AFQR 2016

Airline Fleets Quick Reference

www.air-britain.co.uk

Published by: Air-Britain Publishing

Sales Department: Unit 1A, Munday Works Industrial Estate, Morley Road, Tonbridge, TN9 1RA

Membership Enquiries: 1 Rose Cottages, 179 Penn Road, Hazlemere, Buckinghamshire HP15 7NE

ISBN: 978-0-85130-482-3

PHOTO CAPTIONS:

Front:
Airbus A320-214 JA801P (4887) of Peach landing past the viewing building at Okinawa-Naha on 20.10.15. (Joe Evans)

Back, top to bottom:
Jet Blue Airbus A320-232 N615JB (2461) in a special New York Fire Department colour scheme at Tampa International, 23.10.15 (Rod Simpson)
Airbus A340-313X F-OSEA (438) of Air Tahiti Nui taxies out at Auckland International, 29.1.15. (Dave Partington)
Boeing 737-36E VP-CKW (26322) of Cayman Airways takes off from Tampa International on 23.10.15. (Rod Simpson)

Printed by Bell & Bain Ltd, Glasgow

AFQR 2016

Airline Fleets Quick Reference 2016

Welcome to the 2016 edition of *Airline Fleets Quick Reference*. Comments received are very much appreciated and some slight changes have again been incorporated this year as a result. Please contact us if you can offer any suggestions for further improvements in future editions.

Coverage is, as always, worldwide. Most fleets are included for airlines operating aircraft with more than 19 seats (i.e. Jetstream / Beech 1900 size); this means that any airliner above that size likely to be seen at a major airport should be included (unless it is out of service or stored). In some cases smaller aircraft such as Let 410s are included. Wherever possible expected deliveries in the calendar year have been included.

The fleets are ordered as follows: first, each fleet is listed alphabetically within the country of registration. For the larger fleets the aircraft are then listed in type and registration order. Small fleets are listed in registration order regardless of type. As with any rule, you will find some entries that do not follow this precisely, as we also have to consider that fully laying out any fleet will take up more room than listing in registration order. This whole area is subject to ongoing review and entries may change for airlines as they add aircraft. We hope that what you will see is the best compromise that results in a good combination of space-saving and ease of use.

Information is provided in four columns for each entry, namely registration; type (abridged); constructor's number (and line number for Boeing and McDonnell-Douglas aircraft) plus a column for notes. This last column contains details of fleet number, (where appropriate), aircraft in temporary storage, details of leases between airlines and aircraft on order. In a few cases where a change of marks is imminent the current marks are given in square brackets with the future reserved marks in the first column within round brackets. The type descriptions used in AFQR are the marketing names, rather than the name on the type certificate (e.g. CRJ200 instead of CL-600-2B19). Extra data on the airlines and aircraft listed in this book, plus hundreds of other operators, as well as a decode of airline and airport codes appears in *Airline Fleets 2016*.

Again this year there is a listing of corporate and VIP aircraft whose size falls within the scope of this book, and this listing appears at the end of the book after the fleet listings.

The working file has again been updated this year by Terry Smith with assistance from Air Transport Data Bank (ATDB), *Aviation Letter*, *Airliner World*, Lyn Buttifant, Chris Chatfield, Richard Church (748s), Peter Hillman (Soviet types), Stuart Oldfield (who updated the USA section), Barrie Towey and many websites. Sue Bushell prepared the finished article. Thanks must also be given to all who submitted comments on the 2015 edition, in particular Ray Bowker, John Dyer, Bob Elliott, Paul Gower, Julian Philippe, Bernhard Sternnegger, Andy Stevens and Brian Wilby. Data is believed correct up to early February 2016. Obviously readers will have comments to make on the content and concept of this publication and constructive criticism is welcome at the editorial address below. Please remember, however, that this book (in common with all Air-Britain publications) has been produced entirely in our own time. Of course, don't forget that *AFQR 2016*, like *Airline Fleets 2016*, can be kept up-to-date through the Commercial Scene section of our flagship magazine, *Air-Britain News*.

Please contact us at: afqr@air-britain.co.uk or

Terry Smith
28 Summerfields
Ingatestone
Essex CM4 0BS
United Kingdom

Abbreviations:

♦	New or changed entry in this edition
>	Leased to
<	Leased from
o/o	on order
(xxx)	reserved or expected marks
[xxx]	Storage location
dam & sdam	damaged/seriously damaged
Govt	Government operated
std	storage location unknown at time of compilation
wfs	withdrawn from service
wfu	withdrawn from use

AP- PAKISTAN

AHS AIR INTERNATIONAL / AHS

	Reg	Type	c/n	
☐	AP-BIO	B747-243F	22545/545	
☐	AP-BKS	B747-281BSF	23813/683	

AIRBLUE ED / ABQ

	Reg	Type	c/n	
☐	AP-EDA	A320-214	3974	
☐	AP-EDG	A320-214/S	5891	
☐	AP-EDH	A320-214/S	5943	
☐	AP-BMM	A321-211/S	5966	♦
☐	AP-BMN	A321-211/S	6016	♦
☐	UR-WRH	A321-231	2462	<WRC
☐	UR-WRI	A321-231	2682	<WRC♦
☐	UR-WRJ	A321-231	1869	<WRC
☐	UR-WRQ	A330-223	296	<WRC♦

AIR INDUS I6 / MPK

	Reg	Type	c/n	
☐	AP-BLE	B737-322	24672/1915	
☐	AP-BLG	B737-33A	27910/2873	

PAKISTAN INTERNATIONAL PK / PIA

	Reg	Type	c/n	
☐	AP-BDZ	A310-308	585	
☐	AP-BEB	A310-308	587	[KHI]
☐	AP-BEG	A310-308	653	
☐	AP-BEQ	A310-308	656	
☐	AP-BEU	A310-308	691	
☐	AP-BGN	A310-324ET	676	[KHI]
☐	AP-BGO	A310-324ET	678	
☐	AP-BGP	A310-324ET	682	
☐	AP-BGQ	A310-325ET	660	[KHI]
☐	AP-BGR	A310-325ET	687	
☐	AP-BLA	A320-214	3031	♦
☐	AP-BLB	A320-214	2155	
☐	AP-BLC	A320-214	2212	
☐	AP-BLD	A320-214	2274	
☐	AP-BLS	A320-214	3060	♦
☐	AP-BLT	A320-214	3097	♦
☐	AP-BLU	A320-214	2719	♦
☐	AP-BLV	A320-214	2758	♦
☐	AP-BLW	A320-214	2789	♦
☐	(AP-BLX)	A320-216	2816	o/o♦
☐	AP-BLY	A320-216	2926	♦
☐	AP-BLZ	A320-216	2944	♦
☐	(AP-BMA)	A320-216	2989	o/o♦
☐	9M-XXD	A330-343E	1066	<XAX♦
☐	AP-BHH	ATR 42-500	645	
☐	AP-BHI	ATR 42-500	653	
☐	AP-BHJ	ATR 42-500	657	
☐	AP-BHM	ATR 42-500	659	
☐	AP-BHN	ATR 42-500	661	
☐	AP-BHO	ATR 42-500	663	
☐	AP-BHP	ATR 42-500	665	
☐	AP-BKV	ATR 72-212A	1000	♦
☐	AP-BKW	ATR 72-212A	1036	♦
☐	AP-BKX	ATR 72-212A	1037	♦
☐	AP-BKY	ATR 72-212A	994	♦
☐	AP-BKZ	ATR 72-212A	1029	♦
☐	AP-BCD	B737-340	23297/1122	[KHI]
☐	AP-BCF	B737-340	23299/1235	[KHI]
☐	AP-BFU	B747-367	23392/634	[KHI]
☐	AP-BFY	B747-367	23920/690	[KHI]
☐	AP-BGG	B747-367	24215/709	[KHI]
☐	AP-BGJ	B777-240ER	33775/467	
☐	AP-BGK	B777-240ER	33776/469	
☐	AP-BGL	B777-240ER	33777/473	
☐	AP-BGY	B777-240LR	33781/504	
☐	AP-BGZ	B777-240LR	33782/519	
☐	AP-BHV	B777-340ER	33778/601	
☐	AP-BHW	B777-340ER	33779/611	
☐	AP-BHX	B777-240ER	35296/613	
☐	AP-BID	B777-340ER	33780/705	
☐	AP-BMG	B777-2Q8ER	32716/518	♦
☐	AP-BMH	B777-2Q8ER	32717/541	♦
☐	AP-	B777-2Q8ER	28688/436	o/o♦

SHAHEEN AIR INTERNATIONAL NL / SAI

	Reg	Type	c/n	
☐	AP-BLH	A320-232	0542	
☐	AP-BLI	A320-232	0877	
☐	AP-BLJ	A320-232	1497	
☐	AP-BLK	A320-232	2027	
☐	AP-BLM	A320-232	3105	
☐	AP-BLN	A320-232	3270	
☐	AP-BMC	A320-232	2496	♦
☐	AP-BMD	A320-232	2502	♦
☐	AP-BKL	A330-301	055	
☐	AP-BKM	A330-301	070	
☐	AP-BKN	A330-301	086	
☐	AP-BMI	A330-203	811	o/o♦
☐	AP-	A330-203	819	o/o♦
☐	AP-	A330-203	834	o/o♦
☐	AP-BML	A330-203	900	o/o♦
☐	AP-BJP	B737-4H6	27167/2419	
☐	AP-BJQ	B737-4H6	26449/2491	
☐	AP-BJR	B737-4Q8	25164/2447	
☐	AP-BJT	B737-4Q8	25740/2461	
☐	AP-BJU	B737-4H6	26465/2362	[KHI]
☐	AP-BJV	B737-4H6	27190/2568	
☐	AP-BKO	B737-406	25355/2132	[KHI]

VISION AIR INTERNATIONAL VIS

	Reg	Type	c/n	
☐	AP-BKE	B737-229C	20915/401	
☐	AP-BME	B737-3B3(QC)	26850/2235	♦

A2- BOTSWANA

AIR BOTSWANA BP / BOT

	Reg	Type	c/n	
☐	A2-ABD	BAe146 Srs.100	E1101	
☐	A2-ABF	BAe146 Srs.100	E1160	
☐	A2-ABG	Avro 146-RJ85	E2303	
☐	A2-ABH	Avro 146-RJ85	E2304	
☐	A2-ABN	ATR 42-500	507	
☐	A2-ABO	ATR 42-500	511	
☐	A2-ABP	ATR 42-500	512	
☐	A2-ABR	ATR 72-212A	786	

BLUE SKY AIRWAYS

	Reg	Type	c/n	
☐	A2-FMX	B737-247	23520/1329	

A3- TONGA

REAL TONGA AIRLINE RT / RLT

	Reg	Type	c/n	
☐	A3-RTL	MA60	0904	std
☐	A3-SAM	BAeJetstream 32	982	

	Reg	Type	c/n	Notes
☐	A3-SKY	BAeJetstream 32	974	♦
☐	A3-SPV	Harbin Y-12E	032	

A4O- OMAN

OMAN AIR — WY / OMA

	Reg	Type	c/n	Notes
☐	A4O-DA	A330-243	1038	
☐	A4O-DB	A330-343E	1044	
☐	A4O-DC	A330-243	1049	
☐	A4O-DD	A330-343E	1063	
☐	A4O-DE	A330-343E	1093	
☐	A4O-DF	A330-243	1120	
☐	A4O-DG	A330-243	1227	
☐	A4O-DH	A330-343E	1572	
☐	A4O-DI	A330-343E	1582	
☐	A4O-DJ	A330-343E	1599	
☐	A4O-BB	B737-8Q8/W	30721/2255	
☐	A4O-BC	B737-81M/W	35284/2738	
☐	A4O-BD	B737-81M/W	35287/2804	
☐	A4O-BE	B737-81M/W	37161/2919	
☐	A4O-BF	B737-8FZ/W	29637/3051	
☐	A4O-BG	B737-8FZ/W	29664/3060	
☐	A4O-BH	B737-81M/W	40066/5104	
☐	A4O-BI	B737-91M/W	40069/5150	
☐	A4O-BJ	B737-81M/W	34242/1674	
☐	A4O-BK	B737-91MER/W	40070/5395	♦
☐	A4O-BL	B737-81M/W	40067/5152	
☐	A4O-BM	B737-8FZ/W	29682/2853	
☐	A4O-BO	B737-71M	33103/1154	
☐	A4O-BP	B737-8Q8/W	35272/2537	
☐	A4O-BQ	B737-81M/W	44421/5189	
☐	A4O-BR	B737-81M/W	33104/1337	
☐	A4O-BT	B737-91MER/W	40071/5639	♦
☐	A4O-BU	B737-81M/W	35108/2554	
☐	A4O-BV	B737-81M/W	40068/5160	
☐	A4O-BW	B737-81M/W	44422/5297	
☐	A4O-BX	B737-81M/W	44423/5310	
☐	A4O-BY	B737-91M/W	44424/5320	♦
☐	A4O-BZ	B737-91M/W	44425/5419	♦
☐	OK-TVR	B737-86N/W	38018/3618	<TVS♦
☐	A4O-	B737-8xx/W		o/o♦
☐	A4O-	B737-8xx/W		o/o♦
☐	A4O-	B737-8xx/W		o/o♦
☐	A4O-SA	B787-8	42378/340	♦
☐	A4O-SB	B787-8	42379/372	♦
☐	A4O-	B787-8		o/o
☐	A4O-	B787-8		o/o
☐	A4O-AS	ATR 42-500	574	[MCT]
☐	A4O-AT	ATR 42-500	576	[MCT]
☐	A4O-EA	ERJ-175LR	17000323	
☐	A4O-EB	ERJ-175LR	17000324	
☐	A4O-EC	ERJ-175LR	17000349	
☐	A4O-ED	ERJ-175AR	17000354	std

A5- BHUTAN

BHUTAN AIRLINES — B3 / BTN

	Reg	Type	c/n	Notes
☐	A5-BAB	A319-112	1541	
☐	A5-BAC	A319-112	1551	

DRUKAIR — KB / DRK

	Reg	Type	c/n	Notes
☐	A5-JSW	A319-115/S	6496	♦
☐	A5-RGF	A319-115	2306	
☐	A5-RGG	A319-115	2346	
☐	A5-RGH	ATR 42-500	622	
☐	A5-	A319-115/S		o/o♦

A6- UNITED ARAB EMIRATES

ABU DHABI AVIATION — AXU

	Reg	Type	c/n	Notes
☐	A6-ADA	DHC-8Q-202	471	
☐	A6-ADB	DHC-8Q-315	650	
☐	A6-ADC	DHC-8Q-202	473	
☐	A6-ADD	DHC-8Q-315	627	
☐	A6-ADE	DHC-8Q-315	628	
☐	A6-ADK	DHC-8-402Q	4222	
☐	A6-ADM	DHC-8-402Q	4491	♦
☐	A6-	DHC-8-402Q		o/o♦

AIR ARABIA — G9 / ABY

	Reg	Type	c/n	Notes
☐	A6-ABF	A320-214	2764	
☐	A6-ABT	A320-214	4243	
☐	A6-ABU	A320-214	4310	
☐	A6-ANA	A320-214	4468	
☐	A6-ANB	A320-214	4524	
☐	A6-ANE	A320-214	4806	
☐	A6-ANF	A320-214	4848	
☐	A6-ANG	A320-214	4890	
☐	A6-ANH	A320-214	4958	
☐	A6-ANI	A320-214	5017	
☐	A6-ANL	A320-214	5276	
☐	A6-ANM	A320-214	5307	
☐	A6-ANN	A320-214	5423	
☐	A6-ANO	A320-214/S	5452	
☐	A6-ANP	A320-214/S	5502	
☐	A6-ANQ	A320-214/S	5576	
☐	A6-ANR	A320-214/S	5718	
☐	A6-ANS	A320-214/S	5772	
☐	A6-ANT	A320-214/S	5889	
☐	A6-ANU	A320-214/S	5903	
☐	A6-ANV	A320-214/S	5984	
☐	A6-ANW	A320-214/S	6000	
☐	A6-ANX	A320-214/S	6054	
☐	A6-ANY	A320-214/S	6080	
☐	A6-ANZ	A320-214/S	6166	
☐	A6-AOA	A320-214/S	6176	
☐	A6-AOB	A320-214/S	6234	
☐	A6-AOC	A320-214/S	6293	
☐	A6-AOD	A320-214/S	6365	
☐	A6-AOE	A320-214/S	6430	
☐	A6-AOF	A320-214/S	6444	
☐	A6-AOH	A320-214/S	6481	
☐	A6-AOI	A320-214/S	6553	♦
☐	A6-AOJ	A320-214/S	6665	♦
☐	A6-AOK	A320-214/S	6737	♦
☐	A6-AOL	A320-214/S	6942	♦
☐	A6-	A320-214/S	7096	o/o♦
☐	A6-	A320-214/S	7221	o/o♦
☐	A6-	A320-214/S		o/o♦
☐	A6-	A320-214/S		o/o♦
☐	A6-	A320-214/S		o/o♦
☐	A6-	A320-214/S		o/o♦
☐	A6-	A320-214/S		o/o♦

EASTERN SKYJETS — EE / ESJ

	Reg	Type	c/n	Notes
☐	A6-ESS	B737-33A	25011/2012	

EMIRATES				**EK / UAE**
□	A6-EAF	A330-243	392	[DXB]
□	A6-EAH	A330-243	409	
□	A6-EAK	A330-243	452	
□	A6-EAQ	A330-243	518	
□	A6-EAR	A330-243	536	
□	A6-EAS	A330-243	455	
□	A6-EKQ	A330-243	248	[DXB]
□	A6-EKR	A330-243	251	
□	A6-EKS	A330-243	283	
□	A6-EKT	A330-243	293	
□	A6-EKU	A330-243	295	
□	A6-EKV	A330-243	314	
□	A6-EKX	A330-243	326	
□	A6-EKY	A330-243	328	
□	A6-ERE	A340-541	572	
□	A6-ERF	A340-541	394	[RKT]
□	A6-ERM	A340-313X	236	
□	A6-ERN	A340-313X	166	
□	A6-ERO	A340-313X	163	
□	A6-ERP	A340-313X	185	
□	A6-EDA	A380-861	011	
□	A6-EDB	A380-861	013	
□	A6-EDC	A380-861	016	
□	A6-EDD	A380-861	020	
□	A6-EDE	A380-861	017	
□	A6-EDF	A380-861	007	
□	A6-EDG	A380-861	023	
□	A6-EDH	A380-861	025	
□	A6-EDI	A380-861	028	
□	A6-EDJ	A380-861	009	
□	A6-EDK	A380-861	030	
□	A6-EDL	A380-861	046	
□	A6-EDM	A380-861	042	
□	A6-EDN	A380-861	056	
□	A6-EDO	A380-861	057	
□	A6-EDP	A380-861	077	
□	A6-EDQ	A380-861	080	
□	A6-EDR	A380-861	083	
□	A6-EDS	A380-861	086	
□	A6-EDT	A380-861	090	
□	A6-EDU	A380-861	098	
□	A6-EDV	A380-861	101	
□	A6-EDW	A380-861	103	
□	A6-EDX	A380-861	105	
□	A6-EDY	A380-861	106	
□	A6-EDZ	A380-861	107	
□	A6-EEA	A380-861	108	
□	A6-EEB	A380-861	109	
□	A6-EEC	A380-861	110	
□	A6-EED	A380-861	111	
□	A6-EEE	A380-861	112	
□	A6-EEF	A380-861	113	
□	A6-EEG	A380-861	116	
□	A6-EEH	A380-861	119	
□	A6-EEI	A380-861	123	
□	A6-EEJ	A380-861	127	
□	A6-EEK	A380-861	132	
□	A6-EEL	A380-861	133	
□	A6-EEM	A380-861	134	
□	A6-EEN	A380-861	135	
□	A6-EEO	A380-861	136	
□	A6-EEP	A380-861	138	
□	A6-EEQ	A380-861	141	
□	A6-EER	A380-861	139	
□	A6-EES	A380-861	140	
□	A6-EET	A380-861	142	
□	A6-EEU	A380-861	147	
□	A6-EEV	A380-861	150	
□	A6-EEW	A380-861	153	
□	A6-EEX	A380-861	154	
□	A6-EEY	A380-861	157	
□	A6-EEZ	A380-861	158	
□	A6-EOA	A380-861	159	
□	A6-EOB	A380-861	164	
□	A6-EOC	A380-861	165	
□	A6-EOD	A380-861	168	
□	A6-EOE	A380-861	169	
□	A6-EOF	A380-861	171	
□	A6-EOG	A380-861	172	
□	A6-EOH	A380-861	174	
□	A6-EOI	A380-861	178	
□	A6-EOJ	A380-861	182	
□	A6-EOK	A380-861	184	
□	A6-EOL	A380-861	186	
□	A6-EOM	A380-861	187	
□	A6-EON	A380-861	188	♦
□	A6-EOO	A380-861	190	♦
□	A6-EOP	A380-861	200	♦
□	A6-EOQ	A380-861	201	♦
□	A6-EOR	A380-861	202	♦
□	A6-EOS	A380-861	203	♦
□	A6-EOT	A380-861	204	♦
□	A6-EOU	A380-861	205	♦
□	A6-EOV	A380-861	206	♦
□	A6-EOW	A380-861	207	o/o♦
□	A6-EOX	A380-861	208	o/o♦
□	A6-EOY	A380-861	209	o/o♦
□	A6-EOZ	A380-861	210	o/o♦
□	A6-EUA	A380-861	211	o/o♦
□	A6-EUB	A380-861	213	o/o♦
□	A6-EUC	A380-861	214	o/o♦
□	A6-EUD	A380-861	216	o/o♦
□	N415MC	B747-47UF	32837/1304	<GTI
□	N497MC	B747-47UF	29258/1220	<GTI
□	OO-THC	B747-4HAERF	35235/1389	<TAY
□	OO-THD	B747-4HAERF	35236/1399	<TAY
□	A6-EFD	B777-F1H	35606/766	
□	A6-EFE	B777-F1H	35607/788	
□	A6-EFF	B777-F1H	35612/955	
□	A6-EFG	B777-F1H	35613/996	
□	A6-EFH	B777-F1H	35608/1046	
□	A6-EFI	B777-F1H	35609/1060	
□	A6-EFJ	B777-F1H	35610/1065	
□	A6-EFK	B777-F1H	35611/1088	
□	A6-EFL	B777-F1H	42230/1138	
□	A6-EFM	B777-F1H	42231/1146	
□	A6-EFN	B777-F1H	42232/1212	
□	A6-EFO	B777-F1H	42233/1248	
□	A6-EFS	B777-F1H	42234/1330	♦
□	A6-EMG	B777-21HER	27252/63	
□	A6-EMH	B777-21HER	27251/54	
□	A6-EMI	B777-21HER	27250/47	
□	A6-EMJ	B777-21HER	27253/91	
□	A6-EMK	B777-21HER	29324/171	
□	A6-EML	B777-21HER	29325/176	
□	A6-EWA	B777-21HLR	35572/654	
□	A6-EWB	B777-21HLR	35573/662	
□	A6-EWC	B777-21HLR	35576/677	
□	A6-EWD	B777-21HLR	35577/688	
□	A6-EWE	B777-21HLR	35582/725	

☐	A6-EWF	B777-21HLR	35586/739	
☐	A6-EWG	B777-21HLR	35578/741	
☐	A6-EWH	B777-21HLR	35587/747	
☐	A6-EWI	B777-21HLR	35589/757	
☐	A6-EWJ	B777-21HLR	35590/775	
☐	A6-EBA	B777-31HER	32706/506	
☐	A6-EBB	B777-36NER	32789/508	
☐	A6-EBC	B777-36NER	32790/512	
☐	A6-EBD	B777-31HER	33501/516	
☐	A6-EBE	B777-36NER	32788/532	
☐	A6-EBF	B777-31HER	32708/536	
☐	A6-EBG	B777-36NER	33862/535	
☐	A6-EBH	B777-31HER	32707/539	
☐	A6-EBI	B777-36NER	32785/540	
☐	A6-EBJ	B777-36NER	32787/542	
☐	A6-EBK	B777-31HER	34481/549	
☐	A6-EBL	B777-31HER	32709/551	
☐	A6-EBM	B777-31HER	34482/556	
☐	A6-EBN	B777-36NER	32791/560	
☐	A6-EBO	B777-36NER	32792/568	
☐	A6-EBP	B777-31HER	32710/569	
☐	A6-EBQ	B777-36NER	33863/576	
☐	A6-EBR	B777-31HER	34483/578	
☐	A6-EBS	B777-31HER	32715/582	
☐	A6-EBT	B777-31HER	32730/585	
☐	A6-EBU	B777-31HER	34484/590	
☐	A6-EBV	B777-31HER	32728/594	
☐	A6-EBW	B777-36NER	32793/598	
☐	A6-EBX	B777-31HER	32729/619	
☐	A6-EBY	B777-36NER	33864/622	
☐	A6-EBZ	B777-31HER	32713/628	
☐	A6-ECA	B777-36NER	32794/632	
☐	A6-ECB	B777-31HER	32714/641	
☐	A6-ECC	B777-36NER	33865/664	
☐	A6-ECD	B777-36NER	32795/669	
☐	A6-ECE	B777-31HER	35575/681	
☐	A6-ECF	B777-31HER	35574/690	
☐	A6-ECG	B777-31HER	35579/709	
☐	A6-ECH	B777-31HER	35581/714	
☐	A6-ECI	B777-31HER	35580/728	
☐	A6-ECJ	B777-31HER	35583/734	
☐	A6-ECK	B777-31HER	35584/743	
☐	A6-ECL	B777-31HER	37704/748	
☐	A6-ECM	B777-31HER	37703/755	
☐	A6-ECN	B777-31HER	37705/761	
☐	A6-ECO	B777-31HER	37706/765	
☐	A6-ECP	B777-31HER	37707/768	
☐	A6-ECQ	B777-31HER	35588/779	
☐	A6-ECR	B777-31HER	35592/794	
☐	A6-ECS	B777-31HER	38980/803	
☐	A6-ECT	B777-31HER	35591/808	
☐	A6-ECU	B777-31HER	35593/817	
☐	A6-ECV	B777-31HER	35594/824	
☐	A6-ECW	B777-31HER	38981/828	
☐	A6-ECX	B777-31HER	38982/830	
☐	A6-ECY	B777-31HER	35595/840	
☐	A6-ECZ	B777-31HER	38983/847	
☐	A6-EGA	B777-31HER	38984/861	
☐	A6-EGB	B777-31HER	38985/929	
☐	A6-EGC	B777-31HER	35596/945	
☐	A6-EGD	B777-31HER	38988/946	
☐	A6-EGE	B777-31HER	35597/951	
☐	A6-EGF	B777-31HER	38987/961	
☐	A6-EGG	B777-31HER	41070/965	
☐	A6-EGH	B777-31HER	35585/969	
☐	A6-EGI	B777-31HER	38986/974	
☐	A6-EGJ	B777-31HER	38989/978	
☐	A6-EGK	B777-31HER	41071/981	
☐	A6-EGL	B777-31HER	41072/985	
☐	A6-EGM	B777-31HER	41073/988	
☐	A6-EGN	B777-31HER	41074/993	
☐	A6-EGO	B777-31HER	35598/1000	
☐	A6-EGP	B777-31HER	35599/1010	
☐	A6-EGQ	B777-31HER	41076/1014	
☐	A6-EGR	B777-31HER	41077/1018	
☐	A6-EGS	B777-31HER	41078/1021	
☐	A6-EGT	B777-31HER	35600/1024	
☐	A6-EGU	B777-31HER	41079/1028	
☐	A6-EGV	B777-31HER	38990/1031	
☐	A6-EGW	B777-31HER	35601/1034	
☐	A6-EGX	B777-31HER	35602/1037	
☐	A6-EGY	B777-31HER	41080/1039	
☐	A6-EGZ	B777-31HER	41081/1044	
☐	A6-EMM	B777-31H	29062/256	
☐	A6-EMN	B777-31H	29063/262	
☐	A6-EMO	B777-31H	28680/300	
☐	A6-EMP	B777-31H	29395/326	
☐	A6-EMQ	B777-31H	32697/396	
☐	A6-EMR	B777-31H	29396/402	
☐	A6-EMS	B777-31H	29067/408	
☐	A6-EMT	B777-31H	32699/414	
☐	A6-EMU	B777-31H	29064/418	
☐	A6-EMV	B777-31H	28687/432	
☐	A6-EMW	B777-31H	32700/434	
☐	A6-EMX	B777-31H	32702/444	
☐	A6-ENA	B777-31HER	41082/1047	
☐	A6-ENB	B777-31HER	41075/1055	
☐	A6-ENC	B777-31HER	41083/1058	
☐	A6-END	B777-31HER	41084/1063	
☐	A6-ENE	B777-31HER	35603/1069	
☐	A6-ENF	B777-31HER	41085/1073	
☐	A6-ENG	B777-31HER	35604/1076	
☐	A6-ENH	B777-31HER	41086/1080	
☐	A6-ENI	B777-31HER	41087/1087	
☐	A6-ENJ	B777-31HER	35605/1099	
☐	A6-ENK	B777-31HER	38991/1116	
☐	A6-ENL	B777-31HER	41370/1130	
☐	A6-ENM	B777-31HER	41359/1168	
☐	A6-ENN	B777-31HER	41360/1177	
☐	A6-ENO	B777-31HER	41361/1183	
☐	A6-ENP	B777-31HER	41362/1193	
☐	A6-ENQ	B777-31HER	41363/1201	
☐	A6-ENR	B777-31HER	41364/1207	
☐	A6-ENS	B777-31HER	41365/1220	
☐	A6-ENT	B777-31HER	41366/1225	
☐	A6-ENU	B777-31HER	41367/1236	
☐	A6-ENV	B777-31HER	41368/1243	
☐	A6-ENW	B777-31HER	41369/1249	
☐	A6-ENX	B777-31HER	42318/1261	
☐	A6-ENY	B777-31HER	42122/1276	
☐	A6-ENZ	B777-31HER	42319/1289	♦
☐	A6-EPA	B777-31HER	42320/1317	♦
☐	A6-EPB	B777-31HER	42321/1325	♦
☐	A6-EPC	B777-31HER	42322/1335	♦
☐	A6-EPD	B777-31HER	42323/1341	♦
☐	A6-EPE	B777-31HER	42324/1348	♦
☐	A6-EPF	B777-31HER	42325/1352	♦
☐	A6-EPG	B777-31HER	42326/1357	♦
☐	A6-EPH	B777-31HER	42327/1360	♦
☐	A6-EPI	B777-31HER	42328/1364	♦
☐	A6-EPJ	B777-31HER	42329/1372	♦
☐	A6-EPK	B777-31HER	42330/1379	o/o♦
☐	A6-EPL	B777-31HER	42331/1390	o/o♦

	Reg	Type	c/n	
☐	A6-EPM	B777-31HER	42332/1397	o/o♦
☐	A6-EPN	B777-31HER	42333/1408	o/o♦
☐	A6-EPO	B777-31HER	42334/1415	o/o♦
☐	A6-EPP	B777-31HER	42335/1418	o/o♦
☐	A6-	B777-31HER		o/o♦
☐	A6-	B777-31HER		o/o♦
☐	A6-	B777-31HER		o/o♦
☐	A6-	B777-31HER		o/o♦
☐	A6-	B777-31HER		o/o♦
☐	A6-	B777-31HER		o/o♦
☐	A6-	B777-31HER		o/o♦
☐	A6-	B777-31HER		o/o♦

ETIHAD AIRWAYS — *EY / ETD*

	Reg	Type	c/n	
☐	A6-EID	A319-132	1947	
☐	A6-EIE	A319-132	1955	
☐	A6-EIC	A320-232	2167	
☐	A6-EIF	A320-232	3004	
☐	A6-EIG	A320-232	3050	
☐	A6-EIH	A320-232	3693	
☐	A6-EII	A320-232	3713	
☐	A6-EIJ	A320-232	3902	
☐	A6-EIK	A320-232	3676	
☐	A6-EIL	A320-232	4066	
☐	A6-EIM	A320-232	4077	
☐	A6-EIN	A320-232	4124	
☐	A6-EIO	A320-232	4934	
☐	A6-EIP	A320-232	5095	
☐	A6-EIQ	A320-232	5348	
☐	A6-EIR	A320-232	5407	
☐	A6-EIS	A320-232/S	5714	
☐	A6-EIT	A320-232/S	5791	
☐	A6-EIU	A320-232/S	5821	
☐	A6-EIV	A320-232/S	5882	
☐	A6-EIW	A320-232/S	5924	
☐	A6-EIX	A320-232/S	6134	
☐	A6-EIY	A320-232/S	6226	
☐	A6-EIZ	A320-211	0350	
☐	A6-EJA	A320-232/S	6527	♦
☐	A6-	A320-232/S		o/o♦
☐	A6-AEA	A321-231/S	5836	
☐	A6-AEB	A321-231/S	6108	
☐	A6-AEC	A321-231/S	6143	
☐	A6-AED	A321-232/S	6382	
☐	A6-AEE	A321-231/S	6534	♦
☐	A6-AEF	A321-231/S	6554	♦
☐	A6-AEG	A321-231/S	6731	♦
☐	A6-AEH	A321-231/S	6760	♦
☐	A6-AEI	A321-231/S	6821	♦
☐	A6-AEJ	A321-231/S	6842	♦
☐	A6-	A321-231/S		o/o♦
☐	A6-	A321-231/S		o/o♦
☐	A6-AFA	A330-343E	1071	
☐	A6-AFB	A330-343E	1081	
☐	A6-AFC	A330-343E	1167	
☐	A6-AFD	A330-343E	1205	
☐	A6-AFE	A330-343E	1226	
☐	A6-AFF	A330-343E	1245	
☐	A6-DCA	A330-243F	1032	
☐	A6-DCB	A330-243F	1070	
☐	A6-DCC	A330-243F	1414	
☐	A6-DCD	A330-243F	1524	
☐	A6-	A330-243F	1772	o/o♦
☐	A6-EYC(2)	A330-202	885	
☐	A6-EYD	A330-243	658	
☐	A6-EYE	A330-243	688	
☐	A6-EYF	A330-243	717	
☐	A6-EYG	A330-243	724	
☐	A6-EYH	A330-243	729	
☐	A6-EYI	A330-243	730	
☐	A6-EYJ	A330-243	737	
☐	A6-EYK	A330-243	788	
☐	A6-EYL	A330-243	809	
☐	A6-EYM	A330-243	824	
☐	A6-EYN	A330-243	832	
☐	A6-EYO	A330-243	852	
☐	A6-EYP	A330-243	854	
☐	A6-EYQ	A330-243	868	
☐	A6-EYR	A330-243	975	
☐	A6-EYS	A330-243	991	
☐	A6-EYT	A330-243	1486	
☐	A6-EYU	A330-243	1521	
☐	A6-EYZ	A330-243	807	>SEY
☐	A6-EHB	A340-541	757	
☐	A6-EHC	A340-541	761	
☐	A6-EHD	A340-541	783	
☐	A6-EHE	A340-642HGW	829	
☐	A6-EHF	A340-642HGW	837	
☐	A6-EHH	A340-642HGW	870	
☐	A6-EHI	A340-642HGW	929	
☐	A6-EHJ	A340-642HGW	933	
☐	A6-EHK	A340-642HGW	1030	
☐	A6-EHL	A340-642HGW	1040	
☐	A6-	A350-941		o/o♦
☐	A6-APA	A380-861	166	
☐	A6-APB	A380-861	170	
☐	A6-APC	A380-861	176	
☐	A6-APD	A380-861	180	
☐	A6-APE	A380-861	191	♦
☐	A6-APF	A380-861	195	o/o♦
☐	A6-APG	A380-861	198	o/o♦
☐	A6-APH	A380-861	199	o/o♦
☐	A6-API	A380-861	233	o/o♦
☐	A6-APJ	A380-861	237	o/o♦
☐	N476MC	B747-47UF	29256/1213	<GTI
☐	N855GT	B747-87UF	37567/1476	<GTI
☐	A6-DDA	B777-FFX	39682/939	
☐	A6-DDB	B777-FFX	39692/1072	
☐	A6-DDC	B777-FFX	39691/1100	
☐	A6-DDD	B777-FFX	62744/1374	o/o♦
☐	A6-	B777-FFX		o/o
☐	A6-	B777-FFX		o/o
☐	A6-LRA	B777-237LR	36300/610	
☐	A6-LRB	B777-237LR	36301/621	
☐	A6-LRC	B777-237LR	36302/629	
☐	A6-LRD	B777-237LR	36303/663	
☐	A6-LRE	B777-237LR	36304/698	
☐	A6-ETA	B777-3FXER	34597/538	
☐	A6-ETB	B777-3FXER	34598/543	
☐	A6-ETC	B777-3FXER	34599/544	
☐	A6-ETD	B777-3FXER	34600/547	
☐	A6-ETE	B777-3FXER	34601/548	
☐	A6-ETF	B777-3FXER	39700/832	
☐	A6-ETG	B777-3FXER	39681/932	
☐	A6-ETH	B777-3FXER	39683/957	
☐	A6-ETI	B777-3FXER	39684/987	
☐	A6-ETJ	B777-3FXER	39685/994	
☐	A6-ETK	B777-3FXER	39686/1019	
☐	A6-ETL	B777-3FXER	39687/1064	

Reg	Type	c/n	Notes
A6-ETM	B777-3FXER	39688/1067	
A6-ETN	B777-3FXER	39689/1086	
A6-ETO	B777-3FXER	39690/1105	
A6-ETP	B777-3FXER	41699/1111	
A6-ETQ	B777-3FXER	41700/1137	
A6-ETR	B777-3FXER	41701/1155	
A6-ETS	B777-3FXER	44548/1235	
A6-JAA	B777-35RER	35159/650	
A6-JAB	B777-35RER	35160/653	
A6-JAC	B777-35RER	35157/627	
A6-JAD	B777-35RER	35158/637	♦
A6-JAE	B777-35RER	35163/675	
A6-JAF	B777-35RER	35164/660	
A6-BLA	B787-9	39646/229	
A6-BLB	B787-9	39647/253	
A6-BLC	B787-9	39648/286	♦
A6-BLD	B787-9	39649/302	♦
A6-BLE	B787-9	39650/305	♦
A6-BLF	B787-9	39651/416	♦
A6-BLG	B787-9	39652/432	♦
A6-BLH	B787-9	39653/452	♦
A6-BLI	B787-9	39655/459	♦
A6-BLJ	B787-9	39657/486	♦

FALCON AVIATION SERVICES / FVS

Reg	Type	c/n	Notes
A6-FLA	DHC-8-402Q	4454	
A6-FLQ	DHC-8-402Q	4484	
A6-FLR	DHC-8-402Q	4486	>IKM
P4-AST	DHC-8-402Q	4497	^♦
P4-NUR	DHC-8-402Q	4494	^♦
P4-QAZ	DHC-8-402Q	4502	^♦

Also operates 3 Legacy 650s and 2 Lineage included in the Corporate section; ^ leased to Qazaq Air(UP-)

FLYDUBAI FZ / FDB

Reg	Type	c/n	Notes
A6-FDC	B737-8KN/W	40233/2952	
A6-FDD	B737-8KN/W	40234/2966	
A6-FDE	B737-8KN/W	40235/3053	
A6-FDF	B737-8KN/W	40236/3110	
A6-FDG	B737-8KN/W	29636/3197	
A6-FDH	B737-8KN/W	31716/3270	
A6-FDI	B737-8KN/W	31765/3302	
A6-FDJ	B737-8KN/W	40237/3356	
A6-FDK	B737-8KN/W	40238/3391	
A6-FDL	B737-8KN/W	40239/3460	
A6-FDM	B737-8KN/W	40240/3485	
A6-FDN	B737-8KN/W	40241/3517	
A6-FDO	B737-8KN/W	40242/3540	
A6-FDP	B737-8KN/W	40243/3582	
A6-FDQ	B737-8KN/W	40244/3619	
A6-FDR	B737-8KN/W	40245/3640	
A6-FDS	B737-8KN/W	40246/3659	
A6-FDT	B737-8KN/W	40247/3706	
A6-FDU	B737-8KN/W	40249/3720	
A6-FDV	B737-8KN/W	40248/3768	
A6-FDW	B737-8KN/W	40250/3868	
A6-FDX	B737-8KN/W	40251/3901	
A6-FDY	B737-8KN/W	40252/3923	
A6-FDZ	B737-8KN/W	40253/4081	
A6-FEA	B737-8KN/W	40254/4096	
A6-FEB	B737-8KN/W	40255/4216	
A6-FEC	B737-8KN/W	40256/4243	
A6-FED	B737-8KN/W	40257/4277	
A6-FEE	B737-8KN/W	40258/4433	
A6-FEF	B737-8KN/W	40259/4467	
A6-FEG	B737-8KN/W	40281/4534	
A6-FEH	B737-8KN/W	40260/4648	
A6-FEI	B737-8KN/W	40261/4671	
A6-FEJ	B737-8KN/W	40262/4699	
A6-FEK	B737-8KN/W	40282/4738	
A6-FEL	B737-8KN/W	40263/4781	
A6-FEM	B737-8KN/W	40264/4988	
A6-FEN	B737-8KN/W	40265/4979	
A6-FEO	B737-8KN/W	40266/5004	
A6-FEP	B737-8KN/W	40269/5083	
A6-FEQ	B737-8KN/W	40267/5117	
A6-FER	B737-8KN/W	40268/5163	
A6-FES	B737-8KN/W	40270/5187	
A6-FET	B737-8KN/W	40271/5241	
A6-FEU	B737-8KN/W	40273/5285	
A6-FEV	B737-8KN/W	40275/5323	♦
A6-FEW	B737-8KN/W	40276/5364	♦
A6-FEX	B737-8KN/W	40278/5397	♦
A6-FEY	B737-8KN/W	40274/5465	♦
A6-FEZ	B737-8KN/W	40272/5553	♦
A6-	B737-8KN/W		o/o♦
A6-	B737-8KN/W		o/o♦
A6-	B737-8KN/W		o/o♦
A6-	B737-8KN/W		o/o♦
A6-	B737-8KN/W		o/o♦
A6-	B737-8KN/W		o/o♦
A6-	B737-8KN/W		o/o♦
A6-	B737-8KN/W		o/o♦
A6-	B737-8KN/W		o/o♦

GLOBAL JET AIRLINES 7G / GBG

Reg	Type	c/n	Notes
A6-JMK	B737-322	24674/1928	[SAW]
A6-PHH	B737-3Q8	26314/2707	

MAXIMUS AIR CARGO MXU

Reg	Type	c/n	Notes
A6-MAC	L-100-30 Hercules	5024	
A6-MXB	A300B4-622RF	767	[AUH]
A6-QFY	L-100-30 Hercules	4834	
UR-BXQ	Il-76TD	1023410360	<UKL
UR-ZYD	An-124-100	19530502843	

ROTANA JET RG / RJD

Reg	Type	c/n	Notes
A6-RRA	ERJ-145MP	145398	
A6-RRB	ERJ-145MP	145419	
A6-RRC	A319-112	1618	
A6-RRD	ERJ-145MP	145333	
A6-RRJ	A319-115CJ	5277	

SKIES AIRLINE COMPANY

Reg	Type	c/n	Notes
YR-SKI	B737-46J	27213/2585	<BUR♦

SKYLINK ARABIA SKA

Reg	Type	c/n	Notes
ER-AVA	An-26B-100	11409	<VLN
ER-AVB	An-26-100	3204	<VLN
ER-AZN	An-24RV	37308801	
ER-AZX	An-24RV	47309804	
RDPL-34155	Il-76T	073411338	
RDPL-34157	Il-76T	093418556	
UP-I7611	Il-76T	093418548	
UP-I7630	Il-76T	023441189	
UP-AN203	An-12AP	9347408	
UP-AN204	An-12BK	00347408	
ZS-IRE	B727-2Q9F	21931/1531	
4L-GLT	An-12BK	7345305	

UKAS FZC

	Reg	Type	c/n	
☐	3X-GFX	An-12BK	7345305	
☐	3X-GFY	An-12BK	9346704	
☐	3X-GHF	An-12B	6343810	

UNIQUE AIR 6U / UQA

	Reg	Type	c/n	
☐	A6-JIL	A300B4-605RF	626	
☐	A6-JIM	A300B4-605RF	643	

A7- QATAR

QATAR AIRWAYS QR / QTR

	Reg	Type	c/n	
☐	A7-CJA	A319-133LR	1656	
☐	A7-CJB	A319-133LR	2341	
☐	A7-ADA	A320-232	1566	
☐	A7-ADB	A320-232	1648	
☐	A7-ADC	A320-232	1773	
☐	A7-ADD	A320-232	1895	
☐	A7-ADE	A320-232	1957	
☐	A7-ADF	A320-232	2097	
☐	A7-ADG	A320-232	2121	
☐	A7-ADH	A320-232	2138	
☐	A7-ADI	A320-232	2161	
☐	A7-ADJ	A320-232	2288	
☐	A7-AHA	A320-232	4110	
☐	A7-AHB	A320-232	4130	
☐	A7-AHC	A320-232	4183	
☐	A7-AHD	A320-232	4436	
☐	A7-AHE	A320-232	4479	
☐	A7-AHF	A320-232	4496	
☐	A7-AHG	A320-232	4615	
☐	A7-AHH	A320-232	4700	
☐	A7-AHI	A320-232	4754	
☐	A7-AHJ	A320-232	4784	
☐	A7-AHL	A320-232	4802	
☐	A7-AHO	A320-232	4810	
☐	A7-AHP	A320-232	4858	
☐	A7-AHQ	A320-232	4930	
☐	A7-AHR	A320-232	4968	
☐	A7-AHS	A320-232	5010	
☐	A7-AHT	A320-232	5078	
☐	A7-AHU	A320-232	5127	
☐	A7-AHW	A320-232/S	5217	
☐	A7-AHX	A320-232/S	5361	
☐	A7-AHY	A320-232/S	5395	
☐	A7-AJB	A320-271N	6772	o/o♦
☐	A7-AJC	A320-271N	6829	o/o♦
☐	A7-AJD	A320-271N	6904	o/o♦
☐	A7-AJE	A320-271N	6946	o/o♦
☐	A7-	A320-271N	7083	o/o♦
☐	A7-	A320-271N		o/o♦
☐	A7-LAA	A320-214/S	6347	^
☐	A7-LAB	A320-214/S	6467	^
☐	A7-LAC	A320-214/S	6494	^♦
☐	A7-LAD	A320-214/S	6529	^♦
☐	A7-LAE	A320-214/S	6622	^♦
☐	A7-LAF	A320-214/S	6646	^♦
☐	A7-LAG	A320-214/S	6717	^♦
☐	A7-LAH	A320-214/S	6811	^♦

^ operated by QTR pending Al Maha gaining AOC in Saudi Arabia

	Reg	Type	c/n	
☐	A7-ADK	A321-231	1487	
☐	A7-ADS	A321-231	1928	
☐	A7-ADT	A321-231	2107	
☐	A7-ADV	A321-231	3274	
☐	A7-AIA	A321-231	4173	
☐	A7-AIB	A321-231	4382	
☐	A7-AIC	A321-231	4406	
☐	A7-AID	A321-231	4530	
☐	A7-ACA	A330-202	473	
☐	A7-ACB	A330-202	489	
☐	A7-ACC	A330-202	511	
☐	A7-ACD	A330-202	521	
☐	A7-ACE	A330-202	571	
☐	A7-ACF	A330-202	638	
☐	A7-ACG	A330-202	743	
☐	A7-ACH	A330-202	441	
☐	A7-ACI	A330-202	746	
☐	A7-ACJ	A330-202	760	
☐	A7-ACK	A330-202	792	
☐	A7-ACL	A330-202	820	
☐	A7-ACM	A330-202	849	
☐	A7-AFL	A330-202	612	
☐	A7-AFM	A330-202	616	
☐	A7-AFF	A330-243F	1578	
☐	A7-AFG	A330-243F	1584	
☐	A7-AFH	A330-243F	1594	
☐	A7-AFI	A330-243F	1688	♦
☐	A7-AFJ	A330-243F	1708	o/o♦
☐	A7-AFV	A330-243F	1350	
☐	A7-AFY	A330-243F	1386	
☐	A7-AFZ	A330-243F	1406	
☐	A7-AEA	A330-302	623	
☐	A7-AEB	A330-302	637	
☐	A7-AEC	A330-302	659	
☐	A7-AED	A330-302	680	
☐	A7-AEE	A330-302	711	
☐	A7-AEF	A330-302	721	
☐	A7-AEG	A330-302	734	
☐	A7-AEH	A330-302	789	
☐	A7-AEI	A330-302	813	
☐	A7-AEJ	A330-302	826	
☐	A7-AEM	A330-302	893	
☐	A7-AEN	A330-302	907	
☐	A7-AEO	A330-302	918	
☐	A7-AGA	A340-642HGW	740	
☐	A7-AGB	A340-642HGW	715	
☐	A7-AGC	A340-642HGW	766	
☐	A7-AGD	A340-642HGW	798	
☐	A7-ALA	A350-941	006	
☐	A7-ALB	A350-941	007	
☐	A7-ALC	A350-941	009	♦
☐	A7-ALD	A350-941	010	♦
☐	A7-ALE	A350-941	008	♦
☐	A7-ALF	A350-941	011	♦
☐	A7-ALG	A350-941	013	♦
☐	A7-ALH	A350-941	012	o/o♦
☐	A7-ALI	A350-941	021	o/o♦
☐	A7-ALI	A350-941	025	o/o♦
☐	A7-	A350-941	033	o/o♦
☐	A7-	A350-941	036	o/o♦
☐	A7-	A350-941	042	o/o♦
☐	A7-	A350-941	047	o/o♦
☐	A7-	A350-941	063	o/o♦
☐	A7-	A350-941	069	o/o♦
☐	A7-APA	A380-861	137	
☐	A7-APB	A380-861	143	
☐	A7-APC	A380-861	145	

☐	A7-APD	A380-861	160	
☐	A7-APE	A380-861	181	
☐	A7-APF	A380-861	189	♦
☐	A7-APG	A380-861	193	o/o♦
☐	A7-APH	A380-861	197	o/o♦
☐	A7-API	A380-861	235	o/o♦
☐	A7-	A380-861		o/o♦
☐	TC-ACH	B747-433BCF	24998/840	<RUN♦
☐	A7-BBA	B777-2DZLR	36012/753	
☐	A7-BBB	B777-2DZLR	36013/762	
☐	A7-BBC	B777-2DZLR	36015/825	
☐	A7-BBD	B777-2DZLR	36016/831	
☐	A7-BBE	B777-2DZLR	36017/837	
☐	A7-BBF	B777-2DZLR	36018/842	
☐	A7-BBG	B777-2DZLR	36101/883	
☐	A7-BBH	B777-2DZLR	36102/885	
☐	A7-BBI	B777-2DZLR	41061/962	
☐	A7-BAA	B777-3DZER	36009/676	
☐	A7-BAB	B777-3DZER	36103/686	
☐	A7-BAC	B777-3DZER	36010/731	
☐	A7-BAE	B777-3DZER	36104/769	
☐	A7-BAF	B777-3DZER	37661/815	
☐	A7-BAG	B777-3DZER	36014/819	
☐	A7-BAH	B777-3DZER	37662/849	
☐	A7-BAI	B777-3DZER	36095/742	
☐	A7-BAJ	B777-3DZER	36096/851	
☐	A7-BAK	B777-3DZER	36097/859	
☐	A7-BAL	B777-3DZER	38244/893	
☐	A7-BAM	B777-3DZER	38245/922	
☐	A7-BAN	B777-3DZER	38246/925	
☐	A7-BAO	B777-3DZER	36011/750	
☐	A7-BAP	B777-3DZER	38248/958	
☐	A7-BAQ	B777-3DZER	38247/910	
☐	A7-BAS	B777-3DZER	41062/997	
☐	A7-BAT	B777-3DZER	41738/1149	
☐	A7-BAU	B777-3DZER	41739/1163	
☐	A7-BAV	B777-3DZER	41740/1179	
☐	A7-BAW	B777-3DZER	41741/1071	
☐	A7-BAX	B777-3DZER	41780/1035	
☐	A7-BAY	B777-3DZER	41778/1078	
☐	A7-BAZ	B777-3DZER	41781/1093	
☐	A7-BEA	B777-3DZER	41779/1098	
☐	A7-BEB	B777-3DZER	43215/1218	
☐	A7-BEC	B777-3DZER	43216/1226	
☐	A7-BED	B777-3DZER	60330/1244	
☐	A7-BEE	B777-3DZER	60331/1314	♦
☐	A7-BEF	B777-3DZER	60332/1351	♦
☐	A7-BEG	B777-3DZER	60333/1359	♦
☐	A7-BEH	B777-3DZER	60334/1375	o/o♦
☐	A7-BEI	B777-3DZER	60335/1384	o/o♦
☐	A7-	B777-3DZER		o/o
☐	A7-BFA	B777-FDZ	36098/865	
☐	A7-BFB	B777-FDZ	36100/874	
☐	A7-BFC	B777-FDZ	36099/970	
☐	A7-BFD	B777-FDZ	41427/1004	
☐	A7-BFE	B777-FDZ	39644/1110	
☐	A7-BFF	B777-FDZ	39645/1192	
☐	A7-BFG	B777-FDZ	42299/1238	
☐	A7-BFH	B777-FDZ	42298/1284	
☐	A7-	B777-FDZ		o/o♦
☐	A7-	B777-FDZ		o/o♦
☐	A7-	B777-FDZ		o/o♦
☐	A7-	B777-FDZ		o/o♦
☐	A7-BCA	B787-8	38319/57	
☐	A7-BCB	B787-8	38320/58	
☐	A7-BCC	B787-8	38321/82	
☐	A7-BCD	B787-8	38322/99	
☐	A7-BCE	B787-8	38323/103	
☐	A7-BCF	B787-8	38324/109	
☐	A7-BCG	B787-8	38325/116	
☐	A7-BCH	B787-8	38326/129	
☐	A7-BCI	B787-8	38327/138	
☐	A7-BCJ	B787-8	38328/144	
☐	A7-BCK	B787-8	38329/62	
☐	A7-BCL	B787-8	38330/64	
☐	A7-BCM	B787-8	38331/150	
☐	A7-BCN	B787-8	38332/176	
☐	A7-BCO	B787-8	38333/188	
☐	A7-BCP	B787-8	38334/207	
☐	A7-BCQ	B787-8	38335/215	
☐	A7-BCR	B787-8	38336/225	
☐	A7-BCS	B787-8	38337/261	
☐	A7-BCT	B787-8	38338/266	
☐	A7-BCU	B787-8	38339/277	
☐	A7-BCV	B787-8	38340/292	
☐	A7-BCW	B787-8	38341/328	
☐	A7-BCX	B787-8	38342/352	
☐	A7-BCY	B787-8	38343/354	
☐	A7-BCZ	B787-8	38344/384	
☐	A7-BDA	B787-8	38345/394	o/o♦
☐	A7-BDB	B787-8	38346/410	o/o♦
☐	A7-BDC	B787-8	38347/420	o/o♦
☐	A7-BDD	B787-8	38348/440	o/o♦

A9C- BAHRAIN

DHL INTERNATIONAL AVIATION — ES / DHX

☐	A9C-DHC	B757-225SF	22211/74	
☐	A9C-DHD	B757-225SF	22611/75	
☐	A9C-DHE	B757-225SF	22210/42	
☐	A9C-DHJ	B767-281F	23146/121	♦
☐	A9C-DHK	B767-281F	23434/171	♦

GULF AIR — GF / GFA

☐	A9C-AB	A320-214	4030	
☐	A9C-AC	A320-214	4059	
☐	A9C-AD	A320-214	4083	
☐	A9C-AE	A320-214	4146	
☐	A9C-AF	A320-214	4158	
☐	A9C-AG	A320-214	4188	
☐	A9C-AH	A320-214	4218	
☐	A9C-AI	A320-214	4255	
☐	A9C-AJ	A320-214	4502	
☐	A9C-AK	A320-214	4541	
☐	A9C-AL	A320-214	4780	
☐	A9C-AM	A320-214	4827	
☐	A9C-AN	A320-214	4865	
☐	A9C-AO	A320-214	4860	
☐	A9C-AP	A320-214	5171	
☐	A9C-AQ	A320-214	5175	
☐	A9C-CA	A321-231	5025	
☐	A9C-CB	A321-231	5074	
☐	A9C-CC	A321-231	5180	
☐	A9C-CD	A321-231	5257	
☐	A9C-CE	A321-231	5321	
☐	A9C-CF	A321-231	5336	
☐	A9C-KA	A330-243	276	501
☐	A9C-KB	A330-243	281	502
☐	A9C-KC	A330-243	286	503

	Reg	Type	C/n	
☐	A9C-KD	A330-243	287	504
☐	A9C-KE	A330-243	334	505
☐	A9C-KF	A330-243	340	506

TEXEL AIR **/ XLR**

	Reg	Type	C/n	
☐	A9C-APC	B737-33A(F)	27459/3007	♦
☐	A9C-JNC	B737-3G7(F)	24710/1825	[BAH]
☐	A9C-TXL	B737-3Q8(F)	28200/2854	

B- CHINA

9 AIR (JIU YUAN AIRLINES) **AQ / JYH**

	Reg	Type	C/n	
☐	B-1715	B737-8GP/W	39819/4968	
☐	B-1716	B737-8GP/W	39829/5202	
☐	B-1719	B737-8GP/W	39820/5016	
☐	B-6989	B737-86N/W	38041/4516	♦
☐	B-6990	B737-86N/W	41259/4448	♦
☐	B-	B737-86N/W	41260/4508	o/o♦
☐	B-	B737-86N/W	41261/4573	o/o♦
☐	B-	B737-8xx		o/o♦
☐	B-	B737-8xx		o/o♦
☐	B-	B737-8xx		o/o♦
☐	B-	B737-8xx		o/o♦

AIR CHINA **CA / CCA**

	Reg	Type	C/n	
☐	B-2364	A319-115	2499	
☐	B-2404	A319-131	2454	
☐	B-6004	A319-115	2508	
☐	B-6014	A319-115	2525	
☐	B-6022	A319-131	2000	
☐	B-6023	A319-131	2007	
☐	B-6024	A319-131	2015	
☐	B-6031	A319-131	2172	
☐	B-6032	A319-131	2202	
☐	B-6033	A319-131	2205	
☐	B-6034	A319-115	2237	
☐	B-6035	A319-115	2269	
☐	B-6036	A319-115	2285	
☐	B-6037	A319-115	2293	
☐	B-6038	A319-115	2298	
☐	B-6044	A319-115	2532	
☐	B-6046	A319-115	2545	
☐	B-6047	A319-115	2551	
☐	B-6048	A319-131	2559	
☐	B-6213	A319-131	2614	
☐	B-6216	A319-131	2643	
☐	B-6223	A319-115	2805	
☐	B-6225	A319-115	2819	
☐	B-6226	A319-115	2839	
☐	B-6227	A319-115	2847	
☐	B-6228	A319-115	2890	
☐	B-6235	A319-131	3195	
☐	B-6236	A319-131	3200	
☐	B-6237	A319-131	3226	
☐	B-6238	A319-115	3250	
☐	B-6468	A319-115/S	6514	♦
☐	B-6478	A319-115/S	6603	♦
☐	B-6479	A319-115/S	6699	♦
☐	B-	A319-1xx		o/o♦
☐	B-	A319-1xx		o/o♦
☐	B-	A319-1xx		o/o♦
☐	B-1686	A320-214/S	6466	♦
☐	B-1687	A320-214/S	6743	♦
☐	B-1852	A320-214/S	6239	
☐	B-1853	A320-214/S	6169	
☐	B-1873	A320-214/S	6251	
☐	B-1875	A320-214/S	6283	
☐	B-2210	A320-214	1296	
☐	B-2376	A320-214	0876	
☐	B-2377	A320-214	0921	
☐	B-6606	A320-214	3337	
☐	B-6607	A320-214	3461	
☐	B-6608	A320-214	3601	
☐	B-6609	A320-214	3215	
☐	B-6610	A320-214	3221	
☐	B-6611	A320-214	3506	
☐	B-6676	A320-232	4317	
☐	B-6677	A320-232	4348	
☐	B-6731	A320-232	4473	
☐	B-6733	A320-232	4566	
☐	B-6745	A320-232	4593	
☐	B-6767	A320-214	4803	
☐	B-6773	A320-232	4775	
☐	B-6793	A320-214	4829	
☐	B-6822	A320-214	4900	
☐	B-6828	A320-214	4963	
☐	B-6846	A320-214	4985	
☐	B-6847	A320-232	4895	
☐	B-6881	A320-214	5174	
☐	B-6882	A320-232	4997	
☐	B-6915	A320-214	5014	
☐	B-6916	A320-214	5032	
☐	B-6918	A320-232	5091	
☐	B-6941	A320-214	5386	
☐	B-6967	A320-214	5419	
☐	B-8337	A320-232/S	6882	o/o♦
☐	B-8338	A320-232/S	6932	o/o♦
☐	B-9918	A320-214	5568	
☐	B-9922	A320-232	5600	
☐	B-9923	A320-214	5664	
☐	B-9925	A320-214	5690	
☐	B-9926	A320-232	5771	
☐	B-	A320-214/S	6921	o/o♦
☐	B-	A320-232/S	7041	o/o♦
☐	B-	A320-232/S	7134	o/o♦
☐	B-	A320-232/S	7234	o/o♦
☐	B-	A320-2xx/S		o/o♦
☐	B-	A320-2xx/S		o/o♦
☐	B-	A320-2xx/S		o/o♦
☐	B-	A320-2xx/S		o/o♦
☐	B-	A320-2xx/S		o/o♦
☐	B-	A320-2xx/S		o/o♦
☐	B-1637	A321-213/S	6579	♦
☐	B-1638	A321-213/S	6641	♦
☐	B-1639	A321-213/S	6567	♦
☐	B-1816	A321-213	6013	
☐	B-1833	A321-231	6159	
☐	B-1855	A321-213	6196	
☐	B-1876	A321-213/S	6319	
☐	B-1877	A321-231/S	6273	
☐	B-1878	A321-231/S	6308	
☐	B-1879	A321-231/S	6354	
☐	B-6326	A321-213	3329	
☐	B-6327	A321-213	3307	
☐	B-6361	A321-213	3523	
☐	B-6362	A321-213	3623	
☐	B-6363	A321-213	3653	
☐	B-6365	A321-213	3655	
☐	B-6382	A321-213	3665	
☐	B-6383	A321-213	3678	
☐	B-6385	A321-213	3722	

☐ B-6386 A321-213 3725
☐ B-6555 A321-213 3766
☐ B-6556 A321-213 3806
☐ B-6593 A321-213 3973
☐ B-6595 A321-213 4022
☐ B-6596 A321-213 4031
☐ B-6597 A321-213 4062
☐ B-6599 A321-213 3940
☐ B-6603 A321-213 4131
☐ B-6605 A321-213 4091
☐ B-6631 A321-213 4180
☐ B-6632 A321-213 4221
☐ B-6633 A321-213 4283
☐ B-6665 A321-213 4318
☐ B-6675 A321-213 4377
☐ B-6701 A321-213 4472
☐ B-6711 A321-213 4494
☐ B-6712 A321-213 4538
☐ B-6741 A321-213 4617
☐ B-6742 A321-232 4719
☐ B-6791 A321-232 4771
☐ B-6792 A321-232 4834
☐ B-6823 A321-232 4873
☐ B-6825 A321-213 4949
☐ B-6848 A321-213 5054
☐ B-6883 A321-232 5124
☐ B-6885 A321-232 5199
☐ B-6917 A321-232 5265
☐ B-6919 A321-232 5346
☐ B-6942 A321-232 5432
☐ B-6961 A321-213 5435
☐ B-6973 A321-213 5573
☐ B-9919 A321-213 5743
☐ B- A321-232 7161 o/o♦
☐ B- A321-232 7248 o/o♦
☐ B- A321-213 o/o♦
☐ B- A321-2xx o/o♦
☐ B- A321-2xx o/o♦
☐ B- A321-2xx o/o♦
☐ B- A321-2xx o/o♦
☐ B- A321-2xx o/o♦

☐ B-5901 A330-343E 1353
☐ B-5906 A330-343E 1373
☐ B-5912 A330-343E 1493
☐ B-5913 A330-343E 1509
☐ B-5916 A330-343E 1383
☐ B-5918 A330-243 1396
☐ B-5919 A330-343E 1413
☐ B-5925 A330-243 1434
☐ B-5927 A330-243 1444
☐ B-5932 A330-243 1459
☐ B-5933 A330-243 1471
☐ B-5946 A330-343E 1525
☐ B-5947 A330-343E 1538
☐ B-5948 A330-343E 1541
☐ B-5956 A330-343E 1563
☐ B-5957 A330-343E 1570
☐ B-5958 A330-343E 1587
☐ B-5977 A330-343E 1658 ♦
☐ B-5978 A330-343E 1673 ♦
☐ B-6070 A330-243 750
☐ B-6071 A330-243 756
☐ B-6072 A330-243 759
☐ B-6073 A330-243 780
☐ B-6075 A330-243 785
☐ B-6076 A330-243 797
☐ B-6079 A330-243 810
☐ B-6080 A330-243 815
☐ B-6081 A330-243 839
☐ B-6090 A330-243 860
☐ B-6091 A330-243 867
☐ B-6092 A330-243 873
☐ B-6093 A330-243 884
☐ B-6101 A330-343E 1685 ♦
☐ B-6102 A330-343E 1695 ♦
☐ B-6113 A330-243 890
☐ B-6115 A330-243 909
☐ B-6117 A330-243 903
☐ B-6130 A330-243 930
☐ B-6131 A330-243 941
☐ B-6132 A330-243 944
☐ B-6503 A330-343E 1333
☐ B-6505 A330-243 957
☐ B-6511 A330-343E 1110
☐ B-6512 A330-343E 1087
☐ B-6513 A330-343E 1130
☐ B-6523 A330-343E 1187
☐ B-6525 A330-343E 1199
☐ B-6530 A330-343E 1216
☐ B-6533 A330-243 1237
☐ B-6536 A330-243 1260
☐ B-6540 A330-243 1282
☐ B-6541 A330-243 1304
☐ B-6549 A330-243 1330
☐ B- A330-343E o/o♦

☐ B-2627 B737-36E 26315/2706 std
☐ B-2948 B737-3J6 27361/2631 std

☐ B-2612 B737-79L 33411/1538
☐ B-2613 B737-79L 33412/1544
☐ B-2700 B737-79L 33413/1560
☐ B-5043 B737-79L 33408/1331
☐ B-5044 B737-79L 33409/1351
☐ B-5045 B737-79L 33410/1354
☐ B-5201 B737-79L/W 34023/1795
☐ B-5202 B737-79L/W 34537/1837
☐ B-5203 B737-79L/W 34538/1853
☐ B-5211 B737-79L 34019/1749
☐ B-5213 B737-79L/W 34020/1769
☐ B-5214 B737-79L/W 34021/1774
☐ B-5217 B737-79L/W 34022/1786
☐ B-5220 B737-79L/W 34539/1856
☐ B-5226 B737-79L/W 34540/1877 ^
☐ B-5227 B737-79L/W 34541/1937
☐ B-5228 B737-79L/W 34542/1993
☐ B-5229 B737-79L/W 34543/2006
☐ B-5296 B737-79L/W 41091/4301
☐ B-5297 B737-79L/W 41092/4354
☐ B-5803 B737-79L/W 41093/4658

☐ B-1526 B737-89L/W 41107/5500 ♦
☐ B-1527 B737-89L/W 44919/5515 ♦
☐ B-1528 B737-89L/W 44920/5527 ♦
☐ B-1529 B737-89L/W 44921/5556 ♦
☐ B-1530 B737-89L/W 44922/5585 ♦
☐ B-1531 B737-89L/W 44923/5626 ♦
☐ B-1738 B737-89L/W 41325/5186
☐ B-1760 B737-89L/W 41101/5240
☐ B-1761 B737-89L/W 41102/5265
☐ B-1762 B737-89L/W 41103/5333 ♦
☐ B-1763 B737-89L/W 41104/5381 ♦
☐ B-1764 B737-89L/W 41105/5424 ♦
☐ B-1765 B737-89L/W 41106/5456 ♦

☐ B-1766 B737-89L/W 41108/5327 ♦
☐ B-1767 B737-89L/W 41109/5230
☐ B-1768 B737-89L/W 41110/5276
☐ B-1769 B737-89L/W 44915/5433 ^♦
☐ B-1909 B737-89L/W 40022/4681
☐ B-1942 B737-89L/W 40023/4746
☐ B-1945 B737-89L/W 41094/4790
☐ B-1946 B737-89L/W 41095/4828
☐ B-1947 B737-89L/W 41314/4756
☐ B-1956 B737-89L/W 40024/4864
☐ B-1957 B737-89L/W 40041/4992
☐ B-1958 B737-89L/W 40042/5037
☐ B-1959 B737-89L/W 41321/4982
☐ B-1975 B737-89L/W 41323/5065
☐ B-1976 B737-89L/W 41098/5131
☐ B-1977 B737-89L/W 41099/5181
☐ B-1978 B737-89L/W 41324/5120
☐ B-2509 B737-8Z0 30072/466
☐ B-2510 B737-8Z0 30071/381
☐ B-2511 B737-8Z0 30073/487
☐ B-2641 B737-89L 29876/337
☐ B-2642 B737-89L 29877/359 [PEK]
☐ B-2643 B737-89L 29878/379 [PEK]
☐ B-2645 B737-89L 29879/427
☐ B-2648 B737-89L 29880/511
☐ B-2649 B737-89L 30159/572
☐ B-2650 B737-89L 30160/594
☐ B-2657 B737-89L 30517/1224
☐ B-2670 B737-89L 30514/1055 ^
☐ B-2671 B737-89L 30515/1165
☐ B-2672 B737-89L 30516/1168
☐ B-2673 B737-86N 29888/1133
☐ B-5167 B737-808 34701/1887
☐ B-5170 B737-808 34705/1998
☐ B-5172 B737-8Q8 30704/1985
☐ B-5173 B737-8Q8 30705/2001
☐ B-5175 B737-86N 35209/2067
☐ B-5176 B737-86N 34258/2096
☐ B-5177 B737-86N 35210/2127
☐ B-5178 B737-86N 32682/2117
☐ B-5179 B737-86N 35211/2146
☐ B-5198 B737-89L/W 36491/2759
☐ B-5312 B737-8Q8 29374/2203
☐ B-5325 B737-86N 32692/2275
☐ B-5326 B737-86N 35214/2308
☐ B-5327 B737-86N 35219/2371
☐ B-5328 B737-86N 35221/2444
☐ B-5329 B737-86N 35222/2463
☐ B-5341 B737-89L/W 36483/2403
☐ B-5342 B737-89L/W 36484/2441
☐ B-5343 B737-89L/W 36485/2470
☐ B-5387 B737-89L/W 36492/2828
☐ B-5390 B737-89L/W 36486/2606
☐ B-5391 B737-89L/W 36487/2664
☐ B-5392 B737-89L/W 36488/2674
☐ B-5397 B737-89L/W 36489/2704
☐ B-5398 B737-89L/W 36490/2715
☐ B-5422 B737-89L/W 36741/2845
☐ B-5423 B737-89L/W 36742/2877
☐ B-5425 B737-89L/W 36743/2896
☐ B-5426 B737-89L/W 36744/2969
☐ B-5431 B737-86N 36812/2918
☐ B-5436 B737-86N 36813/2976
☐ B-5437 B737-86N/W 36815/3020
☐ B-5438 B737-86N/W 36816/3032
☐ B-5442 B737-86N/W 36745/3049
☐ B-5443 B737-86N/W 36746/3072
☐ B-5447 B737-89L/W 40015/3509
☐ B-5477 B737-89L/W 36755/3387
☐ B-5485 B737-89L/W 36747/3124
☐ B-5486 B737-89L/W 36748/3127
☐ B-5495 B737-89L/W 36749/3145
☐ B-5496 B737-89L/W 36750/3155
☐ B-5497 B737-89L/W 36751/3167
☐ B-5500 B737-89L/W 36752/3188
☐ B-5507 B737-89L/W 36753/3247
☐ B-5508 B737-89L/W 36545/3275
☐ B-5509 B737-89L/W 36547/3300
☐ B-5510 B737-89L/W 36548/3312
☐ B-5518 B737-89L/W 36754/3336
☐ B-5519 B737-86N 36802/3350
☐ B-5525 B737-86N 37886/3436 ♦
☐ B-5570 B737-89L/W 40032/3608
☐ B-5572 B737-89L/W 40027/3670
☐ B-5582 B737-89L/W 40028/3707
☐ B-5583 B737-89L/W 40016/3749
☐ B-5585 B737-89L/W 40029/3756
☐ B-5621 B737-89L/W 40030/3846
☐ B-5622 B737-89L/W 40031/3859
☐ B-5679 B737-89L/W 40034/4117
☐ B-5680 B737-89L/W 40035/4149
☐ B-5681 B737-89L/W 40025/4202
☐ B-5682 B737-89L/W 40036/4213
☐ B-5696 B737-89L/W 40019/4275
☐ B-5793 B737-89L/W 40021/4595
☐ B-5848 B737-89L/W 41307/4607
☐ B-5849 B737-89L/W 41309/4649
☐ B-5851 B737-89L/W 41313/4725
☐ B-6106 B737-89L/W 44924/5622 ♦
☐ B-6496 B737-89L/W 44926/5648 ♦
☐ B-6497 B737-89L/W 44930/5699 ♦
☐ B-6498 B737-89L/W 44929/5707 ♦
☐ B-6499 B737-89L/W 44927/5679 ♦
☐ B-7180 B737-89L/W 43410/5746 ♦
☐ B-7182 B737-89L/W 44911/5725 ♦
☐ B- B737-89L/W o/o♦
☐ B- B737-89L/W o/o♦
☐ B- B737-89L/W o/o♦

^ operated by Air China Inner Mongolia

☐ B-2443 B747-4J6 25881/957 [PEK]
☐ B-2445 B747-4J6 25882/1021
☐ B-2447 B747-4J6 25883/1054
☐ B-2472 B747-4J6 30158/1243
☐ B-2479 B747-89L 41193/1510
☐ B-2480 B747-89L 41194/1518 ♦
☐ B-2481 B747-89L 41847/1515 ♦
☐ B-2482 B747-89L 44933/1517 ♦
☐ B-2485 B747-89L 41191/1499
☐ B-2486 B747-89L 41192/1507
☐ B-2487 B747-89L 44932/1508

☐ B-2059 B777-2J6 29153/168
☐ B-2060 B777-2J6 29154/173
☐ B-2061 B777-2J6 29155/179
☐ B-2063 B777-2J6 29156/214
☐ B-2064 B777-2J6 29157/240 [PEK]
☐ B-2065 B777-2J6 29744/280
☐ B-2066 B777-2J6 29745/290
☐ B-2067 B777-2J6 29746/338
☐ B-2068 B777-2J6 29747/344
☐ B-2069 B777-2J6 29748/349

☐ B-2006 B777-39LER 44931/1239
☐ B-2031 B777-39LER 38670/1017

	Reg	Type	c/n	
☐	B-2032	B777-39LER	38671/1032	
☐	B-2033	B777-39LER	38673/1045	
☐	B-2035	B777-39LER	38674/1051	
☐	B-2036	B777-39LER	38676/1066	
☐	B-2037	B777-39LER	38677/1094	
☐	B-2038	B777-39LER	38678/1085	
☐	B-2039	B777-39LER	38679/1114	
☐	B-2040	B777-39LER	38680/1123	
☐	B-2043	B777-39LER	41441/1132	
☐	B-2045	B777-39LER	41443/1187	
☐	B-2046	B777-39LER	41442/1165	
☐	B-2047	B777-39LER	60374/1196	
☐	B-2085	B777-39LER	38666/943	
☐	B-2086	B777-39LER	38667/966	
☐	B-2087	B777-39LER	38672/954	
☐	B-2088	B777-39LER	38668/979	
☐	B-2089	B777-39LER	38675/990	
☐	B-2090	B777-39LER	38669/1009	
☐	B-	B777-39LER		o/o♦
☐	B-	B787-9	34305/419	o/o♦
☐	B-	B787-9	34306/433	o/o♦
☐	B-	B787-9	34307/435	o/o♦
☐	B-	B787-9	34308/455	o/o♦
☐	B-	B787-9	34309/462	o/o♦
☐	B-	B787-9	34310/471	o/o♦
☐	B-	B787-9	34311/487	o/o♦

AIR CHINA CARGO — *CA / CAO*

	Reg	Type	c/n	
☐	B-2409	B747-412F	26560/1052	
☐	B-2453	B747-412BCF	27134/981	[MZJ]
☐	B-2458	B747-4J6BCF	24347/775	[PEK]
☐	B-2460	B747-4J6BCF	24348/792	[MZJ]
☐	B-2475	B747-4FTF	34239/1367	
☐	B-2476	B747-4FTF	34240/1373	
☐	B-2836	B757-2Z0F	27258/595	
☐	B-2841	B757-2Z0F	27367/624	
☐	B-2855	B757-2Z0F	29792/822	
☐	B-2856	B757-2Z0F	29793/833	
☐	B-2091	B777-FFT	44682/1230	
☐	B-2092	B777-FFT	44683/1272	
☐	B-2093	B777-FFT	44684/1316	♦
☐	B-2094	B777-FFT	44685/1326	♦
☐	B-2095	B777-FFT	44678/1158	
☐	B-2096	B777-FFT	44679/1180	
☐	B-2097	B777-FFT	44680/1188	
☐	B-2098	B777-FFT	44681/1210	

AIR GUILIN

	Reg	Type	c/n	
☐	B-	A319-1xx		o/o♦
☐	B-	A319-1xx		o/o♦
☐	B-	A319-1xx		o/o♦

CAPITAL AIRLINES — *JD / CBJ*

	Reg	Type	c/n	
☐	B-6169	A319-112	2985	std
☐	B-6177	A319-112	3285	std
☐	B-6178	A319-132	3548	
☐	B-6179	A319-132	3561	
☐	B-6180	A319-132	3578	
☐	B-6181	A319-132	3580	
☐	B-6182	A319-132	3520	
☐	B-6192	A319-132	3768	
☐	B-6193	A319-133	3849	
☐	B-6199	A319-112	2644	
☐	B-6210	A319-115	2557	
☐	B-6211	A319-115	2561	
☐	B-6215	A319-112	2611	
☐	B-6222	A319-112	2733	
☐	B-6245	A319-133	3851	
☐	B-6400	A319-132	3638	
☐	B-6401	A319-133	3842	
☐	B-6402	A319-132	3914	
☐	B-6403	A319-132	3958	
☐	B-6405	A319-132	3982	
☐	B-6415	A319-133	4410	
☐	B-6416	A319-133	4529	
☐	B-6417	A319-133	4522	
☐	B-1603	A320-214/S	6206	
☐	B-1621	A320-232/S	6198	
☐	B-1622	A320-232/S	6212	
☐	B-1623	A320-232/S	6229	
☐	B-1642	A320-232/S	6426	
☐	B-1643	A320-232/S	6480	
☐	B-1691	A320-232/S	6580	♦
☐	B-1809	A320-214/S	5848	
☐	B-1810	A320-214/S	5997	
☐	B-1811	A320-214/S	6041	
☐	B-6709	A320-232	4412	
☐	B-6710	A320-232	4440	
☐	B-6723	A320-232	4483	
☐	B-6725	A320-232	4471	
☐	B-6726	A320-232	4505	
☐	B-6727	A320-232	4513	
☐	B-6746	A320-232	4580	
☐	B-6747	A320-232	4540	
☐	B-6748	A320-232	4602	
☐	B-6769	A320-214	5114	
☐	B-6795	A320-232	4677	
☐	B-6858	A320-214	5008	
☐	B-6859	A320-214	5072	
☐	B-6867	A320-214	5471	
☐	B-6898	A320-232	5185	
☐	B-6952	A320-214	5331	
☐	B-6958	A320-214	5216	
☐	B-6869	A320-214	5630	
☐	B-8072	A320-214/S	6664	♦
☐	B-8169	A320-214/S	6730	♦
☐	B-8170	A320-214/S	6759	std♦
☐	B-8171	A320-214/S	6769	std♦
☐	B-9961	A320-214/S	5722	
☐	B-9962	A320-214	5656	
☐	B-	A320-232/S	7068	o/o♦
☐	B-8107	A321-231/S	6763	♦
☐	B-8187	A321-231/S	6818	♦
☐	B-8188	A321-231/S	6853	♦
☐	B-8189	A321-231/S	6863	♦
☐	B-8200	A321-231/S	6913	♦
☐	B-	A321-231/S	7076	o/o♦
☐	B-	A321-231/S	7144	o/o♦
☐	B-	A321-231/S	7173	o/o♦
☐	B-	A321-231/S	7191	o/o♦
☐	B-	A321-231/S	7220	o/o♦
☐	B-	A321-231/S	7284	o/o♦
☐	B-8019	A330-243	1020	♦
☐	B-8221	A330-243	1052	♦
☐	B-	A330-3xx	1753	o/o♦

CHANG AN AIRLINES — *HU / CGN*

	Reg	Type	c/n	
☐	B-5115	B737-8FH/W	29640/1649	
☐	B-5116	B737-8FH/W	29672/1745	
☐	B-5180	B737-8FH/W	35089/2042	

☐	B-5181	B737-8FH/W	35090/2073	

CHENGDU AIRLINES EU / UEA

☐	B-3321	ARJ21-700	106	♦
☐	B-	ARJ21-700	105	o/o♦
☐	B-6163	A319-112	3024	
☐	B-6229	A319-112	2762	
☐	B-6230	A319-112	2774	
☐	B-1630	A320-216/S	6248	
☐	B-1631	A320-216/S	6281	
☐	B-1632	A320-216/S	6292	
☐	B-1633	A320-216/S	6357	
☐	B-1856	A320-214/S	5957	
☐	B-6728	A320-214	2696	
☐	B-6729	A320-214	2820	
☐	B-6730	A320-214	2835	
☐	B-6850	A320-214	4347	
☐	B-6900	A320-214	2654	
☐	B-6907	A320-214	5003	
☐	B-6940	A320-214	3706	
☐	B-8162	A320-214	4743	♦
☐	B-8185	A320-214	5191	♦
☐	B-8186	A320-214	4988	♦
☐	B-8342	A320-214/S	6830	♦
☐	B-8345	A320-214/S	6922	std♦
☐	B-9985	A320-214	5252	
☐	B-	A320-214/S	7111	o/o♦
☐	B-	A320-214/S	7201	o/o♦
☐	B-	A320-214/S	7211	o/o♦
☐	B-	A320-214/S	7235	o/o♦
☐	B-	A320-214/S	7292	o/o♦
☐	B-	A320-214/S	7319	o/o♦

CHINA CARGO AIRLINES CK / CKK

☐	B-2425	B747-40BERF	35207/1377	
☐	B-2426	B747-40BERF	35208/1392	
☐	B-2428	B747-412F	28263/1094	
☐	B-2076	B777-F6N	37711/846	
☐	B-2077	B777-F6N	37713/856	
☐	B-2078	B777-F6N	37714/869	
☐	B-2079	B777-F6N	37715/876	
☐	B-2082	B777-F6N	37716/942	
☐	B-2083	B777-F6N	37717/949	

CHINA EASTERN AIRLINES MU / CES

☐	B-2217	A319-112	1601	
☐	B-2331	A319-112	1285	[XSP]
☐	B-2333	A319-112	1377	
☐	B-6167	A319-115	3168	
☐	B-6172	A319-115	3186	
☐	B-6217	A319-115	2693	
☐	B-6218	A319-115	2757	
☐	B-6231	A319-115	2825	
☐	B-6423	A319-115	5273	
☐	B-6427	A319-133	5267	
☐	B-6428	A319-115	5330	
☐	B-6429	A319-115	5338	
☐	B-6430	A319-133	5376	
☐	B-6431	A319-115	5380	
☐	B-6432	A319-115	5412	
☐	B-6439	A319-133	5439	
☐	B-6446	A319-133	5623	
☐	B-6450	A319-133/S	5700	
☐	B-6452	A319-115/S	5886	
☐	B-6456	A319-132/S	5920	
☐	B-6457	A319-132/S	5826	
☐	B-6458	A319-115/S	5973	
☐	B-6459	A319-115/S	6116	
☐	B-6460	A319-115/S	6144	
☐	B-6461	A319-115/S	6160	
☐	B-6462	A319-132/S	6052	
☐	B-6463	A319-132/S	6191	
☐	B-6465	A319-115/S	6250	
☐	B-6466	A319-115/S	6269	
☐	B-6469	A319-115/S	6368	
☐	B-6470	A319-115/S	6307	
☐	B-6471	A319-115/S	6453	
☐	B-6472	A319-132/S	6298	
☐	B-6476	A319-115/S	6469	♦
☐	B-6477	A319-115/S	6519	♦
☐	B-8017	A319-132/S	6593	♦
☐	B-	A319-115/S	6836	o/o
☐	B-	A319-115/S	6890	o/o♦
☐	B-	A319-1xx		o/o♦
☐	B-	A319-1xx		o/o♦
☐	B-	A319-1xx		o/o♦
☐	B-	A319-1xx		o/o♦
☐	B-1607	A320-232/S	6180	
☐	B-1608	A320-232/S	6228	
☐	B-1609	A320-214/S	6355	
☐	B-1610	A320-214/S	6373	
☐	B-1611	A320-214/S	6379	
☐	B-1612	A320-214/S	6323	
☐	B-1613	A320-214/S	6274	
☐	B-1635	A320-214/S	6258	~
☐	B-1636	A320-232/S	6284	~
☐	B-1641	A320-232/S	6340	
☐	B-1655	A320-232/S	6431	
☐	B-1678	A320-232/S	6578	~♦
☐	B-1815	A320-232/S	5864	
☐	B-1835	A320-232/S	5942	
☐	B-1836	A320-214/S	6111	
☐	B-1859	A320-232/S	6062	
☐	B-1860	A320-214/S	6213	
☐	B-1861	A320-214/S	6260	
☐	B-1862	A320-214/S	6127	
☐	B-1863	A320-232/S	6137	
☐	B-1865	A320-214/S	6151	
☐	B-2207	A320-214	1028	
☐	B-2208	A320-214	1070	
☐	B-2209	A320-214	1030	
☐	B-2212	A320-214	1316	
☐	B-2213	A320-214	1345	
☐	B-2219	A320-214	1532	
☐	B-2220	A320-214	1542	
☐	B-2221	A320-214	1639	
☐	B-2228	A320-214	1906	
☐	B-2229	A320-214	1911	
☐	B-2230	A320-214	1964	
☐	B-2335	A320-214	1312	
☐	B-2336	A320-214	1330	
☐	B-2337	A320-214	1357	
☐	B-2338	A320-214	1361	
☐	B-2356	A320-214	0665	
☐	B-2357	A320-214	0754	
☐	B-2358	A320-214	0838	
☐	B-2359	A320-214	0854	
☐	B-2372	A320-214	0897	
☐	B-2375	A320-214	0909	
☐	B-2378	A320-214	0939	

	Reg	Type	MSN	
☐	B-2398	A320-214	1108	
☐	B-2399	A320-214	1093	
☐	B-2410	A320-214	2437	
☐	B-2411	A320-214	2451	
☐	B-2412	A320-214	2478	
☐	B-2413	A320-214	2493	
☐	B-2415	A320-214	2498	
☐	B-6001	A320-214	1981	
☐	B-6002	A320-214	2022	
☐	B-6003	A320-214	2034	
☐	B-6005	A320-214	2036	
☐	B-6006	A320-214	2068	
☐	B-6007	A320-214	2056	
☐	B-6008	A320-214	2049	
☐	B-6009	A320-214	2219	
☐	B-6010	A320-214	2221	
☐	B-6011	A320-214	2235	
☐	B-6012	A320-214	2239	
☐	B-6013	A320-214	2244	
☐	B-6333	A320-214	3170	
☐	B-6335	A320-214	3197	
☐	B-6346	A320-232	3481	
☐	B-6370	A320-214	3559	
☐	B-6371	A320-214	3611	
☐	B-6372	A320-232	3613	
☐	B-6373	A320-232	3650	
☐	B-6375	A320-232	3677	
☐	B-6376	A320-232	3692	
☐	B-6399	A320-232	3716	
☐	B-6558	A320-232	3793	
☐	B-6559	A320-232	3904	
☐	B-6560	A320-232	3937	
☐	B-6585	A320-232	3965	
☐	B-6586	A320-232	3775	
☐	B-6587	A320-232	3797	
☐	B-6600	A320-232	3870	
☐	B-6601	A320-232	4037	
☐	B-6616	A320-232	3929	
☐	B-6617	A320-232	4144	
☐	B-6635	A320-232	4027	
☐	B-6636	A320-232	4043	
☐	B-6637	A320-232	4111	
☐	B-6638	A320-232	4240	
☐	B-6639	A320-232	4252	~
☐	B-6671	A320-232	4186	~
☐	B-6672	A320-232	4220	
☐	B-6673	A320-232	4340	
☐	B-6693	A320-232	4239	
☐	B-6695	A320-232	4297	
☐	B-6696	A320-232	4309	
☐	B-6713	A320-232	4342	
☐	B-6715	A320-232	4355	
☐	B-6716	A320-232	4423	
☐	B-6756	A320-214	4659	
☐	B-6757	A320-214	4709	
☐	B-6758	A320-214	4718	
☐	B-6759	A320-214	4723	
☐	B-6760	A320-214	4627	
☐	B-6796	A320-214	4765	
☐	B-6797	A320-214	4685	
☐	B-6798	A320-214	4702	
☐	B-6799	A320-214	4711	
☐	B-6801	A320-214	4722	
☐	B-6802	A320-214	4729	
☐	B-6803	A320-214	4748	
☐	B-6805	A320-214	4877	
☐	B-6829	A320-214	4769	

	Reg	Type	MSN	
☐	B-6830	A320-214	4776	
☐	B-6831	A320-214	4799	
☐	B-6832	A320-214	4831	
☐	B-6870	A320-214	4844	
☐	B-6871	A320-214	4857	
☐	B-6872	A320-214	4886	
☐	B-6873	A320-214	4903	
☐	B-6875	A320-232	5053	
☐	B-6876	A320-214	5135	
☐	B-6877	A320-214	5144	
☐	B-6878	A320-214	4938	
☐	B-6879	A320-214	4946	
☐	B-6880	A320-214	4967	
☐	B-6890	A320-214	5048	
☐	B-6891	A320-214	5047	
☐	B-6892	A320-214	5063	
☐	B-6893	A320-214	5136	
☐	B-6928	A320-214	4987	
☐	B-6929	A320-232	5156	
☐	B-6930	A320-232	5242	~
☐	B-6950	A320-232	5326	
☐	B-6951	A320-232	5363	
☐	B-8018	A320-232/S	6668	~♦
☐	B-8111	A320-232/S	6688	♦
☐	B-8119	A320-232/S	6752	♦
☐	B-8222	A320-232/S	6901	~♦
☐	B-8227	A320-214/S	6582	♦
☐	B-8228	A320-232/S	6624	~♦
☐	B-8229	A320-214/S	6661	♦
☐	B-8237	A320-232/S	6792	♦
☐	B-8276	A320-232/S	6854	♦
☐	B-8281	A320-232/S	6794	♦
☐	B-8391	A320-214/S	6950	o/o♦
☐	B-8392	A320-214/S	6959	o/o♦
☐	B-8393	A320-214/S	7004	o/o♦
☐	B-8395	A320-214/S	7113	o/o♦
☐	B-9900	A320-232	5461	
☐	B-9901	A320-232	5508	
☐	B-9902	A320-232	5524	
☐	B-9921	A320-232/S	5516	
☐	B-9927	A320-214	5527	
☐	B-9941	A320-214/S	5691	
☐	B-9942	A320-214/S	5710	
☐	B-9943	A320-214/S	5726	
☐	B-9945	A320-232/S	5628	
☐	B-9946	A320-214/S	5735	
☐	B-9950	A320-214/S	5668	
☐	B-9970	A320-214/S	5759	
☐	B-9972	A320-232/S	5823	
☐	B-9973	A320-232/S	5852	
☐	B-9975	A320-232/S	5711	
☐	B-	A320-232/S	6900	o/o♦
☐	B-	A320-232/S	6971	o/o♦
☐	B-	A320-214/S	7049	o/o♦
☐	B-	A320-214/S	7168	o/o♦
☐	B-	A320-214/S	7189	o/o♦
☐	B-	A320-214/S	7224	o/o♦
☐	B-	A320-214/S	7238	o/o♦
☐	B-1615	A321-231/S	6396	
☐	B-1640	A321-231/S	6499	
☐	B-1679	A321-231/S	6630	♦
☐	B-1680	A321-231/S	6649	♦
☐	B-1812	A321-231/S	5998	
☐	B-1813	A321-231/S	6089	
☐	B-1837	A321-231/S	6199	
☐	B-1838	A321-231/S	6203	

	Reg	Type	MSN	
☐	B-1858	A321-231/S	6305	
☐	B-2289	A321-211	2309	
☐	B-2290	A321-211	2315	
☐	B-2291	A321-211	2543	
☐	B-2292	A321-211	2549	
☐	B-2419	A321-211	2882	
☐	B-2420	A321-211	2895	
☐	B-6329	A321-211	3233	
☐	B-6330	A321-211	3247	
☐	B-6331	A321-211	3249	
☐	B-6332	A321-211	3262	
☐	B-6345	A321-211	3471	
☐	B-6366	A321-211	3593	
☐	B-6367	A321-211	3612	
☐	B-6368	A321-211	3639	
☐	B-6369	A321-211	3682	
☐	B-6591	A321-231	3969	
☐	B-6592	A321-231	4045	
☐	B-6642	A321-231	4198	
☐	B-6643	A321-231	4209	
☐	B-6668	A321-231	4374	
☐	B-6753	A321-231	4638	
☐	B-6755	A321-231	4746	
☐	B-6886	A321-231	5402	
☐	B-6923	A321-231	5192	
☐	B-6925	A321-231	5210	
☐	B-6926	A321-231	5227	
☐	B-6927	A321-231	5309	
☐	B-8163	A321-211/S	6814	♦
☐	B-8165	A321-231/S	6850	♦
☐	B-8167	A321-211/S	6872	♦
☐	B-8172	A321-231/S	6915	♦
☐	B-8230	A321-231/S	6774	♦
☐	B-8232	A321-211/S	6762	♦
☐	B-8392	A321-214/S	6959	o/o♦
☐	B-8396	A321-211/S	6957	o/o♦
☐	B-8397	A321-211/S	6960	o/o♦
☐	B-8398	A321-211/S	7023	o/o♦
☐	B-8405	A321-211/S	7090	o/o♦
☐	B-8406	A321-211/S	7130	o/o♦
☐	B-9903	A321-231	5481	
☐	B-9905	A321-231	5519	
☐	B-9906	A321-231	5558	
☐	B-9907	A321-231	5575	
☐	B-9947	A321-231	5705	
☐	B-9971	A321-231/S	5770	
☐	B-	A321-211/S	7194	o/o♦
☐	B-	A321-211/S	7212	o/o♦
☐	B-	A321-211/S	7244	o/o♦
☐	B-	A321-211/S	7254	o/o♦
☐	B-	A321-211/S	7265	o/o♦
☐	B-	A321-2xx	7300	o/o♦
☐	B-	A321-2xx	7379	o/o♦

	Reg	Type	MSN	
☐	B-5902	A330-243	1324	
☐	B-5903	A330-243	1331	
☐	B-5908	A330-243	1372	
☐	B-5920	A330-243	1375	
☐	B-5921	A330-243	1402	^
☐	B-5926	A330-243	1421	^
☐	B-5930	A330-243	1429	^
☐	B-5931	A330-243	1440	<CSH
☐	B-5936	A330-243	1461	
☐	B-5937	A330-243	1468	
☐	B-5938	A330-243	1479	
☐	B-5941	A330-243	1484	
☐	B-5942	A330-243	1500	
☐	B-5943	A330-243	1520	
☐	B-5949	A330-243	1537	
☐	B-5952	A330-243	1547	
☐	B-5953	A330-343	1551	
☐	B-5961	A330-243	1569	
☐	B-5962	A330-243	1588	
☐	B-5968	A330-243	1603	
☐	B-5969	A330-343E	1595	
☐	B-5973	A330-243	1617	
☐	B-5975	A330-243	1639	
☐	B-5976	A330-243	1632	♦
☐	B-6082	A330-243	821	
☐	B-6083	A330-343E	830	
☐	B-6085	A330-343E	836	
☐	B-6095	A330-343E	851	
☐	B-6099	A330-243	916	
☐	B-6100	A330-343E	928	
☐	B-6119	A330-343E	713	
☐	B-6120	A330-343E	720	
☐	B-6121	A330-243	728	
☐	B-6122	A330-243	732	
☐	B-6123	A330-243	735	
☐	B-6125	A330-343	773	
☐	B-6126	A330-343	777	
☐	B-6127	A330-343	781	
☐	B-6128	A330-343	782	
☐	B-6129	A330-343	791	
☐	B-6506	A330-343E	936	
☐	B-6507	A330-343E	942	
☐	B-6537	A330-243	1262	
☐	B-6538	A330-243	1267	
☐	B-6543	A330-243	1280	
☐	B-6546	A330-243	1303	
☐	B-8226	A330-243	1655	♦
☐	B-8231	A330-243	1664	♦
☐	B-	A330-243		o/o♦
☐	B-	A330-243		o/o♦

	Reg	Type	MSN	
☐	B-2571	B737-39P	29410/3053	
☐	B-2572	B737-39P	29411/3071	
☐	B-2573	B737-39P	29412/3080	
☐	B-2589	B737-3W0	27127/2377	^ std
☐	B-2594	B737-341	26853/2275	^ std
☐	B-2955	B737-33A	27453/2687	^ std
☐	B-2956	B737-33A	27907/2690	^ std
☐	B-2958	B737-3W0	27522/2727	^
☐	B-2966	B737-33A	27462/2765	^
☐	B-2969	B737-36R	30102/3108	
☐	B-2981	B737-3W0	28972/2919	^ std
☐	B-2983	B737-3W0	28973/2941	^ std
☐	B-2985	B737-3W0	29068/2945	^ std
☐	B-2986	B737-3W0	29069/2951	^ std
☐	B-2988	B737-36R	29087/2970	

	Reg	Type	MSN	
☐	B-2502	B737-7W0	30075/311	^
☐	B-2503	B737-7W0	30074/292	^
☐	B-2639	B737-7W0	29912/140	^
☐	B-2640	B737-7W0	29913/148	^
☐	B-2682	B737-79P	33038/1219	
☐	B-5054	B737-79P	29365/1841	^
☐	B-5074	B737-79P	33008/1718	^
☐	B-5084	B737-79P	33009/1728	^
☐	B-5093	B737-79P/W	29357/1630	^
☐	B-5094	B737-79P/W	29358/1651	^
☐	B-5095	B737-79P/W	29361/1694	^
☐	B-5096	B737-79P/W	29362/1713	^
☐	B-5097	B737-79P	29364/1823	^
☐	B-5225	B737-79P/W	33045/1999	^

	Reg	Type	C/n	Notes
☐	B-5231	B737-79P/W	33046/2034	^
☐	B-5242	B737-79P/W	36269/2357	^
☐	B-5243	B737-79P/W	36270/2398	^
☐	B-5245	B737-79P/W	36271/2697	^
☐	B-5255	B737-79P/W	36757/2902	^
☐	B-5256	B737-79P/W	36758/2949	^
☐	B-5257	B737-79P/W	36759/2968	
☐	B-5258	B737-79P/W	36760/3009	
☐	B-5259	B737-79P/W	36762/3046	^
☐	B-5263	B737-79P/W	36766/3086	^
☐	B-5265	B737-79P/W	36767/3239	^
☐	B-5267	B737-79P/W	36768/3269	^
☐	B-5270	B737-79P/W	36770/3330	^
☐	B-5271	B737-79P/W	36772/3444	^
☐	B-5276	B737-79P/W	39719/3741	^
☐	B-5282	B737-79P/W	39720/3840	^
☐	B-5293	B737-79P/W	39721/4133	
☐	B-5295	B737-79P/W	39723/4258	
☐	B-5802	B737-79P/W	39725/4418	^
☐	B-5807	B737-79P/W	39727/4577	^
☐	B-5809	B737-79P/W	39729/4677	^
☐	B-5815	B737-79P/W	39308/4906	^
☐	B-5816	B737-79P/W	39310/4986	^
☐	B-5817	B737-79P/W	39739/5121	^
☐	B-5819	B737-79P/W	39731/4806	^
☐	B-5820	B737-79P/W	39733/4855	^
☐	B-5821	B737-79P/W	39737/5050	^
☐	B-5822	B737-79P/W	39735/4937	^
☐	B-5828	B737-79P/W	39741/5306	^
☐	B-6141	B737-79P/W	39745/5529	♦
☐	B-6142	B737-79P/W	39747/5629	^♦

	Reg	Type	C/n	Notes
☐	B-1513	B737-89P/W	41477/5561	♦
☐	B-1515	B737-89P/W	41510/5447	♦
☐	B-1702	B737-89P/W	39738/5073	^
☐	B-1703	B737-89P/W	41486/5080	^
☐	B-1722	B737-89P/W	41513/5174	
☐	B-1723	B737-89P/W	41511/5197	
☐	B-1772	B737-89P/W	41470/5244	
☐	B-1773	B737-89P/W	41504/5378	♦
☐	B-1775	B737-89P/W	41507/5466	♦
☐	B-1788	B737-89P/W	39740/5275	^
☐	B-1789	B737-89P/W	41472/5365	♦
☐	B-1790	B737-89P/W	41509/5405	^♦
☐	B-1791	B737-89P/W	41474/5453	^♦
☐	B-1792	B737-89P/W	41475/5497	^♦
☐	B-1907	B737-89P/W	39730/4721	^
☐	B-1908	B737-89P/W	41308/4659	^
☐	B-1910	B737-89P/W	39932/4680	
☐	B-1933	B737-89P/W	41514/4893	
☐	B-1961	B737-89P/W	39732/4820	
☐	B-1965	B737-89P/W	41473/4997	
☐	B-1981	B737-89P/W	41478/5041	
☐	B-5085	B737-89P/W	30691/1702	
☐	B-5086	B737-89P/W	32800/1681	
☐	B-5087	B737-89P/W	32802/1725	
☐	B-5100	B737-89P/W	30681/1645	
☐	B-5101	B737-89P/W	30682/1673	
☐	B-5199	B737-89P/W	36272/2753	
☐	B-5376	B737-86N/W	35226/2641	
☐	B-5472	B737-89P/W	36761/3001	
☐	B-5473	B737-89P/W	36763/3036	
☐	B-5475	B737-89P/W	36765/3062	
☐	B-5492	B737-89P/W	29661/3083	
☐	B-5493	B737-89P/W	29652/3121	
☐	B-5501	B737-89P/W	39388/3203	
☐	B-5515	B737-89P/W	36769/3311	^
☐	B-5516	B737-89N/W	39389/3304	
☐	B-5517	B737-89P/W	29653/3294	
☐	B-5527	B737-89P/W	36771/3343	^
☐	B-5530	B737-89P/W	29655/3351	
☐	B-5589	B737-89P/W	40949/4101	
☐	B-5647	B737-8HX/W	38105/3959	^
☐	B-5683	B737-86N/W	39400/4097	^
☐	B-5689	B737-89P/W	41512/5154	
☐	B-5701	B737-89P/W	39722/4198	^
☐	B-5731	B737-89P/W	40951/4303	
☐	B-5756	B737-89P/W	39724/4383	
☐	B-5779	B737-89P/W	39726/4503	
☐	B-5780	B737-89P/W	39728/4615	
☐	B-5795	B737-89P/W	41305/4587	^
☐	B-5796	B737-89P/W	41306/4599	
☐	B-5857	B737-89P/W	39886/4694	
☐	B-5858	B737-89P/W	39887/4684	
☐	B-6017	B737-89P/W	39744/5485	♦
☐	B-6143	B737-89P/W	41476/5523	^♦
☐	B-6145	B737-89P/W	39746/5581	^♦
☐	B-6146	B737-89P/W	41488/5588	^♦
☐	B-6147	B737-89P/W	41471/5636	^♦
☐	B-6148	B737-89P/W	41479/5661	^♦
☐	B-6149	B737-89P/W	39748/5666	^♦
☐	B-6166	B737-89P/W	41814/5651	♦
☐	B-6249	B737-89P/W	41480/5689	^♦
☐	B-7031	B737-89P/W	41813/5621	♦
☐	B-7170	B737-89P/W	61312/5702	^♦
☐	B-7375	B737-89P/W	41482/5720	♦
☐	B-7376	B737-89P/W	41484/5764	♦
☐	B-7861	B737-89P/W	44384/5803	o/o♦
☐	B-	B737-89P/W	41816/5759	o/o♦
☐	B-	B737-8xx/W		o/o♦
☐	B-	B737-8xx/W		o/o♦
☐	B-	B737-8xx/W		o/o♦

	Reg	Type	C/n	Notes
☐	B-2001	B777-39PER	43269/1232	
☐	B-2002	B777-39PER	43288/1247	
☐	B-2003	B777-39PER	43270/1253	
☐	B-2005	B777-39PER	43271/1259	
☐	B-2020	B777-39PER	43272/1285	♦
☐	B-2021	B777-39PER	43273/1309	♦
☐	B-2022	B777-39PER	43274/1321	♦
☐	B-2023	B777-39PER	43275/1324	♦
☐	B-2025	B777-39PER	43276/1353	♦
☐	B-	B777-39PER		o/o♦
☐	B-	B777-39PER		o/o♦
☐	B-	B777-39PER		o/o♦
☐	B-	B777-39PER		o/o♦
☐	B-	B777-39PER		o/o♦
☐	B-	B777-39PER		o/o♦
☐	B-	B777-39PER		o/o♦

	Reg	Type	C/n	Notes
☐	B-3052	ERJ-145LI	14500905	[LHW]
☐	B-3055	ERJ-145LI	14500921	
☐	B-3056	ERJ-145LI	14500928	dam
☐	B-3057	ERJ-145LI	14500932	
☐	B-3058	ERJ-145LI	14500958	
☐	B-3059	ERJ-145LI	14500949	

^ operated by China Eastern Yunnan division;
~ operated by Jaingsu division

CHINA EXPRESS AIRLINES *G5 / HXA*

	Reg	Type	C/n	Notes
☐	B-3001	CRJ-200ER	7565	[CKG]
☐	B-3012	CRJ-200ER	7557	[CKG]
☐	B-3016	CRJ-200ER	7614	std
☐	B-3565	CRJ-200ER	7690	[CKG]

☐	B-7700	CRJ-200ER	7704	[CKG]
☐	B-3118	CRJ-900LR	15395	♦
☐	B-3360	CRJ-900LR	15289	
☐	B-3361	CRJ-900LR	15290	
☐	B-3362	CRJ-900LR	15291	
☐	B-3363	CRJ-900LR	15312	
☐	B-3366	CRJ-900LR	15321	
☐	B-3368	CRJ-900LR	15332	
☐	B-3369	CRJ-900LR	15344	♦
☐	B-3371	CRJ-900LR	15358	♦
☐	B-3372	CRJ-900LR	15359	♦
☐	B-3377	CRJ-900LR	15363	♦
☐	B-3378	CRJ-900LR	15364	♦
☐	B-3379	CRJ-900LR	15368	♦
☐	B-3380	CRJ-900LR	15369	♦
☐	B-3381	CRJ-900LR	15371	♦
☐	B-3382	CRJ-900LR	15372	♦
☐	B-7691	CRJ-900LR	15288	
☐	B-7692	CRJ-900LR	15280	
☐	B-7693	CRJ-900LR	15281	
☐	B-7760	CRJ-900LR	15282	
☐	B-7762	CRJ-900LR	15285	
☐	B-	CRJ-900LR		o/o
☐	B-	CRJ-900LR		o/o♦
☐	B-	CRJ-900LR		o/o♦
☐	B-	CRJ-900LR		o/o♦
☐	B-	CRJ-900LR		o/o♦
☐	B-	CRJ-900LR		o/o♦
☐	B-	CRJ-900LR		o/o♦
☐	B-	CRJ-900LR		o/o♦
☐	B-	CRJ-900LR		o/o♦

CHINA POSTAL AIRLINES *8Y / CYZ*

☐	B-2135	B737-45R(SF)	29035/3046
☐	B-2513	B737-45R(SF)	29034/3015
☐	B-2525	B737-4Q8(SF)	26337/2811
☐	B-2526	B737-3Y0(SF)	25172/2089
☐	B-2527	B737-3Y0(SF)	25173/2097
☐	B-2528	B737-3Y0(SF)	25174/2168
☐	B-2655	B737-3Q8(SF)	26288/2480
☐	B-2656	B737-3Q8(SF)	26292/2519
☐	B-2661	B737-3Q8(SF)	26284/2418
☐	B-2662	B737-3Q8(SF)	24988/2466
☐	B-2881	B737-45R(SF)	29032/2943
☐	B-2882	B737-45R(SF)	29033/2963
☐	B-2887	B737-4Q8(SF)	26335/2793
☐	B-2891	B737-46J(SF)	28334/2802
☐	B-2892	B737-46J(SF)	28271/2801
☐	B-2961	B737-35N(SF)	28156/2774
☐	B-2962	B737-35N(SF)	28157/2778
☐	B-2968	B737-35N(SF)	28158/2818
☐	B-2996	B737-35N(SF)	29316/3065
☐	B-5065	B737-36Q(SF)	28761/3011
☐	B-5071	B737-341(QC)	24277/1658
☐	B-5072	B737-341(QC)	24279/1673

CHINA SOUTHERN AIRLINES *CZ / CSN*

☐	B-2294	A319-132	2371	
☐	B-2295	A319-132	2408	
☐	B-2296	A319-132	2426	
☐	B-2297	A319-132	2435	
☐	B-6018	A319-132	1971	
☐	B-6019	A319-132	1986	
☐	B-6020	A319-133	2004	
☐	B-6021	A319-133	2008	
☐	B-6039	A319-132	2200	
☐	B-6040	A319-132	2203	
☐	B-6041	A319-132	2232	
☐	B-6158	A319-132	2901	
☐	B-6160	A319-132	2940	
☐	B-6161	A319-132	2948	
☐	B-6162	A319-132	2969	
☐	B-6168	A319-132	3020	
☐	B-6190	A319-132	3860	
☐	B-6191	A319-132	3890	
☐	B-6195	A319-112	3983	
☐	B-6200	A319-115	2519	
☐	B-6201	A319-115	2541	
☐	B-6202	A319-115	2546	
☐	B-6203	A319-112	2554	
☐	B-6205	A319-132	2505	
☐	B-6206	A319-132	2574	
☐	B-6207	A319-132	2579	
☐	B-6208	A319-112	2555	
☐	B-6209	A319-112	2558	
☐	B-6220	A319-132	2815	
☐	B-6239	A319-132	3144	
☐	B-6240	A319-132	3258	
☐	B-6241	A319-132	3269	
☐	B-6242	A319-132	3311	
☐	B-6243	A319-132	3342	
☐	B-6407	A319-132	4036	
☐	B-6408	A319-112	4038	
☐	B-6409	A319-112	4071	
☐	B-1651	A320-232	6462	♦
☐	B-1652	A320-232	6506	♦
☐	B-1653	A320-232	6530	♦
☐	B-1690	A320-232	6551	♦
☐	B-1696	A320-232	6645	♦
☐	B-1697	A320-232	6612	♦
☐	B-1800	A320-214	5976	
☐	B-1801	A320-232/S	6018	
☐	B-1802	A320-232	5837	
☐	B-1803	A320-214	5945	
☐	B-1805	A320-232	5817	
☐	B-1826	A320-232	5875	
☐	B-1828	A320-232/S	6078	
☐	B-1829	A320-232/S	6106	
☐	B-2350	A320-232	0712	
☐	B-2351	A320-233	0718	
☐	B-2352	A320-232	0720	
☐	B-2353	A320-232	0722	
☐	B-2365	A320-232	0849	
☐	B-2366	A320-232	0859	
☐	B-2367	A320-232	0881	
☐	B-2368	A320-232	0895	
☐	B-2369	A320-232	0900	
☐	B-2391	A320-232	0950	
☐	B-2392	A320-232	0966	
☐	B-2393	A320-232	1035	
☐	B-2395	A320-232	1039	
☐	B-2396	A320-232	1057	
☐	B-2406	A320-214	2354	
☐	B-2408	A320-214	2361	
☐	B-6251	A320-214	2484	
☐	B-6252	A320-214	2506	
☐	B-6253	A320-214	2511	
☐	B-6255	A320-214	2637	
☐	B-6263	A320-214	2708	
☐	B-6269	A320-232	2743	
☐	B-6272	A320-214	2770	
☐	B-6275	A320-232	2680	

☐	B-6276	A320-232	2689
☐	B-6277	A320-232	2701
☐	B-6278	A320-232	2714
☐	B-6279	A320-232	2772
☐	B-6281	A320-214	2796
☐	B-6282	A320-214	2824
☐	B-6283	A320-214	2834
☐	B-6287	A320-214	2899
☐	B-6288	A320-214	2855
☐	B-6289	A320-214	2861
☐	B-6290	A320-214	2877
☐	B-6291	A320-214	2915
☐	B-6292	A320-214	2960
☐	B-6293	A320-214	2986
☐	B-6303	A320-214	2950
☐	B-6575	A320-232	3910
☐	B-6577	A320-232	3959
☐	B-6582	A320-232	3999
☐	B-6583	A320-232	4003
☐	B-6588	A320-232	4017
☐	B-6620	A320-214	4172
☐	B-6623	A320-214	4205
☐	B-6627	A320-232	4225
☐	B-6641	A320-232	4140
☐	B-6651	A320-232	4260
☐	B-6652	A320-232	4290
☐	B-6653	A320-232	4232
☐	B-6655	A320-214	4350
☐	B-6656	A320-214	4322
☐	B-6678	A320-232	4248
☐	B-6679	A320-232	4370
☐	B-6680	A320-232	4279
☐	B-6681	A320-214	4365
☐	B-6682	A320-214	4325
☐	B-6702	A320-214	4362
☐	B-6703	A320-214	4396
☐	B-6737	A320-214	4456
☐	B-6738	A320-232	4507>KOC001
☐	B-6739	A320-214	4550
☐	B-6761	A320-232	4696
☐	B-6762	A320-232	4751
☐	B-6766	A320-232	4919
☐	B-6775	A320-214	4613
☐	B-6776	A320-214	4671
☐	B-6782	A320-214	4794
☐	B-6783	A320-214	4808
☐	B-6785	A320-214	4854
☐	B-6786	A320-232	4782
☐	B-6812	A320-232	4883
☐	B-6813	A320-232	4864
☐	B-6815	A320-214	4928
☐	B-6816	A320-232	4912
☐	B-6817	A320-214	4880
☐	B-6826	A320-232	4836
☐	B-6827	A320-232	4982
☐	B-6895	A320-232	5168
☐	B-6896	A320-232	5170
☐	B-6897	A320-232	5214
☐	B-6908	A320-232	5202
☐	B-6909	A320-232	5225
☐	B-6910	A320-232	5061
☐	B-6911	A320-232	5268
☐	B-6945	A320-232	5151
☐	B-6946	A320-232	5183
☐	B-6975	A320-232	5288
☐	B-6976	A320-232	5410
☐	B-6977	A320-232	5503

☐	B-8339	A320-214/S	6974	o/o♦
☐	B-8341	A320-214	6996	o/o♦
☐	B-8357	A320-214	7022	o/o♦
☐	B-9911	A320-232	5480	
☐	B-9912	A320-232	5561	
☐	B-9913	A320-232	5484	
☐	B-9915	A320-232	5506	
☐	B-9916	A320-232	5564	
☐	B-9917	A320-232	5602	
☐	B-9929	A320-214	5693	
☐	B-9930	A320-214	5730	
☐	B-9931	A320-232	5611	
☐	B-9932	A320-232	5579	
☐	B-9951	A320-232	5671	
☐	B-9952	A320-232	5756	
☐	B-9953	A320-232	5832	
☐	B-9958	A320-232	5750	
☐	B-9959	A320-232	5797	
☐	B-	A320-271N	6975	o/o♦
☐	B-	A320-214	7022	o/o♦
☐	B-	A320-214	7039	o/o♦
☐	B-	A320-214	7151	o/o♦
☐	B-	A320-214	7263	o/o♦
☐	B-	A320-2xx	7304	o/o♦
☐	B-	A320-2xxN		o/o♦
☐	B-	A320-2xxN		o/o♦
☐	B-	A320-2xxN		o/o♦
☐	B-	A320-2xxN		o/o♦
☐	B-	A320-2xxN		o/o♦

☐	B-1605	A321-231	6366	
☐	B-1606	A321-231	6385	
☐	B-1616	A321-231	6440	
☐	B-1625	A321-231	6461	
☐	B-1626	A321-231	6504	♦
☐	B-1650	A321-231	6556	♦
☐	B-1806	A321-231/S	5949	
☐	B-1830	A321-231	6049	
☐	B-1831	A321-231	6104	
☐	B-1832	A321-231	6146	
☐	B-1843	A321-231/S	6186	
☐	B-1845	A321-231	6205	
☐	B-1846	A321-231	6211	
☐	B-1847	A321-231	6233	
☐	B-1848	A321-231	6241	
☐	B-1880	A321-231	6261	
☐	B-2280	A321-231	1596	
☐	B-2281	A321-231	1614	
☐	B-2282	A321-231	1776	
☐	B-2283	A321-231	1788	
☐	B-2284	A321-231	1974	
☐	B-2285	A321-231	1995	
☐	B-2287	A321-231	2080	
☐	B-2288	A321-231	2067	
☐	B-2417	A321-231	2521	
☐	B-2418	A321-231	2530	
☐	B-6265	A321-231	2713	
☐	B-6267	A321-231	2741	
☐	B-6270	A321-231	2759	
☐	B-6271	A321-231	2767	
☐	B-6273	A321-231	2809	
☐	B-6302	A321-231	2936	
☐	B-6305	A321-231	2971	
☐	B-6306	A321-231	3067	
☐	B-6307	A321-231	3075	
☐	B-6308	A321-231	3112	
☐	B-6317	A321-231	3217	

☐	B-6318	A321-231	3251	
☐	B-6319	A321-231	3241	
☐	B-6339	A321-231	3507	
☐	B-6342	A321-231	3459	
☐	B-6343	A321-231	3493	
☐	B-6353	A321-231	3552	
☐	B-6355	A321-231	3566	
☐	B-6356	A321-231	3587	
☐	B-6378	A321-231	3645	
☐	B-6379	A321-231	3681	
☐	B-6389	A321-231	3764	
☐	B-6397	A321-231	3784	
☐	B-6398	A321-231	3847	
☐	B-6552	A321-231	3867	
☐	B-6553	A321-231	3920	
☐	B-6578	A321-231	3934	
☐	B-6579	A321-231	3938	
☐	B-6580	A321-231	3951	
☐	B-6581	A321-231	3981	
☐	B-6622	A321-211	4194	
☐	B-6625	A321-231	4184	
☐	B-6626	A321-231	4189	
☐	B-6628	A321-231	4217	
☐	B-6629	A321-231	4224	
☐	B-6630	A321-231	4230	
☐	B-6657	A321-231	4266	
☐	B-6658	A321-231	4271	
☐	B-6659	A321-231	4292	
☐	B-6660	A321-231	4299	
☐	B-6661	A321-231	4341	
☐	B-6662	A321-211	4274	
☐	B-6663	A321-211	4338	
☐	B-6683	A321-211	4369	
☐	B-6685	A321-211	4416	
☐	B-6686	A321-231	4387	
☐	B-6687	A321-231	4430	
☐	B-6912	A321-231	5279	
☐	B-6913	A321-231	5237	
☐	B-6978	A321-231	5534	
☐	B-6979	A321-231	5655	
☐	B-9933	A321-231	5736	
☐	B-9960	A321-231	5890	
☐	B-	A321-211	7064	o/o♦
☐	B-	A321-211	7142	o/o♦
☐	B-	A321-211	7187	o/o♦
☐	B-	A321-211	7222	o/o♦
☐	B-	A321-211	7250	o/o♦
☐	B-	A321-211	7271	o/o♦
☐	B-5917	A330-323E	1392	
☐	B-5922	A330-323E	1425	
☐	B-5928	A330-323E	1430	
☐	B-5939	A330-323E	1494	
☐	B-5940	A330-323E	1519	
☐	B-5951	A330-323E	1536	
☐	B-5959	A330-323E	1575	
☐	B-5965	A330-323E	1593	
☐	B-5966	A330-323E	1625	
☐	B-5967	A330-323E	1636	
☐	B-5970	A330-323E	1645	
☐	B-6056	A330-243	649	
☐	B-6057	A330-243	652	
☐	B-6058	A330-243	656	
☐	B-6059	A330-243	664	
☐	B-6077	A330-243	818	
☐	B-6078	A330-243	840	
☐	B-6086	A330-343E	879	
☐	B-6087	A330-343E	889	
☐	B-6098	A330-343E	908	
☐	B-6111	A330-343E	935	
☐	B-6112	A330-343E	937	
☐	B-6135	A330-223	1096	
☐	B-6500	A330-343E	954	
☐	B-6501	A330-343E	964	
☐	B-6502	A330-343E	958	
☐	B-6515	A330-223	1116	
☐	B-6516	A330-223	1129	
☐	B-6526	A330-223	1220	
☐	B-6528	A330-223	1202	
☐	B-6531	A330-223	1233	
☐	B-6532	A330-223	1244	
☐	B-6542	A330-223	1297	
☐	B-6547	A330-223	1309	
☐	B-6548	A330-223	1335	
☐	B-8358	A330-323E	1699	o/o♦
☐	B-8359	A330-323E	1714	o/o♦
☐	B-	A330-323E	1760	o/o♦
☐	B-	A330-323E		o/o♦
☐	B-6136	A380-841	031	
☐	B-6137	A380-841	036	
☐	B-6138	A380-841	054	
☐	B-6139	A380-841	088	
☐	B-6140	A380-841	120	
☐	B-2574	B737-37K	29407/3100	
☐	B-2575	B737-37K	29408/3104	
☐	B-2959	B737-31B	27520/2775	
☐	B-2169	B737-71B	32936/1531	
☐	B-2620	B737-71B	32937/1569	
☐	B-2622	B737-71B	32938/1603	
☐	B-2916	B737-71B	32939/1607	
☐	B-2917	B737-71B	32940/1624	
☐	B-5068	B737-71B	32933/1430	
☐	B-5069	B737-71B	32934/1465	
☐	B-5070	B737-71B	32935/1507	
☐	B-5221	B737-71B	29366/1872	^
☐	B-5222	B737-71B	29367/1896	^
☐	B-5230	B737-71B	29371/2064	
☐	B-5232	B737-71B	35360/2051	
☐	B-5233	B737-71B	35361/2077	
☐	B-5235	B737-71B	29370/2137	
☐	B-5236	B737-71B	35362/2102	
☐	B-5237	B737-71B	29372/2131	
☐	B-5238	B737-71B	35363/2066	
☐	B-5239	B737-71B	35364/2156	
☐	B-5240	B737-71B	35368/2264	
☐	B-5241	B737-71B	35372/2291	
☐	B-5247	B737-71B	35377/2980	
☐	B-5250	B737-71B	35378/2346	
☐	B-5251	B737-71B	35384/2446	
☐	B-5252	B737-71B	35382/3034	
☐	B-5253	B737-71B	35383/3005	
☐	B-5275	B737-71B	38912/3730	
☐	B-5281	B737-71B/W	38914/3864	
☐	B-5283	B737-71B/W	38919/4000	
☐	B-5285	B737-71B/W	38917/3922	
☐	B-5290	B737-71B/W	38925/4120	
☐	B-5291	B737-71B/W	38962/4103	
☐	B-1520	B737-81B/W	41334/5502	♦
☐	B-1525	B737-81B/W	41611/5448	♦
☐	B-1700	B737-81B/W	43401/5261	
☐	B-1701	B737-86N/W	41251/5008	
☐	B-1717	B737-81B/W	38924/5146	

☐	B-1718	B737-81B/W	38934/5203	
☐	B-1736	B737-81B/W	41326/5247	
☐	B-1737	B737-81B/W	41606/5232	
☐	B-1747	B737-81B/W	41327/5281	
☐	B-1748	B737-81B/W	41328/5334	♦
☐	B-1780	B737-81B/W	41610/5421	^♦
☐	B-1781	B737-86N/W	43404/5426	♦
☐	B-1782	B737-81B/W	41333/5451	♦
☐	B-1916	B737-81B/W	41315/4750	
☐	B-1917	B737-81B/W	41316/4803	
☐	B-1918	B737-81B/W	38915/4831	
☐	B-1919	B737-81B/W	38965/4799	
☐	B-1920	B737-86N/W	41265/4745	
☐	B-1921	B737-86N/W	41245/4766	
☐	B-1923	B737-86N/W	35645/4812	
☐	B-1925	B737-86N/W	41250/4941	
☐	B-1950	B737-81B/W	41317/4880	
☐	B-1951	B737-81B/W	38921/4878	
☐	B-1952	B737-81B/W	41319/4912	
☐	B-1953	B737-81B/W	41320/4946	
☐	B-1955	B737-81B/W	38923/4959	
☐	B-1979	B737-86N/W	41252/5046	
☐	B-1980	B737-86N/W	41268/4993	
☐	B-2693	B737-81B	32921/1187	
☐	B-2694	B737-81B	32922/1199	
☐	B-2695	B737-81B	32923/1213	
☐	B-2696	B737-81B	32924/1230	
☐	B-2697	B737-81B	32925/1250	
☐	B-5020	B737-81B	32926/1268	
☐	B-5021	B737-81B	32927/1290	
☐	B-5022	B737-81B	32928/1323	
☐	B-5040	B737-81B	32929/1348	
☐	B-5041	B737-81B	32930/1355	
☐	B-5042	B737-81B	32931/1362	
☐	B-5067	B737-81B	32932/1395	
☐	B-5112	B737-86N	34248/1806	
☐	B-5113	B737-81B	34250/1784	
☐	B-5120	B737-83N/W	32580/1024	
☐	B-5121	B737-83N/W	32609/1059	
☐	B-5122	B737-83N/W	32610/1110	
☐	B-5123	B737-83N/W	32611/1135	
☐	B-5125	B737-83N/W	32612/1184	
☐	B-5126	B737-83N/W	32613/1197	
☐	B-5127	B737-83N/W	32615/1207	
☐	B-5128	B737-83N/W	32882/1163	
☐	B-5129	B737-83N/W	32884/1181	
☐	B-5147	B737-81B	30697/1915	
☐	B-5149	B737-81B	30699/1933	
☐	B-5155	B737-8K5/W	30783/804	
☐	B-5156	B737-81Q/W	30786/1138	
☐	B-5157	B737-81Q/W	30787/1234	
☐	B-5163	B737-81B	30708/2087	
☐	B-5166	B737-81B	33006/1983	
☐	B-5189	B737-81B	35365/2191	
☐	B-5190	B737-81B	35366/2223	
☐	B-5191	B737-81B	35367/2237	
☐	B-5192	B737-81B	35369/2272	
☐	B-5193	B737-81B	35370/2299	
☐	B-5195	B737-81B	35371/2302	
☐	B-5300	B737-81B	35375/2314	
☐	B-5310	B737-81B	35376/2329	
☐	B-5339	B737-81B	35380/2372	
☐	B-5340	B737-81B	35381/2402	
☐	B-5356	B737-81B	35385/2486	
☐	B-5419	B737-81B	35379/2957	
☐	B-5420	B737-81B	35374/2940	
☐	B-5421	B737-81B	35373/2881	
☐	B-5445	B737-81B	35388/3154	
☐	B-5446	B737-81B	35389/3144	
☐	B-5468	B737-81B	35386/3068	
☐	B-5469	B737-81B	35387/3041	
☐	B-5586	B737-86J/W	36878/3631	
☐	B-5587	B737-81B/W	38966/3650	
☐	B-5596	B737-81B/W	38964/3700	
☐	B-5597	B737-81B/W	38913/3776	
☐	B-5598	B737-86J/W	36877/3784	
☐	B-5609	B737-81B/W	38963/3838	
☐	B-5640	B737-81B/W	38918/3961	~♦
☐	B-5641	B737-81B/W	38916/3898	
☐	B-5643	B737-81B/W	38920/4031	
☐	B-5645	B737-81B/W	38922/4076	
☐	B-5646	B737-81B/W	38932/4064	
☐	B-5675	B737-81B/W	38926/4154	
☐	B-5676	B737-81B/W	38927/4138	
☐	B-5677	B737-81B/W	38928/4178	
☐	B-5678	B737-81B/W	38929/4165	
☐	B-5697	B737-81B/W	38931/4207	
☐	B-5698	B737-81B/W	38933/4244	
☐	B-5699	B737-81B/W	38935/4274	
☐	B-5715	B737-81B/W	38936/4300	
☐	B-5716	B737-81B/W	38937/4307	~♦
☐	B-5717	B737-81B/W	38938/4347	
☐	B-5718	B737-81B/W	38939/4359	~♦
☐	B-5719	B737-81B/W	38940/4370	
☐	B-5720	B737-81B/W	38941/4379	
☐	B-5721	B737-81B/W	38942/4388	~♦
☐	B-5738	B737-81B/W	38930/4443	
☐	B-5739	B737-81B/W	38943/4427	
☐	B-5740	B737-81B/W	38944/4409	
☐	B-5741	B737-81B/W	38945/4464	
☐	B-5742	B737-81B/W	38946/4454	
☐	B-5743	B737-81B/W	38947/4492	
☐	B-5745	B737-81B/W	38948/4498	
☐	B-5746	B737-81B/W	38952/4505	
☐	B-5747	B737-81B/W	38961/4485	
☐	B-5748	B737-81B/W	41302/4415	
☐	B-5749	B737-81B/W	41303/4439	
☐	B-5759	B737-81B/W	38949/4541	
☐	B-5760	B737-81B/W	38957/4533	
☐	B-5761	B737-81B/W	38958/4527	
☐	B-5762	B737-81B/W	38950/4548	
☐	B-5766	B737-81B/W	38951/4570	
☐	B-5767	B737-81B/W	38959/4576	
☐	B-5768	B737-81B/W	38960/4585	
☐	B-5769	B737-81B/W	38953/4617	
☐	B-5770	B737-81B/W	38954/4598	
☐	B-5836	B737-81B/W	38955/4642	
☐	B-5837	B737-81B/W	38956/4662	
☐	B-6067	B737-81B/W	41612/5591	♦
☐	B-6068	B737-81B/W	41613/5632	♦
☐	B-6069	B737-81B/W	41614/5644	♦

☐	B-2461	B747-41BF	32804/1312
☐	B-2473	B747-41BF	32803/1306

☐	B-2812	B757-28S	32341/961
☐	B-2813	B757-28S	32342/966
☐	B-2823	B757-21B	25888/575
☐	B-2824	B757-21B	25889/583
☐	B-2825	B757-21B	25890/585
☐	B-2827	B757-2Y0	26156/503
☐	B-2830	B757-28S	32343/1015
☐	B-2831	B757-2Y0	26153/482
☐	B-2835	B757-236	25598/445
☐	B-2851	B757-28S	29215/797

Reg	Type	c/n	
B-2853	B757-28S	29216/811	
B-2859	B757-28S	29217/868	

Reg	Type	c/n	
B-2007	B777-31BER	43221/1223	
B-2008	B777-31BER	43222/1229	
B-2009	B777-31BER	43223/1260	
B-2010	B777-F1B	41634/1268	
B-2026	B777-F1B	41635/1306	♦
B-2027	B777-F1B	41636/1308	♦
B-2028	B777-F1B	41637/1318	♦
B-2029	B777-31BER	43224/1329	♦
B-2041	B777-F1B	41632/1120	
B-2042	B777-F1B	41633/1126	
B-2048	B777-31BER	43220/1219	
B-2049	B777-31BER	43225/1358	♦
B-2051	B777-21B	27357/20	
B-2052	B777-21B	27358/24	
B-2053	B777-21B	27359/46	
B-2054	B777-21B	27360/48	
B-2071	B777-F1B	37309/760	
B-2072	B777-F1B	37310/770	
B-2073	B777-F1B	37311/811	
B-2075	B777-F1B	37312/820	
B-2080	B777-F1B	37314/983	
B-2081	B777-F1B	37313/888	
B-2099	B777-31BER	43219/1173	
B-	B777-31BER		o/o
B-	B777-31BER		o/o
B-	B777-31BER		o/o

Reg	Type	c/n	
B-2725	B787-8	34923/34	
B-2726	B787-8	34924/36	
B-2727	B787-8	34925/43	
B-2732	B787-8	34926/93	
B-2733	B787-8	34927/95	
B-2735	B787-8	34928/119	
B-2736	B787-8	34929/100	
B-2737	B787-8	34930/104	
B-2787	B787-8	34931/154	
B-2788	B787-8	34932/172	

Reg	Type	c/n	
B-3135	ERJ-190LR	19000535	
B-3136	ERJ-190LR	19000513	
B-3137	ERJ-190LR	19000524	
B-3138	ERJ-190LR	19000539	
B-3139	ERJ-190LR	19000548	
B-3145	ERJ-190LR	19000529	
B-3146	ERJ-190LR	19000476	
B-3147	ERJ-190LR	19000477	
B-3148	ERJ-190LR	19000483	
B-3149	ERJ-190LR	19000488	
B-3197	ERJ-190LR	19000456	
B-3198	ERJ-190LR	19000465	
B-3199	ERJ-190LR	19000469	
B-3205	ERJ-190LR	19000556	
B-3206	ERJ-190LR	19000560	
B-3209	ERJ-190LR	19000564	
B-3210	ERJ-190LR	19000570	
B-3216	ERJ-190LR	19000598	
B-3217	ERJ-190LR	19000605	
B-3218	ERJ-190LR	19000613	

^ operates as Air Guizhou (G4 / CGH) but in China Southern c/s

~ operates as Shantou Airlines but in China Southern c/s

CHINA UNITED AIRLINES — KN / CUA

Reg	Type	c/n	
B-4090	A319-115	5023	
B-4091	A319-115	5088	
B-4092	A319-115	5907	

Reg	Type	c/n	
B-4008	B737-3T0	23839/1507	
B-4009	B737-3T0	23840/1516	
B-4018	B737-33A	25502/2310	
B-4019	B737-33A	25503/2313	
B-4020	B737-34N	28081/2746	
B-4021	B737-34N	28082/2747	
B-4052	B737-3Q8	24701/1957	
B-4053	B737-3Q8	24702/1994	

Reg	Type	c/n	
B-2681	B737-79P	33037/1198	
B-2684	B737-79P	33039/1227	
B-2685	B737-79P	33040/1244	
B-4025	B737-76D	33470/1334	
B-4026	B737-76D	33472/1343	
B-5208	B737-79P/W	33041/1902	
B-5209	B737-79P/W	33042/1947	
B-5210	B737-79P/W	33043/1976	
B-5223	B737-79P/W	33044/1987	
B-5262	B737-79P/W	36764/3067	

Reg	Type	c/n	
B-1523	B737-89P/W	39742/5349	♦
B-1750	B737-89P/W	61308/5201	
B-1751	B737-89P/W	61309/5209	
B-1752	B737-89P/W	61310/5211	
B-1753	B737-89P/W	61311/5215	
B-1989	B737-89P/W	39734/4913	
B-1990	B737-89P/W	39736/5007	
B-4080	B737-86N/W	36774/2944	
B-4081	B737-86N/W	36775/2951	
B-4082	B737-89L/W	40018/4251	
B-4083	B737-89L/W	40037/4262	
B-5183	B737-8Q8/W	30711/2159	
B-5323	B737-8Q8/W	30725/2292	
B-5353	B737-8Q8/W	30728/2386	
B-5399	B737-86N/W	35224/2617	
B-5448	B737-86N/W	38021/3679	
B-5470	B737-86D/W	35774/3010	
B-5471	B737-86D/W	35775/3098	
B-5547	B737-86N/W	36806/3448	
B-5665	B737-8HX/W	38106/3976	
B-5838	B737-89P/W	40953/4575	
B-5839	B737-89P/W	40952/4536	
B-5840	B737-89P/W	41304/4493	
B-7370	B737-89P/W	61313/5685	♦
B-7371	B737-84P/W	61314/5697	♦
B-7372	B737-89P/W	61315/5711	♦
B-	B737-89P/W	61681/5758	o/o♦

Former China United aircraft - CRJs and Tu-154s – are now operated by Chinese Air Force and are included in the Corporate Aircraft section

CHINA XINHUA AIRLINES — XW / CXH

Reg	Type	c/n	
B-5082	B737-883	30193/587	
B-5138	B737-84P/W	32607/1832	
B-5139	B737-84P/W	32608/1855	
B-5141	B737-84P/W	34030/1800	
B-5153	B737-84P/W	34029/1921	

CHONGQING AIRLINES — OQ / CQN

Reg	Type	c/n	
B-1827	A320-232	5930	♦
B-2343	A320-233	0696	
B-2345	A320-233	0698	
B-2346	A320-233	0704	
B-2347	A320-233	0705	
B-6183	A319-115	3828	♦

☐	B-6187	A319-115	3903	
☐	B-6246	A319-133	3836	
☐	B-6247	A319-133	3876	
☐	B-6248	A319-133	3901	
☐	B-6576	A320-232	3941	
☐	B-9976	A320-232	5645	
☐	B-9977	A320-232	5713	

COLORFUL GUIZHOU AIRLINES — *GY /*

☐	B-3115	ERJ-190LR	19000701	♦
☐	B-3116	ERJ-190LR	19000703	♦
☐	B-	ERJ-190LR		o/o♦
☐	B-	ERJ-190LR		o/o♦
☐	B-	ERJ-190LR		o/o♦
☐	B-	ERJ-190LR		o/o♦

DALIAN AIRLINES — *CA / CCD*

☐	B-5196	B737-86N	36810/2699	
☐	B-5197	B737-86N	36811/2777	
☐	B-5553	B737-89L/W	40026/3576	
☐	B-5639	B737-89L/W	40033/4004	
☐	B-5642	B737-8L/W	40017/4060	
☐	B-5729	B737-89L/W	40038/4422	
☐	B-5850	B737-89L/W	41311/4689	
☐	B-6105	B737-89L/W	44917/5484	♦

DONGHAI AIRLINES — *J5 / EPA*

☐	B-2517	B737-3W0(SF)	23396/1166	[SZX]
☐	B-2518	B737-3W0(SF)	23397/1193	std
☐	B-2897	B737-3B7F	24902/1973	
☐	B-2898	B737-3Y0F	24916/2066	
☐	B-5046	B737-341(F)	24276/1645	
☐	B-5047	B737-341(F)	24278/1660	
☐	B-1705	B737-86J/W	39387/4966	
☐	B-1770	B737-8Q8/W	41802/5228	
☐	B-1771	B737-8Q8/W	41803/5274	
☐	B-5311	B737-8Q8	29373/2171	
☐	B-5312	B737-8Q8	29374/2203	o/o
☐	B-5313	B737-8Q8	30716/2210	
☐	B-6980	B737-83Z/W	61268/5537	♦
☐	B-6981	B737-83Z/W	61271/5704	♦
☐	B-6982	B737-83Z/W	61270/5640	♦
☐	B-6983	B737-83Z/W	61269/5592	♦
☐	B-7100	B737-8Q8/W	41810/5594	o/o♦
☐	B-	B737-83Z/W		o/o♦
☐	B-	B737-83Z/W		o/o♦
☐	B-	B737-83Z/W		o/o♦
☐	B-	B737-83Z/W		o/o♦
☐	B-	B737-83Z/W		o/o♦
☐	B-	B737-83Z/W		o/o♦

FUZHOU AIRLINES — *FU / FZA*

☐	B-1905	B737-86J/W	39383/4601	♦
☐	B-1906	B737-86J/W	37768/4118	♦
☐	B-5182	B737-808/W	34708/2097	
☐	B-5430	B737-84P/W	34032/2827	
☐	B-5503	B737-84P/W	36782/3186	
☐	B-7105	B737-84P/W	61321/5612	♦
☐	B-7113	B737-84P/W	61322/5678	♦

GRAND CHINA AIRLINES — *CN / GDC*

☐	B-2652	B737-84P	30475/731	
☐	B-5089	B737-883	28320/551	
☐	B-5482	B737-84P/W	35748/2938	

GX AIRLINES — *GX / CBG*

☐	B-3122	ERJ-190LR	19000186	♦
☐	B-3125	ERJ-190LR	19000194	♦
☐	B-3165	ERJ-190LR	19000340	♦
☐	B-3176	ERJ-190LR	19000406	♦
☐	B-3180	ERJ-190LR	19000442	♦
☐	B-3183	ERJ-190LR	19000472	♦
☐	B-3185	ERJ-190LR	19000480	♦
☐	B-3186	ERJ-190LR	19000489	♦
☐	B-3179	ERJ-190LR	19000426	♦
☐	B-3215	ERJ-190LR	19000591	♦

HAINAN AIRLINES — *HU / CHH*

☐	B-5905	A330-343E	1325	
☐	B-5935	A330-343E	1438	
☐	B-5950	A330-343E	1532	
☐	B-5955	A330-243	1558	
☐	B-5963	A330-243	1573	
☐	B-5971	A330-343E	1614	♦
☐	B-5972	A330-343E	1634	♦
☐	B-5979	A330-243	1591	
☐	B-8015	A330-343E	1656	♦
☐	B-8016	A330-343E	1663	♦
☐	B-8117	A330-343E	1677	♦
☐	B-8118	A330-343E	1686	♦
☐	B-8287	A330-343E	1703	♦
☐	B-6088	A330-243	906	
☐	B-6089	A330-243	919	
☐	B-6116	A330-243	875	
☐	B-6118	A330-243	881	
☐	B-6133	A330-243	982	
☐	B-6519	A330-243	1159	
☐	B-6520	A330-343E	1168	
☐	B-6527	A330-343E	1178	
☐	B-6529	A330-343E	1190	
☐	B-6539	A330-343E	1255	
☐	B-5060	B737-76N	28582/154	
☐	B-5061	B737-76N	28583/163	
☐	B-5062	B737-76N	28585/173	
☐	B-5288	B737-74P/W	39201/4519	♦
☐	B-5289	B737-74P/W	39198/4395	
☐	B-5813	B737-74P/W	39210/4885	
☐	B-1501	B737-84P/W	41382/5442	♦
☐	B-1502	B737-84P/W	43660/5436	♦
☐	B-1503	B737-84P/W	39961/5452	♦
☐	B-1505	B737-84P/W	39962/5460	♦
☐	B-1725	B737-84P/W	38147/5167	
☐	B-1726	B737-84P/W	39217/5155	
☐	B-1727	B737-84P/W	39216/5128	
☐	B-1728	B737-84P/W	39218/5194	
☐	B-1729	B737-84P/W	41377/5175	
☐	B-1733	B737-86N/W	41254/5132	
☐	B-1735	B737-86N/W	41269/5097	
☐	B-1783	B737-84P/W	39219/5233	
☐	B-1785	B737-84P/W	41378/5243	
☐	B-1786	B737-84P/W	39220/5268	
☐	B-1787	B737-84P/W	41379/5277	
☐	B-1793	B737-86J/W	36122/4391	♦
☐	B-1795	B737-84P/W	41568/5308	♦
☐	B-1796	B737-84P/W	41569/5331	♦
☐	B-1797	B737-84P/W	41570/5382	♦
☐	B-1798	B737-86N/W	43403/5359	♦
☐	B-1799	B737-84P/W	41381/5418	♦
☐	B-1902	B737-86J/W	37769/4159	

☐	B-1903	B737-86J/W	36872/4209	
☐	B-1927	B737-84P/W	39207/4760	
☐	B-1928	B737-84P/W	39208/4794	
☐	B-1929	B737-84P/W	39209/4838	
☐	B-1995	B737-84P/W	39213/5006	
☐	B-1996	B737-84P/W	39214/5027	
☐	B-1997	B737-84P/W	39215/5076	
☐	B-2638	B737-8Q8	28220/212	
☐	B-2647	B737-84P	29947/345	
☐	B-2651	B737-84P	30474/607	
☐	B-2676	B737-84P/W	32602/1170	
☐	B-2677	B737-84P/W	32604/1191	
☐	B-5083	B737-883	28319/548	
☐	B-5090	B737-883	28321/577	
☐	B-5135	B737-84P/W	32603/1766	
☐	B-5136	B737-84P/W	32605/1796	
☐	B-5137	B737-84P/W	32606/1805	
☐	B-5337	B737-84P/W	35747/2433	
☐	B-5338	B737-84P/W	35749/2330	
☐	B-5346	B737-8BK/W	29673/2373	
☐	B-5358	B737-84P/W	35077/2419	
☐	B-5359	B737-8FH/W	35101/2459	
☐	B-5371	B737-84P/W	35752/2556	
☐	B-5372	B737-84P/W	35758/2593	
☐	B-5373	B737-84P/W	35754/2618	
☐	B-5375	B737-84P/W	35762/2648	
☐	B-5405	B737-84P/W	35759/2668	
☐	B-5406	B737-84P/W	35760/2678	
☐	B-5408	B737-84P/W	35764/2778	
☐	B-5416	B737-84P/W	34031/2801	
☐	B-5417	B737-86N/W	35639/2821	
☐	B-5418	B737-86N/W	36541/2769	
☐	B-5427	B737-8Q8/W	35285/2772	
☐	B-5428	B737-86N/W	36542/2806	
☐	B-5429	B737-86N/W	36543/2831	
☐	B-5439	B737-808/W	34707/2046	
☐	B-5462	B737-84P/W	36780/3095	
☐	B-5463	B737-84P/W	35755/3339	
☐	B-5465	B737-84P/W	34033/2854	
☐	B-5466	B737-84P/W	34034/2912	
☐	B-5467	B737-84P/W	36779/2885	
☐	B-5478	B737-84P/W	35751/3038	
☐	B-5479	B737-84P/W	35753/3066	
☐	B-5480	B737-86N/W	35648/2973	
☐	B-5481	B737-86N/W	35649/2981	
☐	B-5483	B737-84P/W	35750/3007	
☐	B-5502	B737-84P/W	35757/3192	
☐	B-5520	B737-84P/W	35765/3344	
☐	B-5521	B737-84P/W	35766/3313	
☐	B-5522	B737-84P/W	36781/3278	
☐	B-5538	B737-84P/W	36783/3382	
☐	B-5539	B737-84P/W	35763/3378	
☐	B-5540	B737-84P/W	35761/3392	
☐	B-5579	B737-84P/W	39223/3610	
☐	B-5580	B737-84P/W	39224/3647	
☐	B-5581	B737-84P/W	38143/3713	
☐	B-5611	B737-84P/W	38145/3783	
☐	B-5620	B737-84P/W	38144/3733	
☐	B-5623	B737-84P/W	38148/3865	
☐	B-5625	B737-84P/W	38146/3812	
☐	B-5636	B737-84P/W	38149/3889	
☐	B-5637	B737-84P/W	38150/3937	
☐	B-5638	B737-84P/W	38151/3951	
☐	B-5661	B737-84P/W	38152/3995	
☐	B-5662	B737-84P/W	38153/4036	
☐	B-5663	B737-84P/W	38154/4063	
☐	B-5685	B737-84P/W	38155/4115	
☐	B-5686	B737-84P/W	38156/4147	
☐	B-5687	B737-84P/W	38157/4171	
☐	B-5709	B737-808/W	34709/2121	
☐	B-5710	B737-84P/W	35072/2155	
☐	B-5711	B737-84P/W	39195/4304	
☐	B-5712	B737-84P/W	39196/4355	
☐	B-5713	B737-84P/W	39197/4381	
☐	B-5733	B737-84P/W	37422/3214	
☐	B-5735	B737-84P/W	37953/3299	
☐	B-5765	B737-84P/W	35274/2570	
☐	B-5797	B737-84P/W	39202/4584	
☐	B-5798	B737-84P/W	39203/4596	
☐	B-5835	B737-84P/W	35276/2611	
☐	B-5852	B737-84P/W	39204/4651	
☐	B-5853	B737-84P/W	39205/4678	
☐	B-5855	B737-84P/W	39206/4716	
☐	B-6060	B737-84P/W	39963/5509	♦
☐	B-6061	B737-84P/W	41383/5489	♦
☐	B-6062	B737-84P/W	43658/5493	♦
☐	B-6063	B737-84P/W	41384/5538	♦
☐	B-6065	B737-84P/W	41385/5544	♦
☐	B-6066	B737-84P/W	41387/5577	♦
☐	B-6808	B737-84P/W	41389/5633	♦
☐	B-6809	B737-86N/W	43409/5693	♦
☐	B-7171	B737-86N/W	60688/5731	♦
☐	B-7172	B737-86N/W	60689/5762	♦
☐	B-	B737-84P/W	43663	o/o♦
☐	B-	B737-84P/W		o/o♦
☐	B-	B737-84P/W		o/o♦
☐	B-	B737-84P/W		o/o♦

☐	B-2490	B767-34PER	33047/889	
☐	B-2491	B767-34PER	33048/891	
☐	B-2492	B767-34PER	33049/893	

☐	B-2722	B787-8	34939/76	
☐	B-2723	B787-8	34944/81	
☐	B-2728	B787-8	34938/73	
☐	B-2729	B787-8	34941/79	
☐	B-2730	B787-8	34943/85	
☐	B-2731	B787-8	34945/131	
☐	B-2738	B787-8	34940/151	
☐	B-2739	B787-8	38055/171	
☐	B-2750	B787-8	34942/262	
☐	B-2759	B787-8	38056/274	♦
☐	B-	B787-9	60283/430	o/o♦
☐	B-	B787-9	60284/469	o/o♦
☐	B-	B787-9	62718	o/o♦
☐	B-	B787-9		o/o♦
☐	B-	B787-9		o/o♦

HEBEI AIRLINES — *NS / DBH*

☐	B-1930	B737-85C/W	39335/4796	
☐	B-5212	B737-75C	34024/1703	
☐	B-5215	B737-75C	34025/1724	
☐	B-5456	B737-85C/W	35054/2914	
☐	B-5459	B737-85C/W	35057/2992	♦
☐	B-5660	B737-85C/W	38397/4215	
☐	B-5753	B737-85C/W	39331/4402	
☐	B-6299	B737-8LW/W	42965/5488	♦
☐	B-7195	B737-85C/W	43885/5778	o/o♦

☐	B-3040	ERJ-145LR	145317	[SJW]
☐	B-3041	ERJ-145LR	145349	[SJW]
☐	B-3042	ERJ-145LR	145352	[SJW]
☐	B-3043	ERJ-145LR	145377	[SJW]
☐	B-3045	ERJ-145LR	145470	[SJW]

	Reg	Type	c/n	
☐	B-3140	ERJ-190LR	19000625	
☐	B-3187	ERJ-190LR	19000497	
☐	B-3188	ERJ-190LR	19000502	
☐	B-3207	ERJ-190LR	19000561	
☐	B-3208	ERJ-190LR	19000566	
☐	B-3383	ERJ-190LR	19000694	♦
☐	B-	ERJ-190LR		o/o

HONGTU AIRLINES

☐	B-8285	A321-211/S	6156	♦
☐	B-8318	A321-211/S	6268	o/o♦

JIANGSU JET

☐	B-3005	CRJ-200ER	7435	♦
☐	B-3006	CRJ-200ER	7443	♦
☐	B-3009	CRJ-200ER	7522	♦
☐	B-3007	CRJ-200ER	7498	♦
☐	B-3008	CRJ-200ER	7512	♦

JIANGXI AIRLINES RY / CJX

☐	B-5511	B737-85C/W	37576/3245	♦
☐	B-5512	B737-85C/W	37577/3255	♦

JOY AIR JR / JOY

☐	B-3451	XIAN MA60	0705	
☐	B-3452	XIAN MA60	0706	
☐	B-3453	XIAN MA60	0707	
☐	B-3455	XIAN MA60	0803	
☐	B-3459	XIAN MA60	0804	
☐	B-3716	XIAN MA60	1002	
☐	B-3717	XIAN MA60	1003	
☐	B-3718	XIAN MA60	1103	
☐	B-	XIAN MA60		o/o
☐	B-	XIAN MA60		o/o
☐	B-	XIAN MA60		o/o
☐	B-	XIAN MA60		o/o
☐	B-	XIAN MA60		o/o
☐	B-	XIAN MA60		o/o
☐	B-	XIAN MA60		o/o
☐	B-	XIAN MA60		o/o

It is reported Joy Air will inherit OK Air's MA60 fleet.

JUNEYAO AIRLINES HO / DKH

☐	B-1681	A320-214/S	6542	♦
☐	B-1870	A320-214/S	6315	
☐	B-1871	A320-214/S	6392	
☐	B-6298	A320-214	2975	
☐	B-6311	A320-214	3027	
☐	B-6338	A320-214	3368	
☐	B-6340	A320-214	3234	
☐	B-6341	A320-214	3268	
☐	B-6381	A320-214	3485	
☐	B-6395	A320-214	3596	
☐	B-6396	A320-214	3605	
☐	B-6572	A320-214	3967	
☐	B-6602	A320-214	3984	
☐	B-6618	A320-214	4102	
☐	B-6619	A320-214	4154	
☐	B-6640	A320-214	4064	
☐	B-6670	A320-214	4276	
☐	B-6717	A320-214	4401	
☐	B-6735	A320-214	4429	
☐	B-6736	A320-214	4573	
☐	B-6768	A320-214	4833	
☐	B-6787	A320-214	4587	
☐	B-6788	A320-214	4652	
☐	B-6860	A320-214	4981	
☐	B-6861	A320-214	4840	
☐	B-6901	A320-214	5070	
☐	B-6921	A320-214	5013	
☐	B-6922	A320-214	5071	
☐	B-6948	A320-214	5329	
☐	B-6949	A320-214	5339	
☐	B-6962	A320-214	5491	
☐	B-6963	A320-214	5455	
☐	B-6965	A320-214	5226	
☐	B-6966	A320-214	5131	
☐	B-8035	A320-214/S	6637	♦
☐	B-8235	A320-214/S	6843	♦
☐	B-8236	A320-214/S	6808	♦
☐	B-8408	A320-214/S	6944	std♦
☐	B-9978	A320-214	5737	
☐	B-	A320-214/S	7116	o/o♦
☐	B-	A320-214/S	7169	o/o♦
☐	B-	A320-214/S	7350	o/o♦
☐	B-1645	A321-211/S	6433	
☐	B-1646	A321-211/S	6435	
☐	B-1647	A321-211/S	6477	
☐	B-1808	A321-211/S	5876	
☐	B-1857	A321-211/S	6172	
☐	B-1872	A321-211/S	6221	
☐	B-8036	A321-211/S	6627	♦
☐	B-8068	A321-211/S	6701	♦
☐	B-8315	A321-231/S	6879	♦
☐	B-8317	A321-211/S	6855	♦
☐	B-8407	A321-231/S	6916	♦
☐	B-9957	A321-211	5674	
☐	B-	A321-231/S	7065	o/o♦
☐	B-	A321-231/S	7199	o/o♦
☐	B-	A321-231/S	7208	o/o♦
☐	B-	A321-231/S	7229	o/o♦
☐	B-	A321-231/S	7278	o/o♦

KUNMING AIRLINES KY / KNA

☐	B-1507	B737-87L/W	42050/5407	♦
☐	B-1926	B737-87L/W	41111/4752	
☐	B-1991	B737-87L/W	41112/5093	
☐	B-2666	B737-78S	30169/631	
☐	B-2668	B737-78S	30171/681	
☐	B-2678	B737-76N	32244/895	
☐	B-2679	B737-76N	29893/710	
☐	B-5026	B737-7BX	30742/864	
☐	B-5672	B737-87L/W	39154/4146	
☐	B-5702	B737-87L/W	39131/4265	
☐	B-6491	B737-8LY/W	41337/5657	♦
☐	B-6492	B737-87L/W	44381/5627	♦
☐	B-6493	B737-8LY/W	44382/5580	♦
☐	B-6495	B737-8LY/W	44383/5643	♦
☐	B-	B737-7xx/W		o/o♦
☐	B-	B737-7xx/W		o/o♦
☐	B-	B737-7xx/W		o/o♦

LOONG AIR GJ / CDC

☐	B-1673	A320-214/S	6600	♦
☐	B-1675	A320-214/S	6648	♦
☐	B-1676	A320-214/S	6679	♦
☐	B-1866	A320-214/S	6026	
☐	B-1867	A320-214/S	6055	
☐	B-1868	A320-214/S	6065	
☐	B-1869	A320-214/S	6157	
☐	B-8145	A320-214/S	6671	♦

☐	B-8146	A320-214/S	6714	♦
☐	B-8147	A320-214/S	6789	♦
☐	B-8148	A320-214/S	6764	♦
☐	B-8243	A320-214/S	6847	♦
☐	B-8336	A320-214/S	6805	♦
☐	B-	A320-214/S	6941	o/o♦
☐	B-	A320-214/S	7025	o/o♦
☐	B-	A320-214/S	7027	o/o♦
☐	B-	A320-214/S	7070	o/o♦
☐	B-	A320-214/S	7178	o/o♦
☐	B-2584	B737-3J6F	25891/2385	
☐	B-2949	B737-3J6F	27372/2650	
☐	B-2954	B737-3J6F	27518/2768	

Full name is Zhejiang Loong Airlines.

LUCKY AIR 8L / LKE

☐	B-6198	A319-112	2617	
☐	B-6212	A319-115	2581	
☐	B-6221	A319-112	2746	
☐	B-1825	A320-214	3240	
☐	B-6943	A320-214	5172	
☐	B-6947	A320-214	5220	
☐	B-6959	A320-214	5100	
☐	B-	A320-2xx		o/o
☐	B-	A320-2xx		o/o
☐	B-	A320-2xx		o/o
☐	B-5246	B737-7Q8/W	30674/1511	
☐	B-5248	B737-790/W	30626/1273	
☐	B-5249	B737-790	33011/1291	
☐	B-5268	B737-790/W	30662/1382	
☐	B-5272	B737-790/W	30663/1386	
☐	B-5292	B737-7V3/W	30676/1619	
☐	B-5407	B737-808/W	34967/2239	
☐	B-5409	B737-808/W	34968/2265	
☐	B-5449	B737-808/W	34971/2400	
☐	B-5732	B737-84P/W	35076/2380	
☐	B-5805	B737-74P/W	39199/4449	
☐	B-5806	B737-74P/W	39200/4483	
☐	B-5810	B737-752/W	34299/1829	
☐	B-5823	B737-74P/W	39211/4904	
☐	B-5825	B737-74P/W	39212/4940	
☐	B-6015	B737-84P/W	41809/5483	♦
☐	B-6016	B737-84P/W	41811/5558	♦
☐	B-6800	B737-8MB/W	43883/5569	♦
☐	B-7167	B737-8MB/W	41591/5710	♦

NINGXIA CARGO AIRLINES HT / HTK

☐	B-2584	B737-3J6F	25891/2385	o/o♦
☐	B-2949	B737-3J6F	27372/2650	o/o♦
☐	B-2954	B737-3J6F	27518/2768	o/o♦

NORTHEASTERN AIRWAYS

Plans to start operations in June 2016 with A320 type aircraft.

OK AIRWAYS BK / OKA

☐	B-2117	B737-3Q8(SF)	24961/2133	
☐	B-1732	B737-86N/W	41255/5161	
☐	B-1962	B737-86N/W	41248/4863	
☐	B-1963	B737-86N/W	41249/4905	
☐	B-5367	B737-8Q8/W	30733/2452	
☐	B-5562	B737-8HO/W	37934/3491	
☐	B-5571	B737-86N/W	35643/2884	
☐	B-5573	B737-8HO/W	37932/3498	
☐	B-5575	B737-8AS/W	33554/1418	
☐	B-5577	B737-8AS/W	33557/1438	
☐	B-5578	B737-8AS/W	33560/1447	
☐	B-5841	B737-8Q8/W	41789/4532	
☐	B-5842	B737-86N/W	41262/4624	
☐	B-5843	B737-86N/W	38042/4565	
☐	B-6026	B737-8SH/W	41336/5457	♦
☐	B-	B737-86N/W	43412/5797	o/o♦
☐	B-	B737-8xx/w		o/o♦
☐	B-	B737-8xx/w		o/o♦
☐	B-1521	B737-9KFER/W	41118/5412	♦
☐	B-1522	B737-9KFER/W	41119/5459	♦
☐	B-1739	B737-9KFER/W	41114/5223	
☐	B-	B737-9KFER/W		o/o
☐	B-	B737-9KFER/W		o/o♦
☐	B-	B737-9KFER/W		o/o♦
☐	B-3433	XIAN MA60	0715	
☐	B-3440	XIAN MA60	0714	
☐	B-3705	XIAN MA60	0902	
☐	B-3706	XIAN MA60	0911	
☐	B-3709	XIAN MA60	0509	
☐	B-3710	XIAN MA60	0510	
☐	B-3711	XIAN MA60	0809	
☐	B-3712	XIAN MA60	0913	
☐	B-3713	XIAN MA60	0914	
☐	B-3715	XIAN MA60	0915	
☐	B-3722	XIAN MA60	1004	
☐	B-3723	XIAN MA60	1005	
☐	B-3725	XIAN MA60	1010	

It is reported above MA60s will be transferred to Joy Air.

QINGDAO AIRLINES QW / QDA

☐	B-1617	A320-214/S	6259	
☐	B-1648	A320-214/S	6413	
☐	B-1649	A320-214/S	6547	♦
☐	B-1693	A320-214/S	6608	♦
☐	B-1695	A320-214/S	6681	♦
☐	B-8282	A320-214/S	6893	♦
☐	B-8283	A320-214/S	6784	♦
☐	B-9955	A320-214/S	6061	
☐	B-9956	A320-214/S	6102	
☐	B-	A320-214/S	6993	o/o♦
☐	B-	A320-214/S	6995	o/o♦
☐	B-	A320-214/S	7082	o/o♦
☐	B-3079	CRJ-701ER	10118	o/o♦
☐	B-3080	CRJ-701ER	10120	o/o♦

RUILI AIRLINES DR / RUH

☐	B-1960	B737-86J/W	37786/4732	
☐	B-5811	B737-76J/W	36873/3496	
☐	B-5812	B737-76J/W	36874/3488	
☐	B-5829	B737-7ME/W	60460/5173	
☐	B-5830	B737-7ME/W	60461/5343	
☐	B-6109	B737-76J/W	36116/2730	♦
☐	B-6110	B737-76J/W	36117/2776	♦
☐	B-	B737-7ME/W		o/o
☐	B-	B737-7ME/W		o/o
☐	B-	B737-7ME/W		o/o♦
☐	B-	B737-7ME/W		o/o♦
☐	B-	B737-7ME/W		o/o♦
☐	B-	B737-7ME/W		o/o♦

SF AIRLINES O3 / CSS

	Reg.	Type	C/n	
☐	B-2017	B737-4K5(F)	27102/2394	♦
☐	B-2506	B737-429(F)	25226/2104	
☐	B-2598	B737-3J6(F)	27128/2493	
☐	B-2630	B737-36E(F)	26317/2719	
☐	B-2877	B737-33V(F)	29331/3062	
☐	B-2883	B737-4K5(F)	27830/2670	
☐	B-2924	B737-31B(F)	27287/2575	
☐	B-2941	B737-31B(F)	27344/2622	
☐	B-2951	B737-3Z0(F)	27373/2658	
☐	B-2956	B737-33A(F)	27907/2690	♦
☐	B-2958	B737-3W0(F)	27522/2727	♦
☐	B-2966	B737-33A(F)	27462/2765	♦
☐	B-2817	B757-21B(F)	25258/389	
☐	B-2820	B757-2Z0(F)	25885/476	♦
☐	B-2821	B757-2Z0(PCF)	25886/480	
☐	B-2826	B757-2Y0(F)	26155/495	
☐	B-2828	B757-25C(PCF)	25899/565	
☐	B-2829	B757-25C(PCF)	25900/574	
☐	B-2832	B757-2Z0(PCF)	25887/554	
☐	B-2839	B757-2Z0(F)	27269/615	
☐	B-2840	B757-2Z0(F)	27270/622	
☐	B-2844	B757-2Z0(F)	27511/669	
☐	B-2845	B757-2Z0(F)	27512/674	
☐	B-2899	B757-21B(PCF)	24401/232	
☐	B-6150	B757-25F(F)	30757/928	♦
☐	B-7082	B757-25F(F)	30758/932	♦
☐	B-7342	B757-2G5(F)	26278/671	♦
☐	B-	B757-28A(F)	27621/738	o/o♦
☐	B-7593	B767-338ER(BCF)	29117/710	♦
☐	B-	B767-338ER(BCF)	28153/615	o/o♦
☐	B-	B767-338ER(BCF)	28154/623	o/o♦
☐	B-	B767-338ER(BCF)	29118/713	o/o♦
☐	B-	B767-338ER/F	28724/662	o/o♦

SHANDONG AIRLINES SC / CDG

	Reg.	Type	C/n	
☐	B-	ARJ21-700		o/o♦
☐	B-5205	B737-75N/W	33654/1790	
☐	B-5206	B737-75N/W	33666/1742	
☐	B-5207	B737-75N/W	33663/1838	
☐	B-1506	B737-85N/W	41623/5376	♦
☐	B-1508	B737-85N/W	41624/5403	♦
☐	B-1509	B737-85N/W	44916/5462	♦
☐	B-1510	B737-85N/W	44918/5501	♦
☐	B-1511	B737-85N/W	41625/5504	♦
☐	B-1730	B737-89L/W	41100/5205	
☐	B-1731	B737-85N/W	41619/5139	
☐	B-1743	B737-85N/W	41620/5256	
☐	B-1745	B737-85N/W	41621/5239	
☐	B-1746	B737-85N/W	41622/5266	
☐	B-1931	B737-85N/W	39935/4789	
☐	B-1932	B737-85N/W	39937/4823	
☐	B-1982	B737-85N/W	41615/5003	
☐	B-1983	B737-85N/W	41616/4980	
☐	B-1985	B737-85N/W	41617/5015	
☐	B-1986	B737-85N/W	41618/5082	
☐	B-1987	B737-89L/W	41096/4994	
☐	B-1988	B737-89L/W	41097/5087	
☐	B-5111	B737-85N/W	33660/1752	
☐	B-5117	B737-85N/W	33661/1770	
☐	B-5118	B737-85N/W	33664/1726	
☐	B-5119	B737-85N/W	33665/1775	
☐	B-5321	B737-8AL/W	35073/2197	
☐	B-5331	B737-8AL/W	35075/2287	
☐	B-5332	B737-8FH/W	35095/2295	
☐	B-5333	B737-8FH/W	35096/2336	
☐	B-5335	B737-8FH/W	35097/2345	
☐	B-5336	B737-8FH/W	35098/2361	
☐	B-5347	B737-85N/W	36190/2429	
☐	B-5348	B737-85N/W	36191/2453	
☐	B-5349	B737-85N/W	36192/2642	
☐	B-5350	B737-85N/W	36193/2669	
☐	B-5351	B737-85N/W	36194/2684	
☐	B-5352	B737-85N/W	36195/2823	
☐	B-5450	B737-85N/W	36773/2874	
☐	B-5451	B737-85N/W	36776/2998	
☐	B-5452	B737-85N/W	36777/3045	
☐	B-5453	B737-85N/W	36778/3277	
☐	B-5490	B737-85P/W	35493/3594	
☐	B-5491	B737-85P/W	36584/3626	
☐	B-5513	B737-86N/W	36546/3293	
☐	B-5526	B737-8FZ/W	31717/3237	
☐	B-5531	B737-8FZ/W	29659/3280	
☐	B-5536	B737-8AL/W	37424/3342	
☐	B-5537	B737-8AL/W	37954/3359	
☐	B-5541	B737-85N/W	40882/3368	
☐	B-5542	B737-85N/W	40883/3383	
☐	B-5543	B737-86N/W	39392/3447	
☐	B-5560	B737-86N/W	38013/3560	
☐	B-5561	B737-86N/W	38016/3589	
☐	B-5590	B737-85N/W	39128/3708	
☐	B-5591	B737-8HX/W	38098/3711	
☐	B-5592	B737-8HX/W	38099/3757	
☐	B-5593	B737-85N/W	39115/3742	
☐	B-5626	B737-8HX/W	38103/3903	
☐	B-5627	B737-85N/W	38637/3890	
☐	B-5628	B737-85N/W	39125/3934	
☐	B-5629	B737-85N/W	38638/3957	
☐	B-5648	B737-85N/W	38639/4028	
☐	B-5649	B737-85N/W	38640/4061	
☐	B-5650	B737-85N/W	38641/4102	
☐	B-5651	B737-85N/W	38642/4145	
☐	B-5652	B737-85N/W	39126/4271	
☐	B-5723	B737-85N/W	39329/4311	
☐	B-5725	B737-85N/W	39330/4351	
☐	B-5726	B737-85N/W	38883/4372	
☐	B-5727	B737-85N/W	39110/4406	
☐	B-5728	B737-89L/W	40020/4466	
☐	B-5755	B737-89L/W	40043/4504	
☐	B-5757	B737-89L/W	40039/4542	
☐	B-5758	B737-89L/W	40044/4581	
☐	B-5781	B737-85N/W	39332/4491	
☐	B-5782	B737-85N/W	39111/4486	
☐	B-5783	B737-85N/W	39112/4522	
☐	B-5785	B737-85N/W	39113/4569	
☐	B-5786	B737-85N/W	39127/4556	
☐	B-5787	B737-85N/W	39114/4660	
☐	B-5856	B737-89L/W	40040/4712	
☐	B-6985	B737-85N/W	41626/5534	♦
☐	B-6986	B737-85N/W	41627/5590	♦
☐	B-6987	B737-85N/W	41628/5637	♦
☐	B-6988	B737-85N/W	44925/5630	♦
☐	B-7085	B737-85N/W	41629/5673	♦
☐	B-7086	B737-85N/W	44928/5676	♦
☐	B-7087	B737-85N/W	39969/5688	♦
☐	B-	B737-85N/W		o/o♦
☐	B-	B737-85N/W		o/o♦
☐	B-	B737-85N/W		o/o♦
☐	B-	B737-85N/W		o/o♦
☐	B-	B737-85N/W		o/o♦

	Reg	Type	C/n	
☐	B-	B737-85N/W		o/o♦
☐	B-3079	CRJ-701ER	10118	
☐	B-3080	CRJ-701ER	10120	

SHANGHAI AIRLINES FM / CSH

	Reg	Type	C/n	
☐	B-5931	A330-243	1440	>CES♦
☐	B-6096	A330-343E	862	
☐	B-6097	A330-343E	866	
☐	B-6127	A330-343	781	
☐	B-6545	A330-243	1291	
☐	B-2577	B737-76D	30168/600	
☐	B-2913	B737-76D	30167/550	
☐	B-5260	B737-76D/W	35777/3037	
☐	B-5261	B737-76D/W	35778/3064	
☐	B-5269	B737-76D/W	35779/3235	
☐	B-5298	B737-79P/W	39743/5440	♦
☐	B-5801	B737-76D/W	39303/4349	
☐	B-5808	B737-79P/W	39305/4597	
☐	B-5826	B737-79P/W	39313/5272	
☐	B-5827	B737-76D/W	39315/5356	♦
☐	B-	B737-76D/W		o/o♦
☐	B-1512	B737-89P/W	41506/5508	♦
☐	B-1720	B737-86D/W	41493/5135	
☐	B-1721	B737-86D/W	41501/5193	
☐	B-1740	B737-86D/W	39312/5259	
☐	B-1741	B737-86D/W	39314/5312	
☐	B-1742	B737-86D/W	39316/5409	♦
☐	B-1900	B737-86D/W	39306/4707	
☐	B-1901	B737-86D/W	38060/4653	
☐	B-1948	B737-86D/W	39307/4817	
☐	B-1949	B737-89P/W	39933/4743	
☐	B-1967	B737-86D/W	39309/4948	
☐	B-1968	B737-89D/W	39311/5039	
☐	B-2167	B737-8Q8	30631/1047	
☐	B-2168	B737-8Q8	30632/1086	
☐	B-2686	B737-8Q8	28251/1200	
☐	B-2688	B737-86D/W	33471/1192	
☐	B-5076	B737-86N	32739/1434	
☐	B-5077	B737-86N	32742/1464	
☐	B-5130	B737-8Q8	32801/1666	
☐	B-5131	B737-8Q8	30686/1704	
☐	B-5132	B737-8Q8	30685/1789	
☐	B-5140	B737-8Q8	30698/1911	
☐	B-5142	B737-8Q8	30700/1942	
☐	B-5145	B737-8Q8	33007/1986	
☐	B-5185	B737-8Q8/W	30715/2230	
☐	B-5315	B737-86D	35767/2316	
☐	B-5316	B737-86D	35768/2362	
☐	B-5320	B737-8Q8/W	30718/2251	
☐	B-5368	B737-8Q8	35273/2567	
☐	B-5369	B737-8Q8/W	35281/2709	
☐	B-5370	B737-8Q8/W	35271/2551	
☐	B-5393	B737-86D/W	35769/2632	♦
☐	B-5395	B737-86D/W	35770/2698	
☐	B-5396	B737-86D/W	35771/2740	
☐	B-5460	B737-86D/W	35772/3047	
☐	B-5461	B737-86D/W	35773/2939	
☐	B-5523	B737-86D/W	35776/3360	
☐	B-5545	B737-86N/W	36803/3376	
☐	B-5546	B737-86N/W	39391/3431	
☐	B-5548	B737-86N/W	36807/3479	
☐	B-5549	B737-86N/W	37888/3470	
☐	B-5550	B737-86N/W	39393/3483	
☐	B-5576	B737-86N/W	38011/3531	
☐	B-5610	B737-86D/W	37906/3744	
☐	B-5691	B737-86N/W	39402/4177	
☐	B-5692	B737-8SH/W	41301/4241	
☐	B-5703	B737-89P/W	41784/4170	♦
☐	B-5705	B737-89P/W	38828/4191	♦
☐	B-5722	B737-89P/W	41785/4245	♦
☐	B-5730	B737-86D/W	39302/4313	
☐	B-5799	B737-86D/W	39304/4557	
☐	B-5831	B737-86D/W	38059/4608	
☐	B-5832	B737-86D/W	37907/4545	
☐	B-5833	B737-86D/W	37908/4586	
☐	B-6107	B737-89P/W	41483/5533	♦
☐	B-6108	B737-89P/W	41491/5624	♦
☐	B-6698	B737-89P/W	41489/5674	♦
☐	B-6993	B737-89P/W	41505/5713	♦
☐	B-2498	B767-36D	27684/849	
☐	B-2500	B767-36DER	35155/946	
☐	B-2563	B767-36D	27309/546	
☐	B-2566	B767-36DER	35156/950	
☐	B-2567	B767-36D	27685/686	
☐	B-2570	B767-36D	27941/770	

SHANTOU AIRLINES

Fleet is painted in China Southern c/s and included there.

SHENZHEN AIRLINES ZH / CSZ

	Reg	Type	C/n	
☐	B-6153	A319-115	2841	
☐	B-6159	A319-115	2905	
☐	B-6165	A319-115	2935	
☐	B-6196	A319-115	2672	
☐	B-6197	A319-115	2684	
☐	B-1601	A320-232/S	6197	
☐	B-1602	A320-232/S	6217	
☐	B-1683	A320-214/S	6564	♦
☐	B-1685	A320-214/S	6686	♦
☐	B-1841	A320-232	5986	
☐	B-1842	A320-232/S	6019	
☐	B-6286	A320-214	2909	
☐	B-6296	A320-214	2973	
☐	B-6297	A320-214	2980	
☐	B-6312	A320-214	3131	
☐	B-6313	A320-214	3132	
☐	B-6315	A320-214	3153	
☐	B-6316	A320-214	3206	
☐	B-6351	A320-214	3366	
☐	B-6352	A320-214	3383	
☐	B-6357	A320-214	3440	
☐	B-6358	A320-214	3435	
☐	B-6359	A320-214	3456	
☐	B-6360	A320-214	3528	
☐	B-6377	A320-214	3599	
☐	B-6392	A320-214	3696	
☐	B-6550	A320-214	3756	
☐	B-6563	A320-214	3698	
☐	B-6565	A320-214	3971	
☐	B-6566	A320-214	3855	
☐	B-6567	A320-214	3887	
☐	B-6568	A320-214	3898	
☐	B-6569	A320-214	3848	
☐	B-6570	A320-214	4010	
☐	B-6571	A320-232	3935	
☐	B-6589	A320-214	4028	
☐	B-6613	A320-232	4176	
☐	B-6615	A320-232	4214	
☐	B-6647	A320-214	4226	
☐	B-6648	A320-214	4159	

	Reg	Type	c/n	Notes
☐	B-6649	A320-214	4208	
☐	B-6650	A320-232	4300	
☐	B-6690	A320-232	4359	
☐	B-6691	A320-232	4409	
☐	B-6692	A320-232	4407	
☐	B-6720	A320-214	4474	
☐	B-6721	A320-214	4514	
☐	B-6722	A320-214	4531	
☐	B-6740	A320-232	4435	
☐	B-6749	A320-232	4633	
☐	B-6750	A320-232	4666	
☐	B-6780	A320-232	4726	
☐	B-6781	A320-232	4620	
☐	B-6806	A320-232	4845	
☐	B-6807	A320-232	4897	
☐	B-6833	A320-232	4920	
☐	B-6835	A320-232	4986	
☐	B-6853	A320-232	4866	
☐	B-6855	A320-232	4876	
☐	B-6856	A320-232	4929	
☐	B-6857	A320-232	5002	
☐	B-6935	A320-232	4977	
☐	B-6937	A320-214	5082	
☐	B-6938	A320-214	5110	
☐	B-6939	A320-232	5176	
☐	B-8077	A320-214/S	6708	♦
☐	B-8078	A320-214/S	6728	♦
☐	B-8079	A320-214/S	6742	♦
☐	B-8219	A320-214/S	6721	♦
☐	B-8220	A320-214/S	6911	[TLS]♦
☐	B-9908	A320-214	5369	
☐	B-9909	A320-214	5521	
☐	B-9910	A320-214	5550	
☐	B-9938	A320-214	5589	
☐	B-9939	A320-214/S	5639	
☐	B-9979	A320-214	5731	
☐	B-9980	A320-214/S	5766	
☐	B-	A320-232/S	6984	o/o♦
☐	B-	A320-232/S	7075	o/o♦
☐	B-	A320-232/S	7190	o/o♦
☐	B-	A320-232/S	7197	o/o♦
☐	B-	A320-232/S	7226	o/o♦
☐	B-	A320-232/S	7247	o/o♦
☐	B-	A320-232/S	7270	o/o♦

	Reg	Type	c/n	Notes
☐	B-2667	B737-78S	30170/654	
☐	B-2669	B737-77L	32722/1023	
☐	B-5025	B737-7BX	30741/823	

	Reg	Type	c/n	Notes
☐	B-1516	B737-87L/W	37627/5487	♦
☐	B-1517	B737-87L/W	37626/5461	♦
☐	B-1518	B737-87L/W	40827/5439	♦
☐	B-1519	B737-87L/W	40828/5496	♦
☐	B-1710	B737-87L/W	39158/5182	
☐	B-1711	B737-87L/W	39159/5159	
☐	B-1712	B737-87L/W	39160/5199	
☐	B-1713	B737-87L/W	39161/5213	
☐	B-1755	B737-87L/W	40822/5236	
☐	B-1756	B737-87L/W	40823/5264	
☐	B-1757	B737-87L/W	40824/5326	♦
☐	B-1758	B737-87L/W	40825/5363	♦
☐	B-1759	B737-87L/W	40826/5425	♦
☐	B-1935	B737-87L/W	39140/4754	
☐	B-1936	B737-87L/W	39141/4797	
☐	B-1937	B737-87L/W	37619/4804	
☐	B-1938	B737-87L/W	37618/4834	
☐	B-1939	B737-87L/W	37621/4869	
☐	B-1940	B737-87L/W	37622/4909	
☐	B-1941	B737-87L/W	37625/4877	
☐	B-1972	B737-87L/W	37620/5035	
☐	B-1973	B737-87L/W	37624/5053	
☐	B-1993	B737-87L/W	37623/5010	
☐	B-2691	B737-8Q8	30628/808	
☐	B-2692	B737-8Q8	28241/841	
☐	B-5073	B737-8Q8/W	30680/1402	
☐	B-5075	B737-8Q8	30692/1410	
☐	B-5078	B737-8Q8	30690/1414	
☐	B-5079	B737-8Q8	30693/1422	
☐	B-5186	B737-8BK	33020/2103	
☐	B-5187	B737-8BK	33828/2124	
☐	B-5317	B737-86N/W	32686/2175	
☐	B-5322	B737-86N/W	32688/2218	
☐	B-5345	B737-86N/W	35215/2306	
☐	B-5357	B737-8AL/W	35081/2519	
☐	B-5360	B737-86J/W	30062/485	
☐	B-5361	B737-86J/W	30063/517	
☐	B-5362	B737-86J/W	30499/567	
☐	B-5363	B737-86J/W	30500/593	
☐	B-5365	B737-86J/W	30501/619	
☐	B-5377	B737-8AL/W	35079/2555	
☐	B-5378	B737-8AL/W	35085/2563	
☐	B-5379	B737-8AL/W	35087/2605	
☐	B-5380	B737-87L/W	35527/2616	
☐	B-5381	B737-87L/W	35528/2631	
☐	B-5400	B737-87L/W	35529/2677	
☐	B-5401	B737-87L/W	35530/2703	
☐	B-5402	B737-87L/W	35531/2726	
☐	B-5410	B737-8AL/W	35088/2771	
☐	B-5411	B737-87L/W	35532/2851	
☐	B-5412	B737-87L/W	35533/2900	
☐	B-5413	B737-87L/W	35535/2895	
☐	B-5440	B737-87L/W	35534/3003	
☐	B-5441	B737-87L/W	35536/3019	
☐	B-5606	B737-87L/W	39143/3624	
☐	B-5607	B737-87L/W	39144/3643	
☐	B-5608	B737-87L/W	39145/3656	
☐	B-5612	B737-87L/W	39146/3698	
☐	B-5613	B737-87L/W	39147/3705	
☐	B-5615	B737-87L/W	39148/3736	
☐	B-5616	B737-87L/W	39149/3755	
☐	B-5617	B737-87L/W	39150/3770	
☐	B-5618	B737-87L/W	39151/3828	
☐	B-5619	B737-87L/W	39152/3841	
☐	B-5670	B737-87L/W	39129/4029	
☐	B-5671	B737-87L/W	39153/4107	
☐	B-5673	B737-87L/W	39155/4158	
☐	B-5690	B737-87L/W	39130/4175	
☐	B-5736	B737-87L/W	39132/4470	
☐	B-5737	B737-87L/W	39133/4488	
☐	B-5771	B737-87L/W	39134/4550	
☐	B-5772	B737-87L/W	39135/4554	
☐	B-5773	B737-87L/W	39156/4566	
☐	B-5775	B737-87L/W	39136/4612	
☐	B-5776	B737-87L/W	39157/4604	
☐	B-5778	B737-87L/W	39137/4647	
☐	B-5859	B737-87L/W	39138/4695	
☐	B-5860	B737-87L/W	39139/4703	
☐	B-7083	B737-87L/W	39142/5696	♦

	Reg	Type	c/n	Notes
☐	B-5102	B737-97L	33644/1750	
☐	B-5103	B737-97L	33645/1760	
☐	B-5105	B737-97L	33646/1764	
☐	B-5106	B737-97L	33648/1722	
☐	B-5109	B737-97L	33649/1755	

SICHUAN AIRLINES 3U / CSC

	Reg	Type	C/n	Notes
☐	B-2298	A319-133	2534	
☐	B-2299	A319-133	2597	
☐	B-2300	A319-133	2639	
☐	B-6043	A319-133	2313	
☐	B-6045	A319-133	2348	
☐	B-6054	A319-133	2510	
☐	B-6170	A319-132	2396	
☐	B-6171	A319-132	2431	
☐	B-6173	A319-133	3114	
☐	B-6175	A319-133	3116	
☐	B-6176	A319-133	3124	
☐	B-6185	A319-133	3680	
☐	B-6406	A319-133	3962	
☐	B-6410	A319-133	4018	
☐	B-6419	A319-133	4660	
☐	B-6422	A319-133	5208	
☐	B-6433	A319-133	5286	
☐	B-6442	A319-133	5389	
☐	B-6445	A319-133	5609	
☐	B-6447	A319-133	5650	
☐	B-6448	A319-133	5765	
☐	B-6449	A319-133/S	5868	
☐	B-6453	A319-133/S	5910	
☐	B-6455	A319-133/S	5953	
☐	B-	A319-115/S		o/o♦
☐	B-1660	A320-232/S	6402	
☐	B-1661	A320-232/S	6421	
☐	B-1662	A320-232/S	6486	
☐	B-1665	A320-214/S	6540	♦
☐	B-1818	A320-232/S	5964	
☐	B-1819	A320-232/S	5896	
☐	B-1820	A320-232/S	6008	
☐	B-1821	A320-232/S	5977	
☐	B-1822	A320-232/S	5937	
☐	B-1881	A320-214/S	6339	
☐	B-1882	A320-214/S	6369	
☐	B-1883	A320-214/S	6367	
☐	B-1885	A320-214/S	6386	
☐	B-1886	A320-214/S	6397	
☐	B-1887	A320-232/S	6030	
☐	B-2342	A320-232	0556	
☐	B-2373	A320-233	0919	
☐	B-2397	A320-233	1013	
☐	B-6049	A320-233	0902	[CXG]
☐	B-6256	A320-232	0872	
☐	B-6321	A320-232	3210	
☐	B-6322	A320-232	3158	
☐	B-6323	A320-232	3167	
☐	B-6325	A320-232	3196	
☐	B-6347	A320-232	3386	
☐	B-6348	A320-232	3449	
☐	B-6388	A320-232	3591	
☐	B-6621	A320-232	4068	
☐	B-6697	A320-232	4288	
☐	B-6700	A320-232	4326	
☐	B-6719	A320-232	4424	
☐	B-6732	A320-232	4378	
☐	B-6770	A320-232	4642	
☐	B-6771	A320-232	4619	
☐	B-6772	A320-232	4525	
☐	B-6778	A320-232	4707	
☐	B-6779	A320-232	4575	
☐	B-6843	A320-232	4905	
☐	B-6905	A320-232	4911	
☐	B-6953	A320-232	5041	
☐	B-6955	A320-232	5121	
☐	B-6956	A320-232	5141	
☐	B-8323	A320-214/S	6677	♦
☐	B-8325	A320-214/S	6710	♦
☐	B-8326	A320-214/S	6713	♦
☐	B-8329	A320-232/S	6635	♦
☐	B-8330	A320-214/S	6732	♦
☐	B-8331	A320-214/S	6654	♦
☐	B-8375	A320-214/S	6937	♦
☐	B-9935	A320-232/S	5646	
☐	B-	A320-214/S	6982	o/o♦
☐	B-	A320-214/S		o/o♦
☐	B-	A320-214/S		o/o♦
☐	B-	A320-214/S		o/o♦
☐	B-1663	A321-231/S	6581	♦
☐	B-1677	A321-231/S	6475	
☐	B-1823	A321-231/S	6148	
☐	B-1890	A321-231/S	6303	
☐	B-1891	A321-231/S	6316	
☐	B-2370	A321-231	0878	
☐	B-2371	A321-231	0915	
☐	B-6387	A321-231	3583	
☐	B-6551	A321-231	3730	
☐	B-6590	A321-231	3893	
☐	B-6598	A321-231	3996	
☐	B-6718	A321-231	4420	
☐	B-6810	A321-231	4731	
☐	B-6836	A321-231	4824	
☐	B-6838	A321-231	4856	
☐	B-6839	A321-231	4830	
☐	B-6845	A321-231	4923	
☐	B-6899	A321-231	5233	
☐	B-6906	A321-231	5160	
☐	B-6920	A321-231	5197	
☐	B-6957	A321-231	5303	
☐	B-6968	A321-231	5543	
☐	B-8328	A321-231/S	6703	♦
☐	B-9936	A321-231	5670	
☐	B-9937	A321-231	5647	
☐	B-9967	A321-231/S	5470	
☐	B-	A321-211/S	7010	o/o♦
☐	B-	A321-211/S	7073	o/o♦
☐	B-	A321-211/S	7198	o/o♦
☐	B-	A321-211/S	7227	o/o♦
☐	B-	A321-211/S	7276	o/o♦
☐	B-	A321-211/S	7320	o/o♦
☐	B-	A321-211/S	7383	o/o♦
☐	B-5923	A330-343E	1397	
☐	B-5929	A330-343E	1432	
☐	B-5945	A330-343E	1528	
☐	B-5960	A330-343E	1579	
☐	B-6517	A330-243	1138	
☐	B-6518	A330-243	1082	
☐	B-6535	A330-243	1241	
☐	B-8332	A330-243	1662	♦
☐	B-	A330-243	1746	o/o♦
☐	B-	A330-243	1751	o/o♦

SICHUAN SANXING GENERAL AVIATION

	Reg	Type	C/n	Notes
☐	B-3435	XIAN MA60	1105	♦
☐	B-3726	XIAN MA60	1006	♦

SPRING AIRLINES 9C / CQH

	Reg	Type	C/n	Notes
☐	B-1627	A320-214/S	6403	

	Reg	Type	C/n	
☐	B-1628	A320-214/S	6410	
☐	B-1656	A320-214/S	6452	
☐	B-1657	A320-214/S	6524	♦
☐	B-1670	A320-214/S	6329	
☐	B-1671	A320-214/S	6318	
☐	B-1672	A320-214/S	6358	
☐	B-1807	A320-214/S	5816	
☐	B-1839	A320-214/S	6073	
☐	B-1840	A320-214/S	6117	
☐	B-1892	A320-214/S	6216	
☐	B-1893	A320-214/S	6218	
☐	B-1895	A320-214/S	6220	
☐	B-1896	A320-214/S	6231	
☐	B-6301	A320-214	2939	
☐	B-6309	A320-214	3014	
☐	B-6310	A320-214	3023	
☐	B-6561	A320-214	3819	
☐	B-6562	A320-214	3747	
☐	B-6612	A320-214	4072	
☐	B-6645	A320-214	4168	
☐	B-6646	A320-214	4093	
☐	B-6667	A320-214	4244	
☐	B-6705	A320-214	4331	
☐	B-6706	A320-214	4366	
☐	B-6707	A320-214	4373	
☐	B-6708	A320-214	4375	
☐	B-6751	A320-214	4499	
☐	B-6752	A320-214	4586	
☐	B-6820	A320-214	4738	
☐	B-6821	A320-214	4750	
☐	B-6840	A320-214	4760	
☐	B-6841	A320-214	4816	
☐	B-6851	A320-214	4909	
☐	B-6852	A320-214	4809	
☐	B-6862	A320-214	4983	
☐	B-6863	A320-214	4978	
☐	B-6902	A320-214	5108	
☐	B-6931	A320-214	5022	
☐	B-6932	A320-214	5051	
☐	B-6970	A320-214	5403	
☐	B-6971	A320-214	5434	
☐	B-6972	A320-214	5466	
☐	B-8000	A320-214/S	6497	♦
☐	B-8012	A320-214/S	6591	♦
☐	B-8247	A320-214/S	6765	♦
☐	B-8248	A320-214/S	6786	♦
☐	B-8346	A320-214/S	6874	std♦
☐	B-8347	A320-214/S	6881	std♦
☐	B-8370	A320-214/S	6815	o/o♦
☐	B-8371	A320-214/S	6826	o/o♦
☐	B-8327	A320-214/S	6846	o/o♦
☐	B-8427	A320-214/S	6858	♦
☐	B-9920	A320-214	5378	
☐	B-9928	A320-214/S	5446	
☐	B-9940	A320-214	5562	
☐	B-9965	A320-214/S	5778	
☐	B-9986	A320-214/S	5911	
☐	B-	A320-214/S	6931	o/o♦
☐	B-	A320-214/S	6964	o/o♦
☐	B-	A320-214/S	7016	o/o♦
☐	B-	A320-214/S	7099	o/o♦
☐	B-	A320-214/S	7122	o/o♦
☐	B-	A320-214/S	7159	o/o♦
☐	B-	A320-214/S	7282	o/o♦
☐	B-	A320-214/S		o/o♦

SR JET — *QSR*

	Reg	Type	C/n	
☐	B-3011	CRJ-200ER	7556	♦
☐	B-3013	CRJ-200LR	7571	♦
☐	B-3019	CRJ-200LR	7581	♦
☐	B-3020	CRJ-200ER	7459	♦
☐	B-3021	CRJ-200LR	7596	♦
☐	B-3070	CRJ-200LR	7647	♦
☐	B-3071	CRJ-200LR	7684	♦

TIANJIN AIRLINES — *GS / GCR*

	Reg	Type	C/n	
☐	B-1618	A320-232/S	5835	
☐	B-1619	A320-232/S	5850	
☐	B-1620	A320-232/S	5853	
☐	B-1658	A320-214/S	6449	
☐	B-1659	A320-214/S	6348	
☐	B-1692	A320-214/S	6570	♦
☐	B-1849	A320-232/S	5894	
☐	B-1850	A320-232/S	5928	
☐	B-1851	A320-232/S	5971	
☐	B-6789	A320-232	4739	
☐	B-6837	A320-232	4825	
☐	B-6865	A320-214	5006	
☐	B-6903	A320-214	5117	
☐	B-8062	A320-232/S	6820	♦
☐	B-8066	A320-232/S	6851	♦
☐	B-8069	A320-232/S	6898	♦
☐	B-8075	A320-232/S	6919	♦
☐	B-9948	A320-232	2475	
☐	B-9963	A320-214	4600	
☐	B-9983	A320-214	5799	
☐	B-9987	A320-214	5760	
☐	B-9989	A320-232	2338	
☐	B-	A330-2xx	1756	o/o♦
☐	B-3030	ERJ-145LI	14501009	
☐	B-3031	ERJ-145LI	14501013	
☐	B-3032	ERJ-145LI	14501019	
☐	B-3033	ERJ-145LI	14501022	
☐	B-3036	ERJ-145LI	14501000	
☐	B-3037	ERJ-145LI	14501005	
☐	B-3038	ERJ-145LI	14501024	
☐	B-3067	ERJ-145LI	14501036	
☐	B-3068	ERJ-145LI	14501040	
☐	B-3069	ERJ-145LI	14501043	
☐	B-3081	ERJ-145LI	14501027	
☐	B-3082	ERJ-145LI	14501030	
☐	B-3083	ERJ-145LI	14501033	
☐	B-3085	ERJ-145LI	14501047	
☐	B-3086	ERJ-145LI	14501050	
☐	B-3087	ERJ-145LI	14501053	
☐	B-3088	ERJ-145LI	14501056	
☐	B-3090	ERJ-145LI	14501063	
☐	B-3091	ERJ-145LI	14501065	
☐	B-3092	ERJ-145LI	14501068	
☐	B-3093	ERJ-145LI	14501070	
☐	B-3095	ERJ-145LI	14501073	
☐	B-3100	ERJ-195LR	19000700	♦
☐	B-3108	ERJ-195LR	19000702	♦
☐	B-3117	ERJ-195LR	19000704	♦
☐	B-3120	ERJ-190LR	19000171	
☐	B-3121	ERJ-190LR	19000181	
☐	B-3123	ERJ-190LR	19000192	
☐	B-3127	ERJ-190LR	19000207	
☐	B-3128	ERJ-190LR	19000229	
☐	B-3129	ERJ-190LR	19000246	

	Reg	Type	c/n	
☐	B-3150	ERJ-190LR	19000253	
☐	B-3151	ERJ-190LR	19000268	
☐	B-3152	ERJ-190LR	19000274	
☐	B-3153	ERJ-190LR	19000284	
☐	B-3155	ERJ-190LR	19000293	
☐	B-3156	ERJ-190LR	19000299	
☐	B-3157	ERJ-190LR	19000306	
☐	B-3158	ERJ-190LR	19000313	
☐	B-3159	ERJ-190LR	19000318	
☐	B-3160	ERJ-190LR	19000323	
☐	B-3161	ERJ-190LR	19000328	
☐	B-3162	ERJ-190LR	19000331	
☐	B-3163	ERJ-190LR	19000335	
☐	B-3166	ERJ-190LR	19000348	
☐	B-3167	ERJ-190LR	19000352	
☐	B-3168	ERJ-190LR	19000355	
☐	B-3169	ERJ-190LR	19000369	
☐	B-3170	ERJ-190LR	19000371	
☐	B-3171	ERJ-190LR	19000379	
☐	B-3172	ERJ-190LR	19000385	
☐	B-3173	ERJ-190LR	19000394	
☐	B-3175	ERJ-190LR	19000405	
☐	B-3177	ERJ-190LR	19000410	
☐	B-3178	ERJ-190LR	19000417	
☐	B-3181	ERJ-190LR	19000454	
☐	B-3182	ERJ-190LR	19000459	
☐	B-3189	ERJ-190LR	19000508	
☐	B-3190	ERJ-190LR	19000517	
☐	B-3191	ERJ-190LR	19000527	
☐	B-3192	ERJ-190LR	19000536	
☐	B-3193	ERJ-190LR	19000574	
☐	B-3195	ERJ-190LR	19000582	
☐	B-3212	ERJ-190LR	19000567	
☐	B-3213	ERJ-190LR	19000573	
☐	B-	ERJ-195LR		o/o♦
☐	B-	ERJ-195LR		o/o♦
☐	B-	ERJ-195LR		o/o♦
☐	B-	ERJ-195LR		o/o♦

TIBET AIRLINES — TV / TBA

	Reg	Type	c/n	
☐	B-6425	A319-115	5157	
☐	B-6426	A319-115	5256	
☐	B-6436	A319-115	4766	
☐	B-6437	A319-115	4801	
☐	B-6438	A319-115	4846	
☐	B-6440	A319-115	5451	
☐	B-6441	A319-115/S	5529	
☐	B-6443	A319-115	5563	
☐	B-6451	A319-115/S	5855	
☐	B-6467	A319-115/S	6404	
☐	B-6473	A319-115/S	6380	
☐	B-6475	A319-115/S	6391	
☐	B-6480	A319-115/S	6588	♦
☐	B-6481	A319-115/S	6716	♦
☐	B-1682	A320-214/S	6626	♦
☐	B-	A320-214/S	6986	o/o♦
☐	B-	A320-214/S	7059	o/o♦
☐	B-	A320-214/S	7092	o/o♦
☐	B-	A320-214/S	7258	o/o♦
☐	B-	A330-243	1735	o/o♦

UNI-TOP AIRLINES — UW / UTP

	Reg	Type	c/n	
☐	B-2317	A300B4-605R(F)	741	o/o
☐	B-2318	A300B4-605R(F)	707	o/o
☐	B-2319	A300B4-605R(F)	732	o/o
☐	B-2324	A300B4-622R(F)	725	o/o
☐	B-2325	A300B4-605R(F)	746	o/o
☐	B-2326	A300B4-605R(F)	754	o/o
☐	B-2330	A300B4-605R(F)	763	
☐	B-2448	B747-2J6B (SF)	23461/628	
☐	B-2450	B747-2J6B (SF)	23746/670	
☐	B-2462	B747-2J6F	24960/814	

URUMQI AIR — UQ / CUH

	Reg	Type	c/n	
☐	B-2157	B737-84P/W	32600/1015	
☐	B-2158	B737-84P/W	32601/1033	
☐	B-2159	B737-84P/W	32599/972	
☐	B-6268	B737-8LP/W	41842/5220	♦
☐	B-6995	B737-84P/W	61323/5655	♦
☐	B-7198	B737-84P/W	61324/5695	♦

WEST AIR — PN / CHB

	Reg	Type	c/n	
☐	B-6412	A319-132	4262	
☐	B-6413	A319-132	4452	
☐	B-6420	A319-133	5105	
☐	B-6421	A319-133	4995	
☐	B-1629	A320-232/S	6237	
☐	B-1817	A320-214/S	5912	
☐	B-1897	A320-232/S	6076	
☐	B-1898	A320-232/S	6120	
☐	B-6743	A320-232	4569	
☐	B-6763	A320-232	4482	
☐	B-6765	A320-232	4687	
☐	B-6790	A320-232	4686	
☐	B-6811	A320-232	4644	
☐	B-8102	A320-214	5246	♦
☐	B-8110	A320-214	4231	♦
☐	B-8249	A320-214/S	6924	♦
☐	B-8286	A320-214/S	6870	♦
☐	B-9949	A320-214	5626	
☐	B-9969	A320-232/S	6023	
☐	B-9981	A320-214	5740	
☐	B-9982	A320-214	5679	
☐	B-	A320-232/S		o/o♦

XIAMEN AIRLINES — MF / CXA

	Reg	Type	c/n	
☐	B-2658	B737-75C	30512/637	
☐	B-2659	B737-75C	30513/676	
☐	B-2991	B737-75C	29085/90	
☐	B-2992	B737-75C	29086/108	
☐	B-2998	B737-75C	29042/73	
☐	B-2999	B737-75C	29084/86	
☐	B-5028	B737-75C	30034/1275	
☐	B-5029	B737-75C	30634/1229	
☐	B-5038	B737-7Q8	30656/1304	
☐	B-5039	B737-75C	28258/1315	
☐	B-5216	B737-75C	34026/1733	
☐	B-5218	B737-75C	34027/1767	
☐	B-5219	B737-75C	34028/1771	
☐	B-5277	B737-75C/W	38381/3697	
☐	B-5278	B737-75C/W	38383/3734	
☐	B-5279	B737-75C/W	38384/3721	
☐	B-5280	B737-75C/W	38385/3752	
☐	B-1706	B737-85C/W	39905/5066	
☐	B-1707	B737-85C/W	39906/5126	
☐	B-1708	B737-85C/W	39911/5075	
☐	B-1709	B737-85C/W	39912/5212	
☐	B-1749	B737-85C/W	39909/5234	

	Reg	Type	MSN	
□	B-1911	B737-85C/W	39907/4748	
□	B-1912	B737-85C/W	39908/4862	
□	B-1913	B737-85C/W	39900/4919	
□	B-1915	B737-85C/W	39901/4945	
□	B-1964	B737-85C/W	39914/5545	♦
□	B-1966	B737-85C/W	39910/5321	♦
□	B-1969	B737-85C/W	39902/5005	
□	B-1970	B737-85C/W	39903/4981	
□	B-1971	B737-85C/W	39904/5034	
□	B-5151	B737-86N/W	34255/1975	
□	B-5152	B737-86N/W	34256/1990	
□	B-5159	B737-85C/W	35044/2018	
□	B-5160	B737-85C/W	35045/2050	
□	B-5161	B737-85C/W	35046/2105	
□	B-5162	B737-85C/W	35047/2130	
□	B-5301	B737-85C/W	35048/2194	
□	B-5302	B737-85C/W	35049/2271	
□	B-5303	B737-85C/W	35050/2305	
□	B-5305	B737-85C/W	35051/2364	
□	B-5306	B737-85C/W	35052/2418	
□	B-5307	B737-85C/W	35053/2447	
□	B-5308	B737-86N/W	32687/2229	
□	B-5309	B737-86N/W	32689/2254	
□	B-5318	B737-85C/W	30723/2283	
□	B-5319	B737-8FH/W	35102/2471	
□	B-5355	B737-8FH/W	35104/2495	
□	B-5382	B737-86N/W	36540/2681	
□	B-5383	B737-86N/W	35631/2693	
□	B-5385	B737-86N/W	35633/2741	
□	B-5386	B737-86N/W	35634/2732	
□	B-5388	B737-86N/W	35635/2764	
□	B-5389	B737-86N/W	35636/2775	
□	B-5432	B737-86N/W	35641/2852	
□	B-5433	B737-86N/W	35642/2855	
□	B-5435	B737-86N/W	35644/2922	
□	B-5458	B737-85C/W	35055/3016	
□	B-5476	B737-85C/W	35056/3091	
□	B-5487	B737-85C/W	35058/3150	
□	B-5488	B737-85C/W	37148/3104	
□	B-5489	B737-85C/W	37149/3142	
□	B-5498	B737-85C/W	37574/3160	
□	B-5499	B737-85C/W	37575/3190	
□	B-5528	B737-85C/W	37578/3332	
□	B-5529	B737-85C/W	37150/3386	
□	B-5532	B737-85C/W	37151/3397	
□	B-5533	B737-85C/W	37152/3403	
□	B-5535	B737-85C/W	37579/3424	
□	B-5551	B737-84P/W	36697/3443	
□	B-5552	B737-84P/W	37425/3408	
□	B-5563	B737-86N/W	38012/3550	
□	B-5565	B737-86N/W	38015/3566	
□	B-5566	B737-85C/W	37153/3571	
□	B-5595	B737-86N/W	38017/3614	
□	B-5601	B737-86N/W	36823/3712	
□	B-5602	B737-86N/W	36824/3703	
□	B-5603	B737-86N/W	38020/3638	
□	B-5605	B737-86N/W	38022/3672	
□	B-5630	B737-85C/W	38386/3897	
□	B-5631	B737-85C/W	38387/3929	
□	B-5632	B737-85C/W	38388/3973	
□	B-5633	B737-85C/W	38389/3987	
□	B-5635	B737-85C/W	38390/4012	
□	B-5653	B737-85C/W	38391/4112	
□	B-5655	B737-85C/W	38392/4121	
□	B-5656	B737-85C/W	38393/4135	
□	B-5657	B737-85C/W	38394/4153	
□	B-5658	B737-85C/W	38395/4173	
□	B-5659	B737-85C/W	38396/4187	
□	B-5688	B737-85C/W	41792/4688	
□	B-5706	B737-85C/W	38398/4306	
□	B-5707	B737-85C/W	38399/4375	
□	B-5708	B737-85C/W	38403/4357	
□	B-5750	B737-85C/W	38380/4475	
□	B-5751	B737-85C/W	38400/4419	
□	B-5752	B737-85C/W	38404/4461	
□	B-5788	B737-85C/W	38382/4497	
□	B-5789	B737-85C/W	38401/4525	
□	B-5790	B737-85C/W	38402/4537	
□	B-5791	B737-85C/W	39930/4555	
□	B-5792	B737-85C/W	41790/4568	
□	B-5845	B737-85C/W	39931/4645	
□	B-5846	B737-85C/W	41791/4622	
□	B-5847	B737-85C/W	41793/4709	
□	B-6482	B737-85C/W	41391/5514	♦
□	B-6483	B737-85C/W	39918/5506	♦
□	B-6485	B737-85C/W	39913/5481	♦
□	B-6486	B737-85C/W	41395/5528	♦
□	B-6487	B737-85C/W	39919/5522	♦
□	B-6488	B737-85C/W	41396/5579	♦
□	B-6489	B737-85C/W	39915/5552	♦
□	B-6490	B737-85C/W	41392/5566	♦
□	B-6818	B737-85C/W	39916/5593	♦
□	B-6819	B737-85C/W	39917/5628	♦
□	B-6842	B737-85C/W	40957/5691	♦
□	B-6849	B737-85C/W	40959/5634	♦
□	B-6887	B737-8M8/W	43884/5614	♦
□	B-6889	B737-8M8/W	43914/5647	♦
□	B-7176	B737-85C/W	41393/5721	♦
□	B-7177	B737-85C/W	41394/5736	♦
□	B-7178	B737-85C/W	40958/5756	♦
□	B-7179	B737-85C/W	40960/5745	♦
□	B-	B737-85C/W	42925/5805	o/o♦
□	B-	B737-85C/W	43886/5813	o/o♦
□	B-2848	B757-25C	27513/685	[XMN]
□	B-2849	B757-25C	27517/698	[XMN]
□	B-2862	B757-25C	34008/1047	
□	B-2866	B757-25C	34009/1048	
□	B-2868	B757-25C	32941/993	
□	B-2869	B757-25C	32942/1009	
□	B-2760	B787-8	41540/270	♦
□	B-2761	B787-8	41541/282	♦
□	B-2762	B787-8	41542/304	♦
□	B-2763	B787-8	41543/343	♦
□	B-2768	B787-8	41538/201	
□	B-2769	B787-8	41539/227	
□	B-	B787-9	63040/498	o/o♦
□	B-	B787-9	63041/512	o/o♦

YANGTZE RIVER EXPRESS ***Y8 / YZR***

	Reg	Type	MSN
□	B-2112	B737-36NF	28599/3115
□	B-2113	B737-36NF	28602/3118
□	B-2115	B737-36NF	28606/3124
□	B-2119	B737-332F	25998/2510
□	B-2501	B737-44PF	29914/3067
□	B-2576	B737-44PF	29915/3106
□	B-2578	B737-33AF	25603/2333
□	B-2885	B737-39K(SF)	27274/2559
□	B-2908	B737-341F	26854/2303
□	B-2942	B737-332(F)	25997/2506
□	B-2963	B737-3Q8F	26325/2772
□	B-2993	B737-46Q(F)	28759/2981
□	B-3000	B737-36Q(F)	29326/3020

	Reg	Type	c/n	
☐	B-5053	B737-322F	24378/1704	
☐	B-5055	B737-330(QC)	24283/1677	
☐	B-5056	B737-330(QC)	23836/1508	
☐	B-5057	B737-330(QC)	23837/1514	
☐	B-5058	B737-330(QC)	23835/1465	
☐	B-5059	B737-322F	24362/1696	
☐	B-1992	B737-84P/W	41376/4996	♦
☐	B-5403	B737-84P/W	35756/2691	♦
☐	B-2432	B747-481(SF)	28283/1142	
☐	B-2435	B747-481(SF)	28282/1133	
☐	B-2437	B747-481BDSF	25207/870	

YING'AN ***YI / AYE***

	Reg	Type	c/n	
☐	B-3421	XIAN MA60	0610	♦

YTO EXPRESS AIRLINES ***HYT***

	Reg	Type	c/n	
☐	B-2505	B737-36Q(SF)	28657/2859	♦
☐	B-2608	B737-36Q(SF)	28662/2914	♦
☐	B-2945	B737-39K(F)	27362/2639	♦

ZHUHAI AIRLINES ***CZ***

	Reg	Type	c/n	
☐	B-1776	B737-81B/W	41609/5406	♦
☐	B-1922	B737-86N/W	41246/4792	♦
☐	B-5165	B737-81B	30709/1961	♦

Uses China Southern's AOC.

B-H/K/L CHINA – HONG KONG

AIR HONG KONG ***LD / AHK***

	Reg	Type	c/n	
☐	B-LDA	A300F4-605R	855	
☐	B-LDB	A300F4-605R	856	
☐	B-LDC	A300F4-605R	857	
☐	B-LDD	A300F4-605R	858	
☐	B-LDE	A300F4-605R	859	♦
☐	B-LDF	A300F4-605R	860	
☐	B-LDG	A300F4-605R	870	
☐	B-LDH	A300F4-605R	871	
☐	B-LDM	A300B4-622R(F)	683	
☐	B-LDN	A300B4-622R(F)	770	
☐	B-HOU	B747-467BCF	24925/834	
☐	B-HUR	B747-444BCF	24976/827	DHL c/s
☐	B-HUS	B747-444BCF	25152/861	

CATHAY DRAGON ***KA / HDA***

	Reg	Type	c/n	
☐	B-HSD	A320-232	0756	
☐	B-HSE	A320-232	0784	
☐	B-HSG	A320-232	0812	
☐	B-HSI	A320-232	0930	
☐	B-HSJ	A320-232	1253	
☐	B-HSK	A320-232	1721	
☐	B-HSL	A320-232	2229	
☐	B-HSM	A320-232	2238	
☐	B-HSN	A320-232	2428	
☐	B-HSO	A320-232	4023	
☐	B-HSP	A320-232	4247	
☐	B-HSQ	A320-232	5024	
☐	B-HSR	A320-232	5030	
☐	B-HST	A320-232	5362	
☐	B-HSU	A320-232	5429	
☐	B-HTD	A321-231	0993	
☐	B-HTE	A321-231	1024	
☐	B-HTF	A321-231	0633	
☐	B-HTG	A321-231	1695	
☐	B-HTH	A321-231	1984	
☐	B-HTI	A321-231	2021	
☐	B-HTJ	A321-231	3369	
☐	B-HTK	A321-231	3669	
☐	B-HLA	A330-342	071	
☐	B-HLB	A330-342	083	
☐	B-HLC	A330-342	099	
☐	B-HLE	A330-342	109	
☐	B-HLG	A330-342	118	
☐	B-HLI	A330-342	155	
☐	B-HLJ	A330-342	012	
☐	B-HLK	A330-342	017	
☐	B-HLL	A330-342	244	
☐	B-HWM	A330-343E	1457	
☐	B-HYB	A330-342	106	
☐	B-HYF	A330-342	234	
☐	B-HYG	A330-343	405	
☐	B-HYI	A330-343	479	
☐	B-HYJ	A330-343	512	
☐	B-HYQ	A330-343	581	
☐	B-LAA	A330-342E	669	
☐	B-LAB	A330-342E	673	
☐	B-LBD	A330-343E	1503	♦

CATHAY PACIFIC AIRWAYS ***CX / CPA***

	Reg	Type	c/n	
☐	B-HLD	A330-342	102	
☐	B-HLF	A330-342	113	
☐	B-HLH	A330-342	121	
☐	B-HLM	A330-343E	386	
☐	B-HLN	A330-343E	389	
☐	B-HLO	A330-343E	393	
☐	B-HLP	A330-343E	418	
☐	B-HLQ	A330-343E	420	
☐	B-HLR	A330-343E	421	
☐	B-HLS	A330-343E	423	
☐	B-HLT	A330-343E	439	
☐	B-HLU	A330-343E	539	
☐	B-HLV	A330-343E	548	
☐	B-HLW	A330-343E	565	
☐	B-LAC	A330-342E	679	
☐	B-LAD	A330-342E	776	
☐	B-LAE	A330-342E	850	
☐	B-LAF	A330-342E	855	
☐	B-LAG	A330-342E	895	
☐	B-LAH	A330-342E	915	
☐	B-LAI	A330-342E	959	
☐	B-LAJ	A330-343E	1163	
☐	B-LAK	A330-343E	1196	
☐	B-LAL	A330-343E	1222	
☐	B-LAM	A330-343E	1239	
☐	B-LAN	A330-343E	1285	
☐	B-LAO	A330-343E	1317	
☐	B-LAP	A330-343E	1343	
☐	B-LAQ	A330-343E	1349	
☐	B-LAR	A330-343E	1362	
☐	B-LAX	A330-343E	1366	
☐	B-LAZ	A330-343E	1387	
☐	B-LBA	A330-343E	1409	
☐	B-LBB	A330-343E	1436	
☐	B-LBC	A330-343E	1443	
☐	B-LBE	A330-343E	1523	
☐	B-LBF	A330-343E	1545	
☐	B-LBG	A330-343E	1557	
☐	B-LBH	A330-343E	1567	
☐	B-LBI	A330-343E	1598	

	Reg	Type	C/n	
☐	B-LBJ	A330-343E	1618	♦
☐	B-LBK	A330-343E	1621	♦
☐	B-HXD	A340-313X	147	
☐	B-HXE	A340-313X	157	
☐	B-HXF	A340-313X	160	
☐	B-HXG	A340-313X	208	
☐	B-HXH	A340-313X	218	
☐	B-HXJ	A340-313X	227	
☐	B-LRA	A350-941	029	o/o♦
☐	B-LRB	A350-941	032	o/o♦
☐	B-LRC	A350-941	034	o/o♦
☐	B-LRD	A350-941	038	o/o♦
☐	B-LRE	A350-941	039	o/o♦
☐	B-	A350-941	046	o/o♦
☐	B-	A350-941	053	o/o♦
☐	B-	A350-941	058	o/o♦
☐	B-	A350-941	061	o/o♦
☐	B-	A350-941	070	o/o♦
☐	B-	A350-941	072	o/o♦
☐	B-	A350-941	075	o/o♦
☐	B-	A350-941	085	o/o♦
☐	B-HKT	B747-412	27132/955	
☐	B-HKX	B747-412BCF	26557/1101	♦
☐	B-HOZ	B747-467BCF	25871/925	
☐	B-HUI	B747-467	27230/1033	
☐	B-HUJ	B747-467	27595/1061	
☐	B-HUL	B747-467F	30804/1255	
☐	B-HUO	B747-467F	32571/1271	
☐	B-HUP	B747-467F	30805/1282	
☐	B-HUQ	B747-467F	34150/1356	[MZJ]
☐	B-LIA	B747-467ERF	37299/1404	
☐	B-LIB	B747-467ERF	36867/1409	
☐	B-LIC	B747-467ERF	36868/1413	
☐	B-LID	B747-467ERF	36869/1414	
☐	B-LIE	B747-467ERF	36870/1514	
☐	B-LIF	B747-467ERF	36871/1417	
☐	B-LJA	B747-867F	39238/1427	
☐	B-LJB	B747-867F	39239/1428	
☐	B-LJC	B747-867F	39240/1433	
☐	B-LJD	B747-867F	39241/1438	
☐	B-LJE	B747-867F	39242/1441	
☐	B-LJF	B747-867F	39243/1447	
☐	B-LJG	B747-867F	39244/1450	
☐	B-LJH	B747-867F	39245/1457	
☐	B-LJI	B747-867F	39247/1460	
☐	B-LJJ	B747-867F	39246/1464	
☐	B-LJK	B747-867F	43394/1483	
☐	B-LJL	B747-867F	43536/1484	
☐	B-LJM	B747-867F	43825/1486	
☐	B-	B747-867F		o/o♦
☐	B-	B777-F67		o/o
☐	B-	B777-F67		o/o
☐	B-	B777-F67		o/o
☐	B-	B777-F67		o/o
☐	B-	B777-F67		o/o
☐	B-	B777-F67		o/o♦
☐	B-	B777-F67		o/o♦
☐	B-HNA	B777-267	27265/14	
☐	B-HNB	B777-267	27266/18	
☐	B-HNC	B777-267	27263/28	
☐	B-HND	B777-267	27264/31	
☐	B-HNE	B777-367	27507/94	
☐	B-HNF	B777-367	27506/102	
☐	B-HNG	B777-367	27505/118	
☐	B-HNH	B777-367	27504/136	
☐	B-HNI	B777-367	27508/204	
☐	B-HNJ	B777-367	27509/224	
☐	B-HNK	B777-367	27510/248	
☐	B-HNL	B777-267	27116/1	
☐	B-HNM	B777-367	33702/456	
☐	B-HNN	B777-367	33703/462	
☐	B-HNO	B777-367	33704/470	
☐	B-HNP	B777-367	34243/513	
☐	B-HNQ	B777-367	34244/567	
☐	B-HNR	B777-367ER	60724/1333	♦
☐	B-KPA	B777-367ER	36154/661	
☐	B-KPB	B777-367ER	35299/670	
☐	B-KPC	B777-367ER	34432/674	
☐	B-KPD	B777-367ER	36155/680	
☐	B-KPE	B777-367ER	36156/685	
☐	B-KPF	B777-367ER	36832/692	
☐	B-KPG	B777-367ER	35300/700	
☐	B-KPH	B777-367ER	35301/720	
☐	B-KPI	B777-367ER	36833/746	
☐	B-KPJ	B777-367ER	36157/754	
☐	B-KPK	B777-367ER	36158/783	
☐	B-KPL	B777-367ER	36161/818	
☐	B-KPM	B777-367ER	36159/835	
☐	B-KPN	B777-367ER	36165/839	
☐	B-KPO	B777-367ER	36160/843	
☐	B-KPP	B777-367ER	36164/845	
☐	B-KPQ	B777-367ER	36162/860	
☐	B-KPR	B777-367ER	36163/877	
☐	B-KPS	B777-367ER	39232/921	
☐	B-KPT	B777-367ER	37896/927	
☐	B-KPU	B777-367ER	39233/934	
☐	B-KPV	B777-367ER	37901/941	
☐	B-KPW	B777-367ER	39234/950	
☐	B-KPX	B777-367ER	37897/956	
☐	B-KPY	B777-367ER	37899/991	
☐	B-KPZ	B777-367ER	37900/1003	
☐	B-KQA	B777-367ER	37898/1008	
☐	B-KQB	B777-367ER	39235/1012	
☐	B-KQC	B777-367ER	39236/1040	
☐	B-KQD	B777-367ER	39237/1077	
☐	B-KQE	B777-367ER	41432/1089	
☐	B-KQF	B777-367ER	41428/1101	
☐	B-KQG	B777-367ER	42142/1127	
☐	B-KQH	B777-367ER	42143/1133	
☐	B-KQI	B777-367ER	41429/1139	
☐	B-KQJ	B777-367ER	41760/1147	
☐	B-KQK	B777-367ER	41430/1159	
☐	B-KQL	B777-367ER	41431/1164	
☐	B-KQM	B777-367ER	41433/1195	
☐	B-KQN	B777-367ER	41761/1209	
☐	B-KQO	B777-367ER	41757/1216	
☐	B-KQP	B777-367ER	41758/1224	
☐	B-KQQ	B777-367ER	41762/1231	
☐	B-KQR	B777-367ER	41759/1240	
☐	B-KQS	B777-367ER	42144/1246	
☐	B-KQT	B777-367ER	41766/1255	
☐	B-KQU	B777-367ER	42145/1263	
☐	B-KQV	B777-367ER	41765/1273	
☐	B-KQW	B777-367ER	41763/1282	
☐	B-KQX	B777-367ER	60725/1295	
☐	B-KQY	B777-367ER	41764/1304	
☐	B-KQZ	B777-367ER	60723/1319	

HONG KONG AIRLINES — *HX / CRK*

	Reg	Type	C/n
☐	B-LPC	A320-214	5147

☐	B-LPD	A320-214	5189	
☐	B-LPE	A320-214	5260	
☐	B-LPI	A320-214	5416	
☐	B-LPJ	A320-214	5514	
☐	B-LPK	A320-214	5544	
☐	B-LPL	A320-214/S	6003	
☐	B-LPM	A320-214/S	6246	
☐	B-LPN	A320-214/S	6442	♦
☐	B-LPO	A320-214/S	6776	♦
☐	B-LNC	A330-223	1031	
☐	B-LND	A330-223	1042	
☐	B-LNE	A330-223	1039	
☐	B-LNF	A330-223	1059	
☐	B-LNG	A330-223	1054	
☐	B-LNI	A330-223	1034	
☐	B-LNJ	A330-243	1277	
☐	B-LNK	A330-243	1286	
☐	B-LNL	A330-243	1322	
☐	B-LNM	A330-343E	1358	
☐	B-LNN	A330-343E	1369	♦
☐	B-LNO	A330-343E	1384	
☐	B-LNP	A330-343E	1398	
☐	B-LNQ	A330-343E	1668	♦
☐	B-LNV	A330-243F	1175	
☐	B-LNW	A330-243F	1320	
☐	B-LNX	A330-243F	1115	
☐	B-LNY	A330-243F	1062	
☐	B-LNZ	A330-243F	1051	
☐	B-	B777-FEZ		o/o♦
☐	B-	B777-FEZ		o/o♦
☐	B-	B777-FEZ		o/o♦
☐	B-	B777-FEZ		o/o♦

HONG KONG EXPRESS — UO / HKE

☐	B-LCA	A320-232	2717	
☐	B-LCB	A320-232	2322	
☐	B-LCC	A320-232/S	6142	
☐	B-LCD	A320-232/S	6302	
☐	B-LCE	A320-232	2299	
☐	B-LCF	A320-232/S	5725	♦
☐	B-LCG	A320-232/S	5738	♦
☐	B-LCJ	A320-232/S	5685	♦
☐	B-LPB	A320-214	4970	
☐	B-LPF	A320-214	5264	
☐	B-LPG	A320-214	5266	
☐	B-LPH	A320-214	5341	
☐	B-	A320-2xxN		o/o♦
☐	B-	A320-2xxN		o/o♦

B-M CHINA – MACAU

AIR MACAU — NX / AMU

☐	B-MAK	A319-132	1758	
☐	B-MAL	A319-132	1790	
☐	B-MAN	A319-132	1912	
☐	B-MAO	A319-132	1962	
☐	B-MAX	A320-232	0928	
☐	B-MBC	A320-232	4197	
☐	B-MCB	A320-232	5352	♦
☐	B-MCF	A320-232/S	6934	♦
☐	B-MAF	A321-131	0620	[GYR]
☐	B-MAG	A321-131	0631	
☐	B-MAJ	A321-231	0908	
☐	B-MAP	A321-231	1850	
☐	B-MAQ	A321-231	1926	
☐	B-MBA	A321-231	5459	
☐	B-MBB	A321-231	5523	
☐	B-MBM	A321-231/S	6324	
☐	B-MCA	A321-231/S	6517	
☐	B-MCC	A321-231/S	6827	
☐	B-MCD	A321-231/S	6912	♦
☐	B-MCE	A321-231/S	6938	♦
☐	B-M	A321-231/S		o/o♦

B- CHINA – TAIWAN

CHINA AIRLINES — CI / CAL

☐	B-18301	A330-302	602	
☐	B-18302	A330-302	607	
☐	B-18303	A330-302	641	
☐	B-18305	A330-302	671	
☐	B-18306	A330-302	675	
☐	B-18307	A330-302	691	
☐	B-18308	A330-302	699	
☐	B-18309	A330-302	707	
☐	B-18310	A330-302	714	
☐	B-18311	A330-302	752	
☐	B-18312	A330-302	769	
☐	B-18315	A330-302	823	
☐	B-18316	A330-302	838	
☐	B-18317	A330-302	861	
☐	B-18351	A330-302	725	
☐	B-18352	A330-302	805	
☐	B-18353	A330-302	920	
☐	B-18355	A330-302	1177	
☐	B-18356	A330-302	1272	
☐	B-18357	A330-302	1278	
☐	B-18358	A330-302	1346	
☐	B-18359	A330-302	1367	
☐	B-18360	A330-302	1450	
☐	B-18361	A330-302	1539	
☐	B-18803	A340-313X	411	
☐	B-18805	A340-313X	415	
☐	B-18806	A340-313X	433	
☐	B-18807	A340-313X	541	
☐	B-	A350-941	049	o/o♦
☐	B-	A350-941	057	o/o♦
☐	B-	A350-941	066	o/o♦
☐	B-18601	B737-809/W	28402/113	
☐	B-18605	B737-809/W	28404/130	
☐	B-18606	B737-809/W	28405/132	
☐	B-18607	B737-809/W	29104/139	
☐	B-18608	B737-809/W	28406/141	
☐	B-18609	B737-809/W	28407/161	
☐	B-18610	B737-809/W	29105/295	
☐	B-18612	B737-809/W	30173/695	
☐	B-18615	B737-809/W	30174/1175	
☐	B-18617	B737-809/W	29106/302	
☐	B-18651	B737-8Q8/W	41786/4417	
☐	B-18652	B737-8Q8/W	41787/4455	
☐	B-18653	B737-8Q8/W	41788/4510	
☐	B-18655	B737-8MA/W	40945/4830	
☐	B-18656	B737-8MA/W	40946/4916	
☐	B-18657	B737-8FH/W	39943/4944	
☐	B-18658	B737-8SH/W	61424/5584	♦
☐	B-	B737-8SH/W		o/o♦
☐	B-18201	B747-409	28709/1114	[VCV]
☐	B-18202	B747-409	28710/1132	[VCV]

	Reg	Type	C/n	Notes
☐	B-18203	B747-409	28711/1136	
☐	B-18205	B747-409	28712/1137	
☐	B-18206	B747-409	29030/1145	
☐	B-18207	B747-409	29219/1176	
☐	B-18208	B747-409	29031/1186	
☐	B-18210	B747-409	33734/1353	
☐	B-18211	B747-409	33735/1354	
☐	B-18212	B747-409	33736/1357	
☐	B-18215	B747-409	33737/1358	
☐	B-18251	B747-409	27965/1063	[VCV]
☐	B-18701	B747-409F	30759/1249	
☐	B-18702	B747-409F	30760/1252	[VCV]
☐	B-18703	B747-409F	30761/1254	[VCV]
☐	B-18705	B747-409F	30762/1263	[VCV]
☐	B-18706	B747-409F	30763/1267	
☐	B-18707	B747-409F	30764/1269	
☐	B-18708	B747-409F	30765/1288	
☐	B-18709	B747-409F	30766/1294	
☐	B-18710	B747-409F	30767/1300	
☐	B-18711	B747-409F	30768/1314	
☐	B-18712	B747-409F	33729/1332	
☐	B-18715	B747-409F	33731/1334	
☐	B-18716	B747-409F	33732/1339	
☐	B-18717	B747-409F	30769/1346	
☐	B-18718	B747-409F	30770/1348	
☐	B-18719	B747-409F	33739/1355	
☐	B-18720	B747-409F	33733/1359	
☐	B-18721	B747-409F	33738/1362	
☐	B-18722	B747-409F	34265/1372	
☐	B-18723	B747-409F	34266/1379	
☐	B-18725	B747-409F	30771/1385	
☐	N168CL	B747-409	29906/1219	[VCV]
☐	B-18001	B777-309ER	43978/1301	
☐	B-18002	B777-309ER	43980/1307	
☐	B-18003	B777-309ER	43977/1327	♦
☐	B-18005	B777-309ER	43979/1347	♦
☐	B-18006	B777-309ER	43981/1365	♦
☐	B-18051	B777-36NER	41821/1227	
☐	B-18052	B777-36NER	41822/1245	
☐	B-18053	B777-36NER	41845/1254	
☐	B-18055	B777-36NER	41823/1265	
☐	B-	B777-309ER		o/o♦

EVA AIRWAYS — *BR / EVA*

	Reg	Type	C/n	Notes
☐	B-16201	A321-211	5354	
☐	B-16202	A321-211	5328	
☐	B-16203	A321-211	5377	
☐	B-16205	A321-211/S	5485	
☐	B-16206	A321-211/S	5808	
☐	B-16207	A321-211/S	5849	
☐	B-16208	A321-211/S	6024	
☐	B-16211	A321-211/S	6179	
☐	B-16212	A321-211/S	6276	
☐	B-16213	A321-211/S	6312	
☐	B-16215	A321-211/S	6488	
☐	B-16216	A321-211/S	6545	♦
☐	B-16217	A321-211/S	6585	♦
☐	B-16218	A321-211/S	6653	♦
☐	B-16219	A321-211/S	6707	♦
☐	B-16220	A321-211/S	6747	♦
☐	B-16221	A321-211/S	6935	♦
☐	B-16222	A321-211/S	6999	o/o♦
☐	B-	A321-211/S	7054	o/o♦
☐	B-	A321-211/S	7101	o/o♦
☐	B-	A321-211/S	7317	o/o♦
☐	B-	A321-211/S		o/o♦
☐	B-	A321-211/S		o/o♦
☐	B-	A321-211/S		o/o♦
☐	B-16303	A330-203	555	
☐	B-16305	A330-203	573	
☐	B-16306	A330-203	587	
☐	B-16307	A330-203	634	
☐	B-16308	A330-203	655	
☐	B-16309	A330-203	661	
☐	B-16310	A330-203	678	
☐	B-16311	A330-203	693	
☐	B-16312	A330-203	755	
☐	B-16331	A330-302E	1254	
☐	B-16332	A330-302E	1268	
☐	B-16333	A330-302E	1274	
☐	B-16335	A330-302E	1684	♦
☐	B-16336	A330-302E	1690	♦
☐	B-	A330-302E		o/o♦
☐	B-	A330-302E		o/o♦
☐	B-16401	B747-45ESF	27062/942	
☐	B-16402	B747-45ESF	27063/947	
☐	B-16406	B747-45EMSF	27898/1051	
☐	B-16407	B747-45EMSF	27899/1053	
☐	B-16410	B747-45E	29061/1140	
☐	B-16411	B747-45E	29111/1151	
☐	B-16412	B747-45E	29112/1159	
☐	B-16462	B747-45EMSF	27173/998	[LETL]
☐	B-16481	B747-45EF	30607/1251	
☐	B-16482	B747-45EF	30608/1279	
☐	B-16483	B747-45EF	30609/1309	
☐	B-16701	B777-35EER	32639/524	
☐	B-16702	B777-35EER	32640/531	
☐	B-16703	B777-35EER	32643/572	
☐	B-16705	B777-35EER	32645/597	
☐	B-16706	B777-35EER	33750/612	
☐	B-16707	B777-35EER	33751/634	
☐	B-16708	B777-35EER	33752/658	
☐	B-16709	B777-35EER	33753/683	
☐	B-16710	B777-35EER	32641/707	
☐	B-16711	B777-35EER	33754/721	
☐	B-16712	B777-35EER	33755/735	
☐	B-16713	B777-35EER	33756/758	
☐	B-16715	B777-35EER	33757/810	
☐	B-16716	B777-35EER	32642/822	
☐	B-16717	B777-35EER	32644/863	
☐	B-16718	B777-35EER	43289/1189	
☐	B-16719	B777-35EER	42103/1202	
☐	B-16720	B777-35EER	41820/1213	
☐	B-16721	B777-35EER	43290/1275	
☐	B-16722	B777-35EER	42107/1302	♦
☐	B-16723	B777-35EER	42108/1313	♦
☐	B-16725	B777-35EER	44554/1349	♦
☐	B-16726	B777-35EER	44552/1366	♦
☐	B-	B777-35EER		o/o♦
☐	B-	B777-35EER		o/o♦
☐	B-	B777-Fxx		o/o♦
☐	B-	B777-Fxx		o/o♦

FAR EASTERN AIR TRANSPORT — *FE / FEA*

	Reg	Type	C/n	Notes
☐	B-27013	B757-27A	29608/835	[TPE]
☐	B-27015	B757-27A	29609/876	[TPE]
☐	B-28007	MD-83	49807/1829	
☐	B-28011	MD-82	53118/1954	
☐	B-28017	MD-82	53166/2052	
☐	B-28021	MD-82	53167/2056	
☐	B-28025	MD-83	53602/2214	

	Reg	Type	c/n	
☐	B-28027	MD-83	53603/2218	
☐	B-28035	MD-82	53480/2127	
☐	B-28037	MD-82	53479/2124	

MANDARIN AIRLINES — **AE / MDA**

	Reg	Type	c/n	
☐	B-18659	B737-8SH/W	41335/5560	♦
☐	B-16821	ERJ-190AR	19000087	
☐	B-16822	ERJ-190AR	19000091	
☐	B-16823	ERJ-190AR	19000099	
☐	B-16826	ERJ-190AR	19000175	
☐	B-16827	ERJ-190AR	19000182	
☐	B-16828	ERJ-190AR	19000190	
☐	B-16829	ERJ-190AR	19000302	

TIGERAIR TAIWAN — **IT / TTW**

	Reg	Type	c/n	
☐	B-50001	A320-232/S	6187	
☐	B-50003	A320-232	4804	
☐	B-50005	A320-232/S	6522	
☐	B-50006	A320-232/S	6604	♦
☐	B-50007	A320-232	4874	♦
☐	B-50008	A320-232/S	6700	♦
☐	B-50011	A320-232/S	6917	♦
☐	B-50015	A320-232/S	6943	♦

TRANSASIA AIRWAYS — **GE / TNA**

	Reg	Type	c/n	
☐	B-22310	A320-232	0791	
☐	B-22311	A320-232	0822	
☐	B-22312	A320-232	2914	
☐	B-22317	A320-232	2376	
☐	B-22318	A320-233	3577	♦
☐	B-22320	A320-233	3581	♦
☐	B-	A320-2xxN		o/o♦
☐	B-	A320-2xxN		o/o♦
☐	B-22606	A321-131	0731	
☐	B-22607	A321-131	0746	
☐	B-22611	A321-231/S	6693	♦
☐	B-22612	A321-231/S	6734	♦
☐	B-	A321-231/S	7206	o/o♦
☐	B-	A321-231/S		o/o♦
☐	B-22101	A330-343E	1357	
☐	B-22102	A330-343E	1378	
☐	B-22103	A330-343E	1146	♦
☐	B-22105	A330-343E	1157	♦
☐	B-22807	ATR 72-212A	567	
☐	B-22811	ATR 72-212A	749	
☐	B-22812	ATR 72-212A	774	
☐	B-22815	ATR 72-600	1133	
☐	B-22817	ATR 72-600	1145	
☐	B-22818	ATR 72-600	1198	
☐	B-22820	ATR 72-600	1222	
☐	B-22821	ATR 72-600	1251	♦
☐	B-22822	ATR 72-600	1261	♦
☐	B-	ATR 72-600	1318	o/o♦
☐	B-	ATR 72-600		o/o♦

UNI AIR — **B7 / UIA**

	Reg	Type	c/n	
☐	B-16209	A321-211/S	6042	
☐	B-16210	A321-211/S	6087	♦
☐	B-17001	ATR 72-600	1044	
☐	B-17002	ATR 72-600	1061	
☐	B-17003	ATR 72-600	1078	
☐	B-17005	ATR 72-600	1090	
☐	B-17006	ATR 72-600	1101	
☐	B-17007	ATR 72-600	1111	
☐	B-17008	ATR 72-600	1125	
☐	B-17009	ATR 72-600	1136	
☐	B-17010	ATR 72-600	1150	
☐	B-17011	ATR 72-600	1163	
☐	B-17012	ATR 72-600	1175	
☐	B-17013	ATR 72-600	1183	
☐	B-17015	ATR 72-600	1240	
☐	B-	ATR 72-600		o/o
☐	B-17919	MD-90-30	53569/2173	
☐	B-17920	MD-90-30	53574/2186	

MD-90s reported for delivery to Delta Airlines.

V AIR — **ZV / VAX**

	Reg	Type	c/n	
☐	B-22316	A320-232	5055	♦
☐	B-22608	A321-231/S	6009	
☐	B-22610	A321-231/S	6294	

C- CANADA

AIR CANADA — **AC / ACA**

	Reg	Type	c/n	Fleet no.
☐	C-FYJI	A319-114	0682	258
☐	C-FYKC	A319-114	0691	260
☐	C-FYKR	A319-114	0693	261
☐	C-FZUH	A319-114	0711	264
☐	C-FZUJ	A319-114	0719	265
☐	C-FZUL	A319-114	0721	266
☐	C-GAPY	A319-114	0728	267
☐	C-GAQL	A319-114	0732	268
☐	C-GAQX	A319-114	0736	269
☐	C-GAQZ	A319-114	0740	270
☐	C-GARG	A319-114	0742	271
☐	C-GBHM	A319-114	0769	274
☐	C-GBHN	A319-114	0773	275
☐	C-GBIA	A319-114	0817	280
☐	C-GBIP	A319-114	0546	285
☐	C-GITP	A319-112	1562	286
☐	C-GITR	A319-112	1577	287
☐	C-FDCA	A320-211	0232	405^
☐	C-FDQQ	A320-211	0059	201
☐	C-FDQV	A320-211	0068	202
☐	C-FDRH	A320-211	0073	203
☐	C-FDRK	A320-211	0084	204
☐	C-FDRP	A320-211	0122	205
☐	C-FDSN	A320-211	0126	206
☐	C-FDST	A320-211	0127	207
☐	C-FDSU	A320-211	0141	208
☐	C-FFWI	A320-211	0149	209
☐	C-FFWJ	A320-211	0150	210
☐	C-FFWM	A320-211	0154	211
☐	C-FFWN	A320-211	0159	212
☐	C-FGJI	A320-214	1787	241
☐	C-FGKH	A320-214	1975	242
☐	C-FGYL	A320-211	0254	218
☐	C-FGYS	A320-211	0255	219
☐	C-FKCK	A320-211	0265	220
☐	C-FKCO	A320-211	0277	221
☐	C-FKCR	A320-211	0290	222
☐	C-FKOJ	A320-211	0330	226
☐	C-FKPT	A320-211	0324	225
☐	C-FLSS	A320-211	0284	408
☐	C-FLSU	A320-211	0309	411
☐	C-FMSX	A320-211	0378	232
☐	C-FNVU	A320-211	0403	415
☐	C-FNVV	A320-211	0404	416

☐	C-FPDN	A320-211	0341	228
☐	C-FPWD	A320-211	0231	404^
☐	C-FPWE	A320-211	0175	402^
☐	C-FTJO	A320-211	0183	213
☐	C-FTJQ	A320-211	0242	215
☐	C-FTJR	A320-211	0248	216
☐	C-FTJS	A320-211	0253	217
☐	C-FXCD	A320-214	2018	239
☐	C-FZQS	A320-214	2145	240
☐	C-FZUB	A320-214	1940	238
☐	C-GJVT	A320-214	1719	235
☐	C-GKOD	A320-214	1864	236
☐	C-GKOE	A320-214	1874	237
☐	C-GPWG	A320-211	0174	401^
☐	C-GQCA	A320-211	0210	403^
☐	C-FGKN	A321-212	3051	461♦
☐	C-FGKP	A321-212	3884	462♦
☐	C-FGKZ	A321-212	3401	463♦
☐	C-FJNX	A321-212	1691	♦
☐	C-FLKX	A321-212	1299	473♦
☐	C-GITU	A321-211	1602	451
☐	C-GITY	A321-211	1611	452
☐	C-GIUB	A321-211	1623	453
☐	C-GIUE	A321-211	1632	454
☐	C-GIUF	A321-211	1638	455
☐	C-GJVX	A321-211	1726	456
☐	C-GJWD	A321-211	1748	457
☐	C-GJWI	A321-211	1772	458
☐	C-GJWN	A321-211	1783	459
☐	C-GJWO	A321-211	1811	460
☐	C-GFAF	A330-343E	277	931
☐	C-GFAH	A330-343E	279	932
☐	C-GFAJ	A330-343E	284	933
☐	C-GFUR	A330-343E	344	934
☐	C-GHKR	A330-343E	400	935
☐	C-GHKW	A330-343E	408	936
☐	C-GHKX	A330-343E	412	937
☐	C-GHLM	A330-343E	419	938
☐	C-FCAB	B767-375ER	24082/213	681
☐	C-FCAE	B767-375ER	24083/215	682
☐	C-FCAF	B767-375ER	24084/219	683
☐	C-FCAG	B767-375ER	24085/220	684
☐	C-FOCA	B767-375ER	24575/311	640
☐	C-FPCA	B767-375ER	24306/258	637
☐	C-FTCA	B767-375ER	24307/259	638
☐	C-FXCA	B767-375ER	24574/302	639
☐	C-GBZR	B767-38EER	25404/411	645
☐	C-GDUZ	B767-38EER	25347/399	646
☐	C-GEOQ	B767-375ER	30112/765	647
☐	C-GEOU	B767-375ER	30108/771	648
☐	C-GHLA	B767-35HER	26387/445	656
☐	C-GHLK	B767-35HER	26388/456	657
☐	C-GHOZ	B767-375ER	24087/249	685
☐	C-GLCA	B767-375ER	25120/361	641
☐	C-GSCA	B767-375ER	25121/372	642
☐	C-FIUA	B777-233LR	35239/640	701
☐	C-FIUF	B777-233LR	35243/651	702
☐	C-FIUJ	B777-233LR	35244/679	703
☐	C-FIVK	B777-233LR	35245/689	704
☐	C-FNND	B777-233LR	35246/695	705
☐	C-FNNH	B777-233LR	35247/699	706
☐	C-FITL	B777-333ER	35256/620	731
☐	C-FITU	B777-333ER	35254/626	732
☐	C-FITW	B777-333ER	35298/638	733

☐	C-FIUL	B777-333ER	35255/642	734
☐	C-FIUR	B777-333ER	35242/649	735
☐	C-FIUV	B777-333ER	35248/702	736
☐	C-FIUW	B777-333ER	35249/712	737
☐	C-FIVM	B777-333ER	35251/717	738
☐	C-FIVQ	B777-333ER	35240/749	740
☐	C-FIVR	B777-333ER	35241/763	741
☐	C-FIVS	B777-333ER	35784/797	742
☐	C-FIVW	B777-333ER	42218/1108	743
☐	C-FIVX	B777-333ER	42219/1125	744
☐	C-FNNQ	B777-333ER	43251/1154	745
☐	C-FNNU	B777-333ER	43249/1161	746
☐	C-FNNW	B777-333ER	43250/1174	747
☐	C-FRAM	B777-333ER	35250/726	739
☐	C-	B777-333ER		♦
☐	C-	B777-333ER		♦
☐	C-FGDT	B787-9	37171/393	o/o♦
☐	C-FGDX	B787-9	35269/395	o/o♦
☐	C-FGDZ	B787-9	37173/405	o/o♦
☐	C-FGEI	B787-9	37174/407	o/o♦
☐	C-FGEO	B787-9	37180/409	o/o♦
☐	C-FGFZ	B787-9	37172/417	o/o♦
☐	C-FGHO	B787-9	35270/425	o/o♦
☐	C-FHHZ	B787-9	37169/427	o/o♦
☐	C-FKSV	B787-9	37170/444	o/o♦
☐	C-FNOE	B787-9	35265/323	831♦
☐	C-FNOG	B787-9	35266/332	832♦
☐	C-FNOH	B787-9	35267/366	833♦
☐	C-FNOI	B787-9	35268/371	834♦
☐	C-GHPQ	B787-8	35257/160	801
☐	C-GHPT	B787-8	35258/170	802
☐	C-GHPU	B787-8	35259/174	803
☐	C-GHPV	B787-8	35260/220	804
☐	C-GHPX	B787-8	35261/230	805
☐	C-GHPY	B787-8	35262/235	806
☐	C-GHQQ	B787-8	35263/254	807
☐	C-GHQY	B787-8	35264/265	808
☐	C-	B787-9	37170/444	o/o♦
☐	C-FFYJ	ERJ-190AR	19000013	302
☐	C-FFYM	ERJ-190AR	19000015	303
☐	C-FFYT	ERJ-190AR	19000018	[MZJ]
☐	C-FGMF	ERJ-190AR	19000019	305
☐	C-FHJU	ERJ-190AR	19000044	314
☐	C-FHKA	ERJ-190AR	19000046	315
☐	C-FHKE	ERJ-190AR	19000048	316
☐	C-FHKI	ERJ-190AR	19000052	317
☐	C-FHKP	ERJ-190AR	19000055	318
☐	C-FHKS	ERJ-190AR	19000064	319
☐	C-FHNL	ERJ-190AR	19000070	321
☐	C-FHNP	ERJ-190AR	19000071	322
☐	C-FHNV	ERJ-190AR	19000075	323
☐	C-FHNW	ERJ-190AR	19000077	324
☐	C-FHNX	ERJ-190AR	19000083	325
☐	C-FHNY	ERJ-190AR	19000085	326
☐	C-FHON	ERJ-190AR	19000097	330
☐	C-FHOS	ERJ-190AR	19000101	331
☐	C-FHOY	ERJ-190AR	19000105	332
☐	C-FLWE	ERJ-190AR	19000092	327
☐	C-FLWH	ERJ-190AR	19000094	328
☐	C-FLWK	ERJ-190AR	19000096	329
☐	C-FMYV	ERJ-190AR	19000108	333
☐	C-FMZB	ERJ-190AR	19000111	334
☐	C-FMZD	ERJ-190AR	19000115	335
☐	C-FMZR	ERJ-190AR	19000116	336
☐	C-FMZU	ERJ-190AR	19000118	337
☐	C-FMZW	ERJ-190AR	19000124	338

☐	C-FNAI	ERJ-190AR	19000132	339
☐	C-FNAJ	ERJ-190AR	19000134	340
☐	C-FNAN	ERJ-190AR	19000136	341
☐	C-FNAP	ERJ-190AR	19000142	342
☐	C-FNAW	ERJ-190AR	19000149	344

^ operated for JETZ

AIR CANADA EXPRESS — *QK / JZA*

☐	C-FBJZ	CRJ-705ER	15037	702
☐	C-FCJZ	CRJ-705ER	15040	703
☐	C-FDJZ	CRJ-705ER	15041	704
☐	C-FJJZ	CRJ-705ER	15043	705
☐	C-FKJZ	CRJ-705ER	15044	706
☐	C-FLJZ	CRJ-705ER	15045	707
☐	C-FNJZ	CRJ-705ER	15046	708
☐	C-FTJZ	CRJ-705ER	15047	709
☐	C-FUJZ	CRJ-705ER	15048	710
☐	C-GDJZ	CRJ-705ER	15049	711
☐	C-GFJZ	CRJ-705ER	15050	712
☐	C-GJAZ	CRJ-705ER	15036	701
☐	C-GLJZ	CRJ-705ER	15051	713
☐	C-GNJZ	CRJ-705ER	15052	714
☐	C-GOJZ	CRJ-705ER	15053	715
☐	C-GPJZ	CRJ-705ER	15055	716
☐	C-FSRJ	DHC-8-402Q	4165	945♦
☐	C-FSRN	DHC-8-402Q	4170	946♦
☐	C-FSRW	DHC-8-402Q	4172	947♦
☐	C-FSRY	DHC-8-402Q	4174	948♦
☐	C-FSRZ	DHC-8-402Q	4176	949♦
☐	C-GBJZ	DHC-8-402Q	4503	422♦
☐	C-GGAH	DHC-8-402Q	4432	416
☐	C-GGBF	DHC-8-402Q	4433	417
☐	C-GGCI	DHC-8-402Q	4434	418
☐	C-GGDU	DHC-8-402Q	4435	419
☐	C-GGFJ	DHC-8-402Q	4436	420
☐	C-GGFP	DHC-8-402Q	4437	421
☐	C-GGMI	DHC-8-402Q	4413	415
☐	C-GGMN	DHC-8-402Q	4405	414
☐	C-GGMQ	DHC-8-402Q	4403	413
☐	C-GGMU	DHC-8-402Q	4397	411
☐	C-GGMZ	DHC-8-402Q	4399	412
☐	C-GGND	DHC-8-402Q	4394	410
☐	C-GGNF	DHC-8-402Q	4393	409
☐	C-GGNW	DHC-8-402Q	4388	408
☐	C-GGNY	DHC-8-402Q	4386	407
☐	C-GGNZ	DHC-8-402Q	4384	406
☐	C-GGOF	DHC-8-402Q	4383	405
☐	C-GGOI	DHC-8-402Q	4381	404
☐	C-GGOK	DHC-8-402Q	4372	403
☐	C-GGOY	DHC-8-402Q	4365	401
☐	C-GIJZ	DHC-8-402Q	4509	425♦
☐	C-GJZC	DHC-8-402Q	4181	♦
☐	C-GJZG	DHC-8-402Q	4507	♦
☐	C-GJZK	DHC-8-402Q	4499	♦
☐	C-GJZX	DHC-8-402Q	4508	♦
☐	C-GKUK	DHC-8-402Q	4369	402
☐	C-GSJZ	DHC-8-402Q	4510	429♦
☐	C-GUJZ	DHC-8-402Q	4516	♦
☐	C-	DHC-8-402Q		o/o♦
☐	C-	DHC-8-402Q		o/o♦
☐	C-	DHC-8-402Q		o/o♦
☐	C-	DHC-8-402Q		o/o♦
☐	C-	DHC-8-402Q		o/o♦
☐	C-FEIQ	ERJ-175SU	17000083	371
☐	C-FEIX	ERJ-175SU	17000085	372
☐	C-FEJB	ERJ-175SU	17000086	373
☐	C-FEJC	ERJ-175SU	17000089	374
☐	C-FEJD	ERJ-175SU	17000090	375
☐	C-FEJF	ERJ-175SU	17000091	376
☐	C-FEJL	ERJ-175SU	17000095	377
☐	C-FEJP	ERJ-175SU	17000096	378
☐	C-FEJY	ERJ-175SU	17000097	379
☐	C-FEKD	ERJ-175SU	17000101	380
☐	C-FEKH	ERJ-175SU	17000102	381
☐	C-FEKI	ERJ-175SU	17000103	382
☐	C-FEKJ	ERJ-175SU	17000109	383
☐	C-FEKS	ERJ-175SU	17000110	384
☐	C-FFYG	ERJ-175SU	17000116	385
☐	C-FJBO	ERJ-175LR	17000277	♦
☐	C-FUJA	ERJ-175LR	17000272	♦
☐	C-FUJE	ERJ-175LR	17000291	♦
☐	C-FXJC	ERJ-175LR	17000287	♦
☐	C-FXJF	ERJ-175LR	17000309	♦

See also Air Canada Jazz and Sky Regional Airlines.

AIR CANADA JAZZ — *QK / JZA*

☐	C-FDJA	CRJ-200ER	7979	162
☐	C-FEJA	CRJ-200ER	7983	163
☐	C-FFJA	CRJ-200ER	7985	164
☐	C-FIJA	CRJ-200ER	7987	165
☐	C-FRIA	CRJ-100ER	7045	101
☐	C-FSKE	CRJ-100ER	7065	108
☐	C-FVKM	CRJ-100ER	7074	111
☐	C-FVMD	CRJ-100ER	7082	113
☐	C-FWJB	CRJ-100ER	7087	115
☐	C-FZJA	CRJ-200ER	7988	166
☐	C-GGJA	CRJ-200ER	8002	167
☐	C-GJZJ	CRJ-200ER	7553	157
☐	C-GJZZ	CRJ-200ER	7978	161
☐	C-GKEK	CRJ-200ER	7270	181
☐	C-GKEP	CRJ-200ER	7303	183
☐	C-GKER	CRJ-200ER	7368	184
☐	C-GKEU	CRJ-200ER	7376	185
☐	C-GKEW	CRJ-200ER	7385	186
☐	C-GKEZ	CRJ-200ER	7327	187
☐	C-GKFR	CRJ-200ER	7330	188
☐	C-GKGC	CRJ-200ER	7334	189
☐	C-GMJA	CRJ-200ER	8003	168
☐	C-GQJA	CRJ-200ER	7963	171
☐	C-GUJA	CRJ-200ER	8011	173
☐	C-FABA	DHC-8-102	092	805
☐	C-FABN	DHC-8-102	044	803
☐	C-FABT	DHC-8-102	049	std
☐	C-FACD	DHC-8-102	150	808
☐	C-FACF	DHC-8-311A	259	308
☐	C-FACT	DHC-8-311A	262	309
☐	C-FACV	DHC-8-311A	278	311
☐	C-FADF	DHC-8-311A	272	310
☐	C-FGQK	DHC-8-102	193	819
☐	C-FGRC	DHC-8-102	195	821
☐	C-FGRM	DHC-8-102	199	820
☐	C-FGRP	DHC-8-102	207	822
☐	C-FGRY	DHC-8-102	212	844
☐	C-FJFM	DHC-8-311A	240	324
☐	C-FJMG	DHC-8-102A	255	824
☐	C-FJVV	DHC-8-311A	271	306
☐	C-FJXZ	DHC-8-311A	264	326
☐	C-FMDW	DHC-8-311A	269	305
☐	C-FPON	DHC-8-102	171	836
☐	C-FRUZ	DHC-8-311	293	327
☐	C-FSOU	DHC-8-311A	342	328

	Reg	Type	C/n	Fleet
□	C-FTAK	DHC-8-311A	246	323
□	C-GABO	DHC-8-311A	248	312
□	C-GABP	DHC-8-311A	257	307
□	C-GANF	DHC-8-102	042	802
□	C-GANI	DHC-8-102	064	830
□	C-GANQ	DHC-8-102	096	833
□	C-GANS	DHC-8-102	057	828
□	C-GCTC	DHC-8-102	065	846
□	C-GETA	DHC-8-301	186	321
□	C-GEWQ	DHC-8-311A	202	325
□	C-GHTA	DHC-8-301	198	316
□	C-GION	DHC-8-102	127	832
□	C-GJIG	DHC-8-102	068	826
□	C-GJMI	DHC-8-102	077	825
□	C-GJMO	DHC-8-102	079	834
□	C-GJSV	DHC-8-102	085	814 [YYZ]
□	C-GJSX	DHC-8-102	088	835
□	C-GKON	DHC-8-102	130	815
□	C-GKTA	DHC-8-301	124	317
□	C-GLTA	DHC-8-301	154	318
□	C-GMON	DHC-8-301	131	301
□	C-GMTA	DHC-8-301	174	319
□	C-GNON	DHC-8-301	137	302
□	C-GOND	DHC-8-102	090	840
□	C-GONJ	DHC-8-102	095	839
□	C-GONN	DHC-8-102	101	898
□	C-GONO	DHC-8-102	102	807
□	C-GONR	DHC-8-102	109	841
□	C-GONW	DHC-8-102	112	843
□	C-GONX	DHC-8-102	118	829
□	C-GONY	DHC-8-102	115	827
□	C-GSTA	DHC-8-301	182	320
□	C-GTAG	DHC-8-301	200	315
□	C-GTAI	DHC-8-102	078	853
□	C-GTAQ	DHC-8-301	180	313
□	C-GTAT	DHC-8-301	188	314
□	C-GTBP	DHC-8-102	066	855
□	C-GUON	DHC-8-301	143	303
□	C-GVON	DHC-8-301	149	304
□	C-GVTA	DHC-8-301	190	322

AIR CANADA ROUGE — *RV / ROU*

	Reg	Type	C/n	Fleet
□	C-FYIY	A319-114	0634	252
□	C-FYJE	A319-114	0656	255
□	C-FYJG	A319-114	0670	256
□	C-FYJH	A319-114	0672	257
□	C-FYJP	A319-114	0688	259
□	C-FYKW	A319-114	0695	262
□	C-FYNS	A319-114	0572	251
□	C-FZUG	A319-114	0697	263
□	C-GARJ	A319-114	0752	272
□	C-GARO	A319-114	0757	273
□	C-GBHO	A319-114	0779	276
□	C-GBHR	A319-114	0785	277
□	C-GBHY	A319-114	0800	278
□	C-GBHZ	A319-114	0813	279
□	C-GBIJ	A319-114	0829	281
□	C-GBIK	A319-114	0831	282
□	C-GBIM	A319-114	0840	283
□	C-GBIN	A319-114	0845	284
□	C-GJVY	A319-112	1742	292
□	C-GKOB	A319-112	1853	296
□	C-GSJB	A319-112	1673	290
□	C-FJOK	A321-211/S	6844	468♦
□	C-FJOU	A321-211/S	6873	469♦
□	C-FJQD	A321-211/S	6884	470♦
□	C-FJQH	A321-211/S	6905	471♦
□	C-FJQL	A321-211/S	7117	o/o♦
□	C-FIYA	B767-33AER/W	33421/887	[YYZ]♦
□	C-FIYE	B767-33AER/W	33422/892	694♦
□	C-FJZK	B767-3Q8ER	29386/831	675♦
□	C-FMWP	B767-333ER/W	25583/508	631
□	C-FMWQ	B767-333ER/W	25584/596	632
□	C-FMWU	B767-333ER/W	25585/597	633
□	C-FMWV	B767-333ER/W	25586/599	634
□	C-FMWY	B767-333ER/W	25587/604	635
□	C-FMXC	B767-333ER/W	25588/606	636
□	C-GHLQ	B767-333ER/W	30846/832	658
□	C-GHLT	B767-333ER/W	30850/835	659♦
□	C-GHLU	B767-333ER/W	30851/836	660♦
□	C-GHLV	B767-333ER/W	30852/843	661♦
□	C-GHPE	B767-33AER/W	33423/897	691
□	C-GHPN	B767-33AER/W	33424/901	692
□	C-	B767-316ER/W	26327/621	o/o♦
□	C-	B767-316ER/W	27597/602	o/o♦

AIR CREEBEC — *YN / CRQ*

	Reg	Type	C/n	Fleet
□	C-FCJD	DHC-8-102	158	
□	C-FCLS	DHC-8-102	249	
□	C-FCSK	DHC-8-102	122	
□	C-FCWP	DHC-8-102	111	
□	C-FDWO	DHC-8-106	277	
□	C-FLSX	DHC-8-102	285	♦
□	C-FODL	DHC-8-102	294	♦
□	C-GAIS	DHC-8-102	138	
□	C-GJOP	DHC-8-102	121	
□	C-GTCO	DHC-8-102	119	
□	C-GUXF	DHC-8-102	173	
□	C-GXCN	DHC-8-106	345	♦
□	C-GYWX	DHC-8-102	175	
□	C-GZEW	DHC-8-314	393	
□	C-GZJC	DHC-8-102	060	
□	C-FLIY	HS.748 Srs.2A	1723	
□	C-FPJR	HS.748 Srs.2A	1725	
□	C-FTQR	Beech 1900D	UE-129	

AIR GEORGIAN — *ZX / GGN*

	Reg	Type	C/n	Fleet
□	C-GAAR	Beech 1900D	UE-207	964
□	C-GAAS	Beech 1900D	UE-209	965
□	C-GAAU	Beech 1900D	UE-232	904
□	C-GAAV	Beech 1900D	UE-235	967
□	C-GGGA	Beech 1900D	UE-291	951
□	C-GHGA	Beech 1900D	UE-293	953
□	C-GMGA	Beech 1900D	UE-315	956
□	C-GORA	Beech 1900D	UE-326	957
□	C-GORC	Beech 1900D	UE-320	959
□	C-GORF	Beech 1900D	UE-330	958
□	C-GORN	Beech 1900D	UE-403	974
□	C-GORZ	Beech 1900D	UE-134	973
□	C-GVGA	Beech 1900D	UE-292	952
□	C-GWGA	Beech 1900D	UE-309	955
□	C-GZGA	Beech 1900D	UE-306	954
□	C-FSKM	CRJ-100ER	7071	100
□	C-FWJF	CRJ-100ER	7095	101
□	C-FWJI	CRJ-100ER	7096	103
□	C-FWRR	CRJ-100ER	7107	105
□	C-FWRS	CRJ-100ER	7112	102
□	C-FWRT	CRJ-100ER	7118	104 [YYC]

☐ C-GKEJ CRJ-200ER 7269 180♦
☐ C-GKEM CRJ-200ER 7277 182♦
☐ C-GNJA CRJ-200ER 8004 169♦
☐ C-GOJA CRJ-200ER 8009 170♦
☐ C-GTJA CRJ-200ER 7966 172♦
☐ C-GXJA CRJ-200ER 8017 174♦
☐ C-GZJA CRJ-200ER 8018 175♦

Operates flights on behalf of the Air Canada Express network.

AIR INUIT 3H / AIE

☐ C-FAIY DHC-6 Twin Otter 300 362
☐ C-FJFR DHC-6 Twin Otter 300 784
☐ C-FTJJ DHC-6 Twin Otter 300 325
☐ C-GMDC DHC-6 Twin Otter 300 763
☐ C-GNDO DHC-6 Twin Otter 300 430
☐ C-GTYX DHC-6 Twin Otter 300 631

☐ C-FAID DHC-8Q-314B 400
☐ C-FAIV DHC-8-106 235 std
☐ C-FDAO DHC-8-102 123
☐ C-FEAI DHC-8-314 334
☐ C-FIAI DHC-8Q-314B 485
☐ C-FKTM DHC-8-311A 298 std
☐ C-FOAI DHC-8Q-314B 466
☐ C-FYAI DHC-8-315B 420
☐ C-GAIW DHC-8-311A 300 ♦
☐ C-GIAB DHC-8-311 296
☐ C-GRAI DHC-8Q-314 483
☐ C-GUAI DHC-8Q-314 423
☐ C-GXAI DHC-8Q-314 481

☐ C-FDOX HS.748 Srs.2A 1749
☐ C-GAIG B737-2S2C 21928/603
☐ C-GMAI B737-2Q2C 21467/515

AIR LABRADOR WJ / LAL

☐ C-FCSW DHC-6 Twin Otter 300 355
☐ C-FGON DHC-6 Twin Otter 300 369
☐ C-FOPN DHC-6 Twin Otter 300 291
☐ C-FTWU DHC-6 Twin Otter 300 372
☐ C-GKSN DHC-6 Twin Otter 300 493
☐ C-GLAI DHC-6 Twin Otter 300 296
☐ C-GNQY DHC-6 Twin Otter 300 450

☐ C-FWXL Beech 1900D UE-5
☐ C-FXON DHC-8-102 183
☐ C-GTMB Beech 1900D UE-345

AIR NORTH YUKON'S AIRLINE 4N / ANT

☐ C-FANB B737-48E 25764/2314
☐ C-FANF B737-55D 27417/2392
☐ C-FJLB B737-201 22273/680 [YXY]
☐ C-GANH B737-505/W 27153/2516
☐ C-GANJ B737-548 26287/2427
☐ C-GANU B737-55D 27416/2389
☐ C-GANV B737-2X6C 23122/1036
☐ C-GNAU B737-201 21817/602

☐ C-FAGI HS.748 Srs.2A 1699
☐ C-FCSE HS.748 Srs 2A 1679
☐ C-FYDU HS.748 Srs.2A 1694 [YXY]
☐ C-GANA HS.748 Srs.2A 1758

AIR SPRAY ASB

☐ C-FBAB BAe146 Srs 200A E2090 ♦
☐ C-GRNT BAe146 Srs 200A E2140 o/o♦
☐ C- BAe146 Srs 200A E2156 o/o♦
☐ N908AS BAe146 Srs 200A E2082 o/o♦
☐ N912AS BAe146 Srs 200A E2121 ♦

☐ C-FDTH L-188A Electra 1038 ♦
☐ C-FLJO L-188C Electra 1103 82♦
☐ C-FLXT L-188C Electra 1130 ♦
☐ C-FVFH L-188A Electra 1006 89♦
☐ C-FZCS L-188C Electra 1060 87♦
☐ C-GHZI L-188C Electra 2007 84♦
☐ C-GJTZ L-188C Electra 1133 ♦
☐ C-GNPB L-188A Electra 1028 ♦
☐ C-GOIZ L-188AF Electra 1053 ♦
☐ C-GYVI L-188CF Electra 111283 [YQF]♦
☐ C-GZCF L-188CF Electra 1091 90♦
☐ C-GZVM L-188A Electra 1036 85♦
☐ C-GZYH L-188A Electra 1124 [YQF]♦

AIR TINDI 8T / TID

☐ C-FATM DHC-6 Twin Otter 300 265
☐ C-FATN DHC-6 Twin Otter 300 226
☐ C-FATO DHC-6 Twin Otter 310 674
☐ C-FATW DHC-6 Twin Otter 300 525
☐ C-GMAS DHC-6 Twin Otter 300 438
☐ C-GNPS DHC-6 Twin Otter 300 558

☐ C-FWZV DHC-7-103 081
☐ C-GCEV DHC-7-102 063
☐ C-GCPY DHC-7-102 101
☐ C-GFFL DHC-7-102 074
☐ C-GUAT DHC-7-102 010

AIR TRANSAT TS / TSC

☐ C-FDAT A310-308 658 305
☐ C-GFAT A310-304 545 301
☐ C-GLAT A310-308 588 302
☐ C-GPAT A310-308 597 303
☐ C-GSAT A310-308 600 304
☐ C-GTSF A310-304 472 345
☐ C-GTSH A310-308 599 343
☐ C-GTSW A310-304 483 483
☐ C-GTSY A310-304 447 344

☐ C-GCTS A330-342 177 002
☐ C-GGTS A330-243 250 101
☐ C-GITS A330-243 271 102
☐ C-GKTS A330-342 111 100
☐ C-GPTS A330-243 480 103
☐ C-GTSD A330-343E 407004>TVF
☐ C-GTSI A330-243 427 105
☐ C-GTSJ A330-243 795 203
☐ C-GTSN A330-243 369 104
☐ C-GTSO A330-342 132 003
☐ C-GTSR A330-243 966 >CAJ♦
☐ C-GTSZ A330-243 971 202

☐ C-FTCX B737-8AS/W 29921/560 801♦
☐ C-FTCZ B737-8AS/W 29923/576 802♦
☐ C-FYQN B737-8AS/W 29933/1038 804♦
☐ C-FYQO B737-8AS/W 29934/1050 805♦
☐ C-GTQB B737-8Q8/W 30696/1892 401
☐ C-GTQC B737-8Q8/W 29368/1910 402
☐ C-GTQF B737-8Q8/W 29369/1939
☐ C-GTQG B737-8Q8/W 30701/1946 404
☐ C-GTQI B737-73S/W 29080/211 <FPO
☐ C-GTQP B737-73S/W 29081/215 <FPO
☐ C-GTQX B737-8FH/W 35093/2176 <TVS♦
☐ C-GTQY B737-8Q8/W 30724/2286 <TVS♦

Reg	Type	c/n	Notes
F-GZHA	B737-8GJ/W	34901/2267	<TVF
F-GZHB	B737-8GJ/W	34902/2309	<TVF
F-GZHD	B737-8K2/W	29650/2583	<TVF
F-GZHI	B737-86J/W	36120/4358	<TVF
F-GZHJ	B737-86J/W	37778/4424	<TVF
F-GZTD	B737-73V/W	32418/1300	<FPO♦
OK-TVU	B737-86N/W	38025/3968	<TVS♦
OK-TVV	B737-86N/W	38027/4030	<TVS♦

ALBERTA CENTRAL AIRWAYS

Reg	Type	c/n	Notes
C-FTMU	DHC-6 Twin Otter 300	782	
C-FTSU	DHC-6 Twin Otter 300	451	
C-FTWU	DHC-6 Twin Otter 300	372	

ALKAN AIR AKN

Reg	Type	c/n	Notes
C-FCPV	DHC-6 Twin Otter 300	371	
C-GAKI	Do228-202	8100	♦

BAR XH AIR BXH

Reg	Type	c/n	Notes
C-FFIA	BAeJetstream 31	779	
C-GGIA	BAeJetstream 31	778	
C-GNGI	BAeJetstream 31	739	
C-GZOS	BAeJetstream 31	796	

BEARSKIN AIRLINES JV / BLS

Reg	Type	c/n	Notes
C-FXUS	SA.227CC Metro 23	CC-841B	
C-FYAG	SA.227AC Metro III	AC-670B	
C-FYWG	SA.227AC Metro III	AC-782B	
C-GAFQ	SA.227DC Metro 23	DC-890B	
C-GJVB	SA.227DC Metro 23	DC-902B	
C-GJVC	SA.227DC Metro 23	DC-885B	
C-GJVH	SA.227DC Metro 23	DC-898B	
C-GJVO	SA.227DC Metro 23	DC-846B	
C-GJVW	SA.227DC Metro 23	DC-872B	
C-GSNP	SA.227DC Metro 23	DC-838B	
C-GYHD	SA.227AC Metro III	AC-739B	
C-GYQT	SA.227AC Metro III	AC-644B	
C-GYRL	SA.227AC Metro III	AC-706B	
C-GYTL	SA.227CC Metro 23	CC-829B	
C-GYXL	SA.227AC Metro III	AC-752B	

BUFFALO AIRWAYS J4 / BFL

Reg	Type	c/n	Notes
C-FAYN	CL-215	1105	282
C-FAYU	CL-215	1106	283
C-GBPD	CL-215	1084	291
C-GBYU	CL-215	1083	290
C-GCSX	CL-215	1088	295
C-GDHN	CL-215	1089	296
C-GDKW	CL-215	1095	280
C-GNCS	CL-215	1008	215
C-FBAE	Douglas DC-3	12591	[YQF]
C-FCUE	Douglas DC-3	12983	
C-FDTB	Douglas DC-3	12597	[YQF]
C-FFAY	Douglas DC-3	4785	[YQF]
C-FLFR	Douglas DC-3	13155	
C-GJKM	Douglas DC-3	13580	
C-GPNR	Douglas DC-3	13333	
C-GWIR	Douglas DC-3	9371	
C-GWZS	Douglas DC-3	12327	
CF-BAA	Douglas DC-4	10653	[YZF]
C-FBAJ	Douglas DC-4	308802	[YHY]
C-FBAK	Douglas DC-4	1061313	[YHY]
C-FBAM	Douglas DC-4	36009	[YHY]
C-FBAP	Douglas DC-4	36089	[YHY]
C-FIQM	Douglas DC-4	36088	57
C-GBAJ	Douglas DC-4	27328	
C-GBNV	Douglas DC-4	35988	56 [std]
C-GCTF	Douglas DC-4	27281	58
C-GPSH	Douglas DC-4	7458	1
C-GQIC	Douglas DC-4	27343	
C-GXKN	Douglas DC-4	36090	17
N434TA	Douglas DC-6B/F (ST)	44434/515	[YZF]
C-GTFC	Convair 240	279	
C-FAVO	Curtiss C-46D Commando	33242	[YZF]
C-GTPO	Curtiss C-46F Commando	22556	
C-GTXW	Curtiss C-46A Commando	30386	dbr?
C-FBAQ	L-188AF Electra	1039	
C-FIJV	L-188CF Electra	1140	
C-FIJX	L-188CF Electra	2010	
C-GLBA	L-188AF Electra	1145	
C-GXFC	L-188CF Electra	1100	
C-GZFE	L-188CF Electra	1144	
N922AU	P-3A Orion	5100	

CALM AIR MO / CAV

Reg	Type	c/n	Notes
C-FAFS	ATR 42-300	298	
C-FCIJ	ATR 42-300	139	
C-FCRZ	ATR 72-202	357	
C-FECI	ATR 42-320	203	
C-FJCQ	ATR 72-202(QC)	311	
C-FJYW	ATR 42-300	235	422
C-FMAK	ATR 42-300	142	
C-FULE	ATR 72-212	215	
C-GDSS	ATR 42-300	329	
C-GKKR	ATR 42-320	197	
C-GPBR	ATR 72-202	237	
C-FAMO	HS.748 Srs.2A	1669	746
C-FAPU	Do328-310	3145	
C-GBEU	Do328-310	3185	
C-GDOP	HS.748 Srs.2A	1745	[YTH]
C-GHSC	HS.748 Srs.2B	1790	745
C-GSBF	HS.748 Srs.2A	1662	[YTH]

Some operated as Air Canada Regional.

CANADIAN NORTH 5T / MPE

Reg	Type	c/n	Notes
C-FGCN	B737-36N	28590/3097	595
C-FKCN	B737-36N	28573/3041	597
C-GCNK	B737-36Q	29189/3057	593
C-GCNO	B737-36N	28596/3112	585
C-GCNU	B737-36Q	29140/3013	592
C-GCNW	B737-36Q/W	28760/2989	590
C-GCNZ	B737-36Q/W	28664/2940	591
C-GDPA	B737-2T2C	22056/655	584
C-GICN	B737-36Q/W	29405/3047	594
C-GKCP	B737-217	22729/915	523
C-GNDU	B737-242C	22877/880	562
C-GOPW	B737-275C	22160/688	582
C-GSPW	B737-275C	22618/813	583
C-GPNL	B737-36N	28872/3082	599
C-GZCN	B737-36N(F)	28594/3107	596
C-GECN	DHC-8-106	324	324
C-GRGI	DHC-8-106	304	304
C-GRGO	DHC-8-106	258	258

CARGOJET AIRWAYS W8 / CJT

	Reg	Type	c/n	
☐	C-FCJF	B727-223F	22011/1653	
☐	C-FCJP	B727-223F	22012/1655	[YHM]
☐	C-FCJU	B727-260F	22759/1789	
☐	C-FCJV	B727-223F	22469/1769	
☐	C-GCJB	B727-225F	21855/1535	
☐	C-GCJD	B727-231F	21988/1586	
☐	C-GCJK	B727-223F	22015/1666	
☐	C-GCJN	B727-225F	21451/1310	[BQK]
☐	C-GCJQ	B727-225F	22437/1682	
☐	C-GCJZ	B727-225F	21854/1532	
☐	C-FGKJ	B757-223(F)/W	25298/433	
☐	C-FKAJ	B757-23A(PCF)	24566/255	
☐	C-FKCJ	B757-236(PCF)	24792/279	
☐	C-FLAJ	B757-23A(PCF)	24567/257	
☐	C-GIAJ	B757-28A(PCF)	23767/127	
☐	C-FGAJ	B767-223F	22319/112	
☐	C-FDIJ	B767-39H(ERF)/W	26257/488	♦
☐	C-FGSJ	B767-39H(ERF)/W	26256/484	^
☐	C-FMCJ	B767-223F	22316/95	
☐	C-FMIJ	B767-328ER	27135/493	♦
☐	C-FPIJ	B767-33A(ERF)	27918/603	
☐	C-GCIJ	B767-306(ERF)	26263/592	♦
☐	C-GKLY	B767-223(SCD)	22314/73	
☐	C-GUAJ	B767-35E(ER/F)	26063/434	
☐	C-GVIJ	B767-328ERF	27212/531	
☐	C-GYAJ	B767-35E(ER/F)	26064/438	

^ leased to Purolator Courier Canada

CARGO NORTH

See Kenn Borek Air

CARSON AIR

	Reg	Type	c/n	
☐	C-FAFR	SA.227AC Metro III	AC-684	
☐	C-FBWQ	SA.226TC Metro II	TC-379	
☐	C-FJKK	SA.227AC Metro III	AC-713B	
☐	C-FKKR	SA.226TC Metro II	TC-308	
☐	C-GAMI	SA.227AC Metro III	AC-587	
☐	C-GCAU	SA.226TC Metro II	TC-331E	
☐	C-GCAW	SA.226TC Metro II	TC-358	
☐	C-GKKC	SA.226TC Metro II	TC-370	
☐	C-GKLJ	SA.226TC Metro II	TC-380	
☐	C-GKLK	SA.227AC Metro III	AC-741B	
☐	C-GKLN	SA.226TC Metro II	TC-253	
☐	C-GLSC	SA.226TC Metro II	TC-325	
☐	C-GTTM	SA.227AT Merlin IVC	AT-495B	♦

CENTRAL MOUNTAIN AIR 9M / GLR

	Reg	Type	c/n	
☐	C-FCMB	Beech 1900D	UE-278	916
☐	C-FCME	Beech 1900D	UE-277	915
☐	C-FCMN	Beech 1900D	UE-276	914
☐	C-FCMO	Beech 1900D	UE-281	917
☐	C-FCMP	Beech 1900D	UE-271	912
☐	C-FCMR	Beech 1900D	UE-283	918
☐	C-FCMU	Beech 1900D	UE-285	919
☐	C-FCMV	Beech 1900D	UE-272	913
☐	C-FDTR	Beech 1900D	UE-76	928
☐	C-GCMA	Beech 1900D	UE-289	920
☐	C-GCML	Beech 1900D	UE-243	925
☐	C-GCMY	Beech 1900D	UE-287	921
☐	C-GFSV	Beech 1900D	UE-346	922
☐	C-GGBY	Beech 1900D	UE-351	923
☐	C-FCMG	Do328-110	3055	
☐	C-FDYN	Do328-110	3096	
☐	C-FHVX	Do328-110	3094	std
☐	C-FJFW	DHC-8-311A	315	std
☐	C-GRUR	DHC-8-311A	256	

CONAIR AVIATION CRC

	Reg	Type	c/n	
☐	C-GVFT	Avro 146-RJ85	E2253	♦
☐	C-FEKF	Convair 580F	80	45
☐	C-FFKF	Convair 580	179	44
☐	C-FHKF	Convair 580	374	55
☐	C-FJVD	Convair 580	478	[YXX]
☐	C-FKFA	Convair 580F	100	52
☐	C-FKFB	Convair 580	57	47
☐	C-FKFL	Convair 580	465	49
☐	C-FKFM	Convair 580F	70	54
☐	C-GKFO	Convair 580F	78	53
☐	C-GYXC	Convair 580	507	42
☐	C-GYXS	Convair 580	501	[YXX]
☐	C-GFSK	CL-215T	1085	201
☐	C-GFSL	CL-215T	1086	202
☐	C-GFSM	CL-215T	1098	203
☐	C-GFSN	CL-215	1099	204
☐	C-FYYJ	L-188AC Electra	1143	60
☐	C-GYCG	L-188PF Electra	1138	
☐	G-FIZU	L-188CF Electra	2014	[YYX]

COURTESY AIR

	Reg	Type	c/n
☐	C-FJDF	Beech 1900C	UB-68
☐	C-FJMF	Beech C99	U-180
☐	C-FJTF	Beech 1900C	UB-39

ENERJET EG / ENJ

	Reg	Type	c/n
☐	C-FKEJ	B737-73A	24897/216
☐	C-GDEJ	B737-73V	32427/1489

EXPLOITS VALLEY AIR SERVICES 8K

	Reg	Type	c/n
☐	C-FEVA	Beech 1900D	UE-126
☐	C-FPUB	Beech 1900D	UE-55
☐	C-GAAT	Beech 1900D	UE-217
☐	C-GERI	Beech 1900D	UE-162
☐	C-GLHO	Beech 1900D	UE-266
☐	C-GLXV	Beech 1900D	UE-242
☐	C-GORI	Beech 1900D	UE-47
☐	C-GORZ	Beech 1900D	UE-134
☐	C-GSNQ	Beech 1900D	UE-139
☐	C-GUPW	Beech 1900D	UE-172

Operates flights on behalf of the Air Canada Express network.

FIRST AIR 7F / FAB

	Reg	Type	c/n	
☐	C-FIQR	ATR 42-300(QC)	133	
☐	C-FIQU	ATR 42-300(QC)	138	
☐	C-FTCP	ATR 42-300(QC)	143	
☐	C-FTID	ATR 42-500	510	♦
☐	C-FTIK	ATR 42-500	604	♦
☐	C-FTIQ	ATR 42-500	609	♦
☐	C-FTJB	ATR 42-300(QC)	119	
☐	C-GHCP	ATR 42-300(QC)	123	
☐	C-GKLB	ATR 42-310	331	
☐	C-GSRR	ATR 42-300(QC)	125	
☐	C-GULU	ATR 42-310	155	
☐	C-GUNO	ATR 42-310	132	
☐	C-FLRJ	Avro 146-RJ85	E2302	o/o♦

	Reg	Type	c/n	Notes
☐	C-FACP	B737-2L9	22072/623	
☐	C-GCPT	B737-217	22258/770	
☐	C-FFNC	B737-406(C)	27232/2591	
☐	C-FFNE	B737-406(C)	27233/2601	
☐	C-FFNF	B737-406(C)	25412/2161	
☐	C-FFNM	B737-436	25839/2188	♦
☐	C-FLER	B737-46B	24573/1844	<FLE♦

FLAIR AIRLINES — FY / FLE

	Reg	Type	c/n	Notes
☐	C-FLDX	B737-408	24804/1851	
☐	C-FLEJ	B737-4B3	24751/2107	
☐	C-FLEN	B737-4K5	24769/1839	
☐	C-FLER	B737-46B	24573/1844	>FAB
☐	C-FLHJ	B737-4Q8	25104/2476	
☐	C-FSCO	Do328-130	3109	
☐	C-GSCL	ERJ-175LR	17000241	

HAWKAIR AVIATION SERVICE — BH / BHA

	Reg	Type	c/n	Notes
☐	C-FCJE	DHC-8-102	165	
☐	C-FDNG	DHC-8-102	166	
☐	C-FIDL	DHC-8-311	305	
☐	C-FYDH	DHC-8-102	083	

HYDRO-QUEBEC — OQ / HYD

	Reg	Type	c/n	Notes
☐	C-GHQL	DHC-8-402Q	4115	
☐	C-GHQP	DHC-8-402Q	4004	
☐	C-GJNL	DHC-8-311	422	

KEEWATIN AIR — FK

	Reg	Type	c/n	Notes
☐	C-FJXL	Beech 1900C	UC-102	
☐	C-FJXO	Beech 1900C	UC-124	

KENN BOREK AIR — 4K / KBA

	Reg	Type	c/n	Notes
☐	C-FBKB	Basler BT-67	14170/25615	
☐	C-FGCX	Basler BT-67	19446	
☐	C-FKAL	Basler BT-67	13840	
☐	C-FKGL	Basler BT-67	19066	
☐	C-FMKB	Basler BT-67	19560	
☐	C-GAWI	Basler BT-67	19227	
☐	C-GEAI	Basler BT-67	16305/33053	
☐	C-GEAJ	Basler BT-67	14675/26120	
☐	C-GHGF	Basler BT-67	14519/25964	
☐	C-GJKB	Basler BT-67	13383	
☐	C-GKKB	Basler BT-67	20494	
☐	C-GVKB	Basler BT-67	12300	
☐	C-GHUE	Beech 1900D	UE-52	
☐	C-GSKB	Beech 1900D	UE-180	
☐	C-FBBV	DHC-6 Twin Otter 300	311	
☐	C-FDGV	DHC-6 Twin Otter 200	154	
☐	C-FDHB	DHC-6 Twin Otter 300	338	
☐	C-FGOG	DHC-6 Twin Otter 300	348	
☐	C-FKBK	DHC-6 Twin Otter 300	613	♦
☐	C-FKBX	DHC-6 Twin Otter 300	373	
☐	C-GBPE	DHC-6 Twin Otter 100	21	
☐	C-GCKB	DHC-6 Twin Otter 300	312	
☐	C-GDHC	DHC-6 Twin Otter 300	494	
☐	C-GIKB	DHC-6 Twin Otter 300	64	
☐	C-GKBC	DHC-6 Twin Otter 300	650	
☐	C-GKBG	DHC-6 Twin Otter 300	733	
☐	C-GKBH	DHC-6 Twin Otter 300	732	
☐	C-GKBO	DHC-6 Twin Otter 300	725	
☐	C-GKBR	DHC-6 Twin Otter 300	617	
☐	C-GKBV	DHC-6 Twin Otter 300	287	
☐	C-GKCS	DHC-6 Twin Otter 300	693	
☐	C-GKSQ	DHC-6 Twin Otter 300	276	
☐	C-GLKB	DHC-6 Twin Otter 300	321	♦
☐	C-GOKB	DHC-6 Twin Otter 300	339	>SBS
☐	C-GPOQ	DHC-6 Twin Otter 300	464	♦
☐	C-GSOZ	DHC-6 Twin Otter 300	518	
☐	C-GTKB	DHC-6 Twin Otter 100	60	
☐	C-GVTU	DHC-6 Twin Otter 400	906	♦
☐	C-GXXB	DHC-6 Twin Otter 300	426	

BT-67s are operated as Cargo North & Private Air.

KF AEROSPACE — KW / KFA

	Reg	Type	c/n	Notes
☐	C-GKFA	B737-319	25608/3128	♦
☐	C-FIWM	Convair 580F	128	
☐	C-FKFZ	Convair 580F	151	510 [YVR]
☐	C-GKFF	Convair 580F	160	511 [std]
☐	C-GKFG	Convair 580F	22	516 [YVR]
☐	C-GKFU	Convair 580F	82	501[std]
☐	C-GKFY	Convair 580F	91	[YLW]
☐	C-GLWF	Convair 580	2	
☐	C-GNDK	Convair 580	10	[YLW]
☐	C-GPQY	Convair 580	7	[YLW]
☐	C-GTVJ	Convair 580	9	[YLW]
☐	C-GULQ	Convair 580	1	[YLW]♦
☐	N538JA	Convair 580	34	[YLW]♦
☐	N569JA	Convair 580	69	[YLW]♦
☐	C-GKFB	DC-10-30F	46949/179	102 [YHM]
☐	C-GKFD	DC-10-30F	47928/192	103
☐	C-GKFT	DC-10-30F	46917/211	104

MORNINGSTAR AIR EXPRESS — MAL

	Reg	Type	c/n	Notes
☐	C-FTAR	ATR 72-202F	217	
☐	C-FMAI	B757-2B7SF	27199/586	
☐	C-FMEK	B757-2B7SF	27123/534	
☐	C-FMEP	B757-2B7SF	27144/544	
☐	C-FMEU	B757-2B7SF	27200/589	
☐	C-FMFG	B757-2B7SF	27198/584	
☐	C-FMEQ	B757-2B7SF	27145/546	♦

Operates as FedEx Express in their colours.

NEWFOUNDLAND & LABRADOR A/S

	Reg	Type	c/n	Notes
☐	C-FAYU	CL-215	1106	283
☐	C-FTXA	CL-215	1006	284
☐	C-FYWP	CL-215	1002	285
☐	C-FIZU	CL-415	2076	286
☐	C-FNJC	CL-415	2077	287
☐	C-FOFI	CL-415	2081	288

NOLINOR AVIATION — NRL

	Reg	Type	c/n	Notes
☐	C-GNLK	B737-2K2C	20836/354	
☐	C-GNLN	B737-2B6C	23050/975	
☐	C-GNRD	B737-229C	21738/576	
☐	C-GTUK	B737-2B6C	23049/951	
☐	C-FAWV	Convair 580F	154	
☐	C-FHNM	Convair 580F	454	
☐	C-FTAP	Convair 580	334	
☐	C-GQHB	Convair 580	376	
☐	C-GRLQ	Convair 580	347	

NORTH CARIBOO AIR — NCB

	Reg.	Type	c/n		
☐	C-GSUI	Avro 146-RJ100	E3369		
☐	C-FSUA	Avro 146-RJ100	E3373		
☐	C-FMCN	Beech 1900D	UE-20		
☐	C-FNCL	Beech 1900D	UE-11		
☐	C-FNCP	Beech 1900D	UE-58		
☐	C-FNSN	Beech 1900D	UE-51		
☐	C-FNSV	Beech 1900D	UE-179		
☐	C-FRNC	Beech 1900D	UE-316		
☐	C-GNCE	Beech 1900D	UE-298		
☐	C-FDGP	DHC-8-402Q	4029	[GWO]	
☐	C-FGNJ	DHC-8-402Q	4028	[GWO]	
☐	C-FHNC	DHC-8-311B	412		
☐	C-FNXN	DHC-8Q-311	464		
☐	C-GAQN	DHC-8-311A	548		
☐	C-GLWN	DHC-8-311A	311		
☐	C-GNCF	DHC-8-311A	244		

NORTH WRIGHT AIRWAYS — HW / NWL

	Reg.	Type	c/n		
☐	C-FCSW	DHC-6 Twin Otter 300	355		
☐	C-FNWL	DHC-6 Twin Otter 300	596		
☐	C-GRDD	DHC-6 Twin Otter 100	54		

NORTHWESTERN AIR — J3 / PLR

	Reg.	Type	c/n		
☐	C-FCPE	BAeJetstream 31	825		
☐	C-FNAA	BAeJetstream 32	929		
☐	C-FNAE	BAeJetstream 32	881		
☐	C-FNAF	BAeJetstream 31	789		
☐	C-FNAM	BAeJetstream 31	767		
☐	C-FNAZ	BAeJetstream 32	843		
☐	C-GNAH	BAeJetstream 31	874		
☐	C-GNAQ	BAeJetstream 32EP	837		
☐	C-GPSN	BAeJetstream 31	783		
☐	C-GNAL	Beech 99	U-57		

NT AIR — NTA

	Reg.	Type	c/n		
☐	C-FCPV	DHC-6 Twin Otter 300	371		
☐	C-GCMT	Beech 1900C-1	UC-120		
☐	C-GCMZ	Beech 1900C-1	UC-61	929	
☐	C-GEFA	Beech 1900C-1	UC-94	927	

ONTARIO MINISTRY OF NATURAL RESOURCES

	Reg.	Type	c/n		
☐	C-FOPG	DHC-6 Twin Otter 300	232		
☐	C-FOPI	DHC-6 Twin Otter 300	243		
☐	C-FOPJ	DHC-6 Twin Otter 300	344		
☐	C-GOGA	DHC-6 Twin Otter 300	739		
☐	C-GOGB	DHC-6 Twin Otter 300	761		
☐	C-GOGC	DHC-6 Twin Otter 300	750		

ORCA AIRWAYS — ORK

	Reg.	Type	c/n		
☐	C-FMKH	Beech 99	U-12		♦
☐	C-FWIK	Beech 99	U-39		♦
☐	C-FIOB	SA227AC Metro III	AC-614		♦
☐	C-FIOC	SA227AC Metro III	AC-632		♦

OSPREY WINGS

	Reg.	Type	c/n		
☐	C-FBPK	Beech 1900D	UE-128		
☐	C-GURF	Beech 1900D	UE-279		
☐	C-FDGV	DHC-6 Twin Otter 200	154		
☐	C-FLXP	DHC-6 Twin Otter 200	217		
☐	C-FVEG	DHC-6 Twin Otter 300	260		
☐	C-GIGK	DHC-6 Twin Otter 300	492		
☐	C-GPVQ	DHC-6 Twin Otter 100	99		
☐	C-GQOQ	DHC-6 Twin Otter 200	155		

PACIFIC COASTAL AIRLINES — 8P / PCO

	Reg.	Type	c/n		
☐	C-FPCO	Beech 1900C	UB-52		
☐	C-FPCV	Beech 1900C	UB-9	302	
☐	C-FPCX	Beech 1900C	UB-66		
☐	C-GBPC	Beech 1900C	UB-43		
☐	C-GCPZ	Beech 1900C	UB-71		
☐	C-GIPC	Beech 1900C-1	UC-110		
☐	C-GPCY	Beech 1900C	UB-45	301	
☐	C-FPCU	SAAB SF.340B	340B-338		♦
☐	C-FPCZ	SAAB SF.340B	340B-356		♦
☐	C-GCPU	SAAB SF.340A	340A-140		
☐	C-GPCE	SAAB SF.340A	340A-004		
☐	C-GPCG	SAAB SF.340A	340A-094		
☐	C-GPCN	SAAB SF.340A	340A-027		
☐	C-GPCQ	SAAB SF.340A	340A-043		

PAL AIRLINES — PB / PVL

	Reg.	Type	c/n		
☐	C-FWLG	DHC-6 Twin Otter 300	731		
☐	C-GIED	DHC-6 Twin Otter 300	600		
☐	C-GIMK	DHC-6 Twin Otter 300	352		
☐	C-GJDE	DHC-6 Twin Otter 300	471		
☐	C-FDND	DHC-8-102	129		♦
☐	C-FHRC	DHC-8-102	209		
☐	C-FPAE	DHC-8-315	562		
☐	C-GPAB	DHC-8-106MPA	275		
☐	C-GPAL	DHC-8-102	157		
☐	C-GPAR	DHC-8-311A	519		
☐	C-GPAU	DHC-8-106	282		
☐	C-GRNN	DHC-8-106MPA	314		
☐	C-GYCV	DHC-8Q-314	487		
☐	C-GZPA	DHC-8-102	114		♦
☐	C-GMEW	SA.227AC Metro III	AC-668B		

PASCAN AVIATION — P6 / PSC

	Reg.	Type	c/n		
☐	C-GPEA	ATR 42-300QC	158		
☐	C-GPEB	ATR 42-300QC	122		
☐	C-FFPA	BAeJetstream 32	959		
☐	C-FHQA	BAeJetstream 32	876		
☐	C-FKQA	BAeJetstream 32	877		
☐	C-FPSC	BAeJetstream 32EP	930		
☐	C-FPSI	BAeJetstream 32EP	963		
☐	C-FPSJ	BAeJetstream 32EP	957		
☐	C-FZVY	BAeJetstream 32	833		
☐	C-GPPS	BAeJetstream 32EP	961		
☐	C-GPSK	BAeJetstream 32EP	958		
☐	C-GQJT	BAeJetstream 32	886		
☐	C-GUSC	BAeJetstream 32	902		

PERIMETER AVIATION — YP / PAG

	Reg.	Type	c/n		
☐	C-FOFR	DHC-8-106	317		
☐	C-FPPW	DHC-8-102A	390		
☐	C-GJYZ	DHC-8-314	368		
☐	C-GLKY	DHC-8Q-311	538		
☐	C-GWPS	DHC-8-102	120		
☐	C-FAMC	SA.227AC Metro III	AC-719B		
☐	C-FBTL	SA.226TC Metro II	TC-385		
☐	C-FFJM	SA.227AC Metro III	AC-700		
☐	C-FFDB	SA.226TC Metro II	TC-249		
☐	C-FIHB	SA.226TC Metro II	TC-361		
☐	C-FIHE	SA.226TC Metro II	TC-373		
☐	C-FJLO	SA.227AC Metro III	AC-678B		

☐	C-FJNW	SA.226TC Metro IIA	TC-352	
☐	C-FJTS	SA.227AC Metro III	AC-696B	
☐	C-FLRY	SA.227AC Metro III	AC-756	
☐	C-FMAV	SA.227AC Metro III	AC-616	
☐	C-FSLZ	SA.226TC Metro II	TC-222EE	
☐	C-FSWT	SA.226TC Metro II	TC-382	
☐	C-FTSK	SA.227AC Metro III	AC-874B	
☐	C-FUZY	SA.226TC Metro II	TC-343	
☐	C-GIQF	SA.226TC Metro II	TC-279	
☐	C-GIQG	SA.226TC Metro II	TC-285	
☐	C-GIQK	SA.226TC Metro II	TC-288	
☐	C-GMWW	SA.227DC Metro 23	DC-852B	
☐	C-GPCL	SA.226AT Merlin IV	AT-017	
☐	C-GQAJ	SA.226TC Metro II	TC-295	
☐	C-GQAP	SA.226TC Metro II	TC-263	[YWG]
☐	C-GSWK	SA.226TC Metro II	TC-368	♦
☐	C-GWVH	SA.227AC Metro IIIA	AC-714	
☐	C-GYRD	SA.226TC Metro II	TC-278	

PORTER AIRLINES — *PD / POE*

☐	C-	CS100 C Series		o/o♦
☐	C-	CS100		o/o♦
☐	C-FLQY	DHC-8-402Q	4306	819
☐	C-GKQA	DHC-8-402Q	4357	821
☐	C-GKQB	DHC-8-402Q	4359	822
☐	C-GKQC	DHC-8-402Q	4360	823
☐	C-GKQD	DHC-8-402Q	4361	824
☐	C-GKQE	DHC-8-402Q	4390	825
☐	C-GKQF	DHC-8-402Q	4391	826
☐	C-GLQB	DHC-8-402Q	4130	801
☐	C-GLQC	DHC-8-402Q	4134	802
☐	C-GLQD	DHC-8-402Q	4138	803
☐	C-GLQE	DHC-8-402Q	4140	804
☐	C-GLQF	DHC-8-402Q	4193	805
☐	C-GLQG	DHC-8-402Q	4194	806
☐	C-GLQH	DHC-8-402Q	4225	807
☐	C-GLQJ	DHC-8-402Q	4228	808
☐	C-GLQK	DHC-8-402Q	4247	809
☐	C-GLQL	DHC-8-402Q	4249	810
☐	C-GLQM	DHC-8-402Q	4252	811
☐	C-GLQN	DHC-8-402Q	4254	812
☐	C-GLQO	DHC-8-402Q	4270	813
☐	C-GLQP	DHC-8-402Q	4271	814
☐	C-GLQQ	DHC-8-402Q	4272	815
☐	C-GLQR	DHC-8-402Q	4278	816
☐	C-GLQV	DHC-8-402Q	4279	817
☐	C-GLQX	DHC-8-402Q	4282	818
☐	C-GLQZ	DHC-8-402Q	4308	820

R (REGIONAL) 1 AIRLINES — *TSH*

☐	C-FXMY	CRJ-100ER	7124	♦
☐	C-GEXM	Challenger 850	7187	♦
☐	C-GRIA	CRJ-200ER	7561	
☐	C-GRGK	DHC-8Q-202	522	[YYC]
☐	C-GUZX	DHC-8-311	489	
☐	C-GWRI	DHC-8-103	098	♦

SASKATCHEWAN GOVT AIR — *SGS*

☐	C-GSKQ	Convair 580	217	475
☐	C-GSKR	Convair 580	509	471
☐	C-GVSK	Convair 580	238	473
☐	C-GYSK	Convair 580	234	474

SKYLINK EXPRESS — *SLQ*

☐	C-FKAX	Beech 1900C	UB-67
☐	C-GKGA	Beech 1900C-1	UC-117
☐	C-GSKA	Beech 1900C	UB-32
☐	C-GSKG	Beech 1900C-1	UC-22
☐	C-GSKM	Beech 1900C	UB-21
☐	C-GSKN	Beech 1900C-1	UC-54
☐	C-GSKU	Beech 1900C	UB-35
☐	C-GSKW	Beech 1900C	UB-33
☐	C-GTGA	Beech 1900C-1	UC-62

SKY REGIONAL AIRLINES — *RS / SKV*

Operates DHC-8-402QS & ERJ-175LRs as Air Canada Express in full colours.

STARLINK AVIATION — *Q4 / TLK*

☐	C-GCCN	BAeJetstream 31	704
☐	C-GCCZ	BAeJetstream 31	712
☐	C-GDFW	BAeJetstream 31	720

SUMMIT AIR — *ASC*

☐	C-FUER	ATR 72-202F	241	♦
☐	C-GUSA	ATR 72-202	353	o/o♦
☐	C-GJPY	ATR 72-202F	444	♦
☐	C-FERJ	Avro 146-RJ85	E2290	♦
☐	C-FLRJ	Avro 146-RJ85	E2302	
☐	C-FEQW	Do228-202	8103	
☐	C-FEQX	Do228-202	8101	
☐	C-FPSH	Do228-202	8071	
☐	C-FUCN	Do228-202	8109	>UN
☐	C-GSAX	Do228-202	8153	>UN
☐	C-FASC	DHC-8-102	038	
☐	C-FASQ	DHC-6 Twin Otter 100	78	
☐	C-FTFX	DHC-6 Twin Otter 300	340	
☐	C-FTXQ	DHC-6 Twin Otter 300	308	
☐	C-GASB	DHC-8-102	013	
☐	C-FARA	Short SC.7 Skyvan 3	SH1970	♦
☐	C-GKOA	Short SC.7 Skyvan 3	SH1905	

SUNWEST AVIATION — *CNK*

☐	C-GHCS	Beech 1900D	UE-353	
☐	C-GROK	Beech 1900D	UE-362	
☐	C-GSLX	Beech 1900D	UE-264	
☐	C-GSWB	Beech 1900D	UE-386	
☐	C-GSWV	Beech 1900D	UE-141	
☐	C-GSWX	Beech 1900D	UE-63	
☐	C-FBXG	DHC-8Q-311	443	♦
☐	C-FNSA	DHC-8-315	354	
☐	C-GBOS	DHC-8Q-314	565	
☐	C-GFCD	DHC-8Q-314	576	
☐	C-GYUP	DHC-8-202	536	
☐	C-FGEW	SA.226TC Metro II	TC-347	
☐	C-GAAF	SA.227DC Metro 23	DC-891B	
☐	C-GSAF	SA.227DC Metro 23	DC-866B	
☐	C-GSHV	SA.227DC Metro 23	DC-900B	
☐	C-GSHY	SA.227DC Metro 23	DC-897B	
☐	C-GSHZ	SA.227DC Metro 23	DC-887B	

SUNWING AIRLINES — *KO / SWG*

☐	C-FAWC	B737-8K5/W	39922/3925	<TOM♦
☐	C-FDBD	B737-8Q8/W	30703/1964	

Reg	Type	c/n	Notes
C-FEAK	B737-86Q/W	30292/1451	
C-FFPH	B737-81D/W	39440/4892	
C-FHZZ	B737-8K5/W	37262/3876	<TOM♦
C-FJAU	B737-8K5/W	37250/4345	<JAF
C-FJVE	B737-8DC/W	34596/1875	
C-FLSW	B737-8HX/W	36552/2658	
C-FPRP	B737-8FH/W	39959/5414	♦
C-FTAH	B737-8Q8/W	29351/1471	
C-FTDW	B737-808/W	34704/1958	
C-FTJH	B737-8BK/W	29642/2247	
C-FTLK	B737-8K5/W	35143/2763	<HLX♦
C-FTOH	B737-8HX/W	29647/2865	
C-FVWA	B737-8K5/W	37264/3907	<TOM♦
C-FWGH	B737-86J/W	37752/3835	♦
C-FYBG	B737-8K5/W	35142/2660	<JAF
C-FYJD	B737-8Q8/W	41807/5420	♦
C-FYLC	B737-8BK/W	33029/1945	
C-GBZS	B737-8SH/W	42053/5780	♦
C-GEWO	B737-8K5/W	37255/4384	♦
C-GFEH	B737-8GS/W	41608/5346	♦
C-GHZY	B737-8K5/W	37261/3844	<TOM♦
C-GKVP	B737-8K5/W	32907/1117	<TVS
C-GMWN	B737-8K5/W	37251/4369	♦
C-GNCH	B737-81D/W	39438/4816	
C-GOFW	B737-8BK/W	33018/1488	
C-GOWG	B737-86J/W	37757/3377	
C-GQWM	B737-8K5/W	37249/4360	<TOM♦
C-GTVF	B737-8FH/W	29669/1692	<TVS
C-GTVG	B737-8Q8/W	30719/2257	<TVS
C-GUUL	B737-8K5/W	38820/3653	<HLX♦
C-GVVH	B737-8Q8/W	35275/2604	
C-GWVB	B737-8K5/W	37242/3917	<TOM♦
G-TAWD	B737-8K5/W	37265/3939	<TOM♦
OK-TVM	B737-8FN/W	37077/3163	<TVS
OK-TVS	B737-86N/W	39404/3633	<TVS
OK-TVT	B737-86N/W	39394/3899	<TVS
OK-TVE	B737-86Q/W	30294/1469	<TVS♦
OO-JAA	B737-8BK/W	29660/2355	<JAF♦

Leases aircraft in winter from European airlines & leases aircraft to these airlines in the summer, changing marks.

TRANS CAPITAL AIR

Reg	Type	c/n	Notes
C-FERO	DHC-7-102	113	[YTZ]♦
C-FGOV	DHC-7-103	020	♦
C-FJHQ	DHC-7-103	011	[YTZ]
C-FPBJ	DHC-7-103	009	[YTZ]
C-FWYU	DHC-7-103	012	>UN
C-GCPP	DHC-7-102	087	[YTZ]
C-GNUY	DHC-7-102	033	[YTZ]
C-GTGO	DHC-7-103	106	[YTZ]♦
C-GVPP	DHC-7-102	072	[YTZ]
C-GVWD	DHC-7-102	108	[YTZ]

TRANSWEST AIR — 9T / ABS

Reg	Type	c/n	Notes
C-GTWG	Beech 1900D	UE-79	
C-FCCE	DHC-6 Twin Otter 100	8	
C-FGLF	DHC-6 Twin Otter 200	138	
C-FPGE	DHC-6 Twin Otter 200	197	
C-FSCA	DHC-6 Twin Otter 100	17	
C-FVOG	DHC-6 Twin Otter 100	35	
C-FJVW	SAAB SF.340B	340B-289	♦
C-GKCY	SAAB SF.340A	340A-133	
C-GTJX	SAAB SF.340B	340B-165	
C-GTWK	SAAB SF.340B	340B-190	

VOYAGEUR AIRWAYS — VC / VAL

Reg	Type	c/n	Notes
C-FMCY	CRJ-100LR	7064	
C-FMUV	CRJ-100LR	7073	>UN
C-FWWU	CRJ-200LR	7299	>UN
C-FXHC	CRJ-200ER	7329	
C-FXLH	CRJ-200LR	7283	>UN
C-GIXR	CRJ-200ER	7434	>UN
C-GIXT	CRJ-200ER	7393	
C-GIXU	CRJ-200ER	7345	[YYB]
C-FZKM	DHC-7-102	061	
C-GGUL	DHC-7-102	070	
C-GGXS	DHC-7-102	064	>UN
C-GJPI	DHC-7-102	036	
C-GLOL	DHC-7-102	039	
C-FABW	DHC-8-102	097	♦
C-FEXZ	DHC-8-314	319	
C-FEYG	DHC-8-311	320	
C-FIQT	DHC-8-314	395	>UN
C-FNCU	DHC-8-314A	517	
C-GANK	DHC-8-102	087	♦
C-GHQZ	DHC-8-314	370	

WASAYA AIRWAYS — WT / WSG

Reg	Type	c/n	Notes
C-FQWA	Beech 1900D	UE-75	
C-FWAU	Beech 1900D	UE-164	
C-FWAX	Beech 1900D	UE-297	
C-FWZK	Beech 1900D	UE-8	
C-GSWA	Beech 1900D	UE-34	
C-GWOV	Beech 1900D	UE-332	
C-GWOX	Beech 1900D	UE-333	♦
C-GZVJ	Beech 1900D	UE-223	
C-GMWT	DHC-8-314		<AIE
C-FFFS	HS.748 Srs.2A	1663	806
C-GLTC	HS.748 Srs.2A	1656	801
C-GMAA	HS.748 Srs.2A(F)	1576	807

WEST COAST AIR — 8O

Reg	Type	c/n	Notes
C-FGQH	DHC-6 Twin Otter 100	106	604
C-GQKN	DHC-6 Twin Otter 100	94	606

WESTJET — WS / WJA

Reg	Type	c/n	Notes
C-FAWJ	B737-8CT/W	35502/2323	807
C-FBWI	B737-8CT/W	39090/4364	822
C-FBWJ	B737-7CT/W	32767/1629	230
C-FBWS	B737-7CT/W	37088/3080	255
C-FCNW	B737-8CT/W	39092/3580	816
C-FCSX	B737-8CT/W	60126/5106	832
C-FCWJ	B737-7CT/W	35086/2613	250
C-FDMB	B737-8CT/W	60127/5188	833
C-FEWJ	B737-7CT/W	32769/1665	232
C-FGWJ	B737-7CT/W	32764/1553	226
C-FIBW	B737-7CT/W	37956/3649	266
C-FIWJ	B737-7CT/W	30712/2185	240
C-FIWS	B737-76N/W	32404/851	001
C-FJWS	B737-76N/W	28651/872	002
C-FKIW	B737-7CT/W	37955/3616	265
C-FKRF	B737-8CT/W	60123/5079	829
C-FKWJ	B737-8CT/W	36435/3469	815
C-FKWS	B737-76N/W	30134/905	003
C-FLBV	B737-8CT/W	40836/5624	842♦
C-FLPS	B737-8CT/W	60132/5401	839♦
C-FLSF	B737-8CT/W	40838/5660	845♦
C-FLWJ	B737-7CT/W	38096/3520	262

☐	C-FMWJ	B737-7CT/W	32771/1754	233
☐	C-FONK	B737-8CT/W	40835/5618	841♦
☐	C-FRWA	B737-8CT/W	39085/4293	821
☐	C-FTWJ	B737-7CT/W	30713/2220	241
☐	C-FUCS	B737-8CT/W	60129/5296	836
☐	C-FUJR	B737-8CT/W	60130/5341	837♦
☐	C-FUMF	B737-8CT/W	60128/5248	835
☐	C-FUSM	B737-8CT/W	39081/4641	826
☐	C-FUWS	B737-7CT/W	32765/1574	228
☐	C-FWCN	B737-7CT/W	33698/1346	212
☐	C-FWIJ	B737-8CT/W	39072/4087	819
☐	C-FWJS	B737-8CT/W	39076/4953	827
☐	C-FWSE	B737-8CT/W	36690/2987	811
☐	C-FWSF	B737-7CT/W	32758/1431	218
☐	C-FWSI	B737-7CT/W	36691/2983	253
☐	C-FWSK	B737-7CT/W	36420/2671	251
☐	C-FWSO	B737-7CT/W	32759/1445	219
☐	C-FWSV	B737-7CT/W	32760/1472	220
☐	C-FWSX	B737-7CT/W	32761/1493	221
☐	C-FWSY	B737-7CT/W	32762/1501	222
☐	C-FWVJ	B737-8CT/W	37962/3863	817
☐	C-FXWJ	B737-7CT/W	32768/1648	231
☐	C-FYBK	B737-8CT/W	40336/5650	843♦
☐	C-FYPB	B737-8CT/W	40839/5681	846♦
☐	C-FZWS	B737-76N/W	32731/1044	006
☐	C-GAWS	B737-8CT/W	38880/4268	820
☐	C-GBWS	B737-6CT	34288/1931	608
☐	C-GCWJ	B737-7CT/W	33970/1556	227
☐	C-GDMP	B737-8CT/W	60131/5367	838♦
☐	C-GEWJ	B737-6CT	35571/2045	615
☐	C-GGWJ	B737-7CT/W	35503/2334	242
☐	C-GJLZ	B737-8CT/W	60125/5103	831
☐	C-GJWS	B737-8CT/W	34152/1714	802
☐	C-GKWA	B737-8CT/W	39089/4377	823
☐	C-GKWJ	B737-8CT/W	34151/1684	801
☐	C-GLWS	B737-76N/W	32581/1009	005
☐	C-GMWJ	B737-7CT/W	35985/2135	239
☐	C-GNDG	B737-8CT/W	40337/5717	847♦
☐	C-GPWS	B737-6CT	34284/1759	601
☐	C-GQWJ	B737-7CT/W	35505/2436	246
☐	C-GRWS	B737-76N/W	32881/1155	007
☐	C-GSWJ	B737-7CT/W	37423/3357	261
☐	C-GTWS	B737-76N/W	32883/1179	008
☐	C-GUWJ	B737-7CT/W	36422/2497	248
☐	C-GUWS	B737-76N/W	33378/1206	009
☐	C-GVWA	B737-8CT/W	39088/4641	825
☐	C-GVWJ	B737-7CT/W	36421/2484	247
☐	C-GWAZ	B737-7CT/W	32763/1522	223
☐	C-GWBF	B737-7CT/W	32757/1370	213
☐	C-GWBJ	B737-7CT/W	32754/1385	215
☐	C-GWBL	B737-8CT	34154/1734	806
☐	C-GWBN	B737-7CT/W	34155/1772	235
☐	C-GWBT	B737-7CT/W	32755/1396	216
☐	C-GWBU	B737-8CT/W	39075/4970	828
☐	C-GWBX	B737-7CT/W	34156/1793	236
☐	C-GWCM	B737-7CT/W	32756/1413	217
☐	C-GWCN	B737-7CT/W	34157/1818	237
☐	C-GWCQ	B737-6CT	35111/2004	610
☐	C-GWCT	B737-6CT	35112/2016	611
☐	C-GWCY	B737-6CT	35113/2022	612
☐	C-GWJE	B737-7CT/W	35078/2431	245
☐	C-GWJF	B737-7CT/W	32766/1599	229
☐	C-GWJG	B737-7CT/W	35504/2366	243
☐	C-GWJK	B737-7CT/W	35084/2564	249
☐	C-GWJO	B737-7CT/W	33969/1527	225
☐	C-GWJT	B737-7CT/W	40338/3529	263
☐	C-GWJU	B737-6CT	34289/1956	609
☐	C-GWRG	B737-8CT/W	39071/3931	818
☐	C-GWSA	B737-8CT/W	34153/1731	805
☐	C-GWSB	B737-6CT	34285/1797	602
☐	C-GWSE	B737-76N/W	33379/1216	010
☐	C-GWSH	B737-76N/W	29886/1258	011
☐	C-GWSI	B737-6CT	34286/1816	603
☐	C-GWSJ	B737-6CT	34621/1862	605
☐	C-GWSK	B737-6CT	34287/1912	607
☐	C-GWSL	B737-6CT	34633/1884	606
☐	C-GWSN	B737-7CT/W	37089/3090	256
☐	C-GWSO	B737-7CT/W	37090/3092	257
☐	C-GWSP	B737-7CT/W	36693/3108	258
☐	C-GWSQ	B737-7CT/W	37091/3134	259
☐	C-GWSR	B737-8CT/W	35288/2802	809
☐	C-GWSU	B737-7CT/W	36689/2860	252
☐	C-GWSV	B737-8CT/W	37158/2841	810
☐	C-GWSX	B737-8CT/W	36696/3314	813
☐	C-GWSY	B737-7CT/W	37421/3184	260
☐	C-GWSZ	B737-8CT/W	37092/3164	812
☐	C-GWUX	B737-8CT/W	60124/5090	830
☐	C-GWWJ	B737-8CT/W	35080/2524	808
☐	C-GXRW	B737-8CT/W	39082/5511	840♦
☐	C-GXWJ	B737-6CT	35570/2032	613
☐	C-GYWJ	B737-7CT/W	32772/1879	238
☐	C-GZWS	B737-8CT/W	32770/1719	803
☐	C-	B737-8CT/W		o/o
☐	C-	B737-8CT/W		o/o
☐	C-	B737-8CT/W		o/o
☐	C-	B737-8CT/W		o/o
☐	C-	B737-8CT/W		o/o
☐	C-	B737-8CT/W		o/o

☐	C-FOGJ	B767-338ER/W	25274/396	671
☐	C-FOGT	B767-338ER	25246/387	o/o♦
☐	C-FWAD	B767-338ER	25363/402	672♦
☐	C-GOGN	B767-338ER	25576/549	670♦

WESTJET ENCORE — *WR / WJE*

☐	C-FIWE	DHC-8-402Q	4466	411
☐	C-FENJ	DHC-8-402Q	4496	423♦
☐	C-FENU	DHC-8-402Q	4446	403
☐	C-FENY	DHC-8-402Q	4447	405
☐	C-FHEN	DHC-8-402Q	4441	402
☐	C-FJWE	DHC-8-402Q	4515	428♦
☐	C-FNEN	DHC-8-402Q	4453	406
☐	C-FKWE	DHC-8-402Q	4467	412
☐	C-FOEN	DHC-8-402Q	4440	401
☐	C-FOWE	DHC-8-402Q	4471	413
☐	C-FQWE	DHC-8-402Q	4473	415
☐	C-FSWE	DHC-8-402Q	4517	♦
☐	C-FUWE	DHC-8-402Q	4477	416
☐	C-FWEZ	DHC-8-402Q	4483	417
☐	C-GDEN	DHC-8-402Q	4500	425♦
☐	C-GEEN	DHC-8-402Q	4501	426♦
☐	C-GENM	DHC-8-402Q	4456	407
☐	C-GJWE	DHC-8-402Q	4460	408
☐	C-GENU	DHC-8-402Q	4511	427♦
☐	C-GVWE	DHC-8-402Q	4485	418
☐	C-GWEF	DHC-8-402Q	4487	419
☐	C-GWEG	DHC-8-402Q	4488	420
☐	C-GWEO	DHC-8-402Q	4462	409
☐	C-GWEP	DHC-8-402Q	4463	410
☐	C-GWEQ	DHC-8-402Q	4490	421
☐	C-GWEU	DHC-8-402Q	4493	422♦
☐	C-	DHC-8-402Q		o/o
☐	C-	DHC-8-402Q		o/o
☐	C-	DHC-8-402Q		o/o

☐	C-	DHC-8-402Q		o/o

WESTWIND AVIATION — WEW

	Reg	Type	c/n	
☐	C-GLDE	ATR 42-320	374	
☐	C-GWEA	ATR 42-320	240	
☐	C-GWWC	ATR 42-300	209	
☐	C-GWWD	ATR 42-300	211	
☐	C-GWWR	ATR 42-300	238	
☐	C-FCPD	BAeJetstream 31	822	
☐	C-GHGK	BAeJetstream 31	786	
☐	C-GWEX	BAeJetstream 31	796	
☐	C-GDCG	Beech 1900D	UE-368	
☐	C-GGCA	Beech 1900D	UE-359	
☐	C-GPRL	Beech 1900C	UC-67	
☐	C-GPRT	Beech 1900C-1	UC-140	^
☐	C-GPRZ	Beech 1900C-1	UC-76	
☐	C-GSWZ	Beech 1900D	UE-337	♦
☐	C-GWWX	Beech 1900C-1	UC-44	
☐	C-GWWY	Beech 1900C-1	UC-63	

^ operates as Pronto Airways with 2 others.

CC- CHILE

AEROCARDAL — CDA

	Reg	Type	c/n	
☐	CC-AAQ	Do228-202	8119	
☐	CC-CWC	Do228-202K	8162	
☐	CC-CWX	Do228-101	7027	

AEROVIAS DAP — V5 /DAP

	Reg	Type	c/n	
☐	CC-AAG	B737-247	23608/1399	
☐	CC-ABD	B737-2Q3	22736/896	
☐	CC-ACO	BAe146 Srs.200	E2094	
☐	CC-AJS	Avro 146-RJ85	E2233	
☐	CC-ANS	Avro 146-RJ85	E2273	♦
☐	CC-CHV	DHC-6 Twin Otter 300	709	
☐	CC-CTK	B737-230	22402/744	[CBB]♦
☐	CC-CTO	B737-230	22114/657	♦
☐	CC-CZP	BAe146 Srs.200	E2042	
☐	CC-	BAe146 Srs.200	E2115	o/o♦

ATACAMAIR

	Reg	Type	c/n	
☐	CC-	B737-476	24441/2363	o/o♦

LAN AIRLINES — LA / LAN

	Reg	Type	c/n	
☐	CC-BCD	A319-112	4871	
☐	CC-BCE	A319-112	5005	
☐	CC-BCF	A319-112	5097	
☐	CC-COU	A319-132	2089	^
☐	CC-COX	A319-132	2096	^
☐	CC-COY	A319-132	2295	^
☐	CC-COZ	A319-132	2304	^
☐	CC-CPE	A319-132	2321	^
☐	CC-CPF	A319-132	2572	^
☐	CC-CPI	A319-132	2585	^
☐	CC-CPJ	A319-132	2845	^
☐	CC-CPL	A319-132	2858	^
☐	CC-CPM	A319-132	2864	^
☐	CC-CPO	A319-132	2872	^
☐	CC-CPQ	A319-132	2886	^[QSC]
☐	CC-CQK	A319-132	2892	^
☐	CC-CQL	A319-132	2894	^
☐	CC-CYJ	A319-132	3772	^
☐	CC-CYL	A319-132	3779	

^ operated as LAN Express

	Reg	Type	c/n	
☐	CC-BAA	A320-233	4383	
☐	CC-BAB	A320-233	4400	
☐	CC-BAC	A320-233	4439	
☐	CC-BAD	A320-233	4476	
☐	CC-BAE	A320-233	4509	
☐	CC-BAF	A320-233	4516	
☐	CC-BAG	A320-233	4546	
☐	CC-BAH	A320-233	4549	
☐	CC-BAJ	A320-233	4576	
☐	CC-BAK	A320-233	4597	
☐	CC-BAL	A320-233	4657	
☐	CC-BAM	A320-233	4697	
☐	CC-BAN	A320-214	4758	
☐	CC-BAO	A320-214	4767	>ARE
☐	CC-BAP	A320-214	4815	
☐	CC-BAQ	A320-214	4839	
☐	CC-BAR	A320-214	4892	>ARE
☐	CC-BAS	A320-214	4896	>ARE
☐	CC-BAT	A320-214	4921	>ARE
☐	CC-BAU	A320-214	4943	>ARE
☐	CC-BAV	A320-214	4972	>ARE
☐	CC-BAW	A320-214	5125	>ARE
☐	CC-BAX	A320-214	5178	>ARE
☐	CC-BAY	A320-214	5213	
☐	CC-BAZ	A320-214	5229	>ARE
☐	CC-BFA	A320-214	5234	>ARE
☐	CC-BFB	A320-214	5263	>ARE
☐	CC-BFC	A320-214	5316	>ARE
☐	CC-BFD	A320-214	5324	>ARE
☐	CC-BFE	A320-214	5364	>ARE
☐	CC-BFF	A320-214	5408	
☐	CC-BFG	A320-214	5443	>ARE
☐	CC-BFH	A320-214	5453	>DSM
☐	CC-BFI	A320-214	5483	
☐	CC-BFJ	A320-214	5493	
☐	CC-BFK	A320-214/S	5548	
☐	CC-BFL	A320-214/S	5554	
☐	CC-BFM	A320-214/S	5586	
☐	CC-BFN	A320-214/S	5583	
☐	CC-BFO	A320-214/S	5686	
☐	CC-BFP	A320-214/S	5707	
☐	CC-BFQ	A320-214/S	5764	
☐	CC-BFR	A320-214/S	5801	
☐	CC-BFS	A320-214/S	5818	
☐	CC-BFT	A320-214/S	5859	
☐	CC-BFU	A320-214/S	5929	
☐	CC-BFV	A320-214/S	5965	
☐	CC-BFW	A320-214/S	6135	
☐	CC-BFX	A320-214/S	6183	
☐	CC-BJB	A320-232	3264	
☐	CC-BJC	A320-232	3330	
☐	CC-BJD	A320-214/S	5748	
☐	CC-BJE	A320-214/S	5654	
☐	CC-BJF	A320-214/S	5666	
☐	CC-COF	A320-233	1355	
☐	CC-CQM	A320-233	3280	
☐	CC-CQN	A320-233	3319	
☐	CC-CQO	A320-233	3535	
☐	CC-CQP	A320-233	3556	
☐	CC-	A320-214	6787	o/o
☐	CC-	A320-271N	6286	o/o♦
☐	CC-	A320-271N	7192	o/o♦
☐	CC-	A320-214		o/o
☐	CC-	A320-214		o/o
☐	CC-	A320-214		o/o
☐	CC-	A320-214		o/o
☐	CC-	A320-2xx		o/o

☐	CC-	A320-2xx		o/o
☐	CC-BEA	A321-211/S	6364	
☐	CC-BEB	A321-211/S	6398	
☐	CC-BEC	A321-211/S	6406	
☐	CC-BED	A321-211/S	6484	
☐	CC-BEE	A321-211/S	6698	♦
☐	CC-BEF	A321-211/S	6780	♦
☐	CC-BEG	A321-211/S	6797	♦
☐	CC-BEH	A321-211/S	6894	♦
☐	CC-BEI	A321-211/S	6899	♦
☐	CC-	A321-211/S	7036	o/o♦
☐	CC-	A321-211/S	7127	o/o♦
☐	CC-	A321-211/S	7128	o/o♦
☐	CC-	A321-211/S	7176	o/o♦
☐	CC-	A321-211/S	7237	o/o♦
☐	CC-	A321-211/S	7239	o/o♦
☐	CC-	A321-211/S	7287	o/o♦
☐	CC-	A321-211/S	7298	o/o♦
☐	CC-	A321-211/S	7377	o/o♦
☐	CC-BDA	B767-316ER/W	40798/1011	
☐	CC-BDB	B767-316ER/W	40590/1014	
☐	CC-BDC	B767-316ER/W	40591/1016	"
☐	CC-BDD	B767-316ER/W	40799/1029	
☐	CC-BJA	B767-316ER/W	26329/641	
☐	CC-CML	B767-3Q8ER/W	28206/694	[AUH]
☐	CC-CWF	B767-316ER/W	34626/940	
☐	CC-CWG	B767-316ER/W	34629/944	♦
☐	CC-CWV	B767-316ER/W	35230/955	
☐	CC-CWY	B767-316ER/W	35231/961	
☐	CC-CXC	B767-316ER/W	36710/962	
☐	CC-CXD	B767-316ER/W	35697/967	
☐	CC-CXE	B767-316ER/W	35696/968	^
☐	CC-CXF	B767-316ER/W	36711/970	^
☐	CC-CXG	B767-316ER/W	36712/972	
☐	CC-CXH	B767-316ER/W	35698/973	~
☐	CC-CXI	B767-316ER/W	37800/984	
☐	CC-CXJ	B767-316ER/W	37801/985	
☐	CC-CXK	B767-316ER/W	37802/987	
☐	CC-CXL	B767-31BER/W	26265/570	
☐	CC-CZT	B767-316ER/W	29228/699	
☐	CC-CZU	B767-316ER/W	29229/729	

" operated by LAN Colombia; ^ operated by LAN Ecuador; ~ operated by LAN Peru

☐	CC-BBA	B787-8	38471/68	
☐	CC-BBB	B787-8	38466/74	
☐	CC-BBC	B787-8	38472/80	
☐	CC-BBD	B787-8	38484/118	
☐	CC-BBE	B787-8	38473/113	
☐	CC-BBF	B787-8	38476/185	
☐	CC-BBG	B787-8	38477/195	
☐	CC-BBH	B787-8	42224/205	
☐	CC-BBI	B787-8	38480/210	
☐	CC-BBJ	B787-8	42225/234	
☐	CC	B787-8		o/o♦
☐	CC	B787-8		o/o♦
☐	CC	B787-8		o/o♦
☐	CC	B787-8		o/o♦
☐	CC	B787-8		o/o♦
☐	CC	B787-8		o/o♦
☐	CC-BGA	B787-9	35317/259	
☐	CC-BGB	B787-9	35318/276	♦
☐	CC-BGC	B787-9	35321/309	♦
☐	CC-BGD	B787-9	35322/327	♦
☐	CC-BGE	B787-9	38478/341	♦
☐	CC-BGF	B787-9	38479/350	♦
☐	CC-BGG	B787-9	38461/382	♦
☐	CC-BGH	B787-9	38459/386	♦
☐	CC-BGI	B787-9	38764/399	o/o♦
☐	CC-BGJ	B787-9	38467/403	o/o♦
☐	CC-BGK	B787-9	38474/426	o/o♦
☐	CC-BGL	B787-9	38582/436	o/o♦

LAN CARGO — UC / LCO

☐	CC-CZZ	B767-316F/W	25756/712	
☐	N524LA	B767-346F/W	35816/956	

see also Florida West (N); MAS Air Cargo (XA-); TAM Cargo (ABSA Cargo)(PR-

☐	N772LA	B777-F6N	37708/774	
☐	N774LA	B777-F6N	37710/782	
☐	N776LA	B777-F16	38091/1038	

LATIN AMERICAN WINGS — CHJ

☐	CC-ADZ	B737-3G7	24634/1823	
☐	CC-AIT	B737-36N	28554/2835	o/o

SKY AIRLINE — H2 / SKU

☐	CC-AFX	A319-111	2283	
☐	CC-AFY	A319-111	2129	
☐	CC-AFZ	A319-111	2251	
☐	CC-AHC	A319-111	2119	
☐	CC-AHD	A319-111	2460	
☐	CC-AHE	A319-111	2548	
☐	CC-AIB	A319-111	2378	
☐	CC-AIC	A319-111	2380	
☐	CC-AID	A319-111	2436	
☐	CC-AIY	A319-111	2214	
☐	CC-AJF	A319-111	2249	
☐	CC-AJG	A319-112	3331	
☐	CC-AMP	A319-112	3171	
☐	CC-ABV	A320-233	1400	
☐	CC-ABW	A320-233	1523	

CN- MOROCCO

AIR ARABIA MAROC — 3O / MAC

☐	CN-NMF	A320-214	4539	
☐	CN-NMG	A320-214	4568	
☐	CN-NMH	A320-214	5143	
☐	CN-NMI	A320-214	5206	♦

ROYAL AIR MAROC — AT / RAM

☐	CN-ROX	B737-3M8F	24020/1614	
☐	CN-RNL	B737-7B6/W	28982/236	
☐	CN-RNM	B737-7B6/W	28984/294	
☐	CN-RNQ	B737-7B6/W	28985/501	
☐	CN-RNR	B737-7B6/W	28986/519	
☐	CN-RNV	B737-7B6/W	28988/1261	
☐	CN-ROD	B737-7B6/W	33062/1883	
☐	CN-RGE	B737-86N/W	36822/3746	
☐	CN-RGF	B737-86N/W	36826/3773	
☐	CN-RGG	B737-86N/W	36829/3815	
☐	CN-RGH	B737-86N/W	36828/3850	
☐	CN-RGI	B737-86N/W	36831/3858	
☐	CN-RGJ	B737-8B6/W	33072/3949	
☐	CN-RGK	B737-8B6/W	33073/3970	
☐	CN-RGM	B737-8B6/W	33074/4365	
☐	CN-RGN	B737-8B6/W	33075/4378	
☐	CN-RNJ	B737-8B6/W	28980/55	

☐ CN-RNK	B737-8B6/W	28981/60	
☐ CN-RNP	B737-8B6/W	28983/492	
☐ CN-RNU	B737-8B6/W	28987/1095	
☐ CN-RNW	B737-8B6/W	33057/1347	
☐ CN-RNZ	B737-8B6/W	33058/1432	
☐ CN-ROA	B737-8B6/W	33059/1457	
☐ CN-ROB	B737-8B6/W	33060/1646	
☐ CN-ROC	B737-8B6/W	33061/1661	
☐ CN-ROE	B737-8B6/W	33063/1913	
☐ CN-ROH	B737-85P/W	33978/1957	
☐ CN-ROJ	B737-85P/W	33979/1963	
☐ CN-ROK	B737-8B6/W	33064/2180	
☐ CN-ROL	B737-8B6/W	33065/2206	
☐ CN-ROP	B737-8B6/W	33066/2506	
☐ CN-ROR	B737-8B6/W	33067/2527	
☐ CN-ROS	B737-8B6/W	37718/2773	
☐ CN-ROT	B737-8B6/W	33068/2883	
☐ CN-ROU	B737-8B6/W	33069/2911	
☐ CN-ROY	B737-8B6/W	33070/3233	
☐ CN-ROZ	B737-8B6/W	33071/3258	
☐ CN-RGA	B747-428	25629/956	
☐ CN-RNS	B767-36NER	30115/863	
☐ CN-RNT	B767-36NER	30843/867	
☐ CN-ROV	B767-3Q8ER	27686/793	
☐ CN-ROW	B767-343ER	30008/743	
☐ CN-RGB	B787-8	43817/248	
☐ CN-RGC	B787-8	43818/285	♦
☐ CN-RGD	B787-8	35506/448	o/o♦
☐ CN-	B787-8	35509/457	o/o♦
☐ CN-RGO	ERJ-190AR	19000680	
☐ CN-RGP	ERJ-190AR	19000681	
☐ CN-RGQ	ERJ-190AR	19000682	
☐ CN-RGR	ERJ-190AR	19000684	

ROYAL MAROC EXPRESS — *RXP*

☐ CN-COE	ATR 72-600	960	
☐ CN-COF	ATR 72-600	958	
☐ CN-COG	ATR 72-600	1035	
☐ CN-COH	ATR 72-600	1034	
☐ CN-COI	ATR 42-600	1143	
☐ CN-	ATR 42-600		o/o

CP- BOLIVIA

AMASZONAS — *Z8 / AZN*

☐ CP-2715	CRJ-200ER	7218	
☐ CP-2733	CRJ-200ER	7217	
☐ CP-2742	CRJ-200LR	7195	
☐ CP-2762	CRJ-200ER	7173	
☐ CP-2856	CRJ-200LR	7226	
☐ CP-2867	CRJ-200ER	7612	
☐ CP-2908	CRJ-200ER	7247	
☐ CP-2969	CRJ-200ER	7209	♦

BOLIVIANA DE AVIACION — *OB / BOV*

☐ CP-2550	B737-33A	25118/2065	
☐ CP-2551	B737-382	24449/1857	
☐ CP-2552	B737-3M8	25041/2024	
☐ CP-2554	B737-3Q8	26303/2635	
☐ CP-2640	B737-382	24366/1699	
☐ CP-2684	B737-33A	27455/2709	
☐ CP-2716	B737-3Q8	26309/2674	
☐ CP-2718	B737-33A	25057/2046	
☐ CP-2815	B737-3U3	28738/2988	
☐ CP-2920	B737-37Q	28548/2961	
☐ CP-2921	B737-33R	28868/2881	
☐ CP-2922	B737-7Q8/W	28219/183	♦
☐ CP-2923	B737-7Q8/W	30642/1097	♦
☐ CP-2924	B737-7Q8/W	30037/1449	♦
☐ CP-2925	B737-8Q8/W	28242/942	♦
☐ CP-2926	B737-83N/W	28246/1081	♦
☐ CP-3018	B737-73A/W	28498/775	♦
☐ CP-3019	B737-33A	27458/2959	♦
☐ CP-	B737-37Q	28537/2904	o/o♦
☐ CP-2881	B767-33AER	27377/561	
☐ CP-2880	B767-33AER	27376/560	
☐ CP-	B767-328ER	27427/579	
☐ CP-2851	CRJ-200ER	7544	♦
☐ CP-	CRJ-200ER	7545	o/o♦

ECOJET — *ECD*

☐ CP-2788	Avro 146-RJ85	E2278	
☐ CP-2814	Avro 146-RJ85	E2317	
☐ CP-2850	Avro 146-RJ85	E2277	
☐ CP-2889	Avro 146-RJ85	E2269	

LAMIA BOLIVIA

☐ CP-2933	Avro 146-RJ85	E2348	[DKR]
☐ CP-2997	Avro 146-RJ85	E2370	♦
☐ CP-2998	Avro 146-RJ85	E2350	♦

TAB CARGO — *2L / BOL*

☐ CP-1376	C-130H Hercules	4759	
☐ CP-2184	C-130A Hercules	3228	
☐ CP-2489	DC-10-10F	46903/43	std
☐ CP-2555	DC-10-30F	46937/152	
☐ CP-2791	MD-10-30F	48312/442	

CS- PORTUGAL

AERO VIP — *RVP*

☐ CS-AYT	Do228-200	8084	
☐ CS-DVU	Do228-201	8080	♦

AZORES AIRLINES — *S4 / RZO*

☐ CS-TGU	A310-304	571	
☐ CS-TGV	A310-304	651	
☐ CS-TKJ	A320-212	0795	
☐ CS-TKK	A320-214	2390	
☐ CS-TKN	A310-325ET	624	
☐ CS-TKP	A320-214	2011	
☐ CS-TKQ	A320-214	2325	♦
☐ CS-TRY	A330-223	970	♦

EURO ATLANTIC AIRWAYS — *MM / MMZ*

☐ CS-TFM	B777-212ER	28513/144	
☐ CS-TFT	B767-3Y0ER	26208/505	
☐ CS-TKR	B767-36NER	30854/844	♦
☐ CS-TKS	B767-36NER	30841/841	[OPO]♦
☐ CS-TKT	B767-36NER	30853/837	♦
☐ CS-TLO	B767-383ER	24318/257	
☐ CS-TLZ	B767-375ERF	24086/248	>SRR
☐ CS-TQU	B737-8K2/W	30646/1122	
☐ CS-TRN	B767-33AER	25535/491	

HI FLY — *5K / HFY*

☐ CS-TFZ	A330-243	1008	>BBR

	Reg	Type	c/n	Notes
☐	CS-TMT	A330-322	096	[LDE]
☐	CS-TQP	A330-202	211	>SLM
☐	CS-TQW	A330-223	262	
☐	CS-TQY	A340-313X	190	~
☐	CS-TQZ	A340-313X	202	
☐	CS-TRI	A330-322	127	
☐	CS-TRJ	A321-231	1004	^
☐	CS-	A330-243	437	o/o

^ operated on lease for Belgian Armed Forces;
~ operates for Royal Australian Air Force

LEASE FLY — *RLP / LZF*

	Reg	Type	c/n	Notes
☐	CS-DTO	ATR 42-300	095	♦
☐	CS-DVF	ATR 72-202	350	♦
☐	CS-DVO	ATR 42-320	337	♦

ORBEST — *6O / OBS*

	Reg	Type	c/n	Notes
☐	CS-TRH	A330-343E	833	>EVE
☐	CS-TRL	A320-214	3758	
☐	CS-TRX	A330-223	802	♦

PGA PORTUGALIA AIRLINES — *NI / PGA*

	Reg	Type	c/n	Notes
☐	CS-TRU	ATR 42-600	1011	<WHT
☐	CS-TRV	ATR 42-600	1016	<WHT
☐	CS-DJB	ATR 72-600	1305	<WHT o/o♦
☐	CS-DJC	ATR 72-600	1232	<WHT o/o♦
☐	CS-DJD	ATR 72-600	1233	<WHT o/o♦
☐	CS-	ATR 72-600	1294	<WHT o/o♦
☐	CS-TPG	ERJ-145EP	145014	
☐	CS-TPH	ERJ-145EP	145017	
☐	CS-TPI	ERJ-145EP	145031	
☐	CS-TPJ	ERJ-145EP	145036	
☐	CS-TPK	ERJ-145EP	145041	
☐	CS-TPL	ERJ-145EP	145051	
☐	CS-TPM	ERJ-145EP	145095	
☐	CS-TPN	ERJ-145EP	145099	
☐	CS-TPO	ERJ-190LR	19000432	o/o♦
☐	CS-TPP	ERJ-190LR	19000441	o/o♦
☐	CS-TPQ	ERJ-190LR	19000450	o/o♦
☐	CS-TPR	ERJ-190LR	19000460	o/o♦
☐	CS-TPS	ERJ-190LR	19000493	o/o♦
☐	CS-TPT	ERJ-190LR	19000495	o/o♦
☐	CS-TPU	ERJ-190LR	19000506	o/o♦
☐	CS-TPV	ERJ-190LR	19000541	o/o♦
☐	CS-TPW	ERJ-190LR	19000550	o/o♦
☐	CS-TPA	Fokker 100	11257	
☐	CS-TPB	Fokker 100	11262	
☐	CS-TPC	Fokker 100	11287	
☐	CS-TPD	Fokker 100	11317	
☐	CS-TPE	Fokker 100	11342	
☐	CS-TPF	Fokker 100	11258	

To be rebranded TAP Express.

SATA AIR ACORES — *SP / SAT*

	Reg	Type	c/n
☐	CS-TRB	DHC-8Q-202	476
☐	CS-TRC	DHC-8Q-202	480
☐	CS-TRD	DHC-8-402Q	4291
☐	CS-TRE	DHC-8-402Q	4295
☐	CS-TRF	DHC-8-402Q	4297
☐	CS-TRG	DHC-8-402Q	4298

TAP AIR PORTUGAL — *TP / TAP*

	Reg	Type	c/n
☐	CS-TTA	A319-111	0750
☐	CS-TTB	A319-111	0755
☐	CS-TTC	A319-111	0763
☐	CS-TTD	A319-111	0790
☐	CS-TTE	A319-111	0821
☐	CS-TTF	A319-111	0837
☐	CS-TTG	A319-111	0906
☐	CS-TTH	A319-111	0917
☐	CS-TTI	A319-111	0933
☐	CS-TTJ	A319-111	0979
☐	CS-TTK	A319-111	1034
☐	CS-TTL	A319-111	1100
☐	CS-TTM	A319-111	1106
☐	CS-TTN	A319-111	1120
☐	CS-TTO	A319-111	1127
☐	CS-TTP	A319-111	1165
☐	CS-TTQ	A319-112	0629
☐	CS-TTR	A319-112	1756
☐	CS-TTS	A319-112	1765
☐	CS-TTU	A319-112	1668
☐	CS-TTV	A319-112	1718
☐	CS-TMW	A320-214	1667
☐	CS-TNG	A320-214	0945
☐	CS-TNH	A320-214	0960
☐	CS-TNI	A320-214	0982
☐	CS-TNJ	A320-214	1181
☐	CS-TNK	A320-214	1206
☐	CS-TNL	A320-214	1231
☐	CS-TNM	A320-214	1799
☐	CS-TNN	A320-214	1816
☐	CS-TNP	A320-214	2178
☐	CS-TNQ	A320-214	3769
☐	CS-TNR	A320-214	3883
☐	CS-TNS	A320-214	4021
☐	CS-TNT	A320-214	4095
☐	CS-TNU	A320-214	4106
☐	CS-TNV	A320-214	4145
☐	CS-TNW	A320-214	2792
☐	CS-TNX	A320-214	2822
☐	CS-TQD	A320-214	0870
☐	CS-TJE	A321-211	1307
☐	CS-TJF	A321-211	1399
☐	CS-TJG	A321-211	1713
☐	CS-TOE	A330-223	305
☐	CS-TOF	A330-223	308
☐	CS-TOG	A330-223	312
☐	CS-TOH	A330-223	181
☐	CS-TOI	A330-223	195
☐	CS-TOJ	A330-223	223
☐	CS-TOK	A330-223	317
☐	CS-TOL	A330-223	877
☐	CS-TOM	A330-202	899
☐	CS-TON	A330-202	904
☐	CS-TOO	A330-202	914
☐	CS-TOP	A330-202	934
☐	CS-TOQ	A330-203	477
☐	CS-TOR	A330-203	486
☐	CS-TOA	A340-312	041
☐	CS-TOB	A340-312	044
☐	CS-TOC	A340-312	079
☐	CS-TOD	A340-312	091

WHITE AIRWAYS — WI / WHT

	Reg	Type	c/n	Remarks
☐	CS-TFU	A319-115LR	2440	
☐	CS-TLU	A319-133CJ	1256	
☐	CS-TQJ	A319-115CJ	2675	
☐	CS-TQV	A310-304	494	
☐	CS-TQX	B777-ZFBLR	40668/937	<CEL
☐	CS-TRO	A320-214	0548	
☐	CS-FAF	B737-8FB/W	41159/4973	<CEL
☐	CS-TRU	ATR 42-600	1011	PGA>
☐	CS-TRV	ATR 42-600	1016	PGA>
☐	CS-DJB	ATR 72-600	1305	PGA> o/o♦
☐	CS-DJC	ATR 72-600	1232	PGA> o/o♦
☐	CS-DJD	ATR 72-600	1233	PGA> o/o♦
☐	CS-	ATR 72-600	1294	PGA> o/o♦

CU- CUBA

AEROGAVIOTA — KG / GTV

	Reg	Type	c/n	Remarks
☐	CU-T1228	An-26	12604	♦
☐	CU-T1238	An-26	7803	♦
☐	CU-T1239	An-26	7907	
☐	CU-T1240	An-26	11210	
☐	CU-T1241	An-26	11301	
☐	CU-T1402	An-26B	12605	
☐	CU-T1403	An-26B	12905	
☐	CU-T1406	An-26B	13502	
☐	CU-T1408	An-26	6903	
☐	CU-T1417	An-26		
☐	CU-T1420	An-26	87306607	
☐	CU-T1421	An-26	6610	
☐	CU-T1423	An-26	3806	
☐	CU-T1425	An-26	6904	
☐	CU-T1426	An-26	5603	
☐	CU-T1428	An-26	11303	
☐	CU-T1429	An-26	7006	
☐	CU-T1432	An-26	7306	
☐	CU-T1433	An-26	7309	
☐	CU-T1434	An-26	7701	
☐	CU-T1435	An-26	7702	
☐	CU-T1463	An-24RV	47309405	
☐	CU-T1464	An-24RV		♦

Status of the above fleet uncertain.

	Reg	Type	c/n	Remarks
☐	CU-T1454	ATR 42-500	616	
☐	CU-T1455	ATR 42-500	618	
☐	CU-T1456	ATR 42-500	619	

CUBANA DE AVIACION — CU / CUB

	Reg	Type	c/n	Remarks
☐	LY-COM	A320-212	0528	<NVD
☐	LY-VEQ	A320-214	0709	<NVD
☐	LY-VET	A319-112	1778	<NVD
☐	LY-VEV	A320-211	0211	<NVD
☐	LY-VEW	A320-214	1005	<NVD
☐	CU-T1214	An-24RV	47309404	
☐	CU-T1237	An-24RV	37308909	^
☐	CU-T1244	An-24RV	57310301	^
☐	CU-T1260	An-24RV	57310307	^
☐	CU-T1263	An-24RV	47309610	
☐	CU-T1706	An-24RV	67310701	
☐	CU-T1228	An-26	12604	^
☐	CU-T1238	An-26	7803	
☐	CU-T1230	An-26	14306	
☐	CU-T1710	An-158-200	20101	std
☐	CU-T1711	An-158-200	20102	
☐	CU-T1712	An-158-200	20103	
☐	CU-T1714	An-158-200	20104	
☐	CU-T1715	An-158-200	20105	
☐	CU-T1716	An-158-200	20506	♦
☐	CU-T1240	ATR 42-500	617	VIP
☐	CU-T1509	ATR 42-300	009	♦
☐	CU-T1512	ATR 42-300	136	♦
☐	CU-T1544	ATR 72-212	472	♦
☐	CU-T1545	ATR 72-212	473	♦
☐	CU-T1547	ATR 72-212	485	♦
☐	CU-T1548	ATR 72-212	453	♦
☐	CU-T1550	ATR 42-300	014	♦
☐	CU-T1250	Il-96-300	74393202015	
☐	CU-T1251	Il-96-300	74393202016	
☐	CU-T1254	Il-96-300	74393202017	
☐	CU-T1717	Il-96-300	74393201005	
☐	CU-T	Il-96-300	74393201008	o/o♦
☐	CU-C1700	Tu-204-100SE	64036	
☐	CU-T1701	Tu-204-100E	64035	
☐	CU-T1702	Tu-204-100E	64042	
☐	CU-C1703	Tu-204-100SE	64037	

^ status uncertain

CX- URUGUAY

AIR CLASS — QD / QCL

	Reg	Type	c/n	Remarks
☐	CX-CAR	B727-214F	21958/1533	
☐	CX-CLB	B727-227F	21996/1571	♦

ALAS U — ALY

	Reg	Type	c/n	Remarks
☐	CX-OAA	B737-36N/W	28569/2996	
☐	CX-OAB	B737-33R/W	28869/2887	♦
☐	CX-OAC	B737-36N	28563/2921	♦

C2- NAURU

NAURU AIRLINES — ON / RON

	Reg	Type	c/n	Remarks
☐	VH-INU	B737-3Y0	23684/1353	[ASP]
☐	VH-NLK	B737-33A	23635/1436	
☐	VH-ONU	B737-3U3	28732/2966	
☐	VH-PNI	B737-36N	28555/2846	
☐	VH-VLI	B737-3H6(SF)	27125/2415	
☐	VH-XNU	B737-319	25609/3130	♦
☐	VH-YNU	B737-319	25607/3126	

C5- GAMBIA

AEOLUS AIR — AAZ

	Reg	Type	c/n	Remarks
☐	C5-AAH	A320-231	0295	>AFG♦
☐	C5-AAL	B737-332	25996/2488	>TRQ
☐	C5-AAN	B737-522	26687/2402	>TRQ
☐	C5-AAO	A320-231	0368	[SAW]
☐	C5-MAA	B737-4Q8	25113/2656	std
☐	C5-MAB	B737-3xx	?	>SUD♦
☐	C5-MAD	B737-3xx	?	>TRQ♦
☐	C5-MAE	B737-3xx	?	>TRQ♦

C6- BAHAMAS

BAHAMASAIR			UP / BHS
☐ C6-BFQ	ATR 72-600	1293	♦
☐ C6-BFR	ATR 72-600	1314	♦
☐ C6-	ATR 42-600		o/o♦
☐ C6-	ATR 42-600		o/o♦
☐ C6-	ATR 42-600		o/o♦
☐ C6-BFC	B737-505	27631/2866	
☐ C6-BFD	B737-5H6	26448/2484	
☐ C6-BFE	B737-5H6	26450/2503	
☐ C6-BFG	DHC-8-311A	288	
☐ C6-BFH	DHC-8-311A	291	
☐ C6-BFJ	DHC-8Q-311	323	
☐ C6-BFO	DHC-8-301	164	
☐ C6-BFP	DHC-8Q-311	309	

PINEAPPLE AIR			PNP
☐ N381CR	Beech 1900C	UB-69	
☐ N431CM	Beech 1900C-1	UC-13	♦
☐ N800MX	Beech 1900C	UB-48	
☐ C6-KMC	EMB.110P1	110259	
☐ C6-MIC	EMB.110P1	110407	

SKY BAHAMAS			Q7 / SBM
☐ C6-SBB	SAAB SF.340A	340A-149	
☐ C6-SBD	SAAB SF.340A	340A-021	
☐ C6-SBF	Beech 1900D	UE-2	
☐ C6-SBG	SAAB SF.340A	340A-110	
☐ C6-SBK	SAAB SF.340B	340B-196	
☐ C6-SBL	SAAB SF.340A	340A-131	♦

SOUTHERN AIR CHARTER			PL / SOA
☐ N376SA	Beech 1900C	UB-72	
☐ N378SA	Beech 1900C	UB-31	

WESTERN AIR			WST
☐ C6-HBW	SAAB SF.340A	340A-067	
☐ C6-JAY	SAAB SF.340A	340A-120	
☐ C6-LSR	SAAB SF.340A	340A-122	♦
☐ C6-RMW	SAAB SF.340A	340A-121	
☐ C6-VIP	SAAB SF.340A	340A-098	

C9- MOZAMBIQUE

KAYA AIRLINES			TWM
☐ C9-AUN	LET410UVP	882035	♦
☐ C9-AUQ	EMB.120RT	120139	
☐ C9-AUU	EMB.120RT	120200	

LAM MOZAMBIQUE			TM / LAM
☐ C9-AUL	DHC-8-402Q	4019	
☐ C9-AUM	DHC-8-402Q	4020	
☐ C9-AUY	DHC-8-402Q	4021	
☐ C9-BAJ	B737-205	23464/1223	
☐ C9-BAO	B737-205	23467/1245	
☐ C9-BAP	B737-53S	29074/3086	
☐ C9-BAQ	B737-752/W	33792/1571	
☐ C9-	B737-7xx		o/o
☐ C9-	B737-7xx		o/o♦
☐ C9-EMA	ERJ-190AR	19000301	
☐ C9-EMB	ERJ-190AR	19000309	
☐ C9-MEJ	EMB.120ER	120262	♦
☐ C9-NEJ	EMB.120ER	120252	♦
☐ C9-MEK	ERJ-145MP	145197	♦

MOCAMBIQUE EXPRESSO			MXE
☐ C9-MEH	ERJ-145MP	145294	
☐ C9-MEI	EMB.120RT	120228	♦
☐ C9-MEX	ERJ-145MP	145266	

D- GERMANY

AEROLOGIC			3S / BOX
☐ D-AALA	B777-FZN	36001/780	
☐ D-AALB	B777-FZN	36002/799	
☐ D-AALC	B777-FZN	36003/836	
☐ D-AALD	B777-FZN	36004/838	
☐ D-AALE	B777-FZN	36198/872	
☐ D-AALF	B777-FZN	36201/881	
☐ D-AALG	B777-FZN	36199/894	
☐ D-AALH	B777-FZN	36200/904	

AIR BERLIN			AB / BER
☐ D-ABGQ	A319-112	3700	o/o♦
☐ D-ABGR	A319-112	3704	o/o♦
☐ D-ABGS	A319-112	3865	
☐ D-ASTX	A319-112	3202	
☐ D-ABDB	A320-214	2619	
☐ D-ABDO	A320-214	3055	
☐ D-ABDQ	A320-214	3121	
☐ D-ABDU	A320-214	3516	
☐ D-ABDW	A320-214	3945	
☐ D-ABDY	A320-214	4013	
☐ D-ABFA	A320-214	4101	
☐ D-ABFC	A320-214	4161	
☐ D-ABFE	A320-214	4269	
☐ D-ABFF	A320-214	4329	
☐ D-ABFG	A320-214	4291	
☐ D-ABFK	A320-214	4433	
☐ D-ABFN	A320-214	4510	
☐ D-ABFO	A320-214	4565	
☐ D-ABNE	A320-214	2003	
☐ D-ABNF	A320-214	1961	
☐ D-ABNG	A320-214	4316	o/o
☐ D-ABNH	A320-214	1775	
☐ D-ABNI	A320-214	1717	
☐ D-ABNJ	A320-214/S	5522	
☐ D-ABNK	A320-214	1769	
☐ D-ABNL	A320-214	1852	
☐ D-ABNM	A320-214/S	6856	♦
☐ D-ABNN	A320-214	1889	
☐ D-ABNO	A320-214/S	6831	♦
☐ D-ABNQ	A320-214/S	6877	♦
☐ D-ABNR	A320-214/S	6892	std♦
☐ D-ABNS	A320-214/S	6902	std♦
☐ D-ABNT	A320-214	2562	♦
☐ D-ABNU	A320-214	2591	♦
☐ D-ABNV	A320-214	2606	♦
☐ D-ABNW	A320-214	2627	♦
☐ D-ABNX	A320-214/S	6927	♦
☐ D-ABNY	A320-214/S	6966	♦
☐ D-ABZA	A320-216	3532	
☐ D-ABZB	A320-216	3515	
☐ D-ABZC	A320-216	3502	♦
☐ D-ABZE	A320-216	3464	♦
☐ D-ABZF	A320-216	3482	♦

	Reg	Type	c/n	
☐	D-ABZI	A320-216	3328	♦
☐	D-ABZJ	A320-216	3295	♦
☐	D-ABZK	A320-216	3213	♦
☐	D-ABZL	A320-216	3178	♦
☐	D-ABZN	A320-216	3080	♦
☐	D-ABZL	A320-216	3178	♦
☐	D-	A320-214/S	7224	o/o♦
☐	D-ABCA	A321-211	3708	
☐	D-ABCB	A321-211	3749	
☐	D-ABCC	A321-211	4334	
☐	D-ABCF	A321-211	1966	
☐	D-ABCG	A321-211	1988	
☐	D-ABCH	A321-211	4728	
☐	D-ABCI	A321-211	5038	
☐	D-ABCJ	A321-211	5126	
☐	D-ABCK	A321-211	5133	
☐	D-ABCL	A321-211/S	6168	
☐	D-ABCM	A321-211/S	6432	
☐	D-ABCN	A321-211/S	6454	
☐	D-ABCO	A321-211/S	6501	
☐	D-ABCP	A321-211/S	6629	♦
☐	D-ABCQ	A321-211/S	6639	♦
☐	D-ABCR	A321-211/S	6719	♦
☐	D-A	A321-211/S	7119	o/o♦
☐	D-A	A321-211/S	7171	o/o♦
☐	D-A	A321-211/S	7260	o/o♦
☐	D-ALSA	A321-211	1629	
☐	D-ALSB	A321-211	1994	
☐	D-ALSC	A321-211	2005	
☐	D-ALPA	A330-223	403	
☐	D-ALPB	A330-223	432	
☐	D-ALPC	A330-223	444	
☐	D-ALPD	A330-223	454	
☐	D-ALPE	A330-223	469	
☐	D-ALPF	A330-223	476	
☐	D-ALPG	A330-223	493	
☐	D-ALPH	A330-223	739	
☐	D-ALPI	A330-223	828	
☐	D-ALPJ	A330-223	911	
☐	D-ABXA	A330-223	288	
☐	D-ABXB	A330-223	322	
☐	D-ABXC	A330-223	665	
☐	D-ABXD	A330-223	822	
☐	D-ABXE	A330-223	968	o/o♦
☐	D-ABXF	A330-223	1112	o/o♦
☐	D-AGEC	B737-76J/W	36118/2832	
☐	D-AHXC	B737-7K5/W	34693/2260	<TUI
☐	D-AHXE	B737-7K5/W	35135/2451	<TUI
☐	D-AHXF	B737-7K5/W	35136/2465	<TUI
☐	D-AHXG	B737-7K5/W	35140/2575	<TUI
☐	D-AHXJ	B737-7K5/W	35277/2609	<TUI
☐	D-ABAF	B737-86J/W	30878/844	
☐	D-ABAG	B737-86J/W	30879/871	>HLX
☐	D-ABBD	B737-86J/W	30880/1043	
☐	D-ABBK	B737-8BK/W	33013/1317	
☐	D-ABKA	B737-82R	29329/224	
☐	D-ABKD	B737-86J/W	37742/2796	[MUC]
☐	D-ABKJ	B737-86J/W	37749/3176	
☐	D-ABKK	B737-86J/W	37753/3261	
☐	D-ABKM	B737-86J/W	37755/3349	
☐	D-ABKN	B737-86J/W	37756/3371	
☐	D-ABKS	B737-86J/W	36880/3685	
☐	D-ABMB	B737-86J/W	36121/3853	
☐	D-ABMD	B737-86J/W	37761/3887	
☐	D-ABME	B737-86J/W	37766/4049	
☐	D-ABMF	B737-86J/W	37767/4065	
☐	D-ABMI	B737-86J/W	37770/4184	
☐	D-ABMK	B737-86J/W	37772/4264	
☐	D-ABML	B737-86J/W	37773/4281	
☐	D-ABMP	B737-86J/W	37779/4472	
☐	D-ABMQ	B737-86J/W	37780/4500	
☐	D-ABMR	B737-86J/W	37781/4535	
☐	D-ABMS	B737-86J/W	37782/4564	
☐	D-ABMU	B737-86J/W	39384/4663	
☐	D-ABMV	B737-86J/W	37785/4698	
☐	D-	B737-8xx/W		o/o♦
☐	D-ABQA	DHC-8-402Q	4223	
☐	D-ABQB	DHC-8-402Q	4226	
☐	D-ABQC	DHC-8-402Q	4231	
☐	D-ABQD	DHC-8-402Q	4234	
☐	D-ABQE	DHC-8-402Q	4239	
☐	D-ABQF	DHC-8-402Q	4245	
☐	D-ABQG	DHC-8-402Q	4250	
☐	D-ABQH	DHC-8-402Q	4256	
☐	D-ABQI	DHC-8-402Q	4264	
☐	D-ABQJ	DHC-8-402Q	4274	
☐	D-ABQK	DHC-8-402Q	4265	
☐	D-ABQL	DHC-8-402Q	4184	
☐	D-ABQM	DHC-8-402Q	4119	
☐	D-ABQN	DHC-8-402Q	4124	
☐	D-ABQO	DHC-8-402Q	4129	
☐	D-ABQP	DHC-8-402Q	4137	
☐	D-ABQQ	DHC-8-402Q	4198	
☐	D-A	DHC-8-402Q		o/o♦
☐	D-A	DHC-8-402Q		o/o♦
☐	D-A	DHC-8-402Q		o/o♦

DHC-8-402Qs operated by LGW on behalf of Air Berlin

ARCUS-AIR — ZE / AZE

	Reg	Type	c/n	
☐	D-CAAL	Do228-212	8155	
☐	D-CAAM	Do228-212	8205	
☐	D-CAAR	Do228-212	8211	
☐	D-CAAZ	Do228-212	8212	
☐	D-CUTT	Do228-212	8200	

AVANTI AIR — ATV

	Reg	Type	c/n	
☐	D-AOLG	Fokker 100	11452	
☐	D-AOLH	Fokker 100	11265	o/o[SCN]
☐	D-AGPH	Fokker 100	11308	♦

BINAIR AERO SERVICE — BID

	Reg	Type	c/n	
☐	D-CAVA	SA.227AC Metro III	AC-758B	
☐	D-CBIN	SA.226AT Merlin IVC	AT-440B	
☐	D-CCCC	SA.227AT Merlin IVC	AT-511	
☐	D-CKPP	SA.227DC Metro 23	DC-805B	
☐	D-CNAF	SA.227AC Metro III	AC-505B	
☐	D-CNAG	SA.227DC Metro 23	DC-893B	
☐	D-CNAY	SA.227AT Merlin IVC	AT-493	
☐	D-CPSW	SA.227AC Metro III	AC-757B	
☐	D-CSAL	SA.227AC Metro III	AC-601	
☐	D-ICRK	SA.226TC Metro II	TC-333	

BUSINESSWINGS

	Reg	Type	c/n	
☐	D-CULT	Do228-212	8192	
☐	D-IROL	Do228-100	7003	
☐	D-IVER	DHC-6 Twin Otter 300	411	

CONDOR — DE / CFG

	Reg	Type	c/n	
☐	D-AICA	A320-212	0774	

☐	D-AICC	A320-212	0809	
☐	D-AICD	A320-212	0884	
☐	D-AICE	A320-212	0894	
☐	D-AICF	A320-212	0905	
☐	D-AICG	A320-212	0957	
☐	D-AICH	A320-212	0971	
☐	D-AICK	A320-212	1416	
☐	D-AICL	A320-212	1437	
☐	D-AIAA	A321-211	1607	
☐	D-AIAC	A321-211/S	5969	
☐	D-AIAD	A321-211/S	6053	
☐	D-AIAE	A321-211/S	6376	
☐	D-AIAF	A321-211/S	6459	
☐	D-AIAG	A321-211/S	6590	♦
☐	D-AIAH	A321-211/S	6615	♦
☐	D-ABOA	B757-330/W	29016/804	
☐	D-ABOB	B757-330/W	29017/810	
☐	D-ABOC	B757-330/W	29015/818	
☐	D-ABOE	B757-330/W	29012/839	
☐	D-ABOF	B757-330/W	29013/846	
☐	D-ABOG	B757-330/W	29014/849	
☐	D-ABOH	B757-330/W	30030/855	
☐	D-ABOI	B757-330/W	29018/909	
☐	D-ABOJ	B757-330/W	29019/915	
☐	D-ABOK	B757-330/W	29020/918	
☐	D-ABOL	B757-330/W	29021/923	
☐	D-ABOM	B757-330/W	29022/926	
☐	D-ABON	B757-330/W	29023/929	
☐	D-ABUA	B767-330ER/W	26991/455	
☐	D-ABUB	B767-330ER/W	26987/466	
☐	D-ABUC	B767-330ER/W	26992/470	
☐	D-ABUD	B767-330ER/W	26983/471	
☐	D-ABUE	B767-330ER/W	26984/518	
☐	D-ABUF	B767-330ER/W	26985/537	
☐	D-ABUH	B767-330ER/W	26986/553	
☐	D-ABUI	B767-330ER/W	26988/562	
☐	D-ABUK	B767-343ER/W	30009/746	
☐	D-ABUL	B767-31BER/W	26259/534	
☐	D-ABUM	B767-31BER/W	25170/542	
☐	D-ABUS	B767-38EER/W	30840/829	♦
☐	D-ABUZ	B767-330ER/W	25209/382	
☐	D-ATYG	B767-304ER/W	29137/733	<HLX♦
☐	G-DAJC	B767-31KER/W	27206/533	<TCX♦
☐	G-TCCA	B767-31KER/W	27205/528	<TCX♦
☐	G-TCCB	B767-31KER/W	28865/657	<TCX♦
☐	D-	B767-3Q8ER	29383/747	o/o♦
☐	D-	B767-3Q8ER	29387/840	o/o♦
☐	D-	B767-3Q8ER	30048/828	o/o♦

EAT LEIPZIG — *QY / BCS*

☐	D-AEAA	A300B4-622R(F)	743	♦
☐	D-AEAB	A300B4-622R(F)	837	
☐	D-AEAC	A300B4-622R(F)	602	
☐	D-AEAD	A300B4-622R(F)	617	
☐	D-AEAE	A300B4-622R(F)	753	
☐	D-AEAF	A300B4-622R(F)	836	
☐	D-AEAG	A300B4-622R(F)	621	
☐	D-AEAH	A300B4-622R(F)	783	
☐	D-AEAI	A300B4-622R(F)	637	
☐	D-AEAJ	A300B4-622R(F)	641	
☐	D-AEAK	A300B4-622R(F)	670	
☐	D-AEAL	A300B4-622R(F)	679	
☐	D-AEAM	A300B4-622R(F)	797	
☐	D-AEAN	A300B4-622R(F)	703	
☐	D-AEAO	A300B4-622R(F)	711	
☐	D-AEAP	A300B4-622R(F)	724	
☐	D-AEAQ	A300B4-622R(F)	729	
☐	D-AEAR	A300B4-622R(F)	730	
☐	D-AEAS	A300B4-622R(F)	737	
☐	D-AEAT	A300B4-622R(F)	740	
☐	D-AZMO	A300F4-622R(F)	872	♦
☐	D-ALEA	B757-236(SF)	22172/9	
☐	D-ALEC	B757-236(SF)	22175/13	
☐	D-ALED	B757-236(SF)	22179/24	
☐	D-ALEE	B757-236(SF)	22183/32	
☐	D-ALEF	B757-236(SF)	22189/58	
☐	D-ALEG	B757-236(SF)	23398/77	
☐	D-ALEH	B757-236(SF)	23492/89	
☐	D-ALEJ	B757-23APF	24971/340	
☐	D-ALEK	B757-236(SF)	23533/93	
☐	D-ALEN	B757-2Q8(F)	29380/836	♦
☐	D-ALEO	B757-2Q8(F)	29443/821	o/o♦
☐	D-ALEP	B757-2Q8(F)/W	30046/1006	♦
☐	D-ALEQ	B757-2Q8(F)	26332/688	o/o♦
☐	D-ALER	B757-2Q8(F)	27351/639	o/o♦
☐	D-ALES	B757-2Q8(F)	29442/819	o/o♦

EUROWINGS — *EW / EWG*

☐	D-AEWA	A320-214/S	6953	♦
☐	D-AEWB	A320-214/S	6992	o/o♦
☐	D-AEWC	A320-214/S	7012	o/o♦
☐	D-AEWD	A320-214/S	7019	o/o♦
☐	D-AEWE	A320-214/S	7056	o/o♦
☐	D-AEWF	A320-214/S	7087	o/o♦
☐	D-AEWG	A320-214/S	7121	o/o♦
☐	D-AEWX	A320-214/S	6807	♦
☐	D-AIZQ	A320-214/S	5497	
☐	D-AIZR	A320-214/S	5525	
☐	D-AIZS	A320-214/S	5557	♦
☐	D-AIZT	A320-214/S	5601	♦
☐	D-AIZU	A320-214/S	5635	♦
☐	D-AIZV	A320-214/S	5658	♦
☐	D-A	A320-214/S	7148	o/o♦
☐	D-A	A320-214/S	7210	o/o♦
☐	D-A	A320-214/S	7216	o/o♦
☐	D-A	A320-214/S	7261	o/o♦
☐	D-AXGA	A330-203	530	♦
☐	D-AXGB	A330-202	684	♦
☐	D-AXGC	A330-203	555	o/o♦
☐	D-AXGD	A330-203	573	o/o♦
☐	D-AXGE	A330-202	612	o/o♦
☐	D-AXGF	A330-202	616	o/o♦
☐	D-AXGG	A330-202	504	o/o♦
☐	D-ATYE	B767-304ER/W	28979/691	<HLX♦

Leases CRJ-900ERs to Germanwings/Lufthansa Cityline & included there.

GERMANIA — *ST / GMI*

☐	D-ASTA	A319-112	4663	
☐	D-ASTB	A319-112	4691	
☐	D-ASTC	A319-112	5085	
☐	D-ASTR	A319-112	3950	♦
☐	D-ASTT	A319-112	3560	
☐	D-ASTU	A319-112	3533	
☐	D-ASTY	A319-112	3407	
☐	D-ASTZ	A319-112	3019	
☐	D-ASTE	A321-211/S	6005	
☐	D-ASTP	A321-211	0684	
☐	D-ASTV	A321-211	0995	

☐	D-ASTW	A321-211	0970	
☐	D-ABLA	B737-76J/W	36114/2421	
☐	D-ABLB	B737-76J/W	36115/2692	
☐	D-AGEL	B737-75B/W	28110/5	
☐	D-AGEN	B737-75B/W	28100/16	
☐	D-AGEP	B737-75B/W	28102/18	
☐	D-AGEQ	B737-75B/W	28103/23	
☐	D-AGER	B737-75B	28107/27	
☐	D-AGES	B737-75B/W	28108/28	
☐	D-AGET	B737-75B/W	28109/31	
☐	D-AGEU	B737-75B/W	28104/39	

GERMANWINGS **4U / GWI**

☐	D-AGWA	A319-132	2813	
☐	D-AGWB	A319-132	2833	
☐	D-AGWC	A319-132	2976	
☐	D-AGWD	A319-132	3011	
☐	D-AGWE	A319-132	3128	
☐	D-AGWF	A319-132	3172	
☐	D-AGWG	A319-132	3193	
☐	D-AGWH	A319-132	3352	
☐	D-AGWI	A319-132	3358	
☐	D-AGWJ	A319-132	3375	
☐	D-AGWK	A319-132	3500	
☐	D-AGWL	A319-132	3534	
☐	D-AGWM	A319-132	3839	
☐	D-AGWN	A319-132	3841	
☐	D-AGWO	A319-132	4166	
☐	D-AGWP	A319-132	4227	
☐	D-AGWQ	A319-132	4256	
☐	D-AGWR	A319-132	4285	
☐	D-AGWS	A319-132	4998	
☐	D-AGWT	A319-132	5043	
☐	D-AGWU	A319-132	5457	
☐	D-AGWV	A319-132	5467	
☐	D-AGWW	A319-132	5535	
☐	D-AGWX	A319-132	5569	
☐	D-AGWY	A319-132	5941	
☐	D-AGWZ	A319-132	5978	
☐	D-AKNF	A319-112	0646	
☐	D-AKNG	A319-112	0654	
☐	D-AKNH	A319-112	0794	
☐	D-AKNI	A319-112	1016	
☐	D-AKNJ	A319-112	1172	
☐	D-AKNK	A319-112	1077	
☐	D-AKNL	A319-112	1084	
☐	D-AKNM	A319-112	1089	
☐	D-AKNN	A319-112	1136	
☐	D-AKNO	A319-112	1147	
☐	D-AKNP	A319-112	1155	
☐	D-AKNQ	A319-112	1170	
☐	D-AKNR	A319-112	1209	
☐	D-AKNS	A319-112	1277	
☐	D-AKNT	A319-112	2607	
☐	D-AKNU	A319-112	2628	
☐	D-AKNV	A319-112	2632	
☐	D-AIPL	A320-211	0094	o/o
☐	D-AIPS	A320-211	0116	o/o
☐	D-AIPT	A320-211	0117	
☐	D-AIPU	A320-211	0135	
☐	D-AIPW	A320-211	0137	
☐	D-AIPY	A320-211	0161	
☐	D-AIPZ	A320-211	0162	
☐	D-AIQB	A320-211	0200	
☐	D-AIQC	A320-211	0201	
☐	D-AIQD	A320-211	0202	
☐	D-AIQE	A320-211	0209	
☐	D-AIQF	A320-211	0216	
☐	D-AIQH	A320-211	0217	
☐	D-AIQK	A320-211	0218	
☐	D-AIQL	A320-211	0267	
☐	D-AIQM	A320-211	0268	
☐	D-AIQN	A320-211	0269	
☐	D-AIQP	A320-211	0346	
☐	D-AIQR	A320-211	0382	
☐	D-AIQS	A320-211	0401	
☐	D-AIUO	A320-214/S	6636	♦
☐	D-ACNA	CRJ-900ER	15229	std
☐	D-ACNB	CRJ-900ER	15230	std
☐	D-ACNC	CRJ-900ER	15236	
☐	D-ACND	CRJ-900ER	15238	
☐	D-ACNE	CRJ-900ER	15241	
☐	D-ACNF	CRJ-900ER	15243	
☐	D-ACNG	CRJ-900ER	15245	
☐	D-ACNH	CRJ-900ER	15247	
☐	D-ACNI	CRJ-900ER	15248	
☐	D-ACNJ	CRJ-900ER	15249	
☐	D-ACNK	CRJ-900ER	15251	
☐	D-ACNL	CRJ-900ER	15252	
☐	D-ACNM	CRJ-900ER	15253	
☐	D-ACNN	CRJ-900ER	15254	
☐	D-ACNO	CRJ-900ER	15255	
☐	D-ACNP	CRJ-900ER	15259	
☐	D-ACNQ	CRJ-900ER	15260	
☐	D-ACNR	CRJ-900ER	15263	
☐	D-ACNT	CRJ-900ER	15264	
☐	D-ACNU	CRJ-900ER	15267	
☐	D-ACNV	CRJ-900ER	15268	
☐	D-ACNW	CRJ-900ER	15269	
☐	D-ACNX	CRJ-900ER	15270	

To be merged with Eurowings; CRJ-900ERs leased from Eurowings & operated as Lufthansa Cityline.

LGW **HE / LGW**

☐	D-ILWB	Do228-200	8035
☐	D-ILWS	Do228-200	8002

Also operates DHC-8-402Qs on behalf of Air Berlin, which see.

LUFTHANSA **LH / DLH**

☐	D-AIBA	A319-114	4141
☐	D-AIBB	A319-112	4182
☐	D-AIBC	A319-112	4332
☐	D-AIBD	A319-112	4455
☐	D-AIBE	A319-112	4511
☐	D-AIBF	A319-112	4796
☐	D-AIBG	A319-112	4841
☐	D-AIBH	A319-112	5239
☐	D-AIBI	A319-112	5284
☐	D-AIBJ	A319-112	5293
☐	D-AILA	A319-114	0609
☐	D-AILB	A319-114	0610
☐	D-AILC	A319-114	0616
☐	D-AILD	A319-114	0623
☐	D-AILE	A319-114	0627
☐	D-AILF	A319-114	0636
☐	D-AILH	A319-114	0641
☐	D-AILI	A319-114	0651
☐	D-AILK	A319-114	0679
☐	D-AILL	A319-114	0689
☐	D-AILM	A319-114	0694

	Registration	Type	C/n	Notes
☐	D-AILN	A319-114	0700	
☐	D-AILP	A319-114	0717	
☐	D-AILR	A319-114	0723	
☐	D-AILS	A319-114	0729	
☐	D-AILT	A319-114	0738	
☐	D-AILU	A319-114	0744	
☐	D-AILW	A319-114	0853	
☐	D-AILX	A319-114	0860	
☐	D-AILY	A319-114	0875	
☐	D-AINA	A320-271N	6801	♦
☐	D-AINB	A320-271N	6864	o/o♦
☐	D-AINC	A320-271N	6920	o/o♦
☐	D-AIND	A230-271N	7078	o/o♦
☐	D-AINE	A230-271N		o/o♦
☐	D-AINF	A320-271N		o/o♦
☐	D-AING	A320-271N		o/o♦
☐	D-AINH	A320-271N		o/o♦
☐	D-AINI	A320-271N		o/o♦
☐	D-AIPA	A320-211	0069	
☐	D-AIPB	A320-211	0070	
☐	D-AIPC	A320-211	0071	
☐	D-AIPD	A320-211	0072	
☐	D-AIPE	A320-211	0078	
☐	D-AIPF	A320-211	0083	
☐	D-AIPH	A320-211	0086	
☐	D-AIPK	A320-211	0093	
☐	D-AIPL	A320-211	0094	
☐	D-AIPM	A320-211	0104	
☐	D-AIPP	A320-211	0110	
☐	D-AIPR	A320-211	0111	
☐	D-AIPS	A320-211	0116	
☐	D-AIQA	A320-211	0172	♦
☐	D-AIQT	A320-211	1337	
☐	D-AIQU	A320-211	1365	
☐	D-AIQW	A320-211	1367	
☐	D-AIUA	A320-214/S	5935	
☐	D-AIUB	A320-214/S	5972	
☐	D-AIUC	A320-214/S	6006	
☐	D-AIUD	A320-214/S	6033	
☐	D-AIUE	A320-214/S	6092	
☐	D-AIUF	A320-214/S	6141	
☐	D-AIUG	A320-214/S	6202	
☐	D-AIUH	A320-214/S	6225	
☐	D-AIUI	A320-214/S	6265	
☐	D-AIUJ	A320-214/S	6301	
☐	D-AIUK	A320-214/S	6423	
☐	D-AIUL	A320-214/S	6521	
☐	D-AIUM	A320-214/S	6577	
☐	D-AIUN	A320-214/S	6549	
☐	D-AIUQ	A320-214/S	6947	♦
☐	D-AIUR	A320-214/S	6985	o/o♦
☐	D-AIUS	A320-214/S	7024	o/o♦
☐	D-AIUT	A320-214/S	7115	o/o♦
☐	D-AIZA	A320-214	4097	
☐	D-AIZB	A320-214	4120	
☐	D-AIZC	A320-214	4153	
☐	D-AIZD	A320-214	4191	
☐	D-AIZE	A320-214	4261	
☐	D-AIZF	A320-214	4289	
☐	D-AIZG	A320-214	4324	
☐	D-AIZH	A320-214	4363	
☐	D-AIZI	A320-214	4398	
☐	D-AIZJ	A320-214	4449	
☐	D-AIZK	A320-214	5122	
☐	D-AIZL	A320-214	5181	
☐	D-AIZM	A320-214	5203	

	Registration	Type	C/n	Notes
☐	D-AIZN	A320-214	5425	
☐	D-AIZO	A320-214	5441	
☐	D-AIZP	A320-214/S	5487	
☐	D-AIZW	A320-214/S	5694	
☐	D-AIZX	A320-214/S	5741	
☐	D-AIZY	A320-214/S	5769	
☐	D-AIZZ	A320-214/S	5831	
☐	D-A	A320-214/S	7158	o/o♦
☐	D-A	A320-214/S	7174	o/o♦
☐	D-A	A320-214/S	7312	o/o♦
☐	D-A	A320-214/S	7403	o/o♦
☐	D-A	A320-214/S	7422	o/o♦
☐	D-AIDA	A321-231	4360	
☐	D-AIDB	A321-231	4545	
☐	D-AIDC	A321-231	4560	
☐	D-AIDD	A321-231	4585	
☐	D-AIDE	A321-231	4607	
☐	D-AIDF	A321-231	4626	
☐	D-AIDG	A321-231	4672	
☐	D-AIDH	A321-231	4710	
☐	D-AIDI	A321-231	4753	
☐	D-AIDJ	A321-231	4792	
☐	D-AIDK	A321-231	4819	
☐	D-AIDL	A321-231	4881	
☐	D-AIDM	A321-231	4916	
☐	D-AIDN	A321-231	4976	
☐	D-AIDO	A321-231	4994	
☐	D-AIDP	A321-231	5049	
☐	D-AIDQ	A321-231	5028	
☐	D-AIDT	A321-231	5087	
☐	D-AIDU	A321-231	5186	
☐	D-AIDV	A321-231	5413	
☐	D-AIDW	A321-231	6415	
☐	D-AIDX	A321-231	6451	
☐	D-AIRA	A321-131	0458	
☐	D-AIRB	A321-131	0468	
☐	D-AIRC	A321-131	0473	
☐	D-AIRD	A321-131	0474	
☐	D-AIRE	A321-131	0484	
☐	D-AIRF	A321-131	0493	
☐	D-AIRH	A321-131	0412	
☐	D-AIRK	A321-131	0502	
☐	D-AIRL	A321-131	0505	
☐	D-AIRM	A321-131	0518	
☐	D-AIRN	A321-131	0560	
☐	D-AIRO	A321-131	0563	
☐	D-AIRP	A321-131	0564	
☐	D-AIRR	A321-131	0567	
☐	D-AIRS	A321-131	0595	
☐	D-AIRT	A321-131	0652	
☐	D-AIRU	A321-131	0692	
☐	D-AIRW	A321-131	0699	
☐	D-AIRX	A321-131	0887	
☐	D-AIRY	A321-131	0901	
☐	D-AISB	A321-231	1080	
☐	D-AISC	A321-231	1161	
☐	D-AISD	A321-231	1188	
☐	D-AISE	A321-231	1214	
☐	D-AISF	A321-231	1260	
☐	D-AISG	A321-231	1273	
☐	D-AISH	A321-231	3265	
☐	D-AISI	A321-231	3339	
☐	D-AISJ	A321-231	3360	
☐	D-AISK	A321-231	3387	
☐	D-AISL	A321-231	3434	
☐	D-AISN	A321-231	3592	

	Reg	Type	c/n	
☐	D-AISO	A321-231	3625	
☐	D-AISP	A321-231	3864	
☐	D-AISQ	A321-231	3936	
☐	D-AISR	A321-231	3987	
☐	D-AIST	A321-231	4005	
☐	D-AISU	A321-231	4016	
☐	D-AISV	A321-231	4047	
☐	D-AISW	A321-231	4054	
☐	D-AISX	A321-231	4073	
☐	D-AISZ	A321-231	4085	
☐	D-AIKA	A330-343E	570	
☐	D-AIKB	A330-343E	576	
☐	D-AIKC	A330-343E	579	
☐	D-AIKD	A330-343E	629	
☐	D-AIKE	A330-343E	636	
☐	D-AIKF	A330-343E	642	
☐	D-AIKG	A330-343E	645	
☐	D-AIKH	A330-343E	648	
☐	D-AIKI	A330-343E	687	
☐	D-AIKJ	A330-343E	701	
☐	D-AIKK	A330-343E	896	
☐	D-AIKL	A330-343E	905	
☐	D-AIKM	A330-343E	913	
☐	D-AIKN	A330-343E	922	
☐	D-AIKO	A330-343E	989	
☐	D-AIKP	A330-343E	1292	
☐	D-AIKQ	A330-343E	1305	
☐	D-AIKR	A330-343E	1314	
☐	D-AIKS	A330-343E	1497	
☐	D-AIFC	A340-313X	379	
☐	D-AIFD	A340-313X	390	
☐	D-AIFE	A340-313X	434	
☐	D-AIFF	A340-313X	447	
☐	D-AIGL	A340-313X	135	
☐	D-AIGM	A340-313X	158	
☐	D-AIGN	A340-313X	213	
☐	D-AIGO	A340-313X	233	
☐	D-AIGS	A340-313X	297	
☐	D-AIGT	A340-313X	304	
☐	D-AIGU	A340-313X	321	
☐	D-AIGZ	A340-313X	347	
☐	D-AIHA	A340-642	482	
☐	D-AIHB	A340-642	517	
☐	D-AIHC	A340-642	523	
☐	D-AIHD	A340-642	537	
☐	D-AIHE	A340-642	540	
☐	D-AIHF	A340-642	543	
☐	D-AIHH	A340-642	566	
☐	D-AIHI	A340-642	569	[MUC]
☐	D-AIHK	A340-642	580	
☐	D-AIHL	A340-642	583	
☐	D-AIHM	A340-642	762	
☐	D-AIHN	A340-642	763	
☐	D-AIHO	A340-642	767	
☐	D-AIHP	A340-642	771	
☐	D-AIHQ	A340-642	790	
☐	D-AIHR	A340-642	794	
☐	D-AIHS	A340-642	812	
☐	D-AIHT	A340-642	846	
☐	D-AIHU	A340-642	848	
☐	D-AIHV	A340-642	897	
☐	D-AIHW	A340-642	972	
☐	D-AIHX	A340-642	981	
☐	D-AIHY	A340-642	987	
☐	D-AIHZ	A340-642	1005	
☐	D-AIXA	A350-941	074	o/o♦
☐	D-AIXB	A350-941	080	o/o♦
☐	D-AIXC	A350-941	087	o/o♦
☐	D-AIMA	A380-841	038	
☐	D-AIMB	A380-841	041	
☐	D-AIMC	A380-841	044	
☐	D-AIMD	A380-841	048	
☐	D-AIME	A380-841	061	
☐	D-AIMF	A380-841	066	
☐	D-AIMG	A380-841	069	
☐	D-AIMH	A380-841	070	
☐	D-AIMI	A380-841	072	
☐	D-AIMJ	A380-841	073	
☐	D-AIMK	A380-841	146	
☐	D-AIML	A380-841	149	
☐	D-AIMM	A380-841	175	
☐	D-AIMN	A380-841	177	
☐	D-ABEB	B737-330	25148/2077	std
☐	D-ABEC	B737-330	25149/2081	
☐	D-ABED	B737-330	25215/2082	
☐	D-ABEE	B737-330	25216/2084	
☐	D-ABEF	B737-330	25217/2094	
☐	D-ABEH	B737-330	25242/2102	
☐	D-ABEK	B737-330	25414/2164	
☐	D-ABEN	B737-330	26428/2196	
☐	D-ABIN	B737-530	24938/2023	std
☐	D-ABIW	B737-530	24945/2063	std
☐	D-ABTK	B747-430	29871/1293	
☐	D-ABTL	B747-430	29872/1299	
☐	D-ABVM	B747-430	29101/1143	
☐	D-ABVO	B747-430	28086/1080	
☐	D-ABVP	B747-430	28284/1103	
☐	D-ABVR	B747-430	28285/1106	
☐	D-ABVS	B747-430	28286/1109	
☐	D-ABVT	B747-430	28287/1110	
☐	D-ABVU	B747-430	29492/1191	
☐	D-ABVW	B747-430	29493/1205	
☐	D-ABVX	B747-430	29868/1237	
☐	D-ABVY	B747-430	29869/1261	
☐	D-ABVZ	B747-430	29870/1264	
☐	D-ABYA	B747-830	37827/1443	
☐	D-ABYC	B747-830	37828/1451	
☐	D-ABYD	B747-830	37829/1453	
☐	D-ABYF	B747-830	37830/1456	
☐	D-ABYG	B747-830	37831/1470	
☐	D-ABYH	B747-830	37832/1472	
☐	D-ABYI	B747-830	37833/1475	
☐	D-ABYJ	B747-830	37834/1477	
☐	D-ABYK	B747-830	37835/1480	
☐	D-ABYL	B747-830	37836/1492	
☐	D-ABYM	B747-830	37837/1494	
☐	D-ABYN	B747-830	37838/1497	
☐	D-ABYO	B747-830	37841/1498	
☐	D-ABYP	B747-830	37839/1500	
☐	D-ABYQ	B747-830	37840/1503	
☐	D-ABYR	B747-830	37842/1511	
☐	D-ABYS	B747-830	37843/1512	
☐	D-ABYT	B747-830	37844/1513	
☐	D-ABYU	B747-830	37845/1514	

LUFTHANSA CARGO — *LH / GEC*

	Reg	Type	c/n
☐	D-ALFA	B777-FBT	41674/1144
☐	D-ALFB	B777-FBT	41675/1156
☐	D-ALFC	B777-FBT	41676/1176
☐	D-ALFD	B777-FBT	41677/1208

	Reg	Type	C/n	Notes
☐	D-ALFE	B777-FBT	41678/1274	
☐	D-ALCA	MD-11F	48781/625	
☐	D-ALCB	MD-11F	48782/626	
☐	D-ALCC	MD-11F	48783/627	
☐	D-ALCD	MD-11F	48784/628	
☐	D-ALCE	MD-11F	48785/629	
☐	D-ALCF	MD-11F	48798/637	
☐	D-ALCG	MD-11F	48799/639	[VCV]
☐	D-ALCH	MD-11F	48801/640	
☐	D-ALCI	MD-11F	48800/641	
☐	D-ALCJ	MD-11F	48802/642	
☐	D-ALCK	MD-11F	48803/643	
☐	D-ALCL	MD-11F	48804/644	
☐	D-ALCM	MD-11F	48805/645	
☐	D-ALCN	MD-11F	48806/646	
☐	D-ALCP	MD-11F	48414/491	[TUL]

LUFTHANSA CITYLINE — *CL / CLH*

	Reg	Type	C/n	Notes
☐	D-AIFA	A340-313X	352	♦
☐	D-AIGP	A340-313X	252	♦
☐	D-AIGV	A340-313X	325	♦
☐	D-AIGW	A340-313X	327	♦
☐	D-AIGX	A340-313X	354	♦
☐	D-AIGY	A340-313X	335	♦
☐	D-ACKA	CRJ-900LR	15072	
☐	D-ACKB	CRJ-900LR	15073	
☐	D-ACKC	CRJ-900LR	15078	
☐	D-ACKD	CRJ-900LR	15080	
☐	D-ACKE	CRJ-900LR	15081	
☐	D-ACKF	CRJ-900LR	15083	
☐	D-ACKG	CRJ-900LR	15084	
☐	D-ACKH	CRJ-900LR	15085	
☐	D-ACKI	CRJ-900LR	15088	
☐	D-ACKJ	CRJ-900LR	15089	
☐	D-ACKK	CRJ-900LR	15094	
☐	D-ACKL	CRJ-900LR	15095	
☐	D-AEBB	ERJ-195LR	19000316	
☐	D-AEBC	ERJ-195LR	19000320	
☐	D-AEBD	ERJ-195LR	19000324	
☐	D-AEBE	ERJ-195LR	19000350	
☐	D-AEBG	ERJ-195LR	19000423	
☐	D-AEBH	ERJ-195LR	19000447	[CGN]
☐	D-AEBJ	ERJ-195LR	19000486	
☐	D-AEBK	ERJ-195LR	19000500	
☐	D-AEBL	ERJ-195LR	19000507	
☐	D-AEBM	ERJ-195LR	19000523	
☐	D-AEBN	ERJ-195LR	19000532	
☐	D-AEBO	ERJ-195LR	19000542	
☐	D-AEBP	ERJ-195LR	19000553	
☐	D-AEBQ	ERJ-195LR	19000555	
☐	D-AEBR	ERJ-195LR	19000558	
☐	D-AEBS	ERJ-195LR	19000565	
☐	D-AECA	ERJ-190LR	19000327	
☐	D-AECB	ERJ-190LR	19000332	
☐	D-AECC	ERJ-190LR	19000333	
☐	D-AECD	ERJ-190LR	19000337	
☐	D-AECE	ERJ-190LR	19000341	
☐	D-AECF	ERJ-190LR	19000359	
☐	D-AECG	ERJ-190LR	19000368	
☐	D-AECH	ERJ-190LR	19000376	
☐	D-AECI	ERJ-190LR	19000381	
☐	D-AEMA	ERJ-195LR	19000290	
☐	D-AEMB	ERJ-195LR	19000297	
☐	D-AEMC	ERJ-195LR	19000300	
☐	D-AEMD	ERJ-195LR	19000305	
☐	D-AEME	ERJ-195LR	19000308	♦

See also Germanwings

NIGHTEXPRESS — *EXT*

	Reg	Type	C/n	Notes
☐	D-IEXB	Beech 99	U-70	
☐	D-CCAS	Short SD.3-60	SH3737	
☐	D-CRAS	Short SD.3-60	SH3744	

PRIVATAIR DEUTSCHLAND — *PT / PTG*

	Reg	Type	C/n	Notes
☐	D-APTA	A319-112	1263	[HAM]>
☐	D-ASPA	A319-112	1598	[HAM]>♦
☐	D-ASPB	A319-112	1625	[HAM]>♦
☐	D-ASPG	A320-214	2529	o/o♦
☐	D-APBC	B737-8BK/W	33016/1588	>SAS
☐	D-AWBB	B737-7CN/W (BBJ)	30752/451	>DLH♦

A319s to be leased to Saudia (SVA)

PRIVATE WINGS — *8W / PWF*

	Reg	Type	C/n	Notes
☐	D-BIRD	Do328-300	3180	
☐	D-BJET	Do328-300	3207	
☐	D-CATZ	Do328-110	3090	
☐	D-CAWA	Do328-110	3119	
☐	D-CDAX	Do328-110	3087	
☐	D-CITO	Do328-110	3063	
☐	D-COCA	Beech 1900D	UE-224	
☐	D-COSY	Do328-110	3072	
☐	D-CPWF	Do328-110	3112	
☐	D-CPWG	Do328-120	3012	[ISS]
☐	D-CREW	Do328-110	3113	
☐	D-CSUE	Do328-110	3019	

RHEIN-NECKAR AIR — *M2*

	Reg	Type	C/n	Notes
☐	D-CIRJ	Do328-120	3035	

SUN EXPRESS DEUTSCHLAND — *XG / SXD*

	Reg	Type	C/n	Notes
☐	D-ASXA	B737-8Z9/W	28178/222	
☐	D-ASXB	B737-8Z9/W	30420/1100	
☐	D-ASXD	B737-8AS/W	33562/1466	
☐	D-ASXE	B737-8CX/W	32365/1209	
☐	D-ASXF	B737-8AS/W	33558/1441	
☐	D-ASXG	B737-8CX/W	32366/1235	
☐	D-ASXH	B737-8CX/W	32368/1289	
☐	D-ASXI	B737-8CX/W	32367/1253	o/o♦
☐	D-ASXK	B737-86J/W	28070/106	
☐	D-ASXO	B737-8HX/W	29649/2515	
☐	D-ASXP	B737-8HX/W	29684/2539	
☐	D-ASXQ	B737-8EH/W	37596/3103	o/o♦
☐	D-ASXR	B737-8EH/W	36150/3106	o/o♦
☐	D-ASXS	B737-8AS/W	33563/1473	

TUIFLY — *X3 / HLX*

	Reg	Type	C/n	Notes
☐	D-AHXC	B737-7K5/W	34693/2260	>BER
☐	D-AHXE	B737-7K5/W	35135/2451	>BER
☐	D-AHXF	B737-7K5/W	35136/2465	>BER
☐	D-AHXG	B737-7K5/W	35140/2575	>BER
☐	D-AHXJ	B737-7K5/W	35277/2609	>BER
☐	D-ABAG	B737-86J/W	30879/871	<BER♦
☐	D-ABKI	B737-86J/W	37748/3157	♦
☐	D-AHFT	B737-8K5/W	30413/636	
☐	D-AHFV	B737-8K5/W	30415/719	
☐	D-AHFW	B737-8K5/W	30882/760	
☐	D-AHFZ	B737-8K5/W	30883/783	
☐	D-AHLK	B737-8K5/W	35143/2763	>SWG
☐	D-ASUN	B737-8BK/W	33023/1682	♦

	Reg	Type	c/n	
☐	D-ATUA	B737-8K5/W	37245/3486	
☐	D-ATUB	B737-8K5/W	37247/3497	
☐	D-ATUC	B737-8K5/W	34684/1870	
☐	D-ATUD	B737-8K5/W	34685/1901	
☐	D-ATUE	B737-8K5/W	34686/1903	
☐	D-ATUF	B737-8K5/W	34687/1907	
☐	D-ATUG	B737-8K5/W	34688/1909	
☐	D-ATUH	B737-8K5/W	34689/1935	
☐	D-ATUI	B737-8K5/W	37252/3554	
☐	D-ATUJ	B737-8K5/W	39923/4001	
☐	D-ATUK	B737-8K5/W	39094/3641	♦
☐	D-ATUL	B737-8K5/W	38820/3653	>SWG♦
☐	D-ATUM	B737-8K5/W	37240/4786	
☐	D-ATUN	B737-8K5/W	41660/5252	
☐	D-ATUO	B737-8K5/W	41661/5292	
☐	D-ATUP	B737-8K5/W	41662/5340	
☐	D-ATUQ	B737-8K5/W	41663/5369	
☐	D-ATUR	B737-8K5/W	41664/5380	♦
☐	D-ATUZ	B737-8K5/W	34691/2246	♦
☐	D-ATYE	B767-304ER/W	28979/691	>EWG♦
☐	D-ATYG	B767-304ER/W	29137/733	>CFG♦

WDL AVIATION — WE / WDL

	Reg	Type	c/n	
☐	D-ALIN	BAe146 Srs.300	E3142	[CGN]
☐	D-AMAX	BAe146 Srs.300	E3157	[CGN]
☐	D-AMGL	BAe146 Srs.200	E2055	
☐	D-AWBA	BAe146 Srs.300A	E3134	
☐	D-AWUE	BAe146 Srs.200	E2050	

DQ- FIJI

FIJI AIRWAYS — FJ / FJI

	Reg	Type	c/n	
☐	DQ-FJT	A330-243	1394	
☐	DQ-FJU	A330-243	1416	
☐	DQ-FJV	A330-243	1465	
☐	DQ-FJW	A330-343E	1692	♦
☐	DQ-FJF	B737-7X2/W	28878/96	
☐	DQ-FJG	B737-8X2/W	29968/275	
☐	DQ-FJH	B737-8X2/W	29969/339	
☐	DQ-FJM	B737-86J/W	37754/3306	
☐	DQ-FJN	B737-808/W	34969/2293	♦

FIJI LINK — FJA

	Reg	Type	c/n	
☐	DQ-FJX	ATR 72-600	1221	
☐	DQ-FJY	ATR 42-500	1014	
☐	DQ-FJZ	ATR 72-600	1146	
☐	DQ-FIE	DHC-6 Twin Otter 300	660	
☐	DQ-PSD	DHC-6 Twin Otter 300	414	
☐	DQ-PSE	DHC-6 Twin Otter 300	410	

D2- ANGOLA

AEROJET — MBC

	Reg	Type	c/n	
☐	D2-FDK	EMB.120ER	120281	
☐	D2-FDQ	An-32A	2110	
☐	D2-FET	EMB.120RT	120175	
☐	D2-FHE	BAeJetstream 41	41046	
☐	D2-FHF	BAeJetstream 41	41049	

AIR 26 LINHAS AEREAS — DCD

	Reg	Type	c/n	
☐	D2-EYN	EMB.120ER	120165	
☐	D2-EYO	EMB.120RT	120210	
☐	D2-EYP	EMB.120RT	120146	
☐	D2-EYQ	EMB.120RT	120062	
☐	D2-EYV	EMB.120RT	120145	
☐	D2-EZC	EMB.120ER	120199	
☐	D2-EZZ	EMB.120ER	120102	
☐	D2-SRA	ERJ-135EP	145155	
☐	D2-SRB	ERJ-135LR	145696	
☐	D2-SRC	ERJ-135LR	145724	

ANGOLA AIR CHARTER — AGO

	Reg	Type	c/n	
☐	D2-FCK	B727-44F	18892/148	
☐	D2-FDO	EMB.120ER	120082	
☐	D2-FDT	EMB.120RT	120081	
☐	D2-MBV	An-12BP	5343208	
☐	D2-TBI	B737-214	19681/68	

ANGOLA AIR SERVICES

	Reg	Type	c/n	
☐	ZS-NYK	BAeJetstream 41	41095	
☐	ZS-PCA	Beech 1900C	UC-138	

DIEXIM EXPRESSO

	Reg	Type	c/n	
☐	D2-FFE	EMB.120ER	120242	
☐	D2-FFP	EMB.120ER	120235	
☐	D2-FFU	EMB.120RT	120244	
☐	D2-FFW	ERJ-145MP	145360	
☐	D2-FFY	EMB.120RT	120171	

HM AIRWAYS/HELI MALONGO

	Reg	Type	c/n	
☐	D2-EEA	DHC-8-402Q	4294	Govt
☐	D2-EEB	DHC-8-402Q	4305	Govt
☐	D2-EUO	DHC-8-402Q	4312	
☐	D2-EUP	DHC-8-402Q	4315	
☐	D2-EUQ	DHC-8-402Q	4322	
☐	D2-EUR	DHC-8-402Q	4325	
☐	D2-EYU	DHC-8Q-315	645	

SJL AERONAUTICA — GGL

	Reg	Type	c/n	
☐	D2-ESN	F.27 Friendship 500RF	10610	

SONAIR — SOR

	Reg	Type	c/n	
☐	D2-EVK	Beech 1900D	UE-121	
☐	D2-EVL	Beech 1900D	UE-312	
☐	D2-EVN	Beech 1900D	UE-370	
☐	D2-EVX	Beech 1900D	UE-340	
☐	D2-EVY	Beech 1900D	UE-249	
☐	D2-EWR	Beech 1900D	UE-193	
☐	D2-EWW	Beech 1900D	UE-399	
☐	D2-EWX	Beech 1900D	UE-405	
☐	D2-EWY	Beech 1900D	UE-401	
☐	D2-FFJ	Beech 1900D	UE-412	
☐	D2-FFN	Beech 1900D	UE-329	
☐	D2-EVA	DHC-6 Twin Otter 310	728	
☐	D2-EVB	DHC-6 Twin Otter 300	810	
☐	D2-EVC	DHC-6 Twin Otter 300	809	
☐	D2-EVH	DHC-6 Twin Otter 300	511	
☐	D2-FVM	DHC-6 Twin Otter 300	794	
☐	D2-FVN	DHC-6 Twin Otter 300	817	
☐	D2-FVO	DHC-6 Twin Otter 300	821	
☐	D2-FVP	DHC-6 Twin Otter 300	743	
☐	D2-FVQ	DHC-6 Twin Otter 310	704	
☐	D2-ESU	B727-23F	19431/372	[LAD]
☐	D2-EVW	B737-7HB/W	35954/2310	
☐	D2-EWS	B737-7HBC/W	35956/2736	
☐	N263SG	B747-481	29263/1204	<GTI
☐	N322SG	B747-481	30322/1250	<GTI♦

TAAG ANGOLA AIRLINES			*DT / DTA*
☐ D2-TBC	B737-2M2C	21173/447	
☐ D2-TBF	B737-7M2/W	34559/2013	
☐ D2-TBG	B737-7M2/W	34560/2036	
☐ D2-TBH	B737-7M2/W	34561/2043	
☐ D2-TBJ	B737-7M2/W	34562/2149	
☐ D2-TBK	B737-7HBC/W	35955/2531	
☐ D2-TBO	B737-2M2	22776/891	
☐ D2-TBX	B737-2M2	23351/1117	
☐ D2-TEA	B747-312M	23410/653	[JNB]
☐ D2-TEB	B747-357M	23751/686	[JNB]
☐ D2-TED	B777-2M2ER	34565/581	
☐ D2-TEE	B777-2M2ER	34566/587	
☐ D2-TEF	B777-2M2ER	34567/687	
☐ D2-TEG	B777-3M2ER	40805/935	
☐ D2-TEH	B777-3M2ER	40806/944	
☐ D2-TEI	B777-3M2ER	43252/1198	
☐ D2-TEJ	B777-3M2ER	43253/1356	o/o♦
☐ D2-	B777-3M2ER		o/o♦

D4- CAPE VERDE ISLANDS

BINTER CABO VERDE			
☐ D4-	ATR 72-600		o/o♦
☐ D4-	ATR 72-600		o/o♦

CABO VERDE EXPRESS			*CVE*
☐ D4-CBL	LET L-410UVP-10	902511	
☐ D4-CBR	LET L-410UVP-10	912533	
☐ D4-JCA	LET L-410UVP-20	912604	

SMARTLYNX CABO VERDE			*LCV*
☐ D4-CBZ	A320-211	0359	♦

TACV CABO VERDE AIRLINES			*VR / TCV*
☐ D4-CBP	B757-2Q8	30045/957	
☐ D4-CBT	ATR 72-212A	747	
☐ D4-CBU	ATR 72-212A	755	
☐ D4-CBV	ATR 42-512	669	
☐ D4-CBX	B737-8Q8/W	30039/701	
☐ OM-GTA	B737-4Q8	24332/1866	<RLX

D6- COMORO ISLANDS

COMORES AVIATION INTERNATIONAL			*O5 / KMZ*
☐ D6-CAL	LET L-410UVP	800526	
☐ D6-CAM	LET L-410UVP	851336	
☐ D6-CAN	LET L-410UVP	841331	

EC- SPAIN

AERONOVA			*OV / OVA*
☐ EC-IDG	ATR 42-320	003	
☐ OY-CHT	ATR 42-300	080	<DNM♦
☐ EC-GUS	SA.227AC Metro III	AC-648	
☐ EC-GVE	SA.227AC Metro III	AC-669B	
☐ EC-HCH	SA.227AC Metro III	AC-658B	
☐ EC-HZH	SA.227AC Metro III	AC-720	
☐ EC-IXL	SA.227AC Metro III	AC-689B	
☐ EC-JCU	SA.227AC Metro III	AC-679B	

To be renamed Air Europa Express and operate Air Europa's ERJ-195s & its own ATR 42s.

AIR EUROPA			*UX / AEA*
☐ EC-JPF	A330-202	733	
☐ EC-JQG	A330-202	745	
☐ EC-JQQ	A330-202	749	
☐ EC-JZL	A330-202	814	
☐ EC-KOM	A330-202	931	
☐ EC-KTG	A330-202	950	
☐ EC-LMN	A330-243	597	
☐ EC-LNH	A330-243	551	
☐ EC-LQO	A330-243	505	
☐ EC-LQP	A330-243	526	
☐ EC-LVL	A330-243	461	
☐ EC-LXA	A330-343E	670	
☐ EC-LXR	A330-343E	1097	
☐ EC-MAJ	A330-243	992	
☐ EC-MHL	A330-343E	1574	♦
☐ EC-MIN	A330-343E	1607	♦
☐ EC-MIO	A330-343E	1624	♦
☐ EC-KVI	ATR 72-212A	824	<SWT♦
☐ EC-LHV	ATR 72-202	416	<SWT♦
☐ EC-LST	ATR 72-201	234	<SWT
☐ EC-LYJ	ATR 72-212A	468	<SWT♦
☐ EC-MAF	ATR 72-212A	568	<SWT
☐ EC-IDA	B737-86Q/W	32773/1051	
☐ EC-IDT	B737-86Q/W	30281/1076	
☐ EC-III	B737-86Q/W	30284/1233	
☐ EC-ISN	B737-86Q/W	30291/1435	
☐ EC-JAP	B737-85P/W	33971/1580	
☐ EC-JBJ	B737-85P/W	33972/1598	
☐ EC-JBK	B737-85P/W	33973/1606	
☐ EC-JBL	B737-85P/W	33974/1610	
☐ EC-JHK	B737-85P/W	33975/1716	
☐ EC-JHL	B737-85P/W	33976/1740	
☐ EC-JNF	B737-85P/W	33977/1878	
☐ EC-KCG	B737-85P/W	33981/2269	
☐ EC-LPQ	B737-85P/W	35496/4015	
☐ EC-LPR	B737-85P/W	36588/3989	
☐ EC-LQX	B737-85P/W	36589/4116	
☐ EC-LTM	B737-85P/W	36591/4305	
☐ EC-LUT	B737-85P/W	36592/4434	
☐ EC-LVR	B737-85P/W	36593/4538	
☐ EC-LXV	B737-85P/W	36594/4666	
☐ EC-LYR	B737-85P/W	36595/4735	
☐ EC-MJU	B737-85P/W	60584	o/o♦
☐ EC-	B737-85P/W		o/o
☐ EC-	B737-85P/W		o/o
☐ EC-	B737-85P/W		o/o
☐ EC-	B737-85P/W		o/o
☐ EC-	B737-85P/W		o/o
☐ EC-	B737-85P/W		o/o♦
☐ EC-	B737-85P/W		o/o♦
☐ EC-	B787-8	36412/397	♦
☐ EC-	B787-8	36423/437	♦
☐ EC-	B787-8	36414/482	♦
☐ EC-	B787-8	36415/505	♦
☐ EC-	B787-8	36416/508	♦
☐ SP-LRF	B787-8	35942/161	<LOT♦
☐ EC-KSS	ERJ-145MP	145230	<PVG
☐ EC-KRJ	ERJ-195LR	19000196	
☐ EC-KXD	ERJ-195LR	19000244	

	Reg	Type	c/n	Notes
☐	EC-KYO	ERJ-195LR	19000276	
☐	EC-KYP	ERJ-195LR	19000281	
☐	EC-LCQ	ERJ-195LR	19000303	
☐	EC-LEK	ERJ-195LR	19000344	
☐	EC-LFZ	ERJ-195LR	19000357	
☐	EC-LIN	ERJ-195LR	19000401	
☐	EC-LKM	ERJ-195LR	19000425	
☐	EC-LKX	ERJ-195LR	19000437	
☐	EC-LLR	ERJ-195LR	19000452	

AIR HORIZONT — *HAT*

	Reg	Type	c/n	Notes
☐	9H-ZAZ	B737-436	25349/2156	♦

AIR NOSTRUM — *YW / ANE*

	Reg	Type	c/n	Notes
☐	EC-LQV	ATR 72-600	995	
☐	EC-LRH	ATR 72-600	999	
☐	EC-LRR	ATR 72-600	1023	
☐	EC-LRU	ATR 72-600	1032	
☐	EC-LSQ	ATR 72-600	1041	
☐	EC-	ATR 72-600		o/o
☐	EC-	ATR 72-600		o/o
☐	EC-	ATR 72-600		o/o
☐	EC-	ATR 72-600		o/o
☐	EC-	ATR 72-600		o/o
☐	EC-GYI	CRJ-200ER	7249	
☐	EC-GZA	CRJ-200ER	7252	
☐	EC-HEK	CRJ-200ER	7320	
☐	EC-HHI	CRJ-200ER	7343	
☐	EC-HPR	CRJ-200ER	7430	
☐	EC-HZR	CRJ-200ER	7547	[SGD]
☐	EC-IJS	CRJ-200ER	7706	[LJU]
☐	EC-JNX	CRJ-200ER	8058	
☐	EC-JOD	CRJ-200ER	8061	
☐	EC-JOY	CRJ-200ER	8064	
☐	EC-MJE	CRJ-200ER	7622	std♦
☐	EC-MJX	CRJ-200ER	7466	[ASU]♦
☐	EC-MJY	CRJ-200ER	7915	[ROS]♦
☐	EC-MJZ	CRJ-200ER	7975	[ROS]♦
☐	EC-JNB	CRJ-900ER	15057	
☐	EC-JTS	CRJ-900ER	15071	
☐	EC-JTT	CRJ-900ER	15074	
☐	EC-JTU	CRJ-900ER	15079	
☐	EC-JXZ	CRJ-900ER	15087	
☐	EC-JYA	CRJ-900ER	15090	
☐	EC-JYV	CRJ-900ER	15106	
☐	EC-JZS	CRJ-900ER	15111	
☐	EC-JZT	CRJ-900ER	15113	
☐	EC-JZU	CRJ-900ER	15115	
☐	EC-JZV	CRJ-900ER	15117	>SAS
☐	EC-MEN	CRJ-900ER	15063	>IBB
☐	EC-MFC	CRJ-900ER	15065	>IBB
☐	EC-LJR	CRJ-1000EE	19002	
☐	EC-LJS	CRJ-1000EE	19003	
☐	EC-LJT	CRJ-1000EE	19005	
☐	EC-LJX	CRJ-1000EE	19008	
☐	EC-LKF	CRJ-1000EE	19011	
☐	EC-LOJ	CRJ-1000EE	19018	
☐	EC-LOV	CRJ-1000EE	19019	
☐	EC-LOX	CRJ-1000EE	19020	
☐	EC-LPG	CRJ-1000EE	19021	
☐	EC-LPN	CRJ-1000EE	19022	
☐	EC-MJO	CRJ-1000EE	19045	o/o♦
☐	EC-MJP	CRJ-1000EE	19046	o/o♦
☐	EC-MJQ	CRJ-1000EE	19047	o/o♦
☐	EC-	CRJ-1000EE		o/o
☐	EC-	CRJ-1000EE		o/o
☐	EC-	CRJ-1000EE		o/o
☐	EC-	CRJ-1000EE		o/o
☐	EC-	CRJ-1000EE		o/o
☐	EC-	CRJ-1000EE		o/o
☐	EC-	CRJ-1000EE		o/o
☐	EC-	CRJ-1000EE		o/o
☐	EC-	CRJ-1000EE		o/o
☐	EC-	CRJ-1000EE		o/o
☐	EC-	CRJ-1000EE		o/o
☐	EC-	CRJ-1000EE		o/o
☐	EC-	CRJ-1000EE		o/o
☐	EC-	CRJ-1000EE		o/o
☐	EC-	CRJ-1000EE		o/o
☐	EC-	CRJ-1000EE		o/o
☐	EC-	CRJ-1000EE		o/o

AIR PLUS ULTRA — *PU / PUE*

	Reg	Type	c/n	Notes
☐	EC-MFA	A340-313X	212	
☐	EC-MFB	A340-313X	215	[LETL]

ALBA STAR — *JQ / LAV*

	Reg	Type	c/n	Notes
☐	EC-LAV	B737-408	24352/1705	
☐	EC-LNC	B737-4K5	24130/1827	
☐	EC-LTG	B737-4K5	24129/1783	
☐	EC-MFS	B737-4Y0	25178/2199	♦

BINTER CANARIAS — *NT / IBB*

	Reg	Type	c/n	Notes
☐	EC-GQF	ATR 72-202	489	>CNF
☐	EC-GRP	ATR 72-202	488	>CNF
☐	EC-GRU	ATR 72-202	493	>CNF
☐	EC-IYC	ATR 72-212A	709	^
☐	EC-IZO	ATR 72-212A	711	^
☐	EC-JBI	ATR 72-212A	713	^
☐	EC-JEH	ATR 72-212A	716	^
☐	EC-JEV	ATR 72-212A	717	^
☐	EC-JQL	ATR 72-212A	726	
☐	EC-KGI	ATR 72-212A	752	^
☐	EC-KGJ	ATR 72-212A	753	^
☐	EC-KRY	ATR 72-212A	795	^
☐	EC-KSG	ATR 72-212A	796	^
☐	EC-KYI	ATR 72-212A	850	^
☐	EC-LAD	ATR 72-212A	864	^
☐	EC-LFA	ATR 72-212A	902	*
☐	EC-LGF	ATR 72-212A	907	^
☐	EC-MHI	ATR 72-212A	879	♦
☐	EC-MHJ	ATR 72-212A	982	♦
☐	EC-MIF	ATR 72-600	1278	*♦
☐	EC-MJG	ATR 72-600	1310	*♦
☐	EC-	ATR 72-600		o/o
☐	EC-	ATR 72-600		o/o♦
☐	EC-MEN	CRJ-900ER	15063	<ANS♦
☐	EC-MFC	CRJ-900ER	15065	<ANS♦

^ operated by Canarias Airlines (RSC);
** operated by NAYSA Aerotaxis (ZN / NAY)*

CANARY FLY CANARIAS — *PM / CNF*

	Reg	Type	c/n	Notes
☐	EC-LYZ	ATR 42-300	226	
☐	EC-LZR	ATR 72-201	441	
☐	SX-DIP	ATR 72-202	328	<AZI♦

Also see Binter Canarias above.

CYGNUS AIR — RGN

☐	EC-FTR	B757-256(PCF)	26239/553	♦
☐	EC-KLD	B757-256(PCF)	24121/183	♦

EVELOP AIRLINES — E9 / EVE

☐	CS-TRH	A330-343E	833	<OBS
☐	EC-LZD	A320-214/S	5642	
☐	EC-MII	A330-343E	1691	♦

IBERIA — IB / IBE

☐	EC-HGR	A319-111	1154	
☐	EC-HKO	A319-111	1362	
☐	EC-JAZ	A319-111	2264	
☐	EC-JDL	A319-111	2365	
☐	EC-JEI	A319-111	2311	
☐	EC-JXJ	A319-111	2889	♦
☐	EC-KBX	A319-111	3078	
☐	EC-KHM	A319-111	3209	
☐	EC-KKS	A319-111	3320	
☐	EC-KMD	A319-111	3380	
☐	EC-KOY	A319-111	3443	
☐	EC-KUB	A319-111	3651	
☐	EC-LEI	A319-111	3744	
☐	EC-MFO	A319-111	0938	♦
☐	EC-MFP	A319-111	0998	♦
☐	EC-IEF	A320-214	1655	
☐	EC-IEG	A320-214	1674	
☐	EC-ILR	A320-214	1793	
☐	EC-ILS	A320-214	1809	
☐	EC-IZH	A320-214	2225	
☐	EC-IZR	A320-214	2242	
☐	EC-JFN	A320-214	2391	
☐	EC-LRG	A320-214	1516	♦
☐	EC-LUL	A320-216/S	5486	
☐	EC-LVD	A320-216	5570	
☐	EC-LXQ	A320-216/S	5692	
☐	EC-MCS	A320-214/S	6244	
☐	EC-MDK	A320-214/S	6328	
☐	EC-HUH	A321-211	1021	
☐	EC-HUI	A321-211	1027	
☐	EC-IGK	A321-211	1572	
☐	EC-IJN	A321-211	1836	
☐	EC-ILO	A321-211	1681	
☐	EC-ILP	A321-211	1716	
☐	EC-ITN	A321-211	2115	
☐	EC-IXD	A321-211	2220	
☐	EC-JDM	A321-211	2357	
☐	EC-JDR	A321-211	2488	
☐	EC-JGS	A321-211	2472	
☐	EC-JLI	A321-211	2563	
☐	EC-JNI	A321-211	2270	
☐	EC-JQZ	A321-211	2736	
☐	EC-JRE	A321-211	2756	
☐	EC-JZM	A321-211	2996	
☐	EC-LUB	A330-302	1377	
☐	EC-LUK	A330-302	1385	
☐	EC-LUX	A330-302	1405	
☐	EC-LXK	A330-302	1426	
☐	EC-LYF	A330-302	1437	
☐	EC-LZJ	A330-302	1490	
☐	EC-LZX	A330-302	1507	
☐	EC-MAA	A330-302	1515	
☐	EC-MIL	A330-202	1694	♦
☐	EC-MJA	A330-202	1700	♦
☐	EC-	A330-202	1710	o/o♦
☐	EC-	A330-202	1719	o/o♦
☐	EC-	A330-202	1728	o/o♦
☐	EC-	A330-202	1736	o/o♦
☐	EC-	A330-202	1740	o/o♦
☐	EC-	A330-202	1747	o/o♦
☐	EC-GGS	A340-313	125	[MAD]
☐	EC-GHX	A340-313	134	
☐	EC-GJT	A340-313	145	
☐	EC-GLE	A340-313	146	
☐	EC-GUP	A340-313X	217	
☐	EC-GUQ	A340-313X	221	
☐	EC-HGV	A340-313X	329	
☐	EC-INO	A340-642	431	
☐	EC-IOB	A340-642	440	
☐	EC-IQR	A340-642	460	
☐	EC-IZX	A340-642	601	
☐	EC-IZY	A340-642	604	
☐	EC-JBA	A340-642	606	
☐	EC-JCY	A340-642	617	
☐	EC-JCZ	A340-642	619	
☐	EC-JFX	A340-642	672	
☐	EC-JLE	A340-642	702	
☐	EC-JNQ	A340-642	727	
☐	EC-JPU	A340-642	744	
☐	EC-KZI	A340-642	1017	
☐	EC-LCZ	A340-642	993	
☐	EC-LEU	A340-642	960	
☐	EC-LEV	A340-642	1079	
☐	EC-LFS	A340-642	1122	

IBERIA EXPRESS — I2 / IBS

☐	EC-FDB	A320-211	0173	[MAD]
☐	EC-FGR	A320-211	0224	[MAD]
☐	EC-FGV	A320-211	0207	[MAD]
☐	EC-FLP	A320-211	0266	[MAD]
☐	EC-FQY	A320-211	0356	[MAD]
☐	EC-ILQ	A320-214	1736	♦
☐	EC-JFG	A320-214	2143	
☐	EC-JFH	A320-214	2104	
☐	EC-JSK	A320-214	2807	
☐	EC-KOH	A320-214	2248	
☐	EC-LEA	A320-214	1099	
☐	EC-LKG	A320-214	1047	
☐	EC-LKH	A320-214	1101	
☐	EC-LLE	A320-214	1119	
☐	EC-LUC	A320-214	1059	
☐	EC-LUD	A320-214	1067	
☐	EC-LUS	A320-216/S	5501	
☐	EC-LVQ	A320-216/S	5590	
☐	EC-LYE	A320-216/S	5729	
☐	EC-LYM	A320-216/S	5815	
☐	EC-MBU	A320-214	1198	
☐	EC-MCB	A320-214	1125	
☐	EC-MEG	A320-214	1439	
☐	EC-MEH	A320-214	1450	
☐	EC-JEJ	A321-211	2381	♦

IBERTRANS AEREA — IBT

☐	EC-GQA	EMB.120RT(F)	120027	

NAYSA AEROTAXIS — ZN / NAY

See Binter Canarias

PAN AIR LINEAS AEREAS			PV / PNR
☐ EC-ELT	BAe146 Srs.200QT	E2102	[BRU]
☐ EC-FZE	BAe146 Srs.200QT	E2105	
☐ EC-GQO	BAe146 Srs.200QT	E2086	[YSU]
☐ EC-LMR	BAe146 Srs.300QT	E3151	
☐ EC-LOF	BAe146 Srs.300QT	E3150	
☐ EC-MCK	BAe146 Srs.300QT	E3153	
☐ EC-MCL	BAe146 Srs.300QT	E3154	[EGBP]
☐ EC-MEO	BAe146 Srs.300QT	E3186	
☐ EC-MFT	BAe146 Srs.300QT	E3182	♦
☐ EC-MHR	BAe146 Srs.300QT	E3166	♦
☐ EC-MID	BAe146 Srs.300QT	E3168	♦

Operates for TNT Airways, Belgium.

PRIVILEGE STYLE			P6 / PVG
☐ EC-HDS	B757-256	26252/900	>KNE
☐ EC-ISY	B757-256	26241/572	
☐ EC-KSS	ERJ-145MP	145230	>AEA
☐ EC-LZO	B767-35DER	27902/577	>ELY
☐ EC-MIA	B777-28EER	28685/400	>ELY♦

SERAIR			SEV
☐ EC-GTM	Beech 1900C	UB-30	
☐ EC-GUD	Beech 1900C-1	UC-156	
☐ EC-GZG	Beech 1900C-1	UC-161	
☐ EC-JDY	Beech 1900C-1	UC-91	

SWIFTAIR			7J / SWT
☐ EC-INV	ATR 72-201	274	
☐ EC-ISX	ATR 42-320	242	
☐ EC-IVP	ATR 42-300	231	
☐ EC-IYH	ATR 72-212	330	
☐ EC-JAD	ATR 42-300	321	
☐ EC-JBN	ATR 42-300(QC)	218	
☐ EC-JBX	ATR 42-300	254	
☐ EC-JQF	ATR 72-201F	147	
☐ EC-JRP	ATR 72-212	446	
☐ EC-JXF	ATR 72-201F	150	
☐ EC-KAD	ATR 72-202F	171	
☐ EC-KAI	ATR 42-300F	141	
☐ EC-KIZ	ATR 72-202F	204	
☐ EC-KJA	ATR 72-202F	207	
☐ EC-KKQ	ATR 72-212A	763	>UN
☐ EC-KUL	ATR 72-212A	809	>UN
☐ EC-KVI	ATR 72-212A	824	>AEA
☐ EC-LHV	ATR 72-202	416	>AEA
☐ EC-LSN	ATR 72-202	192	
☐ EC-LST	ATR 72-201	234	>AEA
☐ EC-LYB	ATR 72-212A	550	
☐ EC-LYJ	ATR 72-212A	468	>AEA
☐ EC-MAF	ATR 72-212A	568	>AEA
☐ EC-MEC	ATR 72-212A	595	
☐ EC-MIY	ATR 72-212A	498	>IKM♦
☐ EC-MKE	ATR 72-212A	494	[MAD]
☐ EC-	ATR 72-202F	411	o/o♦
☐ EC-KLR	B737-3Q8(SF)	23766/1375	
☐ EC-LAC	B737-3M8F	24022/1662	
☐ EC-LJI	B737-301(SF)	23512/1291	
☐ EC-MAD	B737-4YO(SF)	25261/2258	
☐ EC-MCI	B737-4Q8(SF)	26298/2564	
☐ EC-MEY	B737-476(F)	24438/2171	
☐ EC-MFE	B737-476(F)	24445/2539	♦
☐ EC-MIE	B737-4YO(SF)	26069/2352	♦
☐ EC-HAK	EMB.120RT	120008	
☐ EC-HCF	EMB.120RT	120007	
☐ EC-HFK	EMB.120RT	120063	
☐ EC-HMY	EMB.120RT	120009	
☐ EC-HTS	EMB.120RT	120168	
☐ EC-IMX	EMB.120ER	120158	
☐ EC-JBD	EMB.120RT	120012	
☐ EC-JBE	EMB.120RT	120013	
☐ EC-JKH	EMB.120RT	120092	
☐ EC-KSF	MD-87	53207/1862	[PGF]♦

VOLOTEA AIRLINES			V7 / VOE
☐ EI-FML	A319-111	2240	o/o♦
☐ EI-FMT	A319-112	2113	♦
☐ EI-FMU	A319-112	2122	♦
☐ EI-FMY	A319-111	2253	♦
☐ EC-LPM	B717-2BL	55185/5145	
☐ EC-MEZ	B717-23S	55059/5023	
☐ EC-MFJ	B717-2CM	55060/5026	♦
☐ EC-MGS	B717-2CM	55061/5029	♦
☐ EC-MGT	B717-23S	55066/5054	♦
☐ EI-EWI	B717-2BL	55170/5120	
☐ EI-EWJ	B717-2BL	55171/5121	
☐ EI-EXA	B717-2BL	55172/5122	
☐ EI-EXB	B717-2BL	55173/5123	
☐ EI-EXI	B717-2BL	55174/5124	
☐ EI-EXJ	B717-2BL	55176/5126	
☐ EI-FBJ	B717-2BL	55177/5127	
☐ EI-FBK	B717-2BL	55182/5138	
☐ EI-FBL	B717-2BL	55183/5140	
☐ EI-FBM	B717-2BL	55192/5152	
☐ EI-FCB	B717-2BL	55191/5151	
☐ EI-FCU	B717-2BL	55190/5149	
☐ EI-FGH	B717-2BL	55169/5119	
☐ EI-FGI	B717-2BL	55167/5117	

VUELING AIRLINES			VY / VLG
☐ EC-JVE	A319-111	2843	
☐ EC-JXV	A319-111	2897	
☐ EC-LRS	A319-112	3704	[MAD]
☐ EC-LRZ	A319-112	3700	[MPL]
☐ EC-MGF	A319-111	3028	♦
☐ EC-MIQ	A319-111	3169	♦
☐ EC-MIR	A319-111	3377	♦
☐ EC-HGZ	A320-214	1208	
☐ EC-HHA	A320-214	1221	
☐ EC-HQI	A320-214	1396	
☐ EC-HQJ	A320-214	1430	
☐ EC-HQL	A320-214	1461	
☐ EC-HTD	A320-214	1550	
☐ EC-IZD	A320-214	2207	
☐ EC-JFF	A320-214	2388	
☐ EC-JGM	A320-214	2407	
☐ EC-JSY	A320-214	2785	
☐ EC-JTQ	A320-214	2794	
☐ EC-JTR	A320-214	2798	
☐ EC-JYX	A320-214	2962	
☐ EC-JZI	A320-214	2988	
☐ EC-KCU	A320-216	3109	
☐ EC-KDG	A320-214	3095	
☐ EC-KDH	A320-214	3083	
☐ EC-KDT	A320-216	3145	
☐ EC-KDX	A320-216	3151	
☐ EC-KFI	A320-216	3174	
☐ EC-KHN	A320-216	3203	

	Reg	Type	c/n	
☐	EC-KJD	A320-216	3237	
☐	EC-KLB	A320-214	3321	
☐	EC-KLT	A320-216	3376	
☐	EC-KMI	A320-216	3400	
☐	EC-KRH	A320-214	3529	
☐	EC-LAA	A320-214	2678	
☐	EC-LAB	A320-214	2761	
☐	EC-LLJ	A320-214	4661	
☐	EC-LLM	A320-214	4681	
☐	EC-LML	A320-214	4742	
☐	EC-LOB	A320-214	4849	
☐	EC-LOC	A320-214	4855	
☐	EC-LOP	A320-214	4937	
☐	EC-LQJ	A320-232	1979	
☐	EC-LQK	A320-232	2589	
☐	EC-LQL	A320-232	1749	
☐	EC-LQM	A320-232	2223	
☐	EC-LQN	A320-232	2168	
☐	EC-LQZ	A320-232	1933	
☐	EC-LRA	A320-232	2479	
☐	EC-LRE	A320-232	1914	
☐	EC-LRM	A320-232	1349	
☐	EC-LRN	A320-214	3995	
☐	EC-LRY	A320-232	1862	
☐	EC-LSA	A320-214	4128	
☐	EC-LUN	A320-232	5479	
☐	EC-LUO	A320-232/S	5530	
☐	EC-LVA	A320-214	1171	
☐	EC-LVB	A320-214	1210	
☐	EC-LVC	A320-214	1372	
☐	EC-LVO	A320-214/S	5533	
☐	EC-LVP	A320-214/S	5587	
☐	EC-LVS	A320-232/S	5599	
☐	EC-LVT	A320-232/S	5612	
☐	EC-LVU	A320-214/S	5616	
☐	EC-LVV	A320-232/S	5620	
☐	EC-LVX	A320-214/S	5673	
☐	EC-LZE	A320-232/S	5885	
☐	EC-LZF	A320-232/S	5940	>PIC
☐	EC-LZM	A320-232/S	5877	>PIC
☐	EC-LZN	A320-214/S	5925	
☐	EC-LZZ	A320-214	2620	
☐	EC-MAH	A320-214/S	6039	
☐	EC-MAI	A320-214/S	6045	
☐	EC-MAN	A320-214/S	6079	
☐	EC-MAO	A320-214/S	6081	
☐	EC-MAX	A320-214	4478	
☐	EC-MBD	A320-214	3444	
☐	EC-MBE	A320-214	3476	
☐	EC-MBF	A320-214	3492	
☐	EC-MBK	A320-214	2658	
☐	EC-MBL	A320-214	3833	
☐	EC-MBM	A320-214	4463	
☐	EC-MBS	A320-232/S	6123	
☐	EC-MBT	A320-232/S	6128	
☐	EC-MBY	A320-214	4674	
☐	EC-MCU	A320-214	3907	
☐	EC-MDZ	A320-232/S	6377	
☐	EC-MEA	A320-232/S	6400	
☐	EC-MEL	A320-232/S	6450	
☐	EC-MEQ	A320-232/S	6483	
☐	EC-MER	A320-232/S	6510	
☐	EC-MES	A320-232/S	6518	
☐	EC-MFK	A320-232/S	6535	♦
☐	EC-MFL	A320-232/S	6557	♦
☐	EC-MFM	A320-232/S	6571	♦
☐	EC-MFN	A320-232/S	6594	♦
☐	EC-MGE	A320-232/S	6607	♦
☐	EC-MJB	A320-232/S	6883	♦
☐	EC-MJC	A320-232/S	6841	♦
☐	EC-	A320-232/S	7017	o/o♦
☐	EC-	A320-232/S	7026	o/o♦
☐	EC-	A320-232/S	7028	o/o♦
☐	EC-	A320-232/S	7109	o/o♦
☐	EC-	A320-232/S		o/o♦
☐	EC-	A320-232/S		o/o♦
☐	EC-	A320-232/S		o/o♦
☐	EC-	A320-232/S		o/o♦
☐	EC-	A320-232/S		o/o♦
☐	EC-	A320-232/S		o/o♦
☐	EC-MGY	A321-231/S	6638	♦
☐	EC-MGZ	A321-231/S	6660	♦
☐	EC-MHA	A321-231/S	6684	♦
☐	EC-MHB	A321-231/S	6691	♦
☐	EC-MHS	A321-231/S	6740	♦
☐	EC-MJR	A321-231/S	6933	♦
☐	EC-	A321-231/S	7105	o/o♦
☐	EC-	A321-231/S	7108	o/o♦
☐	EC-	A321-231/S	7152	o/o♦
☐	EC-	A321-231/S	7218	o/o♦

WAMOS AIR — *EB / PLM*

	Reg	Type	c/n	
☐	EC-MJS	A330-243	265	o/o♦
☐	EC-	A330-243	261	o/o♦
☐	EC-KQC	B747-412	26549/1030	
☐	EC-KSM	B747-412	27178/1015	
☐	EC-KXN	B747-4H6	25703/1025	
☐	EC-LNA	B747-446	26346/897	>VCV
☐	EC-MDS	B747-419	26910/1180	

ZOREX — *ORZ*

	Reg	Type	c/n
☐	EC-HJC	SA.226TC Metro II	TC-318
☐	EC-JYC	SA.226TC Metro II	TC-303

EI- EIRE

AER LINGUS — *EI / EIN*

	Reg	Type	c/n
☐	EI-EPT	A319-111	3054
☐	EI-EPU	A319-111	3102
☐	EI-CVA	A320-214	1242
☐	EI-CVB	A320-214	1394
☐	EI-CVC	A320-214	1443
☐	EI-DEA	A320-214	2191
☐	EI-DEB	A320-214	2206
☐	EI-DEC	A320-214	2217
☐	EI-DEE	A320-214	2250
☐	EI-DEF	A320-214	2256
☐	EI-DEG	A320-214	2272
☐	EI-DEH	A320-214	2294
☐	EI-DEI	A320-214	2374
☐	EI-DEJ	A320-214	2364
☐	EI-DEK	A320-214	2399
☐	EI-DEL	A320-214	2409
☐	EI-DEM	A320-214	2411
☐	EI-DEN	A320-214	2432
☐	EI-DEO	A320-214	2486
☐	EI-DEP	A320-214	2542
☐	EI-DER	A320-214	2583
☐	EI-DES	A320-214	2635
☐	EI-DVE	A320-214	3129
☐	EI-DVG	A320-214	3318

☐	EI-DVH	A320-214	3345	
☐	EI-DVI	A320-214	3501	
☐	EI-DVJ	A320-214	3857	
☐	EI-DVK	A320-214	4572	
☐	EI-DVL	A320-214	4678	
☐	EI-DVM	A320-214	4634	
☐	EI-DVN	A320-214	4715	
☐	EI-EDP	A320-214	3781	
☐	EI-EDS	A320-214	3755	
☐	EI-EZV	A320-214	2001	
☐	EI-EZW	A320-214	1983	
☐	EI-CPE	A321-211	0926	
☐	EI-CPG	A321-211	1023	
☐	EI-CPH	A321-211	1094	
☐	EI-DAA	A330-202	397	
☐	EI-DUO	A330-202	841	
☐	EI-DUZ	A330-302	847	
☐	EI-EAV	A330-302	985	
☐	EI-EDY	A330-302	1025	
☐	EI-ELA	A330-302E	1106	
☐	EI-EWR	A330-202	330	♦
☐	EI-LAX	A330-202	269	
☐	EI-	A330-302	1742	o/o♦
☐	EI-	A330-302	1744	o/o♦
☐	EI-CJX	B757-2Y0	26160/555	<ABRo/o♦
☐	EI-LBR	B757-2Q8/W	28167/775	<ABR
☐	EI-LBS	B757-2Q8/W	27623/792	<ABR
☐	EI-LBT	B757-2Q8/W	28170/801	<ABR

AER LINGUS REGIONAL — *EI / EIN*

Uses ATR42s and ATR72s operated by Stobart Air, listed there.

ASL AIRLINES IRELAND — *AG / ABR*

☐	EI-DGU	A300B4-622R(F)	557	♦
☐	EI-EXR	A300B4-622R(F)	677	
☐	EI-OZL	A300B4-622R(F)	717	♦
☐	EI-OZM	A300B4-622R(F)	722	♦
☐	EI-FXA	ATR 42-320F	282	>FDX
☐	EI-FXB	ATR 42-320F	243	>FDX
☐	EI-FXC	ATR 42-320F	310	>FDX
☐	EI-FXD	ATR 42-300F	273	>FDX
☐	EI-FXE	ATR 42-320F	327	>FDX
☐	EI-FXG	ATR 72-202F	224	>FDX
☐	EI-FXH	ATR 72-202F	229	>FDX
☐	EI-FXI	ATR 72-202F	294	>FDX
☐	EI-FXJ	ATR 72-202F	292	>FDX
☐	EI-FXK	ATR 72-202F	256	>FDX
☐	EI-REJ	ATR 72-202F	126	
☐	EI-SLA	ATR 42-300F	149	
☐	EI-SLF	ATR 72-202F	210	
☐	EI-SLG	ATR 72-202F	183	
☐	EI-SLH	ATR 72-202F	157	
☐	EI-SLJ	ATR 72-201	324	
☐	EI-SLK	ATR 72-212	395	
☐	EI-SLL	ATR 72-212F	387	[LFBF]♦
☐	EI-SLO	ATR 42-320F	121	♦
☐	EI-SLP	ATR 72-212	461	♦
☐	EI-SLR	ATR 72-201F	108	♦
☐	EI-SLT	ATR 72-202F	389	♦
☐	EI-SOP	ATR 72-212A	583	o/o[SGD]♦
☐	EI-STA	B737-31S	29057/2942	
☐	EI-STC	B737-476(F)	24446/2569	
☐	TF-BBD	B737-3Y0(F)	24463/1701	<BBD
☐	EI-	B737-4Y0	24917/2071	o/o♦
☐	EI-	B737-4Y0	26065/2284	o/o♦
☐	EI-	B737-4Y0(F)	25177/2176	o/o♦
☐	EI-CJX	B757-2Y0	26160/555	o/o>EIN♦
☐	EI-LBR	B757-2Q8/W	28167/775	>EIN
☐	EI-LBS	B757-2Q8/W	27623/792	>EIN
☐	EI-LBT	B757-2Q8/W	28170/801	>EIN

CITYJET — *WX / BCY*

☐	EI-RJB	Avro 146-RJ85	E2330	♦
☐	EI-RJC	Avro 146-RJ85	E2333	
☐	EI-RJD	Avro 146-RJ85	E2334	
☐	EI-RJE	Avro 146-RJ85	E2335	
☐	EI-RJF	Avro 146-RJ85	E2337	
☐	EI-RJG	Avro 146-RJ85	E2344	
☐	EI-RJH	Avro 146-RJ85	E2345	
☐	EI-RJI	Avro 146-RJ85	E2346	
☐	EI-RJN	Avro 146-RJ85	E2351	
☐	EI-RJO	Avro 146-RJ85	E2352	
☐	EI-RJR	Avro 146-RJ85	E2364	
☐	EI-RJT	Avro 146-RJ85	E2366	
☐	EI-RJU	Avro 146-RJ85	E2367	
☐	EI-RJW	Avro 146-RJ85	E2371	
☐	EI-RJX	Avro 146-RJ85	E2372	
☐	EI-RJY	Avro 146-RJ85	E2307	
☐	EI-RJZ	Avro 146-RJ85	E2326	
☐	EI-WXA	Avro 146-RJ85	E2310	
☐	EI-	CRJ-900		o/o♦
☐	EI-	CRJ-900		o/o♦
☐	EI-	CRJ-900		o/o♦
☐	EI-	CRJ-900		o/o♦
☐	EI-	Sukhoi SSJ 100-95B	95102	o/o♦
☐	EI-	Sukhoi SSJ 100-95B	95108	o/o♦
☐	EI-	Sukhoi SSJ 100-95B		o/o♦
☐	EI-	Sukhoi SSJ 100-95B		o/o♦

Operates services for Air France; see also Belgium VG/VLM; CRJ-900s to be operated for Blue 1/SAS.

RYANAIR — *FR / RYR*

☐	EI-DAC	B737-8AS/W	29938/1240	
☐	EI-DAD	B737-8AS/W	33544/1249	
☐	EI-DAE	B737-8AS/W	33545/1252	
☐	EI-DAF	B737-8AS/W	29939/1262	
☐	EI-DAG	B737-8AS/W	29940/1265	
☐	EI-DAH	B737-8AS/W	33546/1269	
☐	EI-DAI	B737-8AS/W	33547/1271	
☐	EI-DAJ	B737-8AS/W	33548/1274	
☐	EI-DAK	B737-8AS/W	33717/1310	
☐	EI-DAL	B737-8AS/W	33718/1311	[PIK]
☐	EI-DAM	B737-8AS/W	33719/1312	
☐	EI-DAN	B737-8AS/W	33549/1361	
☐	EI-DAO	B737-8AS/W	33550/1366	
☐	EI-DAP	B737-8AS/W	33551/1368	
☐	EI-DAR	B737-8AS/W	33552/1371	
☐	EI-DAS	B737-8AS/W	33553/1372	
☐	EI-DCF	B737-8AS/W	33804/1529	
☐	EI-DCG	B737-8AS/W	33805/1530	
☐	EI-DCH	B737-8AS/W	33566/1546	
☐	EI-DCI	B737-8AS/W	33567/1547	
☐	EI-DCJ	B737-8AS/W	33564/1562	
☐	EI-DCK	B737-8AS/W	33565/1563	
☐	EI-DCL	B737-8AS/W	33806/1576	
☐	EI-DCM	B737-8AS/W	33807/1578	

	Reg	Type	C/n	
☐	EI-DCN	B737-8AS/W	33808/1590	
☐	EI-DCO	B737-8AS/W	33809/1592	
☐	EI-DCP	B737-8AS/W	33810/1595	
☐	EI-DCR	B737-8AS/W	33811/1613	
☐	EI-DCW	B737-8AS/W	33568/1631	
☐	EI-DCX	B737-8AS/W	33569/1635	
☐	EI-DCY	B737-8AS/W	33570/1637	
☐	EI-DCZ	B737-8AS/W	33815/1638	
☐	EI-DHA	B737-8AS/W	33571/1642	
☐	EI-DHB	B737-8AS/W	33572/1652	
☐	EI-DHC	B737-8AS/W	33573/1655	
☐	EI-DHD	B737-8AS/W	33816/1657	
☐	EI-DHE	B737-8AS/W	33574/1658	
☐	EI-DHF	B737-8AS/W	33575/1660	
☐	EI-DHG	B737-8AS/W	33576/1670	
☐	EI-DHH	B737-8AS/W	33817/1677	
☐	EI-DHN	B737-8AS/W	33577/1782	
☐	EI-DHO	B737-8AS/W	33578/1792	
☐	EI-DHP	B737-8AS/W	33579/1794	
☐	EI-DHR	B737-8AS/W	33822/1798	
☐	EI-DHS	B737-8AS/W	33580/1807	
☐	EI-DHT	B737-8AS/W	33581/1809	
☐	EI-DHV	B737-8AS/W	33582/1811	
☐	EI-DHW	B737-8AS/W	33823/1819	
☐	EI-DHX	B737-8AS/W	33585/1824	
☐	EI-DHY	B737-8AS/W	33824/1826	
☐	EI-DHZ	B737-8AS/W	33583/1834	
☐	EI-DLB	B737-8AS/W	33584/1836	
☐	EI-DLC	B737-8AS/W	33586/1844	
☐	EI-DLD	B737-8AS/W	33825/1847	
☐	EI-DLE	B737-8AS/W	33587/1864	
☐	EI-DLF	B737-8AS/W	33588/1867	
☐	EI-DLG	B737-8AS/W	33589/1869	
☐	EI-DLH	B737-8AS/W	33590/1886	
☐	EI-DLI	B737-8AS/W	33591/1894	
☐	EI-DLJ	B737-8AS/W	34177/1899	
☐	EI-DLK	B737-8AS/W	33592/1904	
☐	EI-DLN	B737-8AS/W	33595/1926	
☐	EI-DLO	B737-8AS/W	34178/1929	
☐	EI-DLR	B737-8AS/W	33596/2057	
☐	EI-DLV	B737-8AS/W	33598/2063	
☐	EI-DLW	B737-8AS/W	33599/2078	
☐	EI-DLX	B737-8AS/W	33600/2082	
☐	EI-DLY	B737-8AS/W	33601/2088	
☐	EI-DPB	B737-8AS/W	33603/2112	
☐	EI-DPC	B737-8AS/W	33604/2120	
☐	EI-DPD	B737-8AS/W	33623/2123	
☐	EI-DPF	B737-8AS/W	33606/2158	
☐	EI-DPG	B737-8AS/W	33607/2163	
☐	EI-DPH	B737-8AS/W	33624/2168	
☐	EI-DPI	B737-8AS/W	33608/2173	
☐	EI-DPJ	B737-8AS/W	33609/2179	
☐	EI-DPK	B737-8AS/W	33610/2183	
☐	EI-DPL	B737-8AS/W	33611/2189	
☐	EI-DPM	B737-8AS/W	33640/2198	
☐	EI-DPN	B737-8AS/W	35549/2200	
☐	EI-DPO	B737-8AS/W	33612/2207	
☐	EI-DPP	B737-8AS/W	33613/2213	
☐	EI-DPR	B737-8AS/W	33614/2219	
☐	EI-DPT	B737-8AS/W	35550/2227	
☐	EI-DPV	B737-8AS/W	35551/2236	
☐	EI-DPW	B737-8AS/W	35552/2263	
☐	EI-DPX	B737-8AS/W	35553/2279	
☐	EI-DPY	B737-8AS/W	33615/2375	
☐	EI-DPZ	B737-8AS/W	33616/2376	
☐	EI-DWA	B737-8AS/W	33617/2377	
☐	EI-DWB	B737-8AS/W	36075/2382	
☐	EI-DWC	B737-8AS/W	36076/2384	
☐	EI-DWD	B737-8AS/W	33642/2389	
☐	EI-DWE	B737-8AS/W	36074/2391	
☐	EI-DWF	B737-8AS/W	33619/2396	
☐	EI-DWG	B737-8AS/W	33620/2397	
☐	EI-DWH	B737-8AS/W	33637/2408	
☐	EI-DWI	B737-8AS/W	33643/2410	
☐	EI-DWJ	B737-8AS/W	36077/2411	
☐	EI-DWK	B737-8AS/W	36078/2415	
☐	EI-DWL	B737-8AS/W	33618/2416	
☐	EI-DWM	B737-8AS/W	36080/2430	
☐	EI-DWO	B737-8AS/W	36079/2440	
☐	EI-DWP	B737-8AS/W	36082/2443	
☐	EI-DWR	B737-8AS/W	36081/2448	
☐	EI-DWS	B737-8AS/W	33625/2472	
☐	EI-DWT	B737-8AS/W	33626/2489	
☐	EI-DWV	B737-8AS/W	33627/2492	
☐	EI-DWW	B737-8AS/W	33629/2507	
☐	EI-DWX	B737-8AS/W	33630/2508	
☐	EI-DWY	B737-8AS/W	33638/2518	
☐	EI-DWZ	B737-8AS/W	33628/2520	
☐	EI-DYA	B737-8AS/W	33631/2529	
☐	EI-DYB	B737-8AS/W	33633/2542	
☐	EI-DYC	B737-8AS/W	36567/2543	
☐	EI-DYD	B737-8AS/W	33632/2544	
☐	EI-DYE	B737-8AS/W	36568/2548	
☐	EI-DYF	B737-8AS/W	36569/2549	
☐	EI-DYL	B737-8AS/W	36574/2635	
☐	EI-DYM	B737-8AS/W	36575/2636	
☐	EI-DYN	B737-8AS/W	36576/2637	
☐	EI-DYO	B737-8AS/W	33636/2728	
☐	EI-DYP	B737-8AS/W	37515/2729	
☐	EI-DYR	B737-8AS/W	37513/2734	
☐	EI-DYT	B737-8AS/W	33634/2745	[DUB]
☐	EI-DYV	B737-8AS/W	37512/2746	
☐	EI-DYW	B737-8AS/W	33635/2747	
☐	EI-DYX	B737-8AS/W	37517/2754	
☐	EI-DYY	B737-8AS/W	37521/2755	
☐	EI-DYZ	B737-8AS/W	37518/2760	
☐	EI-EBA	B737-8AS/W	37516/2761	
☐	EI-EBB	B737-8AS/W	37519/2779	[DUB]
☐	EI-EBC	B737-8AS/W	37520/2780	
☐	EI-EBD	B737-8AS/W	37522/2781	
☐	EI-EBE	B737-8AS/W	37523/2788	
☐	EI-EBF	B737-8AS/W	37524/2791	
☐	EI-EBG	B737-8AS/W	37525/2792	
☐	EI-EBH	B737-8AS/W	37526/2797	
☐	EI-EBI	B737-8AS/W	37527/2798	
☐	EI-EBK	B737-8AS/W	37528/2807	
☐	EI-EBL	B737-8AS/W	37529/2808	
☐	EI-EBM	B737-8AS/W	35002/2839	
☐	EI-EBN	B737-8AS/W	35003/2840	
☐	EI-EBO	B737-8AS/W	35004/2843	
☐	EI-EBP	B737-8AS/W	37531/2844	
☐	EI-EBR	B737-8AS/W	37530/2856	
☐	EI-EBS	B737-8AS/W	35001/2857	
☐	EI-EBT	B737-8AS/W	35000/2858	
☐	EI-EBV	B737-8AS/W	35009/2872	
☐	EI-EBW	B737-8AS/W	35010/2873	
☐	EI-EBX	B737-8AS/W	35007/2882	
☐	EI-EBY	B737-8AS/W	35006/2886	
☐	EI-EBZ	B737-8AS/W	35008/2887	
☐	EI-EFA	B737-8AS/W	35005/2892	
☐	EI-EFB	B737-8AS/W	37532/2893	
☐	EI-EFC	B737-8AS/W	35015/2901	
☐	EI-EFD	B737-8AS/W	35011/2903	
☐	EI-EFE	B737-8AS/W	37533/2905	

	Reg	Type	c/n
☐	EI-EFF	B737-8AS/W	35016/2917
☐	EI-EFG	B737-8AS/W	35014/2921
☐	EI-EFH	B737-8AS/W	35012/2923
☐	EI-EFI	B737-8AS/W	35013/2924
☐	EI-EFJ	B737-8AS/W	37536/2936
☐	EI-EFK	B737-8AS/W	37537/2948
☐	EI-EFL	B737-8AS/W	37534/2958
☐	EI-EFM	B737-8AS/W	37535/2960
☐	EI-EFN	B737-8AS/W	37538/2967
☐	EI-EFO	B737-8AS/W	37539/2978
☐	EI-EFP	B737-8AS/W	37540/2979
☐	EI-EFR	B737-8AS/W	37541/3012
☐	EI-EFS	B737-8AS/W	37542/3021
☐	EI-EFT	B737-8AS/W	37543/3023
☐	EI-EFV	B737-8AS/W	35017/3052
☐	EI-EFW	B737-8AS/W	35018/3078
☐	EI-EFX	B737-8AS/W	35019/3079
☐	EI-EFY	B737-8AS/W	35020/3084
☐	EI-EFZ	B737-8AS/W	38489/3089
☐	EI-EGA	B737-8AS/W	38490/3096
☐	EI-EGB	B737-8AS/W	38491/3097
☐	EI-EGC	B737-8AS/W	38492/3099
☐	EI-EGD	B737-8AS/W	34981/3420
☐	EI-EKA	B737-8AS/W	35022/3139
☐	EI-EKB	B737-8AS/W	38494/3141
☐	EI-EKC	B737-8AS/W	38495/3143
☐	EI-EKD	B737-8AS/W	35024/3146
☐	EI-EKE	B737-8AS/W	35023/3148
☐	EI-EKF	B737-8AS/W	35025/3152
☐	EI-EKG	B737-8AS/W	35021/3161
☐	EI-EKH	B737-8AS/W	38493/3162
☐	EI-EKI	B737-8AS/W	38496/3168
☐	EI-EKJ	B737-8AS/W	38497/3173
☐	EI-EKK	B737-8AS/W	38500/3174
☐	EI-EKL	B737-8AS/W	38498/3179
☐	EI-EKM	B737-8AS/W	38499/3181
☐	EI-EKN	B737-8AS/W	35026/3187
☐	EI-EKO	B737-8AS/W	35027/3198
☐	EI-EKP	B737-8AS/W	35028/3199
☐	EI-EKR	B737-8AS/W	38503/3202
☐	EI-EKS	B737-8AS/W	38504/3203
☐	EI-EKT	B737-8AS/W	38505/3206
☐	EI-EKV	B737-8AS/W	38507/3211
☐	EI-EKW	B737-8AS/W	38506/3220
☐	EI-EKX	B737-8AS/W	35030/3221
☐	EI-EKY	B737-8AS/W	35031/3230
☐	EI-EKZ	B737-8AS/W	38508/3234
☐	EI-EMA	B737-8AS/W	35032/3240
☐	EI-EMB	B737-8AS/W	38511/3241
☐	EI-EMC	B737-8AS/W	38510/3246
☐	EI-EMD	B737-8AS/W	38509/3248
☐	EI-EME	B737-8AS/W	35029/3254
☐	EI-EMF	B737-8AS/W	34978/3256
☐	EI-EMH	B737-8AS/W	34974/3262
☐	EI-EMI	B737-8AS/W	34979/3263
☐	EI-EMJ	B737-8AS/W	34975/3271
☐	EI-EMK	B737-8AS/W	38512/3272
☐	EI-EML	B737-8AS/W	38513/3283
☐	EI-EMM	B737-8AS/W	38514/3284
☐	EI-EMN	B737-8AS/W	38515/3286
☐	EI-EMO	B737-8AS/W	40283/3318
☐	EI-EMP	B737-8AS/W	40285/3322
☐	EI-EMR	B737-8AS/W	40284/3323
☐	EI-ENA	B737-8AS/W	34983/3416
☐	EI-ENB	B737-8AS/W	40289/3418
☐	EI-ENC	B737-8AS/W	34980/3419
☐	EI-ENE	B737-8AS/W	34976/3428
☐	EI-ENF	B737-8AS/W	35034/3451
☐	EI-ENG	B737-8AS/W	34977/3453
☐	EI-ENH	B737-8AS/W	35033/3454
☐	EI-ENI	B737-8AS/W	40300/3514
☐	EI-ENJ	B737-8AS/W	40301/3516
☐	EI-ENK	B737-8AS/W	40303/3524
☐	EI-ENL	B737-8AS/W	35037/3527
☐	EI-ENM	B737-8AS/W	35038/3528
☐	EI-ENN	B737-8AS/W	35036/3533
☐	EI-ENO	B737-8AS/W	40302/3534
☐	EI-ENP	B737-8AS/W	40304/3535
☐	EI-ENR	B737-8AS/W	35041/3538
☐	EI-ENS	B737-8AS/W	40307/3541
☐	EI-ENT	B737-8AS/W	35040/3544
☐	EI-ENV	B737-8AS/W	35039/3546
☐	EI-ENW	B737-8AS/W	40306/3551
☐	EI-ENX	B737-8AS/W	40305/3556
☐	EI-ENY	B737-8AS/W	35042/3559
☐	EI-ENZ	B737-8AS/W	40308/3561
☐	EI-EPA	B737-8AS/W	34987/3568
☐	EI-EPB	B737-8AS/W	34986/3570
☐	EI-EPC	B737-8AS/W	40312/3574
☐	EI-EPD	B737-8AS/W	40310/3578
☐	EI-EPE	B737-8AS/W	34984/3587
☐	EI-EPF	B737-8AS/W	40309/3593
☐	EI-EPG	B737-8AS/W	34985/3597
☐	EI-EPH	B737-8AS/W	40311/3599
☐	EI-ESL	B737-8AS/W	34988/3767
☐	EI-ESM	B737-8AS/W	34992/3772
☐	EI-ESN	B737-8AS/W	34991/3780
☐	EI-ESO	B737-8AS/W	34989/3787
☐	EI-ESP	B737-8AS/W	34990/3789
☐	EI-ESR	B737-8AS/W	34995/3795
☐	EI-ESS	B737-8AS/W	35043/3800
☐	EI-EST	B737-8AS/W	34994/3804
☐	EI-ESV	B737-8AS/W	34993/3814
☐	EI-ESW	B737-8AS/W	34997/3821
☐	EI-ESX	B737-8AS/W	34998/3822
☐	EI-ESY	B737-8AS/W	34999/3829
☐	EI-ESZ	B737-8AS/W	34996/3842
☐	EI-EVA	B737-8AS/W	40288/3884
☐	EI-EVB	B737-8AS/W	34982/3886
☐	EI-EVC	B737-8AS/W	40286/3905
☐	EI-EVD	B737-8AS/W	40287/3908
☐	EI-EVE	B737-8AS/W	35035/3920
☐	EI-EVF	B737-8AS/W	40291/3926
☐	EI-EVG	B737-8AS/W	40292/3928
☐	EI-EVH	B737-8AS/W	40290/3938
☐	EI-EVI	B737-8AS/W	38502/3945
☐	EI-EVJ	B737-8AS/W	38501/3953
☐	EI-EVK	B737-8AS/W	40298/3958
☐	EI-EVL	B737-8AS/W	40299/3992
☐	EI-EVM	B737-8AS/W	40296/3983
☐	EI-EVN	B737-8AS/W	40294/3992
☐	EI-EVO	B737-8AS/W	40297/4011
☐	EI-EVP	B737-8AS/W	40293/4017
☐	EI-EVR	B737-8AS/W	40295/4166
☐	EI-EVS	B737-8AS/W	40313/4169
☐	EI-EVT	B737-8AS/W	40315/4174
☐	EI-EVV	B737-8AS/W	40314/4190
☐	EI-EVW	B737-8AS/W	40318/4204
☐	EI-EVX	B737-8AS/W	40317/4211
☐	EI-EVY	B737-8AS/W	40319/4220
☐	EI-EVZ	B737-8AS/W	40316/4227
☐	EI-EXD	B737-8AS/W	40320/4240
☐	EI-EXE	B737-8AS/W	40321/4249
☐	EI-EXF	B737-8AS/W	40322/4261

	Reg	Type	c/n	
☐	EI-FEE	B737-8AS/W	44686/5072	
☐	EI-FEF	B737-8AS/W	44687/5099	
☐	EI-FEG	B737-8AS/W	44688/5111	
☐	EI-FEH	B737-8AS/W	44689/5124	
☐	EI-FEI	B737-8AS/W	44690/5147	
☐	EI-FIA	B737-8AS/W	44691/5238	
☐	EI-FIB	B737-8AS/W	44692/5257	
☐	EI-FIC	B737-8AS/W	44693/5289	
☐	EI-FID	B737-8AS/W	44694/5301	
☐	EI-FIE	B737-8AS/W	44695/5316	♦
☐	EI-FIF	B737-8AS/W	44696/5344	♦
☐	EI-FIG	B737-8AS/W	44698/5352	♦
☐	EI-FIH	B737-8AS/W	44697/5374	♦
☐	EI-FIJ	B737-8AS/W	44699/5393	♦
☐	EI-FIK	B737-8AS/W	44700/5402	♦
☐	EI-FIL	B737-8AS/W	44702/5429	♦
☐	EI-FIM	B737-8AS/W	61576/5434	♦
☐	EI-FIN	B737-8AS/W	44701/5444	♦
☐	EI-FIO	B737-8AS/W	61579/5448	♦
☐	EI-FIP	B737-8AS/W	61577/5474	♦
☐	EI-FIR	B737-8AS/W	61578/5476	♦
☐	EI-FIS	B737-8AS/W	44704/5562	♦
☐	EI-FIT	B737-8AS/W	44703/5568	♦
☐	EI-FIV	B737-8AS/W	44705/5605	♦
☐	EI-FIW	B737-8AS/W	44706/5625	♦
☐	EI-FIY	B737-8AS/W	44707/5638	♦
☐	EI-FIZ	B737-8AS/W	44709/5653	♦
☐	EI-FOA	B737-8AS/W	44708/5665	♦
☐	EI-FOB	B737-8AS/W	44710/5677	♦
☐	EI-FOC	B737-8AS/W	44714/5719	♦
☐	EI-FOD	B737-8AS/W	44715/5739	♦
☐	EI-FOE	B737-8AS/W	44713/5744	♦
☐	EI-FOF	B737-8AS/W	44716/5748	♦
☐	EI-FOG	B737-8AS/W	44711/5751	♦
☐	EI-FOH	B737-8AS/W	44717/5752	♦
☐	EI-FOI	B737-8AS/W	44712/5755	♦
☐	EI-FOJ	B737-8AS/W	44722/5761	♦
☐	EI-FOK	B737-8AS/W	44719/5779	♦
☐	EI-FOL	B737-8AS/W	61580/5782	o/o♦
☐	EI-FOM	B737-8AS/W	44720/5784	o/o♦
☐	EI-FON	B737-8AS/W	44721/5789	o/o♦
☐	EI-FOO	B737-8AS/W	44724/5792	o/o♦
☐	EI-FOP	B737-8AS/W	44723/5794	o/o♦
☐	EI-FOR	B737-8AS/W	44718/5795	o/o♦
☐	EI-FOS	B737-8AS/W	44727/5801	o/o♦
☐	EI-FOT	B737-8AS/W	44730	o/o♦
☐	EI-	B737-8AS/W		o/o♦
☐	EI-	B737-8AS/W		o/o♦
☐	EI-	B737-8AS/W		o/o♦
☐	EI-	B737-8AS/W		o/o♦
☐	EI-	B737-8AS/W		o/o♦
☐	EI-	B737-8AS/W		o/o♦
☐	EI-	B737-8AS/W		o/o♦
☐	EI-SEV	B737-73S/W	29078/187	^♦

^ standby aircraft used for crew training

STOBART AIR — RE / STK

	Reg	Type	c/n	
☐	EI-CBK	ATR 42-310	199	>EIN
☐	EI-EHH	ATR 42-300	196	>EIN
☐	EI-FAS	ATR 72-600	1083	>EIN
☐	EI-FAT	ATR 72-600	1097	>EIN
☐	EI-FAU	ATR 72-600	1098	>EIN
☐	EI-FAV	ATR 72-600	1105	>EIN
☐	EI-FAW	ATR 72-600	1122	>EIN
☐	EI-FAX	ATR 72-600	1129	>EIN
☐	EI-FCY	ATR 72-600	1139	>EIN
☐	EI-FCZ	ATR 72-600	1159	>EIN
☐	EI-FMJ	ATR 72-600	1295	>EIN♦
☐	EI-FMK	ATR 72-600	1297	>FIN♦
☐	EI-REH	ATR 72-202	260	>EIN
☐	EI-REI	ATR 72-202	267	>EIN
☐	EI-REL	ATR 72-212A	748	>BEE
☐	EI-REM	ATR 72-212A	760	

EK- ARMENIA

AIR ARMENIA CARGO — QN / ARR

	Reg	Type	c/n	
☐	EK32500	An-32B	2009	
☐	EK72928	An-72	36572060640	

SKIVA AIR

	Reg	Type	c/n	
☐	EK2809	PZL An-28	1AJ009-09	
☐	EK2815	PZL An-28	1AJ004-15	♦
☐	EK26005	An-26B	12205	♦
☐	EK32109	An-32A	2109	
☐	EK74036	An-74-200	36547098965	
☐	EK74043	An-74-200	36547098944	
☐	EK74923	An-74-200	36547096923	

SOUTH AIRLINES — STH

	Reg	Type	c/n	
☐	EK26407	An-26	6407	
☐	EK26818	An-26B-100	14101	
☐	EK26819	An-26	4507	
☐	EK26878	An-26	8302	
☐	EK32703	An-32A	1703	
☐	EK32709	An-32A	1709?	
☐	EK72101	An-72-100	36572040548	
☐	EK72903	An-72	36572020385	
☐	EK74045	An-74-200	36547098966	
☐	EK73755	B737-229C	21139/437	
☐	EK74786	B747-281F	25171/886	♦
☐	EK74787	B747-281F	24576/818	♦

TARON AVIA — TRV

	Reg	Type	c/n	
☐	EK73772	B737-55S	28472/3004	>BDR♦
☐	EK73775	B737-55S	28475/3096	>BDR♦
☐	EK73797	B737-505	26297/2578	♦

EP- IRAN

ATA AIR — I3 / TBZ

	Reg	Type	c/n	
☐	EP-TAB	A320-231	0362	
☐	EP-TAC	A320-231	0405	
☐	EP-TAD	A320-231	0361	
☐	EP-TAF	B737-332	25995/2455	♦
☐	EP-	B737-332	25994/2439	o/o♦
☐	EP-TAM	MD-83	53465/2093	
☐	EP-TAN	MD-83	53520/2137	
☐	EP-TAP	MD-83	53466/2101	
☐	EP-TAQ	MD-83	53488/2134	
☐	EP-TAR	MD-83	53198/1847	
☐	EP-TAS	MD-83	49986/1842	

ATRAK AIR — ATR

	Reg	Type	c/n	
☐	EP-TTA	A320-231	0393	
☐	EP-TTB	A320-231	0314	
☐	EP-TTC	A320-231	0373	o/o♦

CASPIAN AIRLINES — RV / CPN

	Reg.	Type	C/n	Notes
☐	UR-COK	B737-31S	29055/2923	<KHO♦
☐	EP-CAP	B737-4H6	26466/2372	♦
☐	EP-CAQ	B737-4H6	?	♦
☐	EP-CAR	B737-4H6	26451/2496	♦
☐		B737-4H6	26467/2378	o/o♦
☐	EP-CQA	B747-2J9F	21507/340	
☐	EP-CQB	B747-131F	19667/5	
☐	EP-CPD	MD-83	53188/2119	
☐	EP-CPU	MD-82	53223/2081	
☐	EP-CPV	MD-83	49938/1785	
☐	EP-CPX	MD-83	53463/2089	
☐	EP-CPZ	MD-83	53464/2091	

IRAN AIR — IR / IRA

	Reg.	Type	C/n	Notes
☐	EP-IBA	A300B4-605R	723	
☐	EP-IBB	A300B4-605R	727	
☐	EP-IBC	A300B4-605R	632	
☐	EP-IBD	A300B4-605R	696	
☐	EP-IBG	A300B4-203F	299	
☐	EP-IBH	A300B4-203F	302	
☐	EP-IBI	A300B4-2C	151	
☐	EP-IBJ	A300B4-2C	256	[THR]
☐	EP-IBS	A300B2-203	080	
☐	EP-IBT	A300B2-203	185	[THR]
☐	EP-IBZ	A300B2-203	226	[THR]
☐	EP-ICE	A300B4-203F	139	
☐	EP-ICF	A300B4-203F	173	
☐	EP-IBK	A310-304	671	
☐	EP-IBL	A310-304	436	
☐	EP-IBN	A310-203	375	[IKA]
☐	EP-IBP	A310-203	370	[THR]
☐	EP-IBQ	A310-203	389	[THR]
☐	EP-IEB	A320-232	0575	
☐	EP-IEC	A320-232	0857	
☐	EP-IED	A320-212	0345	
☐	EP-IEE	A320-211	0303	
☐	EP-IEF	A320-211	0312	
☐	EP-IEG	A320-211	2054	
☐	EP-IRR	B727-286	20946/1052	[THR]
☐	EP-IRS	B727-286	20947/1070	[THR]
☐	EP-IRT	B727-286	21078/1114	[THR]
☐	EP-IAB	B747-SP86	20999/278	[THR]
☐	EP-IAC	B747-SP86	21093/307	
☐	EP-IAD	B747-SP86	21758/371	[THR]
☐	EP-IAG	B747-286M	21217/291	[THR]
☐	EP-IAH	B747-286M	21218/300	[THR]
☐	EP-IAI	B747-230M	22670/550	
☐	EP-ICD	B747-21AC	24134/712	
☐	EP-CFD	Fokker 100	11442	[THR]
☐	EP-CFE	Fokker 100	11422	[THR]
☐	EP-CFH	Fokker 100	11443	[THR]
☐	EP-CFI	Fokker 100	11511	[THR]
☐	EP-CFJ	Fokker 100	11516	[THR]
☐	EP-CFK	Fokker 100	11518	[THR]
☐	EP-CFL	Fokker 100	11343	[THR]
☐	EP-CFM	Fokker 100	11394	
☐	EP-CFO	Fokker 100	11389	[THR]
☐	EP-CFP	Fokker 100	11409	[THR]
☐	EP-CFQ	Fokker 100	11429	
☐	EP-CFR	Fokker 100	11383	
☐	EP-IDA	Fokker 100	11292	[THR]
☐	EP-IDD	Fokker 100	11294	[THR]
☐	EP-IDF	Fokker 100	11298	[THR]
☐	EP-IDG	Fokker 100	11302	
☐	UR-BXI	MD-82	53170/2065	<BKV
☐	UR-CHW	MD-82	49510/1514	<BKV
☐	UR-CHX	MD-82	53162/2010	<BKV

IRAN AIR TOURS AIRLINE — B9 / IRB

	Reg.	Type	C/n	Notes
☐	EP-MDC	MD-82	49524/1746	
☐	EP-MDD	MD-82	49852/1959	
☐	EP-MDE	MD-82	49523/1724	
☐	EP-MDF	MD-83	53184/2088	
☐	EP-MDG	MD-82	53232/2108	
☐	UR-BXL	MD-82	49512/1548	<BKV [MHD]
☐	UR-BXM	MD-82	49505/1381	<BKV
☐	UR-CGS	MD-82	49425/1240	<BKV
☐	UR-CHZ	MD-82	53169/2063	<BKV
☐	UR-CJQ	MD-82	49502/1300	<BKV
☐	UR-CJZ	MD-82	49506/1400	<BKV
☐	UR-CKN	MD-83	53186/2092	<UKM

IRAN ASEMAN AIRLINES — EP / IRC

	Reg.	Type	C/n	Notes
☐	EP-APE	A320-231	0414	
☐	EP-APF	A320-231	0354	
☐	EP-APG	A320-231	0480	♦
☐	EP-APA	A340-311	002	
☐	EP-ATA	ATR 72-212	334	
☐	EP-ATH	ATR 72-212	339	
☐	EP-ATS	ATR 72-212	391	
☐	EP-ATU	ATR 72-212A	697	
☐	EP-ATX	ATR 72-212A	573	
☐	EP-ATZ	ATR 72-212	398	
☐	EP-ASA	B727-228	22081/1594	
☐	EP-ASB	B727-228	22082/1603	
☐	EP-ASD	B727-228	22085/1665	
☐	EP-APO	B737-4H6	26443/2272	♦
☐	EP-APP	B737-4H6	26464/2340	♦
☐	EP-ASG	Fokker 100	11438	
☐	EP-ASI	Fokker 100	11519	
☐	EP-ASJ	Fokker 100	11378	[THR]
☐	EP-ASK	Fokker 100	11388	
☐	EP-ASM	Fokker 100	11433	
☐	EP-ASO	Fokker 100	11454	
☐	EP-ASP	Fokker 100	11504	std
☐	EP-ASQ	Fokker 100	11513	
☐	EP-ASR	Fokker 100	11522	
☐	EP-AST	Fokker 100	11523	
☐	EP-ASU	Fokker 100	11430	
☐	EP-ASX	Fokker 100	11431	std
☐	EP-ATB	Fokker 100	11401	
☐	EP-ATC	Fokker 100	11296	[MHD]
☐	EP-ATD	Fokker 100	11387	[THR]
☐	EP-ATE	Fokker 100	11323	std♦
☐	EP-ATF	Fokker 100	11476	std
☐	EP-ATG	Fokker 100	11329	std

KISH AIR — Y9 / IRK

	Reg.	Type	C/n	Notes
☐	EP-LBV	Fokker 50	20158	
☐	EP-LCG	Fokker 50	20236	
☐	EP-LCP	Fokker 100	11495	
☐	EP-LCQ	Fokker 100	11492	

	Reg	Type	C/n	Notes
☐	EP-LCR	Fokker 100	11330	
☐	EP-LCI	MD-83	49844/1579	
☐	EP-LCJ	MD-82	53221/2079	
☐	EP-LCK	MD-82	53224/2084	
☐	EP-LCL	MD-82	53229/2105	
☐	EP-LCM	MD-82	53226/2087	
☐	EP-LCO	MD-83	53150/1831	
☐	UR-BXN	MD-82	49569/1405	<BKV

MAHAN AIR — *W5 / IRM*

	Reg	Type	C/n	Notes
☐	EP-MHA	A300B2K-3C	160	[KER]
☐	EP-MHF	A300B4-103	055	[IKA]
☐	EP-MHG	A300B4-203	204	
☐	EP-MHL	A300B4-203	175	
☐	EP-MHM	A300B2K-3C	090	[THR]
☐	EP-MMJ	A310-304	526	
☐	EP-MMO	A300B4-622R	838	
☐	EP-MMP	A310-304ET	586	
☐	EP-MNG	A300B4-603	401	
☐	EP-MNH	A300B4-603	405	
☐	EP-MNI	A300B4-603	408	
☐	EP-MNJ	A300B4-603	380	
☐	EP-MNK	A300B4-603	618	
☐	EP-MNL	A300B4-603	623	
☐	EP-MNM	A300B4-605R	773	
☐	EP-MNN	A300B4-605R	701	
☐	EP-MNQ	A300B4-603	553	
☐	EP-MNR	A300B4-603	411	
☐	EP-MNS	A300B4-603	414	
☐	EP-MNT	A300B4-603	546	
☐	EP-MNU	A300B4-605R	608	
☐	EP-MHO	A310-304	488	
☐	EP-MMI	A310-304ET	537	[IKA]♦
☐	EP-MMJ	A310-304	526	♦
☐	EP-MMN	A310-304	524	
☐	EP-MMP	A310-304ET	586	♦
☐	EP-MNF	A310-304	547	
☐	EP-MNO	A310-308	595	
☐	EP-MNP	A310-308	620	
☐	EP-MNV	A310-304	567	
☐	EP-MMA	A340-311	020	♦
☐	EP-MMB	A340-311	056	♦
☐	EP-MMC	A340-313X	282	Govt
☐	EP-MMD	A340-313X	164	♦
☐	EP-MME	A340-642	371	♦
☐	EP-MMF	A340-642	376	♦
☐	EP-MMG	A340-642	383	♦
☐	EP-MMH	A340-642	391	♦
☐	EP-MMI	A340-642	416	♦
☐	EP-MMQ	A340-642	449	♦
☐	EP-MMR	A340-642	615	♦
☐	EP-MMV	BAe146 Srs.200	E2079	
☐	EP-MOB	BAe146 Srs.300	E3212	
☐	EP-MOC	BAe146 Srs.300	E3158	
☐	EP-MOD	BAe146 Srs.300	E3162	
☐	EP-MOE	BAe146 Srs.300	E3129	
☐	EP-MOF	BAe146 Srs.300	E3149	
☐	EP-MOG	Avro 146-RJ100	E3343	♦
☐	EP-MOH	Avro 146-RJ100	E3341	
☐	EP-MOI	Avro 146-RJ100	E3362	
☐	EP-MOK	Avro 146-RJ100	E3146	
☐	EP-MOL	BAe146 Srs.300	E3159	♦
☐	EP-MOM	BAe146 Srs.300	E3165	
☐	EP-MON	Avro 146-RJ100	E3358	♦
☐	EP-MOP	Avro 146-RJ85	E2257	
☐	EP-MOQ	Avro 146-RJ85	E2261	
☐	EP-MOR	Avro 146-RJ85	E2392	♦
☐	EP-MOS	Avro 146-RJ85	E2347	♦
☐	EP-MNA	B747-422	24383/811	[IKA]
☐	EP-MNB	B747-422	24363/740	[IKA]
☐	EP-MNC	B747-422	26879/973	[THR]
☐	EP-MND	B747-3B3 (SCD)	23413/632	[THR]
☐	EP-MNE	B747-3B3 (SCD)	23480/641	[THR]

MERAJ AIR — *MRJ*

	Reg	Type	C/n	Notes
☐	EP-AGB	A321-231	1202	
☐	EP-AJA	A340-313X	257	govt♦
☐	EP-AJC	A320-232	0530	
☐	EP-AJE	B707-386C	21396/928	govt
☐	EP-AJH	A320-233	1353	
☐	EP-AJI	A320-233	1300	
☐	EP-SIF	A300B4-622R	762	
☐	EP-SIG	A300B4-622R	750	

NAFT AIRLINES — *NV / IRG*

	Reg	Type	C/n	Notes
☐	EP-AWZ	Fokker 100	11497	^
☐	EP-EAH	Fokker 50	20234	o/o
☐	EP-GAS	Fokker 50	20224	^
☐	EP-IOS	F.27 Friendship 300	10151	[AWZ]
☐	EP-MIS	Fokker 100	11503	
☐	EP-NFK	Fokker 50	20235	♦
☐	EP-NFT	Fokker 50	20220	
☐	EP-OIL	Fokker 50	20222	^
☐	EP-OPI	Fokker 100	11509	
☐	EP-PET	Fokker 50	20283	
☐	EP-SUS	Fokker 100	11487	

^ operated for National Iranian Oil Co

PAYAM INTERNATIONAL AIR — *2F / IRP*

	Reg	Type	C/n	Notes
☐	EP-TPH	EMB.110P1A	110453	
☐	EP-TPI	EMB.110P1A	110438	
☐	EP-TPJ	EMB.110P1A	110442	
☐	EP-TPK	EMB.110P1	110386	
☐	EP-TPL	EMB.110P1	110423	

POUYA AIR LINES — *PYA*

	Reg	Type	C/n	Notes
☐	EP-PUA	An-74TK-200	3654701211055	♦
☐	EP-PUB	An-74TK-200	3654701211048	♦
☐	EP-PUC	An-74TK-200	3654701211058	♦
☐	EP-PUM	An-74TK-200	3654701211059	♦
☐	EP-PUL	Il-76TD	0033448393	
☐	EP-PUO	Il-76TD	1013409297	
☐	EP-PUS	Il-76TD	1023409321	

QESHM AIR — *IRQ*

	Reg	Type	C/n	Notes
☐	EP-FQK	A300B4-605R	584	[IST]
☐	EP-FQL	A300B4-605R	744	
☐	EP-FQM	A300B4-605R	603	
☐	EP-FQN	A300B4-605R	749	
☐	EP-FQO	A300B4-605R	764	
☐	EP-FQP	A320-214	0617	
☐	EP-FQR	A320-214	0607	
☐	EY-631	A320-214	0611	o/o<TXP
☐	EP-FQS	Avro 146-RJ85	E2363	♦
☐	EP-FQT	Avro 146-RJ100	E3320	♦
☐	EP-FQU	Avro 146-RJ100	E3374	♦
☐	EP-FQV	Avro 146-RJ100	E3375	♦

	Reg.	Type	C/n	
☐	EP-FQX	Avro 146-RJ100	E3356	
☐	EP-FQA	Fokker 50	20274	>SBT
☐	EP-FQB	Fokker 50	20263	>SBT
☐	EP-FQC	Fokker 50	20275	>SBT
☐	EP-FQD	Fokker 50	20265	>SBT
☐	EP-FQF	Fokker 100	11444	♦
☐	EP-FQG	Fokker 100	11462	♦
☐	EP-FQI	Fokker 100	11475	
☐	EP-FQJ	Fokker 100	11477	

SEPEHRAN AIRLINES

	Reg.	Type	C/n	
☐	EP-FSA	B737-5L9	25066/2038	♦
☐	EP-FSB	B737-529	25218/2111	♦
☐	EP-	B737-529	26537/2296	♦
☐	EP-	Do328-310	3165	♦

SAFFATT AIRLINES — IRV

	Reg.	Type	C/n	
☐	EP-SAJ	An-26B	14002	♦
☐	EP-SAK	An-26B	14001	♦
☐	S2-AGA	An-26B	13505	<♦
☐	S2-AGZ	An-26B	13408	<♦

TABAN AIRLINE — HH / TBM

	Reg.	Type	C/n	
☐	EP-TBH	A310-304	565	[IKA]♦
☐	EP-TBG	Avro 146-RJ85	E2289	♦
☐	EY-752	B757-2Q8	27599/696	<TJK♦
☐	EY-754	B737-4Q8	28202/3009	<TJK♦
☐	EP-TBB	MD-88	53549/2185	
☐	EP-TBC	MD-88	53550/2187	
☐	EP-TBD	MD-88	53547/2176	
☐	EP-TBE	MD-88	53548/2180	
☐	EP-TBF	MD-88	53546/2167	

TAFTAN AIR LINES — SBT

	Reg.	Type	C/n	
☐	EP-FQA	Fokker 50	20274	<IRQ
☐	EP-FQB	Fokker 50	20263	<IRQ
☐	EP-FQC	Fokker 50	20275	<IRQ
☐	EP-FQD	Fokker 50	20265	<IRQ
☐	EP-TFN	Fokker 50	20302	[ZAH]
☐	EP-TFT	Fokker 50	20298	[ZAH]

TEHRAN AIR

	Reg.	Type	C/n	
☐	EP-MMX	A310-304ET	499	♦

ZAGROS AIRLINES — ZV / IZG

	Reg.	Type	C/n	
☐	UR-CMW	A319-113	0644	<KHO♦
☐	EP-ZAI	A320-231	0376	
☐	EP-ZAJ	A320-214	0407	
☐	EP-ZAL	A320-212	0400	
☐	EP-ZAR	A320-231	0476	♦
☐	EP-ZAT	A320-214	0999	♦
☐	EP-ZAV	A320-212	0395	♦
☐	EP-ZAZ	A320-231	0430	♦
☐	UR-CNJ	A320-211	0311	<KHO♦
☐	UR-CNK	A320-211	0426	<KHO♦
☐	EP-ZAA	MD-82	49634/1419	
☐	EP-ZAC	MD-83	49949/1906	
☐	EP-ZAE	MD-82	53066/1938	
☐	EP-ZAF	MD-82	53119/1956	
☐	EP-ZAG	MD-82	49372/1252	
☐	EP-ZAK	MD-83	49627/1580	
☐	EP-ZAM	MD-82	49483/1314	♦
☐	EP-ZAQ	MD-83	49769/1559	

ER- MOLDOVA

AEROPORTUL INT'L MARCULESTI — VIH

	Reg.	Type	C/n	
☐	ER-AEJ	An-72	36572094889	♦
☐	ER-AFZ	An-72	36572070698	
☐	ER-AVK	An-26B	13808	
☐	ER-AVL	An-26B	13809	
☐	ER-AWF	An-72	36572070696	

AEROTRANSCARGO — ATG

	Reg.	Type	C/n	
☐	ER-BAM	B747-409(BDSF)	24312/954	
☐	ER-IAF	Il-76T	0003423699	
☐	ER-IAV	Il-76TD	0063471150	

AIR MOLDOVA — 9U / MLD

	Reg.	Type	C/n	
☐	ER-AXL	A319-112	2849	♦
☐	ER-AXP	A320-233	0741	
☐	ER-AXV	A320-211	0622	
☐	ER-ECB	ERJ-190LR	19000325	
☐	ER-ECC	ERJ-190LR	19000130	
☐	ER-EMA	EMB.120RT	120223	
☐	SX-BDT	A320-232	1422	<HRM♦
☐	SX-BHT	A321-211	0666	<HRM

AIR STORK

	Reg.	Type	C/n	
☐	ER-IBI	Il-76M	1013409303	♦
☐	ER-IBU	Il-76TD	1023414450	♦

OSCAR JET

	Reg.	Type	C/n	
☐	ER-IAX	Il-76TD	0063470088	♦
☐	ER-IAY	Il-76MD	1033418596	♦
☐	ER-IAZ	Il-76TD	1023412399	♦

PECOTOX AIR — PXA

	Reg.	Type	C/n	
☐	ER-AZB	An-24RV	27307507	[TMS]
☐	ER-AZP	An-24RV	17307002	[KIV]
☐	ER-AZX	An-24RV	47309804	[KIV]

SKY PRIM AIR — KPM

	Reg.	Type	C/n	
☐	ER-AXO	A320-231	0357	>LAA♦
☐	ER-IAW	Il-76TD	0073479367	♦
☐	ER-ICS	Il-18D	187009903	

VALAN INT'L CARGO — VLN

	Reg.	Type	C/n	
☐	ER-AVA	An-26B-100	11409	>SKA
☐	ER-AVB	An-26-100	3204	>SKA
☐	ER-AZO	An-26B	10606	
☐	ZS-PEL	An-32B	3004	

ES- ESTONIA

AIREST — AEG

	Reg.	Type	C/n	
☐	ES-LSA	SAAB SF.340AF	340A-055	
☐	ES-LSB	SAAB SF.340AF	340A-045	
☐	ES-LSC	SAAB SF.340AF	340A-037	
☐	ES-LSD	SAAB SF.340AF	340A-080	
☐	ES-LSE	SAAB SF.340A	340A-132	
☐	ES-LSF	SAAB SF.340A	340A-144	♦

AVIES AIR COMPANY — U3 / AIA

	Reg.	Type	C/n	
☐	ES-PJA	BAeJetstream 31	749	
☐	ES-PJB	BAeJetstream 31	622	

☐	ES-PJD	BAeJetstream 31	773	
☐	ES-PJE	BAeJetstream 32EP	841	
☐	ES-PJF	BAeJetstream 32EP	854	
☐	ES-PJG	BAeJetstream 31	701	
☐	ES-PJH	BAeJetstream 32EP	855	
☐	ES-PJR	BAeJetstream 32EP	949	

SMART LYNX ESTONIA — MYX

☐	ES-SAK	A320-214	0888	♦
☐	ES-SAL	A320-214	0566	
☐	ES-SAM	A320-232	1896	♦

ET- ETHIOPIA

ETHIOPIAN AIRLINES — ET / ETH

☐	ET-ATQ	A350-941	040	o/o♦
☐	ET-ATR	A350-941	043	o/o♦
☐	ET-	A350-941	089	o/o♦
☐	ET-ALK	B737-760/W	33764/1408	
☐	ET-ALM	B737-760/W	33765/1539	
☐	ET-ALN	B737-760/W	33766/1757	
☐	ET-ANG	B737-7K9/W	34401/2216	>SKK
☐	ET-ANH	B737-7K9/W	34402/2270	>SKK
☐	ET-ANZ	B737-8H0/W	37933/3437	
☐	ET-AOA	B737-8H0/W	37936/3459	
☐	ET-AOB	B737-8H0/W	37937/3467	
☐	ET-AOK	B737-790/W	33012/1306	>SKK
☐	ET-APF	B737-860/W	40961/3827	
☐	ET-APK	B737-860/W	40964/3991	
☐	ET-APL	B737-860/W	40965/4075	
☐	ET-APM	B737-860/W	40962/4250	
☐	ET-APO	B737-860/W	40963/4231	
☐	ET-AQM	B737-860/W	40966/4471	
☐	ET-AQN	B737-860/W	40967/4971	
☐	ET-AQO	B737-860/W	40968/5399	
☐	ET-AQP	B737-860/W	40969/5473	
☐	ET-AQQ	B737-860/W	40970/5507	
☐	ET-ARB	B737-7Q8/W	30687/2252	>MWI
☐	ET-ARD	B737-7Q8/W	30710/2188	
☐	ET-ASJ	B737-860/W	39442/5141	
☐	ET-AJS	B757-260PF	24845/300	
☐	ET-AJX	B757-260(PCF)	25014/348	
☐	ET-ALZ	B757-231	30319/883	
☐	ET-AMK	B757-23N	32449/974	
☐	ET-ALH	B767-3BGER	30565/802	>UN
☐	ET-ALJ	B767-360ER/W	33767/918	
☐	ET-ALO	B767-360ER/W	33768/922	
☐	ET-ALP	B767-360ER	33769/933	
☐	ET-AMF	B767-3BGER	30563/786	
☐	ET-AMG	B767-3BGER	30566/817	
☐	ET-AQG	B767-306ER	28884/738	
☐	ET-ANN	B777-260LR	40770/900	
☐	ET-ANO	B777-260LR	40771/908	
☐	ET-ANP	B777-260LR	40772/914	
☐	ET-ANQ	B777-260LR	40773/930	
☐	ET-ANR	B777-260LR	40774/948	
☐	ET-APS	B777-F6N	41846/1043	
☐	ET-APU	B777-F6N	41817/1054	
☐	ET-APX	B777-36NER	42101/1150	
☐	ET-APY	B777-36NER	42102/1169	
☐	ET-AQL	B777-260LR	43814/1115	
☐	ET-ARH	B777-F60	42031/1242	
☐	ET-ARI	B777-F60	42032/1252	
☐	ET-ARJ	B777-F60	42033/1334	♦
☐	ET-ARK	B777-F60	42034/1346	♦
☐	ET-ASK	B777-360ER	44550/1297	
☐	ET-ASL	B777-360ER	44551/1312	
☐	ET-AOO	B787-8	34743/39	
☐	ET-AOP	B787-8	34744/44	
☐	ET-AOQ	B787-8	34745/49	
☐	ET-AOR	B787-8	34746/71	
☐	ET-AOS	B787-8	34747/75	
☐	ET-AOT	B787-8	34748/167	
☐	ET-AOU	B787-8	34749/164	
☐	ET-AOV	B787-8	34750/168	
☐	ET-ARE	B787-8	34751/196	
☐	ET-ARF	B787-8	34752/216	
☐	ET-ASG	B787-8	36111/258	
☐	ET-ASH	B787-8	38754/283	♦
☐	ET-ASI	B787-8	38758/298	♦
☐	ET-ANI	DHC-8-402Q	4299	
☐	ET-ANJ	DHC-8-402Q	4303	
☐	ET-ANK	DHC-8-402Q	4304	
☐	ET-ANL	DHC-8-402Q	4307	
☐	ET-ANV	DHC-8-402Q	4317	
☐	ET-ANW	DHC-8-402Q	4320	>SKK
☐	ET-ANX	DHC-8-402Q	4330	>SKK
☐	ET-ANY	DHC-8-402Q	4334	
☐	ET-AQB	DHC-8-402Q	4419	>MWI
☐	ET-AQC	DHC-8-402Q	4421	>SKK
☐	ET-AQD	DHC-8-402Q	4427	>SKK
☐	ET-AQE	DHC-8-402Q	4428	>SKK
☐	ET-AQF	DHC-8-402Q	4429	>SKK
☐	ET-ARL	DHC-8-402Q	4469	
☐	ET-ARM	DHC-8-402Q	4472	
☐	ET-ARN	DHC-8-402Q	4475	
☐	ET-ASA	DHC-8-402Q	4476	
☐	ET-AKT	Fokker 50	20331	[ADD]
☐	ET-AKU	Fokker 50	20333	>KUH

EW- BELARUS

BELAVIA BELARUSIAN AIRLINES — B2 / BRU

☐	EW-250PA	B737-524	26319/2748	
☐	EW-251PA	B737-5Q8	27634/2889	
☐	EW-252PA	B737-524	26340/2777	
☐	EW-253PA	B737-524	26339/2771	
☐	EW-254PA	B737-3Q8	26294/2550	
☐	EW-282PA	B737-3Q8	26321/2764	
☐	EW-283PA	B737-3Q8	26333/2786	
☐	EW-290PA	B737-522	27629/2834	
☐	EW-294PA	B737-505	26338/2822	
☐	EW-308PA	B737-3K2	24328/1858	
☐	EW-336PA	B737-3Q8	26312/2693	
☐	EW-366PA	B737-31S	29058/2946	
☐	EW-404PA	B737-3L9	27061/2347	
☐	EW-407PA	B737-36M	28332/2809	
☐	EW-437PA	B737-8K5/W	27988/508	
☐	EW-438PA	B737-86Q/W	30286/1280	
☐	EW-	B737-8xx		o/o♦
☐	EW-	B737-8xx		o/o♦
☐	EW-	B737-8xx		o/o♦
☐	EW-100PJ	CRJ-100LR	7309	
☐	EW-276PJ	CRJ-200ER	7799	
☐	EW-277PJ	CRJ-200ER	7852	
☐	EW-303PJ	CRJ-200LR	7436	
☐	EW-340PO	ERJ-175LR	17000350	

☐ EW-341PO	ERJ-175LR	17000352	
☐ EW-399PO	ERJ-195LR	19000667	
☐ EW-400PO	ERJ-195LR	19000668	
☐ EW-85703	Tu-154M	91A878	std
☐ EW-85741	Tu-154M	91A896	std
☐ EW-85748	Tu-154M	92A924	std

GENEX — GNX

☐ EW-259TG	An-26B	12706	
☐ EW-278TG	An-26B	13306	
☐ EW-328TG	An-26B	12806	

GRODNO AVIAKOMPANIA — GRX

☐ EW-262TK	An-32B	2103	
☐ EW-281CN	An-30	1402	
☐ EW-364TG	An-26B	4206	
☐ EW-378TG	An-26B	14004	^
☐ EW-427TI	An-12AP	2340806	
☐ EW-435TI	An-12B	1347701	♦

^ operates for Vulkan Air

ORSHA AIR

☐ EW-464PS	Yak-40	9510540	♦

RADA AIRLINES — RDA

☐ EW-450TR	Il-62MGr	4546257	♦
☐ EW-	Il-62MGr	4154535	o/o♦

RUBYSTAR — RSB

☐ EW-275TI	An-12BK	00347210	
☐ EW-338TI	An-12BP	1340106	
☐ EW-355TH	Il-76TD	0093495883	
☐ EW-356TH	Il-76TD	1013405159	
☐ EW-383TH	Il-76TD	1013405177	
☐ EW-395TH	Il-76MD	0003499986	♦
☐ EW-412TH	Il-76TD	0023437090	
☐ EW-430TH	Il-76TD	43451528	
☐ EW-448TH	Il-76TD	1023410330	♦
☐ EW-449TH	Il-76TD	1003405167	♦

TRANS AVIA EXPORT CARGO — AL / TXC

☐ EW-445TQ	B747-281BSF	24399/750	♦
☐ EW-460TQ	B747-281BSF	23919/689	♦
☐ EW-466TH	Il-76TD	1033418584	♦
☐ EW-76712	Il-76TD	0063473190	[MSQ]
☐ EW-76734	Il-76TD	0073476312	
☐ EW-76735	Il-76TD	0073476314	[MSQ]
☐ EW-78769	Il-76MD	0083487607	[MSQ]
☐ EW-78779	Il-76TD	0083489662	
☐ EW-78787	Il-76MD	0083490698	
☐ EW-78799	Il-76TD	0093491754	
☐ EW-78839	Il-76TD	1003402047	[MSQ]
☐ EW-78843	Il-76TD	1003403082	

EX- KYRGYZSTAN

AIR BISHKEK — KR / EAA

☐ EX-32002	A320-231	0386	
☐ EY-539	B737-3B7	23700/1461	>ERT

AIR KYRGYZSTAN — QH / LYN

☐ EX-24805	An-24RV	77310805	
☐ EX-37301	B737-382	25162/2241	[FRU]
☐ EX-37401	B737-484	25361/2130	[SAW]
☐ EX-37501	B737-59D	26419/2186	

AVIA TRAFFIC COMPANY — YK / AVJ

☐ EX-27002	BAe146 Srs.200	E2172	
☐ EX-27007	BAe146 Srs.200	E2180	
☐ EX-37008	B737-330	23834/1454	
☐ EX-37010	B737-3L9	25125/2059	
☐ EX-37012	B737-33A	27463/2831	

PEGASUS AIRLINES ASIA — ZM / MBB

☐ EX-37402	B737-42R	29107/2997	
☐ EX-37801	B737-82R/W	35701/2496	♦
☐ TC-CPE	B737-82R/W	38178/4023	<PGT

SKY BISHKEK — GY / BIS

☐ EX-34001	SAAB SF.340A	340A-146	

SKY WAY AIR — SAB

☐ EX-126	An-26	11508	

TRAST AERO — S5 / TSJ

☐ ER-AUR	An-26		
☐ EX-041(2)	An-24B	97304910	
☐ S9-GBC	An-26B & An-32	^	
☐ TN-AGB	An-26B-100	7210	
☐ 3X-GES(1)	An-32A	1408?	
☐ 3X-GET	An-26B-100	4104	
☐ 3X-GFC	An-26		
☐ 3X-GFN	An-26		
☐ 4L-26026(2)	An-26		

Details of this fleet are difficult to confirm; ^ marks used several times by these types.

EY- TAJIKISTAN

ASIA AIRWAYS — ASW

☐ EY-329	Fokker 50	20130	>JUB♦

Operations reported suspended 06Nov15.

ASIAN EXPRESS AIRLINE — TXP

Operates/leases A320s and Avro 146s for Qeshm Air, Iran.

KHATION AIR — KHT

☐ EY-617	Il-76TD	0063467021	
☐ EY-703	Il-76TD	0083488643	♦

SOMON AIR — 4J / SMR

☐ EY-545	B737-3K2	24326/1683	
☐ EY-555	B737-3Y5	25613/2446	
☐ EY-777	B737-8GJ/W	34960/2765	
☐ EY-787	B737-8GJ/W	34955/2512	
☐ P4-SOM	B737-93YER	40889/3837	
☐ P4-TAJ	B737-93YER	40888/3771	

TAJIK AIR — 7J / TJK

☐ EY-46595	An-24B	97305105	
☐ EY-47693	An-24RV	27307510	
☐ EY-47802	An-24RV	17306901	
☐ EY-26205	An-26B-100	14107	
☐ EY-26658	An-26	7904	
☐ EY-28736	PZL An-28	1AJ007-24	
☐ EY-28921	PZL An-28	1AJ008-07	

Reg	Type	c/n	Notes
EY-444	B737-3L9	26441/2250	>
LY-AWF	B737-522	26707/2512	<LLC
LY-AWG	B737-522	26700/2490	<LLC
EY-753	B737-448	25736/2269	
EY-754	B737-4Q8	28202/3009	>TBM
EY-751	B757-2Q8	24964/424	
EY-752	B757-2Q8	27599/696	>TBM
EY-757	B757-231	30338/891	♦
EY-201	XIAN MA60	0701	>EHN
EY-65763	Tu-134A-3	62299	std
EY-85692	Tu-154M	90A865	std
EY-85717	Tu-154M	91A897	

EZ- TURKMENISTAN

TURKMENISTAN AIRLINES — T5 / ASB

Reg	Type	c/n	Notes
EZ-A101	B717-22K	55153/5072	
EZ-A102	B717-22K	55154/5078	
EZ-A103	B717-22K	55155/5086	
EZ-A104	B717-22K	55195/5130	
EZ-A105	B717-22K	55196/5133	
EZ-A106	B717-22K	55186/5146	
EZ-A107	B717-22K	55187/5147	
EZ-A001	B737-341	26855/2305	[ASB]
EZ-A004	B737-82K/W	36088/2181	
EZ-A005	B737-82K/W	36089/2233	
EZ-A006	B737-7GL/W	37236/2986	
EZ-A007	B737-7GL/W	37234/2682	
EZ-A008	B737-7GL/W	37237/2988	
EZ-A009	B737-7GL/W	37235/2993	
EZ-A015	B737-82K/W	39774/4440	
EZ-A016	B737-82K/W	39775/4480	
EZ-A017	B737-82K/W	43863/4731	
EZ-A010	B757-23A	25345/412	[SAW]
EZ-A011	B757-22K	28336/725	[SAW]
EZ-A012	B757-22K	28337/726	[SAW]
EZ-A014	B757-22K	30863/952	
EZ-A777	B777-22KLR	39548/889	Govt
EZ-A778	B777-22KLR	42296/1181	
EZ-A779	B777-22KLR	42297/1194	
EZ-F426	Il-76TD	1033418609	
EZ-F427	Il-76TD	1033418620	
EZ-F428	Il-76TD	1043418624	

E3- ERITREA

ERITREAN AIRLINES — B8 / ERT

Reg	Type	c/n	Notes
EY-539	B737-3B7	23700/1461	<
E3-AAQ	B767-238ER	23309/129	

MASSAWA AIRWAYS

Reg	Type	c/n	Notes
E3-AAV	XIAN MA60	?	
E3-	Beech 1900D	UE-12	
E3-	Beech 1900D	UE-27	

NAS AIR — UE / NAS

Reg	Type	c/n	Notes
E3-NAD	B737-268	21276/468	

E5- COOK ISLANDS

AIR RAROTONGA — GZ

Reg	Type	c/n	Notes
E5-FTS	EMB.110P1A	110239	
E5-TAI	EMB.110P1A	110447	
E5-TAK	EMB.110P1A	110448	
E5-TAL	EMB.110P2	110245	
E5-EFS	SAAB SF.340A	340A-049	

E7- BOSNIA-HERZEGOVINA

ICAR AIR — RAC

Reg	Type	c/n	Notes
E7-AAK	LET L-410UVP-E	892321	

F- FRANCE

AIGLE AZUR — ZI / AAF

Reg	Type	c/n	Notes
F-HBAL	A319-111	2870	
F-HBMI	A319-114	0639	
F-HCZI	A319-112	4268	
F-HBAO	A320-214	4589	
F-HBAP	A320-214	4675	
F-HBIB	A320-214	3289	
F-HBIO	A320-214	3242	
F-HBIS	A320-214	3136	
F-HBIX	A320-214/S	6012	

AIR CORSICA — XK / CCM

Reg	Type	c/n	Notes
F-GHQE	A320-211	0115	[MZJ]
F-HBEV	A320-216	3952	
F-HBSA	A320-216	3882	
F-HZFM	A320-214	5887	
F-HZPD	A320-214	3325	o/o♦
F-HZPG	A320-214	5906	
F-GRPI	ATR 72-212A	722	♦
F-GRPJ	ATR 72-212A	724	
F-GRPX	ATR 72-212A	734	
F-GRPY	ATR 72-212A	742	
F-GRPZ	ATR 72-212A	745	

AIR FRANCE — AF / AFR

Reg	Type	c/n	Notes
F-GUGA	A318-111	2035	
F-GUGB	A318-111	2059	
F-GUGC	A318-111	2071	
F-GUGD	A318-111	2081	
F-GUGE	A318-111	2100	
F-GUGF	A318-111	2109	
F-GUGG	A318-111	2317	
F-GUGH	A318-111	2344	[CDG]
F-GUGI	A318-111	2350	
F-GUGJ	A318-111	2582	
F-GUGK	A318-111	2601	
F-GUGL	A318-111	2686	
F-GUGM	A318-111	2750	
F-GUGN	A318-111	2918	
F-GUGO	A318-111	2951	
F-GUGP	A318-111	2967	
F-GUGQ	A318-111	2972	
F-GUGR	A318-111	3009	[ORY]
F-GPMA	A319-113	0598	
F-GPMB	A319-113	0600	
F-GPMC	A319-113	0608	

☐ F-GPMD	A319-113	0618	
☐ F-GPME	A319-113	0625	
☐ F-GPMF	A319-113	0637	
☐ F-GRHB	A319-111	0985	
☐ F-GRHE	A319-111	1020	
☐ F-GRHF	A319-111	1025	
☐ F-GRHG	A319-111	1036	
☐ F-GRHH	A319-111	1151	
☐ F-GRHI	A319-111	1169	
☐ F-GRHJ	A319-111	1176	
☐ F-GRHK	A319-111	1190	
☐ F-GRHL	A319-111	1201	
☐ F-GRHM	A319-111	1216	
☐ F-GRHN	A319-111	1267	
☐ F-GRHO	A319-111	1271	
☐ F-GRHP	A319-111	1344	
☐ F-GRHQ	A319-111	1404	
☐ F-GRHR	A319-111	1415	
☐ F-GRHS	A319-111	1444	
☐ F-GRHT	A319-111	1449	
☐ F-GRHU	A319-111	1471	
☐ F-GRHV	A319-111	1505	
☐ F-GRHX	A319-111	1524	
☐ F-GRHY	A319-111	1616	
☐ F-GRHZ	A319-111	1622	
☐ F-GRXA	A319-111	1640	
☐ F-GRXB	A319-111	1645	
☐ F-GRXC	A319-111	1677	
☐ F-GRXD	A319-111	1699	
☐ F-GRXE	A319-111	1733	
☐ F-GRXF	A319-111	1938	
☐ F-GRXJ	A319-115LR	2456	
☐ F-GRXK	A319-115LR	2716	
☐ F-GRXL	A319-111	2938	
☐ F-GRXM	A319-111	2961	
☐ F-GFKY	A320-211	0285	
☐ F-GHQJ	A320-211	0214	[ORY]
☐ F-GHQL	A320-211	0239	
☐ F-GHQM	A320-211	0237	[TLS]
☐ F-GHQQ	A320-211	0352	
☐ F-GHQR	A320-211	0377	
☐ F-GKXA	A320-211	0287	
☐ F-GKXC	A320-214	1502	
☐ F-GKXE	A320-214	1879	
☐ F-GKXG	A320-214	1894	
☐ F-GKXH	A320-214	1924	
☐ F-GKXI	A320-214	1949	
☐ F-GKXJ	A320-214	1900	
☐ F-GKXK	A320-214	2140	
☐ F-GKXL	A320-214	2705	
☐ F-GKXM	A320-214	2721	
☐ F-GKXN	A320-214	3008	
☐ F-GKXO	A320-214	3420	
☐ F-GKXP	A320-214	3470	
☐ F-GKXQ	A320-214	3777	
☐ F-GKXR	A320-214	3795	
☐ F-GKXS	A320-214	3825	
☐ F-GKXT	A320-214	3859	
☐ F-GKXU	A320-214	4063	
☐ F-GKXV	A320-214	4084	
☐ F-GKXY	A320-214	4105	
☐ F-GKXZ	A320-214	4137	
☐ F-HBNA	A320-214	4335	
☐ F-HBNB	A320-214	4402	
☐ F-HBNC	A320-214	4601	
☐ F-HBND	A320-214	4604	

☐ F-HBNE	A320-214	4664	
☐ F-HBNF	A320-214	4714	
☐ F-HBNG	A320-214	4747	
☐ F-HBNH	A320-214	4800	
☐ F-HBNI	A320-214	4820	
☐ F-HBNJ	A320-214	4908	
☐ F-HBNK	A320-214	5084	
☐ F-HBNL	A320-214	5129	
☐ F-HEPA	A320-214	4139	
☐ F-HEPB	A320-214	4241	
☐ F-HEPC	A320-214	4267	
☐ F-HEPD	A320-214	4295	
☐ F-HEPE	A320-214	4298	
☐ F-HEPF	A320-214/S	5719	
☐ F-HEPG	A320-214/S	5802	
☐ F-HEPH	A320-214/S	5869	
☐ F-	A320-214/S		o/o
☐ F-GMZA	A321-111	0498	
☐ F-GMZB	A321-111	0509	
☐ F-GMZC	A321-111	0521	
☐ F-GMZD	A321-111	0529	
☐ F-GMZE	A321-111	0544	
☐ F-GTAD	A321-212	0777	
☐ F-GTAE	A321-212	0796	
☐ F-GTAH	A321-212	1133	
☐ F-GTAJ	A321-212	1476	
☐ F-GTAK	A321-212	1658	
☐ F-GTAM	A321-212	1859	
☐ F-GTAO	A321-212	3098	
☐ F-GTAP	A321-212	3372	
☐ F-GTAQ	A321-212	3399	
☐ F-GTAS	A321-212	3419	
☐ F-GTAT	A321-212	3441	
☐ F-GTAU	A321-212	3814	
☐ F-GTAX	A321-212	3930	
☐ F-GTAY	A321-212	4251	
☐ F-GTAZ	A321-212	4901	
☐ F-GZCA	A330-203	422	
☐ F-GZCB	A330-203	443	
☐ F-GZCC	A330-203	448	
☐ F-GZCD	A330-203	458	
☐ F-GZCE	A330-203	465	
☐ F-GZCF	A330-203	481	
☐ F-GZCG	A330-203	498	
☐ F-GZCH	A330-203	500	
☐ F-GZCI	A330-203	502	
☐ F-GZCJ	A330-203	503	
☐ F-GZCK	A330-203	516	
☐ F-GZCL	A330-203	519	
☐ F-GZCM	A330-203	567	
☐ F-GZCN	A330-203	584	
☐ F-GZCO	A330-203	657	
☐ F-GLZH	A340-311	078	
☐ F-GLZI	A340-311	084	
☐ F-GLZJ	A340-313X	186	
☐ F-GLZK	A340-313X	207	
☐ F-GLZM	A340-313X	237	
☐ F-GLZN	A340-313X	245	
☐ F-GLZO	A340-313X	246	
☐ F-GLZP	A340-313X	260	
☐ F-GLZR	A340-313X	307	
☐ F-GLZS	A340-313X	310	
☐ F-GLZU	A340-313X	377	
☐ F-GNII	A340-313X	399	
☐ F-HPJA	A380-861	033	

	Reg	Type	c/n	
☐	F-HPJB	A380-861	040	
☐	F-HPJC	A380-861	043	
☐	F-HPJD	A380-861	049	
☐	F-HPJE	A380-861	052	
☐	F-HPJF	A380-861	064	
☐	F-HPJG	A380-861	067	
☐	F-HPJH	A380-861	099	
☐	F-HPJI	A380-861	115	
☐	F-HPJJ	A380-861	117	
☐	F-GSPA	B777-228ER	29002/129	
☐	F-GSPB	B777-228ER	29003/133	
☐	F-GSPC	B777-228ER	29004/138	
☐	F-GSPD	B777-228ER	29005/187	
☐	F-GSPE	B777-228ER	29006/189	
☐	F-GSPF	B777-228ER	29007/201	
☐	F-GSPG	B777-228ER	27609/195	
☐	F-GSPH	B777-228ER	28675/210	
☐	F-GSPI	B777-228ER	29008/258	
☐	F-GSPJ	B777-228ER	29009/263	
☐	F-GSPK	B777-228ER	29010/267	
☐	F-GSPL	B777-228ER	30457/284	
☐	F-GSPM	B777-228ER	30456/307	
☐	F-GSPN	B777-228ER	29011/314	
☐	F-GSPO	B777-228ER	30614/320	
☐	F-GSPP	B777-228ER	30615/327	
☐	F-GSPQ	B777-228ER	28682/331	
☐	F-GSPR	B777-228ER	28683/367	
☐	F-GSPS	B777-228ER	32306/370	
☐	F-GSPT	B777-228ER	32308/382	
☐	F-GSPU	B777-228ER	32309/383	
☐	F-GSPV	B777-228ER	28684/385	
☐	F-GSPX	B777-228ER	32698/392	
☐	F-GSPY	B777-228ER	32305/395	
☐	F-GSPZ	B777-228ER	32310/401	
☐	F-GSQA	B777-328ER	32723/466	
☐	F-GSQB	B777-328ER	32724/478	
☐	F-GSQC	B777-328ER	32727/480	
☐	F-GSQD	B777-328ER	32726/490	
☐	F-GSQE	B777-328ER	32851/492	
☐	F-GSQF	B777-328ER	32849/494	
☐	F-GSQG	B777-328ER	32850/500	
☐	F-GSQH	B777-328ER	32711/501	
☐	F-GSQI	B777-328ER	32725/502	
☐	F-GSQJ	B777-328ER	32852/510	
☐	F-GSQK	B777-328ER	32845/530	
☐	F-GSQL	B777-328ER	32853/545	
☐	F-GSQM	B777-328ER	32848/558	
☐	F-GSQN	B777-328ER	32960/565	
☐	F-GSQO	B777-328ER	32961/570	
☐	F-GSQP	B777-328ER	35676/573	
☐	F-GSQR	B777-328ER	35677/579	
☐	F-GSQS	B777-328ER	32962/608	
☐	F-GSQT	B777-328ER	32846/616	
☐	F-GSQU	B777-328ER	32847/624	
☐	F-GSQV	B777-328ER	32854/636	
☐	F-GSQX	B777-328ER	32963/645	
☐	F-GSQY	B777-328ER	35678/647	
☐	F-GUOB	B777-F28	32965/732	
☐	F-GUOC	B777-F28	32966/752	
☐	F-GZNA	B777-328ER	35297/671	
☐	F-GZNB	B777-328ER	32964/715	
☐	F-GZNC	B777-328ER	35542/723	
☐	F-GZND	B777-328ER	35543/777	
☐	F-GZNE	B777-328ER	37432/790	
☐	F-GZNF	B777-328ER	37433/792	
☐	F-GZNG	B777-328ER	32968/795	
☐	F-GZNH	B777-328ER	35544/905	
☐	F-GZNI	B777-328ER	39973/924	
☐	F-GZNJ	B777-328ER	38706/928	
☐	F-GZNK	B777-328ER	39971/931	
☐	F-GZNL	B777-328ER	40063/1001	
☐	F-GZNN	B777-328ER	40376/1013	
☐	F-GZNO	B777-328ER	38665/1007	
☐	F-GZNP	B777-328ER	37435/1290	
☐	F-GZNQ	B777-328ER	40064/1298	
☐	F-GZNR	B777-328ER	44553/1343	
☐	F-GZNS	B777-328ER	39970/1380	o/o♦

AIRBUS TRANSPORT INTL — *4Y / BGA*

	Reg	Type	c/n	
☐	F-GSTA	A300B4-608ST	655/001	
☐	F-GSTB	A300B4-608ST	751/002	
☐	F-GSTC	A300B4-608ST	765/003	
☐	F-GSTD	A300B4-608ST	776/004	
☐	F-GSTF	A300B4-608ST	796/005	

AIRLINAIR — *A5 / RLA*

	Reg	Type	c/n	
☐	F-GPYA	ATR 42-500	457	std
☐	F-GPYB	ATR 42-500	480	
☐	F-GPYC	ATR 42-500	484	
☐	F-GPYD	ATR 42-500	490	
☐	F-GPYF	ATR 42-500	495	
☐	F-GPYK	ATR 42-500	537	
☐	F-GPYL	ATR 42-500	542	
☐	F-GPYM	ATR 42-500	520	
☐	F-GPYN	ATR 42-500	539	
☐	F-GPYO	ATR 42-500	544	
☐	F-GVZB	ATR 42-500	524	
☐	F-GVZC	ATR 42-500	516	
☐	F-GVZD	ATR 42-500	530	
☐	F-GVZL	ATR 72-212A	553	
☐	F-GVZM	ATR 72-212A	590	
☐	F-GVZN	ATR 72-212A	563	
☐	F-GVZU	ATR 72-212A	499	
☐	F-GVZV	ATR 72-212A	686	
☐	F-HAPL	ATR 72-212A	654	
☐	F-HOPL	ATR 72-600	1283	♦
☐	F-HOPN	ATR 72-600	1288	♦
☐	F-HOPX	ATR 72-600	1257	♦
☐	F-HOPY	ATR 72-600	1237	♦
☐	F-HOPZ	ATR 72-600	1265	♦

Operates as Hop! by Air France together with Brit Air and Regional.

ASL AIRLINES FRANCE — *5O / FPO*

	Reg	Type	c/n	
☐	F-GFUF	B737-3B3(QC)	24388/1725	
☐	F-GIXB	B737-33A(F)	24789/1953	
☐	F-GIXC	B737-38B(F)	25124/2047	
☐	F-GIXN	B737-4YO(SF)	25181/2203	
☐	F-GIXT	B737-39M(QC)	28898/2906	
☐	F-GZTA	B737-33V(QC)	29333/3084	
☐	F-GZTB	B737-33V(QC)	29336/3102	>REU
☐	F-GZTC	B737-73V/W	32414/1214	
☐	F-GZTD	B737-73V/W	32418/1300	>TSC
☐	F-GZTG	B737-73S/W	29080/211	>TSC♦
☐	F-GZTH	B737-73S/W	29081/215	>TSC♦
☐	F-GZTI	B737-408(SF)	25063/2032	
☐	F-GZTJ	B737-4S3(SF)	25595/2233	
☐	F-GZTK	B737-4Q8(F)	24709/2115	♦
☐	F-GZTM	B737-3B3(QC)	24387/1693	♦

Formerly Europe Airpost

ATLAS ATLANTIQUE AIRLINES — TLB

	Reg	Type	c/n	
☐	LY-SPB	A320-232	2987	<LLC♦
☐	F-GPYY	Beech 1900C-1	UC-115	

BRIT AIR — DB / BZH

	Reg	Type	c/n	
☐	F-GRJG	CRJ-100ER	7143	[MXN]
☐	F-GRJI	CRJ-100ER	7147	[MXN]
☐	F-GRJL	CRJ-100ER	7221	[DNR]
☐	F-GRJN	CRJ-100ER	7262	[MXN]
☐	F-GRJO	CRJ-100ER	7296	[MXN]
☐	F-GRJP	CRJ-100ER	7301	[MXN]
☐	F-GRJQ	CRJ-100ER	7321	[MXN]
☐	F-GRJT	CRJ-100ER	7389	[MXN]
☐	F-GRZC	CRJ-701	10008	
☐	F-GRZD	CRJ-701	10016	
☐	F-GRZE	CRJ-701	10032	
☐	F-GRZF	CRJ-701	10036	
☐	F-GRZG	CRJ-701	10037	
☐	F-GRZH	CRJ-701	10089	
☐	F-GRZI	CRJ-701	10093	
☐	F-GRZJ	CRJ-701	10096	
☐	F-GRZK	CRJ-701	10198	
☐	F-GRZL	CRJ-701	10245	
☐	F-GRZM	CRJ-701	10263	
☐	F-GRZN	CRJ-701	10264	
☐	F-GRZO	CRJ-701	10265	
☐	F-HMLA	CRJ-1000EL	19004	
☐	F-HMLC	CRJ-1000EL	19006	
☐	F-HMLD	CRJ-1000EL	19007	
☐	F-HMLE	CRJ-1000EL	19009	
☐	F-HMLF	CRJ-1000EL	19010	
☐	F-HMLG	CRJ-1000EL	19012	
☐	F-HMLH	CRJ-1000EL	19013	
☐	F-HMLI	CRJ-1000EL	19014	
☐	F-HMLJ	CRJ-1000EL	19015	
☐	F-HMLK	CRJ-1000EL	19016	
☐	F-HMLL	CRJ-1000EL	19017	
☐	F-HMLM	CRJ-1000EL	19023	
☐	F-HMLN	CRJ-1000EL	19024	
☐	F-HMLO	CRJ-1000EL	19041	

Operates as Hop! by Air France together with Airlinair and Regional.

CHALAIR AVIATION — CE / CLG

	Reg	Type	c/n
☐	F-GOOB	Beech 1900C-1	UC-153
☐	F-HBCA	Beech 1900D	UE-188
☐	F-HBCB	Beech 1900D	UE-390
☐	F-HBCC	Beech 1900D	UE-350
☐	F-HBCE	Beech 1900D	UE-323
☐	F-HBCG	Beech 1900D	UE-70

CORSAIR — SS / CRL

	Reg	Type	c/n
☐	F-HBIL	A330-243	320
☐	F-HCAT	A330-243	285
☐	F-HSKY	A330-343E	1359
☐	F-HZEN	A330-343E	1376
☐	F-GTUI	B747-422	26875/931
☐	F-HSEA	B747-422	26877/944
☐	F-HSUN	B747-422	26880/984

FRENCH BLUE

	Reg	Type	c/n	
☐	F-O	A330-323E	1727	o/o♦

HEX'AIR — UD / HER

	Reg	Type	c/n	
☐	F-GUPE	Beech 1900D	UE-248	
☐	F-GYPE	ERJ-135LR	145492	♦

HOP!

See Airlinair, Brit Air and Regional.

LA COMPAGNIE — BO / DJT

	Reg	Type	c/n
☐	F-HCIE	B757-204/W	27208/606
☐	F-HTAG	B757-256/W	29307/924

OPENSKIES — EC / BOS

	Reg	Type	c/n
☐	F-GPEK	B757-236/W	25808/665
☐	F-HAVI	B757-26D/W	24473/301
☐	F-HAVN	B757-230/W	25140/382

OYONNAIR

	Reg	Type	c/n
☐	F-HETS	Beech 1900D	UE-360

PAN EUROPEENNE AIR SERVICE — PEA

	Reg	Type	c/n
☐	F-GOPE	Beech 1900D	UE-103
☐	F-HAPE	Beech 1900D	UE-367
☐	F-HBPE	ERJ-145LR	145106

REGIONAL — YS / RAE

	Reg	Type	c/n
☐	F-GRGR	ERJ-135ER	145236
☐	F-GRGA	ERJ-145EP	145008
☐	F-GRGC	ERJ-145EP	145012
☐	F-GRGD	ERJ-145EP	145043
☐	F-GRGE	ERJ-145EP	145047
☐	F-GRGF	ERJ-145EP	145050
☐	F-GRGG	ERJ-145EP	145118
☐	F-GRGH	ERJ-145EP	145120
☐	F-GRGI	ERJ-145EP	145152
☐	F-GRGJ	ERJ-145EP	145297
☐	F-GRGK	ERJ-145EP	145324
☐	F-GUBC	ERJ-145MP	145556
☐	F-GUBE	ERJ-145MP	145668
☐	F-GUBF	ERJ-145MP	145669
☐	F-GUBG	ERJ-145MP	14500890
☐	F-GUEA	ERJ-145MP	145342
☐	F-GVHD	ERJ-145MP	145178
☐	F-HBXA	ERJ-170STD	17000237
☐	F-HBXB	ERJ-170STD	17000250
☐	F-HBXC	ERJ-170STD	17000263
☐	F-HBXD	ERJ-170STD	17000281
☐	F-HBXE	ERJ-170STD	17000286
☐	F-HBXF	ERJ-170STD	17000292
☐	F-HBXG	ERJ-170STD	17000301
☐	F-HBXH	ERJ-170STD	17000307
☐	F-HBXI	ERJ-170STD	17000310
☐	F-HBXJ	ERJ-170STD	17000312
☐	F-HBXK	ERJ-170LR	17000008
☐	F-HBXL	ERJ-170LR	17000009
☐	F-HBXM	ERJ-170LR	17000010
☐	F-HBXN	ERJ-170LR	17000011
☐	F-HBXO	ERJ-170LR	17000032
☐	F-HBXP	ERJ-170LR	17000036
☐	F-HBLA	ERJ-190LR	19000051
☐	F-HBLB	ERJ-190LR	19000060
☐	F-HBLC	ERJ-190LR	19000080
☐	F-HBLD	ERJ-190LR	19000113

☐ F-HBLE	ERJ-190LR	19000123	
☐ F-HBLF	ERJ-190LR	19000158	
☐ F-HBLG	ERJ-190STD	19000254	
☐ F-HBLH	ERJ-190STD	19000266	
☐ F-HBLI	ERJ-190STD	19000298	
☐ F-HBLJ	ERJ-190STD	19000311	

Operates as Hop! by Air France together with Airlinair and Brit Air.

TRANSAVIA FRANCE — TO / TVF

☐ F-GZHA	B737-8GJ/W	34901/2267	>TSC
☐ F-GZHB	B737-8GJ/W	34902/2309	>TSC
☐ F-GZHC	B737-8K2/W	29651/2534	
☐ F-GZHD	B737-8K2/W	29650/2583	>TSC
☐ F-GZHE	B737-8K2/W	29678/2615	
☐ F-GZHF	B737-8HX/W	29677/2946	
☐ F-GZHG	B737-8K2/W	30650/1158	
☐ F-GZHI	B737-86J/W	36120/4358	>TSC
☐ F-GZHJ	B737-86J/W	37778/4424	>TSC
☐ F-GZHK	B737-8K2/W	37790/4824	
☐ F-GZHL	B737-8K2/W	37791/4858	
☐ F-GZHM	B737-8K2/W	37792/4911	
☐ F-GZHN	B737-85H/W	29445/186	
☐ F-GZHO	B737-8K2/W	43880/5270	
☐ F-GZHP	B737-8K2/W	44566/5345	
☐ F-GZHQ	B737-8K2/W	44567/5396	
☐ F-GZHR	B737-8K2/W	43913/5469	
☐ F-GZHS	B737-84P/W	35074/2217	♦
☐ F-GZHT	B737-8K2/W	41332/5390	
☐ F-GZHU	B737-8K2/W	41352/5491	♦
☐ F-GZHV	B737-85H/W	29444/178	
☐ F-GZHW	B737-8K2/W		o/o♦
☐ F-GZHX	B737-8K2/W		o/o♦
☐ F-HTVA	B737-8K2/W	62158/5733	♦
☐ F-HTVB	B737-8K2/W		o/o♦
☐ F-HTVC	B737-8K2/W		o/o♦

TWIN JET — T7 / TJT

☐ F-GLND	Beech 1900D	UE-196	
☐ F-GLNE	Beech 1900D	UE-197	
☐ F-GLNF	Beech 1900D	UE-69	
☐ F-GLNH	Beech 1900D	UE-73	
☐ F-GLNK	Beech 1900D	UE-269	
☐ F-GRYL	Beech 1900D	UE-301	
☐ F-GTKJ	Beech 1900D	UE-348	
☐ F-GTVC	Beech 1900D	UE-349	
☐ F-GUME	Beech 1900D	UE-371	♦

XL AIRWAYS FRANCE — SE / XLF

☐ C-GTSD	A330-343E	407	<TSC♦
☐ F-GRSQ	A330-243	501	
☐ F-GSEU	A330-243	635	>SGG
☐ F-HXLF	A330-303	1360	
☐ F-HAXL	B737-8Q8/W	35279/2626	
☐ F-HJUL	B737-8Q8/W	38819/3519	>LGL

F-O PACIFIC TERRITORIES

AIR CALEDONIE — TY / TPC

☐ F-OIPI	ATR 42-500	647	
☐ F-OIPN	ATR 72-212A	735	
☐ F-OIPS	ATR 72-212A	764	
☐ F-ONCL	ATR 72-212A	759	
☐ F-O	ATR 72-600		o/o♦
☐ F-O	ATR 72-600		o/o♦

AIR TAHITI — VT / VTA

☐ F-ORVB	ATR 42-600	1007	
☐ F-ORVC	ATR 42-600	1013	
☐ F-OIQN	ATR 72-212A	719	
☐ F-OIQO	ATR 72-212A	731	std
☐ F-OIQR	ATR 72-212A	862	
☐ F-OIQT	ATR 72-212A	829	
☐ F-OIQU	ATR 72-212A	751	
☐ F-OIQV	ATR 72-212A	806	
☐ F-ORVN	ATR 72-600	1255	♦
☐ F-ORVO	ATR 72-600	1289	♦
☐ F-ORVS	ATR 72-600	1192	
☐ F-O	ATR 72-600		o/o♦
☐ F-O	ATR 72-600		o/o♦

AIR TAHITI NUI — TN / THT

☐ F-OJGF	A340-313X	385	
☐ F-OJTN	A340-313X	395	
☐ F-OLOV	A340-313E	668	>CAJ
☐ F-OSEA	A340-313X	438	
☐ F-OSUN	A340-313X	446	

AIRCALIN — SB / ACI

☐ F-OHSD	A330-202	507	
☐ F-OJSB	A320-232	2152	
☐ F-OJSE	A330-202	510	
☐ F-OZNC	A320-232	3547	
☐ F-OCQZ	DHC-6 Twin Otter 300	412	
☐ F-OIAQ	DHC-6 Twin Otter 300	381	

F-O ATLANTIC / INDIAN OCEAN

AIR AUSTRAL — UU / REU

☐ F-OHSF	ATR 72-212A	650	
☐ F-OMRU	ATR 72-212A	855	
☐ F-OZSE	ATR 72-212A	813	>EWR
☐ F-GZTB	B737-33V(QC)	29336/3102	<FPO♦
☐ F-ONGA	B737-89M/W	40910/3484	
☐ F-ONGB	B737-89M/W	40911/3504	
☐ F-ONOU	B777-3Q8ER	35783/786	
☐ F-OREU	B777-39MER	37434/912	
☐ F-OSYD	B777-3Q8ER	35782/778	
☐ F-O	B777-3xx		o/o♦
☐ F-O	B777-3xx		o/o♦
☐ F-O	B787-8	34491/15	o/o
☐ F-O	B787-8	34510/22	o/o

AIR ST PIERRE — PJ / SPM

☐ F-OFSP	ATR 42-500	801	

EWA AIR — ZD / EWR

☐ F-OZSE	ATR 72-212A	813	<REU

F-O FRENCH CARIBBEAN

AIR ANTILLES EXPRESS — 3S / GUY

☐ F-OIXD	ATR 42-500	695	
☐ F-OIXE	ATR 42-500	807	
☐ F-OIXH	ATR 42-500	831	

☐	F-OIXO	ATR 42-600	1010	
☐	F-O	ATR 42-600		o/o♦
☐	F-OHJG	DHC-6 Twin Otter 300	603	
☐	F-OIJL	DHC-6 Twin Otter 320	281	
☐	F-OIJY	DHC-6 Twin Otter 300	797	
☐	F-OIXF	LET L-410UVP-E20	092635	
☐	F-OIXG	LET L-410UVP-E20	2734	
☐	F-OIXT	LET L-410UVP-E20	2903	

AIR CARAIBES — *TX / FWI*

☐	F-OIJH	ATR 72-212A	682	
☐	F-OIJK	ATR 72-212A	736	
☐	F-OIXL	ATR 72-212A	888	
☐	F-O	ATR 72-600		o/o♦
☐	F-O	ATR 72-600		o/o♦

AIR CARAIBES ATLANTIQUE — *TX / CAJ*

☐	C-GTSR	A330-243	966	<TSC♦
☐	F-GOTO	A330-323E	1021	
☐	F-HPTP	A330-323E	1265	
☐	F-OFDF	A330-223	253	
☐	F-OLOV	A340-313E	668	<THT♦
☐	F-OONE	A330-323E	965	
☐	F-ORLY	A330-323E	758	
☐	F-O	A350-941	082	o/o♦

G- UNITED KINGDOM

ATLANTIC AIRLINES — *NPT*

☐	G-JMCL	B737-322F	23951/1532	
☐	G-JMCM	B737-3Y0F	24679/1897	
☐	G-JMCO	B737-3T0(SF)	23569/1258	
☐	G-JMCP	B737-3T0(SF)	23578/1358	>AWC
☐	G-JMCR	B737-4Q8(F)	25372/2280	
☐	G-JMCT	B737-3Y0(SF)	24546/1811	
☐	G-JMCU	B737-301(SF)	23513/1327	
☐	G-JMCV	B737-4K5(F)	24128/1715	♦
☐	G-JMCZ	B737-4K5(F)	24126/1697	♦

AURIGNY AIR SERVICES — *GR / AUR*

☐	G-HUET	ATR 42-500	584	
☐	G-BWDB	ATR 72-202	449	
☐	G-COBO	ATR 72-212A	852	
☐	G-VZON	ATR 72-212A	853	
☐	G-LGIS	Do228-202K	8160	♦
☐	G-SAYE	Do228-201	8046	♦
☐	G-OAUR	Do228-212	8305	♦
☐	G-NSEY	ERJ-195STD	19000671	

BA CITYFLYER — *CJ / CFE*

☐	G-LCYD	ERJ-170STD	17000294	
☐	G-LCYE	ERJ-170STD	17000296	
☐	G-LCYF	ERJ-170STD	17000298	
☐	G-LCYG	ERJ-170STD	17000300	
☐	G-LCYH	ERJ-170STD	17000302	
☐	G-LCYI	ERJ-170STD	17000305	
☐	G-LCYJ	ERJ-190SR	19000339	
☐	G-LCYK	ERJ-190SR	19000343	
☐	G-LCYL	ERJ-190SR	19000346	
☐	G-LCYM	ERJ-190SR	19000351	
☐	G-LCYN	ERJ-190SR	19000392	
☐	G-LCYO	ERJ-190SR	19000430	
☐	G-LCYP	ERJ-190SR	19000443	
☐	G-LCYR	ERJ-190SR	19000563	
☐	G-LCYS	ERJ-190SR	19000663	
☐	G-LCYT	ERJ-190SR	19000670	
☐	G-LCYU	ERJ-190SR	19000674	
☐	G-LCYV	ERJ-190SR	19000255	♦
☐	G-CDKA	SAAB 2000	2000-006	<EZE♦

BLUE ISLANDS — *SI / BCI*

☐	G-ISLF	ATR 42-500	546	
☐	G-ISLG	ATR 42-320	019	
☐	G-ISLH	ATR 42-300	173	
☐	G-ISLI	ATR 72-212A	529	
☐	G-ZEBS	ATR 42-320	066	

BMI REGIONAL — *BM / BMR*

☐	G-EMBI	ERJ-145EP	145126	
☐	G-EMBJ	ERJ-145EP	145134	
☐	G-EMBN	ERJ-145EP	145201	
☐	G-RJXA	ERJ-145EP	145136	
☐	G-RJXB	ERJ-145EP	145142	
☐	G-RJXC	ERJ-145EP	145153	
☐	G-RJXD	ERJ-145EP	145207	
☐	G-RJXE	ERJ-145EP	145245	
☐	G-RJXF	ERJ-145EP	145280	
☐	G-RJXG	ERJ-145EP	145390	
☐	G-RJXH	ERJ-145EP	145442	
☐	G-RJXI	ERJ-145EP	145454	>BEL
☐	G-RJXJ	ERJ-135ER	145473	
☐	G-RJXK	ERJ-135ER	145494	
☐	G-RJXL	ERJ-135ER	145376	
☐	G-RJXM	ERJ-145MP	145216	
☐	G-RJXP	ERJ-135ER	145431	
☐	G-RJXR	ERJ-145EP	145070	

BRITISH AIRWAYS — *BA / BAW*

☐	G-EUNA	A318-112	4007	
☐	G-EUNB	A318-112	4039	
☐	G-DBCA	A319-131	2098	
☐	G-DBCB	A319-131	2188	
☐	G-DBCC	A319-131	2194	
☐	G-DBCD	A319-131	2389	
☐	G-DBCE	A319-131	2429	
☐	G-DBCF	A319-131	2466	
☐	G-DBCG	A319-131	2694	
☐	G-DBCH	A319-131	2697	
☐	G-DBCI	A319-131	2720	
☐	G-DBCJ	A319-131	2981	
☐	G-DBCK	A319-131	3049	
☐	G-EUOA	A319-131	1513	
☐	G-EUOB	A319-131	1529	
☐	G-EUOC	A319-131	1537	
☐	G-EUOD	A319-131	1558	
☐	G-EUOE	A319-131	1574	
☐	G-EUOF	A319-131	1590	
☐	G-EUOG	A319-131	1594	
☐	G-EUOH	A319-131	1604	
☐	G-EUOI	A319-131	1606	
☐	G-EUPA	A319-131	1082	
☐	G-EUPB	A319-131	1115	
☐	G-EUPC	A319-131	1118	
☐	G-EUPD	A319-131	1142	
☐	G-EUPE	A319-131	1193	
☐	G-EUPF	A319-131	1197	
☐	G-EUPG	A319-131	1222	
☐	G-EUPH	A319-131	1225	

	Reg.	Type	C/n	
☐	G-EUPJ	A319-131	1232	
☐	G-EUPK	A319-131	1236	
☐	G-EUPL	A319-131	1239	
☐	G-EUPM	A319-131	1258	
☐	G-EUPN	A319-131	1261	
☐	G-EUPO	A319-131	1279	
☐	G-EUPP	A319-131	1295	
☐	G-EUPR	A319-131	1329	
☐	G-EUPS	A319-131	1338	
☐	G-EUPT	A319-131	1380	
☐	G-EUPU	A319-131	1384	
☐	G-EUPV	A319-131	1423	
☐	G-EUPW	A319-131	1440	
☐	G-EUPX	A319-131	1445	
☐	G-EUPY	A319-131	1466	
☐	G-EUPZ	A319-131	1510	
☐	G-EUUA	A320-232	1661	
☐	G-EUUB	A320-232	1689	
☐	G-EUUC	A320-232	1696	
☐	G-EUUD	A320-232	1760	
☐	G-EUUE	A320-232	1782	
☐	G-EUUF	A320-232	1814	
☐	G-EUUG	A320-232	1829	
☐	G-EUUH	A320-232	1665	
☐	G-EUUI	A320-232	1871	
☐	G-EUUJ	A320-232	1883	
☐	G-EUUK	A320-232	1899	
☐	G-EUUL	A320-232	1708	
☐	G-EUUM	A320-232	1907	
☐	G-EUUN	A320-232	1910	
☐	G-EUUO	A320-232	1958	
☐	G-EUUP	A320-232	2038	
☐	G-EUUR	A320-232	2040	
☐	G-EUUS	A320-232	3301	
☐	G-EUUT	A320-232	3314	
☐	G-EUUU	A320-232	3351	
☐	G-EUUV	A320-232	3468	
☐	G-EUUW	A320-232	3499	
☐	G-EUUX	A320-232	3550	
☐	G-EUUY	A320-232	3607	
☐	G-EUUZ	A320-232	3649	
☐	G-EUYA	A320-232	3697	
☐	G-EUYB	A320-232	3703	
☐	G-EUYC	A320-232	3721	
☐	G-EUYD	A320-232	3726	
☐	G-EUYE	A320-232	3912	
☐	G-EUYF	A320-232	4185	
☐	G-EUYG	A320-232	4238	
☐	G-EUYH	A320-232	4265	
☐	G-EUYI	A320-232	4306	
☐	G-EUYJ	A320-232	4464	
☐	G-EUYK	A320-232	4551	
☐	G-EUYL	A320-232	4725	
☐	G-EUYM	A320-232	4791	
☐	G-EUYN	A320-232	4975	
☐	G-EUYO	A320-232/S	5634	
☐	G-EUYP	A320-232/S	5784	
☐	G-EUYR	A320-232/S	5856	
☐	G-EUYS	A320-232/S	5948	
☐	G-EUYT	A320-232/S	5985	
☐	G-EUYU	A320-232/S	6028	
☐	G-EUYV	A320-232/S	6091	
☐	G-EUYW	A320-232/S	6129	
☐	G-EUYX	A320-232/S	6155	
☐	G-EUYY	A320-232/S	6290	
☐	G-GATH	A320-233	1482	
☐	G-GATJ	A320-233	1509	
☐	G-GATK	A320-233	1902	
☐	G-GATL	A320-233	1834	
☐	G-GATM	A320-233	1892	
☐	G-GATN	A320-232	1613	
☐	G-GATP	A320-232	1804	
☐	G-GATR	A320-232	1771	
☐	G-GATS	A320-232	1672	
☐	G-GATU	A320-232	3089	o/o♦
☐	G-MEDK	A320-232	2441	
☐	G-MIDO	A320-232	1987	
☐	G-MIDS	A320-232	1424	
☐	G-MIDT	A320-232	1418	
☐	G-MIDX	A320-232	1177	
☐	G-MIDY	A320-232	1014	
☐	G-TTOB	A320-232	1687	
☐	G-TTOE	A320-232	1754	
☐	G-EUXC	A321-231	2305	
☐	G-EUXD	A321-231	2320	
☐	G-EUXE	A321-231	2323	
☐	G-EUXF	A321-231	2324	
☐	G-EUXG	A321-231	2351	
☐	G-EUXH	A321-231	2363	
☐	G-EUXI	A321-231	2536	
☐	G-EUXJ	A321-231	3081	
☐	G-EUXK	A321-231	3235	
☐	G-EUXL	A321-231	3254	
☐	G-EUXM	A321-231	3290	
☐	G-MEDF	A321-231	1690	
☐	G-MEDG	A321-231	1711	
☐	G-MEDJ	A321-231	2190	
☐	G-MEDL	A321-231	2653	
☐	G-MEDM	A321-231	2799	
☐	G-MEDN	A321-231	3512	
☐	G-MEDU	A321-231	3926	
☐	G-XLEA	A380-841	095	
☐	G-XLEB	A380-841	121	
☐	G-XLEC	A380-841	124	
☐	G-XLED	A380-841	144	
☐	G-XLEE	A380-841	148	
☐	G-XLEF	A380-841	151	
☐	G-XLEG	A380-841	161	
☐	G-XLEH	A380-841	163	
☐	G-XLEI	A380-841	173	
☐	G-XLEJ	A380-841	192	♦
☐	G-XLEK	A380-841	194	♦
☐	G-XLEL	A380-841	215	o/o♦
☐	G-BNLF	B747-436	24048/773	
☐	G-BNLJ	B747-436	24052/789	
☐	G-BNLK	B747-436	24053/790	
☐	G-BNLN	B747-436	24056/802	
☐	G-BNLO	B747-436	24057/817	
☐	G-BNLP	B747-436	24058/828	
☐	G-BNLV	B747-436	25427/900	
☐	G-BNLY	B747-436	27090/959	
☐	G-BYGA	B747-436	28855/1190	
☐	G-BYGB	B747-436	28856/1194	
☐	G-BYGC	B747-436	25823/1195	
☐	G-BYGD	B747-436	28857/1196	
☐	G-BYGE	B747-436	28858/1198	
☐	G-BYGF	B747-436	25824/1200	
☐	G-BYGG	B747-436	28859/1212	
☐	G-CIVA	B747-436	27092/967	
☐	G-CIVB	B747-436	25811/1018	
☐	G-CIVC	B747-436	25812/1022	

	Reg	Type	c/n	
☐	G-CIVD	B747-436	27349/1048	
☐	G-CIVE	B747-436	27350/1050	
☐	G-CIVF	B747-436	25434/1058	
☐	G-CIVG	B747-436	25813/1059	
☐	G-CIVH	B747-436	25809/1078	
☐	G-CIVI	B747-436	25814/1079	
☐	G-CIVJ	B747-436	25817/1102	
☐	G-CIVK	B747-436	25818/1104	
☐	G-CIVL	B747-436	27478/1108	
☐	G-CIVM	B747-436	28700/1116	
☐	G-CIVN	B747-436	28848/1129	
☐	G-CIVO	B747-436	28849/1135	
☐	G-CIVP	B747-436	28850/1144	
☐	G-CIVR	B747-436	25820/1146	
☐	G-CIVS	B747-436	28851/1148	
☐	G-CIVT	B747-436	25821/1149	
☐	G-CIVU	B747-436	25810/1154	
☐	G-CIVV	B747-436	25819/1156	
☐	G-CIVW	B747-436	25822/1157	
☐	G-CIVX	B747-436	28852/1172	
☐	G-CIVY	B747-436	28853/1178	
☐	G-CIVZ	B747-436	28854/1183	
☐	G-BNWA	B767-336ER	24333/265	
☐	G-BNWB	B767-336ER	24334/281	
☐	G-BNWI	B767-336ER	24341/342	
☐	G-BNWM	B767-336ER	25204/376	
☐	G-BNWT	B767-336ER	25828/476	
☐	G-BNWW	B767-336ER	25831/526	
☐	G-BNWX	B767-336ER	25832/529	
☐	G-BNWY	B767-336ER	25834/608	
☐	G-BNWZ	B767-336ER	25733/648	
☐	G-BZHA	B767-336ER	29230/702	
☐	G-BZHB	B767-336ER	29231/704	
☐	G-BZHC	B767-336ER	29232/708	
☐	G-RAES	B777-236ER	27491/76	
☐	G-VIIA	B777-236ER	27483/41	
☐	G-VIIB	B777-236ER	27484/49	
☐	G-VIIC	B777-236ER	27485/53	
☐	G-VIID	B777-236ER	27486/56	
☐	G-VIIE	B777-236ER	27487/58	
☐	G-VIIF	B777-236ER	27488/61	
☐	G-VIIG	B777-236ER	27489/65	
☐	G-VIIH	B777-236ER	27490/70	
☐	G-VIIJ	B777-236ER	27492/111	
☐	G-VIIK	B777-236ER	28840/117	
☐	G-VIIL	B777-236ER	27493/127	
☐	G-VIIM	B777-236ER	28841/130	
☐	G-VIIN	B777-236ER	29319/157	
☐	G-VIIO	B777-236ER	29320/182	
☐	G-VIIP	B777-236ER	29321/193	
☐	G-VIIR	B777-236ER	29322/203	
☐	G-VIIS	B777-236ER	29323/206	
☐	G-VIIT	B777-236ER	29962/217	
☐	G-VIIU	B777-236ER	29963/221	
☐	G-VIIV	B777-236ER	29964/228	
☐	G-VIIW	B777-236ER	29965/233	
☐	G-VIIX	B777-236ER	29966/236	
☐	G-VIIY	B777-236ER	29967/251	
☐	G-YMMA	B777-236ER	30302/242	
☐	G-YMMB	B777-236ER	30303/265	
☐	G-YMMC	B777-236ER	30304/268	
☐	G-YMMD	B777-236ER	30305/269	
☐	G-YMME	B777-236ER	30306/275	
☐	G-YMMF	B777-236ER	30307/281	
☐	G-YMMG	B777-236ER	30308/301	
☐	G-YMMH	B777-236ER	30309/303	
☐	G-YMMI	B777-236ER	30310/308	
☐	G-YMMJ	B777-236ER	30311/311	
☐	G-YMMK	B777-236ER	30312/312	
☐	G-YMML	B777-236ER	30313/334	
☐	G-YMMN	B777-236ER	30316/346	
☐	G-YMMO	B777-236ER	30317/361	
☐	G-YMMP	B777-236ER	30315/369	
☐	G-YMMR	B777-236ER	36516/771	
☐	G-YMMS	B777-236ER	36517/784	
☐	G-YMMT	B777-236ER	36518/791	
☐	G-YMMU	B777-236ER	36519/796	
☐	G-ZZZA	B777-236	27105/6	
☐	G-ZZZB	B777-236	27106/10	
☐	G-ZZZC	B777-236	27107/15	
☐	G-STBA	B777-336ER	40542/879	
☐	G-STBB	B777-36NER	38286/887	
☐	G-STBC	B777-36NER	38287/901	
☐	G-STBD	B777-36NER	38695/968	
☐	G-STBE	B777-36NER	38696/980	
☐	G-STBF	B777-336ER	40543/995	
☐	G-STBG	B777-336ER	38430/1135	
☐	G-STBH	B777-336ER	38431/1143	
☐	G-STBI	B777-336ER	43702/1171	
☐	G-STBJ	B777-336ER	43703/1182	
☐	G-STBK	B777-336ER	42121/1204	
☐	G-STBL	B777-336ER	42124/1221	
☐	G-	B777-336ER		o/o
☐	G-	B777-336ER		o/o
☐	G-ZBJA	B787-8	38609/108	
☐	G-ZBJB	B787-8	38610/111	
☐	G-ZBJC	B787-8	38611/114	
☐	G-ZBJD	B787-8	38619/121	
☐	G-ZBJE	B787-8	38612/173	
☐	G-ZBJF	B787-8	38613/177	
☐	G-ZBJG	B787-8	38614/187	
☐	G-ZBJH	B787-8	38615/197	
☐	G-	B787-8		o/o♦
☐	G-ZBKA	B787-9	38616/346	
☐	G-ZBKB	B787-9	38617/357	
☐	G-ZBKC	B787-9	38621/360	♦
☐	G-ZBKD	B787-9	38618/361	♦
☐	G-ZBKE	B787-9	38620/374	♦
☐	G-ZBKF	B787-9	38622/392	♦
☐	G-ZBKG	B787-9	38623/396	o/o♦
☐	G-ZBKH	B787-9	38624/404	o/o♦
☐	G-ZBKI	B787-9	38625/406	o/o♦
☐	G-ZBKJ	B787-9	38626/424	o/o♦
☐	G-ZBKK	B787-9	38627/442	o/o♦
☐	G-ZBKL	B787-9	38628/451	o/o♦
☐	G-ZBKM	B787-9	38629/461	o/o♦

CELLO AVIATION — *CLJ*

	Reg	Type	c/n	
☐	G-RAJG	B737-476	24439/2265	>TFL
☐	G-RAJJ	BAe146 Srs.200	E2108	

CITYWING — *V9*

	Reg	Type	c/n	
☐	OK-ASA	LET L-410UVP-E	902439	<VAA
☐	OK-LAZ	LET L-410UVP-E	902504	<VAA♦
☐	OK-RDA	LET L-410UVP-E5	861813	<VAA
☐	OK-UBA	LET L-410UVP-E16	892319	<VAA

All operated by Van Air.

CARGOLOGIC AIR — *P3 / CLU*

	Reg	Type	c/n	
☐	G-CLAA	B747-446F	33749/1352	♦

DHL AIR				**D0 / DHK**
□	G-BIKB	B757-236(SF)	22173/10	♦
□	G-BIKC	B757-236(SF)	22174/11	
□	G-BIKF	B757-236(SF)	22177/16	
□	G-BIKG	B757-236(SF)	22178/23	
□	G-BIKK	B757-236(SF)	22182/30	
□	G-BIKM	B757-236(SF)	22184/33	
□	G-BIKO	B757-236(SF)	22187/52	
□	G-BIKP	B757-236(SF)	22188/54	
□	G-BIKU	B757-236(SF)	23399/78	
□	G-BIKV	B757-236(SF)	23400/81	
□	G-BIKX	B757-236(SF)	23493/90	♦
□	G-BIKZ	B757-236(SF)	23532/98	
□	G-BMRA	B757-236(SF)	23710/123	
□	G-BMRB	B757-236(SF)	23975/145	
□	G-BMRC	B757-236(SF)	24072/160	
□	G-BMRD	B757-236(SF)	24073/166	
□	G-BMRE	B757-236(SF)	24074/168	
□	G-BMRF	B757-236(SF)	24101/175	
□	G-BMRG	B757-236(SF)	24102/179	♦
□	G-BMRH	B757-236(SF)	24266/210	
□	G-BMRI	B757-236(SF)	24267/211	>AXF
□	G-BMRJ	B757-236(SF)	24268/214	
□	G-DHLE	B767-3JHF/W	37805/980	
□	G-DHLF	B767-3JHF/W	37806/981	
□	G-DHLG	B767-3JHF/W	37807/982	
□	G-DHLH	B767-3JHF/W	37808/1036	

EASTERN AIRWAYS				**T3 / EZE**
□	G-MAJA	BAeJetstream 41	41032	
□	G-MAJB	BAeJetstream 41	41018	
□	G-MAJC	BAeJetstream 41	41005	
□	G-MAJD	BAeJetstream 41	41006	
□	G-MAJE	BAeJetstream 41	41007	
□	G-MAJF	BAeJetstream 41	41008	
□	G-MAJG	BAeJetstream 41	41009	
□	G-MAJH	BAeJetstream 41	41010	
□	G-MAJI	BAeJetstream 41	41011	
□	G-MAJJ	BAeJetstream 41	41024	
□	G-MAJK	BAeJetstream 41	41070	
□	G-MAJL	BAeJetstream 41	41087	
□	G-MAJT	BAeJetstream 41	41040	
□	G-MAJU	BAeJetstream 41	41071	
□	G-MAJW	BAeJetstream 41	41015	
□	G-MAJY	BAeJetstream 41	41099	
□	G-MAJZ	BAeJetstream 41	41100	
□	G-CGWV	ERJ-145MP	145362	
□	G-CHMR	ERJ-145MP	145405	
□	G-CISK	ERJ-145LU	145570	♦
□	PH-DND	ERJ-145MP	145406	<DNM♦
□	G-CDEA	SAAB 2000	2000-009	
□	G-CDEB	SAAB 2000	2000-036	
□	G-CDKA	SAAB 2000	2000-006	>CFE
□	G-CDKB	SAAB 2000	2000-032	
□	G-CERY	SAAB 2000	2000-008	
□	G-CERZ	SAAB 2000	2000-042	
□	G-CFLU	SAAB 2000	2000-055	
□	G-CFLV	SAAB 2000	2000-023	
□	G-CIEC	SAAB 2000	2000-037	

EASYJET AIRLINE				**U2 / EZY**
□	G-EJAR	A319-111	2412	
□	G-EZAA	A319-111	2677	
□	G-EZAB	A319-111	2681	
□	G-EZAC	A319-111	2691	
□	G-EZAD	A319-111	2702	[MLA]
□	G-EZAF	A319-111	2715	
□	G-EZAG	A319-111	2727	
□	G-EZAI	A319-111	2735	
□	G-EZAJ	A319-111	2742	
□	G-EZAK	A319-111	2744	
□	G-EZAL	A319-111	2754	
□	G-EZAM	A319-111	2037	
□	G-EZAN	A319-111	2765	
□	G-EZAO	A319-111	2769	
□	G-EZAP	A319-111	2777	
□	G-EZAS	A319-111	2779	
□	G-EZAT	A319-111	2782	
□	G-EZAU	A319-111	2795	
□	G-EZAV	A319-111	2803	
□	G-EZAW	A319-111	2812	
□	G-EZAX	A319-111	2818	
□	G-EZAY	A319-111	2827	
□	G-EZAZ	A319-111	2829	
□	G-EZBA	A319-111	2860	
□	G-EZBB	A319-111	2854	
□	G-EZBC	A319-111	2866	
□	G-EZBD	A319-111	2873	
□	G-EZBE	A319-111	2884	
□	G-EZBF	A319-111	2923	
□	G-EZBG	A319-111	2946	
□	G-EZBH	A319-111	2959	
□	G-EZBI	A319-111	3003	
□	G-EZBJ	A319-111	3036	
□	G-EZBK	A319-111	3041	
□	G-EZBL	A319-111	3053	
□	G-EZBM	A319-111	3059	
□	G-EZBN	A319-111	3061	
□	G-EZBO	A319-111	3082	
□	G-EZBR	A319-111	3088	
□	G-EZBT	A319-111	3090	
□	G-EZBU	A319-111	3118	
□	G-EZBV	A319-111	3122	
□	G-EZBW	A319-111	3134	
□	G-EZBX	A319-111	3137	
□	G-EZBY	A319-111	3176	
□	G-EZBZ	A319-111	3184	
□	G-EZDA	A319-111	3413	
□	G-EZDB	A319-111	3411	
□	G-EZDC	A319-111	2043	
□	G-EZDD	A319-111	3442	
□	G-EZDE	A319-111	3426	
□	G-EZDF	A319-111	3432	
□	G-EZDH	A319-111	3466	
□	G-EZDI	A319-111	3537	
□	G-EZDJ	A319-111	3544	
□	G-EZDK	A319-111	3555	
□	G-EZDL	A319-111	3569	
□	G-EZDM	A319-111	3571	
□	G-EZDN	A319-111	3608	
□	G-EZDO	A319-111	3634	
□	G-EZDP	A319-111	3675	
□	G-EZDR	A319-111	3683	
□	G-EZDS	A319-111	3702	
□	G-EZDT	A319-111	3720	
□	G-EZDU	A319-111	3735	
□	G-EZDV	A319-111	3742	
□	G-EZDW	A319-111	3746	
□	G-EZDX	A319-111	3754	
□	G-EZDY	A319-111	3763	

	Reg	Type	c/n	
☐	G-EZDZ	A319-111	3774	
☐	G-EZEB	A319-111	2120	
☐	G-EZED	A319-111	2170	
☐	G-EZEG	A319-111	2181	
☐	G-EZEH	A319-111	2184	♦
☐	G-EZEN	A319-111	2245	♦
☐	G-EZEV	A319-111	2289	
☐	G-EZEW	A319-111	2300	
☐	G-EZEY	A319-111	2353	♦
☐	G-EZEZ	A319-111	2360	
☐	G-EZFA	A319-111	3788	
☐	G-EZFB	A319-111	3799	
☐	G-EZFC	A319-111	3808	
☐	G-EZFD	A319-111	3810	
☐	G-EZFE	A319-111	3824	
☐	G-EZFF	A319-111	3844	
☐	G-EZFG	A319-111	3845	
☐	G-EZFH	A319-111	3854	
☐	G-EZFI	A319-111	3888	
☐	G-EZFJ	A319-111	4040	
☐	G-EZFK	A319-111	4048	
☐	G-EZFL	A319-111	4056	
☐	G-EZFM	A319-111	4069	
☐	G-EZFN	A319-111	4076	
☐	G-EZFO	A319-111	4080	
☐	G-EZFP	A319-111	4087	
☐	G-EZFR	A319-111	4125	
☐	G-EZFS	A319-111	4129	
☐	G-EZFT	A319-111	4132	
☐	G-EZFU	A319-111	4313	
☐	G-EZFV	A319-111	4327	
☐	G-EZFW	A319-111	4380	
☐	G-EZFX	A319-111	4385	
☐	G-EZFY	A319-111	4418	
☐	G-EZFZ	A319-111	4425	
☐	G-EZGA	A319-111	4427	
☐	G-EZGB	A319-111	4437	
☐	G-EZGC	A319-111	4444	
☐	G-EZGD	A319-111	4451	
☐	G-EZGE	A319-111	4624	
☐	G-EZGF	A319-111	4635	
☐	G-EZIH	A319-111	2463	
☐	G-EZII	A319-111	2471	
☐	G-EZIJ	A319-111	2477	
☐	G-EZIK	A319-111	2481	
☐	G-EZIL	A319-111	2492	
☐	G-EZIM	A319-111	2495	
☐	G-EZIN	A319-111	2503	
☐	G-EZIO	A319-111	2512	
☐	G-EZIP	A319-111	2514	
☐	G-EZIR	A319-111	2527	
☐	G-EZIS	A319-111	2528	
☐	G-EZIT	A319-111	2538	
☐	G-EZIV	A319-111	2565	
☐	G-EZIW	A319-111	2578	
☐	G-EZIX	A319-111	2605	
☐	G-EZIY	A319-111	2636	
☐	G-EZIZ	A319-111	2646	
☐	G-EZMH	A319-111	2053	
☐	G-EZMK	A319-111	2370	♦
☐	G-EZNC	A319-111	2050	
☐	G-EZPG	A319-111	2385	
☐	G-EZSM	A319-111	2062	
☐	G-EZOA	A320-214/S	6412	
☐	G-EZOB	A320-214/S	6416	
☐	G-EZOC	A320-214/S	6485	
☐	G-EZOD	A320-214/S	6502	
☐	G-EZOE	A320-214/S	6509	
☐	G-EZOF	A320-214/S	6525	
☐	G-EZOG	A320-214/S	6541	
☐	G-EZOH	A320-214/S	6546	
☐	G-EZOI	A320-214/S	6562	
☐	G-EZOJ	A320-214/S	6565	
☐	G-EZOK	A320-214/S	6568	
☐	G-EZOL	A320-214/S	6572	
☐	G-EZOM	A320-214/S	6587	
☐	G-EZON	A320-214/S	6605	
☐	G-EZOO	A320-214/S	6606	
☐	G-EZOP	A320-214/S	6633	
☐	G-EZOR	A320-214/S	6675	
☐	G-EZOT	A320-214/S	6680	
☐	G-EZOU	A320-214/S	6754	♦
☐	G-EZOV	A320-214/S	6788	♦
☐	G-EZOW	A320-214/S	6834	♦
☐	G-EZOX	A320-214/S	6837	♦
☐	G-EZOY	A320-214/S	6885	♦
☐	G-EZOZ	A320-214/S	6918	♦
☐	G-EZPA	A320-214/S	6970	♦
☐	G-EZPB	A320-214/S	6977	♦
☐	G-EZPC	A320-214/S	6981	♦
☐	G-EZPD	A320-214/S	7040	o/o♦
☐	G-EZPE	A320-214/S	7044	o/o♦
☐	G-EZPF	A320-214/S	7067	o/o♦
☐	G-EZPH	A320-214/S	7093	o/o♦
☐	G-EZPI	A320-214/S	7104	o/o♦
☐	G-EZPJ	A320-214/S	7132	o/o♦
☐	G-EZPK	A320-214/S	7177	o/o♦
☐	G-EZPL	A320-214/S	7183	o/o♦
☐	G-	A320-214/S	7215	o/o♦
☐	G-	A320-214/S	7228	o/o♦
☐	G-	A320-214/S	7235	o/o♦
☐	G-	A320-214/S	7243	o/o♦
☐	G-EZTA	A320-214	3805	
☐	G-EZTB	A320-214	3843	
☐	G-EZTC	A320-214	3871	
☐	G-EZTD	A320-214	3909	
☐	G-EZTE	A320-214	3913	
☐	G-EZTF	A320-214	3922	
☐	G-EZTG	A320-214	3946	
☐	G-EZTH	A320-214	3953	
☐	G-EZTI	A320-214	3975	
☐	G-EZTJ	A320-214	3979	
☐	G-EZTK	A320-214	3991	
☐	G-EZTL	A320-214	4012	
☐	G-EZTM	A320-214	4014	
☐	G-EZTR	A320-214	4179	
☐	G-EZTT	A320-214	4219	
☐	G-EZTV	A320-214	4234	
☐	G-EZTX	A320-214	4286	
☐	G-EZTY	A320-214	4554	
☐	G-EZTZ	A320-214	4556	
☐	G-EZUA	A320-214	4588	
☐	G-EZUC	A320-214	4591	
☐	G-EZUD	A320-214	4636	
☐	G-EZUF	A320-214	4676	
☐	G-EZUG	A320-214	4680	
☐	G-EZUH	A320-214	4708	
☐	G-EZUI	A320-214	4721	
☐	G-EZUJ	A320-214	4740	
☐	G-EZUK	A320-214	4749	
☐	G-EZUL	A320-214	5019	
☐	G-EZUM	A320-214	5020	
☐	G-EZUN	A320-214	5046	

	Reg	Type	MSN	Notes
☐	G-EZUO	A320-214	5052	
☐	G-EZUP	A320-214	5056	
☐	G-EZUR	A320-214	5064	
☐	G-EZUS	A320-214	5104	
☐	G-EZUT	A320-214	5113	
☐	G-EZUW	A320-214	5116	
☐	G-EZUZ	A320-214	5187	
☐	G-EZWA	A320-214	5201	
☐	G-EZWB	A320-214	5224	
☐	G-EZWC	A320-214	5236	
☐	G-EZWD	A320-214	5249	
☐	G-EZWE	A320-214	5289	
☐	G-EZWF	A320-214	5319	
☐	G-EZWG	A320-214/S	5318	
☐	G-EZWH	A320-214/S	5542	
☐	G-EZWI	A320-214/S	5592	
☐	G-EZWJ	A320-214/S	5638	
☐	G-EZWK	A320-214/S	5688	
☐	G-EZWL	A320-214/S	5702	
☐	G-EZWM	A320-214/S	5739	
☐	G-EZWN	A320-214/S	5757	
☐	G-EZWP	A320-214/S	5927	
☐	G-EZWR	A320-214/S	5981	
☐	G-EZWS	A320-214/S	6011	
☐	G-EZWT	A320-214/S	6047	
☐	G-EZWU	A320-214/S	6095	
☐	G-EZWV	A320-214/S	6177	
☐	G-EZWW	A320-214/S	6188	
☐	G-EZWX	A320-214/S	6192	
☐	G-EZWY	A320-214/S	6267	
☐	G-EZWZ	A320-214/S	6353	

FLYBE ***BE / BEE***

	Reg	Type	MSN	Notes
☐	EI-REL	ATR 72-212A	748	<STK
☐	EI-REM	ATR 72-212A	760	<STK
☐	G-FBXA	ATR 72-600	1260	>SAS♦
☐	G-FBXB	ATR 72-600	1277	>SAS♦
☐	G-FBXC	ATR 72-600	1300	>SAS♦
☐	G-FBXD	ATR 72-600	1315	o/o>SAS♦
☐	G-ECOA	DHC-8-402Q	4180	
☐	G-ECOB	DHC-8-402Q	4185	
☐	G-ECOC	DHC-8-402Q	4197	
☐	G-ECOD	DHC-8-402Q	4206	
☐	G-ECOE	DHC-8-402Q	4212	
☐	G-ECOF	DHC-8-402Q	4216	
☐	G-ECOG	DHC-8-402Q	4220	
☐	G-ECOH	DHC-8-402Q	4221	
☐	G-ECOI	DHC-8-402Q	4224	>BEL
☐	G-ECOJ	DHC-8-402Q	4229	
☐	G-ECOK	DHC-8-402Q	4230	>BEL
☐	G-ECOM	DHC-8-402Q	4233	
☐	G-ECOO	DHC-8-402Q	4237	
☐	G-ECOP	DHC-8-402Q	4242	
☐	G-ECOR	DHC-8-402Q	4248	
☐	G-ECOT	DHC-8-402Q	4251	
☐	G-FLBA	DHC-8-402Q	4253	
☐	G-FLBB	DHC-8-402Q	4255	
☐	G-FLBC	DHC-8-402Q	4257	
☐	G-FLBD	DHC-8-402Q	4259	
☐	G-FLBE	DHC-8-402Q	4261	
☐	G-JECE	DHC-8-402Q	4094	
☐	G-JECF	DHC-8-402Q	4095	
☐	G-JECG	DHC-8-402Q	4098	
☐	G-JECH	DHC-8-402Q	4103	
☐	G-JECI	DHC-8-402Q	4105	
☐	G-JECJ	DHC-8-402Q	4110	
☐	G-JECK	DHC-8-402Q	4113	
☐	G-JECL	DHC-8-402Q	4114	
☐	G-JECM	DHC-8-402Q	4118	
☐	G-JECN	DHC-8-402Q	4120	
☐	G-JECO	DHC-8-402Q	4126	
☐	G-JECP	DHC-8-402Q	4136	
☐	G-JECR	DHC-8-402Q	4139	
☐	G-JECX	DHC-8-402Q	4155	
☐	G-JECY	DHC-8-402Q	4157	
☐	G-JECZ	DHC-8-402Q	4179	
☐	G-JEDM	DHC-8-402Q	4077	
☐	G-JEDP	DHC-8-402Q	4085	
☐	G-JEDR	DHC-8-402Q	4087	
☐	G-JEDT	DHC-8-402Q	4088	
☐	G-JEDU	DHC-8-402Q	4089	
☐	G-JEDV	DHC-8-402Q	4090	
☐	G-JEDW	DHC-8-402Q	4093	
☐	G-KKEV	DHC-8-402Q	4201	
☐	G-PRPA	DHC-8-402Q	4187	
☐	G-PRPB	DHC-8-402Q	4333	
☐	G-PRPC	DHC-8-402Q	4338	
☐	G-PRPD	DHC-8-402Q	4332	
☐	G-PRPE	DHC-8-402Q	4209	o/o
☐	G-PRPF	DHC-8-402Q	4195	o/o♦
☐	G-PRPG	DHC-8-402Q	4204	o/o♦
☐	G-PRPL	DHC-8-402Q	4380	
☐		DHC-8-402Q	4188	o/o
☐		DHC-8-402Q	4190	o/o
☐		DHC-8-402Q	4191	o/o
☐		DHC-8-402Q	4202	o/o
☐		DHC-8-402Q	4203	o/o
☐		DHC-8-402Q	4213	o/o
☐		DHC-8-402Q	4214	o/o
☐		DHC-8-402Q	4323	o/o
☐		DHC-8-402Q	4328	o/o
☐		DHC-8-402Q	4336	o/o
☐		DHC-8-402Q	4339	o/o
☐		DHC-8-402Q	4340	o/o
☐		DHC-8-402Q	4342	o/o
☐		DHC-8-402Q	4345	o/o
☐		DHC-8-402Q	4346	o/o
☐		DHC-8-402Q	4356	o/o
☐	G-CCGS	Do328-110	3101	<LOG♦
☐	G-FBJA	ERJ-175STD	17000326	
☐	G-FBJB	ERJ-175STD	17000327	
☐	G-FBJC	ERJ-175STD	17000328	
☐	G-FBJD	ERJ-175STD	17000329	
☐	G-FBJE	ERJ-175STD	17000336	
☐	G-FBJF	ERJ-175STD	17000341	
☐	G-FBJG	ERJ-175STD	17000344	
☐	G-FBJH	ERJ-175STD	17000351	
☐	G-FBJI	ERJ-175STD	17000355	
☐	G-FBJJ	ERJ-175STD	17000358	
☐	G-FBJK	ERJ-175STD	17000359	
☐	G-FBEF	ERJ-195LR	19000104	
☐	G-FBEG	ERJ-195LR	19000120	
☐	G-FBEH	ERJ-195LR	19000128	
☐	G-FBEI	ERJ-195LR	19000143	
☐	G-FBEJ	ERJ-195LR	19000155	
☐	G-FBEK	ERJ-195LR	19000168	
☐	G-FBEL	ERJ-195LR	19000184	[EXT]
☐	G-FBEM	ERJ-195LR	19000204	
☐	G-FBEN	ERJ-195LR	19000213	
☐	OO-VLM	Fokker 50	20135	<VLM♦
☐	G-LGNC	SAAB SF.340B	340B-318	<LOG♦

☐ G-LGNO	SAAB 2000	2000-013	<LOG
☐ G-LGNP	SAAB 2000	2000-018	<LOG
☐ G-LGNR	SAAB 2000	2000-004	<LOG

FLY SALONE AIRWAYS

☐ TF-FIW	B757-27B	24838/302	♦

ISLES OF SCILLY SKYBUS 5Y / IOS

☐ G-BIHO	DHC-6 Twin Otter 310	738	
☐ G-CBML	DHC-6 Twin Otter 310	695	
☐ G-CEWM	DHC-6 Twin Otter 300	656	
☐ G-ISSG	DHC-6 Twin Otter 310	572	

JET2.COM LS / EXS

☐ G-CELA	B737-377	23663/1323	
☐ G-CELE	B737-33A	24029/1601	
☐ G-CELF	B737-377	24302/1618	
☐ G-CELG	B737-377	24303/1620	
☐ G-CELH	B737-330(QC)	23525/1278	
☐ G-CELI	B737-330	23526/1282	
☐ G-CELJ	B737-330	23529/1293	
☐ G-CELK	B737-330	23530/1297	
☐ G-CELO	B737-33A(QC)	24028/1599	
☐ G-CELP	B737-330(QC)	23522/1246	
☐ G-CELR	B737-330(QC)	23523/1271	
☐ G-CELS	B737-377	23660/1294	
☐ G-CELV	B737-377	23661/1314	
☐ G-CELW	B737-377F	23659/1292	
☐ G-CELX	B737-377	23654/1273	
☐ G-CELY	B737-377F	23662/1316	
☐ G-CELZ	B737-377F	23658/1281	
☐ G-GDFB	B737-33A/W	25743/2206	
☐ G-GDFC	B737-8K2/W	28375/85	
☐ G-GDFD	B737-8K5/W	27982/8	
☐ G-GDFE	B737-3Q8(QC)	24131/1541	
☐ G-GDFF	B737-85P	28385/421	
☐ G-GDFG	B737-36Q	28658/2865	
☐ G-GDFH	B737-3Y5	25615/2478	
☐ G-GDFJ	B737-804	28229/478	
☐ G-GDFK	B737-36N	28572/3031	
☐ G-GDFL	B737-36N/W	28568/2987	
☐ G-GDFM	B737-36N	28586/3090	
☐ G-GDFN	B737-33V/W	29332/3072	
☐ G-GDFO	B737-3U3	28740/3003	
☐ G-GDFP	B737-8Z9/W	28177/69	
☐ G-GDFR	B737-8Z9/W	30421/1345	
☐ G-GDFS	B737-86N/W	32243/869	
☐ G-GDFT	B737-36Q	29141/3035	
☐ G-GDFU	B737-8K5/W	30416/778	
☐ G-GDFV	B737-85F/W	28821/151	
☐ G-GDFW	B737-8K5/W	27986/474	
☐ G-GDFX	B737-8K5/W	27987/499	
☐ G-GDFY	B737-86Q/W	30278/963	
☐ G-GDFZ	B737-86Q/W	30276/920	
☐ G-JZHA	B737-8K5/W	30417/781	
☐ G-JZHB	B737-8K5/W	28623/556	♦
☐ G-JZHC	B737-8K5/W	30593/528	♦
☐ G-JZHD	B737-808	34706/2014	♦
☐ G-JZHE	B737-8K2/W	30390/555	o/o♦
☐ G-JZHF	B737-8K2/W	28378/291	o/o♦
☐ G-JZHG	B737-85P/W	28388/533	o/o♦
☐ G-JZHH	B737-85P/W	28536/540	o/o♦
☐ G-	B737-8xx/W		o/o♦
☐ G-	B737-8xx/W		o/o♦
☐ G-	B737-8xx/W		o/o♦
☐ G-	B737-8xx/W		o/o♦
☐ G-	B737-8xx/W		o/o♦
☐ G-	B737-8xx/W		o/o♦
☐ G-	B737-8xx/W		o/o♦
☐ G-	B737-8xx/W		o/o♦
☐ G-	B737-8xx/W		o/o♦
☐ G-	B737-8xx/W		o/o♦
☐ G-	B737-8xx/W		o/o♦
☐ G-	B737-8xx/W		o/o♦
☐ G-	B737-8xx/W		o/o♦
☐ G-	B737-8xx/W		o/o♦
☐ G-	B737-8xx/W		o/o♦
☐ G-	B737-8xx/W		o/o♦
☐ G-LSAA	B757-236	24122/187	
☐ G-LSAB	B757-27B/W	24136/169	
☐ G-LSAC	B757-23A/W	25488/471	
☐ G-LSAD	B757-236	24397/221	
☐ G-LSAE	B757-27B/W	24135/165	
☐ G-LSAG	B757-21B	24014/144	
☐ G-LSAH	B757-21B	24015/148	
☐ G-LSAI	B757-21B	24016/150	
☐ G-LSAJ	B757-236	24793/292	
☐ G-LSAK	B757-23N/W	27973/735	
☐ G-LSAN	B757-2K2/W	26635/608	

LOGANAIR LC / LOG

☐ G-GNTB	SAAB SF.340A(QC)	340A-082	
☐ G-GNTF	SAAB SF.340A(QC)	340A-113	
☐ G-LGNA	SAAB SF.340B	340B-199	
☐ G-LGNB	SAAB SF.340B	340B-216	
☐ G-LGNC	SAAB SF.340B	340B-318	>BEE
☐ G-LGND	SAAB SF.340B	340B-169	
☐ G-LGNE	SAAB SF.340B	340B-172	
☐ G-LGNF	SAAB SF.340B	340B-192	
☐ G-LGNG	SAAB SF.340B	340B-327	
☐ G-LGNH	SAAB SF.340B	340B-333	
☐ G-LGNI	SAAB SF.340B	340B-160	
☐ G-LGNJ	SAAB SF.340B	340B-173	
☐ G-LGNK	SAAB SF.340B	340B-185	
☐ G-LGNM	SAAB SF.340B	340B-187	
☐ G-LGNN	SAAB SF.340B	340B-197	
☐ G-LGNO	SAAB 2000	2000-013	>BEE
☐ G-LGNP	SAAB 2000	2000-018	>BEE
☐ G-LGNR	SAAB 2000	2000-004	>BEE
☐ G-LGNS	SAAB 2000	2000-041	♦
☐ G-BVVK	DHC-6 Twin Otter 310	666	
☐ G-HIAL	DHC-6 Twin Otter 400	917	♦
☐ G-SGTS	DHC-6 Twin Otter 400	918	♦
☐ G-BYHG	Do328-110	3098	
☐ G-BYMK	Do328-110	3062	
☐ G-BZOG	Do328-110	3088	
☐ G-CCGS	Do328-110	3101	>BEE

MONARCH AIRLINES ZB / MON

☐ G-OZBW	A320-214	1571	
☐ G-OZBX	A320-214	1637	
☐ G-OZBY	A320-214	1320	
☐ G-ZBAH	A320-214	1413	
☐ G-ZBAP	A320-214	1605	
☐ G-ZBAR	A320-214	2142	
☐ G-ZBAS	A320-214/S	6550	
☐ G-ZBAT	A320-214	3278	♦
☐ G-ZBAU	A320-214	3293	o/o♦
☐ G-MARA	A321-231	0983	

	Reg	Type	C/n	
☐	G-OJEG	A321-231	1015	
☐	G-OZBE	A321-231	1707	
☐	G-OZBF	A321-231	1763	
☐	G-OZBG	A321-231	1941	
☐	G-OZBH	A321-231	2105	
☐	G-OZBI	A321-231	2234	
☐	G-OZBL	A321-231	0864	
☐	G-OZBM	A321-231	1045	
☐	G-OZBN	A321-231	1153	
☐	G-OZBO	A321-231	1207	
☐	G-OZBR	A321-231	1794	
☐	G-OZBT	A321-231	3546	
☐	G-OZBU	A321-231	3575	
☐	G-OZBZ	A321-231	1421	
☐	G-ZBAD	A321-231	5582	
☐	G-ZBAE	A321-231	5606	
☐	G-ZBAF	A321-231	2730	
☐	G-ZBAG	A321-231	2793	
☐	G-ZBAI	A321-231	2553	
☐	G-ZBAJ	A321-231	2610	
☐	G-ZBAK	A321-231	3458	
☐	G-ZBAL	A321-231	3522	
☐	G-ZBAM	A321-231/S	6059	
☐	G-ZBAO	A321-231/S	6126	

NORWEGIAN AIR UK

	Reg	Type	C/n	
☐	G-NRWY	B737-8JP/W	39024/4610	♦

THOMAS COOK AIRLINES MT / TCX

	Reg	Type	C/n	
☐	G-DHJH	A321-211	1238	
☐	G-NIKO	A321-211	1250	
☐	G-TCDA	A321-211	2060	
☐	G-TCDB	A321-211/S	5603	
☐	G-TCDC	A321-211/S	5872	
☐	G-TCDD	A321-211/S	6038	
☐	G-TCDE	A321-211/S	6056	
☐	G-TCDF	A321-211/S	6114	
☐	G-TCDG	A321-211/S	6122	
☐	G-TCDH	A321-211/S	6515	
☐	G-TCDJ	A321-211/S	6526	>VKG
☐	G-TCDK	A321-211/S	6548	
☐	G-TCDL	A321-211/S	6968	♦
☐	G-TCDM	A321-211/S	7003	o/o♦
☐	G-TCDN	A321-211/S	7048	o/o♦
☐	G-TCDO	A321-211/S	7055	o/o♦
☐	G-TCDV	A321-211	1972	♦
☐	G-TCDW	A321-211	1921	
☐	G-TCDX	A321-211	1887	
☐	G-TCDY	A321-211	1881	
☐	G-TCDZ	A321-211	1006	
☐	G-CHTZ	A330-243	398	
☐	G-MDBD	A330-243	266	
☐	G-MLJL	A330-243	254	
☐	G-OMYT	A330-243	301	>VKG
☐	G-TCXB	A330-243	948	♦
☐	G-TCXC	A330-243	967	o/o♦
☐	G-VYGK	A330-202	1498	♦
☐	G-FCLI	B757-28A	26275/672	[DGX]
☐	G-JMAA	B757-3CQ/W	32241/960	
☐	G-JMAB	B757-3CQ/W	32242/963	
☐	G-TCBB	B757-236	29945/873	[NZC]
☐	G-TCBC	B757-236	29946/877	[NZC]
☐	G-WJAN	B757-21K	28674/746	std
☐	G-DAJC	B767-31KER/W	27206/533	>CFG
☐	G-TCCA	B767-31KER/W	27205/528	>CFG
☐	G-TCCB	B767-31KER/W	28865/657	>CFG

THOMSON AIRWAYS BY / TOM

	Reg	Type	C/n	
☐	G-FDZA	B737-8K5/W	35134/2152	
☐	G-FDZB	B737-8K5/W	35131/2242	
☐	G-FDZD	B737-8K5/W	35132/2276	
☐	G-FDZE	B737-8K5/W	35137/2482	
☐	G-FDZF	B737-8K5/W	35138/2499	
☐	G-FDZG	B737-8K5/W	35139/2538	
☐	G-FDZJ	B737-8K5/W	34690/2184	
☐	G-FDZR	B737-8K5/W	35145/2849	♦
☐	G-FDZS	B737-8K5/W	35147/2866	
☐	G-FDZT	B737-8K5/W	37248/3532	
☐	G-FDZU	B737-8K5/W	37253/3562	
☐	G-FDZW	B737-8K5/W	37254/3586	
☐	G-FDZX	B737-8K5/W	37258/3655	
☐	G-FDZY	B737-8K5/W	37261/3844	>SWG
☐	G-FDZZ	B737-8K5/W	37262/3876	>SWG
☐	G-TAWA	B737-8K5/W	37264/3907	>SWG
☐	G-TAWB	B737-8K5/W	37242/3917	
☐	G-TAWC	B737-8K5/W	39922/3925	>SWG
☐	G-TAWD	B737-8K5/W	37265/3939	>SWG
☐	G-TAWF	B737-8K5/W	37244/3955	
☐	G-TAWG	B737-8K5/W	37266/3967	
☐	G-TAWH	B737-8K5/W	38107/3997	
☐	G-TAWI	B737-8K5/W	37267/4006	
☐	G-TAWJ	B737-8K5/W	38108/4024	
☐	G-TAWK	B737-8K5/W	37239/4253	
☐	G-TAWL	B737-8K5/W	37243/4299	
☐	G-TAWM	B737-8K5/W	37249/4360	>SWG
☐	G-TAWN	B737-8K5/W	37251/4369	>SWG
☐	G-TAWO	B737-8K5/W	37255/4384	>SWG
☐	G-TAWP	B737-8K5/W	37257/4412	
☐	G-TAWR	B737-8K5/W	37256/4416	
☐	G-TAWS	B737-8K5/W	37241/4842	
☐	G-TAWU	B737-8K5/W	37263/4875	
☐	G-BYAW	B757-204/W	27234/663	
☐	G-BYAY	B757-204/W	28836/861	
☐	G-CPEU	B757-236/W	29941/864	
☐	G-CPEV	B757-236/W	29943/871	
☐	G-OOBA	B757-28A/W	32446/950	
☐	G-OOBB	B757-28A/W	32447/951	
☐	G-OOBC	B757-28A/W	33098/1026	
☐	G-OOBD	B757-28A/W	33099/1028	
☐	G-OOBE	B757-28A/W	33100/1029	
☐	G-OOBF	B757-28A/W	33101/1041	
☐	G-OOBG	B757-236/W	29942/867	
☐	G-OOBH	B757-236/W	29944/872	
☐	G-OOBN	B757-2G5/W	29379/919	
☐	G-OOBP	B757-2G5/W	30394/922	
☐	G-OBYF	B767-304ER/W	28208/705	
☐	G-OBYH	B767-304ER/W	28883/737	
☐	G-TUIA	B787-8	34422/92	
☐	G-TUIB	B787-8	34423/94	
☐	G-TUIC	B787-8	34424/96	
☐	G-TUID	B787-8	36424/106	
☐	G-TUIE	B787-8	37227/191	
☐	G-TUIF	B787-8	36428/198	
☐	G-TUIG	B787-8	36426/260	
☐	G-TUIH	B787-8	37229/291	♦
☐	G-TUII	B787-8	37230/300	♦
☐	G-	B787-9	44578/439	o/o♦
☐	G-	B787-9	34426	o/o♦
☐	G-	B787-9		o/o♦

TITAN AIRWAYS — ZT / AWC

	Reg	Type	c/n	Notes
□	G-POWI	A320-233	2791	
□	G-POWK	A320-233	4701	
□	G-POWM	A320-232	2564	♦
□	G-POWN	A321-211	3830	o/o♦
□	G-	A321-211	4611	o/o♦
□	G-JMCP	B737-3T0(SF)	23578/1358	<NPT
□	G-POWC	B737-33A(QC)	25402/2159	
□	G-ZAPW	B737-3L9(QC)	24219/1600	
□	G-ZAPZ	B737-33A(QC)	25401/2067	
□	G-POWH	B757-256	29308/935	
□	G-ZAPX	B757-256	29309/936	
□	G-POWD	B767-36NER	30847/902	

VIRGIN ATLANTIC AIRWAYS — VS / VIR

	Reg	Type	c/n	Notes
□	G-VGBR	A330-343E	1329	
□	G-VGEM	A330-343E	1215	
□	G-VINE	A330-343E	1231	
□	G-VKSS	A330-343E	1201	
□	G-VLUV	A330-343E	1206	
□	G-VNYC	A330-343E	1315	
□	G-VRAY	A330-343E	1296	
□	G-VSXY	A330-343E	1195	
□	G-VUFO	A330-343E	1352	
□	G-VWAG	A330-343E	1341	

Two A330-300s planned to be operated by Virgin Atlantic International (VGI).

	Reg	Type	c/n	Notes
□	G-VBLU	A340-642	723	
□	G-VBUG	A340-642	804	
□	G-VEIL	A340-642	575	
□	G-VFIT	A340-642	753	
□	G-VFIZ	A340-642	764	
□	G-VGAS	A340-642	639	
□	G-VNAP	A340-642	622	[LDE]
□	G-VRED	A340-642	768	
□	G-VWEB	A340-642	787	
□	G-VWIN	A340-642	736	
□	G-VWKD	A340-642	706	
□	G-VYOU	A340-642	765	
□	G-VAST	B747-41R	28757/1117	
□	G-VBIG	B747-4Q8	26255/1081	
□	G-VGAL	B747-443	32337/1272	
□	G-VLIP	B747-443	32338/1274	
□	G-VROC	B747-41R	32746/1336	
□	G-VROM	B747-443	32339/1275	
□	G-VROS	B747-443	30885/1268	
□	G-VROY	B747-443	32340/1277	
□	G-VXLG	B747-41R	29406/1177	
□	G-VAHH	B787-9	37967/246	
□	G-VBOW	B787-9	37979	o/o♦
□	G-VBZZ	B787-9	37976/401	o/o♦
□	G-VCRU	B787-9	37972/338	
□	G-VDIA	B787-9	37975/377	o/o
□	G-VFAN	B787-9	37978	o/o♦
□	G-VMAP	B787-9	37977/431	o/o♦
□	G-VNEW	B787-9	40956/218	
□	G-VOOH	B787-9	37968/256	
□	G-VOWS	B787-9	37974/373	
□	G-VSPY	B787-9	37973/369	
□	G-VWHO	B787-9	37971/313	♦
□	G-VYUM	B787-9	37970/296	
□	G-VZIG	B787-9	37969/267	
□	G-	B787-9	38047/421	o/o♦

HA- HUNGARY

ABC AIR HUNGARY — AHU

	Reg	Type	c/n	Notes
□	HA-TAE	SAAB SF.340AF	340A-007	
□	HA-TAF	SAAB SF.340AF	340A-011	

ASL AIRLINES HUNGARY — FAH

	Reg	Type	c/n	Notes
□	HA-FAM	Beech 1900D	UE-16	
□	HA-FAO	SA.227AC Metro III	AC-451B	
□	HA-FAR	Beech 1900C-1	UC-68	
□	HA-FAU	B737-43Q(F)	28494/2839	
□	HA-FAV	B737-46Q(F)	29000/3033	
□	HA-FAW	B737-476(F)	24435/1959	♦
□	HA-FAX	B737-476(F)	24437/2162	♦
□	HA-FAY	B737-429F	25729/2217	♦
□	HA-LAS	LET L-410UVP-E4	871924	

BUDAPEST AIR SERVICES — BPS

	Reg	Type	c/n	Notes
□	HA-FAI	EMB.120ER	120123	
□	HA-FAL	EMB.120RT	120176	
□	HA-FAN	EMB.120ER	120104	
□	HA-LAF	LET L-410UVP-E8A	902518	
□	HA-YFD	LET L-410UVP-E17	892324	

FLEET AIR INTERNATIONAL — FRF

	Reg	Type	c/n	Notes
□	HA-TAB	SAAB SF.340A	340A-083	
□	HA-TAD	SAAB SF.340A	340A-126	
□	HA-TAG	SAAB SF.340A	340A-078	
□	HA-TVG	SAAB SF.340B	340B-208	[OSR]♦
□	HA-TVJ	SAAB SF.340A(QC)	340A-066	♦

TRAVEL SERVICE HUNGARY — 7O / TVL

	Reg	Type	c/n	Notes
□	HA-LKG	B737-8CX/W	32362/1125	

WIZZ AIR — W6 / WZZ

	Reg	Type	c/n	Notes
□	HA-LPJ	A320-232	3127	
□	HA-LPK	A320-232	3143	
□	HA-LPL	A320-232	3166	
□	HA-LPM	A320-232	3177	
□	HA-LPN	A320-232	3354	
□	HA-LPO	A320-232	3384	
□	HA-LPQ	A320-232	3409	
□	HA-LPR	A320-232	3430	
□	HA-LPS	A320-232	3771	
□	HA-LPT	A320-232	3807	
□	HA-LPU	A320-232	3877	
□	HA-LPV	A320-232	3927	
□	HA-LPW	A320-232	3947	
□	HA-LPX	A320-232	3968	
□	HA-LPY	A320-232	4109	
□	HA-LPZ	A320-232	4174	
□	HA-LWA	A320-232	4223	
□	HA-LWB	A320-232	4246	
□	HA-LWC	A320-232	4323	
□	HA-LWD	A320-232	4351	
□	HA-LWE	A320-232	4372	
□	HA-LWF	A320-232	3562	
□	HA-LWG	A320-232	4308	
□	HA-LWH	A320-232	4621	
□	HA-LWI	A320-232	4628	
□	HA-LWJ	A320-232	4683	
□	HA-LWK	A320-232	4716	

☐	HA-LWL	A320-232	4736	
☐	HA-LWM	A320-232	5021	
☐	HA-LWN	A320-232	5075	
☐	HA-LWO	A320-232	5123	
☐	HA-LWP	A320-232	5139	
☐	HA-LWQ	A320-232	5196	
☐	HA-LWR	A320-232/S	5604	
☐	HA-LWS	A320-232/S	5608	
☐	HA-LWT	A320-232/S	5615	
☐	HA-LWU	A320-232/S	5617	
☐	HA-LWV	A320-232/S	5660	
☐	HA-LWX	A320-232/S	6001	
☐	HA-LWY	A320-232/S	6058	
☐	HA-LWZ	A320-232/S	6086	
☐	HA-LYA	A320-232/S	6077	
☐	HA-LYB	A320-232/S	6093	
☐	HA-LYC	A320-232/S	6098	
☐	HA-LYD	A320-232/S	6115	
☐	HA-LYE	A320-232/S	6131	
☐	HA-LYF	A320-232/S	6195	
☐	HA-LYG	A320-232/S	5539	
☐	HA-LYH	A320-232/S	6235	
☐	HA-LYI	A320-232/S	6352	
☐	HA-LYJ	A320-232/S	6360	
☐	HA-LYK	A320-232/S	6394	
☐	HA-LYL	A320-232/S	6489	
☐	HA-LYM	A320-232/S	6544	
☐	HA-LYN	A320-232/S	6559	
☐	HA-LYO	A320-232/S	6576	
☐	HA-LYP	A320-232/S	6589	♦
☐	HA-LYQ	A320-232/S	6614	♦
☐	HA-LYR	A320-232/S	6631	♦
☐	HA-LYS	A320-232/S	6662	♦
☐	HA-LYT	A320-232/S	6683	♦
☐	HA-LYU	A320-232	3531	♦
☐	HA-LYV	A320-232	3741	♦
☐	HA-LXA	A321-231/S	6848	♦
☐	HA-LXB	A321-231/S	6910	♦
☐	HA-LXC	A321-231/S	6976	♦
☐	HA-LXD	A321-231/S	7032	o/o♦
☐	HA-	A321-231/S	7114	o/o♦
☐	HA-	A321-231/S	7155	o/o♦
☐	HA-	A321-231/S	7182	o/o♦
☐	HA-	A321-231/S	7217	o/o♦
☐	HA-	A321-231/S	7273	o/o♦
☐	HA-	A321-231/S	7280	o/o♦
☐	HA-	A321-231/S	7316	o/o♦
☐	HA-	A321-231/S	7440	o/o♦

HB- SWITZERLAND

ASL AIRLINES SWITZERLAND — FAT

☐	HB-ACE	ATR 72-212A	577	♦
☐	HB-AFF	ATR 42-320	264	
☐	HB-AFH	ATR 72-202F	313	>DHV
☐	HB-AFJ	ATR 72-202F	154	
☐	HB-AFK	ATR 72-202F	232	
☐	HB-AFL	ATR 72-202F	222	
☐	HB-AFM	ATR 72-202F	364	
☐	HB-AFP	ATR 72-201F	381	>DHV
☐	HB-AFR	ATR 72-201F	195	>DHV
☐	HB-AFS	ATR 72-201F	198	♦
☐	HB-AFV	ATR 72-201F	341	
☐	HB-AFW	ATR 72-201F	419	
☐	HB-AFX	ATR 72-202F	265	

BELAIR AIRLINES — 4T / BHP

☐	HB-IOX	A319-112	3604	
☐	HB-JOY	A319-112	3245	
☐	HB-IOP	A320-214	4187	
☐	HB-IOQ	A320-214	3422	
☐	HB-IOR	A320-214	4033	
☐	HB-IOS	A320-214	2968	
☐	HB-IOZ	A320-214	4294	
☐	HB-JOZ	A320-214	4631	

Aircraft fly in Air Berlin colours.

EASYJET SWITZERLAND — DS / EZS

☐	HB-JXA	A320-214	5138	<EZY
☐	HB-JXB	A320-214	5111	<EZY
☐	HB-JXC	A320-214	5146	<EZY
☐	HB-JXD	A320-214	5150	<EZY
☐	HB-JXE	A320-214/S	5785	<EZY♦
☐	HB-JYA	A320-214	4250	<EZY
☐	HB-JYB	A319-111	4837	<EZY
☐	HB-JYC	A319-111	4785	<EZY
☐	HB-JYD	A320-214	4646	<EZY
☐	HB-JYE	A320-214	4006	<EZY
☐	HB-JYF	A319-111	4778	<EZY
☐	HB-JYG	A319-111	4781	<EZY
☐	HB-JYH	A319-111	4787	<EZY
☐	HB-JYI	A319-111	4744	<EZY♦
☐	HB-JYJ	A319-111	4717	<EZY♦
☐	HB-JZK	A319-111	4705	<EZY♦
☐	HB-JYL	A319-111	4693	<EZY♦
☐	HB-JYM	A319-111	4667	<EZY♦
☐	HB-JYN	A319-111	4640	<EZY♦
☐	HB-JZR	A320-214	4034	<EZY
☐	HB-JZS	A319-111	3084	<EZY
☐	HB-JZU	A319-111	2402	<EZY
☐	HB-JZV	A319-111	2709	[CBG]
☐	HB-JZW	A319-111	2729	<EZY
☐	HB-JZX	A320-214	4157	<EZY
☐	HB-JZY	A320-214	4196	<EZY
☐	HB-JZZ	A320-214	4233	<EZY

EDELWEISS AIR — WK / EDW

☐	HB-IHX	A320-214	0942	
☐	HB-IHY	A320-214	0947	
☐	HB-IHZ	A320-214	1026	
☐	HB-IJU	A320-214	1951	♦
☐	HB-IJV	A320-214	2024	
☐	HB-IJW	A320-214	2134	
☐	HB-IQI	A330-223	291	
☐	HB-JHQ	A330-343E	1193	
☐	HB-JHR	A330-343E	1711	o/o♦

ETIHAD REGIONAL — F7 / DWT

☐	HB-ACA	ATR 72-212A	660	
☐	HB-ACB	ATR 72-212A	662	
☐	HB-ACC	ATR 72-212A	664	
☐	HB-ACD	ATR 72-212A	668	
☐	HB-IYD	SAAB 2000	2000-059	
☐	HB-IYI	SAAB 2000	2000-016	
☐	HB-IZH	SAAB 2000	2000-011	
☐	HB-IZJ	SAAB 2000	2000-015	
☐	HB-IZP	SAAB 2000	2000-031	
☐	HB-IZW	SAAB 2000	2000-039	
☐	HB-IZZ	SAAB 2000	2000-048	

GERMANIA FLUG			GSW
☐ HB-JOI	A321-211/S	5843	♦

HELVETIC AIRWAYS			2L / OAW
☐ HB-JVK	A319-112	1886	
☐ HB-JVL	ERJ-190LR	19000354	
☐ HB-JVM	ERJ-190LR	19000349	
☐ HB-JVN	ERJ-190LR	19000285	
☐ HB-JVO	ERJ-190LR	19000294	
☐ HB-JVP	ERJ-190LR	19000387	♦
☐ HB-JVQ	ERJ-190LR	19000420	♦
☐ HB-JVR	ERJ-190LR	19000435	♦
☐ HB-JVC	Fokker 100	11501	
☐ HB-JVE	Fokker 100	11459	
☐ HB-JVF	Fokker 100	11466	
☐ HB-JVG	Fokker 100	11478	
☐ HB-JVH	Fokker 100	11324	

HOLIDAY JET			GSW
☐ HB-JOG	A319-112	3818	♦
☐ HB-JOH	A319-112	3589	

PRIVATAIR			PT / PTI
☐ HB-JJA	B737-7AK/W	34303/1758	
☐ HB-JJB	B737-306	27421/2438	>LC
☐ HB-JJC	B737-306	27420/2406	[SOF]
☐ HB-JJD	B757-236/W	25807/610	>LC
☐ HB-JJE	B757-204/W	27219/596	>LC
☐ HB-JJF	B767-316ER/W	27613/652	>LC
☐ HB-JJH	B737-752/W	33791/1557	>LC
☐ HB-JJJ	B787-8 (BBJ)	37306/315	o/o♦
☐ HB-	B787-8 (BBJ)		o/o♦

SKYWORK AIRLINES			SX / SRK
☐ HB-AEO	Do328-110	3061	
☐ HB-AER	Do328-110	3066	
☐ HB-AES	Do328-110	3021	
☐ HB-AEV	Do328-110	3056	
☐ HB-AEY	Do328-130	3100	

SWISS GLOBAL AIR LINES			LX / SWU
☐ HB-IXO	Avro 146-RJ100	E3284	
☐ HB-IXP	Avro 146-RJ100	E3283	
☐ HB-IXQ	Avro 146-RJ100	E3282	
☐ HB-IXS	Avro 146-RJ100	E3280	
☐ HB-IXT	Avro 146-RJ100	E3259	
☐ HB-IXU	Avro 146-RJ100	E3276	
☐ HB-IXV	Avro 146-RJ100	E3274	
☐ HB-IYQ	Avro 146-RJ100	E3384	
☐ HB-IYR	Avro 146-RJ100	E3382	
☐ HB-IYS	Avro 146-RJ100	E3381	
☐ HB-IYT	Avro 146-RJ100	E3380	
☐ HB-IYU	Avro 146-RJ100	E3379	
☐ HB-IYV	Avro 146-RJ100	E3377	
☐ HB-IYW	Avro 146-RJ100	E3359	
☐ HB-IYY	Avro 146-RJ100	E3339	
☐ HB-IYZ	Avro 146-RJ100	E3338	
☐ HB-JNA	B777-3DE(ER)	44582/1363	♦
☐ HB-JNB	B777-3DE(ER)	44583	o/o♦
☐ HB-	B777-3DE(ER)		o/o♦
☐ HB-	B777-3DE(ER)		o/o♦

SWISS INTERNATIONAL AIR LINES			LX / SWR
☐ HB-IPT	A319-112	0727	
☐ HB-IPU	A319-112	0713	
☐ HB-IPV	A319-112	0578	
☐ HB-IPX	A319-112	0612	
☐ HB-IPY	A319-112	0621	
☐ HB-IJB	A320-214	0545	
☐ HB-IJD	A320-214	0553	
☐ HB-IJE	A320-214	0559	
☐ HB-IJF	A320-214	0562	
☐ HB-IJH	A320-214	0574	
☐ HB-IJI	A320-214	0577	
☐ HB-IJJ	A320-214	0585	
☐ HB-IJK	A320-214	0596	
☐ HB-IJL	A320-214	0603	
☐ HB-IJM	A320-214	0635	
☐ HB-IJN	A320-214	0643	
☐ HB-IJO	A320-214	0673	
☐ HB-IJP	A320-214	0681	
☐ HB-IJQ	A320-214	0701	
☐ HB-IJR	A320-214	0703	
☐ HB-IJS	A320-214	0782	
☐ HB-IJX	A320-214	1762	
☐ HB-JLP	A320-214	4618	
☐ HB-JLQ	A320-214	4673	
☐ HB-JLR	A320-214	5037	
☐ HB-JLS	A320-214	5069	
☐ HB-JLT	A320-214/S	5518	
☐ HB-IOC	A321-111	0520	
☐ HB-IOD	A321-111	0522	
☐ HB-IOF	A321-111	0541	
☐ HB-IOH	A321-111	0664	
☐ HB-IOK	A321-111	0987	
☐ HB-IOL	A321-111	1144	
☐ HB-IOM	A321-212	4534	
☐ HB-ION	A321-212	5567	
☐ HB-IOO	A321-212	7007	o/o♦
☐ HB-JHA	A330-343E	1000	
☐ HB-JHB	A330-343E	1018	
☐ HB-JHC	A330-343E	1026	
☐ HB-JHD	A330-343E	1029	
☐ HB-JHE	A330-343E	1084	
☐ HB-JHF	A330-343E	1089	
☐ HB-JHG	A330-343E	1101	
☐ HB-JHH	A330-343E	1145	
☐ HB-JHI	A330-343E	1181	
☐ HB-JHJ	A330-343E	1188	
☐ HB-JHK	A330-343E	1276	
☐ HB-JHL	A330-343E	1290	
☐ HB-JHM	A330-343E	1355	
☐ HB-JHN	A330-343E	1403	
☐ HB-	A330-343E	1722	o/o
☐ HB-JMA	A340-313X	538	
☐ HB-JMB	A340-313X	545	
☐ HB-JMC	A340-313X	546	
☐ HB-JMD	A340-313X	556	
☐ HB-JME	A340-313X	559	
☐ HB-JMF	A340-313X	561	
☐ HB-JMG	A340-313X	562	
☐ HB-JMH	A340-313E	585	
☐ HB-JMI	A340-313E	598	
☐ HB-JMJ	A340-313X	150	
☐ HB-JMK	A340-313X	169	
☐ HB-JML	A340-313X	263	

Reg	Type	c/n	Notes
☐ HB-JMM	A340-313X	154	
☐ HB-JMN	A340-313X	175	
☐ HB-JMO	A340-313X	179	
☐ HB-	CS100 C Series		o/o♦
☐ HB-	CS100 C Series		o/o♦
☐ OE-LGR	DHC-8-402Q	4045	<AUA♦

ZIMEX AVIATION — C4 / IMX

Reg	Type	c/n	Notes
☐ HB-LQV	DHC-6 Twin Otter 300	643	
☐ HB-LQX	DHC-6 Twin Otter 300	618	
☐ HB-LRB	DHC-6 Twin Otter 300	705	
☐ HB-LRN	DHC-6 Twin Otter 310	636	
☐ HB-LRO	DHC-6 Twin Otter 300	523	
☐ HB-LRR	DHC-6 Twin Otter 300	505	
☐ HB-LTG	DHC-6 Twin Otter 300	628	
☐ HB-LTR	DHC-6 Twin Otter 300	238	
☐ HB-LUC	DHC-6 Twin Otter 300	351	
☐ HB-LUE	DHC-6 Twin Otter 300	233	
☐ HB-LUM	DHC-6 Twin Otter 300	420	
☐ HB-LUX	DHC-6 Twin Otter 400	845	
☐ HB-AEM	Beech 1900D	UE-379	

HC- ECUADOR

AVIANCA ECUADOR — 2K / GLG

Reg	Type	c/n	Notes
☐ HC-CKL	A319-112	1866	
☐ HC-CKM	A319-112	1872	
☐ HC-CKN	A319-112	1882	
☐ HC-CKO	A319-112	1925	
☐ HC-CKP	A319-112	2126	
☐ HC-CLF	A319-112	2078	
☐ HC-CJM	A320-214	4379	
☐ HC-CJV	A320-214	4547	
☐ HC-CJW	A320-214	4487	

LAC - LINEA AEREA CUENCANA — L5 / LAC

Reg	Type	c/n	Notes
☐ HC-COP	B737-5Y0	25176/2155	♦
☐ HC-CMY	CRJ-700	10004	

LAN ECUADOR — XL / LNE

Reg	Type	c/n	Notes
☐ HC-CPJ	A319-132	3671	
☐ HC-CPQ	A319-132	4563	
☐ HC-CPR	A319-132	3663	
☐ HC-CPY	A319-132	4605	
☐ HC-CPZ	A319-132	4598	
☐ HC-CQU	A319-132	3770	

For B767-300s see LAN Chile.

TAME — EQ / TAE

Reg	Type	c/n	Notes
☐ HC-CGT	A319-132	2659	
☐ HC-CMO	A319-112	0946	
☐ HC-CMP	A319-132	1934	
☐ HC-COF	A319-112	0949	
☐ HC-CGW	A320-233	2084	
☐ HC-CID	A320-232	0934	
☐ HC-COC	A320-232	1368	
☐ HC-COE	A320-233	1339	
☐ HC-CPB	A320-233	1500	
☐ HC-COH	A330-243	348	
☐ HC-CLT	ATR 42-500	844	
☐ HC-CMB	ATR 42-500	849	
☐ HC-CMH	ATR 42-500	854	
☐ HC-CEZ	ERJ-190LR	19000027	
☐ HC-CGF	ERJ-190LR	19000137	
☐ HC-CGG	ERJ-190LR	19000141	
☐ HC-COX	ERJ-190AR	19000372	
☐ HC-COY	ERJ-190AR	19000373	

TRANS AM AERO EXPRESS — 7T / TRM

Reg	Type	c/n	Notes
☐ HC-CDX	ATR 42-320F	081	>DHL

HH- HAITI

SUNRISE AIRWAYS — S6 / KSZ

Reg	Type	c/n	Notes
☐ HH-SUN	BAeJetstream 31	922	
☐ HH-YET	BAeJetstream 32	914	

TORTUG'AIR

Reg	Type	c/n	Notes
☐ HH-JET	BAeJetstream 32	883	
☐ HH-KPS	BAeJetstream 3x		♦
☐ HH-LET	LET L-410UVP-E3	871927	
☐ HH-TOR	LET L-410UVP-E3	871930	

Some of the above are possibly operated by Sunrise Airways.

HI- DOMINICAN REPUBLIC

ACSA – AIR CENTURY — CEY

Reg	Type	c/n	Notes
☐ HI772	BAeJetstream 31	660	
☐ HI840	BAeJetstream 32EP	819	
☐ HI860	BAeJetstream 32EP	944	
☐ HI956	BAeJetstream 32EP	967	♦
☐ HI976	SAAB SF.340B	340B-344	♦

AEROLINEAS MAS — N3 / MAS

Reg	Type	c/n	Notes
☐ HI859	BAeJetstream 31	805	
☐ HI874	BAeJetstream 31	810	

DOMINICAN WINGS — DWI

Reg	Type	c/n	Notes
☐ HI969	A320-233	0561	♦
☐ LY-VEL	A320-232	1998	<NVD♦

PAWA DOMINICANA — 7N / PWD

Reg	Type	c/n	Notes
☐ HI	B757-21B	24402/233	o/o♦
☐ HI817	BAeJetstream 31	673	
☐ HI841	BAeJetstream 31	674	
☐ HI869	DC-9-32	47566/691	
☐ HI876	DC-9-32	47046/168	[SDQ]
☐ HI914	MD-82	49476/1439	[SDQ]
☐ HI937	DC-9-31	48139/1024	[SDQ]♦
☐ HI965	DC-9-32	47235/436	[SDQ]
☐ HI977	MD-83	49845/1573	♦
☐ HI978	MD-87	49780/1674	♦
☐ HI989	MD-83	49568/1380	♦
☐ HI990	MD-83	49904/1680	♦
☐ HI	MD-83	49741/1630	o/o♦

SAPSA — 5S / PSV

Reg	Type	c/n	Notes
☐ HI644	DHC-6 Twin Otter 200	46	
☐ HI657	Short SD.3-60	SH3672	
☐ HI819	BAeJetstream 31	811	
☐ HI851	BAeJetstream 32	940	
☐ HI856	BAeJetstream 32	919	
☐ HI858	BAeJetstream 32	938	

☐	HI875	BAeJetstream 3x	642	
☐	HI918	BAeJetstream 31	641	

HK- COLOMBIA

ADA AEROLINEA DE ANTIOQUIA — ANQ

☐	HK-4364	BAeJetstream 32	897	
☐	HK-4381	BAeJetstream 32	898	
☐	HK-4398	BAeJetstream 32	828	
☐	HK-4515	BAeJetstream 32	900	
☐	HK-4548	BAeJetstream 32	893	
☐	HK-4792	BAeJetstream 32	865	
☐	HK-2548	DHC-6 Twin Otter 300	718	
☐	HK-2603	DHC-6 Twin Otter 300	749	
☐	HK-2669	DHC-6 Twin Otter 300	760	
☐	HK-4533	Do328-120	3092	
☐	HK-4849	Do328-110	3084	
☐	HK-4917	Do328-110	3039	
☐	HK-5053	Do328-110	3018	

AERO CARIBE — ACL

☐	HK-4728	An-26B	8205	[OTU]
☐	HK-4729	An-26B	12602	
☐	HK-4730	An-26B	07309510	
☐	HK-4052	An-32A	1805	
☐	HK-4257	An-32B	3203	
☐	HK-4832X	An-32B	3006	♦
☐	HK-4833	An-32B	3404	♦
☐	HK-5139	B737-476(F)	24431/1863	♦
☐	HK-	B737-476(F)	24430/1820	o/o♦

AEROLINEAS DE LA PAZ

☐	HK-4189	Douglas DC-3	4319	

AEROLINEAS DEL LLANO

☐	HK-1315	Douglas DC-3	4307	♦
☐	HK-3215	Douglas DC-3	14666/26111	♦

AEROLINEAS LLANERAS COLOMBIA

☐	HK-3037	Douglas DC-3	20548	[VVC]
☐	HK-3286	Douglas DC-3	6144	
☐	HK-4971	Douglas DC-3	13860	

AEROSUCRE — 6N / KRE

☐	HK-4216	B737-230C	20253/223	
☐	HK-4253	B737-2H6C	21109/436	
☐	HK-4328	B737-2S5C	22148/663	[BAQ]
☐	HK-4465	B727-222F	19915/681	
☐	HK-4504	B727-2J0F	21108/1174	
☐	HK-4544	B727-2J0F	21105/1158	
☐	HK-5026	B737-230F	22120/715	

AEROVANGUARDIA

☐	HK-2820	Douglas DC-3	20171	
☐	HK-3199	Douglas DC-3	14599/26044	
☐	HK-3286	Douglas DC-3	6144	
☐	HK-4292	Douglas DC-3	13177	

AIR COLOMBIA

☐	HK-1175	Douglas DC-3	20432	
☐	HK-3292	Douglas DC-3	19661	
☐	HK-3293	Douglas DC-3	9186	

ALIANSA

☐	HK-2006	Douglas DC-3	43086	
☐	HK-2820	Douglas DC-3	20171	♦
☐	HK-5016	DC-3-65TP	14101/25546	

AVIANCA — AV / AVA

☐	N589AV	A318-111	2575	
☐	N590EL	A318-111	2328	
☐	N591EL	A318-111	2333	
☐	N592EL	A318-111	2358	
☐	N593EL	A318-111	2367	
☐	N594EL	A318-111	2377	
☐	N595EL	A318-111	2394	
☐	N596EL	A318-111	2523	
☐	N597EL	A318-111	2544	
☐	N598EL	A318-111	2552	
☐	HK-4552	A319-112	3518	
☐	HK-4553	A319-112	3467	
☐	N266CT	A319-112	2662	
☐	N422AV	A319-115	4200	
☐	N519AV	A319-115	5119	
☐	N557AV	A319-115	5057	
☐	N634MX	A319-112	1634	std
☐	N647AV	A319-115	3647	
☐	N690AV	A319-132/S	5944	
☐	N691AV	A319-115	3691	
☐	N726AV	A319-115/S	6174	
☐	N730AV	A319-132/S	6132	
☐	N741AV	A319-115/S	6617	♦
☐	N992TA	A319-112	2066	[GYR]
☐	HK-4549	A320-214	3408	
☐	HK-4659	A320-214	4100	
☐	N195AV	A320-214	5195	
☐	N281AV	A320-214	4281	
☐	N284AV	A320-214	4284	
☐	N345AV	A320-214	4345	
☐	N398AV	A320-214	3988	
☐	N401AV	A320-214	4001	
☐	N411AV	A320-214	4011	
☐	N416AV	A320-214	4167	
☐	N417AV	A320-214	4175	std
☐	N426AV	A320-214	4026	
☐	N446AV	A320-214	4046	
☐	N451AV	A320-214	4051	
☐	N454AV	A320-214	5454	
☐	N477AV	A320-214/S	5477	
☐	N481AV	A320-214	4381	
☐	N536AV	A320-214	5360	
☐	N538AV	A320-214	5398	
☐	N562AV	A320-214/S	5622	
☐	N567AV	A320-214	4567	
☐	N599AV	A320-214	4599	
☐	N632AV	A320-214/S	5632	
☐	N664AV	A320-214	3664	
☐	N688TA	A320-214	5243	
☐	N724AV	A320-214/S	6153	
☐	N728AV	A320-214/S	6209	
☐	N740AV	A320-214/S	6411	
☐	N742AV	A320-214/S	6692	♦
☐	N743AV	A320-214/S	6739	♦
☐	N745AV	A320-214/S	6746	♦
☐	N748AV	A320-214/S	6862	♦
☐	N763AV	A320-214	4763	
☐	N789AV	A320-214	4789	

Registration	Type	c/n	Notes
N821AV	A320-214	4821	
N862AV	A320-214	4862	
N939AV	A320-214	4939	
N961AV	A320-214	3961	
N980AV	A320-214	3980	
N992AV	A320-214	3992	
N	A320-214/S	7120	o/o♦
N	A320-214/S	7253	o/o♦
N696AV	A321-231/S	6138	
N729AV	A321-231/S	6399	
N744AV	A321-211/S	6767	♦
N746AV	A321-211/S	6511	
	A321-231		o/o
	A321-231		o/o
N279AV	A330-243	1279	>TPU
N280AV	A330-243	1400	
N342AV	A330-243	1342	
N508AV	A330-243	1508	[VCV]
N941AV	A330-243	1492	
N967CG	A330-243	967	[MAN]
N968AV	A330-243	1009	
N969AV	A330-243	1016	
N973AV	A330-243	1073	
N974AV	A330-243	1208	
N975AV	A330-243	1224	
HK-4954	ATR 72-600	1092	
HK-4955X	ATR 72-600	1114	
HK-4956X	ATR 72-600	1116	
HK-4999X	ATR 72-600	1126	
HK-5000X	ATR 72-600	1142	
HK-5039	ATR 72-600	1124	
HK-5040	ATR 72-600	1151	
HK-5041X	ATR 72-600	1160	
HK-5109X	ATR 72-600	1231	
N780AV	B787-8	37502/217	
N781AV	B787-8	37503/228	
N782AV	B787-8	37504/239	
N783AV	B787-8	37505/242	
N784AV	B787-8	37506/294	
N785AV	B787-8	37507/347	
N786AV	B787-8	37508/367	
N787AV	B787-8	37509/460	o/o♦
N788AV	B787-8	37510/476	o/o♦
N791AV	B787-8	37511/511	o/o♦
HK-4467	Fokker 50	20301	[MCI]
HK-4468	Fokker 50	20300	[MCI]
HK-4469	Fokker 50	20285	std
HK-4470	Fokker 50	20297	[MCI]
HK-4580	Fokker 50	20281	[MCI]
HK-4581	Fokker 50	20296	[MCI]

Also see Avianca Brazil (PP-); Avianca Cargo (HK-); Avianca Central America (YS-); Avianca Ecuador (HC-); Avianca Guatemala (TG-).

AVIANCA CARGO — *QT / TPA*

Registration	Type	c/n	Notes
N330QT	A330-243F	1368	
N331QT	A330-243F	1380	
N332QT	A330-243F	1428	
N334QT	A330-243F	1448	
N335QT	A330-243F	1534	

COPA COLOMBIA — *P5 / RPB*

Registration	Type	c/n	Notes
HP-1371CMP	B737-7V3/W	30049/388	<CMP
HP-1372CMP	B737-7V3/W	28607/399	<CMP
HP-1373CMP	B737-7V3/W	30458/459	<CMP
HK-4453	ERJ-190LR	19000063	
HK-4454	ERJ-190LR	19000061	
HK-4456	ERJ-190LR	19000074	
HK-4505	ERJ-190LR	19000114	
HK-4508	ERJ-190LR	19000138	[SJO]
HK-4559	ERJ-190LR	19000200	
HK-4560	ERJ-190LR	19000208	
HK-4599	ERJ-190LR	19000269	
HK-4601	ERJ-190LR	19000251	
HP-1562CMP	ERJ-190AR	19000095	<CMP
HP-1563CMP	ERJ-190AR	19000098	<CMP♦
HP-1566CMP	ERJ-190AR	19000165	<CMP♦

EASYFLY — *EF / EFY*

Registration	Type	c/n	Notes
HK-5070X	ATR 42-500	655	
HK-5071X	ATR 42-500	651	
HK-5117X	ATR 42-500	581	♦
HK-5159	ATR 42-500	606	♦
HK-4502	BAeJetstream 4101	41091	
HK-4503	BAeJetstream 4101	41093	
HK-4521	BAeJetstream 4101	41092	
HK-4522	BAeJetstream 4101	41086	
HK-4551	BAeJetstream 4101	41089	
HK-4568	BAeJetstream 4101	41057	
HK-4584X	BAeJetstream 4101	41073	[BOG]
HK-4585X	BAeJetstream 4101	41067	
HK-4596X	BAeJetstream 4101	41079	
HK-4765X	BAeJetstream 4101	41074	
HK-4775X	BAeJetstream 4101	41039	
HK-4786X	BAeJetstream 4101	41098	
HK-4867	BAeJetstream 4101	41101	
HK-4868	BAeJetstream 4101	41030	

LAN COLOMBIA — *4C / ARE*

Registration	Type	c/n	Notes
CC-BAO	A320-214	4767	<LAN♦
CC-BAR	A320-214	4892	<LAN
CC-BAS	A320-214	4896	<LAN
CC-BAT	A320-214	4921	<LAN
CC-BAU	A320-214	4943	<LAN
CC-BAV	A320-214	4972	<LAN
CC-BAW	A320-214	5125	<LAN♦
CC-BAX	A320-214	5178	<LAN♦
CC-BAZ	A320-214	5229	<LAN
CC-BFA	A320-214	5234	<LAN♦
CC-BFB	A320-214	5263	<LAN
CC-BFC	A320-214	5316	<LAN
CC-BFD	A320-214	5324	<LAN
CC-BFE	A320-214	5364	<LAN
CC-BFG	A320-214	5443	<LAN

For B767-300s see LAN Chile.

LAN CARGO COLOMBIA — *L7 / LAE*

Registration	Type	c/n	Notes
N418LA	B767-316F/W	34246/936	
N776LA	B777-F16	38091/1038	

LASER SERO COLOMBIA

Registration	Type	c/n	Notes
HK-2494	Douglas DC-3	16357/33105	♦

LINEAS AEREAS SURAMERICANAS — *LAU*

Registration	Type	c/n	Notes
HK-1271	B727-24C	19524/428	
HK-4154	B727-51F	18804/162	
HK-4261	B727-251F	21156/1170	

	Registration	Type	C/n	Notes
☐	HK-4262	B727-2F9F/W	21427/1291	
☐	HK-4401	B727-2X3F	22609/1731	[BOG]
☐	HK-4636	B727-2S2F	22927/1821	
☐	HK-4637	B727-2S2F	22928/1822	

SADELCA — SDK

	Registration	Type	C/n	Notes
☐	HK-122	Douglas DC-3	4414	♦
☐	HK-1149	Douglas DC-3	26593	
☐	HK-2664	Douglas DC-3	19433	

SARPA COLOMBIA

	Registration	Type	C/n	Notes
☐	HK-4350	BAeJetstream 32	836	
☐	HK-4362	BAeJetstream 32	840	
☐	HK-4394	BAeJetstream 32	905	
☐	HK-4405	BAeJetstream 32	849	
☐	HK-4411	BAeJetstream 32	870	
☐	HK-4541	BAeJetstream 32	937	
☐	HK-4772	BAeJetstream 32	950	
☐	HK-4791	BAeJetstream 32	917	
☐	HK-4803	BAeJetstream 32	924	
☐	HK-4973	EMB.120RT	120161	
☐	HK-5013	EMB.120ER	120147	

SATENA — 9N / NSE

	Registration	Type	C/n	Notes
☐	HK-4747/FAC-1182	ATR 42-500	526	
☐	HK-4748/FAC-1183	ATR 42-500	522	[BLL]
☐	HK-4806/FAC-1184	ATR 42-500	513	
☐	HK-4827/FAC-1185	ATR 42-500	532	
☐	HK-4828X/FAC-1186	ATR 72-212A	521	
☐	HK-4862/FAC-1187	ATR 42-500	571	
☐	HK-4949/FAC-1189	ATR 42-500	621	
☐	HK-4979/FAC-1191	ATR 42-500	603	
☐	HK-5104X/FAC-1190	ATR 42-500	631	
☐	HK-5114/FAC1192	ATR 42-600	1019	♦
☐	HK-5128/FAC1195	ATR 42-600	1204	♦
☐	HK-5129X/FAC-1193	ATR 42-600	1201	♦
☐	HK-5130X/FAC-1194	ATR 42-600	1203	♦
☐	HK-4525/FAC-1171	ERJ-145ER	145774	
☐	HK-4535/FAC-1172	ERJ-145ER	145776	
☐	HK-4528/FAC-1180	ERJ-170LR	17000151	
☐	HK-5036X/FAC-1106	Harbin Y-12E	017	
☐	HK-5037X/FAC-1107	Harbin Y-12E	018	

Frequently wear civil marks in addition to the FAC serial.

SEARCA — SRC

	Registration	Type	C/n	Notes
☐	HK-4266	Beech 1900C-1	UC-64	
☐	HK-4282	Beech 1900C-1	UC-60	
☐	HK-4424	Beech 1900D	UE-125	
☐	HK-4434	Beech 1900D	UE-120	
☐	HK-4476	Beech 1900D	UE-123	
☐	HK-4499	Beech 1900D	UE-110	
☐	HK-4512	Beech 1900D	UE-105	
☐	HK-4537	Beech 1900D	UE-95	
☐	HK-4558	Beech 1900D	UE-156	
☐	HK-4563	Beech 1900D	UE-113	
☐	HK-4598	Beech 1900D	UE-183	
☐	HK-4600	Beech 1900D	UE-99	
☐	HK-4630	Beech 1900D	UE-93	
☐	HK-4673	Beech 1900D	UE-104	
☐	HK-4681	Beech 1900D	UE-213	
☐	HK-4709	Beech 1900D	UE-140	
☐	HK-4780	Beech 1900D	UE-155	
☐	HK-5059	Beech 1900D	UE-181	
☐	HK-4038	LET L-410UVP	841323	
☐	HK-4048	LET L-410UVP-E	892626	
☐	HK-4105	LET L-410UVP-E	861613	
☐	HK-4161	LET L-410UVP-E	861612	
☐	HK-4224	LET L-410UVP-E	902420	
☐	HK-4367	LET L-410UVP	851334	

SELVA COLOMBIA — SDV

	Registration	Type	C/n	Notes
☐	HK-4295	An-26	4702	
☐	HK-4296	An-32A	1704	
☐	HK-4388	An-26B-100	12402	
☐	HK-4607	B727-259F	22476/1747	
☐	HK-4706	An-26B-100	12203	

VIVA COLOMBIA — FC / VVC

	Registration	Type	C/n	Notes
☐	HK-4811	A320-214	1564	
☐	HK-4817	A320-214	1725	
☐	HK-4818	A320-214	1306	
☐	HK-4861	A320-214	1867	
☐	HK-4905	A320-214	1454	
☐	HK-5051	A320-214	1757	
☐	HK-5125	A320-214	1370	
☐	HK-5142	A320-214	1686	♦
☐	HK-5164	A320-214	1578	♦
☐		A320-214	1657	o/o♦

HL- SOUTH KOREA

AIR BUSAN — BX / ABL

	Registration	Type	C/n	Notes
☐	HL7744	A320-232	2808	
☐	HL7745	A320-232	2840	
☐	HL7753	A320-232	2943	
☐	HL8055	A320-232	2732	♦
☐	HL7711	A321-231	1636	
☐	HL7712	A321-231	1670	♦
☐	HL7713	A321-231	1734	♦
☐	HL7722	A321-231	2041	♦
☐	HL7723	A321-231	2045	
☐	HL7729	A321-231	2110	♦
☐	HL7761	A321-231	1227	
☐	HL8213	A321-231	1970	
☐	HL7250	B737-58E	25769/2737	std
☐	HL7508	B737-48E	25772/2791	
☐	HL7510	B737-48E	25771/2816	
☐	HL7513	B737-48E	25776/2860	
☐	HL7517	B737-48E	25774/2909	std

AIR INCHEON — KJ /

	Registration	Type	C/n	Notes
☐	HL8271	B737-4Y0SF	24912/2064	
☐	HL8291	B737-4Y0SF	25190/2256	
☐	HL	B737-348QC	23810/1474	o/o♦

ASIANA AIRLINES — OZ / AAR

	Registration	Type	C/n	Notes
☐	HL7737	A320-232	2397	
☐	HL7738	A320-232	2459	
☐	HL7769	A320-232	3437	
☐	HL7772	A320-232	3483	
☐	HL7773	A320-232	3496	
☐	HL7776	A320-232	3641	
☐	HL7788	A320-232	3873	
☐	HL7594	A321-231	1356	
☐	HL7703	A321-231	1511	
☐	HL7730	A321-231	2226	

	Reg	Type	c/n	
☐	HL7731	A321-231	2247	
☐	HL7735	A321-231	2290	
☐	HL7763	A321-231	3297	
☐	HL7767	A321-231	0802	
☐	HL7789	A321-231	4112	
☐	HL7790	A321-231	4142	
☐	HL8004	A321-231	6299	
☐	HL8018	A321-231	6395	
☐	HL8038	A321-231/S	6768	♦
☐	HL8039	A321-231/S	6796	♦
☐	HL8236	A321-231	1174	
☐	HL8255	A321-231	5035	
☐	HL8256	A321-231	5169	
☐	HL8257	A321-231	5173	
☐	HL8265	A321-231	5287	
☐	HL8266	A321-231	5350	
☐	HL8267	A321-231	5382	
☐	HL8277	A321-231	5462	
☐	HL8278	A321-231	5500	
☐	HL8279	A321-231	5636	
☐	HL8280	A321-231	5767	
☐	HL8281	A321-231	5774	
☐	HL	A321-231/S	7052	o/o♦
☐	HL	A321-231/S	7133	o/o♦
☐	HL	A321-231/S	7266	o/o♦
☐	HL7736	A330-323E	640	
☐	HL7740	A330-323E	676	
☐	HL7741	A330-323E	708	
☐	HL7746	A330-323E	772	
☐	HL7747	A330-323E	803	
☐	HL7754	A330-323E	845	
☐	HL7792	A330-323E	1001	
☐	HL7793	A330-323E	1055	
☐	HL7794	A330-323E	1151	
☐	HL7795	A330-323E	1211	
☐	HL8258	A330-323E	1326	
☐	HL8259	A330-323E	1340	
☐	HL8282	A330-323E	1435	
☐	HL8286	A330-323E	1464	
☐	HL8293	A330-323E	1518	
☐	HL7625	A380-841	152	
☐	HL7626	A380-841	155	
☐	HL7634	A380-841	179	
☐	HL7635	A380-841	183	
☐	HL7413	B747-48EM(SF)	25405/880	
☐	HL7414	B747-48EM(SF)	25452/892	
☐	HL7415	B747-48EM(SF)	25777/946	
☐	HL7417	B747-48EM(SF)	25779/1006	
☐	HL7418	B747-48E	25780/1035	
☐	HL7419	B747-48EF	25781/1044	
☐	HL7420	B747-48EF	25783/1064	
☐	HL7421	B747-48EM	25784/1086	
☐	HL7423	B747-48EM	25782/1115	
☐	HL7428	B747-48E	28552/1160	
☐	HL7436	B747-48EF	29170/1305	
☐	HL7616	B747-446F	33748/1351	
☐	HL7618	B747-446(SF)	26343/918	
☐	HL7620	B747-419(SF)	29375/1228	
☐	HL7247	B767-38E	25757/523	
☐	HL7248	B767-38E	25758/582	
☐	HL7506	B767-38E	25760/639	
☐	HL7507	B767-38EF	25761/616	
☐	HL7514	B767-38E	25763/656	
☐	HL7515	B767-38E	25762/658	
☐	HL7516	B767-38E	25759/668	
☐	HL7528	B767-38E	29129/693	
☐	HL7596	B777-28EER	28681/322	
☐	HL7597	B777-28EER	28686/359	
☐	HL7700	B777-28EER	30859/403	
☐	HL7732	B777-28EER	29174/481	
☐	HL7739	B777-28EER	29175/526	
☐	HL7755	B777-28EER	30861/646	
☐	HL7756	B777-28EER	30860/659	
☐	HL7775	B777-28EER	30862/738	
☐	HL7791	B777-28EER	35525/853	
☐	HL8254	B777-28EER	40198/1027	
☐	HL8284	B777-28EER	40199/1117	

EASTAR JET — ***ZE / ESR***

	Reg	Type	c/n	
☐	HL8022	B737-73V	32426/1474	
☐	HL8023	B737-86N	28574/67	
☐	HL8028	B737-8BK	30625/1248	
☐	HL8029	B737-86N	28576/103	
☐	HL8035	B737-8BK/W	33019/1502	♦
☐	HL8036	B737-86N	28655/965	♦
☐	HL8048	B737-808/W	34710/2144	♦
☐	HL8052	B737-86J/W	37761/3887	o/o♦
☐	HL8205	B737-73V	32412/1151	
☐	HL8207	B737-73V	32413/1202	
☐	HL8264	B737-86J/W	28068/36	
☐	HL8269	B737-8Q8	30684/1689	
☐	HL8289	B737-883	30194/666	
☐	HL8292	B737-883	28323/625	

JEJU AIR — ***7C / JJA***

	Reg	Type	c/n	
☐	HL7779	B737-85F	28824/180	
☐	HL7780	B737-85F	28827/467	
☐	HL8019	B737-86N/W	32694/1960	
☐	HL8020	B737-86N/W	32683/2136	
☐	HL8031	B737-8GJ/W	37361/3506	
☐	HL8032	B737-8GJ/W	36367/3218	♦
☐	HL8033	B737-8AL/W	35071/2138	♦
☐	HL8034	B737-8HX/W	38101/3803	♦
☐	HL8049	B737-8AS/W	36570/2573	♦
☐	HL8050	B737-8AS/W	36571/2574	♦
☐	HL8051	B737-8AS/W	36573/2581	♦
☐	HL8061	B737-8AS/W	37514/2735	♦
☐	HL8063	B737-8AS/W	37519/2779	o/o♦
☐	HL8206	B737-86J/W	30877/782	
☐	HL8214	B737-86N/W	28608/410	
☐	HL8234	B737-86Q/W	30285/1237	
☐	HL8239	B737-82R	29344/849	
☐	HL8260	B737-8BK/W	30622/1108	
☐	HL8261	B737-8BK/W	30624/1193	
☐	HL8263	B737-82R/W	30658/1325	
☐	HL8287	B737-8Q8/W	30665/1436	
☐	HL8295	B737-8Q8/W	30694/1863	
☐	HL8296	B737-8Q8/W	30695/1891	
☐	HL8297	B737-83N/W	30673/1500	
☐	HL	B737-8AS/W	33634/2745[DUB]	o/o♦
☐	HL	B737-7V3/W	30676/1619	o/o♦

JIN AIR — ***LJ / JNA***

	Reg	Type	c/n	
☐	HL7555	B737-86N	30230/460	
☐	HL7556	B737-86N	28615/482	
☐	HL7557	B737-86N	28622/562	
☐	HL7558	B737-86N	28625/590	
☐	HL7559	B737-86N	28626/611	
☐	HL7561	B737-8B5/W	29982/663	
☐	HL7562	B737-8B5/W	29983/678	

	Reg	Type	c/n	
☐	HL7563	B737-86N/W	28636/756	
☐	HL7564	B737-86N	28638/765	
☐	HL7565	B737-8B5/W	29984/848	
☐	HL7567	B737-86N	28647/878	
☐	HL7798	B737-809/W	28236/739	
☐	HL8012	B737-8SH/W	41348/5499	♦
☐	HL8013	B737-8SH/W	41346/5571	♦
☐	HL8014	B737-8SH/W	42051/5611	♦
☐	HL8015	B737-8SH/W	42061/5617	♦
☐	HL7733	B777-2B5ER	34206/520	♦
☐	HL7734	B777-2B5ER	34207/528	♦
☐	HL7743	B777-2B5ER	34208/584	

KOREA EXPRESS AIR XE / KEA

	Reg	Type	c/n	
☐	HL8054	ERJ-145ER	145065	♦
☐	HL	ERJ-145ER		o/o♦

KOREAN AIR KE / KAL

	Reg	Type	c/n	
☐	HL7524	A330-322	206	
☐	HL7525	A330-322	219	
☐	HL7538	A330-223	222	
☐	HL7539	A330-223	226	
☐	HL7540	A330-322	241	
☐	HL7550	A330-322	162	
☐	HL7551	A330-322	172	
☐	HL7552	A330-223	258	
☐	HL7553	A330-323E	267	
☐	HL7554	A330-323E	256	
☐	HL7584	A330-323E	338	
☐	HL7585	A330-323E	350	
☐	HL7586	A330-323E	351	
☐	HL7587	A330-323E	368	
☐	HL7702	A330-323E	428	
☐	HL7709	A330-323E	484	
☐	HL7710	A330-323E	490	
☐	HL7720	A330-323E	550	
☐	HL8001	A330-323E	1556	
☐	HL8002	A330-323E	1576	
☐	HL8003	A330-323E	1590	
☐	HL8025	A330-323E	1611	
☐	HL8026	A330-323E	1638	
☐	HL8027	A330-343E	1647	
☐	HL8211	A330-223	1133	
☐	HL8212	A330-223	1155	
☐	HL8227	A330-223	1200	
☐	HL8228	A330-223	1203	
☐	HL8276	A330-223	1393	
☐	HL7611	A380-861	035	
☐	HL7612	A380-861	039	
☐	HL7613	A380-861	059	
☐	HL7614	A380-861	068	
☐	HL7615	A380-861	075	
☐	HL7619	A380-861	096	
☐	HL7621	A380-861	126	
☐	HL7622	A380-861	128	
☐	HL7627	A380-861	130	
☐	HL7628	A380-861	156	
☐	HL8222	B737-7B5/W BBJ1	37660/2997	
☐	HL7560	B737-8B5/W	29981/622	
☐	HL7566	B737-8B5/W	29985/852	
☐	HL7568	B737-8B5/W	29986/891	
☐	HL7757	B737-8GQ/W	35790/2119	
☐	HL7758	B737-8GQ/W	35791/2150	
☐	HL7785	B737-8GQ/W	37162/2906	
☐	HL7786	B737-8GQ/W	37163/2955	
☐	HL8224	B737-8Q8/W	38822/3704	
☐	HL8225	B737-8Q8/W	38823/3818	
☐	HL8240	B737-8BK/W	39447/3794	
☐	HL8241	B737-8BK/W	38129/3852	
☐	HL8242	B737-8Q8/W	38824/3895	
☐	HL8243	B737-8Q8/W	38825/3927	
☐	HL8244	B737-8Q8/W	38826/3943	
☐	HL8245	B737-8Q8/W	38827/3980	
☐	HL8246	B737-8SH/W	41299/4057	
☐	HL8247	B737-8SH/W	41300/4214	
☐	HL	B737-8SH/W		o/o♦
☐	HL	B737-8SH/W		o/o♦
☐	HL	B737-8SH/W		o/o♦
☐	HL7569	B737-9B5	29987/999	
☐	HL7599	B737-9B5	29988/1026	
☐	HL7704	B737-9B5	29989/1082	
☐	HL7705	B737-9B5	29990/1162	
☐	HL7706	B737-9B5	29991/1188	
☐	HL7707	B737-9B5	29992/1190	
☐	HL7708	B737-9B5	29993/1208	
☐	HL7716	B737-9B5	29994/1320	
☐	HL7717	B737-9B5	29995/1332	
☐	HL7718	B737-9B5	29996/1338	
☐	HL7719	B737-9B5	29997/1416	
☐	HL7724	B737-9B5	29998/1494	
☐	HL7725	B737-9B5	29999/1512	
☐	HL7726	B737-9B5	30001/1729	
☐	HL7727	B737-9B5	30000/1536	
☐	HL7728	B737-9B5	30002/1620	
☐	HL8221	B737-9B5ER/W	37633/3645	
☐	HL8223	B737-9B5ER/W	37634/3681	
☐	HL8248	B737-9B5ER/W	37635/4038	
☐	HL8249	B737-9B5ER/W	37636/4080	
☐	HL8272	B737-9B5ER/W	42173/4468	
☐	HL8273	B737-9B5ER/W	42174/4479	
☐	HL7400	B747-4B5F	26414/1295	
☐	HL7402	B747-4B5	26407/1155	
☐	HL7403	B747-4B5F	26408/1163	
☐	HL7404	B747-4B5	26409/1170	
☐	HL7434	B747-4B5F	32809/1316	
☐	HL7437	B747-4B5F	32808/1323	
☐	HL7438	B747-4B5ERF	33515/1329	
☐	HL7439	B747-4B5ERF	33516/1338	
☐	HL7448	B747-4B5F	26416/1246	
☐	HL7449	B747-4B5F	26411/1248	
☐	HL7460	B747-4B5	26404/1107	
☐	HL7461	B747-4B5	26405/1118	
☐	HL7462	B747-4B5F	26406/1123	
☐	HL7466	B747-4B5F	26413/1286	
☐	HL7467	B747-4B5F	27073/1291	
☐	HL7472	B747-4B5	26403/1095	
☐	HL7473	B747-4B5	28335/1098	
☐	HL7490	B747-4B5	27177/1019	
☐	HL7492	B747-4B5	26397/1055	
☐	HL7494	B747-4B5	27662/1067	
☐	HL7495	B747-4B5	28096/1073	
☐	HL7498	B747-4B5	26402/1092	
☐	HL7499	B747-4B5ERF	33517/1340	
☐	HL7600	B747-4B5ERF	33945/1347	
☐	HL7601	B747-4B5ERF	33946/1350	
☐	HL7602	B747-4B5ERF	34301/1365	
☐	HL7603	B747-4B5ERF	34302/1368	
☐	HL7605	B747-4B5ERF	35526/1375	
☐	HL7609	B747-8B5F	37132/1425	
☐	HL7610	B747-8B5F	37133/1426	

	Reg	Type	c/n	Note
☐	HL7617	B747-8B5F	37654/1474	
☐	HL7623	B747-8B5F	37655/1481	
☐	HL7624	B747-8B5F	37656/1488	
☐	HL7629	B747-8B5F	37657/1516	♦
☐	HL7630	B747-8B5	40905/1506	♦
☐	HL7631	B747-8B5	40906/1509	♦
☐	HL7632	B747-8B5	40907/1524	♦
☐	HL7633	B747-8B5	40908/1525	♦
☐	HL7636	B747-885	60407/1527	♦
☐	HL7637	B747-885	/1529	o/o♦
☐	HL	B747-885	/1531	o/o♦
☐	HL	B747-8B5F		o/o
☐	HL7526	B777-2B5ER	27947/148	
☐	HL7530	B777-2B5ER	27945/59	
☐	HL7531	B777-2B5ER	27946/62	
☐	HL7574	B777-2B5ER	28444/305	
☐	HL7575	B777-2B5ER	28445/309	
☐	HL7598	B777-2B5ER	27949/356	
☐	HL7714	B777-2B5ER	27951/411	
☐	HL7715	B777-2B5ER	28372/416	
☐	HL7721	B777-2B5ER	33727/452	
☐	HL7750	B777-2B5ER	34209/633	
☐	HL7751	B777-2B5ER	34210/657	
☐	HL7752	B777-2B5ER	34211/682	
☐	HL7764	B777-2B5ER	34214/684	
☐	HL7765	B777-2B5ER	34212/711	
☐	HL7766	B777-2B5ER	34213/730	
☐	HL7532	B777-3B5	28371/162	
☐	HL7533	B777-3B5	27948/178	
☐	HL7534	B777-3B5	27950/120	
☐	HL7573	B777-3B5	27952/288	
☐	HL7782	B777-3B5ER	37643/785	
☐	HL7783	B777-3B5ER	37644/806	
☐	HL7784	B777-3B5ER	37136/823	
☐	HL8006	B777-3B5ER	37652/1315	♦
☐	HL8007	B777-3B5ER	43815/1323	♦
☐	HL8008	B777-3B5ER	43816/1339	♦
☐	HL8009	B777-3B5ER	41999/1362	♦
☐	HL8010	B777-3B5ER	42120/1286	
☐	HL8011	B777-3B5ER	42123/1303	
☐	HL8208	B777-3B5ER	37645/867	
☐	HL8209	B777-3B5ER	37646/875	
☐	HL8210	B777-3B5ER	40377/882	
☐	HL8216	B777-3B5ER	37647/933	
☐	HL8217	B777-3B5ER	37648/938	
☐	HL8218	B777-3B5ER	37649/976	
☐	HL8250	B777-3B5ER	37650/1023	
☐	HL8274	B777-3B5ER	41998/1081	
☐	HL8275	B777-3B5ER	37651/1109	
☐	HL	B777-3B5ER		o/o
☐	HL	B777-3B5ER		o/o
☐	HL	B777-3B5ER		o/o♦
☐	HL	B777-3B5ER		o/o♦
☐	HL	B777-3B5ER		o/o♦
☐	HL8005	B777-FB5	37642/1278	
☐	HL8226	B777-FB5	37640/1074	
☐	HL8251	B777-FB5	37639/989	
☐	HL8252	B777-FB5	37638/1026	
☐	HL8285	B777-FB5	37641/1172	
☐	HL	B777-FB5		o/o♦
☐	HL	B777-FB5		o/o♦
☐	HL	B777-FB5		o/o♦
☐	HL	B787-9		o/o♦
☐	HL	B787-9		o/o♦
☐	HL	B787-9		o/o♦
☐	HL	B787-9		o/o♦

T'WAY AIR — TW / TWB

	Reg	Type	c/n	Note
☐	HL8000	B737-86N/W	34249/1857	
☐	HL8021	B737-8GJ/W	34899/2128	
☐	HL8024	B737-8HX/W	36848/3394	
☐	HL8030	B737-8Q8/W	41804/5305	
☐	HL8047	B737-8BK/W	29675/2414	♦
☐	HL8056	B737-8AS/W	36572/2580	♦
☐	HL8232	B737-8K5/W	27979/44	
☐	HL8235	B737-8KG/W	39448/3362	
☐	HL8237	B737-8Q8/W	30654/1295	
☐	HL8253	B737-86J/W	28069/42	
☐	HL8268	B737-83N/W	30660/1330	
☐	HL8294	B737-8Q8/W	32798/1470	

USKY AIR — URI

	Reg	Type	c/n	Note
☐	HL8040	CRJ-200ER	7572	♦

HP- PANAMA

AIR PANAMA — 7P / PST

	Reg	Type	c/n	Note
☐	HP-1923PST	B737-36E(QC)	25159/2068	♦
☐	HP-1507PS	DHC-6 Twin Otter 300	532	
☐	HP-1509PS	DHC-6 Twin Otter 300	360	
☐	HP-1605PST	Fokker 50	20178	
☐	HP-1606PST	Fokker 50	20179	
☐	HP-1793PST	Fokker 50	20162	
☐	HP-1794PST	Fokker 50	20163	
☐	HP-1763PST	Fokker 100	11315	
☐	HP-1764PST	Fokker 100	11364	
☐	HP-1542PST	F.27 Friendship 500F	10560	
☐	HP-1604PST	F.27 Friendship 500F	10471	
☐	HP-1631PST	F.27 Friendship 500F	10658	
☐	HP-1670PST	SAAB SF.340B	340B-299	
☐	HP-1671PST	SAAB SF.340B	340B-294	
☐	HP-1894PST	Fokker 100	11390	
☐	HP-1895PST	Fokker 100	11400	
☐	HP-1896PST	Fokker 100	11320	♦

COPA AIRLINES — CM / CMP

	Reg	Type	c/n	Note
☐	HP-1371CMP	B737-7V3/W	30049/388	>RPB
☐	HP-1372CMP	B737-7V3/W	28607/399	>RPB
☐	HP-1373CMP	B737-7V3/W	30458/459	>RPB
☐	HP-1374CMP	B737-7V3/W	30459/494	674
☐	HP-1375CMP	B737-7V3/W	30460/558	675
☐	HP-1376CMP	B737-7V3/W	30497/574	676
☐	HP-1377CMP	B737-7V3/W	30462/1161	677
☐	HP-1378CMP	B737-7V3/W	30461/1173	678
☐	HP-1520CMP	B737-7V3/W	33707/1376	681
☐	HP-1521CMP	B737-7V3/W	33708/1379	682
☐	HP-1524CMP	B737-7V3/W	33705/1505	683
☐	HP-1525CMP	B737-7V3/W	33706/1518	684
☐	HP-1530CMP	B737-7V3/W	34535/1962	687
☐	HP-1531CMP	B737-7V3/W	34536/1995	688
☐	HP-	B737-7V3/W		o/o♦
☐	HP-	B737-7V3/W		o/o♦
☐	HP-1522CMP	B737-8V3/W	33709/1387	480
☐	HP-1523CMP	B737-8V3/W	33710/1397	481
☐	HP-1526CMP	B737-8V3/W	34006/1585	482
☐	HP-1532CMP	B737-8V3/W	35068/2343	484
☐	HP-1533CMP	B737-8V3/W	35067/2423	485
☐	HP-1534CMP	B737-8V3/W	35125/2624	486
☐	HP-1535CMP	B737-8V3/W	35126/2805	487

	Reg	Type	c/n	Fleet	Notes
□	HP-1536CMP	B737-8V3/W	35127/2963	488	
□	HP-1537CMP	B737-8V3/W	36550/3114	489	
□	HP-1538CMP	B737-8V3/W	36554/3130	490	
□	HP-1539CMP	B737-8V3/W	29667/3151	491	
□	HP-1711CMP	B737-8V3/W	40663/3265	492	
□	HP-1712CMP	B737-8V3/W	40664/3267	493	
□	HP-1713CMP	B737-8V3/W	40890/3455	494	
□	HP-1714CMP	B737-8V3/W	40891/3476	495	
□	HP-1715CMP	B737-8V3/W	40361/3500	496	
□	HP-1716CMP	B737-8V3/W	40666/3567	497	
□	HP-1717CMP	B737-8V3/W	40665/3595	498	
□	HP-1718CMP	B737-8V3/W	38139/3611	499	
□	HP-1719CMP	B737-8V3/W	37957/3695	550	
□	HP-1720CMP	B737-8V3/W	37958/3739	551	
□	HP-1721CMP	B737-8V3/W	40362/3751	552	
□	HP-1722CMP	B737-8V3/W	38100/3761	553	
□	HP-1723CMP	B737-8V3/W	37959/3781	554	
□	HP-1724CMP	B737-8V3/W	38140/3810	555	
□	HP-1725CMP	B737-8V3/W	38102/3839	556	
□	HP-1726CMP	B737-86N/W	38024/3919	557	
□	HP-1727CMP	B737-8V3/W	40778/3956	558	
□	HP-1728CMP	B737-86N/W	39396/3971	559	
□	HP-1729CMP	B737-8V3/W	41088/3977	560	
□	HP-1730CMP	B737-8V3/W	38141/3988	561	
□	HP-1821CMP	B737-8V3/W	41089/4005	562	
□	HP-1822CMP	B737-8V3/W	40779/4033	563	
□	HP-1823CMP	B737-86N/W	39398/4051	564	
□	HP-1824CMP	B737-86N/W	39399/4083	565	
□	HP-1825CMP	B737-8V3/W	40780/4179	566	
□	HP-1826CMP	B737-86N/W	38031/4189	567	
□	HP-1827CMP	B737-8V3/W	38142/4221	568	
□	HP-1828CMP	B737-8V3/W	38879/4233	569	
□	HP-1829CMP	B737-8V3/W	38882/4361	570	
□	HP-1830CMP	B737-8V3/W	40781/4396	571	
H	HP-1831CMP	B737-8V3/W	40788/4398	572	
□	HP-1832CMP	B737-8V3/W	40789/4552	573	
□	HP-1833CMP	B737-8V3/W	39884/4562	574	
□	HP-1834CMP	B737-8V3/W	39885/4588	575	
□	HP-1835CMP	B737-8V3/W	40790/4626	576	
□	HP-1836CMP	B737-8V3/W	40782/4846	577	
□	HP-1837CMP	B737-8V3/W	40783/4857	578	
□	HP-1838CMP	B737-8V3/W	41445/4956	579	
□	HP-1839CMP	B737-8V3/W	41446/4975	580	
□	HP-1840CMP	B737-8V3/W	44155/5014	581	
□	HP-1841CMP	B737-8V3/W	44156/5059	582	
□	HP-1842CMP	B737-8V3/W	40784/5100	583	
□	HP-1843CMP	B737-8V3/W	40785/5144	584	
□	HP-1844CMP	B737-8V3/W	40786/5342	585♦	
□	HP-1845CMP	B737-8V3/W	40787/5357	586♦	
□	HP-1846CMP	B737-8V3/W	41447/5417	587♦	
□	HP-1847CMP	B737-8V3/W	41448/5535	588♦	
□	HP-1848CMP	B737-8V3/W	39965/5543	589♦	
□	HP-1849CMP	B737-8V3/W	41449/5607	590♦	
□	HP-1850CMP	B737-8V3/W	39967/5619	591♦	
□	HP-1851CMP	B737-8V3/W	44153/5631	592♦	
□	HP-1852CMP	B737-8V3/W	39968/5667	593♦	

	Reg	Type	c/n	Notes
□	HP-1540CMP	ERJ-190AR	19000012	
□	HP-1556CMP	ERJ-190AR	19000016	
□	HP-1557CMP	ERJ-190AR	19000034	
□	HP-1558CMP	ERJ-190AR	19000038	
□	HP-1559CMP	ERJ-190AR	19000053	
□	HP-1560CMP	ERJ-190AR	19000056	
□	HP-1561CMP	ERJ-190AR	19000089	
□	HP-1562CMP	ERJ-190AR	19000095	>RPB
□	HP-1563CMP	ERJ-190AR	19000098	>RPB
□	HP-1564CMP	ERJ-190AR	19000100	
□	HP-1565CMP	ERJ-190AR	19000126	
□	HP-1566CMP	ERJ-190AR	19000165	>RPB
□	HP-1567CMP	ERJ-190AR	19000174	
□	HP-1568CMP	ERJ-190AR	19000212	
□	HP-1569CMP	ERJ-190AR	19000222	

DHL AERO EXPRESO — *D5 / DAE*

	Reg	Type	c/n	Notes
□	HP-1610DAE	B727-264F	20780/986	[SFB]
□	HP-1810DAE	B757-27AF	29611/910	
□	HP-1910DAE	B757-27AF	29607/832	
□	HP-2010DAE	B757-27AF	29610/904	

PANAIR CARGO — *I3 / CTW*

	Reg	Type	c/n	Notes
□	HP-1653CTW	B727-277F	21695/1481	[PTY]
□	HP-1754CTW	B727-225F	21857/1539	

UNIWORLD AIR CARGO — *UCG*

	Reg	Type	c/n
□	HP-1813UCG	DC-9-33F	47384/543

HR- HONDURAS

AEROLINEAS SOSA — *P4 / VSO*

	Reg	Type	c/n
□	HR-ARE	LET L-410UVP	841312
□	HR-ASI	LET L-410UVP-E3	871925
□	HR-ASR	Fairchild F-27F	84
□	HR-ASZ	LET L-410UVP	851530
□	HR-ATA	BAeJetstream 31	725
□	HR-ATB	BAeJetstream 31	726
□	HR-ATO	BAeJetstream 31	757
□	HR-AVE	LET L-410UVP-E3	882029
□	HR-AWW	CRJ-100ER	7037
□	HR-AXJ	BAeJetstream 32	896
□	HR-AXT	SAAB SF.340B	340B-267

AEROVIAS CENTROAMERICANAS - AVIAC

	Reg	Type	c/n
□	HR-ALU	Douglas DC-3	4583
□	HR-ATH	Douglas DC-3	6102

AVIASTA — *EKY?*

	Reg	Type	c/n
□	HR-AVR	B737-232	23104/1062
□	HR-EMH	B737-5YO	24900/2095
□	HR-AWG	BAeJetstream 31	764
□	HR-AWH	BAeJetstream 31	766

CM AIRLINES

	Reg	Type	c/n
□	HR-AXC	LET L-410UVP-E	902418

ISLENA AIRLINES — *WC / ISV*

	Reg	Type	c/n	Notes
□	HR-AVA	ATR 42-320	397	[ZAG]
□	HR-AXN	ATR 42-320	378	[ZAG]
□	HR-AYJ	ATR 72-600	1172	^
□	HR-AYM	ATR 72-600	1185	^
□	TG-AGC	ATR 42-300	120	[BLB]
□	TG-AGD	ATR 42-300	004	[BLB]
□	HR-IAP	Short SD.3-60	SH3616	
□	HR-IAW	Short SD.3-60	SH3669	

^ Avianca c/s

LANHSA

	Reg	Type	c/n
□	HR-AXG	BAeJetstream 31	791
□	HR-AXK	Beech 99A	U-134
□	HR-AYE	BAeJetstream 31	747

HS- THAILAND

ASIA ATLANTIC AIRLINES — HB / AAQ

	Reg	Type	c/n	
☐	HS-AAB	B767-383ER	24846/309	
☐	HS-AAC	B767-322ER	25287/449	

ASIAN AIR — DM / DEX

	Reg	Type	c/n	
☐	HS-DCM	B767-2J6ER	23307/126	[UTP]

BANGKOK AIRWAYS — PG / BKP

	Reg	Type	c/n	
☐	HS-PGN	A319-132	3759	
☐	HS-PGT	A319-132	3421	
☐	HS-PGX	A319-132	3424	
☐	HS-PGY	A319-132	3454	
☐	HS-PGZ	A319-132	3694	
☐	HS-PPA	A319-132	3911	
☐	HS-PPB	A319-132	2648	
☐	HS-PPC	A319-132	2660	
☐	HS-PPF	A319-131	2634	
☐	HS-PPG	A319-131	2664	
☐	HS-PPM	A319-132	2273	
☐	HS-PPN	A319-132	2362	♦
☐	HS-PGU	A320-232	2254	
☐	HS-PGV	A320-232	2310	
☐	HS-PGW	A320-232	2509	
☐	HS-PPD	A320-232	2531	
☐	HS-PPE	A320-232	2417	
☐	HS-PPH	A320-232	2783	
☐	HS-PPJ	A320-232	2366	
☐	HS-PPK	A320-232	2600	
☐	HS-PGA	ATR 72-212A	710	
☐	HS-PGB	ATR 72-212A	708	
☐	HS-PGC	ATR 72-212A	715	
☐	HS-PGD	ATR 72-212A	833	
☐	HS-PGF	ATR 72-212A	700	
☐	HS-PGG	ATR 72-212A	692	
☐	HS-PGK	ATR 72-212A	680	
☐	HS-PGM	ATR 72-212A	704	
☐	HS-PZA	ATR 72-600	1194	
☐	HS-PZB	ATR 72-600	1230	
☐	HS-PZC	ATR 72-600	1269	♦
☐	HS-PZD	ATR 72-600	1296	♦
☐	HS-PZE	ATR 72-600	1303	♦
☐	HS-	ATR 72-600		o/o♦
☐	HS-	ATR 72-600		o/o♦

CITY AIRWAYS — E8 / GTA

	Reg	Type	c/n	
☐	HS-GTG	B737-4H6	27191/2676	♦
☐	HS-GTH	B737-86N	30231/515	♦

JET ASIA AIRWAYS — JF / JAA

	Reg	Type	c/n	
☐	HS-JAB	B767-222ER	21868/10	
☐	HS-JAC	B767-222ER	21871/15	[ICN]
☐	HS-JAE	B767-233ER	24324/252	
☐	HS-JAF	B767-233ER	24325/254	[TPE]
☐	HS-JAG	B767-222ER	21872/20	[ICN]
☐	HS-JAK	B767-2J6ER	24007/204	
☐	HS-JAS	B767-336ER	25203/365	

K-MILE AIR — 8K / KMI

	Reg	Type	c/n	
☐	HS-KMA	B737-43Q(F)	28492/2837	
☐	HS-SCK	B727-2J4F	22080/1598	[UTP]
☐	HS-	B737-46Q(F)	29000/3033	o/o♦

KAN AIR — K8 / KND

	Reg	Type	c/n	
☐	HS-KAD	ATR 72-212A	777	
☐	HS-	ATR 72-600		o/o♦
☐	HS-	ATR 72-600		o/o♦

NEWGEN AIRWAYS — E3 / VGO

	Reg	Type	c/n	
☐	HS-NGA	B737-401	23991/1746	
☐	HS-NGB	B737-4H6	27673/2852	
☐	HS-NGC	B737-4Q3	26603/2618	
☐	HS-NGD	B737-4Q3	26604/2684	
☐	HS-NGE	B737-8Q8/W	30661/1186	♦
☐	HS-NGG	B737-8Q8/W	30645/1129	♦

NINE STAR AIRWAYS — NSR

	Reg	Type	c/n	
☐	HS-NSB	A320-231	0308	o/o♦

NOK AIR — DD / NOK

	Reg	Type	c/n	
☐	HS-TRA	ATR 72-201	164	[DMK]
☐	HS-TRB	ATR 72-201	167	[DMK]
☐	HS-DRC	ATR 72-212A	740	
☐	HS-DRD	ATR 72-212A	754	
☐	HS-DBA	B737-8AS/W	33813/1617	
☐	HS-DBB	B737-8AS/W	33814/1618	
☐	HS-DBC	B737-85P	28386/426	
☐	HS-DBD	B737-8AS/W	33821/1698	
☐	HS-DBE	B737-83N/W	32577/973	
☐	HS-DBF	B737-8V3/W	29670/1711	
☐	HS-DBG	B737-8FH/W	35094/2195	
☐	HS-DBH	B737-83N/W	32614/1201	
☐	HS-DBJ	B737-83N/W	32616/1212	
☐	HS-DBK	B737-86J/W	37774/4328	
☐	HS-DBL	B737-8AS/W	33593/1914	
☐	HS-DBM	B737-8AS/W	33594/1923	
☐	HS-DBN	B737-8AS/W	33597/2060	
☐	HS-DBO	B737-8AS/W	33621/2058	
☐	HS-DBP	B737-8FZ/W	39336/4821	
☐	HS-DBQ	B737-86J/W	37794/4991	
☐	HS-DBR	B737-86N/W	43420/5031	
☐	HS-DBS	B737-86N/W	43421/5137	
☐	HS-DBT	B737-88L/W	61293/5519	♦
☐	HS-DBU	B737-88L/W	61294/5672	♦
☐	HS-	B737-88L/W		o/o♦
☐	HS-	B737-88L/W		o/o♦
☐	HS-TDA	B737-4D7	24830/1899	[UTP]
☐	HS-TDB	B737-4D7	24831/1922	[DMK]
☐	HS-TDE	B737-4D7	26612/2330	[DMK]
☐	HS-TDF	B737-4D7	26613/2338	[DMK]
☐	HS-DQA	DHC-8-402Q	4455	
☐	HS-DQB	DHC-8-402Q	4458	
☐	HS-DQC	DHC-8-402Q	4479	
☐	HS-DQD	DHC-8-402Q	4480	
☐	HS-DQE	DHC-8-402Q	4504	♦
☐	HS-DQF	DHC-8-402Q	4506	♦

NOKSCOOT — XW / NCT

	Reg	Type	c/n	
☐	HS-XBA	B777-212ER	28521/330	
☐	HS-XBB	B777-212ER	28522/337	
☐	HS-XBC	B777-212ER	30866/343	

ORIENT THAI AIRLINES — OX / OEA

	Reg	Type	c/n	
☐	HS-BRA	B737-3TO/W	23374/1204	[DMK]
☐	HS-BRB	B737-3TO/W	23375/1207	[UTP]

	Reg.	Type	c/n	Notes
☐	HS-BRD	B737-429	25247/2106	
☐	HS-BRE	B737-429	25248/2120	
☐	HS-BRI	B737-3Z0	27138/2436	[DMK]
☐	HS-BRJ	B737-3Z0	27176/2495	
☐	HS-BRK	B737-3Z0	25896/2558	std
☐	HS-BRL	B737-3J6	25080/2254	
☐	HS-BRQ	B737-3J6	25892/2396	std
☐	HS-STA	B747-412	26876/939	[BKK]
☐	HS-STB	B747-441	24956/917	[TPE]
☐	HS-STC	B747-412	26548/923	
☐	HS-STI	B747-4Q8	28194/1100	[BKK]
☐	HS-BKA	B767-3W0ER	28148/620	>SVA
☐	HS-BKB	B767-346	23961/192	[DMK]
☐	HS-BKD	B767-346	23962/193	
☐	HS-BKE	B767-3W0ER	28264/644	status?
☐	HS-BKH	B767-346	23966/191	std
☐	HS-BKI	B767-346	23965/186	
☐	HS-BKJ	B767-346	23963/224	[DMK]♦

RSU AIRLINES — RK / RCT

	Reg.	Type	c/n	Notes
☐	HS-RCB	A320-212	0466	
☐	HS-RCC	A321-211	1017	

SIAM AIR TRANSPORT — RBR

	Reg.	Type	c/n	Notes
☐	HS-BRU	B737-3J6	25893/2489	
☐	HS-BRV	B737-3L9	26440/2234	
☐	HS-EEE	B737-86J/W	37758/3439	♦
☐	HS-RRR	B737-86J/W	37760/3545	♦

THAI AIRASIA — FD / AIQ

	Reg.	Type	c/n	Notes
☐	HS-ABA	A320-216	3277	
☐	HS-ABB	A320-216	3299	
☐	HS-ABC	A320-216	3338	
☐	HS-ABD	A320-216	3394	
☐	HS-ABE	A320-216	3489	
☐	HS-ABF	A320-216	3505	
☐	HS-ABG	A320-216	3576	
☐	HS-ABH	A320-216	3679	
☐	HS-ABI	A320-216	3729	
☐	HS-ABJ	A320-216	4019	
☐	HS-ABK	A320-216	4088	
☐	HS-ABL	A320-216	4126	
☐	HS-ABM	A320-216	4278	
☐	HS-ABN	A320-216	4302	
☐	HS-ABO	A320-216	4333	
☐	HS-ABP	A320-216	4367	
☐	HS-ABQ	A320-216	4386	
☐	HS-ABR	A320-216	4390	
☐	HS-ABS	A320-216	4426	
☐	HS-ABT	A320-216	4557	
☐	HS-ABU	A320-216	4807	♦
☐	HS-ABV	A320-216	4979	
☐	HS-ABW	A320-216	4980	
☐	HS-ABX	A320-214	4917	
☐	HS-ABY	A320-214	4964	
☐	HS-ABZ	A320-216	5283	
☐	HS-BBA	A320-214	5344	
☐	HS-BBB	A320-214	5353	
☐	HS-BBC	A320-216/S	5468	
☐	HS-BBD	A320-216/S	5593	
☐	HS-BBE	A320-216/S	5703	
☐	HS-BBF	A320-216/S	5762	
☐	HS-BBG	A320-216/S	5812	
☐	HS-BBH	A320-216/S	5839	
☐	HS-BBI	A320-216/S	5851	
☐	HS-BBJ	A320-216/S	5866	
☐	HS-BBK	A320-216/S	5918	
☐	HS-BBL	A320-216/S	5959	
☐	HS-BBM	A320-216/S	6170	
☐	HS-BBN	A320-216/S	6178	
☐	HS-BBO	A320-216/S	6240	
☐	HS-BBP	A320-216/S	6405	
☐	HS-BBQ	A320-216/S	6428	
☐	HS-BBR	A320-216/S	6676	♦
☐	HS-BBS	A320-216	4098	♦
☐	HS-BBT	A320-216	5420?	♦

THAI AIRASIA X — TAX

	Reg.	Type	c/n	Notes
☐	HS-XTA	A330-343E	662	
☐	HS-XTB	A330-343E	786	
☐	HS-XTC	A330-343E	692	
☐	HS-XTD	A330-343E	741	♦
☐	HS-XTE	A330-343E	1619	♦

THAI AIRWAYS INTERNATIONAL — TG / THA

	Reg.	Type	c/n	Notes
☐	HS-TAR	A300B4-622R	681	[DMK]
☐	HS-TXA	A320-232	5198	
☐	HS-TXB	A320-232	5248	
☐	HS-TXC	A320-232	5258	
☐	HS-TXD	A320-232	5301	
☐	HS-TBA	A330-343E	1263	
☐	HS-TBB	A330-343E	1269	
☐	HS-TBC	A330-343E	1289	
☐	HS-TBD	A330-343E	1338	
☐	HS-TBE	A330-343E	1348	
☐	HS-TBF	A330-343E	1374	
☐	HS-TBG	A330-343E	1408	
☐	HS-TEA	A330-321	050	[UTP]
☐	HS-TEB	A330-321	060	[UTP]
☐	HS-TEC	A330-321	062	[DMK]
☐	HS-TED	A330-321	064	[BKK]
☐	HS-TEE	A330-321	065	[BKK]
☐	HS-TEF	A330-321	060	[BKK]
☐	HS-TEG	A330-321	112	[BKK]
☐	HS-TEH	A330-321	122	[BKK]
☐	HS-TEJ	A330-322	209	
☐	HS-TEK	A330-322	224	[UTP]
☐	HS-TEL	A330-322	231	
☐	HS-TEM	A330-323E	346	[UTP]
☐	HS-TEN	A330-343E	990	
☐	HS-TEO	A330-343E	1003	
☐	HS-TEP	A330-343E	1035	
☐	HS-TEQ	A330-343E	1037	
☐	HS-TER	A330-343E	1060	
☐	HS-TES	A330-343E	1074	
☐	HS-TET	A330-343E	1086	
☐	HS-TEU	A330-343E	1090	
☐	HS-TLA	A340-541	624	[DMK]
☐	HS-TLB	A340-541	628	[DMK]
☐	HS-TLC	A340-541	698	[DMK]
☐	HS-TLD	A340-541	775	[DMK]
☐	HS-TNA	A340-642	677	[UTP]
☐	HS-TNB	A340-642	681	[UTP]
☐	HS-TNC	A340-642	689	[UTP]
☐	HS-TND	A340-642	710	[UTP]
☐	HS-TNE	A340-642	719	[BKK]
☐	HS-TNF	A340-642	953	[UTP]
☐	HS-THB	A350-941	044	o/o♦
☐	HS-THC	A350-941	050	o/o♦

	Reg	Type	c/n	
☐	HS-	A350-941	095	o/o♦
☐	HS-TUA	A380-841	087	
☐	HS-TUB	A380-841	093	
☐	HS-TUC	A380-841	100	
☐	HS-TUD	A380-841	122	
☐	HS-TUE	A380-841	125	
☐	HS-TUF	A380-841	131	
☐	HS-TDD	B737-4D7	26611/2318	
☐	HS-TDG	B737-4D7	26614/2481	
☐	HS-TGA	B747-4D7	32369/1273	
☐	HS-TGB	B747-4D7	32370/1278	
☐	HS-TGF	B747-4D7	33770/1335	
☐	HS-TGG	B747-4D7	33771/1337	
☐	HS-TGH	B747-4D7BCF	24458/769	[UTP]
☐	HS-TGJ	B747-4D7BCF	24459/777	[BKK]
☐	HS-TGO	B747-4D7	26609/1001	
☐	HS-TGP	B747-4D7	26610/1047	
☐	HS-TGR	B747-4D7	27723/1071	[UTP]
☐	HS-TGT	B747-4D7	26616/1097	[UTP]
☐	HS-TGW	B747-4D7	27724/1111	
☐	HS-TGX	B747-4D7	27725/1134	
☐	HS-TGY	B747-4D7	28705/1164	
☐	HS-TGZ	B747-4D7	28706/1214	
☐	HS-TJA	B777-2D7	27726/25	
☐	HS-TJB	B777-2D7	27727/32	
☐	HS-TJC	B777-2D7	27728/44	
☐	HS-TJD	B777-2D7	27729/51	
☐	HS-TJE	B777-2D7	27730/89	
☐	HS-TJF	B777-2D7	27731/95	
☐	HS-TJG	B777-2D7	27732/100	
☐	HS-TJH	B777-2D7	27733/113	
☐	HS-TJR	B777-2D7ER	34586/588	
☐	HS-TJS	B777-2D7ER	34587/595	
☐	HS-TJT	B777-2D7ER	34588/596	
☐	HS-TJU	B777-2D7ER	34589/599	
☐	HS-TJV	B777-2D7ER	34590/665	
☐	HS-TJW	B777-2D7ER	34591/672	
☐	HS-TKA	B777-3D7	29150/156	
☐	HS-TKB	B777-3D7	29151/170	
☐	HS-TKC	B777-3D7	29211/250	
☐	HS-TKD	B777-3D7	29212/260	
☐	HS-TKE	B777-3D7	29213/304	
☐	HS-TKF	B777-3D7	29214/310	
☐	HS-TKK	B777-3ALER	41520/1030	
☐	HS-TKL	B777-3ALER	41521/1049	
☐	HS-TKM	B777-3ALER	41522/1082	
☐	HS-TKN	B777-3ALER	41523/1091	
☐	HS-TKO	B777-3ALER	41524/1107	
☐	HS-TKP	B777-3ALER	41525/1119	
☐	HS-TKQ	B777-3ALER	41526/1129	
☐	HS-TKR	B777-3ALER	41527/1145	
☐	HS-TKU	B777-3D7ER	42110/1166	
☐	HS-TKV	B777-3D7ER	42111/1215	
☐	HS-TKW	B777-3D7ER	42112/1228	
☐	HS-TKX	B777-3D7ER	42113/1267	
☐	HS-TKY	B777-3D7ER	42114/1310	♦
☐	HS-TKZ	B777-3D7ER	42115/1338	♦
☐	HS-TQA	B787-8	35315/190	
☐	HS-TQB	B787-8	35316/209	
☐	HS-TQC	B787-8	36110/226	
☐	HS-TQD	B787-8	35320/244	
☐	HS-TQE	B787-8	38757/287	
☐	HS-TQF	B787-8	38759/331	

THAI EXPRESS AIR / TXZ

	Reg	Type	c/n	
☐	HS-EXA	B737-348QC	23809/1458	[UTP]

THAI LION AIR SL / TLM

	Reg	Type	c/n	
☐	HS-LTH	B737-9GPER/W	38739/4657	
☐	HS-LTI	B737-9GPER/W	38738/4643	
☐	HS-LTJ	B737-9GPER/W	39823/5070	
☐	HS-LTK	B737-9GPER/W	38304/5162	
☐	HS-LTL	B737-9GPER/W	38748/4822	
☐	HS-LTM	B737-9GPER/W	38749/4843	
☐	HS-LTO	B737-9GPER/W	39824/5088	
☐	HS-LTP	B737-9GPER/W	38301/5176	
☐	HS-LTQ	B737-9GPER/W	39832/5242	
☐	HS-LTR	B737-9GPER/W	39837/5347	
☐	HS-LTS	B737-9GPER/W	39839/5404	
☐	HS-LTT	B737-9GPER/W	39860/5423	♦
☐	HS-LTU	B737-9GPER/W	39841/5446	♦
☐	HS-LUH	B737-8GP/W	39859/5495	♦
☐	HS-LUI	B737-8GP/W	39861/5524	♦
☐	HS-LUJ	B737-8GP/W	39864/5589	♦
☐	HS-LUK	B737-8GP/W	39868/5608	♦
☐	HS-LUL	B737-8GP/W	39873/5698	♦
☐	HS-LUO	B737-8GP/W	39879/5763	♦

THAI SMILE AIR WE / THD

	Reg	Type	c/n	
☐	HS-TXE	A320-232	5436	♦
☐	HS-TXF	A320-232	5553	
☐	HS-TXG	A320-232/S	5806	
☐	HS-TXH	A320-232/S	5828	
☐	HS-TXJ	A320-232/S	5857	
☐	HS-TXK	A320-232/S	5892	
☐	HS-TXL	A320-232/S	5951	
☐	HS-TXM	A320-232/S	5979	
☐	HS-TXN	A320-232/S	6113	
☐	HS-TXO	A320-232/S	6140	
☐	HS-TXP	A320-232/S	6254	
☐	HS-TXQ	A320-232/S	6297	
☐	HS-TXR	A320-232/S	6374	
☐	HS-TXS	A320-232/S	6417	
☐	HS-TXT	A320-232/S	6775	
☐	HS-TXU	A320-232/S	6795	♦

THAI VIETJET AIR V9 / TVJ

	Reg	Type	c/n	
☐	HS-VKA	A320-214	2745	

HZ- SAUDI ARABIA

AL MAHA AIRWAYS

	Reg	Type	c/n	
☐	A7-LAA	A320-214/S	6347	^
☐	A7-LAB	A320-214/S	6467	^
☐	A7-LAC	A320-214/S	6494	^♦
☐	A7-LAD	A320-214/S	6529	^♦
☐	A7-LAE	A320-214/S	6622	^♦
☐	A7-LAF	A320-214/S	6646	^♦
☐	A7-LAG	A320-214/S	6717	^♦
☐	A7-LAH	A320-214/S	6811	^♦

^ operated by QTR pending Al Maha gaining AOC in Saudi Arabia.

FLYNAS XY / KNE

	Reg	Type	c/n	
☐	LZ-PMX	A320-214	4061	<VIM♦
☐	LZ-PMY	A320-214	3802	<VIM♦
☐	VP-CXC	A320-214	2171	
☐	VP-CXD	A320-214	2182	

	Reg.	Type	c/n	Notes
☐	VP-CXE	A320-214	2199	
☐	VP-CXF	A320-214	1942	
☐	VP-CXG	A320-214	1965	
☐	VP-CXH	A320-214	3256	
☐	VP-CXI	A320-214	3218	
☐	VP-CXJ	A320-214/S	5716	
☐	VP-CXK	A320-214	4055	
☐	VP-CXL	A320-214	4735	
☐	VP-CXM	A320-214	2776	
☐	VP-CXN	A320-214	2569	
☐	VP-CXO	A320-214	3868	
☐	VP-CXP	A320-214	3889	
☐	VP-CXQ	A320-214	3933	
☐	VP-CXR	A320-214	3894	
☐	VP-CXS	A320-214	3787	
☐	VP-CXT	A320-214	3817	
☐	VP-CXU	A320-214	2123	
☐	VP-CXV	A320-214	3809	
☐	VP-CXW	A320-214	3475	
☐	VP-CXX	A320-214	3425	
☐	VP-CXY	A320-214	3396	
☐	VP-CXZ	A320-214	3361	
☐	9M-AZL	A330-243	261	<EZX♦
☐	9M-XXK	A330-343E	1433	<XAX
☐	PK-LHG	B747-412	24065/761	<LNI♦
☐	9M-ACM	B747-428M	25628/934	<EZX
☐	EC-HDS	B757-256	26252/900	<PVG♦

SAUDI ARABIAN AIRLINES SV / SVA

	Reg.	Type	c/n	Notes
☐	D-APTA	A319-112	1263	<PTGo/o♦
☐	D-ASPA	A319-112	1598	<PTGo/o♦
☐	D-ASPB	A319-112	1625	<PTGo/o♦
☐	OK-OER	A319-112	3892	<CSA♦
☐	OK-PET	A319-112	4258	<CSA♦
☐	HZ-ASA	A320-214	4081	
☐	HZ-ASB	A320-214	4090	
☐	HZ-ASC	A320-214	4337	
☐	HZ-ASD	A320-214	4364	
☐	HZ-ASE	A320-214	4408	
☐	HZ-ASF	A320-214	4955	
☐	HZ-ASG	A320-214	5223	
☐	HZ-AS11	A320-214	4015	
☐	HZ-AS12	A320-214	4057	
☐	HZ-AS13	A320-214	4104	
☐	HZ-AS14	A320-214	4115	
☐	HZ-AS15	A320-214	4122	
☐	HZ-AS16	A320-214	4135	
☐	HZ-AS17	A320-214	4349	
☐	HZ-AS18	A320-214	4357	
☐	HZ-AS19	A320-214	4376	
☐	HZ-AS20	A320-214	4392	
☐	HZ-AS21	A320-214	4414	
☐	HZ-AS22	A320-214	4484	
☐	HZ-AS23	A320-214	4519	
☐	HZ-AS31	A320-214	4092	
☐	HZ-AS32	A320-214	4273	
☐	HZ-AS33	A320-214	4314	
☐	HZ-AS34	A320-214	4397	
☐	HZ-AS35	A320-214	4391	
☐	HZ-AS36	A320-214	4393	
☐	HZ-AS37	A320-214	4394	
☐	HZ-AS38	A320-214	4432	
☐	HZ-AS39	A320-214	4442	
☐	HZ-AS40	A320-214	4419	
☐	HZ-AS41	A320-214	4454	
☐	HZ-AS42	A320-214	4501	
☐	HZ-AS43	A320-214	4517	
☐	HZ-AS44	A320-214	4564	
☐	HZ-AS45	A320-214	4823	
☐	HZ-	A320-214		o/o♦
☐	HZ-	A320-214		o/o♦
☐	HZ-ASH	A321-211	4467	
☐	HZ-ASI	A321-211	4542	
☐	HZ-ASJ	A321-211	4577	
☐	HZ-ASK	A321-211	4590	
☐	HZ-ASL	A321-211	4838	
☐	HZ-ASM	A321-211	4811	
☐	HZ-ASN	A321-211	4925	
☐	HZ-ASO	A321-211	4962	
☐	HZ-ASP	A321-211	5009	
☐	HZ-ASQ	A321-211	5065	
☐	HZ-ASR	A321-211	5285	
☐	HZ-AST	A321-211	5314	
☐	HZ-ASU	A321-211	5447	
☐	HZ-ASV	A321-211	5509	
☐	HZ-ASW	A321-211	5549	
☐	TC-OBR	A321-131	1008	<OHY
☐	TC-OBV	A321-231	0806	<OHY
☐	HZ-AQA	A330-343E	1108	
☐	HZ-AQB	A330-343E	1127	
☐	HZ-AQC	A330-343E	1137	
☐	HZ-AQD	A330-343E	1141	
☐	HZ-AQE	A330-343E	1147	
☐	HZ-AQF	A330-343E	1153	
☐	HZ-AQG	A330-343E	1192	
☐	HZ-AQH	A330-343E	1189	
☐	HZ-AQI	A330-343E	1454	
☐	HZ-AQJ	A330-343E	1473	
☐	HZ-AQK	A330-343E	1462	
☐	HZ-AQL	A330-343E	1513	
☐	HZ-	A330-343E	1724	o/o♦
☐	HZ-	A330-343E	1726	o/o♦
☐	HZ-	A330-343E	1729	o/o♦
☐	HZ-	A330-343E	1731	o/o♦
☐	HZ-	A330-343E	1734	o/o♦
☐	HZ-	A330-343E	1738	o/o♦
☐	HZ-	A330-343E	1739	o/o♦
☐	HZ-	A330-343E	1743	o/o♦
☐	HZ-	A330-343E	1749	o/o♦
☐	HZ-	A330-343E		o/o♦
☐	HZ-	A330-343E		o/o♦
☐	HZ-	A330-343E		o/o♦
☐	HZ-	A330-343E		o/o♦
☐	HZ-	A330-343E		o/o♦
☐	TC-OCC	A330-322	143	<OHY
☐	TC-OCD	A330-322	087	<OHY
☐	TC-OCE	A330-223	353	<OHY♦
☐	TC-OCI	A330-243	625	>SVA♦
☐	TC-OCJ	A330-243	632	>SVA♦
☐	TF-EAA	A330-223	343	<ABD
☐	HZ-AIV	B747-468	28339/1122	[JED]
☐	HZ-AIW	B747-468	28340/1138	
☐	HZ-AIX	B747-468	28341/1182	
☐	HZ-AIY	B747-468	28342/1216	[JED]
☐	HZ-AI3	B747-87UF	37562/1429	
☐	HZ-AI4	B747-87UF	37563/1432	
☐	TC-ACF	B747-481BDSF	25645/979	<RUN
☐	TC-ACG	B747-481BDSF	25641/928	<RUN
☐	TC-ACJ	B747-433BCF	25075/868	<RUN
☐	TC-ACM	B747-428ERF	32867/1318	<RUN♦

	Reg	Type	C/n	Notes
☐	TC-ACR	B747-428ERF	32866/1315	<RUN♦
☐	TF-AAD	B747-4H6	28426/1130	<ABD
☐	TF-AAE	B747-4H6	27672/1091	<ABD
☐	TF-AAH	B747-4H6	29901/1301	<ABD
☐	TF-AMI	B747-412(SF)	27066/940	<ABD
☐	TF-AML	B747-4H6BDSF	27044/1041	<ABD
☐	TF-AMM	B747-4H6BDSF	25700/974	<ABD
☐	TF-AMN	B747-4F6BDSF	27602/1161	<ABD♦
☐	TF-AMQ	B747-412F	26553/1069	<ABD
☐	TF-AMU	B747-48EF	27603/1210	<ABD
☐	TF-AMV	B747-412	28022/1082	<ABD
☐	9M-MPD	B747-4H6	25701/997	<EZX
☐	9M-MPK	B747-4H6	28427/1147	<EZX
☐	9M-MPM	B747-4H6	28435/1152	<EZX
☐	HS-BKA	B767-3W0ER	28148/620	<OEA
☐	HZ-AKA	B777-268ER	28344/98	
☐	HZ-AKB	B777-268ER	28345/99	
☐	HZ-AKC	B777-268ER	28346/101	
☐	HZ-AKD	B777-268ER	28347/103	
☐	HZ-AKE	B777-268ER	28348/109	
☐	HZ-AKF	B777-268ER	28349/114	
☐	HZ-AKG	B777-268ER	28350/119	
☐	HZ-AKH	B777-268ER	28351/124	
☐	HZ-AKI	B777-268ER	28352/143	
☐	HZ-AKJ	B777-268ER	28353/147	
☐	HZ-AKK	B777-268ER	28354/154	
☐	HZ-AKL	B777-268ER	28355/166	
☐	HZ-AKM	B777-268ER	28356/175	
☐	HZ-AKN	B777-268ER	28357/181	
☐	HZ-AKO	B777-268ER	28358/186	
☐	HZ-AKP	B777-268ER	28359/194	
☐	HZ-AKQ	B777-268ER	28360/219	
☐	HZ-AKR	B777-268ER	28361/230	
☐	HZ-AKS	B777-268ER	28362/255	
☐	HZ-AKT	B777-268ER	28363/298	
☐	HZ-AKU	B777-268ER	28364/306	
☐	HZ-AKV	B777-268ER	28365/323	
☐	HZ-AKW	B777-268ER	28366/351	
☐	HZ-AK71	B777-FFG	60337/1264	
☐	HZ-AK72	B777-FFG	60338/1328	♦
☐	HZ-AK73	B777-FFG	60339/1342	♦
☐	HZ-AK74	B777-FFG	60340/1354	♦
☐	HZ-AK11	B777-368ER	41048/982	
☐	HZ-AK12	B777-368ER	41050/986	
☐	HZ-AK13	B777-368ER	41049/992	
☐	HZ-AK14	B777-368ER	41051/999	
☐	HZ-AK15	B777-368ER	41052/1025	
☐	HZ-AK16	B777-368ER	41053/1061	
☐	HZ-AK17	B777-368ER	41054/1092	
☐	HZ-AK18	B777-368ER	41055/1131	
☐	HZ-AK19	B777-368ER	41056/1142	
☐	HZ-AK20	B777-368ER	41058/1151	
☐	HZ-AK21	B777-368ER	41057/1157	
☐	HZ-AK22	B777-368ER	41059/1162	
☐	HZ-AK23	B777-368ER	42261/1251	
☐	HZ-AK24	B777-368ER	42262/1262	
☐	HZ-AK25	B777-368ER	42263/1269	
☐	HZ-AK26	B777-368ER	42264/1268	
☐	HZ-AK27	B777-368ER	42265/1311	♦
☐	HZ-AK28	B777-368ER	42266/1322	♦
☐	HZ-AK29	B777-368ER	42267/1350	♦
☐	HZ-AK30	B777-368ER	42268/1389	♦
☐	HZ-ARA	B787-9	41544/376	♦
☐	HZ-ARB	B787-9	41545/379	♦
☐	HZ-ARC	B787-9	41546/383	♦
☐	HZ-ARD	B787-9	41547/413	o/o♦
☐	HZ-	B787-9		o/o♦
☐	HZ-	B787-9		o/o♦
☐	HZ-	B787-9		o/o♦
☐	HZ-	B787-9		o/o♦
☐	HZ-AEA	ERJ-170LR	17000108	
☐	HZ-AEB	ERJ-170LR	17000114	
☐	HZ-AEC	ERJ-170LR	17000118	
☐	HZ-AED	ERJ-170LR	17000119	
☐	HZ-AEE	ERJ-170LR	17000121	
☐	HZ-AEF	ERJ-170LR	17000123	
☐	HZ-AEG	ERJ-170LR	17000124	
☐	HZ-AEH	ERJ-170LR	17000135	
☐	HZ-AEI	ERJ-170LR	17000142	
☐	HZ-AEJ	ERJ-170LR	17000145	
☐	HZ-AEK	ERJ-170LR	17000149	
☐	HZ-AEL	ERJ-170LR	17000152	
☐	HZ-AEM	ERJ-170LR	17000155	
☐	HZ-AEN	ERJ-170LR	17000158	
☐	HZ-AEO	ERJ-170LR	17000161	

SAUDI GULF AIRLINES

	Reg	Type	C/n	Notes
☐	HZ-SGA	A320-232/S	6455	♦
☐	HZ-SGB	A320-232/S	6474	o/o♦
☐	HZ-SGC	A320-232/S	6583	o/o♦
☐	HZ-SGD	A320-232/S	6733	o/o♦
☐	HZ-	CS300 C Series		o/o
☐	HZ-	CS300 C Series		o/o

SNAS AVIATION — RSE

	Reg	Type	C/n	Notes
☐	HZ-SNB	B727-223F	21084/1199	
☐	HZ-SNE	B727-230F	21619/1407	
☐	HZ-SNF	B727-230F	22643/1762	

H4- SOLOMON ISLANDS

SOLOMON AIRLINES — IE / SOL

	Reg	Type	C/n	Notes
☐	H4-BUS	A320-211	0302	
☐	H4-SOL	DHC-8-102A	289	

I - ITALY

AIR DOLOMITI — EN / DLA

	Reg	Type	C/n	Notes
☐	I-ADJK	ERJ-195LR	19000245	
☐	I-ADJL	ERJ-195LR	19000256	
☐	I-ADJM	ERJ-195LR	19000258	
☐	I-ADJN	ERJ-195LR	19000270	
☐	I-ADJO	ERJ-195LR	19000280	
☐	I-ADJP	ERJ-195LR	19000578	
☐	I-ADJQ	ERJ-195LR	19000587	
☐	I-ADJR	ERJ-195LR	19000595	
☐	I-ADJS	ERJ-195LR	19000597	
☐	I-ADJT	ERJ-195LR	19000606	

AIR VALLEE — DO / RVL

	Reg	Type	C/n	Notes
☐	SE-LEZ	Fokker 50	20128	<APF

ALITALIA — AZ / AZA

	Reg	Type	C/n	Notes
☐	EI-IMB	A319-112	2033	
☐	EI-IMC	A319-112	2057	
☐	EI-IMD	A319-112	2074	
☐	EI-IME	A319-112	1740	

	Reg	Type	c/n	
☐	EI-IMF	A319-112	2083	
☐	EI-IMG	A319-112	2086	
☐	EI-IMH	A319-112	2101	
☐	EI-IMI	A319-112	1745	
☐	EI-IMJ	A319-112	1779	
☐	EI-IML	A319-112	2127	
☐	EI-IMM	A319-111	4759	
☐	EI-IMN	A319-111	4764	
☐	EI-IMO	A319-112	1770	
☐	EI-IMP	A319-111	4859	
☐	EI-IMR	A319-111	4875	
☐	EI-IMS	A319-111	4910	
☐	EI-IMT	A319-111	5018	
☐	EI-IMU	A319-111	5130	
☐	EI-IMV	A319-111	5294	
☐	EI-IMW	A319-111	5383	
☐	EI-IMX	A319-111	5424	
☐	I-BIMA	A319-112	1722	
☐	EI-DSA	A320-216	2869	
☐	EI-DSB	A320-216	2932	
☐	EI-DSC	A320-216	2995	
☐	EI-DSD	A320-216	3076	
☐	EI-DSE	A320-216	3079	
☐	EI-DSG	A320-216	3115	
☐	EI-DSL	A320-216	3343	
☐	EI-DSU	A320-216	3563	
☐	EI-DSV	A320-216	3598	
☐	EI-DSW	A320-216	3609	
☐	EI-DSX	A320-216	3643	
☐	EI-DSY	A320-216	3666	
☐	EI-DSZ	A320-216	3695	
☐	EI-DTA	A320-216	3732	
☐	EI-DTB	A320-216	3815	
☐	EI-DTD	A320-216	3846	
☐	EI-DTE	A320-216	3885	
☐	EI-DTF	A320-216	3906	
☐	EI-DTG	A320-216	3921	
☐	EI-DTH	A320-216	3956	
☐	EI-DTI	A320-216	3976	
☐	EI-DTJ	A320-216	3978	
☐	EI-DTK	A320-216	4075	
☐	EI-DTL	A320-216	4108	
☐	EI-DTM	A320-216	4119	
☐	EI-DTN	A320-216	4143	
☐	EI-DTO	A320-216	4152	
☐	EI-EIA	A320-216	4195	
☐	EI-EIB	A320-216	4249	
☐	EI-EIC	A320-216	4520	
☐	EI-EID	A320-216	4523	
☐	EI-EIE	A320-216	4536	
☐	EI-IKB	A320-214	1226	
☐	EI-IKF	A320-214	1473	
☐	EI-IKG	A320-214	1480	
☐	EI-IKL	A320-214	1489	
☐	EI-IKU	A320-214	1217	
☐	I-BIKA	A320-214	0951	
☐	I-BIKC	A320-214	1448	
☐	I-BIKD	A320-214	1457	
☐	I-BIKI	A320-214	1138	
☐	I-BIKO	A320-214	1168	
☐	I-WEBA	A320-214	3138	
☐	I-WEBB	A320-214	3161	
☐	EI-IXC	A321-112	0526	[FCO]
☐	EI-IXH	A321-112	0940	
☐	EI-IXJ	A321-112	0959	
☐	EI-IXV	A321-112	0819	
☐	EI-IXZ	A321-112	0848	
☐	I-BIXK	A321-112	1220	
☐	I-BIXL	A321-112	0513	
☐	I-BIXM	A321-112	0514	
☐	I-BIXN	A321-112	0576	
☐	I-BIXP	A321-112	0583	
☐	I-BIXQ	A321-112	0586	
☐	I-BIXR	A321-112	0593	
☐	I-BIXS	A321-112	0599	
☐	EI-DIP	A330-202	339	
☐	EI-DIR	A330-202	272	
☐	EI-EJG	A330-202	1123	
☐	EI-EJH	A330-202	1135	
☐	EI-EJI	A330-202	1218	
☐	EI-EJJ	A330-202	1225	
☐	EI-EJK	A330-202	1252	
☐	EI-EJL	A330-202	1283	
☐	EI-EJM	A330-202	1308	
☐	EI-EJN	A330-202	1313	
☐	EI-EJO	A330-202	1327	
☐	EI-EJP	A330-202	1354	
☐	I-EJGA	A330-202	825	♦
☐	I-EJGB	A330-202	831	♦
☐	EI-DBK	B777-243ER	32783/455	
☐	EI-DBL	B777-243ER	32781/459	
☐	EI-DBM	B777-243ER	32782/463	
☐	EI-DDH	B777-243ER	32784/477	
☐	EI-ISA	B777-243ER	32855/413	
☐	EI-ISB	B777-243ER	32859/426	
☐	EI-ISD	B777-243ER	32860/439	
☐	EI-ISE	B777-243ER	32856/421	
☐	EI-ISO	B777-243ER	32857/424	
☐	I-DISU	B777-243ER	32858/425	

ALITALIA CITYLINER — CT / CYL

	Reg	Type	c/n
☐	EI-RDA	ERJ-175STD	17000330
☐	EI-RDB	ERJ-175STD	17000331
☐	EI-RDC	ERJ-175STD	17000333
☐	EI-RDD	ERJ-175STD	17000334
☐	EI-RDE	ERJ-175STD	17000335
☐	EI-RDF	ERJ-175STD	17000337
☐	EI-RDG	ERJ-175STD	17000338
☐	EI-RDH	ERJ-175STD	17000339
☐	EI-RDI	ERJ-175STD	17000340
☐	EI-RDJ	ERJ-175STD	17000342
☐	EI-RDK	ERJ-175STD	17000343
☐	EI-RDL	ERJ-175STD	17000345
☐	EI-RDM	ERJ-175STD	17000346
☐	EI-RDN	ERJ-175STD	17000347
☐	EI-RDO	ERJ-175STD	17000348
☐	EI-RNA	ERJ-190STD	19000470
☐	EI-RNB	ERJ-190STD	19000479
☐	EI-RNC	ERJ-190STD	19000503
☐	EI-RND	ERJ-190STD	19000512
☐	EI-RNE	ERJ-190STD	19000520

BLUE PANORAMA AIRLINES — BV / BPA

	Reg	Type	c/n
☐	I-BPAC	B737-4K5	27074/2281
☐	I-BPAG	B737-31S	29059/2967
☐	I-BPAI	B737-31S	29060/2979
☐	I-BPAL	B737-5K5	24927/1968
☐	I-BPAM	B737-3Y0	24909/2021
☐	EI-CMD	B767-324ER	27392/568
☐	EI-DBP	B767-35HER	26389/459

	Registration	Type	c/n	Notes
☐	EI-FCV	B767-3X2ER	26260/552	

CARGOLUX ITALIA — C8 / ICV

	Registration	Type	c/n	Notes
☐	LX-OCV	B747-4R7F	29731/1222	<CLX♦
☐	LX-RCV	B747-4R7F	30400/1235	<CLX♦
☐	LX-SCV	B747-4R7F	29733/1281	<CLX♦
☐	LX-TCV	B747-4R7F	30401/1311	<CLX
☐	LX-YCV	B747-4R7F	35805/1407	<CLX

MERIDIANA FLY — IG / EEZ

	Registration	Type	c/n	Notes
☐	EI-FDS	B737-86N	28595/285	
☐	EI-FFK	B737-81Q/W	29051/479	
☐	EI-FFM	B737-73S	29082/229	
☐	EI-FFW	B737-85F/W	30477/976	
☐	EI-FLM	B737-85F/W	30571/936	♦
☐	EI-FMM	B737-86N	29889/1153	♦
☐	EI-IGR	B737-36N/W	28561/2896	
☐	EI-IGS	B737-36N/W	28562/2908	
☐	EI-IGT	B737-73V/W	32421/1357	
☐	EI-IGU	B737-73V/W	32422/1363	
☐	EI=FMR	B767-304ER/W	28042/649	♦
☐	I-AIGG	B767-304ER	28041/614	
☐	I-AIGH	B767-23BER	23973/208	
☐	I-AIGJ	B767-304ER	28039/610	
☐	I-SMEB	MD-82	53064/1908	[FCO]
☐	I-SMEL	MD-82	49247/1151	[FCO]
☐	I-SMEM	MD-82	49248/1152	[OLB]
☐	I-SMEN	MD-83	53013/1738	
☐	I-SMEP	MD-82	49740/1618	
☐	I-SMER	MD-82	49901/1766	
☐	I-SMES	MD-82	49902/1948	
☐	I-SMET	MD-82	49531/1362	
☐	I-SMEV	MD-82	49669/1493	
☐	I-SMEZ	MD-82	49903/1949	

MINILINER — MNL

	Registration	Type	c/n	Notes
☐	I-MLGT	F.27 Friendship 500	10379	[BGY]
☐	I-MLHT	F.27 Friendship 500	10382	[BGY]
☐	I-MLRT	F.27 Friendship 500	10377	[BGY]
☐	I-MLTT	F.27 Friendship 500	10378	[BGY]
☐	I-MLUT	F.27 Friendship 500	10369	>SKG
☐	I-MLXT	F.27 Friendship 500	10374	>
☐	9H-MQT	F.27 Friendship 400	10295	[QRA]
☐	I-MLCT	Fokker 50	20191	std
☐	I-MLDT	Fokker 50	20197	

Reported ceased operations Feb15 but still leases aircraft out.

MISTRAL AIR — M4 / MSA

	Registration	Type	c/n	Notes
☐	I-ADLK	ATR 72-212A	706	^
☐	I-ADLW	ATR 72-212A	707	^
☐	OY-CNJ	ATR 72-212(F)	414	^
☐	OY-YAB	ATR 72-212A	588	^
☐	OY-YAE	ATR 72-212A	705	^
☐	EI-CFQ	B737-3YO(QC)	24255/1625	^
☐	EI-ELZ	B737-4Q8	26308/2665	^
☐	EI-FGX	B737-3Q8(F)	28054/3016	
☐	OM-GTB	B737-49R	28882/2845	<RLX

^ operated for Posta Italiana

NEOS — NO / NOS

	Registration	Type	c/n	Notes
☐	I-NDDL	B767-324ER/W	27568/593	♦
☐	I-NDMJ	B767-306ER/W	27958/589	
☐	I-NDOF	B767-306ER	27610/605	
☐	I-NEOS	B737-86N/W	32733/1078	
☐	I-NEOT	B737-86N/W	33004/1144	
☐	I-NEOU	B737-86N/W	29887/1263	
☐	I-NEOW	B737-86N/W	32685/2186	
☐	I-NEOX	B737-86N/W	33677/1486	
☐	I-NEOZ	B737-86N/W	34257/2024	

SILK WAY ITALIA AIRLINES — CSW

	Registration	Type	c/n	Notes
☐	I-SWIA	B747-4R7F	29729/1189	

SKYBRIDGE AIROPS — KYB

	Registration	Type	c/n	Notes
☐	I-SKYB	EMB.120ER	120087	

JA JAPAN

AIRASIA JAPAN

	Registration	Type	c/n	Notes
☐	JA01DJ	A320-216/S	6702	♦
☐	JA02DJ	A320-216/S	6972	o/o♦

AIR DO - HOKKAIDO INTERNATIONAL — HD / ADO

	Registration	Type	c/n	Notes
☐	JA8595	B737-54K	28461/2850	[HND]
☐	JA01AN	B737-781/W	33916/1781	
☐	JA07AN	B737-781/W	33900/2071	
☐	JA08AN	B737-781/W	33877/2086	
☐	JA09AN	B737-781/W	33878/2145	♦
☐	JA11AN	B737-781/W	33882/2268	
☐	JA12AN	B737-781/W	33881/2301	
☐	JA14AN	B737-781/W	33883/2370	♦
☐	JA15AN	B737-781/W	33888/2394	
☐	JA16AN	B737-781/W	33889/2488	♦
☐	JA01HD	B767-33AER	28159/689	
☐	JA98AD	B767-33AER	27476/687	
☐	JA601A	B767-381	27943/669	
☐	JA8359	B767-381	25617/439	

AMAKUSA AIRLINES — MZ / AHX

	Registration	Type	c/n	Notes
☐	JA01AM	ATR 42-600	1202	♦
☐	JA81AM	DHC-8Q-103	537	

ANA - ALL NIPPON AIRWAYS — NH / ANA

	Registration	Type	c/n	Notes
☐	JA8300	A320-211	0549	
☐	JA8304	A320-211	0531	
☐	JA8313	A320-211	0534	
☐	JA8382	A320-211	0139	
☐	JA8393	A320-211	0365	
☐	JA8396	A320-211	0482	
☐	JA8400	A320-211	0554	
☐	JA8609	A320-211	0501	
☐	JA8654	A320-211	0507	
☐	JA8946	A320-211	0669	
☐	JA8947	A320-211	0685	
☐	JA8997	A320-211	0658	
☐	JA380A	A380-841	162	o/o♦
☐	JA380B	A380-841	167	o/o♦
☐	JA380C	A380-841	185	o/o♦
☐	JA02AN	B737-781/W	33872/1850	
☐	JA03AN	B737-781/W	33873/1871	
☐	JA04AN	B737-781/W	33874/1890	
☐	JA05AN	B737-781/W	33875/1971	
☐	JA06AN	B737-781/W	33876/1992	
☐	JA10AN	B737-781ER/W	33879/2157	

☐	JA13AN	B737-781ER/W	33880/2232	
☐	JA17AN	B737-781/W	33884/2513	
☐	JA18AN	B737-781/W	33885/2582	
☐	JA51AN	B737-881/W	33886/2607	
☐	JA52AN	B737-881/W	33887/2643	
☐	JA53AN	B737-881/W	33891/2739	
☐	JA54AN	B737-881/W	33890/2833	
☐	JA55AN	B737-881/W	33892/2889	
☐	JA56AN	B737-881/W	33893/2926	
☐	JA57AN	B737-881/W	33894/2975	
☐	JA58AN	B737-881/W	33895/3029	
☐	JA59AN	B737-881/W	33896/3073	
☐	JA60AN	B737-881/W	33897/3126	
☐	JA61AN	B737-881/W	33898/3379	
☐	JA62AN	B737-881/W	33899/3414	
☐	JA63AN	B737-881/W	33901/3449	
☐	JA64AN	B737-881/W	33902/3478	
☐	JA65AN	B737-881/W	33903/3502	
☐	JA66AN	B737-881/W	33909/3598	
☐	JA67AN	B737-881/W	33911/3682	
☐	JA68AN	B737-881/W	33910/4151	
☐	JA69AN	B737-881/W	33912/4228	
☐	JA70AN	B737-881/W	33913/4282	
☐	JA71AN	B737-881/W	33914/4334	
☐	JA72AN	B737-881/W	33915/4426	
☐	JA73AN	B737-881/W	33904/4561	
☐	JA74AN	B737-881/W	33905/4634	
☐	JA75AN	B737-881/W	33906/4851	
☐	JA76AN	B737-881/W	33907/4922	
☐	JA77AN	B737-881/W	44556/4985	
☐	JA78AN	B737-881/W	33908/5025	
☐	JA79AN	B737-881/W	44557/5101	
☐	JA80AN	B737-881/W	44558/5216	
☐	JA81AN	B737-881/W	44559/5330	
☐	JA82AN	B737-881/W	62637/5683	♦
☐	JA83AN	B737-881/W	62638/5705	♦
☐	JA84AN	B737-881/W	62639/5724	♦
☐	JA85AN	B737-881/W	62640/5766	♦
☐	JA	B737-881/W		o/o♦
☐	JA601F	B767-381F	33404/885	♦
☐	JA602A	B767-381	27944/684	
☐	JA602F	B767-381F	33509/937	
☐	JA603A	B767-381ERF	32972/877	
☐	JA604A	B767-381ER	32973/881	
☐	JA604F	B767-381F	35709/947	
☐	JA605A	B767-381ER	32974/882	
☐	JA605F	B767-316F/W	30842/860	
☐	JA606A	B767-381ER	32975/883	
☐	JA607A	B767-381ER	32976/884	
☐	JA608A	B767-381ER	32977/886	
☐	JA609A	B767-381ER	32978/888	
☐	JA610A	B767-381ER	32979/895	
☐	JA611A	B767-381ER	32980/914	
☐	JA612A	B767-381ER	33506/920	
☐	JA613A	B767-381ER	33507/924	
☐	JA614A	B767-381ER	33508/931	
☐	JA615A	B767-381ER	35877/951	
☐	JA616A	B767-381ER	35876/953	
☐	JA617A	B767-381ER	37719/971	
☐	JA618A	B767-381ER	37720/976	
☐	JA619A	B767-381ER	40564/993	
☐	JA620A	B767-381ER	40565/996	
☐	JA621A	B767-381ER	40566/998	
☐	JA622A	B767-381ER	40567/1000	
☐	JA623A	B767-381ER	40894/1001	
☐	JA624A	B767-381ER	40895/1010	
☐	JA625A	B767-381ER	40896/1012	
☐	JA626A	B767-381ER	40897/1018	
☐	JA627A	B767-381ER	40898/1023	
☐	JA8256	B767-381	23756/176	
☐	JA8257	B767-381	23757/177	
☐	JA8259	B767-381	23759/185	
☐	JA8271	B767-381	24002/199	
☐	JA8272	B767-381	24003/212	
☐	JA8273	B767-381	24004/218	
☐	JA8286	B767-381ERBCF	24400/269	
☐	JA8322	B767-381	25618/458	
☐	JA8323	B767-381ERBCF	25654/463	
☐	JA8324	B767-381	25655/465	
☐	JA8342	B767-381	27445/573	
☐	JA8356	B767-381ERBCF	25136/379	
☐	JA8357	B767-381	25293/401	
☐	JA8358	B767-381ERBCF	25616/432	
☐	JA8362	B767-381ERBCF	24632/285	
☐	JA8567	B767-381	25656/510	
☐	JA8568	B767-381	25657/515	
☐	JA8569	B767-381	27050/516	
☐	JA8578	B767-381	25658/519	
☐	JA8579	B767-381	25659/520	
☐	JA8664	B767-381ERBCF	27339/556	
☐	JA8669	B767-381	27444/567	
☐	JA8670	B767-381	25660/539	
☐	JA8674	B767-381	25661/543	
☐	JA8677	B767-381	25662/551	
☐	JA8970	B767-381ERBCF	25619/645	
☐	JA8971	B767-381ER	27942/651	
☐	JA701A	B777-281	27938/77	
☐	JA702A	B777-281	27033/75	
☐	JA703A	B777-281	27034/81	
☐	JA704A	B777-281	27035/131	
☐	JA705A	B777-281	29029/137	
☐	JA706A	B777-281	27036/141	
☐	JA707A	B777-281ER	27037/247	
☐	JA708A	B777-281ER	28277/278	
☐	JA709A	B777-281ER	28278/286	
☐	JA710A	B777-281ER	28279/302	
☐	JA711A	B777-281	33406/482	
☐	JA712A	B777-281	33407/495	
☐	JA713A	B777-281	32647/509	
☐	JA714A	B777-281	28276/523	
☐	JA715A	B777-281ER	32646/563	
☐	JA716A	B777-281ER	33414/574	
☐	JA717A	B777-281ER	33415/580	
☐	JA731A	B777-381ER	28281/488	
☐	JA732A	B777-381ER	27038/511	
☐	JA733A	B777-381ER	32648/529	
☐	JA734A	B777-381ER	32649/557	
☐	JA735A	B777-381ER	34892/571	
☐	JA736A	B777-381ER	34893/589	
☐	JA741A	B777-281ER	40900/1005	
☐	JA742A	B777-281ER	40901/1016	
☐	JA743A	B777-281ER	40902/1090	
☐	JA744A	B777-281ER	40903/1102	
☐	JA745A	B777-281ER	40904/1112	
☐	JA751A	B777-381	28272/142	
☐	JA752A	B777-381	28274/160	
☐	JA753A	B777-381	28273/132	
☐	JA754A	B777-381	27939/172	
☐	JA755A	B777-381	28275/104	
☐	JA756A	B777-381	27039/440	
☐	JA757A	B777-381	27040/442	
☐	JA777A	B777-381ER	32650/593	

	Reg	Type	c/n	
☐	JA778A	B777-381ER	32651/606	
☐	JA779A	B777-381ER	34894/631	
☐	JA780A	B777-381ER	34895/639	
☐	JA781A	B777-381ER	27041/667	
☐	JA782A	B777-381ER	33416/691	
☐	JA783A	B777-381ER	27940/737	
☐	JA784A	B777-381ER	37950/833	
☐	JA785A	B777-381ER	37951/855	
☐	JA786A	B777-381ER	37948/866	
☐	JA787A	B777-381ER	37949/870	
☐	JA788A	B777-381ER	40686/873	
☐	JA789A	B777-381ER	40687/878	
☐	JA790A	B777-381ER	60136/1283	
☐	JA791A	B777-381ER	60137/1293	
☐	JA792A	B777-381ER	60381/1300	♦
☐	JA	B777-381ER		o/o
☐	JA	B777-381ER		o/o
☐	JA	B777-381ER		o/o
☐	JA	B777-381ER		o/o
☐	JA	B777-381ER		o/o
☐	JA	B777-381ER		o/o
☐	JA8197	B777-281	27027/16	
☐	JA8198	B777-281	27028/21	
☐	JA8199	B777-281	27029/29	
☐	JA8967	B777-281	27030/37	
☐	JA8968	B777-281	27031/38	
☐	JA8969	B777-281	27032/50	

	Reg	Type	c/n	
☐	JA801A	B787-8	34488/8	
☐	JA802A	B787-8	34497/24	
☐	JA803A	B787-8	34485/7	
☐	JA804A	B787-8	34486/9	
☐	JA805A	B787-8	34514/31	
☐	JA806A	B787-8	34515/40	♦
☐	JA807A	B787-8	34508/41	
☐	JA808A	B787-8	34490/42	
☐	JA809A	B787-8	34494/47	
☐	JA810A	B787-8	34506/48	
☐	JA811A	B787-8	34502/51	
☐	JA812A	B787-8	40748/56	
☐	JA813A	B787-8	34521/67	
☐	JA814A	B787-8	34493/69	
☐	JA815A	B787-8	40899/66	
☐	JA816A	B787-8	34507/63	
☐	JA817A	B787-8	40749/59	
☐	JA818A	B787-8	42243/83	
☐	JA819A	B787-8	42244/97	
☐	JA820A	B787-8	34511/101	
☐	JA821A	B787-8	42245/107	
☐	JA822A	B787-8	34512/110	
☐	JA823A	B787-8	42246/120	
☐	JA824A	B787-8	42247/132	
☐	JA825A	B787-8	34516/148	
☐	JA827A	B787-8	34509/147	
☐	JA828A	B787-8	42248/140	
☐	JA829A	B787-8	34520/179	
☐	JA831A	B787-8	34496/199	
☐	JA832A	B787-8	42249/203	
☐	JA834A	B787-8	40750/206	
☐	JA835A	B787-8	34525/243	
☐	JA838A	B787-8	34528/299	♦
☐	JA840A	B787-8	34518/322	♦
☐	JA874A	B787-8	34503/358	♦
☐	JA878A	B787-8	34501/428	o/o♦

	Reg	Type	c/n	
☐	JA830A	B787-9	34522/146	
☐	JA833A	B787-9	34524/202	
☐	JA836A	B787-9	34527/280	
☐	JA837A	B787-9	34526/295	
☐	JA839A	B787-9	34529/310	
☐	JA871A	B787-9	34534/319	♦
☐	JA872A	B787-9	34504/329	♦
☐	JA873A	B787-9	34530/345	♦
☐	JA875A	B787-9	34531/370	♦
☐	JA876A	B787-9	43871/408	o/o♦
☐	JA877A	B787-9	34532/414	o/o♦
☐	JA879A	B787-9	34533/447	o/o♦
☐	JA880A	B787-9	43869/454	o/o♦
☐	JA882A	B787-9	43872/467	o/o♦
☐	JA883A	B787-9	43873/472	o/o♦
☐	JA884A	B787-9	34523/479	o/o♦
☐	JA885A	B787-9	43870/484	o/o♦
☐	JA886A	B787-9	61522/491	o/o♦
☐	JA887A	B787-9	43864/497	o/o♦
☐	JA888A	B787-9	43874/504	o/o♦

ANA WINGS — *EH / AKX*

	Reg	Type	c/n	
☐	JA300K	B737-54K	27434/2872	♦
☐	JA301K	B737-54K	27435/2875	
☐	JA302K	B737-54K	28990/3002	
☐	JA303K	B737-54K	28991/3017	
☐	JA304K	B737-54K	28992/3030	
☐	JA305K	B737-54K	28993/3075	
☐	JA306K	B737-54K	29794/3109	
☐	JA307K	B737-54K	29795/3116	
☐	JA353K	B737-5Y0	26104/2552	[MZJ]
☐	JA355K	B737-5L9	28129/2823	[MZJ]
☐	JA356K	B737-5L9	28083/2784	
☐	JA357K	B737-5L9	28131/2828	
☐	JA358K	B737-5L9	28130/2825	
☐	JA359K	B737-5L9	28128/2817	
☐	JA8195	B737-54K	27433/2815	
☐	JA8196	B737-54K	27966/2824	
☐	JA8404	B737-54K	27381/2708	
☐	JA8419	B737-54K	27430/2723	
☐	JA8500	B737-54K	27431/2751	
☐	JA8504	B737-54K	27432/2783	♦
☐	JA8596	B737-54K	28462/2853	

	Reg	Type	c/n
☐	JA460A	DHC-8-402Q	4416
☐	JA461A	DHC-8-402Q	4430
☐	JA462A	DHC-8-402Q	4445
☐	JA841A	DHC-8-402Q	4080
☐	JA842A	DHC-8-402Q	4082
☐	JA843A	DHC-8-402Q	4084
☐	JA844A	DHC-8-402Q	4091
☐	JA845A	DHC-8-402Q	4096
☐	JA846A	DHC-8-402Q	4097
☐	JA847A	DHC-8-402Q	4099
☐	JA848A	DHC-8-402Q	4102
☐	JA850A	DHC-8-402Q	4108
☐	JA851A	DHC-8-402Q	4109
☐	JA852A	DHC-8-402Q	4131
☐	JA853A	DHC-8-402Q	4135
☐	JA854A	DHC-8-402Q	4151
☐	JA855A	DHC-8-402Q	4292
☐	JA856A	DHC-8-402Q	4335
☐	JA857A	DHC-8-402Q	4362
☐	JA858A	DHC-8-402Q	4385
☐	JA859A	DHC-8-402Q	4401

FUJI DREAM AIRLINES — *JH / FDA*

	Reg	Type	c/n
☐	JA01FJ	ERJ-170STD	17000271
☐	JA02FJ	ERJ-170STD	17000289
☐	JA03FJ	ERJ-175STD	17000304

	Registration	Type	Serial	Notes
□	JA04FJ	ERJ-170SU	17000129	
□	JA05FJ	ERJ-175STD	17000317	
□	JA06FJ	ERJ-175STD	17000332	
□	JA07FJ	ERJ-175STD	17000361	
□	JA08FJ	ERJ-175STD	17000391	
□	JA09FJ	ERJ-175STD	17000464	♦

HOKKAIDO AIR SYSTEM — NTH

	Registration	Type	Serial	Notes
□	JA01HC	SAAB SF.340B	340B-432	
□	JA02HC	SAAB SF.340B	340B-440	
□	JA03HC	SAAB SF.340B	340B-458	

IBEX AIRLINES/ANA CONNECTION — FW / IBX

	Registration	Type	Serial	Notes
□	JA03RJ	CRJ-200ER	7624	
□	JA04RJ	CRJ-200ER	7798	
□	JA05RJ	CRJ-702	10279	
□	JA06RJ	CRJ-702	10303	
□	JA07RJ	CRJ-702	10327	
□	JA08RJ	CRJ-702	10333	
□	JA09RJ	CRJ-702	10334	
□	JA10RJ	CRJ-702	10340	
□	JA11RJ	CRJ-702	10344	♦

J-AIR — XM / JLJ

	Registration	Type	Serial	Notes
□	JA201J	CRJ-200ER	7452	
□	JA202J	CRJ-200ER	7484	
□	JA203J	CRJ-200ER	7626	
□	JA204J	CRJ-200ER	7643	
□	JA205J	CRJ-200ER	7767	
□	JA206J	CRJ-200ER	7834	
□	JA207J	CRJ-200ER	8050	
□	JA208J	CRJ-200ER	8059	
□	JA209J	CRJ-200ER	8062	
□	JA211J	ERJ-170STD	17000251	
□	JA212J	ERJ-170STD	17000268	
□	JA213J	ERJ-170STD	17000285	
□	JA214J	ERJ-170STD	17000295	
□	JA215J	ERJ-170STD	17000297	
□	JA216J	ERJ-170STD	17000299	
□	JA217J	ERJ-170STD	17000308	
□	JA218J	ERJ-170STD	17000314	
□	JA219J	ERJ-170STD	17000315	
□	JA220J	ERJ-170STD	17000322	
□	JA221J	ERJ-170STD	17000353	
□	JA222J	ERJ-170STD	17000356	
□	JA223J	ERJ-170STD	17000362	
□	JA224J	ERJ-170STD	17000379	
□	JA225J	ERJ-170STD	17000389	
□	JA226J	ERJ-170STD	17000514	♦
□	JA227J	ERJ-170STD	17000524	♦
□	JA	ERJ-170STD		o/o♦
□	JA	ERJ-170STD		o/o♦
□	JA	ERJ-170STD		o/o♦
□	JA	ERJ-190		o/o♦
□	JA	ERJ-190		o/o♦
□	JA	ERJ-190		o/o♦
□	JA	ERJ-190		o/o♦
□	JA	ERJ-190		o/o♦
□	JA	ERJ-190		o/o♦

JAPAN AIR COMMUTER — 3X / JAC

	Registration	Type	Serial	Notes
□	JA841C	DHC-8-402Q	4072	
□	JA842C	DHC-8-402Q	4073	
□	JA843C	DHC-8-402Q	4076	
□	JA844C	DHC-8-402Q	4092	
□	JA845C	DHC-8-402Q	4101	std
□	JA846C	DHC-8-402Q	4107	
□	JA847C	DHC-8-402Q	4111	
□	JA848C	DHC-8-402Q	4121	
□	JA849C	DHC-8-402Q	4133	
□	JA850C	DHC-8-402Q	4158	
□	JA851C	DHC-8-402Q	4177	
□	JA001C	SAAB SF.340B	340B-419	
□	JA002C	SAAB SF.340B	340B-459	
□	JA8594	SAAB SF.340B	340B-399	
□	JA8642	SAAB SF.340B	340B-365	
□	JA8649	SAAB SF.340B	340B-368	
□	JA8703	SAAB SF.340B	340B-355	
□	JA8704	SAAB SF.340B	340B-361	
□	JA8886	SAAB SF.340B	340B-281	
□	JA8888	SAAB SF.340B	340B-331	
□	JA8900	SAAB SF.340B	340B-378	

JAPAN AIRLINES — JL / JAL

	Registration	Type	Serial	Notes
□	JA301J	B737-846/W	35330/2095	
□	JA302J	B737-846/W	35331/2162	
□	JA303J	B737-846/W	35332/2225	
□	JA304J	B737-846/W	35333/2253	
□	JA305J	B737-846/W	35334/2289	
□	JA306J	B737-846/W	35335/2395	
□	JA307J	B737-846/W	35336/2450	
□	JA308J	B737-846/W	35337/2479	
□	JA309J	B737-846/W	35338/2522	
□	JA310J	B737-846/W	35339/2510	
□	JA311J	B737-846/W	35340/2571	
□	JA312J	B737-846/W	35341/2584	
□	JA313J	B737-846/W	35342/2633	
□	JA314J	B737-846/W	35343/2701	
□	JA315J	B737-846/W	35344/2731	
□	JA316J	B737-846/W	35345/2762	
□	JA317J	B737-846/W	35346/2824	
□	JA318J	B737-846/W	35347/2830	
□	JA319J	B737-846/W	35348/2867	
□	JA320J	B737-846/W	35349/2953	
□	JA321J	B737-846/W	35350/2977	
□	JA322J	B737-846/W	35351/3002	
□	JA323J	B737-846/W	35352/3057	
□	JA324J	B737-846/W	35353/3105	
□	JA325J	B737-846/W	35354/3117	
□	JA326J	B737-846/W	35355/3159	
□	JA327J	B737-846/W	35356/3201	
□	JA328J	B737-846/W	35357/3279	
□	JA329J	B737-846/W	35358/3315	
□	JA330J	B737-846/W	35359/3341	
□	JA331J	B737-846/W	40346/3366	
□	JA332J	B737-846/W	40347/3385	
□	JA333J	B737-846/W	40348/3465	
□	JA334J	B737-846/W	40349/3489	
□	JA335J	B737-846/W	40350/3525	
□	JA336J	B737-846/W	40351/3543	
□	JA337J	B737-846/W	40352/3604	
□	JA338J	B737-846/W	40355/3609	
□	JA339J	B737-846/W	40354/3687	
□	JA340J	B737-846/W	39190/3882	
□	JA341J	B737-846/W	40356/3906	
□	JA342J	B737-846/W	39191/4002	
□	JA343J	B737-846/W	39192/4048	
□	JA344J	B737-846/W	39193/4074	
□	JA345J	B737-846/W	40947/4062	
□	JA346J	B737-846/W	40948/4091	

	Reg	Type	c/n	
☐	JA347J	B737-846/W	39194/4104	
☐	JA348J	B737-846/W	40353/4122	
☐	JA349J	B737-846/W	40950/4152	
☐	JA350J	B737-846/W	40954/4621	
☐	JA601J	B767-346ER	32886/875	
☐	JA602J	B767-346ER	32887/879	
☐	JA603J	B767-346ER	32888/880	
☐	JA604J	B767-346ER	33493/905	
☐	JA605J	B767-346ER	33494/911	
☐	JA606J	B767-346ER	33495/915	
☐	JA607J	B767-346ER	33496/917	
☐	JA608J	B767-346ER	33497/919	
☐	JA609J	B767-346ER	33845/921	
☐	JA610J	B767-346ER	33846/925	
☐	JA611J	B767-346ER	33847/927	
☐	JA612J	B767-346ER	33848/929	
☐	JA613J	B767-346ER	33849/935	
☐	JA614J	B767-346ER	33851/938	
☐	JA615J	B767-346ER	33850/942	
☐	JA616J	B767-346ER	35813/954	
☐	JA617J	B767-346ER	35814/957	
☐	JA618J	B767-346ER	35815/964	
☐	JA619J	B767-346ER	37550/969	
☐	JA620J	B767-346ER	37547/974	
☐	JA621J	B767-346ER	37548/975	
☐	JA622J	B767-346ER	37549/977	
☐	JA623J	B767-346ER	36131/978	
☐	JA651J	B767-346ER	40363/994	
☐	JA652J	B767-346ER	40364/995	
☐	JA653J	B767-346ER	40365/997	
☐	JA654J	B767-346ER	40366/999	
☐	JA655J	B767-346ER	40367/1007	
☐	JA656J	B767-346ER	40368/1009	
☐	JA657J	B767-346ER	40369/1013	
☐	JA658J	B767-346ER	40370/1015	
☐	JA659J	B767-346ER	40371/1017	
☐	JA8397	B767-346	27311/547	
☐	JA8398	B767-346	27312/548	
☐	JA8399	B767-346	27313/554	
☐	JA8975	B767-346	27658/581	
☐	JA8976	B767-346	27659/667	
☐	JA8980	B767-346	28837/673	
☐	JA8986	B767-346	28838/680	
☐	JA8987	B767-346	28553/688	
☐	JA8988	B767-346	29863/772	
☐	JA007D	B777-289	27639/134	
☐	JA008D	B777-289	27640/146	
☐	JA009D	B777-289	27641/159	
☐	JA010D	B777-289	27642/213	
☐	JA701J	B777-246ER	32889/410	
☐	JA702J	B777-246ER	32890/417	
☐	JA703J	B777-246ER	32891/427	
☐	JA704J	B777-246ER	32892/435	
☐	JA705J	B777-246ER	32893/446	
☐	JA706J	B777-246ER	33394/464	
☐	JA707J	B777-246ER	32894/475	
☐	JA708J	B777-246ER	32895/483	
☐	JA709J	B777-246ER	32896/489	
☐	JA710J	B777-246ER	33395/525	
☐	JA711J	B777-246ER	33396/533	
☐	JA731J	B777-346ER	32431/429	
☐	JA732J	B777-346ER	32430/423	
☐	JA733J	B777-346ER	32432/521	
☐	JA734J	B777-346ER	32433/527	
☐	JA735J	B777-346ER	32434/577	
☐	JA736J	B777-346ER	32435/583	
☐	JA737J	B777-346ER	36126/668	
☐	JA738J	B777-346ER	32436/724	
☐	JA739J	B777-346ER	32437/736	
☐	JA740J	B777-346ER	36127/744	
☐	JA741J	B777-346ER	36128/812	
☐	JA742J	B777-346ER	36129/816	
☐	JA743J	B777-346ER	36130/821	
☐	JA751J	B777-346	27654/458	
☐	JA752J	B777-346	27655/460	
☐	JA771J	B777-246	27656/437	
☐	JA772J	B777-246	27657/507	
☐	JA773J	B777-246	27653/635	
☐	JA8944	B777-346	28396/212	
☐	JA8945	B777-346	28397/238	
☐	JA8977	B777-289	27636/45	
☐	JA8978	B777-289	27637/79	
☐	JA8979	B777-289	27638/107	
☐	JA8984	B777-246	27651/68	
☐	JA8985	B777-246	27652/72	
☐	JA821J	B787-8	34831/20	
☐	JA822J	B787-8	34832/23	
☐	JA823J	B787-8	34833/21	
☐	JA824J	B787-8	34834/27	
☐	JA825J	B787-8	34835/33	
☐	JA826J	B787-8	34836/37	
☐	JA827J	B787-8	34837/38	
☐	JA828J	B787-8	34838/70	
☐	JA829J	B787-8	34839/84	
☐	JA830J	B787-8	34840/89	
☐	JA831J	B787-8	34847/152	
☐	JA832J	B787-8	34844/105	
☐	JA833J	B787-8	34846/125	
☐	JA834J	B787-8	34842/98	
☐	JA835J	B787-8	34850/159	
☐	JA836J	B787-8	38135/237	
☐	JA837J	B787-8	34860/222	
☐	JA838J	B787-8	34849/231	
☐	JA839J	B787-8	34853/252	
☐	JA840J	B787-8	34856/271	
☐	JA841J	B787-8	34855/312	♦
☐	JA842J	B787-8	34854/301	♦
☐	JA843J	B787-8	34859/385	♦
☐	JA844J	B787-8	38136/434	o/o♦
☐	JA845J	B787-8	34857/441	o/o♦
☐	JA	B787-8	34843	o/o♦
☐	JA	B787-8	34845	o/o♦
☐	JA	B787-8	34848	o/o♦
☐	JA	B787-8	34851	o/o♦
☐	JA	B787-8	34852	o/o♦
☐	JA	B787-8	38134	o/o♦
☐	JA861J	B787-9	35422/139	♦
☐	JA862J	B787-9	34841/362	♦
☐	JA863J	B787-9	38137/391	o/o♦
☐	JA864J	B787-9	34858/438	o/o♦
☐	JA865J	B787-9	38138/458	o/o♦
☐	JA866J	B787-9	35423/494	o/o♦

JAPAN TRANSOCEAN AIR NU / JTA

	Reg	Type	c/n
☐	JA8525	B737-4Q3	26605/2752
☐	JA8597	B737-4Q3	27660/3043
☐	JA8938	B737-4Q3	29485/3085
☐	JA8939	B737-4Q3	29486/3088
☐	JA8991	B737-446	27916/2718
☐	JA8992	B737-446	27917/2729
☐	JA8993	B737-446	28087/2812

	Reg	Type	c/n	
☐	JA8994	B737-446	28097/2907	
☐	JA8995	B737-446	28831/2911	
☐	JA8996	B737-446	28832/2953	
☐	JA8998	B737-446	28994/3044	
☐	JA8999	B737-446	29864/3111	
☐	JA01RK	B737-8Q3/W	61475/5722	♦
☐	JA	B737-8Q3/W		o/o♦
☐	JA	B737-8Q3/W		o/o♦
☐	JA	B737-8Q3/W		o/o♦
☐	JA	B737-8Q3/W		o/o♦
☐	JA	B737-8Q3/W		o/o♦

JETSTAR JAPAN GK / JJP

	Reg	Type	c/n	
☐	JA01JJ	A320-232	5093	
☐	JA02JJ	A320-232	5145	
☐	JA03JJ	A320-232	5161	
☐	JA04JJ	A320-232	5245	
☐	JA05JJ	A320-232	5274	
☐	JA06JJ	A320-232/S	5281	
☐	JA07JJ	A320-232/S	5355	
☐	JA08JJ	A320-232/S	5492	
☐	JA09JJ	A320-232	5499	
☐	JA10JJ	A320-232	5520	
☐	JA11JJ	A320-232/S	5598	
☐	JA12JJ	A320-232/S	5618	
☐	JA13JJ	A320-232/S	5649	
☐	JA14JJ	A320-232/S	5695	
☐	JA15JJ	A320-232/S	5701	
☐	JA16JJ	A320-232/S	5717	
☐	JA17JJ	A320-232/S	5732	
☐	JA18JJ	A320-232/S	5796	
☐	JA19JJ	A320-232/S	6296	
☐	JA20JJ	A320-232/S	6381	

NIPPON CARGO AIRLINES KZ / NCA

	Reg	Type	c/n	
☐	JA04KZ	B747-4KZF	34283/1384	
☐	JA05KZ	B747-4KZF	36132/1394	
☐	JA06KZ	B747-4KZF	36133/1397	
☐	JA07KZ	B747-4KZF	36134/1405	
☐	JA08KZ	B747-4KZF	36135/1408	
☐	JA11KZ	B747-8KZF	36136/1421	
☐	JA12KZ	B747-8KZF	36137/1422	
☐	JA13KZ	B747-8KZF	36138/1431	
☐	JA14KZ	B747-8KZF	37394/1469	
☐	JA15KZ	B747-8KZF	36139/1479	
☐	JA16KZ	B747-8KZF	37393/1485	
☐	JA17KZ	B747-8KZF	36140/1487	
☐	JA18KZ	B747-8KZF	36141/1489	
☐	JA19KZ	B747-8KZF	36142	o/o
☐	JA20KZ	B747-8KZF	36143	o/o
☐	JA21KZ	B747-8KZF	37395	o/o
☐	JA23KZ	B747-8KZF	37396	o/o
☐	JA24KZ	B747-8KZF	37397	o/o
☐	JA25KZ	B747-8KZF	37398	o/o

ORIENTAL AIR BRIDGE NGK

	Reg	Type	c/n	
☐	JA801B	DHC-8Q-201	566	
☐	JA802B	DHC-8Q-201	579	

PEACH AVIATION MM / APJ

	Reg	Type	c/n	
☐	JA801P	A320-214	4887	
☐	JA802P	A320-214	4936	
☐	JA803P	A320-214	5015	
☐	JA804P	A320-214	5166	
☐	JA805P	A320-214	5304	
☐	JA806P	A320-214	5384	
☐	JA807P	A320-214	5440	
☐	JA808P	A320-214	5540	
☐	JA809P	A320-214	5640	
☐	JA810P	A320-214	5724	
☐	JA811P	A320-214	5874	
☐	JA812P	A320-214	6004	
☐	JA813P	A320-214	6107	
☐	JA814P	A320-214	6335	
☐	JA815P	A320-214	6640	♦
☐	JA816P	A320-214	6674	♦
☐	JA817P	A320-214	6824	♦
☐	JA	A320-214		o/o♦
☐	JA	A320-214		o/o♦
☐	JA	A320-214		o/o♦
☐	JA	A320-214		o/o♦
☐	JA	A320-214		o/o♦
☐	JA	A320-214		o/o♦

RYUKYU AIR COMMUTER RAC

	Reg	Type	c/n	
☐	JA8935	DHC-8Q-103B	593	
☐	JA8936	DHC-8Q-314	635	
☐	JA8972	DHC-8Q-103	472	
☐	JA8973	DHC-8Q-103	501	
☐	JA8974	DHC-8Q-103B	540	
☐	JA81RC	DHC-8-402Q(C)	4505	♦
☐	JA	DHC-8-402Q(C)		o/o♦
☐	JA	DHC-8-402Q(C)		o/o♦

SKYMARK AIRLINES BC / SKY

	Reg	Type	c/n	
☐	JA73NA	B737-8HX/W	36849/3372	
☐	JA73NC	B737-8FZ/W	31743/3450	
☐	JA73ND	B737-8FZ/W	33440/3474	
☐	JA73NE	B737-82Y/W	40713/3501	
☐	JA73NF	B737-86N/W	38019/3642	
☐	JA73NG	B737-86N/W	36821/3738	
☐	JA73NJ	B737-86N/W	39405/3845	
☐	JA73NK	B737-86N/W	38023/3883	
☐	JA73NL	B737-8HX/W	38104/3933	
☐	JA73NM	B737-81D/W	39421/3940	
☐	JA73NN	B737-81D/W	39422/3975	
☐	JA73NP	B737-8HX/W	38109/4034	
☐	JA73NQ	B737-81D/W	39432/4310	
☐	JA73NR	B737-8FH/W	39927/4340	
☐	JA73NT	B737-86N/W	41264/4460	
☐	JA73NU	B737-86N/W	38046/4511	
☐	JA73NX	B737-86N/W	38045/4606	
☐	JA73NY	B737-86N/W	41263/4633	
☐	JA737N	B737-8HX	36845/2339	
☐	JA737Q	B737-86N/W	35228/2630	
☐	JA737R	B737-86N/W	35630/2666	
☐	JA737T	B737-8Q8/W	35290/2818	
☐	JA737U	B737-8FZ/W	29680/2888	
☐	JA737X	B737-8AL/W	36692/3088	
☐	JA737Y	B737-8FZ/W	29663/3113	
☐	JA737Z	B737-82Y/W	40712/3308	

Filed for bankrupcy protection 28Jan15 but continues to operate.

SOLASEED AIR 6J / SNA

	Reg	Type	c/n	
☐	JA801X	B737-81D/W	39415/3666	
☐	JA802X	B737-81D/W	39418/3816	
☐	JA803X	B737-86N/W	39395/3915	
☐	JA804X	B737-86N/W	38026/4016	
☐	JA805X	B737-86N/W	38035/4327	

	Reg	Type	C/n	Notes
☐	JA806X	B737-86N/W	38036/4339	
☐	JA807X	B737-81D/W	39431/4526	
☐	JA808X	B737-81D/W	39433/4611	
☐	JA809X	B737-86N/W	41247/4826	
☐	JA810X	B737-84N/W	41271/4920	
☐	JA811X	B737-86N/W	43406/5062	
☐	JA812X	B737-86N/W	43402/5319	♦

SPRING AIRLINES JAPAN — 9C / SJO

	Reg	Type	C/n	Notes
☐	JA01GR	B737-81D/W	39429/4413	
☐	JA02GR	B737-86N/W	41256/4714	
☐	JA03GR	B737-86N/W	41272/4819	
☐	JA	B737-81D/W		o/o

STARFLYER — 7G / SFJ

	Reg	Type	C/n	Notes
☐	JA05MC	A320-214	4555	
☐	JA06MC	A320-214	4720	
☐	JA07MC	A320-214	5102	
☐	JA08MC	A320-214	5393	
☐	JA09MC	A320-214	5512	
☐	JA20MC	A320-214/S	5652	
☐	JA21MC	A320-214/S	5773	
☐	JA22MC	A320-214/S	5862	
☐	JA23MC	A320-214/S	5931	
☐	JA	A320-214/S		o/o

VANILLA AIR — JW / VNL

	Reg	Type	C/n	Notes
☐	JA01VA	A320-214/S	5844	
☐	JA02VA	A320-214/S	5901	
☐	JA03VA	A320-216/S	5926	
☐	JA04VA	A320-214/S	6257	
☐	JA05VA	A320-214/S	6282	
☐	JA06VA	A320-214/S	6320	
☐	JA07VA	A320-214/S	6422	
☐	JA08VA	A320-214/S	6447	
☐	JA	A320-214/S	7080	o/o♦
☐	JA8385	A320-211	0167	[TUS]
☐	JA8388	A320-211	0212	[TUS]
☐	JA8391	A320-211	0300	[TUS]

JU- MONGOLIA

AERO MONGOLIA — MNG

	Reg	Type	C/n	Notes
☐	JU-8250	Fokker 50	20210	
☐	JU-8251	Fokker 50	20251	
☐	JU-8257	Fokker 50	20257	
☐	JU-8258	Fokker 50	20258	

HUNNU AIR — MR / MML

	Reg	Type	C/n	Notes
☐	JU-8881	Fokker 50	20183	
☐	JU-8882	Fokker 50	20184	
☐	JU-8883	Fokker 50	20181	

MIAT - MONGOLIAN AIRLINES — OM / MGL

	Reg	Type	C/n	Notes
☐	EI-CSG	B737-8AS/W	29922/571	
☐	EI-CXV	B737-8CX/W	32364/1166	
☐	JU-1015	B737-8SH/W	41318/4902	
☐		B737-8xx		o/o♦
☐	JU-1011	B767-3WOER	28149/627	
☐	JU-1021	B767-34GER	41519/1050	

JY- JORDAN

AIR ARABIA JORDAN — 9P / JAD

	Reg	Type	C/n	Notes
☐	JY-JAU	A320-212	0537	♦
☐	JY-PTC	A320-214	3246	

FLYJORDAN

	Reg	Type	C/n	Notes
☐	JY-SOA	B737-33V	293383114	♦
☐	JY-SOB	B737-33V	29342/3127	♦

JORDAN AVIATION — R5 / JAV

	Reg	Type	C/n	Notes
☐	JY-JAC	A320-211	0029	
☐	JY-JAT	A320-211	2061	
☐	JY-JAB	B737-33A	23630/1312	[AMM]
☐	JY-JAD	B737-322	24662/1862	
☐	JY-JAP	B737-46B	24124/1679	
☐	JY-JAQ	B737-46J	27826/2694	>FBA
☐	JY-JAX	B737-322	23955/1550	
☐	JY-JAY	B737-3S3	29244/3059	>AWZ♦
☐	JY-JAG	B767-204ER	24757/299	
☐	JY-JAL	B767-204ER	24239/243	

JORDAN INTERNATIONAL CARGO — J4 / JCI

	Reg	Type	C/n	Notes
☐	JY-JIC	Il-76MF	1063421724	^
☐	JY-JID	Il-76MF	20.3423808	^

^ carry dual marks JY-JIC serial 360 & JY-JID serial 361

ROYAL FALCON — RF / RFJ

	Reg	Type	C/n	Notes
☐	JY-JRG	A320-212	0814	
☐	JY-RFF	B737-4K5	27831/2677	

ROYAL JORDANIAN — RJ / RJA

	Reg	Type	C/n	Notes
☐	JY-AGQ	A310-304F	445	
☐	JY-AGR	A310-304F	490	
☐	JY-AYL	A319-132	3428	
☐	JY-AYM	A319-132	3685	
☐	JY-AYN	A319-132	3803	
☐	JY-AYP	A319-132	3832	
☐	JY-AYQ	A320-232	4670	
☐	JY-AYR	A320-232	4817	
☐	JY-AYS	A320-232	4853	
☐	JY-AYU	A320-232	5128	
☐	JY-AYW	A320-232	5367	
☐	JY-AYX	A320-231	2953	
☐	JY-AYT	A321-231	5099	
☐	JY-AYV	A321-231	5177	
☐	JY-AIF	A330-223	979	
☐	JY-AIG	A330-223	1002	
☐	JY-BAA	B787-8	37983/194	
☐	JY-BAB	B787-8	35319/214	
☐	JY-BAC	B787-8	37164/219	
☐	JY-BAE	B787-8	37166/221	
☐	JY-BAF	B787-8	36112/233	
☐	JY-	B787-8	37984/499	o/o♦
☐	JY-EMA	ERJ-195AR	19000107	
☐	JY-EMB	ERJ-195AR	19000131	
☐	JY-EMC	ERJ-175LR	17000223	
☐	JY-EMD	ERJ-175LR	17000232	
☐	JY-EMH	ERJ-175LR	17000316	

ROYAL WINGS AIRLINES			**RY / RYW**
☐ JY-AYI	A320-212	0569	

J2- DJIBOUTI

AIR DJIBOUTI			
☐ J2-	B767-216ER	23624/144	o/o♦
☐ 5Y-JUU	F.27 Friendship 500	10448	♦

DAALLO AIRLINES			**D3 / DAO**
☐ LZ-DAL	BAe146 srs. 200A	E2074	♦

J8- ST. VINCENT & GRENADINES

SVG AIR			**SVD**
☐ J8-GAA	DHC-6 Twin Otter 300	239	
☐ J8-GAL	DHC-6 Twin Otter 300	510	
☐ J8-GAW	DHC-6 Twin Otter 300	834	♦
☐ J8-GLS	DHC-6 Twin Otter 300	766	♦
☐ J8-MUS	DHC-6 Twin Otter 300	553	
☐ J8-SUN	DHC-6 Twin Otter 300	477	
☐ J8-UNI	DHC-6 Twin Otter 300	792	♦
☐ J8-VBQ	DHC-6 Twin Otter 300	604	
☐ J8-VBS	DHC-6 Twin Otter 300	249	

LN- NORWAY

LUFTTRANSPORT			**L5 / LTR**
☐ LN-LTS	Do228-212NG	8301	
☐ LN-LYR	Do228-202K	8166	

NORWEGIAN			**DY / NAX**
☐ LN-	A320-271N	7150	o/o♦
☐ LN-	A320-271N	7273	o/o♦
☐ LN-	A320-271N	7288	o/o♦
☐ LN-	A320-271N	7307	o/o♦
☐ LN-	A320-271N		o/o♦
☐ LN-KHA	B737-31S/W	29100/2984	[BUD]
☐ LN-KHB	B737-31S/W	29264/3070	[SVG]
☐ LN-KHC	B737-31S/W	29265/3073	[SVG]
☐ LN-KKX	B737-33S/W	29072/3012	[BUD]
☐ LN-DYA	B737-8JP/W	39162/2994	
☐ LN-DYB	B737-8JP/W	39163/3054	
☐ LN-DYC	B737-8JP/W	39164/3196	
☐ LN-DYD	B737-8JP/W	39002/3231	
☐ LN-DYE	B737-8JP/W	39003/3401	
☐ LN-DYF	B737-8JP/W	39004/3482	
☐ LN-DYG	B737-8JP/W	39165/3507	
☐ LN-DYM	B737-8JP/W	39005/3572	
☐ LN-DYN	B737-8JP/W	39006/3583	
☐ LN-DYO	B737-8JP/W	40868/3591	
☐ LN-DYP	B737-8JP/W	39047/3630	
☐ LN-DYQ	B737-8JP/W	40869/3651	
☐ LN-DYT	B737-8JP/W	39048/3686	
☐ LN-DYU	B737-8JP/W	39008/3725	
☐ LN-DYV	B737-8JP/W	39009/3790	
☐ LN-DYW	B737-8JP/W	39010/3871	
☐ LN-DYZ	B737-8JP/W	39013/4037	
☐ LN-NGA	B737-8JP/W	39014/4067	
☐ LN-NGB	B737-8JP/W	39015/4090	
☐ LN-NGC	B737-8JP/W	39016/4157	
☐ LN-NGD	B737-8JP/W	39049/4161	
☐ LN-NGE	B737-8JP/W	39050/4196	
☐ LN-NGF	B737-8JP/W	39017/4234	
☐ LN-NGG	B737-8JP/W	39018/4289	
☐ LN-NGK	B737-8JP/W	39022/4528	
☐ LN-NGL	B737-8JP/W	39023/4572	
☐ LN-NGN	B737-8JP/W	39025/4652	
☐ LN-NGO	B737-8JP/W	39026/4676	
☐ LN-NGP	B737-8JP/W	39028/4701	
☐ LN-NGQ	B737-8JP/W	39027/4729	
☐ LN-NGR	B737-8JP/W	41121/4739	
☐ LN-NGS	B737-8JP/W	39029/4767	
☐ LN-NGT	B737-8JP/W	41125/4774	
☐ LN-NGU	B737-8JP/W	39030/4785	
☐ LN-NGV	B737-8JP/W	39031/4841	
☐ LN-NGW	B737-8JP/W	39032/4889	
☐ LN-NGX	B737-8JP/W	39033/4927	
☐ LN-NGY	B737-8JP/W	41126/4972	
☐ LN-NGZ	B737-8JP/W	41127/5013	
☐ LN-NHA	B737-8JP/W	41129/5069	
☐ LN-NHB	B737-8JP/W	41134/5102	
☐ LN-NHC	B737-8JP/W	41128/5235	
☐ LN-NHD	B737-8JP/W	41131/5317	
☐ LN-NHE	B737-8JP/W	41136/5415	
☐ LN-NHF	B737-8JP/W	42075/5470	♦
☐ LN-NHG	B737-8JP/W	41139/5526	♦
☐ LN-NIA	B737-8JP/W	39444/3965	
☐ LN-NIB	B737-8JP/W	36879/3805	
☐ LN-NIC	B737-8JP/W	38881/4316	
☐ LN-NID	B737-8JP/W	40544/4474	
☐ LN-NIE	B737-8JP/W	39435/4330	
☐ LN-NIF	B737-8JP/W	39434/4337	
☐ LN-NIG	B737-8JP/W	43878/5123	
☐ LN-NIH	B737-8JP/W	43879/5177	
☐ LN-NII	B737-8JP/W	43877/5204	
☐ LN-NOF	B737-86N/W	36809/2647	
☐ LN-NOI	B737-86N/W	36820/3131	
☐ LN-NOM	B737-86N/W	28642/813	
☐ LN-NON	B737-86N/W	28620/542	
☐ LN-NOO	B737-86Q/W	30289/1399	
☐ LN-NOT	B737-8JP/W	37816/3194	
☐ LN-NOW	B737-8FZ/W	37817/3364	
☐ LN-NOX	B737-8JP/W	37818/3384	
☐ LN-	B737-81D/W		o/o♦
☐ LN-	B737-81D/W		o/o♦
☐ LN-	B737-8JP/W		o/o♦
☐ LN-	B737-8JP/W		o/o♦
☐ LN-	B737-8JP/W		o/o♦
☐ LN-	B737-8JP/W		o/o♦

NORWEGIAN AIR INTERNATIONAL			**D8 / IBK**
☐ EI-FHA	B737-8JP/W	39012/3982	
☐ EI-FHB	B737-8Q8/W	35283/2742	
☐ EI-FHC	B737-8Q8/W	37159/2868	
☐ EI-FHD	B737-8JP/W	39011/3946	
☐ EI-FHE	B737-8Q8/W	35280/2629	
☐ EI-FHF	B737-8FZ/W	34954/2483	[BUD]
☐ EI-FHG	B737-86N/W	37884/3223	
☐ EI-FHH	B737-8FZ/W	31713/3215	
☐ EI-FHJ	B737-8JP/W	42069/5541	♦
☐ EI-FHK	B737-8JP/W	41140/5555	♦
☐ EI-FHL	B737-8JP/W	42078/5575	♦
☐ EI-FHM	B737-8JP/W	42070/5583	♦
☐ EI-FHN	B737-8JP/W	39046/3557	♦
☐ EI-FHO	B737-86N/W	35647/2927	♦
☐ EI-FHP	B737-8JP/W	40865/3410	♦
☐ EI-FHR	B737-8JP/W	39045/3530	♦

☐	EI-FHS	B737-8JP/W	39021/4371	♦
☐	EI-FHT	B737-8JP/W	40867/3565	♦
☐	EI-FHU	B737-8JP/W	39019/4295	♦
☐	EI-FHV	B737-8JP/W	40870/3660	♦
☐	EI-FHW	B737-8JP/W	39007/3665	♦
☐	EI-FHX	B737-8JP/W	40866/3432	♦
☐	EI-FHY	B737-8JP/W	39020/4343	♦
☐	EI-FJA	B737-8JP/W	39419/3878	♦
☐	EI-FJB	B737-8JP/W	42081/5714	♦
☐	EI-FJC	B737-81D/W	39412/3553	♦
☐	EI-FJD	B737-8JP/W	41143/5737	♦
☐	EI-FJE	B737-8JP/W	39420/3891	♦
☐	EI-FJF	B737-86N/W	36814/3015	♦
☐	EI-FJH	B737-8JP/W	42071/5777	♦
☐	EI-FJJ	B737-8JP/W	41148/5807	o/o♦

NORWEGIAN LONG HAUL — *DU / NLH*

☐	EI-LNH	B787-8	36526/279	
☐	EI-LNI	B787-9	37307/400	o/o♦
☐	EI-	B787-9	37308/418	o/o♦
☐	EI-	B787-9	37931/488	o/o♦
☐	EI-	B787-9	62082/450	o/o♦
☐	LN-LNA	B787-8	35304/102	♦
☐	LN-LNB	B787-8	35305/112	♦
☐	LN-LNC	B787-8	34795/136	♦
☐	LN-LND	B787-8	35310/153	♦
☐	LN-LNE	B787-8	34796/165	♦
☐	LN-LNF	B787-8	35313/178	♦
☐	LN-LNG	B787-8	35314/183	♦

Norwegian-registered aircaft operated by Norwegian (Air Shuttle).

WIDEROE — *WF / WIF*

☐	LN-ILS	DHC-8-103	396
☐	LN-RDV	DHC-8-402Q	4054
☐	LN-RDY	DHC-8-402Q	4062
☐	LN-RDZ	DHC-8-402Q	4063
☐	LN-WDE	DHC-8-402Q	4183
☐	LN-WDF	DHC-8-402Q	4244
☐	LN-WDG	DHC-8-402Q	4266
☐	LN-WDH	DHC-8-402Q	4273
☐	LN-WDI	DHC-8-402Q	4286
☐	LN-WDJ	DHC-8-402Q	4290
☐	LN-WDK	DHC-8-402Q	4337
☐	LN-WDL	DHC-8-402Q	4392
☐	LN-WFC	DHC-8-311A	236
☐	LN-WFH	DHC-8-311A	238
☐	LN-WFO	DHC-8Q-311	493
☐	LN-WFP	DHC-8Q-311	495
☐	LN-WFS	DHC-8Q-311	535
☐	LN-WFT	DHC-8Q-311	532
☐	LN-WFU	DHC-8Q-314	592
☐	LN-WIA	DHC-8-103B	359
☐	LN-WIB	DHC-8-103B	360
☐	LN-WIC	DHC-8-103B	367
☐	LN-WID	DHC-8-103B	369
☐	LN-WIE	DHC-8-103B	371
☐	LN-WIF	DHC-8-103B	372
☐	LN-WIG	DHC-8-103B	382
☐	LN-WIH	DHC-8-103B	383
☐	LN-WII	DHC-8-103B	384
☐	LN-WIJ	DHC-8-103B	386
☐	LN-WIL	DHC-8-103B	398
☐	LN-WIM	DHC-8-103B	403
☐	LN-WIN	DHC-8-103B	409
☐	LN-WIO	DHC-8-103B	417
☐	LN-WIP	DHC-8-103A	239
☐	LN-WIR	DHC-8-103A	273
☐	LN-WIT	DHC-8-103	310
☐	LN-WIU	DHC-8-103	378
☐	LN-WIV	DHC-8-103	343
☐	LN-WSA	DHC-8Q-202	435
☐	LN-WSB	DHC-8Q-202	440
☐	LN-WSC	DHC-8Q-202	441

LV- ARGENTINA

AEROLINEAS ARGENTINAS — *AR / ARG*

☐	LV-FNI	A330-223	290	
☐	LV-FNJ	A330-223	300	
☐	LV-FNK	A330-223	358	
☐	LV-FNL	A330-223	364	
☐	LV-FVH	A330-202	1605	
☐	LV-FVI	A330-202	1623	♦
☐	LV-	A330-202	1737	o/o♦
☐	LV-	A330-202	1748	o/o♦
☐	LV-CEK	A340-312	094	
☐	LV-CSD	A340-313X	123	
☐	LV-CSE	A340-313X	126	
☐	LV-CSF	A340-313X	128	
☐	LV-CSX	A340-313X	373	
☐	LV-FPU	A340-313X	170	
☐	LV-FPV	A340-313X	193	
☐	LV-ZRA	A340-211	085	[EZE]
☐	LV-BYY	B737-7BD/W	33938/2863	
☐	LV-BZA	B737-76N/W	32674/1952	
☐	LV-BZO	B737-76N/W	32676/1974	
☐	LV-CAD	B737-76N/W	32680/2089	
☐	LV-CAP	B737-76N/W	32695/1919	
☐	LV-CBF	B737-76N/W	32696/1922	
☐	LV-CBT	B737-76N/W	34756/2208	
☐	LV-CCR	B737-73V/W	30237/730	[EZE]
☐	LV-CMK	B737-7Q8/W	28240/832	
☐	LV-CPH	B737-7Q8/W	28238/817	
☐	LV-CSC	B737-7Q8/W	30630/1032	
☐	LV-CSI	B737-7Q8/W	30707/975	
☐	LV-CVX	B737-7Q8/W	30641/1080	
☐	LV-CWL	B737-7Q8/W	30644/1107	
☐	LV-CXN	B737-7Q8/W	30638/858	
☐	LV-CYJ	B737-7Q8/W	30647/1159	
☐	LV-CYN	B737-7Q8/W	30648/1171	
☐	LV-CYO	B737-7Q8/W	30633/1220	
☐	LV-GOO	B737-7BD	35962/2932	
☐	LV-CTB	B737-85F/W	30478/997	
☐	LV-CTC	B737-86J/W	30570/879	
☐	LV-CXS	B737-81D/W	39425/4167	
☐	LV-CXT	B737-81D/W	39426/4186	
☐	LV-FQB	B737-86J/W	36886/3777	
☐	LV-FQC	B737-86J/W	37744/3694	
☐	LV-FQY	B737-81D/W	39436/4764	
☐	LV-FQZ	B737-8BK/W	41563/5086	
☐	LV-FRK	B737-8BK/W	41560/4759	
☐	LV-FRQ	B737-8BK/W	41561/4860	
☐	LV-FSK	B737-8BK/W	41562/4960	
☐	LV-FUA	B737-8HX/W	40548/4995	
☐	LV-FUB	B737-81D/W	39893/5056	
☐	LV-FUC	B737-8SH/W	41347/5169	
☐	LV-FVM	B737-8SH/W	41329/5313	
☐	LV-FVN	B737-8SH/W	41331/5373	♦
☐	LV-FVO	B737-8SH/W	41356/5550	♦

Reg	Type	c/n	Notes
LV-FWS	B737-8LP/W	41711/5136	♦
LV-FXQ	B737-8MB/W	43881/5539	♦
LV-FYK	B737-8MB/W	43882/5546	♦
LV-GFQ	B737-8SH/W	41338/5735	♦
LV-GGK	B737-8SH/W	41339/5774	♦

AMERICAN JET

Reg	Type	c/n	Notes
LV-CZJ	ATR 42-320	257	

ANDES LINEAS AEREAS — *OY / ANS*

Reg	Type	c/n	Notes
LV-ARF	MD-83	49252/1169	[SFB]
LV-AYD	MD-83	53015/1818	
LV-BAY	MD-83	49284/1209	[SFB]
LV-BHF	MD-82	49508/1449	[SLA]
LV-BZR	MD-87	49706/1614	[SLA]
LV-CCJ	MD-83	49621/1495	
LV-CDD	MD-83	49579/1465	[SLA]
LV-VBX	MD-88	53047/2016	♦
LV-WGM	MD-83	49784/1627	
LV-WGN	MD-83	49934/1764	♦

AUSTRAL LINEAS AEREAS — *AU / AUT*

Reg	Type	c/n	Notes
LV-CDY	ERJ-190AR	19000365	
LV-CDZ	ERJ-190AR	19000377	
LV-CET	ERJ-190AR	19000383	
LV-CEU	ERJ-190AR	19000389	
LV-CEV	ERJ-190AR	19000390	
LV-CHO	ERJ-190AR	19000395	
LV-CHQ	ERJ-190AR	19000397	
LV-CHR	ERJ-190AR	19000400	
LV-CHS	ERJ-190AR	19000402	
LV-CID	ERJ-190AR	19000409	
LV-CIE	ERJ-190AR	19000414	
LV-CIF	ERJ-190AR	19000421	
LV-CIG	ERJ-190AR	19000427	
LV-CIH	ERJ-190AR	19000428	
LV-CKZ	ERJ-190AR	19000439	
LV-CMA	ERJ-190AR	19000445	
LV-CMB	ERJ-190AR	19000448	
LV-CPI	ERJ-190AR	19000457	
LV-CPJ	ERJ-190AR	19000463	
LV-CPK	ERJ-190AR	19000474	
LV-FPS	ERJ-190AR	19000639	
LV-FPT	ERJ-190AR	19000640	

LAN ARGENTINA — *4M / DSM*

Reg	Type	c/n	Notes
CC-BFH	A320-214	5453	<LAN♦
LV-BET	A320-233	1854	
LV-BFO	A320-233	1877	
LV-BFY	A320-233	1858	
LV-BGI	A320-233	1903	
LV-BHU	A320-233	1512	
LV-BOI	A320-233	1491	
LV-BRA	A320-233	1304	
LV-BRY	A320-233	1351	
LV-BSJ	A320-233	1332	
LV-BTM	A320-233	1548	
LV-CKV	A320-233	1568	
LV-CQS	A320-233	1526	
LV-FUX	A320-233	4543	
LV-CDQ	B767-316ER/W	35229/949	
LV-CKU	B767-316ER/W	34628/945	♦

MACAIR JET — *VM / MCJ*

Reg	Type	c/n	Notes
LV-ZOW	BAeJetstream 32EP	869	
LV-ZPW	BAeJetstream 32EP	861	
LV-ZPZ	BAeJetstream 32EP	931	
LV-ZRL	BAeJetstream 32EP	928	
LV-ZSB	BAeJetstream 32EP	942	
LV-ZST	BAeJetstream 32EP	941	

SOL LINEAS AEREAS — *8R / OLS*

Reg	Type	c/n	Notes
LV-BEW	SAAB SF.340A	340A-150	
LV-BEX	SAAB SF.340A	340A-014	
LV-BTP	SAAB SF.340A	340A-131	
LV-CEI	SAAB SF.340A	340A-012	
LV-CSK	SAAB SF.340B	340B-168	
LV-CYC	SAAB SF.340B	340B-310	

Operations suspended 15Jan16.

LX- LUXEMBOURG

CARGOLUX AIRLINES INTERNATIONAL CV / CLX

Reg	Type	c/n	Notes
LX-DCV	B747-4B5BCF	24619/793	
LX-ECV	B747-4HQF	37303/1416	
LX-FCL	B747-467F	27503/1065	♦
LX-JCV	B747-4EVFER	35171/1380	♦
LX-OCV	B747-4R7F	29731/1222	>ICV
LX-RCV	B747-4R7F	30400/1235	>ICV
LX-SCV	B747-4R7F	29733/1281	>ICV
LX-TCV	B747-4R7F	30401/1311	>ICV
LX-UCV	B747-4R7F	33827/1345	
LX-VCA	B747-8R7F	35808/1420	
LX-VCB	B747-8R7F	35806/1423	
LX-VCC	B747-8R7F	35807/1424	
LX-VCD	B747-8R7F	35809/1436	
LX-VCE	B747-8R7F	35810/1454	
LX-VCF	B747-8R7F	35811/1461	
LX-VCG	B747-8R7F	35812/1465	
LX-VCH	B747-8R7F	35821/1473	
LX-VCI	B747-8R7F	35822/1478	
LX-VCJ	B747-8R7F	38077/1490	
LX-VCK	B747-8R7F	38078/1491	
LX-VCL	B747-8R7F	35823/1504	
LX-VCM	B747-8R7F	61169/1522	♦
LX-VCV	B747-4R7F	34235/1366	
LX-WCV	B747-4R7F	35804/1390	
LX-YCV	B747-4R7F	35805/1407	>ICV
LX-	B747-8R7F		o/o♦

LUXAIR — *LG / LGL*

Reg	Type	c/n	Notes
F-HJUL	B737-8Q8/W	38819/3519	<XLF♦
LX-LBA	B737-8C9/W	43537/5293	
LX-LBB	B737-86J/W	36875/5353	♦
LX-LGQ	B737-7C9/W	33802/1442	
LX-LGS	B737-7C9/W	33956/1634	
LX-LGU	B737-8C9/W	41047/4272	
LX-LGV	B737-8C9/W	41190/4755	
LX-LGE	DHC-8-402Q	4284	
LX-LGF	DHC-8-402Q	4349	
LX-LGG	DHC-8-402Q	4418	
LX-LGM	DHC-8-402Q	4425	
LX-LGN	DHC-8-402Q	4426	
LX-LQA	DHC-8-402Q	4468	
LX-LQB	DHC-8-402Q	4512	♦
LX-LQC	DHC-8-402Q	4513	♦
LX-	DHC-8-402Q		o/o♦

	Reg	Type	c/n	Notes
☐	LX-LGI	ERJ-145LU	145369	
☐	LX-LGW	ERJ-145LU	145135	[DNR]
☐	LX-LGX	ERJ-145LU	145147	
☐	LX-LGZ	ERJ-145LU	145258	

LY- LITHUANIA

AVION EXPRESS — X9 / NVD

	Reg	Type	c/n	Notes
☐	LY-COM	A320-212	0528	>CUB
☐	LY-VEL	A320-232	1998	>DWI
☐	LY-VEN	A320-233	1626	
☐	LY-VEO	A320-233	0558	
☐	LY-VEQ	A320-214	0709	>CUB
☐	LY-VET	A319-112	1778	>CUB
☐	LY-VEV	A320-211	0211	>CUB
☐	LY-VEW	A320-214	1005	>CUB
☐	LY-	A320-233	0902	o/o♦

DOT LU — R6 / DNU

	Reg	Type	c/n	Notes
☐	LY-	A320-231	0113	o/o♦
☐	OY-RUP	A320-231	0406	<DTR♦
☐	LY-DAT	ATR 42-500	445	>SEH
☐	LY-MCA	ATR 72-201	212	
☐	LY-OOV	ATR 42-300F	005	[OTP]
☐	LY-RUM	ATR 42-300	010	
☐	LY-RUN	SAAB SF.340A	340A-086	
☐	LY-RUS	SAAB SF.340A	340A-074	

GRAND CRU AIRLINES — GCA

	Reg	Type	c/n	Notes
☐	LY-CGC	B737-4YO	23870/1647	
☐	LY-GGC	B737-3Q8	24492/1808	>ELB
☐	LY-LGC	B737-382	24365/1695	

SMALL PLANET AIRLINES — LLC

	Reg	Type	c/n	Notes
☐	LY-ONJ	A320-214	4203	♦
☐	LY-ONL	A320-214	4489	♦
☐	LY-SPA	A320-232	1715	
☐	LY-SPB	A320-232	2987	>TLB
☐	LY-SPC	A320-231	0415	
☐	LY-SPD	A320-232	0990	
☐	LY-SPF	A320-214	0967	♦
☐	LY-SPG	A320-214	1041	♦
☐	LY-AWD	B737-522	26739/2494	>VSV
☐	LY-AWE	B737-522	26684/2388	>VSV
☐	LY-AWF	B737-522	26707/2512	>TJK
☐	LY-AWG	B737-522	26700/2490	>TJK
☐	LY-FLH	B737-382	25161/2226	[VNO]
☐	LY-FLJ	B737-3K2	24327/1712	[VNO]♦
☐	LY-FLG	B757-204	27237/602	>VSV

TRANSAVIABALTIKA — KTB

	Reg	Type	c/n	Notes
☐	LY-AVA	LET L-410UVP-E3	882036	
☐	LY-AVT	LET L-410UVP-E3	882033	
☐	LY-AVZ	LET L-410UVP-E	892336	

LZ- BULGARIA

AIR MAX — RMX

	Reg	Type	c/n	Notes
☐	LZ-MNG	LET L-410UVP	841326	
☐	LZ-RMK	LET L-410UVP	851406	[SOF]
☐	LZ-RMV	LET L-410UVP-E	892215	
☐	LZ-RMW	LET L-410UVP-E8A	902517	

AIR SCORPIO — SCU

	Reg	Type	c/n	Notes
☐	LZ-SAB	SAAB SF.340A	340A-020	

BH AIR — 8H / BGH

	Reg	Type	c/n	Notes
☐	LZ-AOA	A319-112	3139	>SEJ
☐	LZ-BHF	A320-214	1087	
☐	LZ-BHG	A320-232	2844	>VJC
☐	LZ-BHH	A320-232	2863	
☐	LZ-BHI	A320-232	3125	>VJC♦
☐	LZ-AWA	A330-223	255	

BRIGHT FLIGHT

	Reg	Type	c/n	Notes
☐	LZ-FLA	An-26B	12010	
☐	LZ-FLL	An-26B	12201	

BULGARIA AIR — FB / LZB

	Reg	Type	c/n	Notes
☐	LZ-FBA	A319-112	3564	<HMS
☐	LZ-FBB	A319-112	3309	<HMS
☐	LZ-FBE	A320-214	3780	
☐	LZ-HBZ	BAe146 Srs.200	E2103	<HMS
☐	LZ-BOO	B737-341	26852/2273	♦
☐	LZ-BOT	B737-322	24665/1889	♦
☐	LZ-BUR	ERJ-190AR	19000551	
☐	LZ-PLO	ERJ-190AR	19000584	
☐	LZ-SOF	ERJ-190AR	19000492	
☐	LZ-VAR	ERJ-190AR	19000496	
☐	LZ-	ERJ-190AR		o/o
☐	LZ-	ERJ-190AR		o/o
☐	LZ-	ERJ-190AR		o/o
☐	LZ-	ERJ-190AR		o/o
☐	LZ-	ERJ-190AR		o/o

BULGARIAN AIR CHARTER — H6 / BUC

	Reg	Type	c/n	Notes
☐	LZ-LAA	A320-231	0256	♦
☐	LZ-LDC	MD-82	49217/1268	[SOF]
☐	LZ-LDF	MD-82	49219/1310	[SOF]
☐	LZ-LDG	MD-83	53149/1817	[SOF]
☐	LZ-LDJ	MD-82	53230/2106	
☐	LZ-LDK	MD-82	49432/1378	[BOJ]
☐	LZ-LDM	MD-82	53228/2104	
☐	LZ-LDN	MD-82	53216/2048	
☐	LZ-LDP	MD-82	49973/1762	
☐	LZ-LDS	MD-82	53218/2060	
☐	LZ-LDT	MD-82	53058/1927	
☐	LZ-LDU	MD-82	53204/2009	
☐	LZ-LDW	MD-82	49795/1639	
☐	LZ-LDY	MD-82	49213/1243	

CARGO AIR — VEA

	Reg	Type	c/n	Notes
☐	LZ-CGO	B737-301F	23237/1222	
☐	LZ-CGP	B737-35BF	23970/1467	
☐	LZ-CGQ	B737-3Y5F	25614/2467	
☐	LZ-CGR	B737-448SF	24474/1742	
☐	LZ-CGS	B737-4Q8F	26306/2653	
☐	LZ-CGT	B737-4Y0F	24691/1904	♦
☐	LZ-CGU	B737-448F	24773/1850	♦

HELI AIR — HLR

	Reg	Type	c/n	Notes
☐	LZ-CCJ	LET L-410UVP-E9	022634	
☐	LZ-CCP	LET L-410UVP-E20	912540	
☐	LZ-CCR	LET L-410UVP-E10	892301	
☐	LZ-CCS	LET L-410UVP-E	902425	

	Reg	Type	c/n	
☐	LZ-CCT	LET L-410UVP-E20	912528	
☐	LZ-CCV	LET L-410UVP-E20	2720	
☐	LZ-CCW	LET L-410UVP-E	912609	
☐	LZ-LSB	LET L-410UVP-E2	861802	

HEMUS AIR — DU / HMS

	Reg	Type	c/n	
☐	LZ-FBA	A319-112	3564	>LZB
☐	LZ-FBB	A319-112	3309	>LZB
☐	LZ-FBC	A320-214	2540	>OHY
☐	LZ-FBD	A320-214	2596	>OHY
☐	LZ-HBA	BAe146 Srs.200	E2072	[SOF]
☐	LZ-HBB	BAe146 Srs.200	E2073	[SOF]
☐	LZ-HBC	BAe146 Srs.200	E2093	[SOF]
☐	LZ-HBD	BAe146 Srs.300	E3141	[SOF]
☐	LZ-HBZ	BAe146 Srs.200	E2103	>LZB
☐	LZ-TIM	Avro 146-RJ70	E1258	[SOF]

ROSE AIR — REM

	Reg	Type	c/n	
☐	LZ-ABR	An-26B	13905	♦

VIA - AIR VIA — VL / VIM

	Reg	Type	c/n	
☐	LZ-PMX	A320-214	4061	>KNE
☐	LZ-PMY	A320-214	3802	>KNE♦
☐	LZ-PMZ	A321-231	1060	>VJC♦

N UNITED STATES OF AMERICA

10 TANKER AIR CARRIER — TNK

	Reg	Type	c/n	
☐	N450AX	DC-10-10	46942/162	[OSC]
☐	N522AX	DC-10-30ER	48315/436	
☐	N612AX	DC-10-30ER	48290/435	
☐	N17085	DC-10-30	47957/201	

21 AIR

	Reg	Type	c/n	
☐	N881YV	B767-241ER(SF)	23803/161	
☐	N999YV	B767-241ER(SF)	23801/170	

ABX AIR — GB / ABX

	Reg	Type	c/n	
☐	N219CY	B767-383F	24358/263	
☐	N220CY	B767-383F	24729/358	
☐	N226CY	B767-383(ER/BDSF)	26544/412	
☐	N312AA	B767-233SF	22315/94	♦
☐	N315AA	B767-223F	22317/109	
☐	N317CM	B767-338ERF	24317/246	
☐	N362CM	B767-338ERF	24316/242	
☐	N363CM	B767-338ERF	24853/319	
☐	N371CM	B767-338ER	25577/550	♦
☐	N372CM	B767-338ER	25575/451	
☐	N740AX	B767-232(SCD)	22213/6	
☐	N744AX	B767-232(SCD)	22221/53	
☐	N750AX	B767-232(SCD)	22227/83	
☐	N767AX	B767-281F	22785/51	
☐	N768AX	B767-281F	22786/54	
☐	N769AX	B767-281F	22787/58	
☐	N773AX	B767-281F	22788/61	
☐	N774AX	B767-281F	22789/67	
☐	N775AX	B767-281F	22790/69	
☐	N783AX	B767-281F	23016/80	
☐	N787AX	B767-281F	23020/96	
☐	N788AX	B767-281F	23021/103	
☐	N792AX	B767-281F	23142/110	
☐	N793AX	B767-281F	23143/114	
☐	N794AX	B767-281F	23144/115	
☐	N795AX	B767-281F	23145/116	
☐	N797AX	B767-281F	23147/123	
☐	N798AX	B767-281F	23431/143	

ADI CHARTER SERVICES — DYN

	Reg	Type	c/n	
☐	N359AD	ERJ-145MP	145169	♦
☐	N459AD	ERJ-145MP	145185	♦
☐	N974RP	ERJ-145MP	145203	♦

AERO-FLITE

	Reg	Type	c/n	
☐	N354AC	Avro 146-RJ85	E2256	
☐	N355AC	Avro 146-RJ85	E2293	
☐	N366AC	Avro 146-RJ85	E2288	
☐	N374AC	Avro 146-RJ85	E2266	
☐	N379AC	Avro 146-RJ85	E2246	
☐	N839AC	Avro 146-RJ85	E2270	

AIR CARGO CARRIERS — 2Q / SNC

	Reg	Type	c/n	
☐	N106SW	Short SD.3-30	SH3072	♦
☐	N167RC	Short SD.3-30	SH3038	
☐	N264AC	Short SD.3-30	SH3103	
☐	N334AC	Short SD.3-30	SH3029	
☐	N336MV	Short SD.3-30	SH3018	
☐	N393AC	Short SD.3-30	SH3111	♦
☐	N875AC	Short SD.3-30	SH3207	♦
☐	N936MA	Short SD.3-30	SH3036	
☐	N2629P	Short SD.3-30	SH3079	
☐	N124CA	Short SD.3-60	SH3652	
☐	N151CA	Short SD.3-60	SH3653	
☐	N360AB	Short SD.3-60	SH3756	
☐	N360RW	Short SD.3-60	SH3613	
☐	N360SA	Short SD.3-60	SH3601	
☐	N367AC	Short SD.3-60	SH3626	
☐	N368AC	Short SD.3-60	SH3651	
☐	N376AC	Short SD.3-60	SH3736	
☐	N386AC	Short SD.3-60	SH3709	♦
☐	N564AC	Short SD.3-60	SH3620	♦
☐	N567AC	Short SD.3-60	SH3622	♦
☐	N601CA	Short SD.3-60	SH3623	
☐	N618AN	Short SD.3-60	SH3691	
☐	N642AN	Short SD.3-60	SH3611	
☐	N688AN	Short SD.3-60	SH3633	
☐	N701A	Short SD.3-60	SH3627	
☐	N733CH	Short SD.3-60	SH3733	
☐	N764JR	Short SD.3-60	SH3764	♦
☐	N972AA	Short SD.3-60	SH3754	
☐	N973AA	Short SD.3-60	SH3749	
☐	N974AA	Short SD.3-60	SH3742	
☐	N3732X	Short SD.3-60	SH3732	
☐	N4498Y	Short SD.3-60	SH3625	

AIR FLAMENCO — F4 / WAF

	Reg	Type	c/n	
☐	N915GD	Short SD.3-60	SH3755	♦
☐	N918GD	Short SD.3-60	SH3741	♦

AIR WISCONSIN — ZW / AWI

Operates aircraft for US Airways Express, for which see this fleet.

ALASKA AIRLINES — AS / ASA

	Reg	Type	c/n	Fleet No
☐	N703AS	B737-490	28893/3039	703
☐	N705AS	B737-490	29318/3042	705
☐	N706AS	B737-490	28894/3050	706
☐	N708AS	B737-490	28895/3098	708
☐	N709AS	B737-490(SF)	28896/3099	709

	Reg	Type	c/n	Fleet
☐	N713AS	B737-490	30161/3110	713
☐	N756AS	B737-4Q8	25097/2299	756
☐	N760AS	B737-4Q8	25098/2320	760
☐	N762AS	B737-4Q8F	25099/2334	762
☐	N763AS	B737-4Q8F	25100/2346	763
☐	N764AS	B737-4Q8F	25101/2348	764
☐	N765AS	B737-4Q8F	25102/2350	765
☐	N767AS	B737-490	27081/2354	767
☐	N768AS	B737-490F	27082/2356	768
☐	N769AS	B737-4Q8	25103/2452	769
☐	N778AS	B737-4Q8	25110/2586	778
☐	N779AS	B737-4Q8	25111/2605	779
☐	N788AS	B737-490	28885/2891	788
☐	N791AS	B737-490	28886/2902	791
☐	N792AS	B737-490	28887/2903	792
☐	N793AS	B737-490	28888/2990	793
☐	N794AS	B737-490	28889/3000	794
☐	N795AS	B737-490	28890/3006	795
☐	N796AS	B737-490	28891/3027	796
☐	N797AS	B737-490	28892/3036	797
☐	N799AS	B737-490	29270/3038	799
☐	N607AS	B737-790/W	29751/313	607
☐	N609AS	B737-790/W	29752/350	609
☐	N611AS	B737-790/W	29753/385	611
☐	N612AS	B737-790/W	30162/406	612
☐	N613AS	B737-790/W	30163/430	613
☐	N614AS	B737-790/W	30343/439	614
☐	N615AS	B737-790/W	30344/472	615
☐	N618AS	B737-790/W	30543/536	618
☐	N619AS	B737-790/W	30164/597	619
☐	N622AS	B737-790/W	30165/661	622
☐	N625AS	B737-790/W	30792/754	625
☐	N626AS	B737-790/W	30793/763	626
☐	N627AS	B737-790/W/F	30794/796	627
☐	N644AS	B737-790/W	30795/1277	644
☐	N506AS	B737-890/W	35690/2627	506
☐	N508AS	B737-890/W	35691/2662	508
☐	N512AS	B737-890/W	39043/2711	512
☐	N513AS	B737-890/W	35192/2721	513
☐	N514AS	B737-890/W	35193/2727	514
☐	N516AS	B737-890/W	39044/2751	516
☐	N517AS	B737-890/W	35197/2770	517
☐	N518AS	B737-890/W	35693/2785	518
☐	N519AS	B737-890/W	36482/2800	519
☐	N520AS	B737-890/W	36481/2812	520
☐	N523AS	B737-890/W	35194/2816	523
☐	N524AS	B737-890/W	35195/2850	524
☐	N525AS	B737-890/W	35692/2859	525
☐	N526AS	B737-890/W	35196/2862	526
☐	N527AS	B737-890/W	35694/2913	527
☐	N528AS	B737-890/W	35695/2930	528
☐	N529AS	B737-890/W	35198/3229	529
☐	N530AS	B737-890/W	36578/3257	530
☐	N531AS	B737-890/W	35199/3287	531
☐	N532AS	B737-890/W	36346/3317	532
☐	N533AS	B737-890/W	35201/3511	533
☐	N534AS	B737-890/W	35202/3523	534
☐	N535AS	B737-890/W	35200/3558	535
☐	N536AS	B737-890/W	35203/3893	536
☐	N537AS	B737-890/W	35204/3913	537
☐	N538AS	B737-890/W	41188/4045	538
☐	N546AS	B737-890/W	30022/1640	546
☐	N548AS	B737-890/W	30020/1738	548
☐	N549AS	B737-8FH/W	30824/1664	549
☐	N551AS	B737-890/W	34593/1860	551
☐	N552AS	B737-890/W	34595/1882	552
☐	N553AS	B737-890/W	34594/1906	553
☐	N556AS	B737-890/W	35175/1980	556
☐	N557AS	B737-890/W	35176/2010	557
☐	N558AS	B737-890/W	35177/2031	558
☐	N559AS	B737-890/W	35178/2026	559
☐	N560AS	B737-890/W	35179/2072	560
☐	N562AS	B737-890/W	35091/2084	562
☐	N563AS	B737-890/W	35180/2090	563
☐	N564AS	B737-890/W	35103/2099	564
☐	N565AS	B737-890/W	35181/2134	565
☐	N566AS	B737-890/W	35182/2164	566
☐	N568AS	B737-890/W	35183/2166	568
☐	N569AS	B737-890/W	35184/2192	569
☐	N570AS	B737-890/W	35185/2212	570
☐	N577AS	B737-890/W	35186/2221	577
☐	N579AS	B737-890/W	35187/2226	579
☐	N581AS	B737-890/W	35188/2259	581
☐	N583AS	B737-890/W	35681/2333	583
☐	N584AS	B737-890/W	35682/2365	584
☐	N585AS	B737-890/W	35683/2385	585
☐	N586AS	B737-890/W	35189/2393	586
☐	N587AS	B737-890/W	35684/2422	587
☐	N588AS	B737-890/W	35685/2454	588
☐	N589AS	B737-890/W	35686/2458	589
☐	N590AS	B737-890/W	35687/2478	590
☐	N592AS	B737-890/W	35190/2511	592
☐	N593AS	B737-890/W	35107/2545	593
☐	N594AS	B737-890/W	35191/2560	594
☐	N596AS	B737-890/W	35688/2587	596
☐	N597AS	B737-890/W	35689/2601	597
☐	N224AK	B737-990ER/W	62680	o/o♦
☐	N236AK	B737-990ER/W	36351	o/o♦
☐	N302AS	B737-990	30017/596	302
☐	N303AS	B737-990	30016/683	303
☐	N305AS	B737-990	30013/774	305
☐	N306AS	B737-990/W	30014/802	306
☐	N307AS	B737-990/W	30015/838	307
☐	N309AS	B737-990/W	30857/902	309
☐	N315AS	B737-990/W	30019/1218	315
☐	N317AS	B737-990/W	30856/1296	317
☐	N318AS	B737-990/W	30018/1326	318
☐	N319AS	B737-990/W	33679/1344	319
☐	N320AS	B737-990/W	33680/1380	320
☐	N323AS	B737-990/W	30021/1454	323
☐	N402AS	B737-990ER/W	41189/4212	402
☐	N403AS	B737-990ER/W	41730/4242	403
☐	N407AS	B737-990ER/W	41731/4278	407
☐	N408AS	B737-990ER/W	41732/4296	408
☐	N409AS	B737-990ER/W	41733/4338	409
☐	N413AS	B737-990ER/W	35205/4386	413
☐	N419AS	B737-990ER/W	41734/4403	419
☐	N423AS	B737-990ER/W	35206/4425	423
☐	N431AS	B737-990ER/W	43255/4636	431
☐	N433AS	B737-990ER/W	41704/4646	433
☐	N434AS	B737-990ER/W	61620	o/o♦
☐	N435AS	B737-990ER/W	43292/4668	435
☐	N440AS	B737-990ER/W	41705/4675	440
☐	N442AS	B737-990ER/W	43293/4700	442
☐	N448AS	B737-990ER/W	36356	o/o♦
☐	N453AS	B737-990ER/W	36354/4747	453
☐	N457AS	B737-990ER/W	36355/4784	457
☐	N459AS	B737-990ER/W	36352/4832	459
☐	N461AS	B737-990ER/W	36363/4850	461
☐	N462AS	B737-990ER/W	36361/4887	462
☐	N464AS	B737-990ER/W	40714/4903	464
☐	N467AS	B737-990ER/W	36362/4925	467

☐ N468AS	B737-990ER/W	41735/5012	468
☐ N469AS	B737-990ER/W	40702/5043	469
☐ N471AS	B737-990ER/W	41703/5110	471
☐ N472AS	B737-990ER/W	60580/5358	472
☐ N474AS	B737-990ER/W	40715/5431	474
☐ N477AS	B737-990ER/W	40716/5454	477
☐ N478AS	B737-990ER/W	44105/5482	478♦
☐ N479AS	B737-990ER/W	60576/5494	479♦
☐ N481AS	B737-990ER/W	44106/5540	481♦
☐ N482AS	B737-990ER/W	36353	o/o♦
☐ N483AS	B737-990ER/W	36350/5563	483♦
☐ N486AS	B737-990ER/W	44107/5578	486♦
☐ N487AS	B737-990ER/W	44108/5597	487♦
☐ N491AS	B737-990ER/W	44109/5682	491♦
☐ N492AS	B737-990ER/W	44110/5686	492♦
☐ N493AS	B737-990ER/W	41727/5738	493♦
☐ N494AS	B737-990ER/W	41729/5768	494♦
☐ N495AS	B737-990ER/W	41728/5787	495♦
☐ N215AG	CRJ-701	10009	^ 215
☐ N216AG	CRJ-701	10023	^ 216
☐ N217AG	CRJ-701	10031	^ 217
☐ N218AG	CRJ-701	10205	^ 218
☐ N219AG	CRJ-701	10246	^ 219
☐ N223AG	CRJ-701ER	10010	^ 223
☐ N224AG	CRJ-701ER	10024	^ 224
☐ N225AG	CRJ-701ER	10033	^ 225
☐ N227AG	CRJ-701ER	10015	^ 227
☐ N170SY	ERJ-175LR	17000483	♦
☐ N171SY	ERJ-175LR	17000485	♦
☐ N173SY	ERJ-175LR	17000486	♦
☐ N174SY	ERJ-175LR	17000517	♦
☐ N175SY	ERJ-175LR	17000527	♦
☐ N176SY	ERJ-175LR	17000533	♦
☐ N177SY	ERJ-175LR	17000535	♦

^ operates as Alaska Skywest

ALASKA CENTRAL EXPRESS — KO / AER

☐ N110AX	Beech 1900C-1	UC-93	
☐ N111AX	Beech 1900C-1	UC-81	
☐ N113AX	Beech 1900C-1	UC-41	
☐ N115AX	Beech 1900C-1	UC-2	
☐ N117AX	Beech 1900C-1	UC-79	
☐ N118AX	Beech 1900C-1	UC-116	
☐ N119AX	Beech 1900C-1	UC-43	
☐ N258SL	Beech 1900C-1	UC-158	♦

ALLEGIANT AIR — G4 / AAY

☐ N301NV	A319-111	2319	301
☐ N302NV	A319-111	2387	302
☐ N303NV	A319-112	2271	303
☐ N304NV	A319-112	2265	304
☐ N305NV	A319-111	2398	305
☐ N306NV	A319-112	2420	306
☐ N307NV	A319-111	2427	307
☐ N308NV	A319-111	2450	308
☐ N310NV	A319-111	2224	310
☐ N326NV	A319-111	2586	326♦
☐ N327NV	A319-111	2556	327♦
☐ N	A319-112	2625	o/o♦
☐ N	A319-112	2638	o/o♦
☐ N	A319-111	2702	o/o♦
☐ N	A319-112	2786	o/o♦
☐ N	A319-112	2790	o/o♦
☐ N215NV	A320-214	1292	215
☐ N216NV	A320-214	1318	216
☐ N217NV	A320-214	1347	217
☐ N218NV	A320-214	1229	218
☐ N219NV	A320-214	1255	219
☐ N220NV	A320-214	1262	220
☐ N221NV	A320-214	1288	221
☐ N222NV	A320-214	1530	222
☐ N223NV	A320-214	1540	223
☐ N224NV	A320-214	1694	224♦
☐ N225NV	A320-214	0706	225♦
☐ N226NV	A320-214	0745	226♦
☐ N227NV	A320-214	0714	227♦
☐ N228NV	A320-214	0716	228♦
☐ N229NV	A320-214	0730	229♦
☐ N234NV	A320-214	1467	234♦
☐ N902NV	B757-204/W	26964/452	902
☐ N903NV	B757-204/W	26966/520	903
☐ N905NV	B757-204/W	27235/598	905
☐ N906NV	B757-204/W	27236/600	906
☐ N401NV	MD-88	49761/1623	401
☐ N402NV	MD-88	49763/1626	402
☐ N403NV	MD-88	49764/1632	403
☐ N404NV	MD-88	49765/1645	404
☐ N405NV	MD-83	49623/1499	405
☐ N406NV	MD-82	49900/1765	406
☐ N407NV	MD-82	53244/1901	407
☐ N408NV	MD-82	53246/1918	408
☐ N409NV	MD-83	49574/1413	409
☐ N410NV	MD-83	49965/2044	410
☐ N411NV	MD-82	53245/1978	411
☐ N412NV	MD-88	49759/1606	412
☐ N414NV	MD-88	49766/1657	414
☐ N415NV	MD-82	49909/1625	415
☐ N416NV	MD-82	49555/1402	416
☐ N417NV	MD-83	53347/1979	417
☐ N418NV	MD-82	49615/1543	418
☐ N419NV	MD-82	53366/1999	419
☐ N420NV	MD-83	49424/1284	420
☐ N421NV	MD-83	53275/1896	421
☐ N422NV	MD-82	49381/1231	422
☐ N423NV	MD-82	53008/1895	423
☐ N424NV	MD-82	49421/1263	424
☐ N425NV	MD-83	49438/1353	425
☐ N426NV	MD-83	49437/1345	426
☐ N427NV	MD-83	49436/1303	427
☐ N429NV	MD-82	49385/1244	429
☐ N861GA	MD-83	49557/1436	861
☐ N862GA	MD-83	49556/1415	862
☐ N863GA	MD-83	49911/1653	863
☐ N864GA	MD-83	49912/1659	864
☐ N865GA	MD-83	49998/1800	865
☐ N866GA	MD-83	49910/1638	866
☐ N868GA	MD-83	49554/1379	868
☐ N869GA	MD-83	53294/1917	869
☐ N871GA	MD-83	53296/1937	871
☐ N872GA	MD-83	53295/1922	872
☐ N873GA	MD-83	49658/1461	873
☐ N874GA	MD-83	49643/1423	874
☐ N875GA	MD-83	53468/2130	875
☐ N876GA	MD-83	53469/2116	876
☐ N877GA	MD-83	53467/2102	877
☐ N878GA	MD-83	53487/2132	878
☐ N879GA	MD-83	53486/2130	879
☐ N881GA	MD-83	49708/1561	881
☐ N883GA	MD-83	49710/1547	883
☐ N884GA	MD-83	49401/1357	884

☐	N886GA	MD-82	49931/1754	886
☐	N887GA	MD-82	49932/1756	887
☐	N891GA	MD-83	49423/1283	891
☐	N892GA	MD-83	49826/1578	892
☐	N893GA	MD-83	53051/1718	893

ALOHA AIR CARGO — *KH / AAH*

☐	N301KH	B737-330F	27904/2691	
☐	N302KH	B737-330F	27905/2705	
☐	N303KH	B737-319F	25606/3123	♦
☐	N320DL	B737-232F	23092/1023	♦
☐	N842AL	B737-290QC	23136/1032	[TUS]
☐	N843KH	SAAB SF.340A	340A-046	
☐	N844KH	SAAB SF.340A	340A-108	
☐	N845KH	SAAB SF.340A	340A-111	

ALPINE AIR EXPRESS — *5A / AIP*

☐	N60MJ	Beech 1900D	UE-60	
☐	N101UE	Beech 1900C-1	UC-101	♦
☐	N125BA	Beech 1900C	UB-6	
☐	N127BA	Beech 1900C	UB-7	
☐	N133BA	Beech 1900C	UB-54	
☐	N153GA	Beech 1900C	UB-34	
☐	N172GA	Beech 1900C	UB-11	
☐	N190GA	Beech 1900C	UB-1	
☐	N192GA	Beech 1900C	UB-17	
☐	N194GA	Beech 1900C	UB-8	
☐	N197GA	Beech 1900C	UB-16	
☐	N198GA	Beech 1900C	UB-5	
☐	N218SL	Beech 1900C-1	UC-113	♦
☐	N422AX	Beech 1900C-1	UC-95	♦
☐	N575F	Beech 1900C-1	UC-99	
☐	N821SF	Beech 1900C-1	UC-121	

AMERICAN AIRLINES — *AA / AAL*

☐	N700UW	A319-112	0885	
☐	N701UW	A319-112	0890	
☐	N702UW	A319-112	0896	
☐	N703UW	A319-112	0904	
☐	N704US	A319-112	0922	
☐	N705UW	A319-112	0929	
☐	N708UW	A319-112	0972	
☐	N709UW	A319-112	0997	
☐	N710UW	A319-112	1019	
☐	N711UW	A319-112	1033	
☐	N712US	A319-112	1038	
☐	N713UW	A319-112	1040	
☐	N714US	A319-112	1046	
☐	N715UW	A319-112	1051	
☐	N716UW	A319-112	1055	
☐	N717UW	A319-112	1069	
☐	N721UW	A319-112	1095	
☐	N722US	A319-112	1097	
☐	N723UW	A319-112	1109	
☐	N724UW	A319-112	1122	
☐	N725UW	A319-112	1135	
☐	N730US	A319-112	1182	
☐	N732US	A319-112	1203	
☐	N733UW	A319-112	1205	
☐	N737US	A319-112	1245	
☐	N738US	A319-112	1254	
☐	N740UW	A319-112	1265	
☐	N741UW	A319-112	1269	
☐	N742PS	A319-112	1275	
☐	N744P	A319-112	1287	
☐	N745VJ	A319-112	1289	
☐	N746UW	A319-112	1297	
☐	N747UW	A319-112	1301	
☐	N748UW	A319-112	1311	
☐	N749US	A319-112	1313	
☐	N750UW	A319-112	1315	
☐	N751UW	A319-112	1317	
☐	N752US	A319-112	1319	
☐	N753US	A319-112	1326	
☐	N754UW	A319-112	1328	
☐	N755US	A319-112	1331	
☐	N756US	A319-112	1340	
☐	N757UW	A319-112	1342	
☐	N758US	A319-112	1348	
☐	N760US	A319-112	1354	
☐	N762US	A319-112	1358	
☐	N763US	A319-112	1360	
☐	N764US	A319-112	1369	
☐	N765US	A319-112	1371	
☐	N766US	A319-112	1378	
☐	N767UW	A319-112	1382	
☐	N768US	A319-112	1389	
☐	N769US	A319-112	1391	
☐	N770UW	A319-112	1393	
☐	N801AW	A319-132	0889	
☐	N802AW	A319-132	0924	
☐	N803AW	A319-132	0931	
☐	N804AW	A319-132	1043	
☐	N805AW	A319-132	1049	
☐	N806AW	A319-132	1056	
☐	N807AW	A319-132	1064	
☐	N808AW	A319-132	1088	
☐	N809AW	A319-132	1111	
☐	N810AW	A319-132	1116	
☐	N812AW	A319-132	1178	
☐	N813AW	A319-132	1223	
☐	N814AW	A319-132	1281	
☐	N815AW	A319-132	1323	
☐	N816AW	A319-132	1350	
☐	N817AW	A319-132	1373	
☐	N818AW	A319-132	1375	
☐	N819AW	A319-132	1395	
☐	N820AW	A319-132	1397	
☐	N821AW	A319-132	1406	
☐	N822AW	A319-132	1410	
☐	N823AW	A319-132	1463	
☐	N824AW	A319-132	1490	
☐	N825AW	A319-132	1527	
☐	N826AW	A319-132	1534	
☐	N827AW	A319-132	1547	
☐	N828AW	A319-132	1552	
☐	N829AW	A319-132	1563	
☐	N830AW	A319-132	1565	
☐	N831AW	A319-132	1576	
☐	N832AW	A319-132	1643	
☐	N833AW	A319-132	1844	
☐	N834AW	A319-132	2302	
☐	N835AW	A319-132	2458	
☐	N836AW	A319-132	2570	
☐	N837AW	A319-132	2595	
☐	N838AW	A319-132	2615	
☐	N839AW	A319-132	2669	
☐	N840AW	A319-132	2690	
☐	N3014R	A319-115/S	5842	014
☐	N4005X	A319-115/S	5753	005
☐	N4032T	A319-115/S	6644	032♦
☐	N5007E	A319-115/S	5781	007

☐	N8001N	A319-115/S	5678	001
☐	N8009T	A319-115/S	5788	009
☐	N8027D	A319-115/S	6437	027
☐	N8030F	A319-115/S	6552	030
☐	N8031M	A319-115/S	6595	031
☐	N9002U	A319-115/S	5698	002
☐	N9004F	A319-115/S	5745	004
☐	N9006	A319-115/S	5761	006
☐	N9008U	A319-115/S	5786	008
☐	N9010R	A319-115/S	5789	010
☐	N9011P	A319-115/S	5798	011
☐	N9012	A319-115/S	5810	012
☐	N9013A	A319-115/S	5827	013
☐	N9015D	A319-115/S	5327	015
☐	N9016	A319-115/S	6040	016
☐	N9017P	A319-115/S	6085	017
☐	N9018E	A319-115/S	6150	018
☐	N9019F	A319-115/S	6154	019
☐	N9021H	A319-115/S	6277	021
☐	N9022G	A319-115/S	6310	022
☐	N9023N	A319-115/S	6349	023
☐	N9025B	A319-115/S	6393	025
☐	N9026C	A319-115/S	6429	026
☐	N9029F	A319-115/S	6491	029
☐	N12028	A319-115/S	6456	028
☐	N70020	A319-115/S	6263	020
☐	N90024	A319-115/S	6384	024
☐	N93003	A319-115/S	5704	003
☐	N102UW	A320-214	0844	
☐	N103US	A320-214	0861	
☐	N104UW	A320-214	0863	
☐	N105UW	A320-214	0868	
☐	N107US	A320-214	1052	
☐	N108UW	A320-214	1061	
☐	N109UW	A320-214	1065	
☐	N110UW	A320-214	1112	
☐	N111US	A320-214	1114	
☐	N112US	A320-214	1134	
☐	N114UW	A320-214	1148	
☐	N117UW	A320-214	1224	
☐	N118US	A320-214	1264	
☐	N119US	A320-214	1268	
☐	N121UW	A320-214	1294	
☐	N122US	A320-214	1298	
☐	N123UW	A320-214	1310	
☐	N124US	A320-214	1314	
☐	N125UW	A320-214	4086	
☐	N126UW	A320-214	4149	
☐	N127UW	A320-214	4202	
☐	N128UW	A320-214	4242	
☐	N601AW	A320-232	1935	
☐	N604AW	A320-232	1196	
☐	N640AW	A320-232	0448	
☐	N647AW	A320-232	0762	
☐	N648AW	A320-232	0770	[GYR]
☐	N649AW	A320-232	0803	
☐	N650AW	A320-232	0856	
☐	N651AW	A320-232	0866	
☐	N652AW	A320-232	0953	
☐	N653AW	A320-232	1003	
☐	N654AW	A320-232	1050	
☐	N655AW	A320-232	1075	
☐	N656AW	A320-232	1079	
☐	N657AW	A320-232	1083	
☐	N658AW	A320-232	1110	
☐	N659AW	A320-232	1166	
☐	N660AW	A320-232	1234	
☐	N661AW	A320-232	1284	
☐	N662AW	A320-232	1274	
☐	N663AW	A320-232	1419	
☐	N664AW	A320-232	1621	
☐	N665AW	A320-232	1644	
☐	N667AW	A320-232	1710	
☐	N668AW	A320-232	1764	
☐	N669AW	A320-232	1792	
☐	N672AW	A320-232	2193	
☐	N673AW	A320-232	2312	
☐	N675AW	A320-232	2405	
☐	N676AW	A320-232	2422	std
☐	N677AW	A320-232	2430	
☐	N678AW	A320-232	2482	
☐	N679AW	A320-232	2613	
☐	N680AW	A320-232	2630	
☐	N101NN	A321-231/S	5834	783
☐	N102NN	A321-231/S	5860	784
☐	N103NN	A321-231/S	5884	785
☐	N104NN	A321-231/S	5895	786
☐	N105NN	A321-231/S	5904	787
☐	N106NN	A321-231/S	5932	788
☐	N107NN	A321-231/S	5938	789
☐	N108NN	A321-231/S	5946	790
☐	N109NN	A321-231/S	5955	791
☐	N110AN	A321-231/S	5975	792
☐	N111ZM	A321-231/S	5983	793
☐	N112AN	A321-231/S	5991	794
☐	N113AN	A321-231/S	6020	795
☐	N114NN	A321-231/S	6046	796
☐	N115NN	A321-231/S	6063	797
☐	N116AN	A321-231/S	6070	798
☐	N117AN	A321-231/S	6094	799
☐	N118NN	A321-231/S	6162	850
☐	N119NN	A321-231/S	6222	851
☐	N120EE	A321-231/S	6227	852
☐	N121AN	A321-231/S	6238	853
☐	N122NN	A321-231/S	6252	854
☐	N123NN	A321-231/S	6256	855
☐	N124AA	A321-231/S	6271	856
☐	N125AA	A321-231/S	6272	857
☐	N126AN	A321-231/S	6313	858
☐	N127AA	A321-231/S	6334	859
☐	N128AN	A321-231/S	6346	860
☐	N129AA	A321-231/S	6401	861
☐	N130AN	A321-231/S	6407	862
☐	N131NN	A321-231/S	6472	863
☐	N132AN	A321-231/S	6473	864
☐	N133AN	A321-231/S	6482	865
☐	N134AN	A321-231/S	6495	866
☐	N135NN	A321-231/S	6520	867
☐	N136AN	A321-231/S	6532	868
☐	N137AA	A321-231/S	6647	869♦
☐	N138AN	A321-231/S	6650	870♦
☐	N139AN	A321-231/S	6687	871♦
☐	N140AN	A321-231/S	6667	872♦
☐	N141NN	A321-231/S	6656	873♦
☐	N142AN	A321-231/S	6711	874♦
☐	N143AN	A321-231/S	6745	875♦
☐	N144AN	A321-231/S	6723	876♦
☐	N145AN	A321-231/S	6783	877♦
☐	N146AA	A321-231/S	6761	878♦
☐	N147AA	A321-231/S	6802	879♦
☐	N148AN	A321-231/S	6790	880♦
☐	N149AN	A321-231/S	6812	881♦

	Registration	Type	c/n		
☐	N150NN	A321-231/S	6828	882♦
☐	N150UW	A321-211	5504	
☐	N151AN	A321-231/S	6840	883♦
☐	N151UW	A321-211	5513	
☐	N152AA	A321-231/S	6887	884♦
☐	N152UW	A321-211	5588	
☐	N153AN	A321-231/S	6908	885♦
☐	N153UW	A321-211	5594	
☐	N154AA	A321-231/S	6928	886♦
☐	N154UW	A321-211	5644	
☐	N155NN	A321-231/S	6940	887♦
☐	N155UW	A321-211	5659	
☐	N156AN	A321-231/S	6983	♦
☐	N156UW	A321-211	5684	
☐	N157UW	A321-211	5696	
☐	N161UW	A321-211	1403	
☐	N162UW	A321-211	1412	
☐	N163US	A321-211	1417	
☐	N165US	A321-211	1431	
☐	N167US	A321-211	1442	
☐	N169UW	A321-211	1455	
☐	N170US	A321-211	1462	
☐	N171US	A321-211	1465	
☐	N172US	A321-211	1472	
☐	N173US	A321-211	1481	
☐	N174US	A321-211	1492	
☐	N176UW	A321-211	1499	
☐	N177US	A321-211	1517	
☐	N178US	A321-211	1519	
☐	N179UW	A321-211	1521	
☐	N180US	A321-211	1525	
☐	N181UW	A321-211	1531	
☐	N182UW	A321-211	1536	
☐	N183UW	A321-211	1539	
☐	N184US	A321-211	1651	
☐	N185UW	A321-211	1666	
☐	N186US	A321-211	1701	
☐	N187US	A321-211	1704	
☐	N188US	A321-211	1724	
☐	N189UW	A321-211	1425	
☐	N190UW	A321-211	1436	
☐	N191UW	A321-211	1447	
☐	N192UW	A321-211	1496	
☐	N193UW	A321-211	3584	
☐	N194UW	A321-211	3629	
☐	N195UW	A321-211	3633	
☐	N196UW	A321-211	3879	
☐	N197UW	A321-211	3928	
☐	N198UW	A321-211	5444	
☐	N199UW	A321-211	5475	
☐	N507AY	A321-231	3712	
☐	N508AY	A321-231	3740	
☐	N509AY	A321-231	3796	
☐	N510UW	A321-231	3858	
☐	N519UW	A321-231	3881	
☐	N521UW	A321-231	3944	
☐	N523UW	A321-231	3960	
☐	N524UW	A321-231	3977	
☐	N534UW	A321-231	3989	
☐	N535UW	A321-231	3993	
☐	N536UW	A321-231	4025	
☐	N537UW	A321-231	4041	
☐	N538UW	A321-231	4050	
☐	N539UW	A321-231	4082	
☐	N540UW	A321-231	4107	
☐	N542UW	A321-231	4134	
☐	N543UW	A321-231	4843	
☐	N544UW	A321-231	4847	
☐	N545UW	A321-231	4850	
☐	N546UW	A321-231	4885	
☐	N549UW	A321-231	4932	
☐	N551UW	A321-231	4940	
☐	N552UW	A321-231	4957	
☐	N553UW	A321-231	4960	
☐	N554UW	A321-231	4966	
☐	N556UW	A321-231	5244	
☐	N557UW	A321-231	5269	
☐	N558UW	A321-231	5282	
☐	N559UW	A321-231	5292	
☐	N560UW	A321-231	5300	
☐	N561UW	A321-231	5317	
☐	N562UW	A321-231	5332	
☐	N563UW	A321-231	5368	
☐	N567UW	A321-231	5728	
☐	N568UW	A321-231	5751	
☐	N572UW	A321-231	5899	
☐	N573UW	A321-231	5939	
☐	N575UW	A321-231	5980	
☐	N576UW	A321-231	6027	
☐	N578UW	A321-231	6035	
☐	N579UW	A321-231	6100	
☐	N580UW	A321-231	6133	
☐	N581UW	A321-231	6152	
☐	N582UW	A321-231	6175	
☐	N583UW	A321-231	6181	
☐	N584UW	A321-231	6194	
☐	N585UW	A321-231	6214	
☐	N586UW	A321-231	6230	
☐	N587UW	A321-231	6236	
☐	N912UY	A321-231	6264	
☐	N913US	A321-231	6255	
☐	N914UY	A321-231	6337	
☐	N915US	A321-231	6387	
☐	N916US	A321-231	6420	
☐	N917UY	A321-231	6427	
☐	N918US	A321-231	6443	
☐	N919US	A321-231	6479	
☐	N920US	A321-231	6490	
☐	N921US	A321-231	6523	
☐	N922US	A321-231	6537	
☐	N923US	A321-231	6543	
☐	N924US	A321-231	6569	
☐	N925UY	A321-231	6613	♦
☐	N926UW	A321-231	6618	♦
☐	N927UW	A321-231	6625	♦
☐	N970UY	A321-231	3924	♦
☐	N971UY	A321-231	6249	
☐	N972UY	A321-231	4123	♦
☐	N973UY	A321-231	4893	♦
☐	N974UY	A321-231	4898	♦
☐	N975UY	A321-231	4935	♦
☐	N976UY	A321-231	5235	♦
☐	N977UY	A321-231	5409	♦
☐	N978UY	A321-231	5422	♦
☐	N979UY	A321-231	5763	♦
☐	N980UY	A321-231	5795	♦
☐	N981UY	A321-231	5800	♦
☐	N982VJ	A321-231	5374	♦
☐	N270AY	A330-323E	315	
☐	N271AY	A330-323E	323	
☐	N272AY	A330-323E	333	
☐	N273AY	A330-323E	337	
☐	N274AY	A330-323E	342	

☐	N275AY	A330-323E	370	
☐	N276AY	A330-323E	375	
☐	N277AY	A330-323E	380	
☐	N278AY	A330-323E	388	
☐	N279AY	A330-243	1011	
☐	N280AY	A330-243	1022	
☐	N281AY	A330-243	1041	
☐	N282AY	A330-243	1069	
☐	N283AY	A330-243	1076	
☐	N284AY	A330-243	1095	
☐	N285AY	A330-243	1100	
☐	N286AY	A330-243	1415	
☐	N287AY	A330-243	1417	
☐	N288AY	A330-243	1441	
☐	N289AY	A330-243	1455	
☐	N290AY	A330-243	1480	
☐	N291AY	A330-243	1502	
☐	N292AY	A330-243	1512	
☐	N293AY	A330-243	1526	

☐	N800NN	B737-823/W	29564/2964	3DY
☐	N801NN	B737-823/W	29565/2972	3EA
☐	N802NN	B737-823/W	31073/2982	3EB
☐	N803NN	B737-823/W	29566/2995	3EC
☐	N804NN	B737-823/W	29567/3004	3ED
☐	N805NN	B737-823/W	31075/3013	3EE
☐	N806NN	B737-823/W	29561/3028	3EF
☐	N807NN	B737-823/W	31077/3035	3EG
☐	N808NN	B737-823/W	33206/3042	3EH
☐	N809NN	B737-823/W	33519/3050	3EJ
☐	N810NN	B737-823/W	33207/3056	3EK
☐	N811NN	B737-823/W	31079/3063	3EL
☐	N812NN	B737-823/W	33520/3070	3EM
☐	N813NN	B737-823/W	30918/3077	3EN
☐	N814NN	B737-823/W	29562/3085	3EP
☐	N815NN	B737-823/W	33208/3094	3ER
☐	N816NN	B737-823/W	31081/3102	3ES
☐	N817NN	B737-823/W	29558/3107	3ET
☐	N818NN	B737-823/W	30910/3112	3EU
☐	N819NN	B737-823/W	31083/3118	3EV
☐	N820NN	B737-823/W	29559/3125	3EW
☐	N821NN	B737-823/W	30912/3137	3EX
☐	N822NN	B737-823/W	31085/3149	3EY
☐	N823NN	B737-823/W	29560/3156	3FA
☐	N824NN	B737-823/W	30916/3170	3FB
☐	N825NN	B737-823/W	31087/3178	3FC
☐	N826NN	B737-823/W	31089/3185	3FD
☐	N827NN	B737-823/W	33209/3193	3FE
☐	N829NN	B737-823/W	33210/3200	3FF
☐	N830NN	B737-823/W	31091/3209	3FG
☐	N831NN	B737-823/W	33211/3217	3FH
☐	N832NN	B737-823/W	33521/3228	3FJ
☐	N833NN	B737-823/W	31093/3236	3FK
☐	N834NN	B737-823/W	29576/3244	3FL
☐	N835NN	B737-823/W	29577/3252	3FM
☐	N836NN	B737-823/W	31095/3260	3FN
☐	N837NN	B737-823/W	30908/3268	3FP
☐	N838NN	B737-823/W	31097/3276	3FR
☐	N839NN	B737-823/W	29557/3282	3FS
☐	N840NN	B737-823/W	33518/3291	3FT
☐	N841NN	B737-823/W	30914/3298	3FU
☐	N842NN	B737-823/W	31099/3307	3FV
☐	N843NN	B737-823/W	30906/3328	3FW
☐	N844NN	B737-823/W	33212/3334	3FX
☐	N845NN	B737-823/W	40579/3340	3FY
☐	N846NN	B737-823/W	31101/3347	3GA
☐	N847NN	B737-823/W	29575/3361	3GB
☐	N848NN	B737-823/W	31103/3367	3GC
☐	N849NN	B737-823/W	33213/3373	3GD
☐	N850NN	B737-823/W	40580/3380	3GE
☐	N851NN	B737-823/W	29556/3390	3GF
☐	N852NN	B737-823/W	40581/3396	3GG
☐	N853NN	B737-823/W	31105/3404	3GH
☐	N854NN	B737-823/W	33214/3412	3GJ
☐	N855NN	B737-823/W	40582/3422	3GK
☐	N856NN	B737-823/W	31107/3427	3GL
☐	N857NN	B737-823/W	30907/3434	3GM
☐	N858NN	B737-823/W	30904/3440	3GN
☐	N859NN	B737-823/W	29555/3456	3GP
☐	N860NN	B737-823/W	40583/3462	3GR
☐	N861NN	B737-823/W	31109/3468	3GS
☐	N862NN	B737-823/W	30905/3475	3GT
☐	N863NN	B737-823/W	30903/3481	3GU
☐	N864NN	B737-823/W	31111/3487	3GV
☐	N865NN	B737-823/W	29554/3493	3GW
☐	N866NN	B737-823/W	40584/3499	3GX
☐	N867NN	B737-823/W	40762/3634	3GY
☐	N868NN	B737-823/W	40763/3668	3HA
☐	N869NN	B737-823/W	40764/3689	3HB
☐	N870NN	B737-823/W	40765/3748	3HE
☐	N871NN	B737-823/W	31127/3731	3HC
☐	N872NN	B737-823/W	33219/3740	3HD
☐	N873NN	B737-823/W	40766/3775	3HG
☐	N874NN	B737-823/W	31129/3764	3HF
☐	N875NN	B737-823/W	33220/3782	3HH
☐	N876NN	B737-823/W	40767/3793	3HJ
☐	N877NN	B737-823/W	31131/3808	3HK
☐	N878NN	B737-823/W	40768/3820	3HL
☐	N879NN	B737-823/W	31133/3833	3HM
☐	N880NN	B737-823/W	40769/3854	3HN
☐	N881NN	B737-823/W	31135/3862	3HP
☐	N882NN	B737-823/W	33221/3880	3HR
☐	N883NN	B737-823/W	31137/3892	3HS
☐	N884NN	B737-823/W	33222/3914	3HT
☐	N885NN	B737-823/W	31139/3935	3HU
☐	N886NN	B737-823/W	33223/3950	3HV
☐	N887NN	B737-823/W	31141/3964	3HW
☐	N889NN	B737-823/W	33314/3981	3HX
☐	N890NN	B737-823/W	31143/3999	3HY
☐	N891NN	B737-823/W	33315/4022	3JA
☐	N892NN	B737-823/W	31145/4040	3JB
☐	N893NN	B737-823/W	33316/4053	3JC
☐	N894NN	B737-823/W	31147/4066	3JD
☐	N895NN	B737-823/W	31149/4079	3JE
☐	N896NN	B737-823/W	33224/4093	3JF
☐	N897NN	B737-823/W	33318/4106	3JG
☐	N898NN	B737-823/W	33225/4129	3JH
☐	N899NN	B737-823/W	31151/4142	3JJ
☐	N901AN	B737-823/W	29503/184	3AA
☐	N901NN	B737-823/W	33226/4155	3JK
☐	N902AN	B737-823/W	29504/190	3AB
☐	N902NN	B737-823/W	31154/4168	3JL
☐	N903AN	B737-823/W	29505/196	3AC
☐	N903NN	B737-823/W	31153/4183	3JM
☐	N904AN	B737-823/W	29506/207	3AD
☐	N904NN	B737-823/W	33317/4197	3JN
☐	N905AN	B737-823/W	29507/231	3AE
☐	N905NN	B737-823/W	31156/4210	3JP
☐	N906AN	B737-823/W	29508/240	3AF
☐	N906NN	B737-823/W	31155/4223	3JR
☐	N907AN	B737-823/W	29509/254	3AG
☐	N907NN	B737-823/W	31158/4235	3JS
☐	N908AN	B737-823/W	29510/263	3AH
☐	N908NN	B737-823/W	31157/4247	3JT

	Registration	Type	c/n / l/n	Code
☐	N909AN	B737-823/W	29511/267	3AJ
☐	N909NN	B737-823/W	31159/4259	3JU
☐	N910AN	B737-823/W	29512/271	3AK
☐	N910NN	B737-823/W	31160/4273	3JV
☐	N912AN	B737-823/W	29513/289	3AL
☐	N912NN	B737-823/W	33319/4286	3JW
☐	N913AN	B737-823/W	29514/293	3AM
☐	N913NN	B737-823/W	29571/4309	3JX
☐	N914AN	B737-823/W	29515/316	3AN
☐	N914NN	B737-823/W	31161/4315	3JY
☐	N915AN	B737-823/W	29516/322	3AP
☐	N915NN	B737-823/W	33227/4322	3KA
☐	N916AN	B737-823/W	29517/332	3AR
☐	N916NN	B737-823/W	31163/4333	3KB
☐	N917AN	B737-823/W	29518/344	3AS
☐	N917NN	B737-823/W	29572/4341	3KC
☐	N918AN	B737-823/W	29519/353	3AT
☐	N918NN	B737-823/W	33228/4352	3KD
☐	N919AN	B737-823/W	29520/363	3AU
☐	N919NN	B737-823/W	29573/4363	3KE
☐	N920AN	B737-823/W	29521/378	3AV
☐	N920NN	B737-823/W	31165/4373	3KF
☐	N921AN	B737-823/W	29522/383	3AW
☐	N921NN	B737-823/W	33229/4390	3KG
☐	N922AN	B737-823/W	29523/398	3AX
☐	N922NN	B737-823/W	29574/4401	3KH
☐	N923AN	B737-823/W	29524/405	3AY
☐	N923NN	B737-823/W	31167/4410	3KJ
☐	N924AN	B737-823/W	29525/434	3BA
☐	N924NN	B737-823/W	33486/4438	3KK
☐	N925AN	B737-823/W	29526/440	3BB
☐	N925NN	B737-823/W	31169/4444	3KL
☐	N926AN	B737-823/W	29527/453	3BC
☐	N926NN	B737-823/W	33321/4451	3KM
☐	N927AN	B737-823/W	30077/462	3BD
☐	N927NN	B737-823/W	31171/4459	3KN
☐	N928AN	B737-823/W	29528/473	3BE
☐	N928NN	B737-823/W	31172/4478	3KP
☐	N929AN	B737-823/W	30078/488	3BF
☐	N929NN	B737-823/W	33322/4489	3KR
☐	N930AN	B737-823/W	29529/503	3BG
☐	N930NN	B737-823/W	33487/4507	3KS
☐	N931AN	B737-823/W	30079/509	3BH
☐	N931NN	B737-823/W	33230/4523	3KT
☐	N932AN	B737-823/W	29530/527	3BJ
☐	N932NN	B737-823/W	33488/4530	3KU
☐	N933AN	B737-823/W	30080/531	3BK
☐	N933NN	B737-823/W	31173/4540	3KV
☐	N934AN	B737-823/W	29531/553	3BL
☐	N934NN	B737-823/W	33489/4558	3KW
☐	N935AN	B737-823/W	30081/559	3BM
☐	N935NN	B737-823/W	33231/4563	3KX
☐	N936AN	B737-823/W	29532/575	3BN
☐	N936NN	B737-823/W	31176/4580	3KY
☐	N937AN	B737-823/W	30082/579	3BP
☐	N937NN	B737-823/W	31178/4594	3LA
☐	N938AN	B737-823/W	29533/608	3BR
☐	N938NN	B737-823/W	33490/4605	3LB
☐	N939AN	B737-823/W	30083/612	3BS
☐	N939NN	B737-823/W	33491/4629	3LC
☐	N940AN	B737-823/W	30598/616	3BT
☐	N940NN	B737-823/W	33323/4655	3LD
☐	N941AN	B737-823/W	29534/624	3BU
☐	N941NN	B737-823/W	33232/4683	3LE
☐	N942AN	B737-823/W	30084/629	3BV
☐	N942NN	B737-823/W	33492/4691	3LF
☐	N943AN	B737-823/W	30599/635	3BW
☐	N943NN	B737-823/W	31177/4724	3LG
☐	N944AN	B737-823/W	29535/645	3BX
☐	N944NN	B737-823/W	31185/4742	3LH
☐	N945AN	B737-823/W	30085/649	3BY
☐	N945NN	B737-823/W	33233/4763	3LJ
☐	N946AN	B737-823/W	30600/655	3CA
☐	N946NN	B737-823/W	33234/4776	3LK
☐	N947AN	B737-823/W	29536/671	3CB
☐	N947NN	B737-823/W	31190/4811	3LL
☐	N948AN	B737-823/W	30086/679	3CC
☐	N948NN	B737-823/W	31189/4835	3LM
☐	N949AN	B737-823/W	29537/699	3CD
☐	N949NN	B737-823/W	31192/4871	3LN
☐	N950AN	B737-823/W	30087/704	3CE
☐	N950NN	B737-823/W	31194/4891	3LP
☐	N951AA	B737-823/W	29538/720	3CF
☐	N951NN	B737-823/W	33327/4923	3LR
☐	N952AA	B737-823/W	30088/726	3CG
☐	N952NN	B737-823/W	31196/4951	3LS
☐	N953AN	B737-823/W	29539/741	3CH
☐	N953NN	B737-823/W	33328/4929	3LT
☐	N954AN	B737-823/W	30089/745	3CJ
☐	N954NN	B737-823/W	31197/4983	3LU
☐	N955AN	B737-823/W	29540/762	3CK
☐	N955NN	B737-823/W	31199/5033	3LV
☐	N956AN	B737-823/W	30090/764	3CL
☐	N956NN	B737-823/W	31200/5024	3LW
☐	N957AN	B737-823/W	29541/788	3CM
☐	N957NN	B737-823/W	31202/5071	3LX
☐	N958AN	B737-823/W	30091/797	3CN
☐	N958NN	B737-823/W	31203/5113	3LY
☐	N959AN	B737-823/W	30828/801	3CP
☐	N959NN	B737-823/W	33329/5142	3MA
☐	N960AN	B737-823/W	29542/818	3CR
☐	N960NN	B737-823/W	33330/5156	3MB
☐	N961AN	B737-823/W	30092/822	3CS
☐	N961NN	B737-823/W	31205/5171	3MC
☐	N962AN	B737-823/W	30858/825	3CT
☐	N962NN	B737-823/W	33331/5191	3MD
☐	N963AN	B737-823/W	29543/834	3CU
☐	N963NN	B737-823/W	31208/5207	3ME
☐	N964AN	B737-823/W	30093/837	3CV
☐	N964NN	B737-823/W	31210/5226	3MF
☐	N965AN	B737-823/W	29544/860	3CW
☐	N965NN	B737-823/W	33239/5251	3MG
☐	N966AN	B737-823/W	30094/863	3CX
☐	N966NN	B737-823/W	33240/5288	3MH
☐	N967AN	B737-823/W	29545/883	3CY
☐	N967NN	B737-823/W	31214/5304	3MJ
☐	N968AN	B737-823/W	30095/886	3DA
☐	N968NN	B737-823/W	33241/5348	3MK
☐	N969AN	B737-823/W	29546/910	3DB
☐	N969NN	B737-823/W	31215/5360	3ML
☐	N970AN	B737-823/W	30096/915	3DC
☐	N970NN	B737-823/W	31218/5394	3MM♦
☐	N971AN	B737-823/W	29547/937	3DD
☐	N971NN	B737-823/W	31217/5413	3MN♦
☐	N972AN	B737-823/W	30097/941	3DE
☐	N972NN	B737-823/W	33334/5449	3MP♦
☐	N973AN	B737-823/W	29548/971	3DF
☐	N973NN	B737-823/W	31219/5455	3MR♦
☐	N974AN	B737-823/W	30098/977	3DG
☐	N975AN	B737-823/W	29549/992	3DH
☐	N976AN	B737-823/W	30099/1001	3DJ
☐	N976NN	B737-823/W	33243/5521	3MU♦
☐	N977NN	B737-823/W	31225/5565	3MV♦
☐	N978AN	B737-823/W	30100/1022	3DL

	Reg	Type	c/n	Fleet
□	N978NN	B737-823/W	31226/5573	3MW♦
□	N979AN	B737-823/W	29568/2838	3DM
□	N979NN	B737-823/W	31228/5603	3MX♦
□	N980AN	B737-823/W	33203/2846	3DN
□	N980NN	B737-823/W	31229/5658	3MY♦
□	N981AN	B737-823/W	29569/2870	3DP
□	N981NN	B737-823/W	31230/5670	3NA♦
□	N982AN	B737-823/W	31067/2876	3DR
□	N982NN	B737-823/W	31231/5687	3NB♦
□	N983AN	B737-823/W	29570/2899	3DS
□	N983NN	B737-823/W	33337/5692	3NC♦
□	N984NN	B737-823/W	31234/5727	3ND♦
□	N985NN	B737-823/W	31233/5732	3NE♦
□	N986NN	B737-823/W	31236/5781	o/o♦
□	N987AN	B737-823/W	31069/2907	3DT
□	N987NN	B737-823/W	33247/5802	o/o♦
□	N988NN	B737-823/W	31237/5806	o/o♦
□	N989AN	B737-823/W	33205/2915	3DU
□	N990AN	B737-823/W	29563/2935	3DV
□	N991AN	B737-823/W	30920/2945	3DW
□	N992AN	B737-823/W	31071/2954	3DX
□	N	B737-823/W	31221	o/o
□	N	B737-823/W	31222	o/o
□	N	B737-823/W	31241	o/o♦
□	N	B737-823/W	31242	o/o♦
□	N	B737-823/W	31244	o/o♦
□	N	B737-823/W	31245	o/o♦
□	N	B737-823/W	31248	o/o♦
□	N	B737-823/W	31250	o/o♦
□	N	B737-823/W	31253	o/o♦
□	N	B737-823/W	31255	o/o♦
□	N	B737-823/W	31257	o/o♦
□	N175AN	B757-223/W	32394/992	5FK
□	N176AA	B757-223/W	32395/994	5FL
□	N177AN	B757-223/W	32396/996	5FM
□	N178AA	B757-223/W	32398/1002	5FN
□	N179AA	B757-223/W	32397/1000	5FP
□	N181AN	B757-223/W	29591/852	5EN
□	N182AN	B757-223/W	29592/853	5EP
□	N183AN	B757-223ER/W	29593/862	5ER
□	N184AN	B757-223ER/W	29594/866	5ES
□	N185AN	B757-223/W	32379/962	5ET
□	N186AN	B757-223/W	32380/964	5EU
□	N187AN	B757-223/W	32381/965	5EV
□	N188AN	B757-223/W	32382/969	5EW
□	N189AN	B757-223/W	32383/970	5EX
□	N190AA	B757-223/W	32384/973	5EY
□	N191AN	B757-223/W	32385/977	5FA
□	N192AN	B757-223/W	32386/979	5FB
□	N193AN	B757-223/W	32387/981	5FC
□	N194AA	B757-223/W	32388/983	5FD
□	N195AN	B757-223/W	32389/984	5FE
□	N196AA	B757-223/W	32390/986	5FF
□	N197AN	B757-223/W	32391/988	5FG
□	N198AA	B757-223/W	32392/989	5FH
□	N199AN	B757-223/W	32393/991	5FJ
□	N200UU	B757-2B7/W	27809/673	
□	N201UU	B757-2B7/W	27810/678	
□	N202UW	B757-2B7/W	27811/681	
□	N203UW	B757-23N/W	30548/930	
□	N204UW	B757-23N/W	30886/945	
□	N205UW	B757-23N/W	30887/946	
□	N206UW	B757-2B7/W	27808/666	
□	N207UW	B757-28A	32448/967	
□	N602AN	B757-223/W	27053/664	5DV
□	N606AA	B757-223/W	27057/707	5EA
□	N676AN	B757-223/W	29426/827	5EH
□	N677AN	B757-223/W	29427/828	5EJ♦
□	N678AN	B757-223/W	29428/837	5EK
□	N679AN	B757-223/W	29589/842	5EL
□	N688AA	B757-223ER/W	25730/548	5DF
□	N689AA	B757-223ER/W	25731/562	5DG
□	N691AA	B757-223ER/W	25697/568	5DJ
□	N692AA	B757-223/W	26972/578	5DK
□	N901AW	B757-2S7	23321/76	
□	N904AW	B757-2S7	23566/96	[GYR]
□	N906AW	B757-2S7	23568/99	
□	N908AW	B757-2G7/W	24233/244	
□	N909AW	B757-2G7/W	24522/252	
□	N910AW	B757-2G7/W	24523/256	
□	N935UW	B757-2B7/W	27201/605	
□	N936UW	B757-2B7/W	27244/607	
□	N937UW	B757-2B7/W	27245/630	
□	N938UW	B757-2B7/W	27246/643	
□	N939UW	B757-2B7/W	27303/647	
□	N940UW	B757-2B7/W	27805/655	
□	N941UW	B757-2B7/W	27806/657	
□	N942UW	B757-2B7/W	27807/662	
□	N342AN	B767-323ER/W	33081/896	342
□	N343AN	B767-323ER/W	33082/899	343
□	N344AN	B767-323ER/W	33083/900	344
□	N345AN	B767-323ER/W	33084/906	345
□	N346AN	B767-323ER/W	33085/907	346
□	N347AN	B767-323ER/W	33086/908	347
□	N348AN	B767-323ER/W	33087/910	348
□	N349AN	B767-323ER/W	33088/913	349
□	N350AN	B767-323ER/W	33089/916	350
□	N351AA	B767-323ER/W	24032/202	351
□	N353AA	B767-323ER/W	24034/206	353
□	N354AA	B767-323ER/W	24035/211	354
□	N361AA	B767-323ER/W	24042/235	361
□	N362AA	B767-323ER/W	24043/237	362
□	N368AA	B767-323ER	25195/404	368
□	N369AA	B767-323ER	25196/422	369
□	N373AA	B767-323ER/W	25200/435	373
□	N377AN	B767-323ER/W	25446/453	377
□	N379AA	B767-323ER/W	25448/481	379
□	N380AN	B767-323ER/W	25449/489	380
□	N381AN	B767-323ER/W	25450/495	381
□	N382AN	B767-323ER/W	25451/498	382
□	N383AN	B767-323ER/W	26995/500	383
□	N384AA	B767-323ER/W	26996/512	384
□	N385AM	B767-323ER/W	27059/536	385
□	N387AM	B767-323ER/W	27184/541	387
□	N388AA	B767-323ER/W	27448/563	388
□	N389AA	B767-323ER/W	27449/564	389
□	N390AA	B767-323ER/W	27450/565	390
□	N391AA	B767-323ER/W	27451/566	391
□	N392AN	B767-323ER/W	29429/700	392
□	N393AN	B767-323ER/W	29430/701	393
□	N394AN	B767-323ER/W	29431/703	394
□	N395AN	B767-323ER/W	29432/709	[BFM]
□	N396AN	B767-323ER/W	29603/739	396
□	N397AN	B767-323ER/W	29604/744	397
□	N398AN	B767-323ER/W	29605/748	398
□	N399AN	B767-323ER/W	29606/752	399
□	N39356	B767-323ER/W	24037/226	356
□	N39365	B767-323ER/W	24046/241	365
□	N39367	B767-323ER	25194/394	367
□	N750AN	B777-223ER	30259/332	7BJ
□	N751AN	B777-223ER	30798/333	7BK
□	N752AN	B777-223ER	30260/339	7BL

	Reg.	Type	c/n	Fleet
☐	N753AN	B777-223ER	30261/341	7BM
☐	N754AN	B777-223ER	30262/345	7BN
☐	N755AN	B777-223ER	30263/354	7BP
☐	N756AM	B777-223ER	30264/358	7BR
☐	N757AN	B777-223ER	32636/363	7BS
☐	N758AN	B777-223ER	32637/371	7BT
☐	N759AN	B777-223ER	32638/376	7BU
☐	N760AN	B777-223ER	31477/379	7BV
☐	N761AJ	B777-223ER	31478/393	7BW
☐	N762AN	B777-223ER	31479/399	7BX
☐	N765AN	B777-223ER	32879/433	7BY
☐	N766AN	B777-223ER	32880/445	7CA
☐	N767AJ	B777-223ER	33539/555	7CB
☐	N768AA	B777-223ER	33540/566	7CC
☐	N770AN	B777-223ER	29578/185	7AA
☐	N771AN	B777-223ER	29579/190	7AB
☐	N772AN	B777-223ER	29580/198	7AC
☐	N773AN	B777-223ER	29583/199	7AD
☐	N774AN	B777-223ER	29581/208	7AE
☐	N775AN	B777-223ER	29584/209	7AF
☐	N776AN	B777-223ER	29582/215	7AG
☐	N777AN	B777-223ER	29585/218	7AH
☐	N778AN	B777-223ER	29587/223	7AJ
☐	N779AN	B777-223ER	29955/225	7AK
☐	N780AN	B777-223ER	29956/241	7AL
☐	N781AN	B777-223ER	29586/266	7AM
☐	N782AN	B777-223ER	30003/270	7AN
☐	N783AN	B777-223ER	30004/271	7AP
☐	N784AN	B777-223ER	29588/272	7AR
☐	N785AN	B777-223ER	30005/274	7AS
☐	N786AN	B777-223ER	30250/276	7AT
☐	N787AL	B777-223ER	30010/277	7AU
☐	N788AN	B777-223ER	30011/283	7AV
☐	N789AN	B777-223ER	30252/285	7AW
☐	N790AN	B777-223ER	30251/287	7AX
☐	N791AN	B777-223ER	30254/289	7AY
☐	N792AN	B777-223ER	30253/292	7BA
☐	N793AN	B777-223ER	30255/299	7BB
☐	N794AN	B777-223ER	30256/313	7BC
☐	N795AN	B777-223ER	30257/315	7BD
☐	N796AN	B777-223ER	30796/316	7BE
☐	N797AN	B777-223ER	30012/321	7BF
☐	N798AN	B777-223ER	30797/324	7BG
☐	N799AN	B777-223ER	30258/328	7BH
☐	N717AN	B777-323ER	31543/1053	7LA
☐	N718AN	B777-323ER	41665/1062	7LB
☐	N719AN	B777-323ER	41668/1070	7LC
☐	N720AN	B777-323ER	33522/1075	7LD
☐	N721AN	B777-323ER	31546/1083	7LE
☐	N722AN	B777-323ER	31547/1095	7LF
☐	N723AN	B777-323ER	33125/1103	7LG
☐	N724AN	B777-323ER	31548/1113	7LH
☐	N725AN	B777-323ER	41666/1122	7LJ
☐	N726AN	B777-323ER	31550/1160	7LK
☐	N727AN	B777-323ER	33541/1176	7LL
☐	N728AN	B777-323ER	31553/1191	7LM
☐	N729AN	B777-323ER	33127/1200	7LN
☐	N730AN	B777-323ER	31554/1217	7LP
☐	N731AN	B777-323ER	33523/1241	7LR
☐	N732AN	B777-323ER	31549/1257	7LS
☐	N733AR	B777-323ER	33524/1270	7LT
☐	N734AR	B777-323ER	31480/1344	7LU♦
☐	N735AT	B777-323ER	32439/1371	7LV♦
☐	N736AT	B777-323ER	33538/1377	o/o♦
☐	N	B777-323ER	41669	o/o
☐	N800AN	B787-8	40618/241	8AA

	Reg.	Type	c/n	Fleet
☐	N801AC	B787-8	40619/249	8AB
☐	N802AN	B787-8	40620/255	8AC
☐	N803AL	B787-8	40621/268	8AD
☐	N804AN	B787-8	40622/288	8AE
☐	N805AN	B787-8	40623/290	8AF
☐	N806AA	B787-8	40624/306	8AG
☐	N807AA	B787-8	40625/320	8AH
☐	N808AN	B787-8	40626/326	8AJ
☐	N809AA	B787-8	40627/336	8AK
☐	N810AN	B787-8	40628/339	8AL♦
☐	N811AB	B787-8	40629/364	8AM♦
☐	N812AA	B787-8	40630/378	8AN♦
☐	N813AN	B787-8	40631/387	8AP♦
☐	N814AA	B787-8	40632/389	o/o♦
☐	N815AA	B787-8	40633/423	o/o♦
☐	N816AA	B787-8	40634/429	o/o♦
☐	N817AN	B787-8	40635/519	o/o♦
☐	N	B787-9	40639/466	o/o♦
☐	N	B787-9	40640/478	o/o♦
☐	N	B787-9	40641/503	o/o♦
☐	N	B787-9	40642/485	o/o♦
☐	N	B787-9	40643/510	o/o♦
☐	N	B787-9	40644/517	o/o♦
☐	N944UW	ERJ-190AR	19000058	
☐	N945UW	ERJ-190AR	19000062	
☐	N946UW	ERJ-190AR	19000072	
☐	N947UW	ERJ-190AR	19000078	
☐	N948UW	ERJ-190AR	19000081	
☐	N949UW	ERJ-190AR	19000102	
☐	N950UW	ERJ-190AR	19000106	
☐	N951UW	ERJ-190AR	19000112	
☐	N952UW	ERJ-190AR	19000119	
☐	N953UW	ERJ-190AR	19000133	
☐	N954UW	ERJ-190AR	19000139	
☐	N955UW	ERJ-190AR	19000152	
☐	N956UW	ERJ-190AR	19000156	
☐	N957UW	ERJ-190AR	19000161	
☐	N958UW	ERJ-190AR	19000164	
☐	N959UW	ERJ-190AR	19000166	
☐	N961UW	ERJ-190AR	19000183	
☐	N963UW	ERJ-190AR	19000191	
☐	N965UW	ERJ-190AR	19000198	
☐	N967UW	ERJ-190AR	19000211	
☐	N403A	MD-82	49314/1256	403
☐	N424AA	MD-82	49336/1321	424
☐	N426AA	MD-82	49338/1327	426
☐	N434AA	MD-83	49452/1389	434
☐	N436AA	MD-83	49454/1391	436
☐	N437AA	MD-83	49455/1392	437
☐	N438AA	MD-83	49456/1393	438
☐	N439AA	MD-83	49457/1398	439
☐	N466AA	MD-82	49596/1510	466
☐	N467AA	MD-82	49597/1511	467
☐	N468AA	MD-82	49598/1513	468
☐	N469AA	MD-82	49599/1515	469
☐	N470AA	MD-82	49600/1516	470
☐	N471AA	MD-82	49601/1518	471
☐	N472AA	MD-82	49647/1520	472
☐	N473AA	MD-82	49648/1521	473
☐	N474	MD-82	49649/1526	474
☐	N475AA	MD-82	49650/1527	475
☐	N477AA	MD-82	49652/1529	477
☐	N479AA	MD-82	49654/1535	479
☐	N480AA	MD-82	49655/1536	480
☐	N481AA	MD-82	49656/1545	481

☐ N482AA	MD-82	49675/1546	482
☐ N483A	MD-82	49676/1550	483
☐ N484AA	MD-82	49677/1551	484
☐ N485AA	MD-82	49678/1555	485
☐ N486AA	MD-82	49679/1557	486
☐ N487AA	MD-82	49680/1558	487
☐ N488AA	MD-82	49681/1560	488
☐ N489AA	MD-82	49682/1562	489
☐ N493AA	MD-82	49731/1566	493
☐ N494AA	MD-82	49732/1567	494
☐ N499AA	MD-82	49737/1641	499
☐ N501AA	MD-82	49738/1648	501
☐ N513AA	MD-82	49890/1686	513
☐ N555AN	MD-82	53085/1839	555
☐ N564AA	MD-83	49346/1372	564
☐ N565AA	MD-83	49347/1373	565
☐ N566AA	MD-83	49348/1374	566
☐ N570AA	MD-83	49352/1386	570
☐ N571AA	MD-83	49353/1387	571
☐ N590AA	MD-83	53253/1919	590
☐ N954U	MD-82	49426/1399	4UB
☐ N955U	MD-82	49427/1401	4UC
☐ N961TW	MD-83	53611/2264	4XT
☐ N962TW	MD-83	53612/2265	4XU
☐ N963TW	MD-83	53613/2266	4XV
☐ N964TW	MD-83	53614/2267	4XW
☐ N965TW	MD-83	53615/2268	4XX
☐ N966TW	MD-83	53616/2269	4XY
☐ N967TW	MD-83	53617/2270	4YA
☐ N968TW	MD-83	53618/2271	4YB
☐ N969TW	MD-83	53619/2272	4YC
☐ N970TW	MD-83	53620/2273	4YD
☐ N971TW	MD-83	53621/2274	4YE
☐ N972TW	MD-83	53622/2275	4YF
☐ N979TW	MD-83	53629/2282	4YN
☐ N980TW	MD-83	53630/2283	4YP
☐ N982TW	MD-83	53632/2285	4YR
☐ N983TW	MD-83	53633/2286	4YS
☐ N984TW	MD-83	53634/2287	4YT
☐ N7514A	MD-82	49891/1694	514
☐ N7520A	MD-82	49897/1708	520
☐ N7528A	MD-82	49920/1750	528
☐ N7541A	MD-82	49995/1791	541
☐ N7547A	MD-82	53029/1814	547
☐ N7548A	MD-82	53030/1816	548
☐ N7550	MD-82	53032/1820	550
☐ N9401W	MD-83	53137/1872	4WJ
☐ N9402W	MD-83	53138/1886	4WK
☐ N9403W	MD-83	53139/1899	4WL
☐ N9404V	MD-83	53140/1923	4WM
☐ N9405T	MD-83	53141/1935	4WN
☐ N9409F	MD-83	53121/1971	4WT
☐ N9615W	MD-83	53562/2192	4XB
☐ N9616G	MD-83	53563/2196	4XC
☐ N9617R	MD-83	53564/2199	4XD
☐ N9618A	MD-83	53565/2201	4XE
☐ N9619V	MD-83	53566/2206	4XF
☐ N9620D	MD-83	53591/2208	4XG
☐ N9621A	MD-83	53592/2234	4XH
☐ N9622A	MD-83	53593/2239	4XJ
☐ N9624T	MD-83	53594/2241	4XK
☐ N9625W	MD-83	53595/2244	4XL
☐ N9626F	MD-83	53596//2247	4XM
☐ N9628W	MD-83	53598/2252	4XP
☐ N9629H	MD-83	53599/2254	4XR
☐ N9630A	MD-83	53561/2174	4XS
☐ N9677W	MD-83	53627/2280	4YL
☐ N9681B	MD-83	53631/2284	4XT
☐ N33502	MD-82	49739/1649	502
☐ N70425	MD-82	49337/1325	425
☐ N70504	MD-82	49798/1651	504

AMERICAN EAGLE — MQ / EGF

Incorporating US Airways Express.

☐ N202PS	CRJ-200ER	7858	202
☐ N206PS	CRJ-200ER	7860	206
☐ N207PS	CRJ-200ER	7873	207
☐ N209PS	CRJ-200ER	7874	209
☐ N213PS	CRJ-200ER	7879	213
☐ N215PS	CRJ-200ER	7880	215
☐ N216PS	CRJ-200ER	7882	216
☐ N218PS	CRJ-200ER	7885	218
☐ N220PS	CRJ-200ER	7887	220
☐ N221PS	CRJ-200ER	7889	221
☐ N223JS	CRJ-200ER	7892	223
☐ N226JS	CRJ-200ER	7895	226
☐ N228PS	CRJ-200ER	7897	228
☐ N229PS	CRJ-200ER	7898	229
☐ N230PS	CRJ-200ER	7904	230
☐ N237PS	CRJ-200ER	7906	237
☐ N241PS	CRJ-200ER	7909	241
☐ N242JS	CRJ-200ER	7911	242
☐ N244PS	CRJ-200ER	7912	244
☐ N245PS	CRJ-200ER	7919	245
☐ N246PS	CRJ-200ER	7920	246
☐ N247JS	CRJ-200ER	7922	247
☐ N248PS	CRJ-200ER	7925	248
☐ N249PS	CRJ-200ER	7926	249
☐ N250PS	CRJ-200ER	7929	250
☐ N251PS	CRJ-200ER	7931	251
☐ N253PS	CRJ-200ER	7934	253
☐ N254PS	CRJ-200ER	7935	254
☐ N256PS	CRJ-200ER	7937	256
☐ N257PS	CRJ-200ER	7939	257
☐ N258PS	CRJ-200ER	7941	258
☐ N259PS	CRJ-200ER	7945	259
☐ N260JS	CRJ-200ER	7957	260
☐ N261PS	CRJ-200ER	7959	261
☐ N262PS	CRJ-200ER	7962	262
☐ N401AW	CRJ-200LR	7280	401
☐ N402AW	CRJ-200LR	7281	402
☐ N403AW	CRJ-200LR	7288	403
☐ N404AW	CRJ-200LR	7294	404
☐ N405AW	CRJ-200LR	7362	405
☐ N406AW	CRJ-200LR	7402	406
☐ N407AW	CRJ-200LR	7424	407
☐ N408AW	CRJ-200LR	7568	408
☐ N409AW	CRJ-200LR	7447	409
☐ N410AW	CRJ-200LR	7490	410
☐ N411ZW	CRJ-200LR	7569	411
☐ N412AW	CRJ-200LR	7582	412
☐ N413AW	CRJ-200LR	7585	413
☐ N414ZW	CRJ-200LR	7586	414
☐ N415AW	CRJ-200LR	7593	415
☐ N416AW	CRJ-200LR	7603	416
☐ N417AW	CRJ-200LR	7610	417
☐ N417SW	CRJ-200ER	7400	
☐ N418AW	CRJ-200LR	7618	418
☐ N419AW	CRJ-200LR	7633	419
☐ N420AW	CRJ-200LR	7640	420
☐ N421ZW	CRJ-200LR	7346	421
☐ N422AW	CRJ-200LR	7341	422
☐ N423AW	CRJ-200LR	7636	423

☐	N423SW	CRJ-200ER	7456	
☐	N424AW	CRJ-200LR	7656	424
☐	N425AW	CRJ-200LR	7663	425
☐	N426AW	CRJ-200LR	7669	426
☐	N427ZW	CRJ-200LR	7685	427
☐	N428AW	CRJ-200LR	7695	428
☐	N429AW	CRJ-200LR	7711	429
☐	N430AW	CRJ-200LR	7719	430
☐	N431AW	CRJ-200LR	7256	431
☐	N432AW	CRJ-200LR	7257	432
☐	N433AW	CRJ-200LR	7289	433
☐	N434AW	CRJ-200LR	7322	434
☐	N435AW	CRJ-200LR	7724	435
☐	N435SW	CRJ-200ER	7555	
☐	N436AW	CRJ-200LR	7734	436
☐	N437AW	CRJ-200LR	7744	437
☐	N438AW	CRJ-200LR	7748	438
☐	N439AW	CRJ-200LR	7753	439
☐	N440AW	CRJ-200LR	7766	440
☐	N441ZW	CRJ-200LR	7777	441
☐	N442AW	CRJ-200LR	7778	442
☐	N443AW	CRJ-200LR	7781	443
☐	N444ZW	CRJ-200LR	7788	444
☐	N445AW	CRJ-200LR	7804	445
☐	N446AW	CRJ-200LR	7806	446
☐	N447AW	CRJ-200LR	7812	447
☐	N448AW	CRJ-200LR	7814	448
☐	N449AW	CRJ-200LR	7818	449
☐	N450AW	CRJ-200LR	7823	450
☐	N451AW	CRJ-200LR	7832	451
☐	N452AW	CRJ-200LR	7835	452
☐	N453AW	CRJ-200LR	7838	453
☐	N454AW	CRJ-200LR	7842	454
☐	N455AW	CRJ-200LR	7848	455
☐	N456ZW	CRJ-200LR	7849	456
☐	N457AW	CRJ-200LR	7854	457
☐	N458AW	CRJ-200LR	7861	458
☐	N459AW	CRJ-200LR	7863	459
☐	N460AW	CRJ-200LR	7867	460
☐	N461AW	CRJ-200LR	7870	461
☐	N462AW	CRJ-200LR	7875	462
☐	N463AW	CRJ-200LR	7878	463
☐	N464AW	CRJ-200LR	7890	464
☐	N464SW	CRJ-200ER	7827	
☐	N465AW	CRJ-200LR	7893	465
☐	N466AW	CRJ-200LR	7899	466
☐	N467AW	CRJ-200LR	7900	467
☐	N468AW	CRJ-200LR	7916	468
☐	N469AW	CRJ-200LR	7917	469
☐	N470ZW	CRJ-200LR	7927	470
☐	N471ZW	CRJ-200ER	7457	471
☐	N492SW	CRJ-200ER	7168	
☐	N821AS	CRJ-200ER	7194	
☐	N862AS	CRJ-200ER	7476	
☐	N863AS	CRJ-200ER	7487	
☐	N864AS	CRJ-200ER	7502	
☐	N866AS	CRJ-200ER	7517	
☐	N868CA	CRJ-200ER	7427	
☐	N869AS	CRJ-200ER	7479	
☐	N875AS	CRJ-200ER	7559	
☐	N876AS	CRJ-200ER	7576	
☐	N877AS	CRJ-200ER	7579	
☐	N879AS	CRJ-200ER	7600	
☐	N880AS	CRJ-200ER	7606	
☐	N901EV	CRJ-200ER	7616	
☐	N902EV	CRJ-200ER	7620	
☐	N903EV	CRJ-200ER	7621	
☐	N904EV	CRJ-200ER	7628	
☐	N905EV	CRJ-200ER	7632	
☐	N906EV	CRJ-200ER	7642	
☐	N906SW	CRJ-200ER	7510	
☐	N907EV	CRJ-200ER	7648	
☐	N907SW	CRJ-200ER	7511	
☐	N908EV	CRJ-200ER	7654	
☐	N909EV	CRJ-200ER	7658	
☐	N955SW	CRJ-200ER	7817	

☐	N500AE	CRJ-701ER	10025	500
☐	N501BG	CRJ-701ER	10017	501
☐	N502AE	CRJ-701ER	10018	502
☐	N503AE	CRJ-701ER	10021	503
☐	N504AE	CRJ-701ER	10044	544
☐	N505AE	CRJ-701ER	10053	505
☐	N506AE	CRJ-701ER	10056	506
☐	N507AE	CRJ-701ER	10059	507
☐	N508AE	CRJ-701ER	10072	508
☐	N509AE	CRJ-701ER	10078	509
☐	N510AE	CRJ-701ER	10105	510
☐	N511AE	CRJ-701ER	10107	511
☐	N512AE	CRJ-701ER	10110	512
☐	N513AE	CRJ-701ER	10114	513
☐	N514AE	CRJ-701ER	10119	514
☐	N515AE	CRJ-701ER	10121	515
☐	N516AE	CRJ-701ER	10123	516
☐	N517AE	CRJ-701ER	10124	517
☐	N518AE	CRJ-701ER	10126	518
☐	N519AE	CRJ-701ER	10131	519
☐	N520DC	CRJ-701ER	10140	520
☐	N521AE	CRJ-701ER	10142	521
☐	N522AE	CRJ-701ER	10147	522
☐	N523AE	CRJ-701ER	10152	523
☐	N524AE	CRJ-701ER	10154	524
☐	N525AE	CRJ-702ER NG	10302	525
☐	N526EA	CRJ-702ER NG	10304	526
☐	N527EA	CRJ-702ER NG	10305	527
☐	N528EG	CRJ-702ER NG	10306	528
☐	N529EA	CRJ-702ER NG	10307	529
☐	N530EA	CRJ-702ER NG	10308	530
☐	N531EG	CRJ-702ER NG	10309	531
☐	N532EA	CRJ-702ER NG	10310	532
☐	N533AE	CRJ-702ER NG	10311	533
☐	N534AE	CRJ-702ER NG	10312	534
☐	N535EA	CRJ-702ER NG	10313	535
☐	N536EA	CRJ-702ER NG	10315	536
☐	N537EA	CRJ-702ER NG	10316	537
☐	N538EG	CRJ-702ER NG	10317	538
☐	N539EA	CRJ-702ER NG	10318	539
☐	N540EG	CRJ-702ER NG	10319	540
☐	N541EA	CRJ-702ER NG	10320	541
☐	N542EA	CRJ-702ER NG	10321	542
☐	N543EA	CRJ-702ER NG	10323	543
☐	N544EA	CRJ-702ER NG	10324	544
☐	N545PB	CRJ-702ER NG	10325	545
☐	N546FF	CRJ-702ER NG	10326	546
☐	N702PS	CRJ-701ER	10135	702
☐	N703PS	CRJ-701ER	10137	703
☐	N705PS	CRJ-701ER	10144	705
☐	N706PS	CRJ-701ER	10150	706
☐	N708PS	CRJ-701ER	10160	708
☐	N709PS	CRJ-701ER	10165	709
☐	N710PS	CRJ-701ER	10167	710
☐	N712PS	CRJ-701ER	10168	712
☐	N716PS	CRJ-701ER	10171	716
☐	N718PS	CRJ-701ER	10175	718

☐	N719PS	CRJ-701ER	10177	719
☐	N720PS	CRJ-701ER	10178	720
☐	N723PS	CRJ-701ER	10181	723
☐	N725PS	CRJ-701ER	10186	725
☐	N241LR	CRJ-900ER	15066	
☐	N242LR	CRJ-900ER	15076	
☐	N243LR	CRJ-900LR	15064	
☐	N244LR	CRJ-900LR	15233	
☐	N245LR	CRJ-900LR	15234	
☐	N246LR	CRJ-900LR	15239	
☐	N247LR	CRJ-900LR	15273	
☐	N248LR	CRJ-900LR	15274	
☐	N249LR	CRJ-900LR	15275	
☐	N326MS	CRJ-900LR	15124	
☐	N329MS	CRJ-900LR	15126	
☐	N547NN	CRJ-900LR	15317	
☐	N548NN	CRJ-900LR	15318	
☐	N549NN	CRJ-900LR	15322	
☐	N550NN	CRJ-900LR	15323	
☐	N551NN	CRJ-900LR	15327	
☐	N552NN	CRJ-900LR	15328	
☐	N553NN	CRJ-900LR	15333	
☐	N554NN	CRJ-900LR	15334	
☐	N555NN	CRJ-900LR	15338	
☐	N556NN	CRJ-900LR	15339	
☐	N557NN	CRJ-900LR	15340	557
☐	N558NN	CRJ-900LR	15342	558
☐	N559NN	CRJ-900LR	15343	559
☐	N560NN	CRJ-900LR	15345	560
☐	N561NN	CRJ-900LR	15346	561
☐	N562NN	CRJ-900LR	15347	562
☐	N563NN	CRJ-900LR	15350	
☐	N564NN	CRJ-900LR	15351	
☐	N565NN	CRJ-900LR	15352	
☐	N566NN	CRJ-900LR	15353	
☐	N567NN	CRJ-900LR	15354	
☐	N568NN	CRJ-900LR	15355	
☐	N569NN	CRJ-900LR	15356	
☐	N570NN	CRJ-900LR	15357	
☐	N571NN	CRJ-900LR	15360	♦
☐	N572NN	CRJ-900LR	15361	♦
☐	N573NN	CRJ-900LR	15362	♦
☐	N574NN	CRJ-900LR	15365	♦
☐	N575NN	CRJ-900LR	15366	♦
☐	N576NN	CRJ-900LR	15367	♦
☐	N577NN	CRJ-900LR	15380	♦
☐	N578NN	CRJ-900LR	15381	♦
☐	N579NN	CRJ-900LR	15382	♦
☐	N580NN	CRJ-900LR	15383	580♦
☐	N581NN	CRJ-900LR	15384	♦
☐	N582NN	CRJ-900LR	15385	♦
☐	N583NN	CRJ-900LR	15386	♦
☐	N584NN	CRJ-900LR	15387	♦
☐	N585NN	CRJ-900LR	15388	♦
☐	N896SK	CRJ-900ER	15102	
☐	N897SK	CRJ-900ER	15103	
☐	N898SK	CRJ-900ER	15110	
☐	N899SK	CRJ-900ER	15112	
☐	N902FJ	CRJ-900ER	15002	
☐	N903FJ	CRJ-900ER	15003	
☐	N904FJ	CRJ-900ER	15004	
☐	N905J	CRJ-900ER	15005	
☐	N906FJ	CRJ-900ER	15006	
☐	N907FJ	CRJ-900ER	15007	
☐	N908FJ	CRJ-900ER	15008	
☐	N909FJ	CRJ-900ER	15009	

☐	N910FJ	CRJ-900ER	15010	
☐	N911FJ	CRJ-900ER	15011	
☐	N912FJ	CRJ-900ER	15012	
☐	N913FJ	CRJ-900ER	15013	
☐	N914FJ	CRJ-900ER	15014	
☐	N915FJ	CRJ-900ER	15015	
☐	N916FJ	CRJ-900ER	15016	
☐	N917FJ	CRJ-900ER	15017	
☐	N918FJ	CRJ-900ER	15018	
☐	N919FJ	CRJ-900ER	15019	
☐	N920FJ	CRJ-900ER	15020	
☐	N921FJ	CRJ-900ER	15021	
☐	N922FJ	CRJ-900ER	15022	
☐	N923FJ	CRJ-900ER	15023	
☐	N924FJ	CRJ-900ER	15024	
☐	N925FJ	CRJ-900ER	15025	
☐	N926LR	CRJ-900ER	15026	
☐	N927LR	CRJ-900ER	15027	
☐	N928LR	CRJ-900ER	15028	
☐	N929LR	CRJ-900ER	15029	
☐	N930LR	CRJ-900ER	15030	
☐	N931LR	CRJ-900ER	15031	
☐	N932LR	CRJ-900ER	15032	
☐	N933LR	CRJ-900ER	15033	
☐	N934FJ	CRJ-900ER	15034	
☐	N935LR	CRJ-900ER	15035	
☐	N938LR	CRJ-900ER	15038	
☐	N939LR	CRJ-900ER	15039	
☐	N942LR	CRJ-900ER	15042	
☐	N943LR	CRJ-900ER	15068	
☐	N944LR	CRJ-900ER	15075	
☐	N945LR	CRJ-900ER	15077	
☐	N946LR	CRJ-900ER	15104	
☐	N947LR	CRJ-900ER	15116	
☐	N948LR	CRJ-900ER	15118	
☐	N950LR	CRJ-900ER	15119	
☐	N951LR	CRJ-900ER	15123	
☐	N952LR	CRJ-900LR	15373	♦
☐	N953LR	CRJ-900LR	15374	♦
☐	N954LR	CRJ-900LR	15375	♦
☐	N955LR	CRJ-900LR	15376	♦
☐	N956LR	CRJ-900ER	15056	
☐	N957LR	CRJ-900LR	15377	♦
☐	N958LR	CRJ-900LR	15378	♦
☐	N959LR	CRJ-900LR	15379	♦
☐	N326EN	DHC-8-311	234	HDF
☐	N327EN	DHC-8-311A	261	HDD
☐	N328EN	DHC-8-311A	281	HDC
☐	N329EN	DHC-8-311	290	HDG
☐	N330EN	DHC-8-311A	274	HDI
☐	N331EN	DHC-8-311A	279	HDJ
☐	N333EN	DHC-8-311	221	HDK
☐	N335EN	DHC-8-311	375	HDN
☐	N336EN	DHC-8-311A	336	HAD
☐	N337EN	DHC-8-311A	284	HDH
☐	N343EN	DHC-8-311A	340	HDE
☐	N804EX	DHC-8-102A	227	ESA
☐	N805EX	DHC-8-102A	228	ESB
☐	N806EX	DHC-8-102A	263	ESC
☐	N807EX	DHC-8-102A	292	ESD
☐	N808EX	DHC-8-102A	299	ESE
☐	N809EX	DHC-8-102A	302	ESF
☐	N810EX	DHC-8-102A	308	ESG
☐	N812EX	DHC-8-102A	312	ESH
☐	N814EX	DHC-8-102A	318	ESI
☐	N815EX	DHC-8-102A	321	ESJ

☐	N816EX	DHC-8-102A	329	ESK
☐	N837EX	DHC-8-102A	217	ERH
☐	N838EX	DHC-8-102A	220	ERK
☐	N839EX	DHC-8-102A	226	
☐	N914HA	DHC-8-102	053	HSH
☐	N930HA	DHC-8-102	126	HSW
☐	N931HA	DHC-8-102	132	HSZ
☐	N933HA	DHC-8-102	134	HBA
☐	N934HA	DHC-8-102	139	HBB
☐	N935HA	DHC-8-102	142	HBC
☐	N936HA	DHC-8-102	145	HRA
☐	N937HA	DHC-8-102	148	HRB
☐	N938HA	DHC-8-102	152	HRC
☐	N940HA	DHC-8-102	156	HRE
☐	N941HA	DHC-8-102	161	HRF
☐	N942HA	DHC-8-102	163	HRG
☐	N943HA	DHC-8-102	167	HRH
☐	N975HA	DHC-8-201	176	
☐	N800AE	ERJ-140LR	145425	[SJT]
☐	N801AE	ERJ-140LR	145469	[SJT]
☐	N802AE	ERJ-140LR	145471	[SJT]
☐	N803AE	ERJ-140LR	145483	[SJT]
☐	N804AE	ERJ-140LR	145487	[SJT]
☐	N805AE	ERJ-140LR	145489	[SJT]
☐	N806AE	ERJ-140LR	145503	std
☐	N807AE	ERJ-140LR	145506	[SJT]
☐	N808AE	ERJ-140LR	145519	808
☐	N809AE	ERJ-140LR	145521	809
☐	N810AE	ERJ-140LR	145525	[SJT]
☐	N811AE	ERJ-140LR	145529	[SJT]
☐	N812AE	ERJ-140LR	145531	[SJT]
☐	N813AE	ERJ-140LR	145539	813
☐	N814AE	ERJ-140LR	145541	[SJT]
☐	N815AE	ERJ-140LR	145545	std
☐	N816AE	ERJ-140LR	145552	[SJT]
☐	N817AE	ERJ-140LR	145554	std
☐	N818AE	ERJ-140LR	145561	818
☐	N819AE	ERJ-140LR	145566	819
☐	N820AE	ERJ-140LR	145576	std
☐	N821AE	ERJ-140LR	145577	std
☐	N822AE	ERJ-140LR	145581	std
☐	N823AE	ERJ-140LR	145582	[SJT]
☐	N824AE	ERJ-140LR	145584	824
☐	N825AE	ERJ-140LR	145589	std
☐	N826AE	ERJ-140LR	145592	std
☐	N827AE	ERJ-140LR	145602	827
☐	N828AE	ERJ-140LR	145604	[SJT]
☐	N829AE	ERJ-140LR	145609	[SJT]
☐	N830AE	ERJ-140LR	145615	830
☐	N831AE	ERJ-140LR	145616	831
☐	N832AE	ERJ-140LR	145627	[SJT]
☐	N833AE	ERJ-140LR	145629	833
☐	N834AE	ERJ-140LR	145631	[SJT]
☐	N835AE	ERJ-140LR	145634	[SJT]
☐	N836AE	ERJ-140LR	145635	836
☐	N837AE	ERJ-140LR	145647	[SJT]
☐	N838AE	ERJ-140LR	145651	838
☐	N839AE	ERJ-140LR	145653	[SJT]
☐	N840AE	ERJ-140LR	145656	[SJT]
☐	N841AE	ERJ-140LR	145667	[SJT]
☐	N842AE	ERJ-140LR	145673	[SJT]
☐	N843AE	ERJ-140LR	145680	843
☐	N844AE	ERJ-140LR	145682	[SJT]
☐	N845AE	ERJ-140LR	145685	845
☐	N846AE	ERJ-140LR	145692	[SJT]
☐	N847AE	ERJ-140LR	145707	[SJT]

☐	N848AE	ERJ-140LR	145710	[SJT]
☐	N849AE	ERJ-140LR	145716	[SJT]
☐	N850AE	ERJ-140LR	145722	[SJT]
☐	N851AE	ERJ-140LR	145734	[SJT]
☐	N852AE	ERJ-140LR	145736	[SJT]
☐	N853AE	ERJ-140LR	145742	[SJT]
☐	N854AE	ERJ-140LR	145743	[SJT]
☐	N855AE	ERJ-140LR	145747	std
☐	N856AE	ERJ-140LR	145748	856
☐	N857AE	ERJ-140LR	145752	[SJT]
☐	N858AE	ERJ-140LR	145754	[SJT]
☐	N600BP	ERJ-145LR	145044	600
☐	N601DW	ERJ-145LR	145046	601
☐	N602AE	ERJ-145LR	145048	602
☐	N603KC	ERJ-145LR	145055	603
☐	N604AE	ERJ-145LR	145058	604
☐	N605KS	ERJ-145LR	145059	605
☐	N606AE	ERJ-145LR	145062	606
☐	N607AE	ERJ-145LR	145064	607
☐	N608LM	ERJ-145LR	145068	608
☐	N609DP	ERJ-145LR	145069	609
☐	N610AE	ERJ-145LR	145073	610
☐	N611AE	ERJ-145LR	145074	611
☐	N612AE	ERJ-145LR	145079	612
☐	N613AE	ERJ-145LR	145081	613
☐	N614AE	ERJ-145LR	145086	614
☐	N615AE	ERJ-145LR	145087	615
☐	N616AE	ERJ-145LR	145092	616
☐	N617AE	ERJ-145LR	145093	617
☐	N618AE	ERJ-145LR	145097	618
☐	N619AE	ERJ-145LR	145101	619
☐	N620AE	ERJ-145LR	145102	620
☐	N621AE	ERJ-145LR	145105	
☐	N622AE	ERJ-145LR	145108	
☐	N623AE	ERJ-145LR	145109	
☐	N624AE	ERJ-145LR	145111	
☐	N625AE	ERJ-145LR	145115	
☐	N626AE	ERJ-145LR	145117	
☐	N627AE	ERJ-145LR	145121	
☐	N628AE	ERJ-145LR	145124	
☐	N629AE	ERJ-145LR	145130	
☐	N630AE	ERJ-145LR	145132	
☐	N631AE	ERJ-145LR	145139	
☐	N632AE	ERJ-145LR	145143	
☐	N633AE	ERJ-145LR	145148	
☐	N634AE	ERJ-145LR	145150	
☐	N635AE	ERJ-145LR	145158	
☐	N636AE	ERJ-145LR	145160	
☐	N637AE	ERJ-145LR	145170	
☐	N638AE	ERJ-145LR	145172	
☐	N639AE	ERJ-145LR	145182	
☐	N640AE	ERJ-145LR	145183	
☐	N641AE	ERJ-145LR	145191	
☐	N642AE	ERJ-145LR	145193	
☐	N643AE	ERJ-145LR	145200	
☐	N644AE	ERJ-145LR	145204	
☐	N645AE	ERJ-145LR	145212	
☐	N646AE	ERJ-145LR	145213	
☐	N647AE	ERJ-145LR	145222	
☐	N648AE	ERJ-145LR	145225	
☐	N649PP	ERJ-145LR	145234	
☐	N650AE	ERJ-145LR	145417	
☐	N651AE	ERJ-145LR	145422	
☐	N652RS	ERJ-145LR	145432	
☐	N653AE	ERJ-145LR	145433	
☐	N654AE	ERJ-145LR	145437	

☐	N655AE	ERJ-145LR	145452	
☐	N656AE	ERJ-145LR	145740	
☐	N657AE	ERJ-145LR	145744	
☐	N658AE	ERJ-145LR	145760	
☐	N659AE	ERJ-145LR	145762	
☐	N660CL	ERJ-145LR	145764	
☐	N661JA	ERJ-145LR	145766	
☐	N662EH	ERJ-145LR	145777	
☐	N663AR	ERJ-145LR	145778	
☐	N664MS	ERJ-145LR	145779	
☐	N665BC	ERJ-145LR	145783	
☐	N667GB	ERJ-145LR	145784	
☐	N668HH	ERJ-145LR	145785	
☐	N669MB	ERJ-145LR	145788	
☐	N670AE	ERJ-145LR	145790	
☐	N671AE	ERJ-145LR	145793	
☐	N672AE	ERJ-145LR	145794	
☐	N673AE	ERJ-145LR	145797	
☐	N674RJ	ERJ-145LR	14500801	
☐	N675AE	ERJ-145LR	14500806	
☐	N676AE	ERJ-145LR	14500807	
☐	N677AE	ERJ-145LR	14500810	
☐	N678AE	ERJ-145LR	14500813	
☐	N679AE	ERJ-145LR	14500814	
☐	N680AE	ERJ-145LR	14500820	
☐	N681AE	ERJ-145LR	14500824	
☐	N682AE	ERJ-145LR	14500826	
☐	N683AE	ERJ-145LR	14500833	
☐	N684JW	ERJ-145LR	14500835	
☐	N685AE	ERJ-145LR	14500836	
☐	N686AE	ERJ-145LR	14500843	
☐	N687JS	ERJ-145LR	14500846	
☐	N688AE	ERJ-145LR	14500849	
☐	N689EC	ERJ-145LR	14500853	
☐	N690AE	ERJ-145LR	14500858	
☐	N691AE	ERJ-145LR	14500860	
☐	N692AE	ERJ-145LR	14500866	
☐	N693AE	ERJ-145LR	14500868	
☐	N694AE	ERJ-145LR	14500869	
☐	N695AE	ERJ-145LR	14500870	
☐	N696AE	ERJ-145LR	14500874	
☐	N697AB	ERJ-145LR	14500875	
☐	N698CB	ERJ-145LR	14500877	
☐	N699AE	ERJ-145LR	14500883	
☐	N900AE	ERJ-145LR	14500885	
☐	N902BC	ERJ-145LR	14500887	
☐	N905JH	ERJ-145LR	14500892	
☐	N906AE	ERJ-145LR	14500894	
☐	N907AE	ERJ-145LR	14500895	
☐	N908AE	ERJ-145LR	14500897	
☐	N909AE	ERJ-145LR	14500899	
☐	N918AE	ERJ-145LR	14500902	
☐	N922AE	ERJ-145LR	14500906	
☐	N923AE	ERJ-145LR	14500907	
☐	N925AE	ERJ-145LR	14500908	
☐	N928AE	ERJ-145LR	14500911	
☐	N931AE	ERJ-145LR	14500912	
☐	N932AE	ERJ-145LR	14500915	
☐	N933JN	ERJ-145LR	14500918	
☐	N935AE	ERJ-145LR	14500920	
☐	N939AE	ERJ-145LR	14500923	
☐	N941LT	ERJ-145LR	14500926	
☐	N942LL	ERJ-145LR	14500930	
☐	N801MA	ERJ-170SU	17000012	801
☐	N802MD	ERJ-170SU	17000013	802
☐	N803MD	ERJ-170SU	17000015	803

☐	N804MD	ERJ-170SU	17000016	804
☐	N805MD	ERJ-170SU	17000018	805
☐	N807MD	ERJ-170SU	17000020	807
☐	N808MD	ERJ-170SU	17000021	808
☐	N809MD	ERJ-170SU	17000022	809
☐	N811MD	ERJ-170SU	17000028	811
☐	N812MD	ERJ-170SU	17000030	812
☐	N813MA	ERJ-170SU	17000031	813
☐	N814MD	ERJ-170SU	17000033	814
☐	N816MA	ERJ-170SU	17000037	816
☐	N817MD	ERJ-170SU	17000038	817
☐	N819MD	ERJ-170SU	17000040	819
☐	N820MD	ERJ-170SU	17000041	820
☐	N822MD	ERJ-170SU	17000043	822
☐	N827MD	ERJ-170SU	17000047	827
☐	N828MD	ERJ-170SU	17000048	828
☐	N829MD	ERJ-170SU	17000049	829
☐	N101HQ	ERJ-175LR	17000156	
☐	N102HQ	ERJ-175LR	17000157	
☐	N103HQ	ERJ-175LR	17000159	
☐	N104HQ	ERJ-175LR	17000160	
☐	N105HQ	ERJ-175LR	17000163	
☐	N106HQ	ERJ-175LR	17000164	
☐	N107HQ	ERJ-175LR	17000165	
☐	N108HQ	ERJ-175LR	17000166	
☐	N109HQ	ERJ-175LR	17000168	
☐	N110HQ	ERJ-175LR	17000172	
☐	N111HQ	ERJ-175LR	17000173	
☐	N112HQ	ERJ-175LR	17000174	
☐	N113HQ	ERJ-175LR	17000177	
☐	N114HQ	ERJ-175LR	17000179	
☐	N115HQ	ERJ-175LR	17000182	
☐	N116HQ	ERJ-175LR	17000183	
☐	N117HQ	ERJ-175LR	17000184	
☐	N118HQ	ERJ-175LR	17000189	
☐	N119HQ	ERJ-175LR	17000190	
☐	N120HQ	ERJ-175LR	17000193	
☐	N121HQ	ERJ-175LR	17000194	
☐	N122HQ	ERJ-175LR	17000196	
☐	N123HQ	ERJ-175LR	17000199	
☐	N124HQ	ERJ-175LR	17000200	
☐	N125HQ	ERJ-175LR	17000202	
☐	N126HQ	ERJ-175LR	17000204	
☐	N127HQ	ERJ-175LR	17000206	
☐	N128HQ	ERJ-175LR	17000208	
☐	N129HQ	ERJ-175LR	17000211	
☐	N130HQ	ERJ-175LR	17000212	
☐	N131HQ	ERJ-175LR	17000215	
☐	N132HQ	ERJ-175LR	17000216	
☐	N133HQ	ERJ-175LR	17000217	
☐	N134HQ	ERJ-175LR	17000220	
☐	N135HQ	ERJ-175LR	17000224	
☐	N136HQ	ERJ-170LR	17000228	
☐	N137HQ	ERJ-170LR	17000231	
☐	N138HQ	ERJ-170LR	17000234	
☐	N200NN	ERJ-175LR	17000456	000
☐	N201NN	ERJ-175LR	17000461	001
☐	N202NN	ERJ-175LR	17000467	002♦
☐	N203NN	ERJ-175LR	17000473	003♦
☐	N204NN	ERJ-175LR	17000477	004♦
☐	N205NN	ERJ-175LR	17000481	005♦
☐	N206NN	ERJ-175LR	17000489	006♦
☐	N207AN	ERJ-175LR	17000490	007♦
☐	N208AN	ERJ-175LR	17000494	008♦
☐	N209NN	ERJ-175LR	17000497	009♦
☐	N210NN	ERJ-175LR	17000500	010♦

	Reg	Type	c/n	
☐	N211NN	ERJ-175LR	17000501	011♦
☐	N212NN	ERJ-175LR	17000504	012♦
☐	N213NN	ERJ-175LR	17000505	013♦
☐	N214NN	ERJ-175LR	17000508	014♦
☐	N215NN	ERJ-175LR	17000511	015♦
☐	N216NN	ERJ-175LR	17000513	016♦
☐	N217NN	ERJ-175LR	17000515	017♦
☐	N218NN	ERJ-175LR	17000519	018♦
☐	N219NN	ERJ-175LR	17000522	019♦
☐	N220NN	ERJ-175LR	17000523	020♦
☐	N221NN	ERJ-175LR	17000525	021♦
☐	N222NS	ERJ-175LR	17000528	022♦
☐	N223NN	ERJ-175LR	17000529	023♦
☐	N224NN	ERJ-175LR	17000536	024♦
☐	N225NN	ERJ-175LR	17000537	025♦
☐	N401YX	ERJ-175LR	17000363	A01
☐	N402YX	ERJ-175LR	17000364	A02
☐	N403YX	ERJ-175LR	17000365	A03
☐	N404YX	ERJ-175LR	17000367	A04
☐	N405YX	ERJ-175LR	17000368	A05
☐	N406YX	ERJ-175LR	17000369	A06
☐	N407YX	ERJ-175LR	17000370	A07
☐	N408YX	ERJ-175LR	17000371	A08
☐	N409YX	ERJ-175LR	17000372	A09
☐	N410YX	ERJ-175LR	17000373	A10
☐	N411YX	ERJ-175LR	17000374	A11
☐	N412YX	ERJ-175LR	17000375	A12
☐	N413YX	ERJ-175LR	17000376	A13
☐	N414YX	ERJ-175LR	17000377	A14
☐	N415YX	ERJ-175LR	17000378	A15
☐	N416YX	ERJ-175LR	17000381	A16
☐	N417YX	ERJ-175LR	17000382	A17
☐	N418YX	ERJ-175LR	17000383	A18
☐	N419YX	ERJ-175LR	17000384	A19
☐	N420YX	ERJ-175LR	17000385	A20
☐	N421YX	ERJ-175LR	17000386	A21
☐	N422YX	ERJ-175LR	17000387	A22
☐	N423YX	ERJ-175LR	17000392	A23
☐	N424YX	ERJ-175LR	17000393	A24
☐	N425YX	ERJ-175LR	17000396	A25
☐	N426YX	ERJ-175LR	17000397	A26
☐	N427YX	ERJ-175LR	17000402	A27
☐	N428YX	ERJ-175LR	17000403	A28
☐	N429YX	ERJ-175LR	17000408	A29
☐	N430YX	ERJ-175LR	17000409	A30
☐	N431YX	ERJ-175LR	17000413	A31
☐	N432YX	ERJ-175LR	17000415	A32
☐	N433YX	ERJ-175LR	17000417	A33
☐	N434YX	ERJ-175LR	17000418	A34
☐	N435YX	ERJ-175LR	17000423	A35
☐	N436YX	ERJ-175LR	17000424	A36
☐	N437YX	ERJ-175LR	17000366	A37
☐	N438YX	ERJ-175LR	17000428	A38
☐	N439YX	ERJ-175LR	17000434	A39
☐	N440YX	ERJ-175LR	17000435	A40
☐	N441YX	ERJ-175LR	17000444	A41
☐	N442YX	ERJ-175LR	17000446	A42
☐	N443YX	ERJ-175LR	17000447	A43
☐	N444YX	ERJ-175LR	17000453	A44
☐	N445YX	ERJ-175LR	17000455	A45
☐	N446YX	ERJ-175LR	17000457	A46
☐	N447YX	ERJ-175LR	17000463	A47

AMERIFLIGHT *A8 / AMF*

	Reg	Type	c/n	
☐	N19RZ	Beech 1900C-1	UC-75	
☐	N21RZ	Beech 1900C-1	UC-106	
☐	N26RZ	Beech 1900C-1	UC-134	
☐	N34RZ	Beech 1900C-1	UC-151	
☐	N49UC	Beech 1900C-1	UC-49	
☐	N111YV	Beech 1900C-1	UC-111	
☐	N112YV	Beech 1900C-1	UC-112	
☐	N330AF	Beech 1900C	UB-38	
☐	N331AF	Beech 1900C	UB-44	
☐	N338AF	Beech 1900C-1	UC-57	
☐	N346AF	Beech 1900C-1	UC-71	
☐	N347AF	Beech 1900C-1	UC-66	
☐	N575G	Beech 1900C-1	UC-155	
☐	N718AF	Beech 1900C-1	UC-162	
☐	N1568G	Beech 1900C-1	UC-58	
☐	N2049K	Beech 1900C-1	UC-164	
☐	N3052K	Beech 1900C	UB-70	
☐	N3071A	Beech 1900C	UB-46	
☐	N3229A	Beech 1900C	UB-51	
☐	N7203C	Beech 1900C	UB-28	
☐	N31701	Beech 1900C	UB-2	
☐	N31702	Beech 1900C	UB-3	
☐	N31703	Beech 1900C	UB-10	
☐	N31704	Beech 1900C	UB-12	
☐	N31705	Beech 1900C	UB-60	
☐	N179CA	EMB.120ER	120179	
☐	N189CA	EMB.120ER	120189	
☐	N201YW	EMB.120RT	120201	
☐	N246AS	EMB.120ER	120100	
☐	N247CA	EMB.120ER	120225	
☐	N257AS	EMB.120ER	120126	
☐	N258AS	EMB.120ER	120131	
☐	N560SW	EMB.120ER	120334	♦
☐	N152AF	SA.227AC Metro III	AC-520	
☐	N155AF	SA.227AC Metro III	AC-455	
☐	N191AF	SA.227AC Metro III	AC-491	
☐	N240DH	SA.227AT Expediter	AT-602B	
☐	N241DH	SA.227AT Expediter	AT-607B	
☐	N242DH	SA.227AT Expediter	AT-608B	
☐	N243DH	SA.227AT Expediter	AT-609B	
☐	N244DH	SA.227AT Expediter	AT-618B	
☐	N245DH	SA.227AT Expediter	AT-624B	
☐	N246DH	SA.227AT Expediter	AT-625B	
☐	N247DH	SA.227AT Expediter	AT-626B	
☐	N248DH	SA.227AT Expediter	AT-630B	
☐	N249DH	SA.227AT Expediter	AT-631B	
☐	N360AE	SA.227AC Metro III	AC-675	
☐	N362AE	SA.227AC Metro III	AC-677B	
☐	N370AE	SA.227AC Metro III	AC-506	♦
☐	N377PH	SA.227AC Metro III	AC-574	
☐	N421MA	SA.227AC Metro III	AC-634	
☐	N422MA	SA.227AC Metro III	AC-635	
☐	N423MA	SA.227AC Metro III	AC-636	
☐	N424MA	SA.227AC Metro III	AC-639	
☐	N426MA	SA.227AC Metro III	AC-645	
☐	N428MA	SA.227AC Metro III	AC-646	
☐	N443AF	SA.227AC Metro III	AC-443	
☐	N473AF	SA.227AC Metro III	AC-473	
☐	N475AF	SA.227AC Metro III	AC-475	
☐	N476AF	SA.227AC Metro III	AC-476	
☐	N488AF	SA.227AC Metro III	AC-488	
☐	N529AF	SA.227AC Metro III	AC-752	
☐	N544UP	SA.227AT Expediter	AT-544	
☐	N548UP	SA.227AT Expediter	AT-548	
☐	N556UP	SA.227AT Expediter	AT-556	
☐	N560UP	SA.227AT Expediter	AT-560	
☐	N561UP	SA.227AT Expediter	AT-561	
☐	N566UP	SA.227AT Expediter	AT-566	

	Reg	Type	c/n	Notes
☐	N569UP	SA.227AT Expediter	AT-569	
☐	N573G	SA.227AT Merlin IVC	AT-446B	
☐	N578AF	SA.227AC Metro III	AC-578	
☐	N671AV	SA.227AC Metro III	AC-671	
☐	N672AV	SA.227AC Metro III	AC-672	
☐	N673AV	SA.227AC Metro III	AC-673	
☐	N698AF	SA.227AC Metro III	AC-698	
☐	N709TR	SA.227AC Metro III	AC-709B	
☐	N801AF	SA.227AC Metro III	AC-701	
☐	N807M	SA.227AT Merlin IVC	AT-454B	
☐	N838AF	SA.227AC Metro III	AC-738	

AMERIJET INTERNATIONAL — M6 / AJT

	Reg	Type	c/n	Notes
☐	N199AJ	B727-2F9F/W	21426/1285	♦
☐	N395AJ	B727-233F/W	21100/1148	[LAL]
☐	N495AJ	B727-233F/W	20937/1103	♦
☐	N598AJ	B727-212F/W	21947/1506	
☐	N905AJ	B727-231F	21989/1590	[LAL]
☐	N316CM	B767-338ERF	24146/231	
☐	N319CM	B767-338ERF	24407/247	
☐	N739AX	B767-232(SCD)	22216/26	
☐	N741AX	B767-232 (SCD)	22215/17	
☐	N743AX	B767-232 (SCD)	22218/31	

AMERISTAR JET CHARTER — 7Z / AJI

	Reg	Type	c/n	Notes
☐	N782TW	DC-9-15RC	45826/79	
☐	N783TW	DC-9-15F	47010/97	
☐	N784TW	DC-9-15F	47014/141	
☐	N785TW	DC-9-15F	47015/156	
☐	N786TW	MD-83	53123/1987	
☐	N787TW	MD-83	49945/1889	

ASIA PACIFIC AIRLINES — P9 / MGE

	Reg	Type	c/n	Notes
☐	N319NE	B727-212F/W	21349/1289	
☐	N705AA	B727-223F/W	22462/1751	
☐	N86425	B727-212F/W	21459/1329	
☐	N757MQ	B757-230	25436/419	[GYR]
☐	N757QM	B757-29JF/W	27203/588	

ATI - AIR TRANSPORT INTL — 8C / ATN

	Reg	Type	c/n	Notes
☐	N531UA	B757-222(PCF)	25042/361	
☐	N557CM	B757-2B6F/W	23687/106	
☐	N588GT	B757-26DF	24471/1713	♦
☐	N605DL	B757-232F	22812/46	
☐	N620DL	B757-232F	22910/111	
☐	N751CX	B757-2Q8/W(PC)	26273/597	
☐	N752CX	B757-25GSF	24451/227	
☐	N753CX	B757-2Y0ER	26152/478	
☐	N754CX	B757-2Y0ERF	26154/486	
☐	N364CM	B767-338ERF	24531/278	♦
☐	N761CX	B767-223(SCD)	22318/111	>RMY
☐	N762CX	B767-232(SCD)	22225/77	
☐	N763CX	B767-232(SCD)	22223/74	
☐	N791AX	B767-281F	23141/108	>SWN

ATLANTIC AIR CARGO

	Reg	Type	c/n	Notes
☐	N437GB	Douglas DC-3	19999	

ATLAS AIR — 5Y / GTI

	Reg	Type	c/n	Notes
☐	N249BA	B747-409LCF	24309/766	^
☐	N263SG	B747-481	29263/1204	>SOR
☐	N322SG	B747-481	30322/1250	>SOR
☐	N408MC	B747-47UF	29261/1192	
☐	N409MC	B747-47UF	30558/1242	>ETD
☐	N412MC	B747-47UF	30559/1244	
☐	N415MC	B747-47UF	32837/1304	
☐	N416MC	B747-47UF	32838/1307	>PAC
☐	N418MC	B747-47UF	32840/1319	
☐	N419MC	B747-48EF	28367/1096	
☐	N429MC	B747-481SCF	24833/812	♦
☐	N464MC	B747-446	26341/902	
☐	N465MC	B747-446	24784/798	
☐	N473MC	B747-45EBDSF	27174/1004	♦
☐	N475MC	B747-47UF	29252/1165	
☐	N476MC	B747-47UF	29256/1213	>ETD
☐	N477MC	B747-47UF	29255/1184	
☐	N492MC	B747-47UF	29253/1169	
☐	N493MC	B747-47UF	29254/1179	
☐	N496MC	B747-47UF	29257/1217	
☐	N497MC	B747-47UF	29258/1220	
☐	N498MC	B747-47UF	29259/1227	
☐	N499MC	B747-47UF	29260/1240	
☐	N718BA	B747-4H6LCF	27042/932	^
☐	N747BC	B747-4J6LCF	25879/904	^
☐	N780BA	B747-409LCF	24310/778	^
☐	N850GT	B747-87UF	37570/1455	*
☐	N851GT	B747-87UF	37565/1458	*>PAC
☐	N852GT	B747-87UF	37571/1462	>PAC
☐	N853GT	B747-87UF	37572/1467	>PAC
☐	N854GT	B747-87UF	37566/1471	
☐	N855GT	B747-87UF	37567/1476	>ETD
☐	N856GT	B747-87UF	37561/1442	>PAC
☐	N857GT	B747-87UF	37568/1444	>PAC
☐	N858GT	B747-87UF	37569/1445	>PAC
☐	N859GT	B747-87UF	62441/1526	♦

^ operated for Boeing to transport 787 components;
** flies in Panalpina c/s*

	Reg	Type	c/n	Notes
☐	(N632GT)	B767-375ER/W	25865/430	♦ [N258CT]
☐	N640GT	B767-3S1ER	25221/384	
☐	N641GT	B767-38EER	25132/417	
☐	N642GT	B767-3YOER	26207/503	[TLV]
☐	N643GT	B767-3JHF/W	37809/1039	>PAC
☐	N644GT	B767-3JHF/W	37810/1041	>PAC
☐	N645GT	B767-324ER/W	27393/571	♦
☐	N647GT	B767-306ER/F	27611/633	>PAC♦
☐	N648GT	B767-33AER	27310/545	o/o♦
☐	(N649GT)	B767-375ER/W	25864/426	♦ [N661CS]
☐	N650GT	B767-231ERF	22566/29	
☐	N651GT	B767-231ERF	22570/63	
☐	N652GT	B767-231ERF	22571/64	
☐	N653GT	B767-231ERF	22572/65	
☐	N655GT	B767-205ERF	23058/101	
☐	N656GT	B767-281F	23017/82	
☐	N657GT	B767-281F	23018/84	♦
☐	N658GT	B767-281F	23019/85	
☐	N659GT	B767-281F	23140/106	
☐	N767MW	B767-277	22694/32	

BALTIA AIRLINES — BTL

	Reg	Type	c/n	Notes
☐	N706BL	B747-251B	21705/374	

BERING AIR — 8E / BRG

	Reg	Type	c/n	Notes
☐	N15GA	Beech 1900D	UE-37	
☐	N148SK	Beech 1900D	UE-148	
☐	N349TA	CASA 212-200	CC60-9-349	

BERRY AVIATION — BYA

	Registration	Type	c/n	
☐	N92FE	DHC-6 Twin Otter 300	242	
☐	N675BA	DHC-6 Twin Otter 300	675	
☐	N969AC	DHC-6 Twin Otter 300	286	
☐	N437YV	DHC-8-202	437	
☐	N449YV	DHC-8-202	449	
☐	N541AV	DHC-8-201	541	
☐	N989HA	DHC-8-201	427	
☐	N339PH	Do328-100	3015	
☐	N473PS	Do328-100	3010	
☐	N229SW	EMB.120ER	120305	
☐	N233SW	EMB.120ER	120307	
☐	N235SW	EMB.120ER	120310	
☐	N290SW	EMB.120ER	120317	♦
☐	N297SW	EMB.120ER	120327	♦
☐	N651CT	EMB.120ER	120197	
☐	N707TG	EMB.120RT	120182	
☐	N165BA	SA.226TC Metro II	TC-215	
☐	N660EA	SA.227AC Metro III	AC-660	♦
☐	N680AX	SA.227AC Metro III	AC-680	
☐	N691AX	SA.227AC Metro III	AC-691	
☐	N27442	SA.227AC Metro III	AC-750B	

BIGHORN AIRWAYS — BHR

	Registration	Type	c/n	
☐	N107BH	CASA 212-200	CC20-4-165	
☐	N109BH	CASA 212-200	CC35-1-192	
☐	N112BH	CASA 212-200	CC50-11-292	
☐	N117BH	CASA 212-200	CC23-1-171	
☐	N217BH	CASA 212-200	CD51-6-318	♦
☐	N257MC	Do228-202	8102	
☐	N263MC	Do228-202	8141	
☐	N266MC	Do228-202	8150	

BLUE RIDGE AERO SERVICES

	Registration	Type	c/n
☐	N212AZ	ATR 42-320	016
☐	N315CR	ATR 42-320	252
☐	N470JF	ATR 42-320	247

C & M AIRWAYS — RWG

	Registration	Type	c/n
☐	N563PC	DC-9-15RC	47055/194

CAPE AIR — 9K / CAP

	Registration	Type	c/n	Fleet no.
☐	N14834	ATR 42-320	193	834
☐	N42836	ATR 42-320	200	836

Operates in Micronesia for United as United Express.

CENTURION II AIR CARGO — WE / CWC

	Registration	Type	c/n	
☐	N902AR	B747-428ERF	32870/1344	
☐	N903AR	B747-428ERF	33096/1317	
☐	N904AR	B747-428ERF	33097/1361	
☐	(N906AR)	B747-412BDSF	27071/1072 [N742WA]	♦
☐	N984AR	MD-11BCF	48429/500	
☐	N986AR	MD-11F	48426/468	
☐	N987AR	MD-11F	48427/471	

CHARTER AIR TRANSPORT — VC / SRY

	Registration	Type	c/n
☐	N650CT	EMB.120RT	120198
☐	N651CT	EMB.120RT	120197
☐	N654CT	EMB.120ER	120251

CHAUTAUQUA AIRLINES — RP / CHQ

Operates as American Connection, Delta Connection, United Express & US Airways Express, see these fleets.

COMMUTAIR — C5 / UCA

Operates as United Express, see this fleet.

COMPASS AIRLINES — CP / CPZ

Operates as Delta Connection, see this fleet.

CONQUEST AIR

	Registration	Type	c/n	
☐	N145GT	Convair 340 (C-131B)	256	
☐	N341GS	Convair 340 (C-131F)	281	♦
☐	N342GS	Convair 340 (C-131F)	299	♦
☐	N343GS	Convair 340 (C-131F)	305	♦
☐	N344GS	Convair 340 (C-131F)	311	♦
☐	N345GS	Convair 340 (C-131F)	291	♦

CORPORATE AIR — CPT

	Registration	Type	c/n
☐	N330SB	Short SD.3-30	SH3013
☐	N331SB	Short SD.3-30	SH3015

CORPORATE FLIGHT — VTE

	Registration	Type	c/n
☐	N913AE	BAeJetstream 32	913
☐	N564HK	BAeJetstream 41	41081
☐	N569HK	BAeJetstream 41	41088

DELTA AIR LINES — DL / DAL

	Registration	Type	c/n	Fleet no.
☐	N301NB	A319-114	1058	3101
☐	N302NB	A319-114	1062	3102
☐	N314NB	A319-114	1191	3114
☐	N315NB	A319-114	1230	3115
☐	N316NB	A319-114	1249	3116
☐	N317NB	A319-114	1324	3117
☐	N318NB	A319-114	1325	3118
☐	N319NB	A319-114	1346	3119
☐	N320NB	A319-114	1392	3120
☐	N321NB	A319-114	1414	3121
☐	N322NB	A319-114	1434	3122
☐	N323NB	A319-114	1453	3123
☐	N324NB	A319-114	1456	3124
☐	N325NB	A319-114	1483	3125
☐	N326NB	A319-114	1498	3126
☐	N327NB	A319-114	1501	3127
☐	N328NB	A319-114	1520	3128
☐	N329NB	A319-114	1543	3129
☐	N330NB	A319-114	1549	3130
☐	N331NB	A319-114	1567	3131
☐	N332NB	A319-114	1570	3132
☐	N333NB	A319-114	1582	3133
☐	N334NB	A319-114	1659	3134
☐	N335NB	A319-114	1662	3135
☐	N336NB	A319-114	1683	3136
☐	N337NB	A319-114	1685	3137
☐	N338NB	A319-114	1693	3138
☐	N339NB	A319-114	1709	3139
☐	N340NB	A319-114	1714	3140
☐	N341NB	A319-114	1738	3141
☐	N342NB	A319-114	1746	3142
☐	N343NB	A319-114	1752	3143
☐	N344NB	A319-114	1766	3144
☐	N345NB	A319-114	1774	3145
☐	N346NB	A319-114	1796	3146

☐	N347NB	A319-114	1800	3147
☐	N348NB	A319-114	1810	3148
☐	N349NB	A319-114	1815	3149
☐	N351NB	A319-114	1820	3151
☐	N352NB	A319-114	1824	3152
☐	N353NB	A319-114	1828	3153
☐	N354NB	A319-114	1833	3154
☐	N355NB	A319-114	1839	3155
☐	N357NB	A319-114	1875	3157
☐	N358NB	A319-114	1897	3158
☐	N359NB	A319-114	1923	3159
☐	N360NB	A319-114	1959	3160
☐	N361NB	A319-114	1976	3161
☐	N362NB	A319-114	1982	3162
☐	N363NB	A319-114	1990	3163
☐	N364NB	A319-114	2002	3164
☐	N365NB	A319-114	2013	3165
☐	N366NB	A319-114	2026	3166
☐	N368NB	A319-114	2039	3168
☐	N369NB	A319-114	2047	3169
☐	N370NB	A319-114	2087	3170
☐	N371NB	A319-114	2095	3171
☐	N309US	A320-211	0118	3209
☐	N310NW	A320-211	0121	3210
☐	N311US	A320-211	0125	3211
☐	N312US	A320-211	0152	3212
☐	N313US	A320-211	0153	3213
☐	N314US	A320-211	0160	3214
☐	N315US	A320-211	0171	3215
☐	N316US	A320-211	0192	3216
☐	N317US	A320-211	0197	3217
☐	N318US	A320-211	0206	3218
☐	N319US	A320-211	0208	3219
☐	N320US	A320-211	0213	3220
☐	N321US	A320-211	0262	3221
☐	N322US	A320-211	0263	3222
☐	N323US	A320-211	0272	3223
☐	N324US	A320-211	0273	3224
☐	N325US	A320-211	0281	3225
☐	N326US	A320-211	0282	3226
☐	N327NW	A320-211	0297	3227
☐	N328NW	A320-211	0298	3228
☐	N329NW	A320-211	0306	3229
☐	N330NW	A320-211	0307	3230
☐	N331NW	A320-211	0318	3231
☐	N332NW	A320-211	0319	3232
☐	N333NW	A320-211	0329	3233
☐	N334NW	A320-212	0339	3234
☐	N335NW	A320-212	0340	3235
☐	N336NW	A320-212	0355	3236
☐	N337NW	A320-212	0358	3237
☐	N338NW	A320-212	0360	3238
☐	N339NW	A320-212	0367	3239
☐	N340NW	A320-212	0372	3240
☐	N341NW	A320-212	0380	3241
☐	N342NW	A320-212	0381	3242
☐	N343NW	A320-212	0387	3243
☐	N344NW	A320-212	0388	3244
☐	N345NW	A320-212	0399	3245
☐	N347NW	A320-212	0408	3247
☐	N348NW	A320-212	0410	3248
☐	N349NW	A320-212	0417	3249
☐	N350NA	A320-212	0418	3250
☐	N351NW	A320-212	0766	3251
☐	N352NW	A320-212	0778	3252
☐	N353NW	A320-212	0786	3253
☐	N354NW	A320-212	0801	3254
☐	N355NW	A320-212	0807	3255
☐	N356NW	A320-212	0818	3256
☐	N357NW	A320-212	0830	3257
☐	N358NW	A320-212	0832	3258
☐	N359NW	A320-212	0846	3259
☐	N360NW	A320-212	0903	3260
☐	N361NW	A320-212	0907	3261
☐	N362NW	A320-212	0911	3262
☐	N363NW	A320-212	0923	3263
☐	N364NW	A320-212	0962	3264
☐	N365NW	A320-212	0964	3265
☐	N366NW	A320-212	0981	3266
☐	N367NW	A320-212	0988	3267
☐	N368NW	A320-212	0996	3268
☐	N369NW	A320-212	1011	3269
☐	N370NW	A320-212	1037	3270
☐	N371NW	A320-212	1535	3271
☐	N372NW	A320-212	1633	3272
☐	N373NW	A320-212	1641	3273
☐	N374NW	A320-212	1646	3274
☐	N375NC	A320-212	1789	3275
☐	N376NW	A320-212	1812	3276
☐	N377NW	A320-212	2082	3277
☐	N378NW	A320-212	2092	3278
☐	N301DN	A321-211/S	6923	o/o♦
☐	N302DN	A321-211/S	7031	o/o♦
☐	N303DN	A321-211/S	7061	o/o♦
☐	N804DN	A321-211/S	7112	o/o♦
☐	N805DN	A321-211/S	7149	o/o♦
☐	N806DN	A321-211/S	7165	o/o♦
☐	N807DX	A321-211/S	7214	o/o♦
☐	N808DN	A321-211/S	7233	o/o♦
☐	N809DN	A321-211/S	7259	o/o♦
☐	N810DN	A321-211/S	7262	o/o♦
☐	N811DN	A321-211/S	7275	o/o♦
☐	N812DN	A321-211/S	7281	o/o♦
☐	N813DN	A321-211/S	7356	o/o♦
☐	N814DN	A321-211/S	7360	o/o♦
☐	N815DN	A321-211/S	7376	o/o♦
☐	N801NW	A330-323E	524	3301
☐	N802NW	A330-323E	533	3302
☐	N803NW	A330-323E	542	3303
☐	N804NW	A330-323E	549	3304
☐	N805NW	A330-323E	552	3305
☐	N806NW	A330-323E	578	3306
☐	N807NW	A330-323E	588	3307
☐	N808NW	A330-323E	591	3308
☐	N809NW	A330-323E	663	3309
☐	N810NW	A330-323E	674	3310
☐	N811NW	A330-323E	690	3311
☐	N812NW	A330-323E	784	3312
☐	N813NW	A330-323E	799	3313
☐	N814NW	A330-323E	806	3314
☐	N815NW	A330-323E	817	3315
☐	N816NW	A330-323E	827	3316
☐	N817NW	A330-323E	843	3317
☐	N818NW	A330-323E	857	3318
☐	N819NW	A330-323E	858	3319
☐	N820NW	A330-323E	859	3320
☐	N821NW	A330-323E	865	3321
☐	N822NW	A330-302	1627	3322
☐	N823NW	A330-302	1628	3323
☐	N824NW	A330-302	1637	3324
☐	N825NW	A330-302	1679	3325♦
☐	N826NW	A330-302	1701	3326♦

	Reg.	Type	c/n	Fleet no.
☐	N827NW	A330-302	1716	o/o♦
☐	N828NW	A330-302	1720	o/o♦
☐	N829NW	A330-302	1721	o/o♦
☐	N851NW	A330-223	609	3351
☐	N852NW	A330-223	614	3352
☐	N853NW	A330-223	618	3353
☐	N854NW	A330-223	620	3354
☐	N855NW	A330-223	621	3355
☐	N856NW	A330-223	631	3356
☐	N857NW	A330-223	633	3357
☐	N858NW	A330-223	718	3358
☐	N859NW	A330-223	722	3359
☐	N860NW	A330-223	778	3360
☐	N861NW	A330-223	796	3361
☐	N603AT	B717-22A	55127/5074	9594
☐	N608AT	B717-231	55081/5045	9576♦
☐	N607AT	B717-231	55074/5030	9569
☐	N717JL	B717-2BD	55042/5115	9550♦
☐	N891AT	B717-2BD	55043/5131	9551
☐	N892AT	B717-2BD	55044/5134	9552
☐	N893AT	B717-2BD	55045/5136	9553
☐	N894AT	B717-2BD	55046/5137	9554
☐	N895AT	B717-2BD	55047/5139	9555
☐	N896AT	B717-2BD	55048/5141	9556
☐	N899AT	B717-2BD	55049/5143	9557
☐	N906AT	B717-231	55087/5060	9582
☐	N910AT	B717-231	55086/5056	9581
☐	N915AT	B717-231	55085/5055	9580
☐	N919AT	B717-231	55084/5052	9579
☐	N920AT	B717-231	55083/5049	9578
☐	N921AT	B717-231	55082/5046	9577
☐	N922AT	B717-2BD	55050/5144	9553
☐	N923AT	B717-2BD	55051/5148	9559
☐	N924AT	B717-231	55080/5043	9575
☐	N925AT	B717-231	55079/5042	9574
☐	N926AT	B717-231	55078/5039	9573
☐	N927AT	B717-231	55077/5038	9572
☐	N928AT	B717-231	55076/5035	9571♦
☐	N929AT	B717-231	55075/5032	9570
☐	N930AT	B717-231	55072/5025	9567♦
☐	N932AT	B717-231	55073/5028	9568♦
☐	N933AT	B717-231	55071/5024	9566
☐	N934AT	B717-231	55070/5022	9565
☐	N935AT	B717-231	55069/5019	9564
☐	N936AT	B717-231	55058/5017	9563♦
☐	N937AT	B717-231	55091/5075	9586
☐	N938AT	B717-2BD	55098/5155	9561
☐	N939AT	B717-2BD	55099/5156	9562♦
☐	N940AT	B717-2BD	55004/5005	9501♦
☐	N942AT	B717-2BD	55005/5006	9502♦
☐	N943AT	B717-2BD	55006/5007	9503♦
☐	N944AT	B717-2BD	55007/5008	9504♦
☐	N945AT	B717-2BD	55008/5009	9505♦
☐	N946AT	B717-2BD	55009/5010	9506♦
☐	N947AT	B717-2BD	55010/5011	9507♦
☐	N948AT	B717-2BD	55011/5012	9508♦
☐	N949AT	B717-2BD	55003/5004	9500♦
☐	N950AT	B717-2BD	55012/5018	9509♦
☐	N951AT	B717-2BD	55013/5021	9510♦
☐	N952AT	B717-2BD	55014/5027	9511♦
☐	N953AT	B717-2BD	55015/5033	9512
☐	N954AT	B717-2BD	55016/5036	9513
☐	N955AT	B717-2BD	55017/5040	9514
☐	N956AT	B717-2BD	55018/5044	9515
☐	N957AT	B717-2BD	55019/5047	9516
☐	N958AT	B717-2BD	55020/5051	9517
☐	N959AT	B717-2BD	55021/5057	9518
☐	N960AT	B717-2BD	55022/5058	9519
☐	N961AT	B717-2BD	55023/5062	9520
☐	N963AT	B717-2BD	55024/5066	9522
☐	N964AT	B717-2BD	55025/5071	9523♦
☐	N965AT	B717-2BD	55026/5076	9524♦
☐	N966AT	B717-2BD	55027/5081	9525
☐	N967AT	B717-2BD	55028/5082	9526
☐	N968AT	B717-2BD	55029/5091	9530
☐	N969AT	B717-2BD	55030/5094	9531
☐	N970AT	B717-2BD	55031/5096	9532
☐	N971AT	B717-2BD	55032/5097	9533♦
☐	N972AT	B717-2BD	55033/5099	9534♦
☐	N974AT	B717-2BD	55034/5101	9536
☐	N975AT	B717-2BD	55035/5102	9537
☐	N977AT	B717-2BD	55036/5106	9541
☐	N978AT	B717-2BD	55037/5108	9543
☐	N979AT	B717-2BD	55038/5109	9544
☐	N980AT	B717-2BD	55039/5111	9546♦
☐	N981AT	B717-2BD	55040/5113	9548
☐	N982AT	B717-2BD	55041/5114	9549♦
☐	N983AT	B717-2BD	55052/5150	9560♦
☐	N985AT	B717-231	55090/5068	9585
☐	N986AT	B717-231	55089/5067	9584
☐	N987AT	B717-231	55088/5063	9583
☐	N987DN	B717-23S	55064/5037	o/o♦
☐	N988AT	B717-23S	55068/5065	9521
☐	N988DN	B717-23S	55065/5048	o/o♦
☐	N989AT	B717-23S	55152/5085	9527
☐	N989DN	B717-23S	55067/5059	o/o♦
☐	N990AT	B717-23S	55134/5088	9528
☐	N991AT	B717-23S	55135/5090	9529
☐	N992AT	B717-2BD	55136/5100	9535♦
☐	N993AT	B717-2BD	55137/5103	9538
☐	N994AT	B717-2BD	55138/5104	9539
☐	N995AT	B717-2BD	55139/5105	9540
☐	N996AT	B717-2BD	55140/5107	9542♦
☐	N997AT	B717-2BD	55141/5110	9545♦
☐	N998AT	B717-2BD	55142/5112	9547
☐	N301DQ	B737-732/W	29687/2667	3601
☐	N302DQ	B737-732/W	29648/2683	3602
☐	N303DQ	B737-732/W	29688/2720	3603
☐	N304DQ	B737-732/W	29683/2724	3604
☐	N305DQ	B737-732/W	29645/2743	3605
☐	N306DQ	B737-732/W	29633/2758	3606
☐	N307DQ	B737-732/W	29679/2767	3607
☐	N308DE	B737-732/W	29656/3022	3608
☐	N309DE	B737-732/W	29634/3031	3609
☐	N310DE	B737-732/W	29665/3058	3610
☐	N371DA	B737-832/W	29619/115	3701
☐	N372DA	B737-832/W	29620/118	3702
☐	N373DA	B737-832/W	29621/123	3703
☐	N374DA	B737-832/W	29622/128	3704
☐	N375DA	B737-832/W	29623/145	3705
☐	N376DA	B737-832/W	29624/176	3706
☐	N377DA	B737-832/W	29625/264	3707
☐	N378DA	B737-832/W	30265/340	3708
☐	N379DA	B737-832/W	30349/351	3709
☐	N380DA	B737-832/W	30266/361	3710
☐	N381DN	B737-832/W	30350/365	3711
☐	N382DA	B737-832/W	30345/389	3712
☐	N383DN	B737-832/W	30346/393	3713
☐	N384DA	B737-832/W	30347/412	3714
☐	N385DN	B737-832/W	30348/418	3715
☐	N386DA	B737-832/W	30373/446	3716
☐	N387DA	B737-832/W	30374/457	3717

☐	N388DA	B737-832/W	30375/469	3718
☐	N389DA	B737-832/W	30376/513	3719
☐	N390DA	B737-832/W	30536/518	3720
☐	N391DA	B737-832/W	30560/535	3721
☐	N392DA	B737-832/W	30561/564	3722
☐	N393DA	B737-832/W	30377/584	3723
☐	N394DA	B737-832/W	30562/589	3724
☐	N395DN	B737-832/W	30773/604	3725
☐	N396DA	B737-832/W	30378/632	3726
☐	N397DA	B737-832/W	30537/638	3727
☐	N398DA	B737-832/W	30774/641	3728
☐	N399DA	B737-832/W	30379/657	3729
☐	N3730B	B737-832/W	30538/662	3730
☐	N3731T	B737-832/W	30775/665	3731
☐	N3732J	B737-832/W	30380/674	3732
☐	N3733Z	B737-832/W	30539/685	3733
☐	N3734B	B737-832/W	30776/689	3734
☐	N3735D	B737-832/W	30381/694	3735
☐	N3736C	B737-832/W	30540/709	3736
☐	N3737C	B737-832/W	30799/712	3737
☐	N3738B	B737-832/W	30382/723	3738
☐	N3739P	B737-832/W	30541/729	3739
☐	N3740C	B737-832/W	30800/732	3740
☐	N3741S	B737-832/W	30487/750	3741
☐	N3742C	B737-832/W	30835/755	3742
☐	N3743H	B737-832/W	30836/770	3743
☐	N3744F	B737-832/W	30837/805	3744
☐	N3745B	B737-832/W	32373/831	3745
☐	N3746H	B737-832/W	30488/842	3746
☐	N3747D	B737-832/W	32374/846	3747
☐	N3748Y	B737-832/W	30489/865	3748
☐	N3749D	B737-832/W	30490/867	3749
☐	N3750D	B737-832/W	32375/870	3750
☐	N3751B	B737-832/W	30491/892	3751
☐	N3752	B737-832/W	30492/894	3752
☐	N3753	B737-832/W	32626/899	3753
☐	N3754A	B737-832/W	29626/907	3754
☐	N3755D	B737-832/W	29627/914	3755
☐	N3756	B737-832/W	30493/917	3756
☐	N3757D	B737-832/W	30813/921	3757
☐	N3758Y	B737-832/W	30814/923	3758
☐	N3759	B737-832/W	30815/949	3759
☐	N3760C	B737-832/W	30816/952	3760
☐	N3761R	B737-832/W	29628/964	3761
☐	N3762Y	B737-832/W	30817/968	3762
☐	N3763D	B737-832/W	29629/1003	3763
☐	N3764D	B737-832/W	30818/1006	3764
☐	N3765	B737-832/W	30819/1008	3765
☐	N3766	B737-832/W	30820/1029	3766
☐	N3767	B737-832/W	30821/1031	3767
☐	N3768	B737-832/W	29630/1053	3768
☐	N3769L	B737-832/W	30822/1057	3769
☐	N3771K	B737-832/W	29632/1103	3771
☐	N3772H	B737-832/W	30823/3274	3772
☐	N3773D	B737-832/W	30825/3338	3773
☐	N37700	B737-832/W	29631/1074	3770
☐	N801DZ	B737-932ER/W	31912/4603	3801
☐	N802DN	B737-932ER/W	31917/4628	3802
☐	N803DN	B737-932ER/W	31919/4639	3803
☐	N804DN	B737-932ER/W	31918/4650	3804
☐	N805DN	B737-932ER/W	31913/4664	3805
☐	N806DN	B737-932ER/W	31914/4672	3807
☐	N807DN	B737-932ER/W	31921/4682	3808
☐	N808DN	B737-932ER/W	31920/4693	3809
☐	N809DN	B737-932ER/W	31915/4704	3809
☐	N810DN	B737-932ER/W	31922/4708	3810

☐	N811DZ	B737-932ER/W	31916/4715	3811
☐	N812DN	B737-932ER/W	31923/4722	3812
☐	N813DN	B737-932ER/W	31925/4744	3813
☐	N814DN	B737-932ER/W	31924/4751	3814
☐	N815DN	B737-932ER/W	31926/4780	3815
☐	N816DN	B737-932ER/W	31927/4791	3816
☐	N817DN	B737-932ER/W	31929/4818	3817
☐	N818DA	B737-932ER/W	31928/4829	3818
☐	N819DN	B737-932ER/W	31930/4861	3819
☐	N820DN	B737-932ER/W	31931/4883	3820
☐	N821DN	B737-932ER/W	31932/4899	3821
☐	N822DN	B737-932ER/W	31933/4947	3822
☐	N823DN	B737-932ER/W	31934/4987	3823
☐	N824DN	B737-932ER/W	31935/4998	3824
☐	N825DN	B737-932ER/W	31936/5021	3825
☐	N826DN	B737-932ER/W	31937/5036	3826
☐	N827DN	B737-932ER/W	31938/5067	3827
☐	N828DN	B737-932ER/W	31939/5114	3828
☐	N829DN	B737-932ER/W	31941/5143	3829
☐	N830DN	B737-932ER/W	31940/5172	3830
☐	N831DN	B737-932ER/W	31942/5210	3831
☐	N832DN	B737-932ER/W	31943/5231	3832
☐	N833DN	B737-932ER/W	31944/5250	3833
☐	N834DN	B737-932ER/W	31946/5290	3834
☐	N835DN	B737-932ER/W	31945/5299	3835
☐	N836DN	B737-932ER/W	31947/5324	3836
☐	N837DN	B737-932ER/W	31948/5332	3837
☐	N838DN	B737-932ER/W	31949/5362	3838
☐	N839DN	B737-932ER/W	31950/5371	3839
☐	N840DN	B737-932ER/W	31951/5391	3840
☐	N841DN	B737-932ER/W	31952/5450	3841
☐	N842DN	B737-932ER/W	31953/5475	3842
☐	N843DN	B737-932ER/W	31954/5498	3843♦
☐	N844DN	B737-932ER/W	31955/5520	3844
☐	N845DN	B737-932ER/W	31956/5551	3845
☐	N846DN	B737-932ER/W	31957/5582	3846
☐	N847DN	B737-932ER/W	31958/5604	3847♦
☐	N848DN	B737-932ER/W	31959/5663	3848♦
☐	N849DN	B737-932ER/W	31960/5675	3849♦
☐	N850DN	B737-932ER/W	31961/5694	3850♦
☐	N851DN	B737-932ER/W	31962/5730	3851♦
☐	N852DN	B737-932ER/W	31963/5743	3852♦
☐	N853DN	B737-932ER/W	31964/5776	3853♦
☐	N854DN	B737-932ER/W	31965	o/o♦
☐	N855DN	B737-932ER/W	31966	o/o♦
☐	N856DN	B737-932ER/W	31967	o/o♦
☐	N857DZ	B737-932ER/W	31968	o/o♦
☐	N858DZ	B737-932ER/W	31969	o/o♦
☐	N859DZ	B737-932ER/W	31970	o/o♦
☐	N860DN	B737-932ER/W	31971	o/o♦
☐	N861DN	B737-932ER/W		o/o♦
☐	N862DN	B737-932ER/W		o/o♦
☐	N863DN	B737-932ER/W		o/o♦
☐	N864DN	B737-932ER/W		o/o♦
☐	N865DN	B737-932ER/W		o/o♦
☐	N662US	B747-451	23720/708	6302
☐	N665US	B747-451	23820/726	6305
☐	N666US	B747-451	23821/742	6306
☐	N667US	B747-451	24222/799	6307
☐	N668US	B747-451	24223/800	6308
☐	N669US	B747-451	24224/803	6309
☐	N670US	B747-451	24225/804	6310
☐	N673US	B747-451	30268/1226	6313
☐	N674US	B747-451	30269/1232	6314
☐	N675NW	B747-451	33001/1297	[MZJ]
☐	N535US	B757-251/W	26482/693	5635

☐	N536US	B757-251/W	26483/695	5636
☐	N537US	B757-251/W	26484/697	5637
☐	N538US	B757-251/W	26485/699	5638
☐	N539US	B757-251/W	26486/700	5639
☐	N540US	B757-251/W	26487/701	5640
☐	N541US	B757-251/W	26488/703	5641
☐	N542US	B757-251/W	26489/705	5642
☐	N543US	B757-251/W	26490/709	5643
☐	N544US	B757-251/W	26491/710	5644
☐	N545US	B757-251/W	26492/711	5645
☐	N546US	B757-251/W	26493/713	5646
☐	N547US	B757-251/W	26494/714	5647
☐	N548US	B757-251/W	26495/715	5648
☐	N549US	B757-251/W	26496/716	5649
☐	N550NW	B757-251	26497/968	5550
☐	N551NW	B757-251/W	26498/971	5551
☐	N552NW	B757-251/W	26499/975	5652
☐	N553NW	B757-251/W	26500/982	5653
☐	N554NW	B757-251/W	26501/987	5654
☐	N555NW	B757-251/W	33391/1011	5655
☐	N556NW	B757-251/W	33392/1013	5656
☐	N557NW	B757-251/W	33393/1016	5657
☐	N617DL	B757-232	22907/92	617
☐	N623DL	B757-232	22913/118	623
☐	N624AG	B757-2Q8/W	25624/541	6818
☐	N627DL	B757-232/W	22917/129	627
☐	N633DL	B757-232	23614/157	633
☐	N635DL	B757-232	23762/159	635
☐	N650DL	B757-232/W	24390/230	650♦
☐	N651DL	B757-232/W	24391/238	651
☐	N652DL	B757-232	24392/239	652
☐	N659DL	B757-232/W	24421/293	659
☐	N661DN	B757-232/W	24972/335	661
☐	N662DN	B757-232/W	24991/342	662
☐	N663DN	B757-232/W	24992/343	663
☐	N664DN	B757-232/W	25012/347	664
☐	N665DN	B757-232/W	25013/349	665
☐	N666DN	B757-232/W	25034/354	666
☐	N667DN	B757-232/W	25035/355	667
☐	N668DN	B757-232	25141/376	668
☐	N669DN	B757-232/W	25142/377	669
☐	N670DN	B757-232	25331/415	670
☐	N671DN	B757-232	25332/416	671
☐	N672DL	B757-232/W	25977/429	672
☐	N673DL	B757-232	25978/430	673
☐	N674DL	B757-232	25979/439	674
☐	N675DL	B757-232	25980/448	675
☐	N676DL	B757-232	25981/455	676
☐	N678DL	B757-232	25983/465	678
☐	N679DA	B757-232	26955/500	679
☐	N680DA	B757-232	26956/502	680
☐	N681DA	B757-232	26957/516	681
☐	N682DA	B757-232	26958/518	682
☐	N683DA	B757-232	27103/533	683
☐	N684DA	B757-232	27104/535	684
☐	N685DA	B757-232/W	27588/667	685
☐	N686DA	B757-232/W	27589/689	686
☐	N687DL	B757-232/W	27586/800	687
☐	N688DL	B757-232/W	27587/803	688
☐	N689DL	B757-232/W	27172/807	689
☐	N690DL	B757-232/W	27585/808	690
☐	N692DL	B757-232/W	29724/820	692
☐	N693DL	B757-232/W	29725/826	693
☐	N694DL	B757-232/W	29726/831	694
☐	N695DL	B757-232/W	29727/838	695
☐	N696DL	B757-232	29728/845	696
☐	N697DL	B757-232	30318/880	697
☐	N698DL	B757-232	29911/885	698
☐	N699DL	B757-232/W	29970/887	699
☐	N702TW	B757-2Q8/W	28162/732	6801
☐	N703TW	B757-2Q8ER/W	27620/736	6802
☐	N704X	B757-2Q8/W	28163/741	6803
☐	N705TW	B757-231/W	28479/742	6811
☐	N706TW	B757-2Q8/W	28165/743	6804
☐	N707TW	B757-2Q8ER/W	27625/744	6805
☐	N709TW	B757-2Q8/W	28168/754	6806
☐	N710TW	B757-2Q8/W	28169/757	6807
☐	N711ZX	B757-231/W	28481/758	6814
☐	N712TW	B757-2Q8ER/W	27624/760	6808
☐	N713TW	B757-2Q8/W	28173/764	6809
☐	N717TW	B757-231/W	28485/854	6812
☐	N718TW	B757-231/W	28486/869	6815
☐	N721TW	B757-231/W	29954/874	6810
☐	N722TW	B757-231/W	29385/893	6816
☐	N723TW	B757-231/W	29378/907	6817
☐	N727TW	B757-231/W	30340/901	6813
☐	N750AT	B757-212ER	23126/45	6902
☐	N751AT	B757-212ER	23125/44	6901
☐	N752AT	B757-212ER	23128/48	6904
☐	N819DX	B757-26D	33959/1044	♦
☐	N820DX	B757-26D	33960/1045	♦
☐	N821DX	B757-26D	33961/1046	♦
☐	N822DX	B757-26D	33966/1049	♦
☐	N823DX	B757-26D	33967/1050	♦
☐	N900PC	B757-26D/W	28446/740	691
☐	N6700	B757-232/W	30337/890	6700
☐	N6701	B757-232	30187/892	6701
☐	N6702	B757-232/W	30188/898	6702
☐	N6703D	B757-232	30234/908	6703
☐	N6704Z	B757-232	30396/914	6704
☐	N6705Y	B757-232	30397/917	6705
☐	N6706Q	B757-232	30422/921	6706
☐	N6707A	B757-232	30395/927	6707
☐	N6708D	B757-232	30480/934	6708
☐	N6709	B757-232	30481/937	6709
☐	N6710E	B757-232/W	30482/939	6710
☐	N6711M	B757-232	30483/941	6711
☐	N6712B	B757-232/W	30484/942	6712
☐	N6713Y	B757-232/W	30777/944	6713
☐	N6714Q	B757-232/W	30485/949	6714
☐	N6715C	B757-232/W	30486/953	6715
☐	N6716C	B757-232	30838/955	6716
☐	N67171	B757-232/W	30839/959	6717

☐	N581NW	B757-351/W	32982/1001	5801
☐	N582NW	B757-351/W	32981/1014	5802
☐	N583NW	B757-351/W	32983/1019	5803
☐	N584NW	B757-351/W	32984/1020	5804
☐	N585NW	B757-351/W	32985/1021	5805
☐	N586NW	B757-351/W	32987/1022	5806
☐	N587NW	B757-351/W	32986/1023	5807
☐	N588NW	B757-351/W	32988/1024	5808
☐	N589NW	B757-351/W	32989/1025	5809
☐	N590NW	B757-351/W	32990/1027	5810
☐	N591NW	B757-351/W	32991/1030	5811
☐	N592NW	B757-351/W	32992/1033	5812
☐	N593NW	B757-351/W	32993/1034	5813
☐	N594NW	B757-351/W	32994/1035	5814
☐	N595NW	B757-351/W	32995/1036	5815
☐	N596NW	B757-351/W	32996/1037	5816

☐	N121DE	B767-332	23435/162	121
☐	N125DL	B767-332	24075/200	125
☐	N126DL	B767-332	24076/201	126
☐	N127DL	B767-332	24077/203	127

☐ N128DL	B767-332	24078/207	128
☐ N129DL	B767-332	24079/209	129
☐ N130DL	B767-332	24080/216	130
☐ N136DL	B767-332	25146/374	136
☐ N138DL	B767-332	25409/410	138
☐ N139DL	B767-332	25984/427	139
☐ N140LL	B767-332	25988/499	1401
☐ N143DA	B767-332	25991/721	1403
☐ N144DA	B767-332	27584/751	1404
☐ N152DL	B767-3P6ER/W	24984/339	1502
☐ N153DL	B767-3P6ER/W	24985/340	1503
☐ N154DL	B767-3P6ER	25241/389	1504
☐ N155DL	B767-3P6ER/W	25269/390	1505
☐ N156DL	B767-3P6ER/W	25354/406	1506
☐ N169DZ	B767-332ER/W	29689/706	1601
☐ N171DN	B767-332ER/W	24759/304	171
☐ N171DZ	B767-332ER/W	29690/717	1701
☐ N172DN	B767-332ER/W	24775/312	172
☐ N172DZ	B767-332ER/W	29691/719	1702
☐ N173DZ	B767-332ER/W	29692/723	1703
☐ N174DN	B767-332ER/W	24802/317	174
☐ N174DZ	B767-332ER/W	29693/725	1704
☐ N175DN	B767-332ER/W	24803/318	175
☐ N175DZ	B767-332ER/W	29696/740	1705
☐ N176DN	B767-332ER/W	25061/341	176
☐ N176DZ	B767-332ER/W	29697/745	1706
☐ N177DN	B767-332ER/W	25122/346	177
☐ N177DZ	B767-332ER/W	29698/750	1707
☐ N178DN	B767-332ER/W	25143/349	178
☐ N178DZ	B767-332ER/W	30596/795	1708
☐ N179DN	B767-332ER/W	25144/350	179
☐ N180DN	B767-332ER/W	25985/428	180
☐ N181DN	B767-332ER/W	25986/446	181
☐ N182DN	B767-332ER/W	25987/461	182
☐ N183DN	B767-332ER/W	27110/492	183
☐ N184DN	B767-332ER/W	27111/496	184
☐ N185DN	B767-332ER/W	27961/576	185
☐ N186DN	B767-332ER/W	27962/585	186
☐ N187DN	B767-332ER/W	27582/617	187
☐ N188DN	B767-332ER/W	27583/631	188
☐ N189DN	B767-332ER/W	25990/646	189
☐ N190DN	B767-332ER/W	28447/653	190
☐ N191DN	B767-332ER/W	28448/654	191
☐ N192DN	B767-332ER/W	28449/664	192
☐ N193DN	B767-332ER/W	28450/671	193
☐ N194DN	B767-332ER/W	28451/675	194
☐ N195DN	B767-332ER/W	28452/676	195
☐ N196DN	B767-332ER/W	28453/679	196
☐ N197DN	B767-332ER/W	28454/683	197
☐ N198DN	B767-332ER/W	28455/685	198
☐ N199DN	B767-332ER/W	28456/690	199
☐ N394DL	B767-324ER/W	27394/572	1521
☐ N764RD	B767-3Y0ER	26204/464	[MZJ]
☐ N1200K	B767-332ER/W	28457/696	1200
☐ N1201P	B767-332ER/W	28458/697	1201
☐ N1402A	B767-332	25989/506	1402
☐ N1501P	B767-3P6ER/W	24983/334	1501
☐ N1602	B767-332ER/W	29694/735	1602
☐ N1603	B767-332ER/W	29695/736	1603
☐ N1604R	B767-332ER/W	30180/749	1604
☐ N1605	B767-332ER/W	30198/753	1605
☐ N1607B	B767-332ER/W	30388/787	1607
☐ N1608	B767-332ER/W	30573/788	1608
☐ N1609	B767-332ER/W	30574/789	1609
☐ N1610D	B767-332ER/W	30594/790	1610
☐ N1611B	B767-332ER/W	30595/794	1611
☐ N1612T	B767-332ER/W	30575/838	1612
☐ N1613B	B767-332ER/W	32776/847	1613
☐ N16065	B767-332ER/W	30199/755	1606
☐ N825MH	B767-432ER	29703/758	1801
☐ N826MH	B767-432ER	29713/769	1802
☐ N827MH	B767-432ER	29705/773	1803
☐ N828MH	B767-432ER	29699/791	1804
☐ N829MH	B767-432ER	29700/801	1805
☐ N830MH	B767-432ER	29701/803	1806
☐ N831MH	B767-432ER	29702/804	1807
☐ N832MH	B767-432ER	29704/807	1808
☐ N833MH	B767-432ER	29706/810	1809
☐ N834MH	B767-432ER	29707/813	1810
☐ N835MH	B767-432ER	29708/814	1811
☐ N836MH	B767-432ER	29709/818	1812
☐ N837MH	B767-432ER	29710/820	1813
☐ N838MH	B767-432ER	29711/821	1814
☐ N839MH	B767-432ER	29712/824	1815
☐ N840MH	B767-432ER	29718/830	1816
☐ N841MH	B767-432ER	29714/855	1817
☐ N842MH	B767-432ER	29715/856	1818
☐ N843MH	B767-432ER	29716/865	1819
☐ N844MH	B767-432ER	29717/871	1820
☐ N845MH	B767-432ER	29719/874	1821
☐ N701DN	B777-232LR	29740/697	7101
☐ N702DN	B777-232LR	29741/704	7102
☐ N703DN	B777-232LR	32222/767	7103
☐ N704DK	B777-232LR	29739/772	7104
☐ N705DN	B777-232LR	29742/773	7105
☐ N706DN	B777-232LR	30440/776	7106
☐ N707DN	B777-232LR	39091/782	7107
☐ N708DN	B777-232LR	39254/789	7108
☐ N709DN	B777-232LR	40559/854	7109
☐ N710DN	B777-232LR	40560/857	7110
☐ N860DA	B777-232ER	29951/202	7001
☐ N861DA	B777-232ER	29952/207	7002
☐ N862DA	B777-232ER	29734/235	7003
☐ N863DA	B777-232ER	29735/245	7004
☐ N864DA	B777-232ER	29736/249	7005
☐ N865DA	B777-232ER	29737/257	7006
☐ N866DA	B777-232ER	29738/261	7007
☐ N867DA	B777-232ER	29743/387	7008
☐ N900DE	MD-88	53372/1970	9000
☐ N901DE	MD-88	53378/1980	9001
☐ N902DE	MD-88	53379/1983	9002
☐ N903DE	MD-88	53380/1986	9003
☐ N904DE	MD-88	53409/1990	9004
☐ N904DL	MD-88	49535/1347	904
☐ N905DE	MD-88	53410/1992	9005
☐ N905DL	MD-88	49536/1348	905
☐ N906DE	MD-88	53415/2027	9006
☐ N906DL	MD-88	49537/1355	906
☐ N907DE	MD-88	53416/2029	9007
☐ N907DL	MD-88	49538/1365	907
☐ N908DE	MD-88	53417/2032	9008
☐ N908DL	MD-88	49539/1366	908
☐ N909DE	MD-88	53418/2033	9009
☐ N910DE	MD-88	53419/2036	9010
☐ N910DL	MD-88	49541/1416	910
☐ N911DE	MD-88	49967/2037	9011
☐ N911DL	MD-88	49542/1433	911
☐ N912DE	MD-88	49997/2038	9012
☐ N912DL	MD-88	49543/1434	912
☐ N913DE	MD-88	49956/2039	9013
☐ N913DL	MD-88	49544/1443	913
☐ N914DE	MD-88	49957/2049	9014

☐	N914DL	MD-88	49545/1444	914
☐	N915DE	MD-88	53420/2050	9015
☐	N915DL	MD-88	49546/1447	915
☐	N916DE	MD-88	53421/2051	9016
☐	N916DL	MD-88	49591/1448	916
☐	N917DE	MD-88	49958/2054	9017
☐	N917DL	MD-88	49573/1469	917
☐	N918DE	MD-88	49959/2055	9018
☐	N918DL	MD-88	49583/1470	918
☐	N919DE	MD-88	53422/2058	9019
☐	N919DL	MD-88	49584/1471	919
☐	N920DE	MD-88	53423/2059	9020
☐	N920DL	MD-88	49644/1473	920
☐	N921DL	MD-88	49645/1480	921
☐	N922DL	MD-88	49646/1481	922
☐	N923DL	MD-88	49705/1491	923
☐	N924DL	MD-88	49711/1492	924
☐	N925DL	MD-88	49712/1500	925
☐	N926DL	MD-88	49713/1523	926
☐	N927DA	MD-88	49714/1524	927
☐	N928DL	MD-88	49715/1530	928
☐	N929DL	MD-88	49716/1531	929
☐	N930DL	MD-88	49717/1532	930
☐	N931DL	MD-88	49718/1533	931
☐	N932DL	MD-88	49719/1570	932
☐	N933DL	MD-88	49720/1571	933
☐	N934DL	MD-88	49721/1574	934
☐	N935DL	MD-88	49722/1575	935
☐	N936DL	MD-88	49723/1576	936
☐	N937DL	MD-88	49810/1588	937
☐	N938DL	MD-88	49811/1590	938
☐	N939DL	MD-88	49812/1593	939
☐	N940DL	MD-88	49813/1599	940
☐	N941DL	MD-88	49814/1602	941
☐	N942DL	MD-88	49815/1605	942
☐	N943DL	MD-88	49816/1608	943
☐	N944DL	MD-88	49817/1612	944
☐	N945DL	MD-88	49818/1613	945
☐	N946DL	MD-88	49819/1629	946
☐	N947DL	MD-88	49878/1664	947
☐	N948DL	MD-88	49879/1666	948
☐	N949DL	MD-88	49880/1676	949
☐	N950DL	MD-88	49881/1677	950
☐	N951DL	MD-88	49882/1679	951
☐	N952DL	MD-88	49883/1683	952
☐	N953DL	MD-88	49884/1685	953
☐	N954DL	MD-88	49885/1689	954
☐	N955DL	MD-88	49886/1691	955
☐	N956DL	MD-88	49887/1699	956
☐	N957DL	MD-88	49976/1700	957
☐	N958DL	MD-88	49977/1701	958
☐	N959DL	MD-88	49978/1710	959
☐	N960DL	MD-88	49979/1711	960
☐	N961DL	MD-88	49980/1712	961
☐	N962DL	MD-88	49981/1725	962
☐	N963DL	MD-88	49982/1726	963
☐	N964DL	MD-88	49983/1747	964
☐	N965DL	MD-88	49984/1748	965
☐	N966DL	MD-88	53115/1795	966
☐	N967DL	MD-88	53116/1796	967
☐	N968DL	MD-88	53161/1808	968
☐	N969DL	MD-88	53172/1810	969
☐	N970DL	MD-88	53173/1811	970
☐	N971DL	MD-88	53214/1823	971
☐	N972DL	MD-88	53215/1824	972
☐	N973DL	MD-88	53241/1832	973
☐	N974DL	MD-88	53242/1833	974
☐	N975DL	MD-88	53243/1834	975
☐	N976DL	MD-88	53257/1845	976
☐	N977DL	MD-88	53258/1848	977
☐	N978DL	MD-88	53259/1849	978
☐	N979DL	MD-88	53266/1859	979
☐	N980DL	MD-88	53267/1860	980
☐	N981DL	MD-88	53268/1861	981
☐	N982DL	MD-88	53273/1870	982
☐	N983DL	MD-88	53274/1873	983
☐	N984DL	MD-88	53311/1912	984
☐	N985DL	MD-88	53312/1914	985
☐	N986DL	MD-88	53313/1924	986
☐	N987DL	MD-88	53338/1926	987
☐	N988DL	MD-88	53339/1928	988
☐	N989DL	MD-88	53341/1936	989
☐	N990DL	MD-88	53342/1939	990
☐	N991DL	MD-88	53343/1941	991
☐	N992DL	MD-88	53344/1943	992
☐	N993DL	MD-88	53345/1950	993
☐	N994DL	MD-88	53346/1952	994
☐	N995DL	MD-88	53362/1955	995
☐	N996DL	MD-88	53363/1958	996
☐	N997DL	MD-88	53364/1961	997
☐	N998DL	MD-88	53370/1963	998
☐	N999DN	MD-88	53371/1965	999
☐	N901DA	MD-90-30	53381/2100	9201
☐	N902DA	MD-90-30	53382/2094	9202
☐	N903DA	MD-90-30	53383/2095	9203
☐	N904DA	MD-90-30	53384/2096	9204
☐	N905DA	MD-90-30	53385/2097	9205
☐	N906DA	MD-90-30	53386/2099	9206
☐	N907DA	MD-90-30	53387/2115	9207
☐	N908DA	MD-90-30	53388/2117	9208
☐	N909DA	MD-90-30	53389/2122	9209
☐	N910DN	MD-90-30	53390/2123	9210
☐	N911DA	MD-90-30	53391/2126	9211
☐	N912DN	MD-90-30	53392/2136	9212
☐	N913DN	MD-90-30	53393/2154	9213
☐	N914DN	MD-90-30	53394/2156	9214
☐	N915DN	MD-90-30	53395/2159	9215
☐	N916DN	MD-90-30	53396/2161	9216
☐	N917DN	MD-90-30	53552/2163	9217
☐	N918DH	MD-90-30	53553/2165	9218
☐	N919DN	MD-90-30	53576/2195	9219
☐	N920DN	MD-90-30	53582/2198	9220
☐	N921DN	MD-90-30	53583/2200	9221
☐	N922DX	MD-90-30	53584/2203	9222
☐	N923DN	MD-90-30	53585/2224	9223
☐	N924DN	MD-90-30	53586/2233	9224
☐	N925DN	MD-90-30	53587/2240	9225
☐	N926DH	MD-90-30	53588/2248	9226
☐	N927DN	MD-90-30	53589/2259	9227
☐	N928DN	MD-90-30	53590/2261	9228
☐	N929DN	MD-90-30	53459/2141	9229
☐	N930DN	MD-90-30	53458/2140	9230
☐	N931DN	MD-90-30	53544/2197	9231
☐	N932DN	MD-90-30	53457/2138	9232
☐	N933DN	MD-90-30	53543/2194	9233
☐	N934DN	MD-90-30	53462/2149	9234
☐	N935DN	MD-90-30	53460/2142	9235
☐	N936DN	MD-90-30	53461/2147	9236
☐	N937DN	MD-90-30	53352/2098	9237
☐	N938DN	MD-90-30	53353/2120	9238
☐	N939DN	MD-90-30	53356/2157	9239
☐	N940DN	MD-90-30	53359/2164	9240
☐	N941DN	MD-90-30	53555/2207	9241

☐	N942DN	MD-90-30	53556/2210	9242
☐	N943DN	MD-90-30	53557/2211	9243
☐	N944DN	MD-90-30	53558/2212	9244
☐	N945DN	MD-90-30	53559/2236	9345
☐	N946DN	MD-90-30	53354/2125	9346
☐	N947DN	MD-90-30	53355/2131	9347
☐	N948DN	MD-90-30	53357/2164	9348
☐	N949DN	MD-90-30	53358/2179	9349
☐	N950DN	MD-90-30	53360/2190	9350
☐	N951DN	MD-90-30	53361/2202	9351
☐	N952DN	MD-90-30	53560/2245	9252
☐	N953DN	MD-90-30	53523/2143	9253
☐	N954DN	MD-90-30	53524/2146	9254
☐	N955DN	MD-90-30	53525/2150	9255
☐	N956DN	MD-90-30	53526/2170	9256
☐	N957DN	MD-90-30	53527/2175	9257
☐	N958DN	MD-90-30	53528/2177	9258
☐	N959DN	MD-90-30	53529/2220	9259
☐	N960DN	MD-90-30	53530/2222	9260
☐	N961DN	MD-90-30	53531/2228	9261
☐	N962DN	MD-90-30	53532/2253	9262
☐	N963DN	MD-90-30	53533/2258	9263
☐	N964DN	MD-90-30	60001/4001	9264
☐	N965DN	MD-90-30	60002/4002	9265

DELTA CONNECTION — DL / DAL

☐	N416SW	CRJ-200ER	7089	7089
☐	N418SW	CRJ-200ER	7446	7446
☐	N426SW	CRJ-200ER	7468	7468
☐	N427SW	CRJ-200ER	7497	7497
☐	N429SW	CRJ-200ER	7518	7518
☐	N430SW	CRJ-200ER	7523	7523
☐	N431SW	CRJ-200ER	7536	7536
☐	N432SW	CRJ-200ER	7548	7548
☐	N433SW	CRJ-200ER	7550	7550
☐	N437SW	CRJ-200ER	7564	7564
☐	N438SW	CRJ-200ER	7574	7574
☐	N439SW	CRJ-200ER	7578	7578
☐	N440SW	CRJ-200ER	7589	7589
☐	N441SW	CRJ-200ER	7602	7602
☐	N442SW	CRJ-200ER	7609	7609
☐	N443SW	CRJ-200ER	7638	
☐	N445SW	CRJ-200ER	7651	7651
☐	N446SW	CRJ-200ER	7666	7666
☐	N447SW	CRJ-200ER	7677	7677
☐	N448SW	CRJ-200ER	7678	7678
☐	N449SW	CRJ-200ER	7699	7699
☐	N452SW	CRJ-200ER	7716	7716
☐	N453SW	CRJ-200ER	7743	7743
☐	N454SW	CRJ-200ER	7749	7749
☐	N455CA	CRJ-200ER	7592	7592
☐	N455SW	CRJ-200ER	7760	7760
☐	N457SW	CRJ-200ER	7773	7773
☐	N459SW	CRJ-200ER	7782	7782
☐	N460SW	CRJ-200ER	7803	7803
☐	N461SW	CRJ-200ER	7811	7811
☐	N463SW	CRJ-200ER	7820	7820
☐	N466SW	CRJ-200LR	7856	♦
☐	N468CA	CRJ-200ER	7649	♦
☐	N477CA	CRJ-200ER	7670	♦
☐	N495CA	CRJ-200ER	7774	♦
☐	N496CA	CRJ-200ER	7791	♦
☐	N506CA	CRJ-200ER	7793	♦
☐	N594SW	CRJ-100ER	7285	♦
☐	N601XJ	CRJ-200LR	8044	8044
☐	N602XJ	CRJ-200LR	8045	8045
☐	N629BR	CRJ-200ER	7251	7251
☐	N652BR	CRJ-200ER	7429	♦
☐	N659BR	CRJ-200ER	7509	7509
☐	N675BR	CRJ-200ER	7635	7635
☐	N685BR	CRJ-200ER	7712	7712
☐	N686BR	CRJ-200ER	7715	7715
☐	N779CA	CRJ-100ER	7306	7306
☐	N781CA	CRJ-100ER	7312	7312
☐	N783CA	CRJ-100ER	7315	7315
☐	N801AY	CRJ-200LR	8001	8001
☐	N809CA	CRJ-100ER	7366	7366
☐	N819AY	CRJ-200LR	8019	8019
☐	N820AY	CRJ-200LR	8020	8020
☐	N823AS	CRJ-200ER	7196	823
☐	N832AY	CRJ-200LR	8032	8032
☐	N833AY	CRJ-200LR	8033	8033
☐	N834AY	CRJ-200LR	8034	8034
☐	N835AY	CRJ-200LR	8035	8035
☐	N836AY	CRJ-200LR	8036	8036
☐	N840AY	CRJ-200LR	8040	8040
☐	N843AS	CRJ-200ER	7310	843
☐	N846AS	CRJ-200ER	7328	846
☐	N847AS	CRJ-200ER	7335	847
☐	N848AS	CRJ-200ER	7339	848
☐	N849AS	CRJ-200ER	7347	849
☐	N850AS	CRJ-200ER	7355	850
☐	N851AS	CRJ-200ER	7360	851
☐	N852AS	CRJ-200ER	7369	852
☐	N853AS	CRJ-200ER	7374	853
☐	N854AS	CRJ-200ER	7382	854
☐	N855AS	CRJ-200ER	7395	855
☐	N856AS	CRJ-200ER	7404	856
☐	N857AS	CRJ-200ER	7411	857
☐	N858AS	CRJ-200ER	7417	858
☐	N859AS	CRJ-200ER	7421	859
☐	N860AS	CRJ-200ER	7433	860
☐	N861AS	CRJ-200ER	7445	861
☐	N867AS	CRJ-200ER	7463	867
☐	N868AS	CRJ-200ER	7474	868
☐	N870AS	CRJ-200ER	7530	870
☐	N871AS	CRJ-200ER	7537	871
☐	N872AS	CRJ-200ER	7542	872
☐	N873AS	CRJ-200ER	7549	873
☐	N878AS	CRJ-200ER	7590	878
☐	N881AS	CRJ-200ER	7496	881
☐	N882AS	CRJ-200ER	7503	882
☐	N883AS	CRJ-200ER	7504	883
☐	N884AS	CRJ-200ER	7513	884
☐	N885AS	CRJ-200ER	7521	♦
☐	N886AS	CRJ-200ER	7531	♦
☐	N889AS	CRJ-200ER	7538	♦
☐	N900EV	CRJ-200ER	7608	900
☐	N910EV	CRJ-200ER	7727	7727
☐	N912EV	CRJ-200ER	7728	7728
☐	N913EV	CRJ-200ER	7731	7731
☐	N914EV	CRJ-200ER	7752	914
☐	N915EV	CRJ-200ER	7754	7754
☐	N916EV	CRJ-200ER	7757	916
☐	N917EV	CRJ-200ER	7769	917
☐	N919EV	CRJ-200ER	7780	919
☐	N920EV	CRJ-200ER	7810	920
☐	N921EV	CRJ-200ER	7819	921
☐	N922EV	CRJ-200ER	7822	922
☐	N923EV	CRJ-200ER	7826	923
☐	N924EV	CRJ-200ER	7830	924
☐	N925EV	CRJ-200ER	7831	925
☐	N926EV	CRJ-200ER	7843	926

☐	N927EV	CRJ-200ER	7844	927
☐	N931EV	CRJ-200ER	8015	931
☐	N933EV	CRJ-200ER	8022	933
☐	N935SW	CRJ-200ER	7725	
☐	N936EV	CRJ-200ER	8038	936
☐	N936SW	CRJ-200ER	7726	
☐	N937EV	CRJ-200ER	8042	937
☐	N944SW	CRJ-200LR	7764	♦
☐	N953SW	CRJ-200LR	7813	♦
☐	N979EV	CRJ-200ER	7737	979
☐	N980EV	CRJ-200ER	7759	980
☐	N981EV	CRJ-200ER	7768	981
☐	N8390A	CRJ-200LR	7390	♦
☐	N8416B	CRJ-200LR	7416	♦
☐	N8506C	CRJ-200LR	7506	♦
☐	N8516C	CRJ-200LR	7516	♦
☐	N8721B	CRJ-200LR	7721	8721
☐	N8828D	CRJ-200LR	7828	8828
☐	N8836A	CRJ-440LR	7836	♦
☐	N8837B	CRJ-440LR	7837	♦
☐	N8839E	CRJ-200LR	7839	8839
☐	N8847A	CRJ-200LR	7847	8847
☐	N8855A	CRJ-440LR	7855	♦
☐	N8869B	CRJ-200LR	7869	8869
☐	N8877A	CRJ-200LR	7877	8877
☐	N8883E	CRJ-200LR	7883	8883
☐	N8884E	CRJ-200LR	7884	8884
☐	N8888D	CRJ-200LR	7888	♦
☐	N8891A	CRJ-200LR	7891	8891
☐	N8896A	CRJ-200LR	7896	♦
☐	N8903A	CRJ-200LR	7903	8903
☐	N8905F	CRJ-200LR	7905	8905
☐	N8907A	CRJ-200LR	7907	8907
☐	N8913A	CRJ-200LR	7913	8913
☐	N8923A	CRJ-200LR	7923	8923
☐	N8924B	CRJ-200LR	7924	8924
☐	N8930E	CRJ-200LR	7930	8930
☐	N8932C	CRJ-200LR	7932	8932
☐	N8933B	CRJ-200LR	7933	8933
☐	N8938A	CRJ-200LR	7938	8938
☐	N8940E	CRJ-200LR	7940	8940
☐	N8942A	CRJ-200LR	7942	8942
☐	N8944B	CRJ-200LR	7944	8944
☐	N8946A	CRJ-440LR	7946	8946♦
☐	N8960A	CRJ-200LR	7960	8960
☐	N8964E	CRJ-200LR	7964	8964
☐	N8965E	CRJ-200LR	7965	8965
☐	N8968E	CRJ-200LR	7968	8968
☐	N8969A	CRJ-200LR	7969	8969
☐	N8970D	CRJ-200LR	7970	8970
☐	N8972E	CRJ-200LR	7972	8972
☐	N8974C	CRJ-200LR	7974	8974
☐	N8977A	CRJ-200LR	7977	8977
☐	N8980A	CRJ-200LR	7980	8980
☐	N8982A	CRJ-200LR	7982	8982
☐	N8986B	CRJ-200LR	7986	8986

☐	N317CA	CRJ-701ER	10055	10055
☐	N331CA	CRJ-701ER	10061	10061
☐	N340CA	CRJ-701ER	10062	10062
☐	N354CA	CRJ-701ER	10064	10064
☐	N355CA	CRJ-701ER	10067	10067
☐	N367CA	CRJ-701ER	10069	10069
☐	N368CA	CRJ-701ER	10075	10075
☐	N369CA	CRJ-701ER	10079	10079
☐	N371CA	CRJ-701ER	10082	10082
☐	N374CA	CRJ-701ER	10090	10090
☐	N376CA	CRJ-701ER	10092	10092
☐	N378CA	CRJ-701ER	10097	10097
☐	N379CA	CRJ-701ER	10102	10102
☐	N390CA	CRJ-701ER	10106	10106
☐	N391CA	CRJ-701ER	10108	10108
☐	N398CA	CRJ-701ER	10112	10112
☐	N603QX	CRJ-701	10011	10011
☐	N603SK	CRJ-702ER	10248	10248
☐	N604QX	CRJ-701	10019	10019
☐	N604SK	CRJ-702ER	10249	10249
☐	N605QX	CRJ-701	10022	10022
☐	N606SK	CRJ-702ER	10250	10250
☐	N607SK	CRJ-702ER	10251	10251
☐	N608QX	CRJ-701	10026	10026
☐	N608SK	CRJ-702ER	10252	10252
☐	N609SK	CRJ-701ER	10020	10020
☐	N611QX	CRJ-701	10041	10041
☐	N611SK	CRJ-701ER	10035	10035
☐	N612QX	CRJ-701	10042	10042
☐	N613QX	CRJ-701	10045	10045
☐	N613SK	CRJ-701ER	10038	10038
☐	N614QX	CRJ-701	10049	10049
☐	N614SK	CRJ-701ER	10051	10051
☐	N615QX	CRJ-701	10065	10065
☐	N616QX	CRJ-701	10128	10128
☐	N617QX	CRJ-701	10130	10130
☐	N625CA	CRJ-701ER	10113	10113
☐	N630SK	CRJ-701	10328	10328
☐	N631SK	CRJ-701	10329	10329
☐	N632SK	CRJ-702	10330	10330
☐	N633SK	CRJ-702	10331	10331
☐	N641CA	CRJ-701ER	10122	10122
☐	N642CA	CRJ-701ER	10125	10125
☐	N653CA	CRJ-701ER	10129	10129
☐	N655CA	CRJ-701ER	10134	10134
☐	N656CA	CRJ-701ER	10143	10143
☐	N658CA	CRJ-701ER	10148	10148
☐	N659CA	CRJ-701ER	10153	10153
☐	N668CA	CRJ-701ER	10162	10162
☐	N669CA	CRJ-701ER	10176	10176
☐	N690CA	CRJ-701ER	10182	10182
☐	N707EV	CRJ-701ER	10057	707
☐	N708EV	CRJ-701ER	10060	708
☐	N709EV	CRJ-701ER	10068	709
☐	N710EV	CRJ-701ER	10071	710
☐	N712EV	CRJ-701ER	10074	712
☐	N713EV	CRJ-701ER	10081	713
☐	N716EV	CRJ-701ER	10084	716
☐	N717EV	CRJ-701ER	10088	717
☐	N718EV	CRJ-701ER	10095	718
☐	N719EV	CRJ-701ER	10099	719
☐	N720EV	CRJ-701ER	10115	720
☐	N722EV	CRJ-701ER	10127	722
☐	N723EV	CRJ-701ER	10132	723
☐	N724EV	CRJ-701ER	10138	724
☐	N730EV	CRJ-701ER	10141	730
☐	N738EV	CRJ-701ER	10146	738
☐	N740EV	CRJ-701ER	10151	740
☐	N741EV	CRJ-701ER	10155	741
☐	N744EV	CRJ-701ER	10157	744
☐	N748EV	CRJ-701ER	10158	748
☐	N750EV	CRJ-701ER	10161	750
☐	N751EV	CRJ-701ER	10163	751
☐	N752EV	CRJ-701ER	10166	752
☐	N753EV	CRJ-701ER	10169	753
☐	N754EV	CRJ-701ER	10173	754
☐	N755EV	CRJ-701ER	10185	755

☐	N758EV	CRJ-701ER	10210	758
☐	N759EV	CRJ-701ER	10211	759
☐	N760EV	CRJ-701ER	10212	760
☐	N761ND	CRJ-701ER	10213	761
☐	N131EV	CRJ-900ER	15217	131
☐	N132EV	CRJ-900ER	15219	132
☐	N133EV	CRJ-900ER	15222	133
☐	N134EV	CRJ-900ER	15223	134
☐	N135EV	CRJ-900ER	15225	135
☐	N136EV	CRJ-900ER	15226	136
☐	N137EV	CRJ-900ER	15227	137
☐	N138EV	CRJ-900ER	15235	138
☐	N146PQ	CRJ-900ER	15146	15146
☐	N147PQ	CRJ-900ER	15147	15147
☐	N153PQ	CRJ-900ER	15153	15153
☐	N161PQ	CRJ-900ER	15161	15161
☐	N162PQ	CRJ-900ER	15162	15162
☐	N166PQ	CRJ-900ER	15166	15166
☐	N170PQ	CRJ-900ER	15170	15170
☐	N176PQ	CRJ-900ER	15176	15176
☐	N181GJ	CRJ-900LR	15204	♦
☐	N182GJ	CRJ-900LR	15175	♦
☐	N183GJ	CRJ-900LR	15209	♦
☐	N184GJ	CRJ-900LR	15169	♦
☐	N185GJ	CRJ-900LR	15185	♦
☐	N186GJ	CRJ-900LR	15165	♦
☐	N187GJ	CRJ-900LR	15180	♦
☐	N181PQ	CRJ-900ER	15181	15181
☐	N186PQ	CRJ-900ER	15186	15186
☐	N187PQ	CRJ-900ER	15187	15187
☐	N195PQ	CRJ-900ER	15195	15195
☐	N197PQ	CRJ-900ER	15197	15197
☐	N200PQ	CRJ-900ER	15200	15200
☐	N228PQ	CRJ-900ER	15228	15228
☐	N232PQ	CRJ-900ER	15232	15232
☐	N272PQ	CRJ-900ER	15272	15272
☐	N279PQ	CRJ-900LR	15279	15279
☐	N292PQ	CRJ-900LR	15292	15292
☐	N293PQ	CRJ-900LR	15293	15293
☐	N294PQ	CRJ-900LR	15294	15294
☐	N295PQ	CRJ-900LR	15295	15295
☐	N296PQ	CRJ-900LR	15296	15296
☐	N297PQ	CRJ-900LR	15297	15297
☐	N298PQ	CRJ-900LR	15298	15298
☐	N299PQ	CRJ-900LR	15299	15299
☐	N300PQ	CRJ-900LR	15300	15300
☐	N301PQ	CRJ-900LR	15301	15301
☐	N302PQ	CRJ-900LR	15302	15302
☐	N303PQ	CRJ-900LR	15303	15303
☐	N304PQ	CRJ-900LR	15304	15304
☐	N305PQ	CRJ-900LR	15305	15305
☐	N306PQ	CRJ-900LR	15306	15306
☐	N307PQ	CRJ-900LR	15307	15307
☐	N308PQ	CRJ-900LR	15308	15308
☐	N309PQ	CRJ-900LR	15309	15309
☐	N310PQ	CRJ-900LR	15310	15310
☐	N311PQ	CRJ-900LR	15311	15311
☐	N313PQ	CRJ-900LR	15313	15313
☐	N314PQ	CRJ-900LR	15314	15314
☐	N315PQ	CRJ-900LR	15315	15315
☐	N316PQ	CRJ-900LR	15316	15316
☐	N319PQ	CRJ-900LR	15319	15319
☐	N320PQ	CRJ-900LR	15320	15320
☐	N324PQ	CRJ-900LR	15324	15324
☐	N325PQ	CRJ-900LR	15325	15325
☐	N326PQ	CRJ-900LR	15326	15326
☐	N329PQ	CRJ-900LR	15329	15329
☐	N330PQ	CRJ-900LR	15330	15330
☐	N331PQ	CRJ-900LR	15331	15331
☐	N335PQ	CRJ-900LR	15335	15335
☐	N336PQ	CRJ-900LR	15336	15336
☐	N337PQ	CRJ-900LR	15337	15337
☐	N341PQ	CRJ-900LR	15341	15341
☐	N348PQ	CRJ-900LR	15348	15348
☐	N349PQ	CRJ-900LR	15349	15349
☐	N538CA	CRJ-900ER	15157	15157
☐	N548CA	CRJ-900ER	15159	15159
☐	N549CA	CRJ-900ER	15164	15164
☐	N554CA	CRJ-900ER	15168	15168
☐	N582CA	CRJ-900ER	15171	15171
☐	N600LR	CRJ-900ER	15142	950
☐	N601LR	CRJ-900ER	15145	951
☐	N602LR	CRJ-900ER	15151	952
☐	N604LR	CRJ-900ER	15152	953
☐	N605LR	CRJ-900ER	15160	954
☐	N606LR	CRJ-900ER	15173	606
☐	N607LR	CRJ-900ER	15178	607
☐	N676CA	CRJ-900ER	15127	15127
☐	N678CA	CRJ-900ER	15125	15125
☐	N679CA	CRJ-900ER	15132	15132
☐	N689CA	CRJ-900ER	15133	15133
☐	N691CA	CRJ-900ER	15136	15136
☐	N692CA	CRJ-900ER	15092	15092
☐	N693CA	CRJ-900ER	15096	15096
☐	N695CA	CRJ-900ER	15097	15097
☐	N800SK	CRJ-900ER	15060	15060
☐	N802SK	CRJ-900ER	15061	15061
☐	N803SK	CRJ-900ER	15062	15062
☐	N804SK	CRJ-900ER	15067	15067
☐	N805SK	CRJ-900ER	15069	15069
☐	N806SK	CRJ-900ER	15070	15070
☐	N807SK	CRJ-900ER	15082	15082
☐	N809SK	CRJ-900ER	15086	15086
☐	N810SK	CRJ-900ER	15093	15093
☐	N812SK	CRJ-900ER	15098	15098
☐	N813SK	CRJ-900ER	15099	15099
☐	N814SK	CRJ-900ER	15100	15100
☐	N815SK	CRJ-900ER	15101	15101
☐	N816SK	CRJ-900ER	15105	15105
☐	N817SK	CRJ-900ER	15107	15107
☐	N820SK	CRJ-900ER	15108	15108
☐	N821SK	CRJ-900ER	15109	15109
☐	N822SK	CRJ-900ER	15203	15203
☐	N823SK	CRJ-900ER	15205	15205
☐	N824SK	CRJ-900ER	15208	15208
☐	N825SK	CRJ-900ER	15212	15212
☐	N901XJ	CRJ-900	15130	901
☐	N902XJ	CRJ-900	15131	902
☐	N903XJ	CRJ-900	15134	903
☐	N904XJ	CRJ-900	15135	904
☐	N905XJ	CRJ-900	15137	905
☐	N906XJ	CRJ-900	15138	906
☐	N907XJ	CRJ-900	15139	907
☐	N908XJ	CRJ-900	15140	908
☐	N909XJ	CRJ-900	15141	909
☐	N910XJ	CRJ-900	15143	910
☐	N912XJ	CRJ-900	15144	912
☐	N913XJ	CRJ-900	15148	913
☐	N914XJ	CRJ-900	15149	914
☐	N915XJ	CRJ-900	15150	915
☐	N916XJ	CRJ-900	15154	916
☐	N917XJ	CRJ-900	15155	917
☐	N918XJ	CRJ-900	15156	918

☐	N919XJ	CRJ-900	15163	919
☐	N920XJ	CRJ-900	15167	920
☐	N921XJ	CRJ-900	15172	921
☐	N922XJ	CRJ-900	15174	922
☐	N923XJ	CRJ-900	15177	923
☐	N924XJ	CRJ-900	15179	924
☐	N925XJ	CRJ-900	15183	925
☐	N926XJ	CRJ-900	15184	926
☐	N927XJ	CRJ-900	15188	927
☐	N928XJ	CRJ-900	15190	928
☐	N929XJ	CRJ-900	15191	929
☐	N930XJ	CRJ-900	15192	930
☐	N931XJ	CRJ-900	15193	931
☐	N932XJ	CRJ-900	15194	932
☐	N933XJ	CRJ-900	15196	933
☐	N934XJ	CRJ-900	15198	934
☐	N935XJ	CRJ-900	15199	935
☐	N936XJ	CRJ-900	15201	936
☐	N937XJ	CRJ-900	15210	937

☐	N257JQ	ERJ-145LR	145812	257
☐	N258JQ	ERJ-145LR	145768	258
☐	N259JQ	ERJ-145LR	145763	259
☐	N266SK	ERJ-145LR	145241	266
☐	N269SK	ERJ-145LR	145293	269
☐	N270SK	ERJ-145LR	145304	270
☐	N271SK	ERJ-145LR	145305	271
☐	N272SK	ERJ-145LR	145306	8272
☐	N273SK	ERJ-145LR	145331	8273
☐	N274SK	ERJ-145LR	145344	8274
☐	N276SK	ERJ-145LR	145348	8275
☐	N278SK	ERJ-145LR	145370	278♦
☐	N280SK	ERJ-145LR	145381	280
☐	N281SK	ERJ-145LR	145391	281
☐	N286SK	ERJ-145LR	145443	
☐	N287SK	ERJ-145LR	145460	♦
☐	N290SK	ERJ-145LR	145474	290
☐	N293SK	ERJ-145LR	145500	293
☐	N294SK	ERJ-145LR	145497	294
☐	N296SK	ERJ-145LR	145514	296
☐	N298SK	ERJ-145LR	145508	298
☐	N370SK	ERJ-145LR	145515	370
☐	N561RP	ERJ-145LR	145447	8561
☐	N562RP	ERJ-145LR	145451	8562
☐	N563RP	ERJ-145LR	145509	8563
☐	N565RP	ERJ-145LR	145679	8565
☐	N566RP	ERJ-145LR	145691	8566
☐	N567RP	ERJ-145LR	145698	8567
☐	N568RP	ERJ-145LR	145800	8568
☐	N569RP	ERJ-145LR	14500816	8569
☐	N570RP	ERJ-145LR	14500821	8570
☐	N571RP	ERJ-145LR	14500827	8571
☐	N572RP	ERJ-145LR	14500828	8572
☐	N573RP	ERJ-145LR	14500837	8573
☐	N574RP	ERJ-145LR	14500845	8574
☐	N575RP	ERJ-145LR	14500847	8575
☐	N576RP	ERJ-145LR	14500856	8576
☐	N577RP	ERJ-145LR	14500862	8577
☐	N578RP	ERJ-145LR	14500865	8578
☐	N579RP	ERJ-145LR	14500871	8579

☐	N201JQ	ERJ-175LR	17000235	8201
☐	N202JQ	ERJ-175LR	17000240	8202
☐	N203JQ	ERJ-175LR	17000242	8203
☐	N204JQ	ERJ-175LR	17000243	8204
☐	N205JQ	ERJ-175LR	17000248	8205♦
☐	N206JQ	ERJ-175LR	17000249	8206
☐	N207JQ	ERJ-175LR	17000254	8207
☐	N208JQ	ERJ-175LR	17000257	8208
☐	N209JQ	ERJ-175LR	17000258	8209
☐	N210JQ	ERJ-175LR	17000260	8210
☐	N211JQ	ERJ-175LR	17000261	8211
☐	N212JQ	ERJ-175LR	17000264	8212
☐	N213JQ	ERJ-175LR	17000265	8213
☐	N214JQ	ERJ-175LR	17000267	8214
☐	N215JQ	ERJ-175LR	17000270	8215
☐	N216JQ	ERJ-175LR	17000273	8216
☐	N602CZ	ERJ-175LR	17000171	602
☐	N603CZ	ERJ-175LR	17000176	603
☐	N604CZ	ERJ-175LR	17000181	604
☐	N605CZ	ERJ-175LR	17000186	605
☐	N606CZ	ERJ-175LR	17000188	606
☐	N607CZ	ERJ-175LR	17000192	607
☐	N608CZ	ERJ-175LR	17000195	608
☐	N609CZ	ERJ-175LR	17000197	609
☐	N610CZ	ERJ-175LR	17000198	610
☐	N612CZ	ERJ-175LR	17000201	612
☐	N613CZ	ERJ-175AR	17000203	613
☐	N614CZ	ERJ-175AR	17000205	614
☐	N615CZ	ERJ-175LR	17000207	615
☐	N616CZ	ERJ-175LR	17000209	616
☐	N617CZ	ERJ-175LR	17000210	617
☐	N619CZ	ERJ-175LR	17000213	619
☐	N620CZ	ERJ-175LR	17000214	620
☐	N621CZ	ERJ-175LR	17000218	621
☐	N622CZ	ERJ-175LR	17000219	622
☐	N623CZ	ERJ-175LR	17000221	623
☐	N624CZ	ERJ-175LR	17000222	624
☐	N625CZ	ERJ-175AR	17000225	625
☐	N626CZ	ERJ-175AR	17000226	626
☐	N627CZ	ERJ-175AR	17000229	627
☐	N628CZ	ERJ-175AR	17000233	628
☐	N629CZ	ERJ-175AR	17000236	629
☐	N630CZ	ERJ-175AR	17000238	630
☐	N631CZ	ERJ-175AR	17000239	631
☐	N632CZ	ERJ-175AR	17000244	632
☐	N633CZ	ERJ-175AR	17000245	633
☐	N634CZ	ERJ-175AR	17000246	634
☐	N635CZ	ERJ-175AR	17000252	635
☐	N636CZ	ERJ-175AR	17000253	636
☐	N637CZ	ERJ-175AR	17000256	637
☐	N638CZ	ERJ-175AR	17000259	638
☐	N639CZ	ERJ-175AR	17000262	639
☐	N746CZ	ERJ-170LR	17000180	
☐	N747CZ	ERJ-170LR	17000187	
☐	N748CZ	ERJ-170LR	17000191	
☐	N749CZ	ERJ-170LR	17000227	
☐	N751CZ	ERJ-170LR	17000247	
☐	N752CZ	ERJ-170LR	17000255	
☐	N810MD	ERJ-170SU	17000026	<TCF
☐	N815MD	ERJ-170SU	17000034	<TCF
☐	N818MD	ERJ-170SU	17000039	<RPA
☐	N823MD	ERJ-170SU	17000044	
☐	N824MD	ERJ-170SU	17000045	
☐	N860RW	ERJ-170SE	17000084	
☐	N867RW	ERJ-170SU	17000130	
☐	N868RW	ERJ-170SU	17000131	
☐	N869RW	ERJ-170SE	17000133	<RPA
☐	N870RW	ERJ-170SE	17000138	
☐	N871RW	ERJ-170SU	17000140	<TCF
☐	N872RW	ERJ-170SU	17000143	<TCF
☐	N873RW	ERJ-170SU	17000144	<RPA
☐	N874RW	ERJ-170SU	17000148	<RPA

Operated by the following airlines; Chautauqua Airlines, Compass Airlines, Endeavor Air, ExpressJet Airlines, GoJet Airlines, Shuttle America and Skywest Airlines.

DYNAMIC INTERNATIONAL AIRWAYS D2 / DYA

	Reg	Type	c/n	Notes
☐	N250MY	B767-238ER	23306/125	[MZJ]♦
☐	N253MY	B767-23BER	23974/214	
☐	N254MY	B767-336ER	25443/219	
☐	N767DA	B767-246	23213/118	
☐	N769DA	B767-246	23212/117	[SHD]♦
☐	N770JM	B767-233	24145/236	[GYR]
☐	N796JM	B767-336ER	24339/298	♦

DYNAMIC AVIATION

	Reg	Type	c/n	Notes
☐	N49FE	DHC-8-102A	241	♦
☐	N805WP	DHC-8-103	353	♦
☐	N806WP	DHC-8-103	357	♦
☐	N8100A	DHC-8-102A	225	♦
☐	N8100V	DHC-8-102	024	♦
☐	N8200H	DHC-8Q-202	494	♦
☐	N8200L	DHC-8Q-202	455	♦
☐	(N8200R)	DHC-8-202	425 [N987HA]	♦
☐	N8300C	DHC-8-311	307	♦

EG & G

	Reg	Type	c/n	Notes
☐	N273RH	B737-66N	29890/1276	
☐	N288DP	B737-66N	29892/1305	
☐	N319BD	B737-66N	28649/887	
☐	N365SR	B737-66N	29891/1294	
☐	N859WP	B737-66N	28652/938	
☐	N869HH	B737-66N	28650/932	
☐	N20RA	Beech 1900C	UB-42	
☐	N623RA	Beech 1900C-1	UC-163	

EASTERN AIR LINES EA / EAL

	Reg	Type	c/n	Notes
☐	N276EA	B737-8AL/W	35070/2115	
☐	N277EA	B737-8CX/W	32359/1041	♦
☐	N278EA	B737-7L9/W	2800626	♦
☐	N279EA	B737-86J/W	36881/3671	
☐	N280EA	B737-85P/W	33982/2338	♦

ELITE AIRWAYS MNU

	Reg	Type	c/n	Notes
☐	N91EA	CRJ-200ER	7705	
☐	N92EA	CRJ-200ER	7732	
☐	N93EA	CRJ-200ER	7563	
☐	N96EA	CRJ-200ER	7700	
☐	N97EA	CRJ-100ER	7027	
☐	N155MW	CRJ-200LR	7021	♦
☐	N11EA	CRJ-701ER	10043	♦
☐	N24EA	CRJ-701ER	10040	♦
☐	N54EA	CRJ-701ER	10100	♦
☐	N86EA	CRJ-701ER	10086	♦
☐		CRJ-701ER	10103	std♦

EMPIRE AIRLINES EM / CFS

Operates aircraft for FedEX see their fleet.

ERICKSON AERO TANKER (AERO AIR) WIL

	Reg	Type	c/n	Notes
☐	N401US	Douglas DC-7	45145/767	62
☐	N838D	Douglas DC-7	45347/936	60
☐	N6353C	Douglas DC-7	45486/964	66
☐	N291EA	MD-87	53039/1881	101
☐	N292EA	MD-87	53208/1865	
☐	N293EA	MD-87	53209/1867	103
☐	N294EA	MD-87	53210/1871	
☐	N295EA	MD-87	53211/1874	
☐	N296EA	MD-87	53212/1877	
☐	N297EA	MD-87	53213/1879	
☐	N950NS	MD-83	53023/1821	o/o

EVERGREEN HELICOPTERS 7E

	Reg	Type	c/n	Notes
☐	N104EV	Beech 1900D	UE-166	
☐	N105EV	Beech 1900D	UE-64	
☐	N171CJ	Beech 1900D	UE-71	
☐	N172MJ	Beech 1900D	UE-72	
☐	N348CA	CASA 212-200	CC20-7-175	
☐	N392CA	CASA 212-300	DF72-2-398	
☐	N422CA	CASA 212-200	CC40-5-238	
☐	N437CA	CASA 212-200	CC29-1-180	
☐	N502FS	CASA 212-200	CD58-1-294	

EVERTS AIR CARGO 3K / VTS

	Reg	Type	c/n	Notes
☐	N904CE	DC-9-32CF	47040/172	
☐	N930CE	DC-9-33F	47363/445	
☐	N932CE	DC-9-33CF	47465/584	
☐	N935CE	DC-9-33RC	47413/521	
☐	N952AX	DC-9-41F	47615/751	
☐	N964CE	MD-83	53078/1996	o/o♦
☐	N965AS	MD-83	53079/2004	
☐	N73444	MD-82SF	49470/1417	
☐	N100CE	Douglas C-118A	44662/629	
☐	N151	Douglas DC-6B	45496/992	
☐	N170UA	Douglas DC-6A	45518/998	♦
☐	N251CE	Douglas C-118A	44612/532	
☐	N351CE	Douglas C-118A	44599/505	
☐	N400UA	Douglas DC-6A	44258/467	[FAI]
☐	N451CE	Douglas C-118B	43712/358	♦
☐	N500UA	Douglas DC-6A	44597/501	♦
☐	N551CE	Douglas DC-6A/B	45179/865	
☐	N555SQ	Douglas DC-6B	45137/830	
☐	N651CE	Douglas DC-6B	45501/953	♦
☐	N747CE	Douglas C-118A	44661/628	
☐	N751CE	Douglas DC-6A/B	45177/859	♦
☐	N851CE(2)	Douglas DC-6A/B	45531/1015	
☐	N888DG	Douglas C-118A	44675/642	[FAI]
☐	N6174C	Douglas DC-6A	44075/451	
☐	N9056R	Douglas DC-6A/B	45498/1005	
☐	N1105G	EMB.120FC	120105	
☐	N1110J	EMB.120FC	120110	
☐	N7848B	Curtiss C-46R Commando	273	
☐	N12703	EMB.120FC	120084	
☐	N54514	Curtiss C-46D Commnado	33285	[FAI]

The DC-9s and the MD-80s fly as Everts Air Alaska.

EVERTS AIR FUEL

	Reg	Type	c/n	Notes
☐	N444CE	Douglas DC-6B	45478/962	
☐	N951CE	Douglas C-118B	44669/328	[FAI]
☐	N1822M	Curtiss C-46F Commando	22521	
☐	N1837M	Curtiss C-46F Commando	22388	
☐	N6586C	Douglas DC-6BF	45222/849	
☐	N7780B	Douglas DC-6A	45372/875	
☐	N9148F	Douglas VC-118A	44669/636	[FAI]

EXPRESSJET AIRLINES CO / BTA

Operates services for Delta Connection and United Express and some ad hoc flights with unidentified ERJ-145s.

FEDEX EXPRESS *FX / FDX*

	Reg.	Type	C/n	
☐	N650FE	A300F4-605R	726	
☐	N651FE	A300F4-605R	728	
☐	N652FE	A300F4-605R	735	
☐	N653FE	A300F4-605R	736	
☐	N654FE	A300F4-605R	738	
☐	N655FE	A300F4-605R	742	
☐	N656FE	A300F4-605R	745	
☐	N657FE	A300F4-605R	748	
☐	N658FE	A300F4-605R	752	
☐	N659FE	A300F4-605R	757	
☐	N660FE	A300F4-605R	759	
☐	N661FE	A300F4-605R	760	
☐	N662FE	A300F4-605R	761	
☐	N663FE	A300F4-605R	766	
☐	N664FE	A300F4-605R	768	
☐	N665FE	A300F4-605R	769	
☐	N667FE	A300F4-605R	771	
☐	N668FE	A300F4-605R	772	
☐	N669FE	A300F4-605R	774	
☐	N670FE	A300F4-605R	777	
☐	N671FE	A300F4-605R	778	
☐	N672FE	A300F4-605R	779	
☐	N673FE	A300F4-605R	780	
☐	N674FE	A300F4-605R	781	
☐	N675FE	A300F4-605R	789	
☐	N676FE	A300F4-605R	790	
☐	N677FE	A300F4-605R	791	
☐	N678FE	A300F4-605R	792	
☐	N679FE	A300F4-605R	793	
☐	N680FE	A300F4-605R	794	
☐	N681FE	A300F4-605R	799	
☐	N682FE	A300F4-605R	800	
☐	N683FE	A300F4-605R	801	
☐	N684FE	A300F4-605R	802	
☐	N685FE	A300F4-605R	803	
☐	N686FE	A300F4-605R	804	
☐	N687FE	A300F4-605R	873	
☐	N688FE	A300F4-605R	874	
☐	N689FE	A300F4-605R	875	
☐	N690FE	A300F4-605R	876	
☐	N691FE	A300F4-605R	877	
☐	N692FE	A300F4-605R	878	
☐	N716FD	A300B4-622F	358	
☐	N717FD	A300B4-622F	361	
☐	N718FD	A300B4-622F	365	♦
☐	N719FD	A300B4-622F	388	
☐	N720FD	A300B4-622F	417	
☐	N721FD	A300B4-622RF	477	
☐	N722FD	A300B4-622RF	479	
☐	N723FD	A300B4-622RF	543	
☐	N724FD	A300B4-622RF	530	
☐	N725FD	A300B4-622RF	572	
☐	N726FD	A300B4-622RF	575	
☐	N727FD	A300B4-622RF	579	
☐	N728FD	A300B4-622RF	581	
☐	N729FD	A300B4-622RF	657	
☐	N730FD	A300B4-622RF	659	
☐	N731FD	A300B4-605RF	709	
☐	N732FD	A300B4-605RF	713	
☐	N733FD	A300B4-605RF	715	
☐	N740FD	A300B4-622RF	559	
☐	N741FD	A300B4-622RF	611	
☐	N742FD	A300B4-622RF	613	
☐	N743FD	A300B4-622RF	630	
☐	N744FD	A300B4-622RF	664	
☐	N745FD	A300B4-622RF	668	
☐	N746FD	A300B4-622RF	688	
☐	N748FD	A300B4-622RF	633	
☐	N749FD	A300B4-622RF	536	
☐	N750FD	A300B4-622RF	555	
☐	N751FD	A300B4-622RF	625	
☐	N429FE	A310-203F	364	
☐	N454FE	A310-222F	278	
☐	N801FD	A310-324F	539	
☐	N803FD	A310-324F	378	
☐	N804FD	A310-324F	549	
☐	N805FD	A310-324F	456	
☐	N807FD	A310-324F	492	
☐	N808FD	A310-324F	439	
☐	N809FD	A310-324F	449	
☐	N810FD	A310-324F	452	
☐	N811FD	A310-324F	457	
☐	N900FX	ATR 42-320F	170	
☐	N901FX	ATR 42-320F	172	
☐	N903FX	ATR 42-320F	179	
☐	N906FX	ATR 42-320F	280	
☐	N907FX	ATR 42-320F	286	
☐	N908FX	ATR 42-300F	023	
☐	N909FX	ATR 42-300F	275	
☐	N910FX	ATR 42-300F	277	
☐	N911FX	ATR 42-300F	045	
☐	N912FX	ATR 42-300F	047	
☐	N913FX	ATR 42-320F	250	
☐	N914FX	ATR 42-300F	293	
☐	N915FX	ATR 42-320F	269	
☐	N916FX	ATR 42-300F	314	
☐	N917FX	ATR 42-320F	354	
☐	N918FX	ATR 42-300F	262	
☐	N919FX	ATR 42-320F	266	
☐	N920FX	ATR 42-320F	325	
☐	N921FX	ATR 42-300F	319	
☐	N923FX	ATR 42-310F	135	
☐	EI-FXG	ATR 72-202F	224	
☐	EI-FXH	ATR 72-202F	229	<ABR
☐	EI-FXI	ATR 72-202F	294	<ABR
☐	EI-FXJ	ATR 72-202F	292	<ABR
☐	EI-FXK	ATR 72-202F	256	<ABR
☐	N800FX	ATR 72-212	336	
☐	N801FX	ATR 72-212	338	
☐	N802FX	ATR 72-212	344	
☐	N803FX	ATR 72-212	362	
☐	N804FX	ATR 72-212	370	
☐	N805FX	ATR 72-212	372	
☐	N806FX	ATR 72-212	375	
☐	N807FX	ATR 72-212	383	
☐	N810FX	ATR 72-202F	220	
☐	N811FX	ATR 72-202F	283	
☐	N812FX	ATR 72-212F	404	
☐	N816FX	ATR 72-212F	347	
☐	N819FX	ATR 72-212F	359	
☐	N820FX	ATR 72-212F	248	
☐	N821FX	ATR 72-212F	253	
☐	N770FD	B757-222F	24743/270	
☐	N771FD	B757-222F	24799/291	
☐	N772FD	B757-222F	24840/306	
☐	N773FD	B757-222F	24872/312	
☐	N774FD	B757-222F	26709/563	
☐	N775FD	B757-222F	25043/353	
☐	N776FD	B757-222F	25129/372	
☐	N777FD	B757-222F	25222/385	

	Registration	Type	c/n	
☐	N778FD	B757-222F	25223/386	
☐	N779FD	B757-222F	25252/393	
☐	N780FD	B757-222F	25253/394	
☐	N781FD	B757-222F	26673/497	
☐	N782FD	B757-222F	26677/499	♦
☐	N783FD	B757-222F	26678/501	
☐	N784FD	B757-222F	26681/506	
☐	N785FD	B757-222F	26682/508	
☐	N786FD	B757-222F	24995/341	
☐	N787FD	B757-222F	26685/512	
☐	N788FD	B757-222F	26686/513	
☐	N789FD	B757-222F	26689/515	♦
☐	N790FD	B757-222F	26693/527	♦
☐	N791FD	B757-222F	26694/531	
☐	N792FD	B757-222F	26697/539	♦
☐	N793FD	B757-222F	26698/542	♦
☐	N794FD	B757-222F	26701/543	
☐	N795FD	B757-222F	26706/559	
☐	N796FD	B757-222F	26710/567	
☐	N797FD	B757-222F	28143/719	
☐	N798FD	B757-222F	28144/724	
☐	N799FD	B757-222F	28145/727	♦
☐	N901FD	B757-2B7SF	27122/525	
☐	N903FD	B757-2B7SF	27124/540	
☐	N906FD	B757-2B7SF	27148/564	
☐	N910FD	B757-236SF	25054/362	
☐	N912FD	B757-28ASF	24260/204	
☐	N913FD	B757-28ASF	24017/162	
☐	N914FD	B757-28ASF	24367/208	
☐	N915FD	B757-236SF	24120/174	
☐	N916FD	B757-27BSF	24137/178	
☐	N917FD	B757-23ASF	24291/215	
☐	N918FD	B757-23AER	24290/212	
☐	N919FD	B757-23ASF	24636/259	
☐	N920FD	B757-23AER	24289/209	
☐	N921FD	B757-23ASF	24924/333	
☐	N922FD	B757-23ASF	24293/220	
☐	N923FD	B757-204SF	26266/514	
☐	N924FD	B757-204SF	26267/538	
☐	N925FD	B757-204SF	27238/604	
☐	N926FD	B757-257SF	23323/80	
☐	N927FD	B757-204SF	27220/618	
☐	N928FD	B757-28ASF	24369/226	
☐	N930FD	B757-2Y0SF	25240/388	
☐	N933FD	B757-21BSF	24330/200	
☐	N934FD	B757-21BSF	24331/203	
☐	N935FD	B757-2T7ERSF	22780/15	
☐	N936FD	B757-2T7ERSF	23293/56	
☐	N937FD	B757-2T7SF	23895/132	
☐	N938FD	B757-23ASF	24292/219	
☐	N939FD	B757-23ASF	24528/250	
☐	N940FD	B757-236SF	24772/271	
☐	N941FD	B757-225SF	22691/155	
☐	N942FD	B757-225SF	22612/114	
☐	N943FD	B757-2G5SF	23929/153	
☐	N944FD	B757-2G5SF	24497/228	
☐	N946FD	B757-236SF	24398/224	
☐	N947FD	B757-236ERSF	24882/323	
☐	N948FD	B757-236ERSF	25059/363	
☐	N949FD	B757-236ERSF	25060/364	
☐	N950FD	B757-236SF	25806/601	
☐	N951FD	B757-236SF	28665/747	
☐	N952FD	B757-236SF	28666/751	
☐	N953FD	B757-236SF	28667/762	
☐	N954FD	B757-236SF	29113/784	
☐	N955FD	B757-236SF	29114/793	
☐	N956FD	B757-236SF	29115/798	

	Registration	Type	c/n	
☐	N957FD	B757-21BSF	24774/288	
☐	N958FD	B757-236SF	24371/225	
☐	N959FD	B757-236SF	25133/374	
☐	N960FD	B757-236SF	25593/466	
☐	N961FD	B757-2Y0SF	25268/400	
☐	N962FD	B757-2G5SF	24176/173	
☐	N963FD	B757-28ASF	24368/213	
☐	N964FD	B757-258SF	24884/325	
☐	N965FD	B757-258SF	27622/745	
☐	N966FD	B757-204SF	25626/549	
☐	N967FD	B757-28ASF	26269/612	
☐	N968FD	B757-28ASF	26274/676	
☐	N969FD	B757-28ASF	28164/749	
☐	N970FD	B757-28ASF	28166/756	
☐	N971FD	B757-28ASF	26277/658	
☐	N972FD	B757-28AERF	28203/802	
☐	N973FD	B757-2Y0SF	26151/472	
☐	N974FD	B757-2Y0ERF	26158/526	
☐	N975FD	B757-2B7F	27146/551	
☐	N976FD	B757-2B7F	27147/552	
☐	N977FD	B757-236SF	24118/163	
☐	N978FD	B757-236SF	24119/167	
☐	N979FD	B757-236SF	25592/453	
☐	N985FD	B757-230ERSF	24737/267	
☐	N986FD	B757-231SF	28482/770	
☐	N987FD	B757-231F	28483/777	
☐	N988FD	B757-222SF	26705/556	
☐	N989FD	B757-231SF	28480/750	
☐	N990FD	B757-232SF	22909/101	
☐	N991FD	B757-232SF	22911/112	
☐	N992FD	B757-232SF	22912/113	
☐	N993FD	B757-2Q8SF	24965/438	
☐	N994FD	B757-23ASF	25490/510	
☐	N995FD	B757-2Q8SF	25131/458	
☐	N996FD	B757-2Q8SF	26270/558	
☐	N997FD	B757-230SF	24738/274	
☐	N998FD	B757-230SF	24747/275	
☐	N999FD	B757-230SF	24748/285	
☐	N68087	B757-222F	24891/319	[VCV]
☐	N101FE	B767-3S2F(ER)	42706/1058	
☐	N102FE	B767-3S2F(ER)	42707/1061	
☐	N103FE	B767-3S2F(ER)	43544/1063	
☐	N104FE	B767-3S2F(ER)	42708/1064	
☐	N106FE	B767-3S2F(ER)	42709/1070	
☐	N107FE	B767-3S2F(ER)	44377/1071	
☐	N108FE	B767-3S2F(ER)	44378/1072	
☐	N109FE	B767-3S2F(ER)	42710/1073	
☐	N110FE	B767-3S2F(ER)	43542/1074	
☐	N112FE	B767-3S2F(ER)	43543/1075	
☐	N113FE	B767-3S2F(ER)	42711/1076	
☐	N114FE	B767-3S2F(ER)	42712/1077	
☐	N115FE	B767-3S2F(ER)	42713/1078	
☐	N117FE	B767-3S2F(ER)	44379/1079	♦
☐	N118FE	B767-3S2F(ER)	42714/1080	♦
☐	N120FE	B767-3S2F(ER)	44380/1081	♦
☐	N121FE	B767-3S2F(ER)	43545/1082	♦
☐	N122FE	B767-3S2F(ER)	42715/1083	♦
☐	N123FE	B767-3S2F(ER)	42716/1085	♦
☐	N124FE	B767-3S2F(ER)	43546/1084	♦
☐	N125FE	B767-3S2F(ER)	42717/1086	♦
☐	N126FE	B767-3S2F(ER)	42718/1087	♦
☐	N127FE	B767-3S2F(ER)	43547/1088	♦
☐	N128FE	B767-3S2F(ER)	42719/1089	♦
☐	N129FE	B767-3S2F(ER)	43548/1090	♦
☐	N130FE	B767-3S2F(ER)	42720/1093	♦
☐	N131FE	B767-3S2F(ER)	61205	o/o♦

	Reg	Type	c/n	Notes
☐	N132FE	B767-3S2F(ER)	42721	o/o♦
☐	N133FE	B767-3S2F(ER)	43549	o/o♦
☐	N297FE	B767-32LERF/W	41068/1027	
☐	N298FE	B767-32LERF	41069/1032	
☐	N68077	B767-316F/W	30780/806	♦
☐	N68078	B767-316F/W	32572/846	
☐	N68079	B767-316F/W	32573/848	

	Reg	Type	c/n	Notes
☐	N850FD	B777-FS2	37721/813	
☐	N851FD	B777-FS2	37722/834	
☐	N852FD	B777-FS2	37723/848	
☐	N853FD	B777-FS2	37724/829	
☐	N854FD	B777-FS2	37725/890	
☐	N855FD	B777-FS2	37726/892	
☐	N856FD	B777-FS2	37727/884	
☐	N857FD	B777-FS2	37728/886	
☐	N858FD	B777-FS2	37729/936	
☐	N859FD	B777-FS2	37730/1134	
☐	N861FD	B777-FS2	37732/973	
☐	N862FD	B777-FS2	37733/975	
☐	N863FD	B777-FS2	37734/998	
☐	N864FD	B777-FS2	37735/1015	
☐	N868FD	B777-FS2	40674/1320	♦
☐	N869FD	B777-FS2	40675/1336	♦
☐	N880FD	B777-F28	32967/718	
☐	N882FD	B777-F28	32969/827	
☐	N883FD	B777-FHT	39285/897	
☐	N884FD	B777-FHT	37137/917	
☐	N885FD	B777-FS2	41064/967	
☐	N886FD	B777-FS2	41065/1041	
☐	N887FD	B777-FS2	41066/1048	
☐	N889FD	B777-FS2	41067/1057	
☐	N890FD	B777-FS2	41439/1033	
☐	N892FD	B777-FS2	38707/960	
☐	N895FD	B777-FS2	41749/1152	

	Reg	Type	c/n	Notes
☐	N303FE	MD-10-30CF	46802/110	
☐	N304FE	MD-10-30CF	46992/257	
☐	N306FE	MD-10-30F	48287/409	
☐	N307FE	MD-10-30F	48291/412	
☐	N308FE	MD-10-30F	48297/416	
☐	N311FE	MD-10-30CF	46871/219	
☐	N313FE	MD-10-30F	48311/440	
☐	N315FE	MD-10-30F	48313/443	
☐	N316FE	MD-10-30F	48314/444	
☐	N318FE	MD-10-30CF	46837/282	
☐	N319FE	MD-10-30CF	47820/317	
☐	N320FE	MD-10-30F	47835/326	
☐	N321FE	MD-10-30F	47836/330	
☐	N357FE	MD-10-10F	46939/203	
☐	N358FE	MD-10-10F	46633/297	
☐	N359FE	MD-10-10F	46635/307	
☐	N360FE	MD-10-10F	46636/309	
☐	N361FE	MD-10-10F	48260/344	
☐	N363FE	MD-10-10F	48263/353	
☐	N365FE	MD-10-10F	46601/6	
☐	N370FE	MD-10-10F	46608/26	
☐	N372FE	MD-10-10F	46610/32	
☐	N373FE	MD-10-10F	46611/35	
☐	N375FE	MD-10-10F	46613/42	
☐	N381FE	MD-10-10F	46615/76	
☐	N383FE	MD-10-10F	46616/86	
☐	N385FE	MD-10-10F	46619/119	
☐	N389FE	MD-10-10F	46623/154	
☐	N390FE	MD-10-10F	46624/155	
☐	N394FE	MD-10-10F	46628/207	
☐	N550FE	MD-10-10F	46521/55	
☐	N554FE	MD-10-10F	46708/62	
☐	N559FE	MD-10-10F	46930/112	
☐	N560FE	MD-10-10F	46938/153	
☐	N562FE	MD-10-10F	46947/247	
☐	N564FE	MD-10-10F	46984/250	
☐	N566FE	MD-10-10F	46989/271	
☐	N567FE	MD-10-10F	46994/273	
☐	N571FE	MD-10-10F	47830/323	
☐	N10060	MD-10-10F	46970/269	
☐	N40061	MD-10-10F	46973/272	
☐	N68049	MD-10-10CF	47803/139	
☐	N68053	MD-10-10CF	47807/173	

	Reg	Type	c/n	Notes
☐	N412SN	MD-11F	48412/454	<WGN♦
☐	N415JN	MD-11F	48415/576	<WGN♦
☐	N521FE	MD-11F	48478/514	
☐	N522FE	MD-11F	48476/510	
☐	N523FE	MD-11F	48479/536	
☐	N525FE	MD-11F	48565/542	
☐	N528FE	MD-11F	48623/605	
☐	N529FE	MD-11F	48624/622	
☐	N542KD	MD-11F	48542/570	<WGN♦
☐	N546JN	MD-11F	48546/589	<WGN♦
☐	N572FE	MD-11F	48755/613	
☐	N573FE	MD-11F	48769/603	
☐	N574FE	MD-11F	48499/486	
☐	N575FE	MD-11F	48500/493	
☐	N576FE	MD-11F	48501/513	
☐	N577FE	MD-11F	48469/519	
☐	N578FE	MD-11F	48458/449	
☐	N580FE	MD-11F	48471/558	
☐	N582FE	MD-11F	48420/451	
☐	N583FE	MD-11F	48421/452	
☐	N584FE	MD-11F	48436/483	
☐	N585FE	MD-11F	48481/482	
☐	N586FE	MD-11F	48487/469	
☐	N587FE	MD-11F	48489/492	
☐	N588FE	MD-11F	48490/499	
☐	N589FE	MD-11F	48491/503	
☐	N590FE	MD-11F	48505/462	
☐	N591FE	MD-11F	48527/504	
☐	N592FE	MD-11F	48550/526	
☐	N593FE	MD-11F	48551/527	
☐	N594FE	MD-11F	48552/530	
☐	N595FE	MD-11F	48553/531	
☐	N596FE	MD-11F	48554/535	
☐	N597FE	MD-11F	48596/537	
☐	N598FE	MD-11F	48597/540	
☐	N599FE	MD-11F	48598/550	
☐	N601FE	MD-11F	48401/447	
☐	N602FE	MD-11F	48402/448	
☐	N604FE	MD-11F	48460/497	
☐	N605FE	MD-11F	48514/515	
☐	N606FE	MD-11F	48602/549	
☐	N607FE	MD-11F	48547/517	
☐	N608FE	MD-11F	48548/521	
☐	N609FE	MD-11F	48549/545	
☐	N610FE	MD-11F	48603/551	
☐	N612FE	MD-11F	48605/555	
☐	N613FE	MD-11F	48749/598	
☐	N614FE	MD-11F	48528/507	
☐	N615FE	MD-11F	48767/602	
☐	N616FE	MD-11F	48747/594	
☐	N617FE	MD-11F	48748/595	
☐	N618FE	MD-11F	48754/604	
☐	N619FE	MD-11F	48770/607	
☐	N620FE	MD-11F	48791/635	
☐	N621FE	MD-11F	48792/636	

☐	N623FE	MD-11F	48794/638	
☐	N624FE	MD-11F	48443/458	
☐	N625FE	MD-11F	48753/608	
☐	N628FE	MD-11F	48447/464	
☐	N631FE	MD-11F	48454/477	
☐	N642FE	MD-11F	48485/502	
☐	N643FE	MD-11F	48486/509	

FLORIDA AIR TRANSPORT *FBN*

☐	N55CW	Douglas C-54D	10673	16
☐	N70BF	Douglas C-118B	43720/373	
☐	N381AA	Douglas DC-7BF	44921/666	
☐	N406WA	Douglas C-54G	35944	
☐	N460WA	Douglas C-54E	27359	
☐	N9015Q	Douglas C-54D	22178	

FREEDOM AIR *FP / FRE*

☐	N74NF	Short SD.3-60	SH3721
☐	N330FA	Short SD.3-30	SH3112
☐	N2843F	Short SD.3-60	SH3739

FREIGHT RUNNERS EXPRESS *FRG*

☐	N191CZ	Beech 1900C	UB-59
☐	N192CZ	Beech 1900C-1	UC-118
☐	N193CZ	Beech 1900C-1	UC-73

FRONTIER AIRLINES *F9 / FFT*

☐	N902FR	A319-111	1515	
☐	N905FR	A319-111	1583	
☐	N906FR	A319-111	1684	
☐	N908FR	A319-111	1759	
☐	N910FR	A319-112	1781	
☐	N918FR	A319-111	1943	
☐	N919FR	A319-111	1980	
☐	N920FR	A319-111	1997	
☐	N921FR	A319-111	2010	
☐	N922FR	A319-111	2012	
☐	N923FR	A319-111	2019	
☐	N924FR	A319-111	2030	
☐	N925FR	A319-111	2103	
☐	N926FR	A319-111	2198	
☐	N927FR	A319-111	2209	
☐	N928FR	A319-111	2236	
☐	N932FR	A319-111	2258	
☐	N933FR	A319-111	2260	
☐	N934FR	A319-111	2287	
☐	N935FR	A319-111	2318	
☐	N938FR	A319-112	2406	
☐	N939FR	A319-112	2448	
☐	N941FR	A319-112	2483	
☐	N943FR	A319-112	2518	
☐	N947FR	A319-111	2806	
☐	N948FR	A319-112	2836	
☐	N949FR	A319-112	2857	
☐	N951FR	A319-112	4127	
☐	N952FR	A319-112	4204	
☐	N953FR	A319-112	4254	
☐	N954FR	A319-112	1786	
☐	N201FR	A320-214	3389	
☐	N202FR	A320-214	3431	
☐	N203FR	A320-214	1806	
☐	N205FR	A320-214	4253	
☐	N206FR	A320-214	4272	
☐	N207FR	A320-214	4307	
☐	N208FR	A320-214	4562	
☐	N209FR	A320-214	4641	
☐	N210FR	A320-214	4668	
☐	N211FR	A320-214	4688	
☐	N213FR	A320-214	4704	
☐	N214FR	A320-214	4727	
☐	N216FR	A320-214	4745	
☐	N218FR	A320-214	1615	
☐	N219FR	A320-214	1860	
☐	N220FR	A320-214/S	5661	
☐	N221FR	A320-214	3205	
☐	N223FR	A320-214	2695	
☐	N227FR	A320-214/S	6184	
☐	N228FR	A320-214/S	5526	
☐	N229FR	A320-214/S	5581	♦
☐	N230FR	A320-214/S	6773	♦
☐	N232FR	A320-214/S	6838	♦
☐	N233FR	A320-214/S	7095	o/o♦
☐	N	A320-251N	7141	o/o♦
☐	N	A320-251N	7175	o/o♦
☐	N	A320-251N	7209	o/o♦
☐	N701FR	A321-211/S	6793	♦
☐	N702FR	A321-211/S	6825	♦
☐	N704FR	A321-211/S	6845	♦
☐	N705FR	A321-211/S	6891	♦
☐	N706FR	A321-211/S	6926	♦
☐	N	A321-211/S	7042	o/o♦
☐	N	A321-211/S	7097	o/o♦
☐	N	A321-211/S	7179	o/o♦
☐	N	A321-211/S	7184	o/o♦
☐	N	A321-211/S	7204	o/o♦
☐	N	A321-211/S	7286	o/o♦
☐	N	A321-211/S	7294	o/o♦

GOJET *G7 / GJS*

Operates flights for Delta Connection and United Express see for their fleets for details.

GRAND CANYON AIRLINES *CVU*

☐	N72GC	DHC-6 Twin Otter 300	264	♦
☐	N74GC	DHC-6 Twin Otter 300	559	
☐	N171GC	DHC-6 Twin Otter 300	406	
☐	N173GC	DHC-6 Twin Otter 300	295	
☐	N177GC	DHC-6 Twin Otter 300	263	
☐	N178GC	DHC-6 Twin Otter 300	697	♦
☐	N190GC	DHC-6 Twin Otter 300	285	
☐	N227SA	DHC-6 Twin Otter 300	517	

GREAT LAKES AIRLINES *ZK / GLA*

☐	N100UX	Beech 1900D	UE-100
☐	N122UX	Beech 1900D	UE-122
☐	N153GL	Beech 1900D	UE-153
☐	N154GL	Beech 1900D	UE-154
☐	N165YV	Beech 1900D	UE-165
☐	N169GL	Beech 1900D	UE-169
☐	N170GL	Beech 1900D	UE-170
☐	N178YV	Beech 1900D	UE-178
☐	N184UX	Beech 1900D	UE-184
☐	N192GL	Beech 1900D	UE-192
☐	N195GL	Beech 1900D	UE-195
☐	N201GL	Beech 1900D	UE-201
☐	N202UX	Beech 1900D	UE-202
☐	N208GL	Beech 1900D	UE-208
☐	N210GL	Beech 1900D	UE-210
☐	N211GL	Beech 1900D	UE-211
☐	N219GL	Beech 1900D	UE-219

☐	N220GL	Beech 1900D	UE-220	
☐	N231YV	Beech 1900D	UE-231	
☐	N240GL	Beech 1900D	UE-240	
☐	N245GL	Beech 1900D	UE-245	
☐	N247GL	Beech 1900D	UE-247	
☐	N251GL	Beech 1900D	UE-251	
☐	N253GL	Beech 1900D	UE-253	
☐	N254GL	Beech 1900D	UE-254	
☐	N255GL	Beech 1900D	UE-255	
☐	N257GL	Beech 1900D	UE-257	
☐	N261GL	Beech 1900D	UE-261	
☐	N71GL	EMB.120ER	120071	
☐	N96ZK	EMB.120ER	120096	
☐	N108UX	EMB.120ER	120108	
☐	N293UX	EMB.120ER	120293	
☐	N297UX	EMB.120ER	120297	
☐	N299UX	EMB.120ER	120299	

GULF AND CARIBBEAN AIR — TSU

☐	N215WE	B727-2S2F	22936/1830	
☐	N216WE	B727-2S2F	22937/1831	
☐	N281FL	B727-281F/W	21455/1316	
☐	N131FL	Convair 580	155	13
☐	N141FL	Convair 580	111	14
☐	N151FL	Convair 580	51	15
☐	N171FL	Convair 580	318	17
☐	N181FL	Convair 580	387	18
☐	N191FL	Convair 580	326	19
☐	N351FL	Convair 5800	279	
☐	N361FL	Convair 5800	343	
☐	N371FL	Convair 5800	309	
☐	N381FL	Convair 5800	276	
☐	N391FL	Convair 5800	278	
☐	N991FL	Convair 580	508	
☐	N405SW	CRJ-200SF	7029	o/o

HAWAIIAN AIRLINES — HA / HAL

☐	N370HA	A330-243	1511	
☐	N373HA	A330-243	1530	
☐	N374HA	A330-243	1565	
☐	N375HA	A330-243	1606	
☐	N378HA	A330-243	1615	♦
☐	N379HA	A330-243	1672	♦
☐	N380HA	A330-243	1104	
☐	N381HA	A330-243	1114	
☐	N382HA	A330-243	1171	
☐	N383HA	A330-243	1217	
☐	N384HA	A330-243	1259	
☐	N385HA	A330-243	1295	
☐	N386HA	A330-243	1302	
☐	N388HA	A330-243	1310	
☐	N389HA	A330-243	1316	
☐	N390HA	A330-243	1389	
☐	N391HA	A330-243	1399	
☐	N392HA	A330-243	1404	
☐	N393HA	A330-243	1422	
☐	N395HA	A330-243	1469	
☐	N396HA	A330-243	1488	
☐	N399HA	A330-243	1496	
☐	N	A330-243	1732	o/o♦
☐	N475HA	B717-22A	55121/5050	
☐	N476HA	B717-22A	55118/5053	
☐	N477HA	B717-22A	55122/5061	
☐	N478HA	B717-22A	55123/5064	
☐	N479HA	B717-22A	55124/5069	
☐	N480HA	B717-22A	55125/5070	
☐	N481HA	B717-22A	55126/5073	
☐	N483HA	B717-22A	55128/5079	
☐	N484HA	B717-22A	55129/5080	
☐	N485HA	B717-22A	55130/5089	
☐	N486HA	B717-22A	55131/5092	
☐	N487HA	B717-22A	55132/5098	
☐	N488HA	B717-23S	55001/5002	
☐	N489HA	B717-23S	55002/5003	
☐	N490HA	B717-23S	55151/5041	
☐	N491HA	B717-2BL	55175/5125	
☐	N492HA	B717-2BL	55181/5135	
☐	N493HA	B717-2BL	55184/5142	
☐	N580HA	B767-33AER/W	28140/850	
☐	N581HA	B767-33AER/W	28141/853	
☐	N582HA	B767-33AER/W	28139/857	
☐	N583HA	B767-33AER	25531/423	
☐	N588HA	B767-3CBER/W	33466/890	
☐	N590HA	B767-3CBER/W	33467/894	
☐	N592HA	B767-3CBER/W	33468/898	
☐	N594HA	B767-332	23275/136	

HORIZON AIR — QX / QXE

☐	N400QX	DHC-8-402Q	4030
☐	N401QX	DHC-8-402Q	4031
☐	N402QX	DHC-8-402Q	4032
☐	N403QX	DHC-8-402Q	4037
☐	N404QX	DHC-8-402Q	4046
☐	N405QX	DHC-8-402Q	4047
☐	N406QX	DHC-8-402Q	4048
☐	N407QX	DHC-8-402Q	4049
☐	N408QX	DHC-8-402Q	4050
☐	N409QX	DHC-8-402Q	4051
☐	N410QX	DHC-8-402Q	4053
☐	N411QX	DHC-8-402Q	4055
☐	N412QX	DHC-8-402Q	4059
☐	N413QX	DHC-8-402Q	4060
☐	N414QX	DHC-8-402Q	4061
☐	N415QX	DHC-8-402Q	4081
☐	N416QX	DHC-8-402Q	4083
☐	N417QX	DHC-8-402Q	4086
☐	N418QX	DHC-8-402Q	4143
☐	N419QX	DHC-8-402Q	4145
☐	N420QX	DHC-8-402Q	4147
☐	N421QX	DHC-8-402Q	4149
☐	N422QX	DHC-8-402Q	4150
☐	N423QX	DHC-8-402Q	4153
☐	N426QX	DHC-8-402Q	4154
☐	N427QX	DHC-8-402Q	4156
☐	N428QX	DHC-8-402Q	4160
☐	N429QX	DHC-8-402Q	4161
☐	N430QX	DHC-8-402Q	4163
☐	N431QX	DHC-8-402Q	4164
☐	N432QX	DHC-8-402Q	4166
☐	N433QX	DHC-8-402Q	4210
☐	N434MK	DHC-8-402Q	4227
☐	N435QX	DHC-8-402Q	4232
☐	N436QX	DHC-8-402Q	4236
☐	N437QX	DHC-8-402Q	4240
☐	N438QX	DHC-8-402Q	4243
☐	N439QX	DHC-8-402Q	4246
☐	N440QX	DHC-8-402Q	4347
☐	N441QX	DHC-8-402Q	4348
☐	N442QX	DHC-8-402Q	4352
☐	N443QX	DHC-8-402Q	4353

☐	N444QX	DHC-8-402Q	4355	
☐	N445QX	DHC-8-402Q	4358	
☐	N446QX	DHC-8-402Q	4363	
☐	N447QX	DHC-8-402Q	4364	
☐	N448QX	DHC-8-402Q	4409	
☐	N449QX	DHC-8-402Q	4410	
☐	N450QX	DHC-8-402Q	4452	
☐	N451QX	DHC-8-402Q	4457	
☐	N452QX	DHC-8-402Q	4459	
☐	N453QX	DHC-8-402Q	4489	
☐	N	DHC-8-402Q		o/o
☐	N	DHC-8-402Q		o/o

IBC AIRWAYS — *II / CSQ*

☐	N241BC	ERJ-145ER	145077	
☐	N261BC	ERJ-145ER	145082	
☐	N367PX	SAAB SF.340B	340B-271	
☐	N431BC	SAAB SF.340B	340B-260	
☐	N481BC	SAAB SF.340B	340B-274	
☐	N611BC	SAAB SF.340A	340A-060	
☐	N631BC	SAAB SF.340A	340A-061	
☐	N641BC	SAAB SF.340A	340A-069	
☐	N651BC	SAAB SF.340A	340A-076	
☐	N661BC	SAAB SF.340A	340A-125	
☐	N671BC	SAAB SF.340A	340A-084	
☐	N691BC	SAAB SF.340A	340A-041	
☐	N901BC	SAAB SF.340A	340A-088	
☐	N841BC	SA.227TC Metro II	TC-282	

INTERNATIONAL AIR RESPONSE

☐	N117TG	C-130A-1A Hercules	3018	31
☐	N118TG	C-130A-1A Hercules	3219	32
☐	N119TG	C-130A Hercules	3227	[CHD]
☐	N120TG	C-130A Hercules	3035	
☐	N121TG	C-130A Hercules	3119	
☐	N133HP	C-130A-1A Hercules	3189	
☐	N4887C	Douglas DC-7B	45351/903	33

ISLAND AIR HAWAII — *WP / MKU*

☐	N941WP	ATR 72-212	349	
☐	N942WP	ATR 72-212	425	
☐	N943WP	ATR 72-212	420	
☐	N944WP	ATR 72-212	345	♦
☐	N945WP	ATR 72-212	434	
☐	N360WP	DHC-8-402Q	4481	
☐	N361WP	DHC-8-402Q	4482	
☐	N364PX	SAAB SF.340B	340B-262	<PEN

JETBLUE AIRWAYS — *B6 / JBU*

☐	N503JB	A320-232	1123
☐	N504JB	A320-232	1156
☐	N505JB	A320-232	1173
☐	N506JB	A320-232	1235
☐	N507JT	A320-232	1240
☐	N508JL	A320-232	1257
☐	N509JB	A320-232	1270
☐	N510JB	A320-232	1280
☐	N516JB	A320-232	1302
☐	N517JB	A320-232	1327
☐	N519JB	A320-232	1398
☐	N520JB	A320-232	1446
☐	N521JB	A320-232	1452
☐	N523JB	A320-232	1506
☐	N524JB	A320-232	1528
☐	N526JL	A320-232	1546
☐	N527JL	A320-232	1557
☐	N529JB	A320-232	1610
☐	N531JL	A320-232	1650
☐	N534JB	A320-232	1705
☐	N535JB	A320-232	1739
☐	N536JB	A320-232	1784
☐	N537JT	A320-232	1785
☐	N547JB	A320-232	1849
☐	N552JB	A320-232	1861
☐	N554JB	A320-232	1898
☐	N556JB	A320-232	1904
☐	N558JB	A320-232	1915
☐	N559JB	A320-232	1917
☐	N561JB	A320-232	1927
☐	N562JB	A320-232	1948
☐	N563JB	A320-232	2006
☐	N564JB	A320-232	2020
☐	N565JB	A320-232	2031
☐	N566JB	A320-232	2042
☐	N568JB	A320-232	2063
☐	N569JB	A320-232	2075
☐	N570JB	A320-232	2099
☐	N571JB	A320-232	2125
☐	N579JB	A320-232	2132
☐	N580JB	A320-232	2136
☐	N583JB	A320-232	2150
☐	N584JB	A320-232	2149
☐	N585JB	A320-232	2159
☐	N586JB	A320-232	2160
☐	N587JB	A320-232	2177
☐	N588JB	A320-232	2201
☐	N589JB	A320-232	2215
☐	N590JB	A320-232	2231
☐	N591JB	A320-232	2246
☐	N592JB	A320-232	2259
☐	N593JB	A320-232	2280
☐	N594JB	A320-232	2284
☐	N595JB	A320-232	2286
☐	N597JB	A320-232	2307
☐	N598JB	A320-232	2314
☐	N599JB	A320-232	2336
☐	N603JB	A320-232	2352
☐	N605JB	A320-232	2368
☐	N606JB	A320-232	2384
☐	N607JB	A320-232	2386
☐	N608JB	A320-232	2415
☐	N612JB	A320-232	2447
☐	N613JB	A320-232	2449
☐	N615JB	A320-232	2461
☐	N618JB	A320-232	2489
☐	N621JB	A320-232	2491
☐	N623JB	A320-232	2504
☐	N624JB	A320-232	2520
☐	N625JB	A320-232	2535
☐	N627JB	A320-232	2577
☐	N629JB	A320-232	2580
☐	N630JB	A320-232	2640
☐	N632JB	A320-232	2647
☐	N633JB	A320-232	2671
☐	N634JB	A320-232	2710
☐	N635JB	A320-232	2725
☐	N636JB	A320-232	2755
☐	N637JB	A320-232	2781
☐	N638JB	A320-232	2802
☐	N639JB	A320-232	2814
☐	N640JB	A320-232	2832

	Reg	Type	c/n	
☐	N641JB	A320-232	2848	
☐	N643JB	A320-232	2871	
☐	N644JB	A320-232	2880	
☐	N645JB	A320-232	2900	
☐	N646JB	A320-232	2945	
☐	N648JB	A320-232	2970	
☐	N649JB	A320-232	2977	
☐	N651JB	A320-232	2992	
☐	N652JB	A320-232	3029	
☐	N653JB	A320-232	3039	
☐	N655JB	A320-232	3072	
☐	N656JB	A320-232	3091	
☐	N657JB	A320-232	3119	
☐	N658JB	A320-232	3150	
☐	N659JB	A320-232	3190	
☐	N661JB	A320-232	3228	
☐	N662JB	A320-232	3263	
☐	N663JB	A320-232	3287	
☐	N665JB	A320-232	3348	
☐	N703JB	A320-232	3381	
☐	N705JB	A320-232	3416	
☐	N706JB	A320-232	3451	
☐	N708JB	A320-232	3479	
☐	N709JB	A320-232	3488	
☐	N712JB	A320-232	3517	
☐	N715JB	A320-232	3554	
☐	N729JB	A320-232	3572	
☐	N746JB	A320-232	3622	
☐	N760JB	A320-232	3659	
☐	N763JB	A320-232	3707	
☐	N766JB	A320-232	3724	
☐	N768JB	A320-232	3760	
☐	N775JB	A320-232	3800	
☐	N779JB	A320-232	3811	
☐	N784JB	A320-232	4578	
☐	N789JB	A320-232	4612	
☐	N793JB	A320-232	4647	
☐	N794JB	A320-232	4904	
☐	N796JB	A320-232	5060	
☐	N804JB	A320-232/S	5142	
☐	N805JB	A320-232/S	5148	
☐	N806JB	A320-232/S	5302	
☐	N807JB	A320-232/S	5312	
☐	N809JB	A320-232/S	5349	
☐	N821JB	A320-232/S	5417	
☐	N827JB	A320-232/S	5677	
☐	N828JB	A320-232/S	5723	
☐	N834JB	A320-232/S	5782	
☐	N	A320-271N	7309	o/o♦
☐	N903JB	A321-231/S	5783	
☐	N905JB	A321-231/S	5854	
☐	N907JB	A321-231/S	5865	
☐	N913JB	A321-231/S	5909	
☐	N923JB	A321-231/S	5960	
☐	N929JB	A321-231/S	6031	
☐	N934JB	A321-231/S	6130	
☐	N935JB	A321-231/S	6185	
☐	N937JB	A321-231/S	6245	
☐	N942JB	A321-231/S	6279	
☐	N943JT	A321-231/S	6326	
☐	N944JT	A321-231/S	6359	
☐	N945JT	A321-231/S	6390	
☐	N946JL	A321-231/S	6425	
☐	N947JB	A321-231/S	6448	
☐	N948JB	A321-231/S	6560	♦
☐	N949JT	A321-231/S	6575	♦
☐	N950JT	A321-231/S	6609	♦
☐	N952JB	A321-231/S	6663	♦
☐	N954JB	A321-231/S	6725	♦
☐	N955JB	A321-231/S	6757	♦
☐	N956JT	A321-231/S	6791	♦
☐	N957JB	A321-231/S	6809	♦
☐	N958JB	A321-231/S	6859	♦
☐	N959JB	A321-231/S	6903	♦
☐	N961JT	A321-231/S	6930	♦
☐	N962JT	A321-231/S	6988	o/o♦
☐	N964JT	A321-231/S	7018	o/o♦
☐	N965JT	A321-231/S	6512	o/o♦
☐	N	A321-231/S	7230	o/o♦
☐	N	A321-231/S	7279	o/o♦
☐	N	A321-231/S	7358	o/o♦
☐	N	A321-231/S	7366	o/o♦
☐	N	A321-231/S	7408	o/o♦
☐	N178JB	ERJ-190AR	19000004	
☐	N179JB	ERJ-190AR	19000006	
☐	N183JB	ERJ-190AR	19000007	
☐	N184JB	ERJ-190AR	19000008	
☐	N187JB	ERJ-190AR	19000009	
☐	N190JB	ERJ-190AR	19000011	
☐	N192JB	ERJ-190AR	19000014	
☐	N193JB	ERJ-190AR	19000017	
☐	N197JB	ERJ-190AR	19000020	
☐	N198JB	ERJ-190AR	19000021	
☐	N203JB	ERJ-190AR	19000023	
☐	N206JB	ERJ-190AR	19000025	
☐	N216JB	ERJ-190AR	19000026	
☐	N228JB	ERJ-190AR	19000030	
☐	N229JB	ERJ-190AR	19000032	
☐	N231JB	ERJ-190AR	19000033	
☐	N236JB	ERJ-190AR	19000035	
☐	N238JB	ERJ-190AR	19000039	
☐	N239JB	ERJ-190AR	19000040	
☐	N247JB	ERJ-190AR	19000042	
☐	N249JB	ERJ-190AR	19000045	
☐	N258JB	ERJ-190AR	19000047	
☐	N265JB	ERJ-190AR	19000049	
☐	N266JB	ERJ-190AR	19000054	
☐	N267JB	ERJ-190AR	19000065	
☐	N273JB	ERJ-190AR	19000073	
☐	N274JB	ERJ-190AR	19000082	
☐	N279JB	ERJ-190AR	19000090	
☐	N281JB	ERJ-190AR	19000103	
☐	N283JB	ERJ-190AR	19000125	
☐	N284JB	ERJ-190AR	19000144	
☐	N292JB	ERJ-190AR	19000179	
☐	N294JB	ERJ-190AR	19000185	
☐	N296JB	ERJ-190AR	19000219	
☐	N298JB	ERJ-190AR	19000249	
☐	N304JB	ERJ-190AR	19000257	
☐	N306JB	ERJ-190AR	19000272	
☐	N307JB	ERJ-190AR	19000286	
☐	N309JB	ERJ-190AR	19000289	
☐	N316JB	ERJ-190AR	19000292	
☐	N317JB	ERJ-190AR	19000363	
☐	N318JB	ERJ-190AR	19000364	
☐	N323JB	ERJ-190AR	19000384	
☐	N324JB	ERJ-190AR	19000388	
☐	N328JB	ERJ-190AR	19000422	
☐	N329JB	ERJ-190AR	19000433	
☐	N334JB	ERJ-190AR	19000446	
☐	N337JB	ERJ-190AR	19000473	
☐	N339JB	ERJ-190AR	19000490	

☐ N346JB ERJ-190AR 19000504
☐ N348JB ERJ-190AR 19000511
☐ N351JB ERJ-190AR 19000549
☐ N353JB ERJ-190AR 19000576
☐ N354JB ERJ-190AR 19000601
☐ N355JB ERJ-190AR 19000617
☐ N358JB ERJ-190AR 19000618
☐ N368JB ERJ-190AR 19000623
☐ N373JB ERJ-190AR 19000624
☐ N374JB ERJ-190AR 19000629
☐ N375JB ERJ-190AR 19000637

JIM HANKINS AIR SERVICE — HKN

☐ N3BA Douglas DC-3 12172
☐ N366MQ Short SD.3-60 SH3639
☐ N8061A Douglas DC-3 6085

KALITTA AIR — K4 / CKS

☐ N402KZ B747-481F 34017/1363
☐ N403KZ B747-4KZF 34018/1378
☐ N700CK B747-4R7F 25868/1125 ♦
☐ N704CK B747-246F 23391/654 [OSC]
☐ N740CK B747-4H6FCF 24405/745
☐ N741CK B747-4H6FCF 24315/738
☐ N742CK B747-446BCF 24424/760
☐ N743CK B747-446BCF 26350/961
☐ N744CK B747-446BCF 26353/980
☐ N745CK B747-446BCF 26361/1188
☐ N746CK B747-246F 22989/571
☐ N782CK B747-4HQERF 37304/1419
☐ N793CK B747-222B(SF) 23736/673
☐ N794CK B747-222B(SF) 23737/675
☐ N795CK B747-251B(SF) 23111/594

☐ N170CR B767-341ERF 24752/289 ♦
☐ N173CR B767-341ERF 24753/291 ♦
☐ N783CK B767-346 24782/327 ♦
☐ N784CK B767-346 24783/329 ♦

KALITTA CHARTERS II — K9 / KFS

☐ N720CK B727-2B6F 21298/1246
☐ N722CK B727-2H3F 20948/1084
☐ N723CK B727-2H3F 20545/877 [OSC]
☐ N724CK B727-225F 20383/831
☐ N725CK B727-224F/W 22252/1697
☐ N726CK B727-2M7F 21951/1680
☐ N728CK B727-221 22541/1797 [OSC]
☐ N729CK B727-264F/W 22982/1802
☐ N752DH B727-223F 22466/1763 [OSC]
☐ N730CK B737-4C9(F) 26437/2249
☐ N915CK DC-9-15RC 47086/219
☐ N916CK DC-9-33RC 47291/343
☐ N917CK DC-9-15RC 47152/170

KEY LIME AIR — LYM

☐ N259DS Do328-300 3197 ♦
☐ N356SK Do328-310 3163 ♦
☐ N358SK Do328-310 3188 ♦
☐ N394DC Do328-310 3174
☐ N395DC Do328-300 3178
☐ N398DC Do328-310 3206

☐ N366DC EMB.120ER 120288

☐ N62Z SA.226TC Metro II TC-237
☐ N184SW SA.227AC Metro III AC-647
☐ N276CA SA.226TC Metro II TC-276
☐ N326BA SA.226TC Metro II TC-269
☐ N425MA SA.227AC Metro III AC-640
☐ N508FA SA.227AC Metro III AC-508
☐ N509SS SA.226TC Metro II TC-206
☐ N542FA SA.227AC Metro III AC-542
☐ N765FA SA.227AC Metro III AC-765
☐ N769KL SA.227AC Metro III AC-769B
☐ N770S SA.226TC Metro II TC-248
☐ N779BC SA.227AC Metro III BC-779B
☐ N787C SA.227AC Metro III AC-550
☐ N787KL SA.227BC Metro III BC-787B
☐ N788KL SA.227AC Metro III AC-788B
☐ N820DC SA.227DC Metro 23 DC-820B
☐ N882DC SA.227DC Metro 23 DC-882B
☐ N2691W SA.227AC Metro III AC-655B
☐ N2728G SA.227AC Metro III AC-731
☐ N81418 SA.226TC Metro II TC-223

KOLOB CANYONS AIR SERVICES

☐ N649KA SA.227AC Metro III AC-649
☐ N652KA SA.227AC Metro III AC-652B
☐ N746KA SA.227AC Metro III AC-746B

LYNDEN AIR CARGO — L2 / LYC

☐ N401LC L-382G-31C Hercules 4606
☐ N403LC L-382G-31C Hercules 4590
☐ N404LC L-382G-38C Hercules 4763
☐ N405LC L-382G-69C Hercules 5025 ^
☐ N408LC L-328G-31C Hercules 4600 ♦
☐ P2-LAC L-382G-35C Hercules 4676 >TOK
☐ P4-LAD L-382G-35C Hercules 4698 ♦
☐ P4-LAE L-382G-70C Hercules 5225

^ leased to Coulson Flying Tankers in Canada

MARTINAIRE — MRA

☐ N354AE SA.227AC Metro III AC-633
☐ N370AE SA.227AC Metro III AC-506
☐ N592BA SA.227AC Metro III AC-592

MAVERICK AIRLINES

☐ N567MA Beech 1900D UE-67
☐ N886MA Beech 1900D UE-86

McNEELY CHARTER SERVICE — MDS

☐ N262AG Short SD.3-30 SH3120
☐ N320MC SA.227AC Metro III AC-688
☐ N654AR SA.227DC Metro 23 DC-864B ♦
☐ N2699Y SA.227AC Metro III AC-666

MESA AIRLINES — YV / ASH

Operates for United Express and US Airways Express.

MIAMI AIR INTERNATIONAL — LL / BSK

☐ N732MA B737-81Q/W 30618/830
☐ N733MA B737-81Q/W 30619/856
☐ N738MA B737-8Q8/W 32799/1467
☐ N739MA B737-8Q8/W 30670/1481
☐ N752MA B737-48E 28198/2806
☐ N753MA B737-48E 28053/2954

MOUNTAIN AIR CARGO — MTN

☐ N2679U Short SD.3-30 SH3071
☐ N26288 Short SD.3-30 SH3074

NATIONAL AIRLINES — N8 / MUA

	Reg	Type	C/n	Notes
☐	N919CA	B747-428BCF	25302/884	
☐	N952CA	B747-428MBCF	25238/872	
☐	N153CA	B757-2Y0	26161/557	[GYR]
☐	N168CA	B757-2Z0	27259/609	[ROW]
☐	N176CA	B757-28AF	24543/268	
☐	N567CA	B757-223/W	24608/384	

NEPTUNE AVIATION SERVICES

	Reg	Type	C/n	Notes
☐	N470NA	BAe146-200A	E2049	o/o♦
☐	N471NA	BAe146-200A	E2136	♦
☐	N472NA	BAe146-200A	E2138	♦
☐	N473NA	BAe146-200A	E2045	♦
☐	N474NA	BAe146-200A	E2084	♦
☐	N475NA	BAe146-200	E2192	♦
☐	N476NA	BAe146-200	E2196	♦

NORD AVIATION

	Reg	Type	C/n	Notes
☐	N321L	Douglas C-117D	43345	
☐	N57626	Douglas DC-3	4564	

NORTH STAR AIR CARGO — SBX

	Reg	Type	C/n	Notes
☐	N50DA	Short SC.7 Skyvan	SH1852	
☐	N50NS	Short SC.7 Skyvan	SH1856	
☐	N549WB	Short SC.7 Skyvan	SH1911	
☐	N731E	Short SC.7 Skyvan	SH1853	
☐	N754BD	Short SC.7 Skyvan	SH1907	

NORTHERN AIR CARGO — NC / NAC

	Reg	Type	C/n	Notes
☐	N321DL	B737-232F	23093/1024	
☐	N322DL	B737-232F	23094/1026	
☐	N360WA	B737-301F	23553/1406	
☐	N361NC	B737-301F	23260/1146	

OHANA BY HAWAIIAN

	Reg	Type	C/n	Notes
☐	N801HC	ATR 42-500	629	
☐	N804HC	ATR 42-500	623	
☐	N805HC	ATR 42-500	625	
☐	N807HC	ATR 72-212	432	♦
☐	N810HC	ATR 72-212F	423	♦
☐	N811HC	ATR 72-201F	227	♦

Operated by Empire Airlines.

OMNI AIR INTERNATIONAL — OY / OAE

	Reg	Type	C/n	Notes
☐	N207AX	B767-224ER	30438/845	♦
☐	N225AX	B767-224ER	30434/825	
☐	N234AX	B767-224ER	30436/833	
☐	N342AX	B767-328ER	27136/497	
☐	N351AX	B767-33AER	27908/578	
☐	N378AX	B767-33AER	28147/622	
☐	N387AX	B767-319ER	24875/371	
☐	N396AX	B767-319ER	26264/555	
☐	N423AX	B767-324ER	27569/601	♦
☐	N441AX	B767-36NER	29898/754	
☐	N846AX	B777-2U8ER	36124/614	♦
☐	N918AX	B777-222ER	26935/88	
☐	N927AX	B777-222ER	26943/92	

ORANGE AIR

	Reg	Type	C/n	Notes
☐	N918AV	MD-82	49104/1085	
☐	N926AV	MD-83	49630/1591	

PENAIR — KS / PEN

	Reg	Type	C/n	Notes
☐	N331AG	SAAB SF.340B	340B-430	♦
☐	N340AQ	SAAB SF.340AF	340A-019	
☐	N364PX	SAAB SF.340B	340B-262	
☐	N365PX	SAAB SF.340B	340B-265	
☐	N369PX	SAAB SF.340B	340B-295	
☐	N403XJ	SAAB SF.340B	340B-403	
☐	N404XJ	SAAB SF.340B	340B-404	
☐	N406XJ	SAAB SF.340B	340B-406	
☐	N410XJ	SAAB SF.340B	340B-410	
☐	N424XJ	SAAB SF.340B	340B-424	
☐	N662PA	SAAB SF.340AF	340A-109	
☐	N665PA	SAAB SF.340B	340B-181	
☐	N675PA	SAAB SF.340B	340B-206	
☐	N677PA	SAAB SF.340B	340B-328	
☐	N679PA	SAAB SF.340B	340B-345	
☐	N685PA	SAAB SF.340B	340B-212	
☐	N	SAAB 2000	2000-032	o/o
☐	N680PA	SAAB 2000	2000-020	♦
☐	N681PA	SAAB 2000	2000-027	♦
☐	N682PA	SAAB 2000	2000-030	♦
☐	(N686PA)	SAAB 2000	2000-017 [N519JG]	♦
☐	(N687PA)	SAAB 2000	2000-021 [N517JG]	♦

POLAR AIR CARGO — PO / PAC

	Reg	Type	C/n	Notes
☐	N416MC	B747-47UF	32838/1307	<GTI
☐	N450PA	B747-46NF	30808/1257	
☐	N451PA	B747-46NF	30809/1259	
☐	N452PA	B747-46NF	30810/1260	
☐	N453PA	B747-46NF	30811/1283	
☐	N454PA	B747-46NF	30812/1310	
☐	N851GT	B747-87UF	37565/1458	<GTI♦
☐	N852GT	B747-87UF	37571/1462	<GTI
☐	N853GT	B747-87UF	37572/1467	<GTI
☐	N856GT	B747-87UF	37561/1442	<GTI
☐	N857GT	B747-87UF	37568/1444	<GTI
☐	N858GT	B747-87UF	37569/1445	<GTI
☐	N643GT	B767-3JHF/W	37809/1039	<GTI
☐	N644GT	B767-3JHF/W	37810/1041	<GTI♦
☐	N647GT	B767-306ERF/W	27611/633	<GTI♦

PRESIDENTAL AIRWAYS

Associated with EP Aviation.

	Reg	Type	C/n	Notes
☐	N602AR	CASA 212-200	CC15-1-161	
☐	N603AR	CASA 212-200	CC15-2-162	
☐	N604AR	CASA 212-200	CC50-10-289	
☐	N605AR	CASA 212-200	CC44-1-290	
☐	N606AR	CASA 212-200	CD51-2-304	
☐	N607AR	CASA 212-200	CD51-2-309	
☐	(N608AR)	CASA 212-200	CC40-8-248 [N961BW]	♦
☐	(N609AR)	CASA 212-200	CC50-1-262 [N969BW]	♦
☐	N620AR	CASA 212-200	MS03-08-379	
☐	N963BW	CASA 212-200	CC60-3-320	
☐	N4399T	CASA 212-300	DF-1-393	
☐	N982BW	CASA CN235-10	C010	
☐	N1269J	CASA CN235-10	C012	
☐	N2696S	CASA CN235-10	C007	
☐	N511AV	DHC-8-102	051	

	Reg	Type	C/n	Notes
☐	N634AR	DHC-8-103	003	
☐	N635AR	DHC-8-103	047	
☐	N636AR	DHC-8-103	086	
☐	N637AR	DHC-8-102A	265	
☐	N979HA	DHC-8-102A	373	
☐	N990AV	DHC-8-102	099	
☐	N654AR	SA.227DC Metro 23	DC-868B	
☐	N955BW	SA.227DC Metro 23	DC-821B	
☐	N956BW	SA.227DC Metro 23	DC-864B	

PRIORITY AIR CHARTER — *PRY*

	Reg	Type	C/n	Notes
☐	N467KS	Basler BT-67	20175	
☐	N467PA	Basler BT-67	14995/26439	

RAVN ALASKA — *7H / ERH*

	Reg	Type	C/n	Notes
☐	N404GV	Beech 1900C-1	UC-154	
☐	N575A	Beech 1900C-1	UC-83	
☐	N575Q	Beech 1900C-1	UC-160	
☐	N575Z	Beech 1900C-1	UC-136	
☐	N815GV	Beech 1900C-1	UC-78	
☐	N971EA	Beech 1900D	UE-387	
☐	N972EA	Beech 1900D	UE-389	
☐	N973EA	Beech 1900D	UE-391	
☐	N1553C	Beech 1900C-1	UC-24	
☐	N15503	Beech 1900C-1	UC-72	
☐	N880EA	DHC-8-102A	392	
☐	N883EA	DHC-8-106	260	
☐	N884EA	DHC-8-106	387	
☐	N885EA	DHC-8-106	341	
☐	N886EA	DHC-8-103	215	
☐	N887EA	DHC-8-106	351	
☐	N889EA	DHC-8-106	322	
☐	N891EA	DHC-8-106	335	
☐	N892EA	DHC-8-106	389	♦
☐	N168LM	Short SD.3-30	SH3104	
☐	N261AG	Short SD.3-30	SH3117	

REPUBLIC AIRWAYS — *RW / RPA*

	Reg	Type	C/n	Notes
☐	N502LX	DHC-8-402Q	4168	
☐	N508LX	DHC-8-402Q	4182	
☐	N510LX	DHC-8-402Q	4186	
☐	N818MD	ERJ-170SU	17000039	>DAL
☐	N869RW	ERJ-170SE	17000133	>DAL
☐	N873RW	ERJ-170SU	17000144	>DAL
☐	N874RW	ERJ-170SU	17000148	>DAL

Operates for American Eagle and United Express.

ROYAL AIR FREIGHT — *RAX*

	Reg	Type	C/n	Notes
☐	N34A	EMB.110P1	110350	
☐	N49RA	EMB.110P1	110424	
☐	N64DA	EMB.110P1	110385	
☐	N73RA	EMB.110P1	110413	

SCENIC AIRLINES — *YR / SCE*

	Reg	Type	C/n	Notes
☐	N142SA	DHC-6 Twin Otter 300	241	
☐	N146SA	DHC-6 Twin Otter 300	514	
☐	N148SA	DHC-6 Twin Otter 300	409	
☐	N297SA	DHC-6 Twin Otter 300	297	
☐	N359AR	DHC-6 Twin Otter 300	359	
☐	N692AR	DHC-6 Twin Otter 300	692	

SEABORNE AIRLINES — *BB / SBS*

	Reg	Type	C/n	Notes
☐	C-GOKB	DHC-6 Twin Otter 300	339	<KBA♦
☐	N189GC	DHC-6 Twin Otter 300	772	
☐	N327SA	SAAB SF.340B	340B-166	
☐	N334CJ	SAAB SF.340B	340B-334	
☐	N335SA	SAAB SF.340B	340B-351	
☐	N336SA	SAAB SF.340B	340B-336	
☐	N341CJ	SAAB SF.340B	340B-341	
☐	N343CJ	SAAB SF.340B	340B-343	
☐	N350CJ	SAAB SF.340B	340B-350	
☐	N224SA	DHC-6 Twin Otter 300	247	
☐	N562CP	DHC-6 Twin Otter 300	562	
☐	N888PV	DHC-6 Twin Otter 300	620	

SHUTTLE AMERICA — *S5 / TCF*

Operates for Delta Connection, United Express and US Airways Express.

SIERRA PACIFIC AIRLINES — *SI / SPA*

	Reg	Type	C/n	Notes
☐	N703S	B737-2T4	22529/750	
☐	N708S	B737-528	27424/2720	♦
☐	N712S	B737-2Y5	23038/949	

SIERRA WEST AIRLINES — *P8 / PKW*

	Reg	Type	C/n	Notes
☐	N209TR	B727-223F	20994/1190	
☐	N63NE	SA.227AC Metro III	AC-763B	
☐	N681TR	SA.227AC Metro III	AC-682	

SILVER AIRWAYS — *3M / GFT*

	Reg	Type	C/n	Notes
☐	N303AG	SAAB SF.340B	340B-414	
☐	N304AG	SAAB SF.340B	340B-418	
☐	N327AG	SAAB SF.340B	340B-427	
☐	N328AG	SAAB SF.340B	340B-428	
☐	N334AG	SAAB SF.340B	340B-434	
☐	N336AG	SAAB SF.340B	340B-436	
☐	N341AG	SAAB SF.340B	340B-437	
☐	N343AG	SAAB SF.340B	340B-443	
☐	N344AG	SAAB SF.340B	340B-444	
☐	N346AG	SAAB SF.340B	340B-446	
☐	N347AG	SAAB SF.340B	340B-447	
☐	N348AG	SAAB SF.340B	340B-448	
☐	N350AG	SAAB SF.340B	340B-450	
☐	N351AG	SAAB SF.340B	340B-445	
☐	N362AG	SAAB SF.340B	340B-438	
☐	N412XJ	SAAB SF.340B	340B-412	
☐	N413XJ	SAAB SF.340B	340B-413	
☐	N415XJ	SAAB SF.340B	340B-415	
☐	N417XJ	SAAB SF.340B	340B-417	[BGR]♦
☐	N433XJ	SAAB SF.340B	340B-433	
☐	N435XJ	SAAB SF.340B	340B-435	♦
☐	N442XJ	SAAB SF.340B	340B-442	♦

SKYLEASE AERO — *GG / KYE*

	Reg	Type	C/n	Notes
☐	N950AR	MD-11F	48461/475	
☐	N951AR	MD-11F	48495/461	[MIA]
☐	N952AR	MD-11F	48497/512	[MIA]
☐	N953AR	MD-11F	48520/541	
☐	N955AR	MD-11F	48496/496	
☐	N956AR	MD-11CF	48629/586	

SKYWAY ENTERPRISES — *SKZ*

	Reg	Type	C/n	Notes
☐	N112PS	DC-9-15F	47013/129	
☐	N435NA	Short SD.3-30	SH3201	♦

	Reg	Type	c/n	
☐	N367MQ	Short SD.3-60	SH3640	
☐	N377MQ	Short SD.3-60	SH3699	
☐	N378MQ	Short SD.3-60	SH3700	
☐	N381MQ	Short SD.3-60	SH3703	
☐	N382MQ	Short SD.3-60	SH3704	
☐	N383MQ	Short SD.3-60	SH3706	
☐	N385MQ	Short SD.3-60	SH3707	

SKYWEST AIRLINES *OO / SKW*

Operates services for Delta Connection, United Express and US Airways Express some in own colours.

SONGBIRD AIRWAYS *SK / SGB*

	Reg	Type	c/n	
☐	N417XA	B737-484	25417/2160	♦
☐	N761XA	B767-27GER	27048/475	♦

SOUTHERN AIR *9S / SOO*

	Reg	Type	c/n	
☐	N494SA	B737-4H6F	27674/2877	
☐	N495SA	B737-45DF	27157/2502	
☐	N496SA	B737-4H6F	26455/2507	
☐	N498SA	B737-4Q8(F)	26334/2782	
☐	N499SA	B737-4K5(F)	26316/2711	♦
☐	N743WA	B747-412SF	26562/1074	[MZJ]
☐	N714SA	B777-FZB	37988/1002	
☐	N774SA	B777-FZB	37986/844	DHL c/s
☐	N775SA	B777-FZB	37987/852	DHL c/s
☐	N777SA	B777-FZB	37989/1011	
☐	N778LA	B777-F16	41518/1050	♦

To be acquired by Atlas Air, subject to DoT approval.

SOUTHWEST AIRLINES *WN / SWA*

	Reg	Type	c/n
☐	N317WN	B737-3Q8	24068/1506
☐	N340LV	B737-3K2	23738/1360
☐	N345SA	B737-3K2	23786/1386
☐	N352SW	B737-3H4/W	24888/1942
☐	N353SW	B737-3H4/W	24889/1947
☐	N354SW	B737-3H4/W	25219/2092
☐	N355SW	B737-3H4/W	25250/2103
☐	N356SW	B737-3H4/W	25251/2105
☐	N357SW	B737-3H4/W	26594/2294
☐	N358SW	B737-3H4/W	26595/2295
☐	N359SW	B737-3H4/W	26596/2297
☐	N360SW	B737-3H4/W	26571/2307
☐	N361SW	B737-3H4/W	26572/2309
☐	N362SW	B737-3H4/W	26573/2322
☐	N363SW	B737-3H4/W	26574/2429
☐	N364SW	B737-3H4/W	26575/2430
☐	N365SW	B737-3H4/W	26576/2433
☐	N366SW	B737-3H4/W	26577/2469
☐	N367SW	B737-3H4/W	26578/2470
☐	N368SW	B737-3H4/W	26579/2473
☐	N369SW	B737-3H4/W	26580/2477
☐	N370SW	B737-3H4/W	26597/2497
☐	N371SW	B737-3H4/W	26598/2500
☐	N372SW	B737-3H4/W	26599/2504
☐	N373SW	B737-3H4/W	26581/2509
☐	N374SW	B737-3H4/W	26582/2515
☐	N375SW	B737-3H4/W	26583/2520
☐	N376SW	B737-3H4/W	26584/2570
☐	N378SW	B737-3H4/W	26585/2579
☐	N379SW	B737-3H4/W	26586/2580
☐	N380SW	B737-3H4/W	26587/2610
☐	N382SW	B737-3H4/W	26588/2611
☐	N383SW	B737-3H4/W	26589/2612
☐	N384SW	B737-3H4/W	26590/2613
☐	N385SW	B737-3H4/W	26600/2617
☐	N386SW	B737-3H4/W	26601/2626
☐	N387SW	B737-3H4/W	26602/2627
☐	N388SW	B737-3H4/W	26591/2628
☐	N389SW	B737-3H4/W	26592/2629
☐	N390SW	B737-3H4/W	26593/2642
☐	N391SW	B737-3H4/W	27378/2643
☐	N392SW	B737-3H4/W	27379/2644
☐	N394SW	B737-3H4/W	27380/2645
☐	N395SW	B737-3H4/W	27689/2667
☐	N396SW	B737-3H4/W	27690/2668
☐	N397SW	B737-3H4/W	27691/2695
☐	N398SW	B737-3H4/W	27692/2696
☐	N399WN	B737-3H4/W	27693/2697
☐	N600WN	B737-3H4/W	27694/2699
☐	N601WN	B737-3H4/W	27695/2702
☐	N602SW	B737-3H4/W	27953/2713
☐	N603SW	B737-3H4/W	27954/2714
☐	N604SW	B737-3H4/W	27955/2715
☐	N605SW	B737-3H4/W	27956/2716
☐	N606SW	B737-3H4/W	27926/2740
☐	N607SW	B737-3H4/W	27927/2741
☐	N608SW	B737-3H4/W	27928/2742
☐	N609SW	B737-3H4/W	27929/2744
☐	N610WN	B737-3H4/W	27696/2745
☐	N611SW	B737-3H4/W	27697/2750
☐	N612SW	B737-3H4/W	27930/2753
☐	N613SW	B737-3H4/W	27931/2754
☐	N614SW	B737-3H4/W	28033/2755
☐	N615SW	B737-3H4/W	27698/2757
☐	N616SW	B737-3H4/W	27699/2758
☐	N617SW	B737-3H4/W	27700/2759
☐	N618WN	B737-3H4/W	28034/2761
☐	N619SW	B737-3H4/W	28035/2762
☐	N620SW	B737-3H4/W	28036/2766
☐	N621SW	B737-3H4/W	28037/2767
☐	N622SW	B737-3H4/W	27932/2779
☐	N623SW	B737-3H4/W	27933/2780
☐	N624SW	B737-3H4/W	27934/2781
☐	N625SW	B737-3H4/W	27701/2787
☐	N626SW	B737-3H4/W	27702/2789
☐	N627SW	B737-3H4/W	27935/2790
☐	N628SW	B737-3H4/W	27703/2795
☐	N629SW	B737-3H4/W	27704/2796
☐	N630WN	B737-3H4/W	27705/2797
☐	N631SW	B737-3H4/W	27706/2798
☐	N632SW	B737-3H4/W	27707/2799
☐	N633SW	B737-3H4/W	27936/2807
☐	N634SW	B737-3H4/W	27937/2808
☐	N635SW	B737-3H4/W	27708/2813
☐	N636WN	B737-3H4/W	27709/2814
☐	N637SW	B737-3H4/W	27710/2819
☐	N638SW	B737-3H4/W	27711/2820
☐	N639SW	B737-3H4/W	27712/2821
☐	N640SW	B737-3H4/W	27713/2840
☐	N641SW	B737-3H4/W	27714/2841
☐	N642WN	B737-3H4/W	27715/2842
☐	N643SW	B737-3H4/W	27716/2843
☐	N644SW	B737-3H4/W	28329/2869
☐	N645SW	B737-3H4/W	28330/2870
☐	N646SW	B737-3H4/W	28331/2871
☐	N647SW	B737-3H4/W	27717/2892
☐	N648SW	B737-3H4/W	27718/2893
☐	N649SW	B737-3H4/W	27719/2894
☐	N650SW	B737-3H4/W	27720/2901
☐	N651SW	B737-3H4/W	27721/2915

	Registration	Type	Serial	
☐	N652SW	B737-3H4/W	27722/2916	
☐	N653SW	B737-3H4/W	28398/2917	
☐	N654SW	B737-3H4/W	28399/2918	
☐	N655WN	B737-3H4/W	28400/2931	
☐	N656SW	B737-3H4/W	28401/2932	
☐	N657SW	B737-3L9	23331/1111	
☐	N658SW	B737-3L9	23332/1118	
☐	N659SW	B737-301	23229/1112	
☐	N660SW	B737-301	23230/1115	
☐	N663SW	B737-3Q8	23256/1128	
☐	N665WN	B737-3Y0	23497/1227	
☐	N669SW	B737-3A4	23752/1484	
☐	N684WN	B737-3T0	23941/1520	
☐	N685SW	B737-3Q8	23401/1209	
☐	N687SW	B737-3Q8	23388/1187	
☐	N694SW	B737-3T5	23061/1080	
☐	N697SW	B737-3T0	23838/1505	
☐	N511SW	B737-5H4	24188/2029	[NZC]
☐	N514SW	B737-5H4	25153/2078	
☐	N515SW	B737-5H4	25154/2080	
☐	N520SW	B737-5H4	25319/2134	
☐	N521SW	B737-5H4	25320/2136	
☐	N522SW	B737-5H4	26564/2202	
☐	N523SW	B737-5H4	26565/2204	
☐	N524SW	B737-5H4	26566/2224	
☐	N525SW	B737-5H4	26567/2283	
☐	N526SW	B737-5H4	26568/2285	
☐	N527SW	B737-5H4	26569/2287	
☐	N200WN	B737-7H4/W	32482/1638	
☐	N201LV	B737-7H4/W	29854/1650	
☐	N202WN	B737-7H4/W	33999/1653	
☐	N203WN	B737-7H4/W	32483/1656	
☐	N204WN	B737-7H4/W	29855/1663	
☐	N205WN	B737-7H4/W	34010/1668	
☐	N206WN	B737-7H4/W	34011/1675	
☐	N207WN	B737-7H4/W	34012/1678	
☐	N208WN	B737-7H4/W	29856/1679	
☐	N209WN	B737-7H4/W	32484/1683	
☐	N210WN	B737-7H4/W	34162/1690	
☐	N211WN	B737-7H4/W	34163/1699	
☐	N212WN	B737-7H4/W	32485/1708	
☐	N213WN	B737-7H4/W	34217/1717	
☐	N214WN	B737-7H4/W	32486/1721	
☐	N215WN	B737-7H4/W	32487/1723	
☐	N216WR	B737-7H4/W	32488/1735	
☐	N217JC	B737-7H4/W	34232/1737	
☐	N218WN	B737-7H4/W	32489/1741	
☐	N219WN	B737-7H4/W	32490/1744	
☐	N220WN	B737-7H4/W	32491/1756	
☐	N221WN	B737-7H4/W	34259/1776	
☐	N222WN	B737-7H4/W	34290/1780	
☐	N223WN	B737-7H4/W	32492/1799	
☐	N224WN	B737-7H4/W	32493/1801	
☐	N225WN	B737-7H4/W	34333/1820	
☐	N226WN	B737-7H4/W	32494/1822	
☐	N227WN	B737-7H4/W	34450/1831	
☐	N228WN	B737-7H4/W	32496/1835	
☐	N229WN	B737-7H4/W	32498/1858	
☐	N230WN	B737-7H4/W	34592/1868	
☐	N231WN	B737-7H4/W	32499/1881	
☐	N232WN	B737-7H4/W	32500/1888	
☐	N233LV	B737-7H4/W	32501/1893	
☐	N234WN	B737-7H4/W	32502/1905	
☐	N235WN	B737-7H4/W	34630/1916	
☐	N236WN	B737-7H4/W	34631/1928	
☐	N237WN	B737-7H4/W	34632/1930	
☐	N238WN	B737-7H4/W	34713/1950	
☐	N239WN	B737-7H4/W	34714/1954	
☐	N240WN	B737-7H4/W	32503/1959	
☐	N241WN	B737-7H4/W	32504/1965	
☐	N242WN	B737-7H4/W	32505/1969	
☐	N243WN	B737-7H4/W	34863/1973	
☐	N244WN	B737-7H4/W	34864/1977	
☐	N245WN	B737-7H4/W	32506/1982	
☐	N246LV	B737-7H4/W	32507/1984	
☐	N247WN	B737-7H4/W	32508/1989	
☐	N248WN	B737-7H4/W	32509/2000	
☐	N249WN	B737-7H4/W	34951/2005	
☐	N250WN	B737-7H4/W	34972/2019	
☐	N251WN	B737-7H4/W	32510/2025	
☐	N252WN	B737-7H4/W	34973/2027	
☐	N253WN	B737-7H4/W	32511/2038	
☐	N254WN	B737-7H4/W	32512/2040	
☐	N255WN	B737-7H4/W	32513/2049	
☐	N256WN	B737-7H4/W	32514/2059	
☐	N257WN	B737-7H4/W	32515/2062	
☐	N258WN	B737-7H4/W	32516/2076	
☐	N259WN	B737-7H4/W	35554/2092	
☐	N260WN	B737-7H4/W	32518/2114	
☐	N261WN	B737-7H4/W	32517/2133	
☐	N262WN	B737-7H4/W	32519/2139	
☐	N263WN	B737-7H4/W	32520/2153	
☐	N264LV	B737-7H4/W	32521/2161	
☐	N265WN	B737-7H4/W	32522/2174	
☐	N266WN	B737-7H4/W	32523/2182	
☐	N267WN	B737-7H4/W	32525/2193	
☐	N268WN	B737-7H4/W	32524/2199	
☐	N269WN	B737-7H4/W	32526/2204	
☐	N270WN	B737-705/W	29089/83	
☐	N271LV	B737-705/W	29090/109	
☐	N272WN	B737-7H4/W	32527/2224	
☐	N273WN	B737-7H4/W	32528/2238	
☐	N274WN	B737-7H4/W	32529/2244	
☐	N275WN	B737-7H4/W	36153/2256	
☐	N276WN	B737-7H4/W	32530/2262	
☐	N277WN	B737-7H4/W	32531/2274	
☐	N278WN	B737-7H4/W	36441/2281	
☐	N279WN	B737-7H4/W	32532/2284	
☐	N280WN	B737-7H4/W	32533/2294	
☐	N281WN	B737-7H4/W	36528/2307	
☐	N282WN	B737-7H4/W	32534/2318	
☐	N283WN	B737-7H4/W	36610/2322	
☐	N284WN	B737-7H4/W	32535/2328	
☐	N285WN	B737-7H4/W	32536/2337	
☐	N286WN	B737-7H4/W	32471/1535	
☐	N287WN	B737-7H4/W	32537/2344	
☐	N288WN	B737-7H4/W	36611/2350	
☐	N289CT	B737-7H4/W	36633/2354	
☐	N290WN	B737-7H4/W	36632/2363	
☐	N291WN	B737-7H4/W	32539/2378	
☐	N292WN	B737-7H4/W	32538/2383	
☐	N293WN	B737-7H4/W	36612/2387	
☐	N294WN	B737-7H4/W	32540/2390	
☐	N295WN	B737-7H4/W	32541/2409	
☐	N296WN	B737-7H4/W	36613/2413	
☐	N297WN	B737-7H4/W	32542/2417	
☐	N298WN	B737-7H4/W	32543/2438	
☐	N299WN	B737-7H4/W	36614/2442	
☐	N400WN	B737-7H4/W	27891/806	
☐	N401WN	B737-7H4/W	29813/810	
☐	N402WN	B737-7H4/W	29814/811	
☐	N403WN	B737-7H4/W	29815/821	
☐	N404WN	B737-7H4/W	27892/880	

☐	N405WN	B737-7H4/W	27893/881
☐	N406WN	B737-7H4/W	27894/885
☐	N407WN	B737-7H4/W	29817/903
☐	N408WN	B737-7H4/W	27895/934
☐	N409WN	B737-7H4/W	27896/945
☐	N410WN	B737-7H4/W	27897/946
☐	N411WN	B737-7H4/W	29821/950
☐	N412WN	B737-7H4/W	29818/956
☐	N413WN	B737-7H4/W	29819/960
☐	N414WN	B737-7H4/W	29820/967
☐	N415WN	B737-7H4/W	29836/980
☐	N416WN	B737-7H4/W	32453/990
☐	N417WN	B737-7H4/W	29822/993
☐	N418WN	B737-7H4/W	29823/1000
☐	N419WN	B737-7H4/W	29824/1017
☐	N420WN	B737-7H4/W	29825/1039
☐	N421LV	B737-7H4/W	32452/1040
☐	N422WN	B737-7H4/W	29826/1093
☐	N423WN	B737-7H4/W	29827/1101
☐	N424WN	B737-7H4/W	29828/1105
☐	N425LV	B737-7H4/W	29829/1109
☐	N426WN	B737-7H4/W	29830/1114
☐	N427WN	B737-7H4/W	29831/1119
☐	N428WN	B737-7H4/W	29844/1243
☐	N429WN	B737-7H4/W	33658/1256
☐	N430WN	B737-7H4/W	33659/1257
☐	N431WN	B737-7H4/W	29845/1259
☐	N432WN	B737-7H4/W	33715/1297
☐	N433LV	B737-7H4/W	33716/1301
☐	N434WN	B737-7H4/W	32454/1313
☐	N435WN	B737-7H4/W	32455/1328
☐	N436WN	B737-7H4/W	32456/1342
☐	N437WN	B737-7H4/W	29832/1349
☐	N438WN	B737-7H4/W	29833/1353
☐	N439WN	B737-7H4/W	29834/1356
☐	N440LV	B737-7H4/W	29835/1358
☐	N441WN	B737-7H4/W	29837/1360
☐	N442WN	B737-7H4/W	32459/1365
☐	N443WN	B737-7H4/W	29838/1369
☐	N444WN	B737-7H4/W	29839/1374
☐	N445WN	B737-7H4/W	29841/1388
☐	N446WN	B737-7H4/W	29842/1401
☐	N447WN	B737-7H4/W	33720/1405
☐	N448WN	B737-7H4/W	33721/1409
☐	N449WN	B737-7H4/W	32469/1427
☐	N450WN	B737-7H4/W	32470/1429
☐	N451WN	B737-7H4/W	32495/1458
☐	N452WN	B737-7H4/W	29846/1461
☐	N453WN	B737-7H4/W	29847/1476
☐	N454WN	B737-7H4/W	29851/1477
☐	N455WN	B737-7H4/W	32462/1480
☐	N456WN	B737-7H4/W	32463/1484
☐	N457WN	B737-7H4/W	33856/1485
☐	N458WN	B737-7H4/W	33857/1490
☐	N459WN	B737-7H4/W	32497/1492
☐	N460WN	B737-7H4/W	32464/1499
☐	N461WN	B737-7H4/W	32465/1510
☐	N462WN	B737-7H4/W	32466/1513
☐	N463WN	B737-7H4/W	32467/1515
☐	N464WN	B737-7H4/W	32468/1517
☐	N465WN	B737-7H4/W	33829/1519
☐	N466WN	B737-7H4/W	30677/1520
☐	N467WN	B737-7H4/W	33830/1521
☐	N468WN	B737-7H4/W	33858/1523
☐	N469WN	B737-7H4/W	33859/1525
☐	N470WN	B737-7H4/W	33860/1528
☐	N472WN	B737-7H4/W	33831/1537

☐	N473WN	B737-7H4/W	33832/1541
☐	N474WN	B737-7H4/W	33861/1543
☐	N475WN	B737-7H4/W	32474/1545
☐	N476WN	B737-7H4/W	32475/1549
☐	N477WN	B737-7H4/W	33988/1552
☐	N478WN	B737-7H4/W	33989/1555
☐	N479WN	B737-7H4/W	33990/1558
☐	N480WN	B737-7H4/W	33998/1561
☐	N481WN	B737-7H4/W	29853/1564
☐	N482WN	B737-7H4/W	29852/1568
☐	N483WN	B737-7H4/W	32472/1570
☐	N484WN	B737-7H4/W	33841/1575
☐	N485WN	B737-7H4/W	32473/1577
☐	N486WN	B737-7H4/W	33852/1579
☐	N487WN	B737-7H4/W	33854/1583
☐	N488WN	B737-7H4/W	33853/1587
☐	N489WN	B737-7H4/W	33855/1589
☐	N490WN	B737-7H4/W	32476/1591
☐	N491WN	B737-7H4/W	33867/1596
☐	N492WN	B737-7H4/W	33866/1605
☐	N493WN	B737-7H4/W	32477/1616
☐	N494WN	B737-7H4/W	33868/1621
☐	N495WN	B737-7H4/W	33869/1625
☐	N496WN	B737-7H4/W	32478/1626
☐	N497WN	B737-7H4/W	32479/1628
☐	N498WN	B737-7H4/W	32480/1633
☐	N499WN	B737-7H4/W	32481/1636
☐	N550WN	B737-76Q/W	30279/1010
☐	N551WN	B737-76Q/W	30280/1025
☐	N552WN	B737-7BX/W	30744/989
☐	N553WN	B737-7BX/W	30745/1027
☐	N554WN	B737-7BX/W	30746/1085
☐	N555LV	B737-7BD/W	36726/3585
☐	N556WN	B737-7BD/W	33936/3613
☐	N557WN	B737-790/W	30166/700
☐	N558WN	B737-73V/W	30248/1118
☐	N559WN	B737-73V/W	30249/1128
☐	N560WN	B737-790/W	30542/532
☐	N561WN	B737-73V	32417/1285
☐	N562WN	B737-790/W	30778/724
☐	N563WN	B737-752/W	34296/1783
☐	N564WN	B737-73V/W	30244/1148
☐	N565WN	B737-76Q	30282/1143
☐	N566WN	B737-7CT/W	32753/1222
☐	N567WN	B737-7CT/W	32747/1239
☐	N568WN	B737-76N/W	32583/994
☐	N569WN	B737-7CT/W	33656/1246
☐	N570WN	B737-7CT/W	33657/1254
☐	N700GS	B737-7H4/W	27835/4
☐	N701GS	B737-7H4/W	27836/6
☐	N703SW	B737-7H4/W	27837/12
☐	N704SW	B737-7H4/W	27838/15
☐	N705SW	B737-7H4/W	27839/20
☐	N706SW	B737-7H4/W	27840/24
☐	N707SA	B737-7H4/W	27841/1
☐	N708SW	B737-7H4/W	27842/2
☐	N709SW	B737-7H4/W	27843/3
☐	N710SW	B737-7H4/W	27844/34
☐	N711HK	B737-7H4/W	27845/38
☐	N712SW	B737-7H4/W	27846/53
☐	N713SW	B737-7H4/W	27847/54
☐	N714CB	B737-7H4/W	27848/61
☐	N715SW	B737-7H4/W	27849/62
☐	N716SW	B737-7H4/W	27850/64
☐	N717SA	B737-7H4/W	27851/70
☐	N718SW	B737-7H4/W	27852/71
☐	N719SW	B737-7H4/W	27853/82

	Reg	Type	c/n
☐	N720WN	B737-7H4/W	27854/121
☐	N723SW	B737-7H4/W	27855/199
☐	N724SW	B737-7H4/W	27856/201
☐	N725SW	B737-7H4/W	27857/208
☐	N726SW	B737-7H4/W	27858/213
☐	N727SW	B737-7H4/W	27859/274
☐	N728SW	B737-7H4/W	27860/276
☐	N729SW	B737-7H4/W	27861/278
☐	N730SW	B737-7H4/W	27862/284
☐	N731SA	B737-7H4/W	27863/318
☐	N732SW	B737-7H4/W	27864/319
☐	N733SA	B737-7H4/W	27865/320
☐	N734SA	B737-7H4/W	27866/324
☐	N735SA	B737-7H4/W	27867/354
☐	N736SA	B737-7H4/W	27868/357
☐	N737JW	B737-7H4/W	27869/358
☐	N738CB	B737-7H4/W	27870/360
☐	N739GB	B737-7H4/W	29275/144
☐	N740SW	B737-7H4/W	29276/155
☐	N741SA	B737-7H4/W	29277/157
☐	N742SW	B737-7H4/W	29278/172
☐	N743SW	B737-7H4/W	29279/175
☐	N744SW	B737-7H4/W	29490/232
☐	N745SW	B737-7H4/W	29491/237
☐	N746SW	B737-7H4/W	29798/299
☐	N747SA	B737-7H4/W	29799/306
☐	N748SW	B737-7H4/W	29800/331
☐	N749SW	B737-7H4/W	29801/343
☐	N750SA	B737-7H4/W	29802/366
☐	N751SW	B737-7H4/W	29803/373
☐	N752SW	B737-7H4/W	29804/387
☐	N754SW	B737-7H4/W	29849/416
☐	N755SA	B737-7H4/W	27871/419
☐	N756SA	B737-7H4/W	27872/422
☐	N757LV	B737-7H4/W	29850/425
☐	N758SW	B737-7H4/W	27873/437
☐	N759GS	B737-7H4/W	30544/448
☐	N760SW	B737-7H4/W	27874/468
☐	N761RR	B737-7H4/W	27875/495
☐	N762SW	B737-7H4/W	27876/512
☐	N763SW	B737-7H4/W	27877/520
☐	N764SW	B737-7H4/W	27878/521
☐	N765SW	B737-7H4/W	29805/525
☐	N766SW	B737-7H4/W	29806/537
☐	N767SW	B737-7H4/W	29807/541
☐	N768SW	B737-7H4/W	30587/580
☐	N769SW	B737-7H4/W	30588/592
☐	N770SA	B737-7H4/W	30589/595
☐	N771SA	B737-7H4/W	27879/599
☐	N772SW	B737-7H4/W	27880/601
☐	N773SA	B737-7H4/W	27881/603
☐	N774SW	B737-7H4/W	27882/609
☐	N775SW	B737-7H4/W	30590/617
☐	N776WN	B737-7H4/W	30591/620
☐	N777QC	B737-7H4/W	30592/621
☐	N778SW	B737-7H4/W	27883/626
☐	N779SW	B737-7H4/W	27884/628
☐	N780SW	B737-7H4/W	27885/643
☐	N781WN	B737-7H4/W	30601/646
☐	N782SA	B737-7H4/W	29808/670
☐	N783SW	B737-7H4/W	29809/675
☐	N784SW	B737-7H4/W	29810/677
☐	N785SW	B737-7H4/W	30602/693
☐	N786SW	B737-7H4/W	29811/698
☐	N787SA	B737-7H4/W	29812/705
☐	N788SA	B737-7H4/W	30603/707
☐	N789SW	B737-7H4/W	29816/718

	Reg	Type	c/n
☐	N790SW	B737-7H4/W	30604/721
☐	N791SW	B737-7H4/W	27886/736
☐	N792SW	B737-7H4/W	27887/737
☐	N793SA	B737-7H4/W	27888/744
☐	N794SW	B737-7H4/W	30605/748
☐	N795SW	B737-7H4/W	30606/780
☐	N796SW	B737-7H4/W	27889/784
☐	N797MX	B737-7H4/W	27890/803
☐	N798SW	B737-7AD/W	28436/41
☐	N799SW	B737-7Q8/W	28209/14
☐	N900WN	B737-7H4/W	32544/2460
☐	N901WN	B737-7H4/W	32545/2462
☐	N902WN	B737-7H4/W	36615/2469
☐	N903WN	B737-7H4/W	32457/2473
☐	N904WN	B737-7H4/W	36616/2480
☐	N905WN	B737-7H4/W	36617/2491
☐	N906WN	B737-7H4/W	36887/2494
☐	N907WN	B737-7H4/W	36619/2500
☐	N908WN	B737-7H4/W	36620/2509
☐	N909WN	B737-7H4/W	32458/2517
☐	N910WN	B737-7H4/W	36618/2521
☐	N912WN	B737-7H4/W	36621/2532
☐	N913WN	B737-7H4/W	29840/2536
☐	N914WN	B737-7H4/W	36622/2540
☐	N915WN	B737-7H4/W	36888/2546
☐	N916WN	B737-7H4/W	36623/2558
☐	N917WN	B737-7H4/W	36624/2562
☐	N918WN	B737-7H4/W	29843/2572
☐	N919WN	B737-7H4/W	36625/2591
☐	N920WN	B737-7H4/W	32460/2597
☐	N921WN	B737-7H4/W	36626/2600
☐	N922WN	B737-7H4/W	32461/2620
☐	N923WN	B737-7H4/W	36627/2634
☐	N924WN	B737-7H4/W	36628/2640
☐	N925WN	B737-7H4/W	36630/2656
☐	N926WN	B737-7H4/W	36629/2663
☐	N927WN	B737-7H4/W	36889/2679
☐	N928WN	B737-7H4/W	36890/2687
☐	N929WN	B737-7H4/W	36631/2689
☐	N930WN	B737-7H4/W	36636/2784
☐	N931WN	B737-7H4/W	36637/2799
☐	N932WN	B737-7H4/W	36639/2837
☐	N933WN	B737-7H4/W	36640/2847
☐	N934WN	B737-7H4/W	36642/2878
☐	N935WN	B737-7H4/W	36641/2894
☐	N936WN	B737-7H4/W	36643/2909
☐	N937WN	B737-7H4/W	36644/2925
☐	N938WN	B737-7H4/W	36645/2929
☐	N939WN	B737-7H4/W	36646/2933
☐	N940WN	B737-7H4/W	36900/2943
☐	N941WN	B737-7H4/W	36647/2961
☐	N942WN	B737-7H4/W	36648/2985
☐	N943WN	B737-7H4/W	36913/3195
☐	N944WN	B737-7H4/W	36659/3220
☐	N945WN	B737-7H4/W	36660/3226
☐	N946WN	B737-7H4/W	36918/3251
☐	N947WN	B737-7H4/W	36924/3290
☐	N948WN	B737-7H4/W	36662/3296
☐	N949WN	B737-7H4/W	36663/3358
☐	N950WN	B737-7H4/W	36664/3365
☐	N951WN	B737-7H4/W	36665/3388
☐	N952WN	B737-7H4/W	36667/3477
☐	N953WN	B737-7H4/W	36668/3510
☐	N954WN	B737-7H4/W	36669/3547
☐	N955WN	B737-7H4/W	36671/3603
☐	N956WN	B737-7H4/W	36672/3629
☐	N957WN	B737-7H4/W	41528/3657

	Reg	Type	c/n	
☐	N958WN	B737-7H4/W	36673/3661	
☐	N959WN	B737-7H4/W	36674/3696	
☐	N960WN	B737-7H4/W	36675/3715	
☐	N961WN	B737-7H4/W	36962/3719	
☐	N962WN	B737-7H4/W	36963/3724	
☐	N963WN	B737-7H4/W	36676/3726	
☐	N964WN	B737-7H4/W	36965/3759	
☐	N965WN	B737-7H4/W	36677/3774	
☐	N966WN	B737-7H4/W	36966/3788	
☐	N967WN	B737-7H4/W	36967/3791	
☐	N968WN	B737-7H4/W	36679/3872	
☐	N969WN	B737-7H4/W	41777/3874	
☐	N7701B	B737-76N/W	32681/1526	
☐	N7702A	B737-7BD/W	33917/1550	
☐	N7703A	B737-76N/W	32653/1566	
☐	N7704B	B737-7BD/W	33918/1572	
☐	N7705A	B737-76N/W	32744/1584	
☐	N7706A	B737-76N/W	32661/1593	
☐	N7707C	B737-76N/W	32667/1623	
☐	N7708E	B737-76N/W	32652/1627	
☐	N7709A	B737-76N/W	32654/1641	
☐	N7710A	B737-76N/W	32656/1671	
☐	N7711N	B737-76N/W	32657/1687	
☐	N7712G	B737-76N/W	32660/1710	
☐	N7713A	B737-7BD/W	33919/1730	
☐	N7714B	B737-76N/W	32679/1514	
☐	N7715E	B737-7BD/W	33921/1778	
☐	N7716A	B737-76N/W	32662/1788	
☐	N7717D	B737-76N/W	32664/1804	
☐	N7718B	B737-76N/W	32665/1827	
☐	N7719A	B737-76N/W	32666/1833	
☐	N7720F	B737-78D/W	33922/1845	
☐	N7721E	B737-7BD/W	34479/1874	
☐	N7722B	B737-76N/W	32668/1876	
☐	N7723E	B737-76N/W	32670/1898	
☐	N7724A	B737-7BD/W	36725/2815	
☐	N7725A	B737-76N/W	32671/1925	
☐	N7726A	B737-7BD/W	33924/1940	
☐	N7727A	B737-76N/W	32673/1943	
☐	N7728D	B737-7BD/W	33925/1967	
☐	N7729A	B737-76N/W	32675/1970	
☐	N7730A	B737-7BD/W	33926/1997	
☐	N7731A	B737-76N/W	32677/2002	
☐	N7732A	B737-7BD/W	34861/2041	
☐	N7733B	B737-76N/W	32678/2055	
☐	N7734H	B737-7BD/W	33923/2083	
☐	N7735A	B737-7BD/W	34862/2094	
☐	N7736A	B737-7BD/W	35109/2126	
☐	N7737E	B737-7BD/W	33929/2129	
☐	N7738A	B737-7BD/W	33930/2143	
☐	N7739A	B737-7BD/W	35110/2147	
☐	N7740A	B737-7BD/W	33927/2169	
☐	N7741C	B737-7BD/W	35788/2178	
☐	N7742B	B737-7BD/W	33928/2190	
☐	N7743B	B737-7BD/W	36718/2568	
☐	N7744A	B737-7BD/W	33931/2214	
☐	N7745A	B737-7BD/W	33933/2278	
☐	N7746C	B737-7BD/W	33934/2296	
☐	N7747C	B737-7BD/W	36091/2304	
☐	N7748A	B737-7BD/W	36399/2312	
☐	N7749B	B737-7BD/W	36724/2813	
☐	N7750A	B737-7BD/W	36716/2505	
☐	N7751A	B737-7BD/W	36717/2526	
☐	N7752B	B737-7BD/W	33943/2552	
☐	N7811F	B737-76N/W	28654/986	
☐	N7812G	B737-76N/W	32582/1013	
☐	N7813P	B737-7K9/W	30041/909	
☐	N7814B	B737-7K9/W	30042/931	
☐	N7815L	B737-76Q/W	30288/1322	
☐	N7816B	B737-7L9/W	28009/221	
☐	N7817J	B737-7L9/W	28013/682	
☐	N7818L	B737-76N/W	28609/417	
☐	N7819A	B737-7Q8/W	30649/1048	
☐	N7820L	B737-79P/W	28253/1247	
☐	N7821L	B737-7CT/W	32748/1266	
☐	N7822A	B737-76N/W	32596/1028	♦
☐	N7823A	B737-7CT/W	32749/1281	
☐	N7824A	B737-7BK/W	30617/812	♦
☐	N7825A	B737-7CT/W	32750/1286	
☐	N7826A	B737-79P/W	30035/1288	♦
☐	N7827A	B737-79P/W	28255/1284	♦
☐	N7828A	B737-7CT/W	33697/1303	♦
☐	N7829B	B737-7CT/W	32751/1333	♦
☐	N7830A	B737-7L9/W	28008/203	♦
☐	N7831B	B737-7CT/W	32752/1339	♦
☐	N7832A	B737-79P/W	30657/1319	♦
☐	N7833A	B737-79P/W	30036/1336	♦
☐	N7834A	B737-752/W	33789/1524	
☐	N7835A	B737-752/W	34294/1761	♦
☐	N7836A	B737-7L9/W	28010/396	♦
☐	N7837A	B737-752/W	33785/1398	♦
☐	N7838A	B737-73V/W	30235/672	♦
☐	N7839A	B737-73V/W	30243/919	♦
☐	N7840A	B737-73V/W	30236/715	♦
☐	N7841A	B737-7L9/W	28015/785	o/o♦
☐	N7842A	B737-73V/W	30237/730	o/o♦
☐	N7843A	B737-752/W	35786/2098	♦
☐	N7844A	B737-752/W	35118/2151	♦
☐	N7846A	B737-76N/W	35218/2342	♦
☐	N7873A	B737-7Q8/W	29350/1452	♦
☐	N7874B	B737-7Q8/W	29352/1491	♦
☐	N7875A	B737-7Q8/W	29354/1581	♦
☐	N7876A	B737-7Q8/W	29355/1609	♦
☐	N7877H	B737-7Q8W	29359/1659	♦
☐	N	B737-752/W	34297/1808	o/o♦
☐	N	B737-71B/W	29366/1872	o/o♦
☐	N500WR	B737-8H4/W	36898/4967	
☐	N8301J	B737-8H4/W	36980/3952	
☐	N8302F	B737-8H4/W	36680/3979	
☐	N8303R	B737-8H4/W	36681/3993	
☐	N8305E	B737-8H4/W	36683/4009	
☐	N8306H	B737-8H4/W	36983/4019	
☐	N8307K	B737-8H4/W	36987/4027	
☐	N8308K	B737-8H4/W	36682/4039	
☐	N8309C	B737-8H4/W	36985/4043	
☐	N8310C	B737-8H4/W	38807/4058	
☐	N8311Q	B737-8H4/W	38808/4073	
☐	N8312C	B737-8H4/W	38809/4084	
☐	N8313F	B737-8H4/W	38810/4088	
☐	N8314L	B737-8H4/W	36990/4100	
☐	N8315C	B737-8H4/W	38811/4108	
☐	N8316H	B737-8H4/W	36684/4113	
☐	N8317M	B737-8H4/W	36992/4126	
☐	N8318F	B737-8H4/W	36685/4143	
☐	N8319F	B737-8H4/W	36994/4162	
☐	N8320J	B737-8H4/W	36686/4163	
☐	N8321D	B737-8H4/W	36687/4195	
☐	N8322X	B737-8H4/W	36997/4200	
☐	N8323C	B737-8H4/W	37005/4232	
☐	N8324A	B737-8H4/W	35966/4239	
☐	N8325D	B737-8H4/W	37003/4255	
☐	N8326F	B737-8H4/W	35969/4263	

	Reg	Type	c/n	
☐	N8327A	B737-8H4/W	37009/4269	
☐	N8328A	B737-8H4/W	38818/4285	
☐	N8329B	B737-8H4/W	37006/4292	
☐	N8600F	B737-8H4/W	39882/4007	
☐	N8601C	B737-8H4/W	38874/4050	
☐	N8602F	B737-8H4/W	38110/4059	
☐	N8603F	B737-8H4/W	38875/4069	
☐	N8604K	B737-8H4/W	39883/4078	
☐	N8605E	B737-8H4/W	36891/4297	
☐	N8606C	B737-8H4/W	35964/4312	
☐	N8607M	B737-8H4/W	36634/4318	
☐	N8608N	B737-8H4/W	36638/4323	
☐	N8609A	B737-8H4/W	36893/4335	
☐	N8610A	B737-8H4/W	36635/4362	
☐	N8611F	B737-8H4/W	36892/4367	
☐	N8612K	B737-8H4/W	36973/4389	
☐	N8613K	B737-8H4/W	36998/4397	
☐	N8614M	B737-8H4/W	36908/4420	
☐	N8615E	B737-8H4/W	36933/4613	
☐	N8616C	B737-8H4/W	36914/4627	
☐	N8617E	B737-8H4/W	36912/4631	
☐	N8618N	B737-8H4/W	36915/4667	
☐	N8619F	B737-8H4/W	33939/4670	
☐	N8620H	B737-8H4/W	42526/4674	
☐	N8621A	B737-8H4/W	36917/4706	
☐	N8622A	B737-8H4/W	36919/4717	
☐	N8623F	B737-8H4/W	36731/4734	
☐	N8624J	B737-8H4/W	37004/4845	
☐	N8625A	B737-8H4/W	36896/4849	
☐	N8626B	B737-8H4/W	36894/4854	
☐	N8627B	B737-8H4/W	36895/4874	
☐	N8628A	B737-8H4/W	42384/4888	
☐	N8629A	B737-8H4/W	36897/4896	
☐	N8630B	B737-8H4/W	42521/4914	
☐	N8631A	B737-8H4/W	42385/4928	
☐	N8632A	B737-8H4/W	60082/4935	
☐	N8633A	B737-8H4/W	36905/4942	
☐	N8634A	B737-8H4/W	42522/4955	
☐	N8635F	B737-8H4/W	60083/4962	
☐	N8637A	B737-8H4/W	42523/4974	
☐	N8638A	B737-8H4/W	36911/4977	
☐	N8639B	B737-8H4/W	60086/4999	
☐	N8640D	B737-8H4/W	60084/5001	
☐	N8641B	B737-8H4/W	60085/5011	
☐	N8642E	B737-8H4/W	42525/5022	
☐	N8643A	B737-8H4/W	42524/5030	
☐	N8644C	B737-8H4/W	35973/5032	
☐	N8645A	B737-8H4/W	36907/5038	
☐	N8646B	B737-8H4/W	36935/5042	
☐	N8647A	B737-8H4/W	42528/5044	
☐	N8648A	B737-8H4/W	42531/5064	
☐	N8649A	B737-8H4/W	42527/5084	
☐	N8650F	B737-8H4/W	36909/5105	
☐	N8651A	B737-8H4/W	36920/5125	
☐	N8652B	B737-8H4/W	36971/5151	
☐	N8653A	B737-8H4/W	37037/5192	
☐	N8654B	B737-8H4/W	37045/5198	
☐	N8655D	B737-8H4/W	42529/5200	
☐	N8656B	B737-8H4/W	42530/5221	
☐	N8657B	B737-8H4/W	42535/5227	
☐	N8658A	B737-8H4/W	36899/5229	
☐	N8659D	B737-8H4/W	36901/5269	
☐	N8660A	B737-8H4/W	36654/5273	
☐	N8661A	B737-8H4/W	36906/5283	
☐	N8662F	B737-8H4/W	36936/5309	
☐	N8663A	B737-8H4/W	36902/5329	
☐	N8664J	B737-8H4/W	36649/5350	
☐	N8665D	B737-8H4/W	36652/5370	
☐	N8667D	B737-8H4/W	36657/5392	
☐	N8668A	B737-8H4/W	36903/5411	
☐	N8669B	B737-8H4/W	36655/5432	
☐	N8670A	B737-8H4/W	36656/5443	
☐	N8671D	B737-8H4/W	36715/5646	♦
☐	N8672F	B737-8H4/W	36940/5662	♦
☐	N8673F	B737-8H4/W	36937/5671	♦
☐	N8674B	B737-8H4/W	36734/5684	♦
☐	N8675A	B737-8H4/W	35976/5701	♦
☐	N8676A	B737-8H4/W	36941/5706	♦
☐	N8677A	B737-8H4/W	36650/5742	♦
☐	N8678E	B737-8H4/W	36735/5753	♦
☐	N8679A	B737-8H4/W	36932/5771	♦
☐	N8680C	B737-8H4/W	36737/5775	♦
☐	N8681M	B737-8H4/W	36904/5786	o/o♦
☐	N8682B	B737-8H4/W	36651	o/o♦
☐	N8683D	B737-8H4/W	36738	o/o♦
☐	N8684F	B737-8H4/W	36653	o/o♦
☐	N8685B	B737-8H4/W	36723	o/o♦
☐	N8686A	B737-8H4/W	36938	o/o♦
☐	N8687A	B737-8H4/W	33837	o/o♦
☐	N8688J	B737-8H4/W	36939	o/o♦
☐	N8689C	B737-8H4/W	36658	o/o♦
☐	N8690A	B737-8H4/W	36916	o/o♦
☐	N	B737-8H4/W		o/o♦
☐	N	B737-8H4/W		o/o♦
☐	N	B737-8H4/W		o/o♦
☐	N	B737-8H4/W		o/o♦
☐	N	B737-8H4/W		o/o♦
☐	N	B737-8H4/W		o/o♦
☐	N	B737-8H4/W		o/o♦
☐	N	B737-8H4/W		o/o♦
☐	N	B737-8H4/W		o/o♦
☐	N	B737-8H4/W		o/o♦
☐	N	B737-8H4/W		o/o♦
☐	N	B737-8H4/W		o/o♦
☐	N	B737-8H4/W		o/o♦
☐	N	B737-8H4/W		o/o♦
☐	N	B737-8H4/W		o/o♦
☐	N	B737-8H4/W		o/o♦

SPIRIT AIRLINES *NK / NKS*

	Reg	Type	c/n
☐	N502NK	A319-132	2433
☐	N503NK	A319-132	2470
☐	N504NK	A319-132	2473
☐	N505NK	A319-132	2485
☐	N506NK	A319-132	2490
☐	N507NK	A319-132	2560
☐	N508NK	A319-132	2567
☐	N509NK	A319-132	2603
☐	N510NK	A319-132	2622
☐	N512NK	A319-132	2673
☐	N514NK	A319-132	2679
☐	N515NK	A319-132	2698
☐	N516NK	A319-132	2704
☐	N517NK	A319-132	2711
☐	N519NK	A319-132	2723
☐	N521NK	A319-132	2797
☐	N522NK	A319-132	2893
☐	N523NK	A319-132	2898
☐	N524NK	A319-132	2929
☐	N525NK	A319-132	2942
☐	N526NK	A319-132	2963
☐	N527NK	A319-132	2978
☐	N528NK	A319-132	2983

	Reg	Type	C/n	
☐	N529NK	A319-132	3007	
☐	N530NK	A319-132	3017	
☐	N531NK	A319-132	3026	
☐	N532NK	A319-132	3165	
☐	N533NK	A319-132	3393	
☐	N534NK	A319-132	3395	
☐	N601NK	A320-232	4206	
☐	N602NK	A320-232	4264	
☐	N603NK	A320-232	4321	
☐	N604NK	A320-232	4431	
☐	N605NK	A320-232	4548	
☐	N606NK	A320-232	4592	
☐	N607NK	A320-232	4595	
☐	N608NK	A320-232	4902	
☐	N609NK	A320-232	4951	
☐	N611NK	A320-232	4996	
☐	N612NK	A320-232	5029	
☐	N613NK	A320-232	5042	
☐	N614NK	A320-232	5132	
☐	N615NK	A320-232	5159	
☐	N616NK	A320-232	5370	
☐	N617NK	A320-232	5387	
☐	N618NK	A320-232/S	5458	
☐	N619NK	A320-232/S	5517	
☐	N620NK	A320-232/S	5624	
☐	N621NK	A320-232/S	5672	
☐	N622NK	A320-232/S	5804	
☐	N623NK	A320-232/S	5861	
☐	N624NK	A320-232/S	5880	
☐	N625NK	A320-232/S	5954	
☐	N626NK	A320-232/S	5999	
☐	N627NK	A320-232/S	6082	
☐	N628NK	A320-232/S	6193	
☐	N629NK	A320-232/S	6300	
☐	N630NK	A320-232/S	6304	
☐	N631NK	A320-232/S	6327	
☐	N632NK	A320-232/S	6331	
☐	N633NK	A320-232/S	6345	
☐	N634NK	A320-232/S	6370	
☐	N635NK	A320-232/S	6383	
☐	N636NK	A320-232/S	6424	
☐	N637NK	A320-232/S	6436	
☐	N638NK	A320-232/S	6463	
☐	N639NK	A320-232/S	6487	
☐	N640NK	A320-232/S	6507	
☐	N641NK	A320-232/S	6566	♦
☐	N642NK	A320-232/S	6586	♦
☐	N643NK	A320-232/S	6616	♦
☐	N645NK	A320-232/S	7008	o/o♦
☐	N	A320-232/S	7062	o/o♦
☐	N	A320-232/S	7156	o/o♦
☐	N901NK	A320-271N	6833	o/o♦
☐	N902NK	A320-271N	6907	o/o♦
☐	N903NK	A320-271N	7011	o/o♦
☐	N	A320-271N	7094	o/o♦
☐	N	A320-271N	7249	o/o♦
☐	N587NK	A321-231	2476	
☐	N588NK	A321-231	2590	
☐	N657NK	A321-231/S	6672	♦
☐	N658NK	A321-231/S	6736	♦
☐	N659NK	A321-231/S	6770	♦
☐	N660NK	A321-231/S	6804	♦
☐	N661NK	A321-231/S	6867	♦
☐	N662NK	A321-231/S	6897	♦
☐	N663NK	A321-231/S	6994	o/o♦
☐	N	A321-231/S	7021	o/o♦
☐	N	A321-231/S	7045	o/o♦
☐	N	A321-231/S	7058	o/o♦
☐	N	A321-231/S	7106	o/o♦
☐	N	A321-231/S	7135	o/o♦
☐	N	A321-231/S	7246	o/o♦
☐	N	A321-231/S	7296	o/o♦
☐	N	A321-231/S	7301	o/o♦

SUBURBAN AIR FREIGHT — *SUB*

	Reg	Type	C/n	
☐	N124GP	Beech 1900C	UB-23	
☐	N103SX	Beech 1900C-1	UC-103	
☐	N131SF	Beech 1900C-1	UC-131	♦
☐	N149SF	Beech 1900C-1	UC-149	
☐	N253SF	Beech 1900C-1	UC-53	
☐	N719GL	Beech 1900C	UB-19	

SUN COUNTRY AIRLINES — *SY / SCX*

	Reg	Type	C/n	
☐	N710SY	B737-73V/W	30241/1034	
☐	N711SY	B737-73V/W	30245/1058	
☐	N713SY	B737-7Q8	30635/713	
☐	N714SY	B737-752/W	33786/1403	
☐	N715SY	B737-752/W	33787/1421	
☐	N716SY	B737-7Q8/W	30629/1011	
☐	N801SY	B737-8Q8/W	30332/777	
☐	N804SY	B737-8Q8/W	30689/908	
☐	N805SY	B737-8Q8/W	30032/985	
☐	N808SY	B737-8BK/W	33021/1667	
☐	N809SY	B737-8Q8/W	30683/1669	
☐	N813SY	B737-8Q8	28237/769	
☐	N814SY	B737-8BK/W	30620/991	
☐	N815SY	B737-8BK/W	30623/1136	
☐	N816SY	B737-8Q8/W	30637/800	
☐	N817SY	B737-8K2/W	30392/833	
☐	N818SY	B737-8BK/W	29646/2282	
☐	N819SY	B737-86N/W	34254/1897	
☐	N820SY	B737-8FH/W	39951/5166	
☐	N821SY	B737-8FH/W	39952/5217	
☐	PH-HZG	B737-8K2/W	28379/498	<TRA
☐	PH-HZL	B737-8K2/W	30391/814	<TRA♦
☐	PH-HZO	B737-8K2/W	34169/2243	<TRA♦

SWIFT AIR — *Q7 / SWQ*

	Reg	Type	C/n	
☐	N418US	B737-401	23985/1676	
☐	N420US	B737-401	23987/1698	
☐	N440US	B737-4B7	24811/1890	
☐	N458UW	B737-4B7	25022/2010	
☐	N529AU	B737-3B7	24411/1713	^♦
☐	N801TJ	B737-4B7	24892/1944	
☐	N802TJ	B737-4B7	24874/1936	
☐	N803TJ	B737-45D	27156/2492	
☐	N804TJ	B737-401	23988/1714	♦
☐	N811TJ	B737-306F	23538/1288	♦
☐	N812TJ	B737-375F	23708/1395	o/o♦

^ *operates for Choice Aire*

TBM

	Reg	Type	C/n	
☐	N466TM	C-130A-1A Hercules	3173	64
☐	N531BA	C-130A-1A Hercules	3139	67

TEPPER AVIATION

	Reg	Type	C/n
☐	N2679C	L-382G-69C Hercules	4796
☐	N2731G	L-382G-30C Hercules	4582
☐	N3796B	L-382G-39C Hercules	5027

TRANSAIR			**P6 / MUI**
☐ N306AL	B737-2T4C	23066/992	[CLU]
☐ N413JG	B737-2QB	23148/1059	♦
☐ N737CS	B737-2T4F	23272/1093	
☐ N809TA	B737-209F	23796/1420	
☐ N810TA	B737-275C	21116/427	
☐ N221LM	Short SD.3-60	SH3722	
☐ N351TA	Short SD.3-60	SH3759	
☐ N729PC	Short SD.3-60	SH3729	
☐ N808KR	Short SD.3-60	SH3734	
☐ N808TR	Short SD.3-60	SH3718	
☐ N827BE	Short SD.3-60	SH3746	
☐ N4476F	Short SD.3-60	SH3731	

TRANS NORTHERN AVIATION			**TNV**
☐ N27TN	Douglas C-117D	43332	
☐ N28TN	Douglas C-117D	43354	
☐ N29TN	Douglas C-117D	43302	
☐ N30TN	Douglas C-117D	43159	
☐ N782C	SA.227AC Metro III	AC-525	
☐ N3114G	SA.227AC Metro III	AC-583	

UNITED AIR LINES **UA / UAL**

Former Continental aircraft are listed in order of the last three digits of their registrations, and fleet numbers, within types.

Reg	Type	C/n	Fleet
☐ N801UA	A319-131	0686	4001
☐ N802UA	A319-131	0690	4002
☐ N803UA	A319-131	0748	4003
☐ N804UA	A319-131	0759	4004
☐ N805UA	A319-131	0783	4005
☐ N806UA	A319-131	0788	4006
☐ N807UA	A319-131	0798	4007
☐ N808UA	A319-131	0804	4008
☐ N809UA	A319-131	0825	4009
☐ N810UA	A319-131	0843	4010
☐ N811UA	A319-131	0847	4011
☐ N812UA	A319-131	0850	4012
☐ N813UA	A319-131	0858	4013
☐ N814UA	A319-131	0862	4014
☐ N815UA	A319-131	0867	4015
☐ N816UA	A319-131	0871	4016
☐ N817UA	A319-131	0873	4017
☐ N818UA	A319-131	0882	4018
☐ N819UA	A319-131	0893	4019
☐ N820UA	A319-131	0898	4020
☐ N821UA	A319-131	0944	4021
☐ N822UA	A319-131	0948	4022
☐ N823UA	A319-131	0952	4023
☐ N824UA	A319-131	0965	4024
☐ N825UA	A319-131	0980	4025
☐ N826UA	A319-131	0989	4026
☐ N827UA	A319-131	1022	4027
☐ N828UA	A319-131	1031	4028
☐ N829UA	A319-131	1211	4029
☐ N830UA	A319-131	1243	4030
☐ N831UA	A319-131	1291	4031
☐ N832UA	A319-131	1321	4032
☐ N833UA	A319-131	1401	4033
☐ N834UA	A319-131	1420	4034
☐ N835UA	A319-131	1426	4035
☐ N836UA	A319-131	1460	4036
☐ N837UA	A319-131	1474	4037
☐ N838UA	A319-131	1477	4038
☐ N839UA	A319-131	1507	4039
☐ N840UA	A319-131	1522	4040
☐ N841UA	A319-131	1545	4041
☐ N842UA	A319-131	1569	4042
☐ N843UA	A319-131	1573	4043
☐ N844UA	A319-131	1581	4044
☐ N845UA	A319-131	1585	4045
☐ N846UA	A319-131	1600	4046
☐ N847UA	A319-131	1627	4047
☐ N848UA	A319-131	1647	4048
☐ N849UA	A319-131	1649	4049
☐ N850UA	A319-131	1653	4050
☐ N851UA	A319-131	1664	4051
☐ N852UA	A319-131	1671	4052
☐ N853UA	A319-131	1688	4053
☐ N854UA	A319-131	1731	4054
☐ N855UA	A319-131	1737	4055
☐ N889UA	A319-132	2667	♦
☐	A319-132	2433	o/o♦
☐	A319-132	2470	o/o♦
☐	A319-132	2473	o/o♦
☐	A319-132	2485	o/o♦
☐	A319-132	2490	o/o♦
☐	A319-132	2673	o/o♦
☐	A319-132	2679	o/o♦
☐	A319-132	2698	o/o♦
☐	A319-132	2704	o/o♦
☐	A319-132	2711	o/o♦
☐	A319-132	2723	o/o♦
☐	A319-132	2797	o/o♦
☐	A319-132	2978	o/o♦
☐	A319-132	3007	o/o♦
☐	A319-132	3017	o/o♦
☐	A319-132	3026	o/o♦
☐	A319-132	3165	o/o♦
☐ N401UA	A320-232	0435	4501
☐ N402UA	A320-232	0439	4502
☐ N403UA	A320-232	0442	4703
☐ N404UA	A320-232	0450	4704
☐ N405UA	A320-232	0452	4705
☐ N406UA	A320-232	0454	4506
☐ N407UA	A320-232	0456	4507
☐ N408UA	A320-232	0457	4508
☐ N409UA	A320-232	0462	4709
☐ N410UA	A320-232	0463	4910
☐ N411UA	A320-232	0464	4711
☐ N412UA	A320-232	0465	4712
☐ N413UA	A320-232	0470	4713
☐ N414UA	A320-232	0472	4814
☐ N415UA	A320-232	0475	4615
☐ N416UA	A320-232	0479	4616
☐ N417UA	A320-232	0483	4617
☐ N418UA	A320-232	0485	4618
☐ N419UA	A320-232	0487	4619
☐ N420UA	A320-232	0489	4620
☐ N421UA	A320-232	0500	4621
☐ N422UA	A320-232	0503	4622
☐ N423UA	A320-232	0504	4623
☐ N424UA	A320-232	0506	4624
☐ N425UA	A320-232	0508	4625
☐ N426UA	A320-232	0510	4626
☐ N427UA	A320-232	0512	4627
☐ N428UA	A320-232	0523	4628
☐ N429UA	A320-232	0539	4629
☐ N430UA	A320-232	0568	4630
☐ N431UA	A320-232	0571	4631

☐	N432UA	A320-232	0587	4632
☐	N433UA	A320-232	0589	4633
☐	N434UA	A320-232	0592	4634
☐	N435UA	A320-232	0613	4635
☐	N436UA	A320-232	0638	4636
☐	N437UA	A320-232	0655	4637
☐	N438UA	A320-232	0678	4838
☐	N439UA	A320-232	0683	4839
☐	N440UA	A320-232	0702	4840
☐	N441UA	A320-232	0751	4841
☐	N442UA	A320-232	0780	4842
☐	N443UA	A320-232	0820	4643
☐	N444UA	A320-232	0824	4844
☐	N445UA	A320-232	0826	4845
☐	N446UA	A320-232	0834	4846
☐	N447UA	A320-232	0836	4847
☐	N448UA	A320-232	0842	4848
☐	N449UA	A320-232	0851	4849
☐	N451UA	A320-232	0865	4851
☐	N452UA	A320-232	0955	4852
☐	N453UA	A320-232	1001	4853
☐	N454UA	A320-232	1104	4654
☐	N455UA	A320-232	1105	4655
☐	N456UA	A320-232	1128	4656
☐	N457UA	A320-232	1146	4857
☐	N458UA	A320-232	1163	4858
☐	N459UA	A320-232	1192	4859
☐	N460UA	A320-232	1248	4860
☐	N461UA	A320-232	1266	4661
☐	N462UA	A320-232	1272	4962
☐	N463UA	A320-232	1282	4663
☐	N464UA	A320-232	1290	4664
☐	N465UA	A320-232	1341	4865
☐	N466UA	A320-232	1343	4666
☐	N467UA	A320-232	1359	4867
☐	N468UA	A320-232	1363	4668
☐	N469UA	A320-232	1409	4869
☐	N470UA	A320-232	1427	4870
☐	N471UA	A320-232	1432	4871
☐	N472UA	A320-232	1435	4872
☐	N473UA	A320-232	1469	4873
☐	N474UA	A320-232	1475	4874
☐	N475UA	A320-232	1495	4875
☐	N476UA	A320-232	1508	4876
☐	N477UA	A320-232	1514	4877
☐	N478UA	A320-232	1533	4878
☐	N479UA	A320-232	1538	4879
☐	N480UA	A320-232	1555	4880
☐	N481UA	A320-232	1559	4881
☐	N482UA	A320-232	1584	4882
☐	N483UA	A320-232	1586	4883
☐	N484UA	A320-232	1609	4884
☐	N485UA	A320-232	1617	4885
☐	N486UA	A320-232	1620	4886
☐	N487UA	A320-232	1669	4887
☐	N488UA	A320-232	1680	4888
☐	N489UA	A320-232	1702	4889
☐	N490UA	A320-232	1728	4890
☐	N491UA	A320-232	1741	4891
☐	N492UA	A320-232	1755	4892
☐	N493UA	A320-232	1821	4893
☐	N494UA	A320-232	1840	4894
☐	N495UA	A320-232	1842	4895
☐	N496UA	A320-232	1845	4896
☐	N497UA	A320-232	1847	4897
☐	N498UA	A320-232	1865	4898

☐	N16701	B737-724/W	28762/29	0701
☐	N24702	B737-724/W	28763/32	0702
☐	N16703	B737-724/W	28764/37	0703
☐	N14704	B737-724/W	28765/43	0704
☐	N25705	B737-724/W	28766/46	0705
☐	N24706	B737-724/W	28767/47	0706
☐	N23707	B737-724/W	28768/48	0707
☐	N23708	B737-724/W	28769/52	0708
☐	N16709	B737-724/W	28779/93	0709
☐	N15710	B737-724/W	28780/94	0710
☐	N54711	B737-724/W	28782/97	0711
☐	N15712	B737-724/W	28783/105	0712
☐	N16713	B737-724/W	28784/107	0713
☐	N33714	B737-724/W	28785/119	0714
☐	N24715	B737-724/W	28786/125	0715
☐	N13716	B737-724/W	28787/156	0716
☐	N29717	B737-724/W	28936/182	0717
☐	N13718	B737-724/W	28937/185	0718
☐	N17719	B737-724/W	28938/195	0719
☐	N13720	B737-724/W	28939/214	0720
☐	N23721	B737-724/W	28940/219	0721
☐	N27722	B737-724/W	28789/247	0722
☐	N21723	B737-724/W	28790/253	0723
☐	N27724	B737-724/W	28791/283	0724
☐	N39726	B737-724/W	28796/315	0726
☐	N38727	B737-724/W	28797/317	0727
☐	N39728	B737-724/W	28944/321	0728
☐	N24729	B737-724/W	28945/325	0729
☐	N17730	B737-724/W	28798/338	0730
☐	N14731	B737-724/W	28799/346	0731
☐	N16732	B737-724/W	28948/352	0732
☐	N27733	B737-724/W	28800/364	0733
☐	N27734	B737-724/W	28949/371	0734
☐	N14735	B737-724/W	28950/376	0735
☐	N24736	B737-724/W	28803/380	0736
☐	N13750	B737-724/W	28941/286	0750
☐	N15751	B737-71Q/W	29047/235	0751♦
☐	N17752	B737-71Q/W	29048/288	0752♦
☐	N17753	B737-7V3/W	30463/1221	0753♦
☐	N12754	B737-7V3/W	30464/1241	0754♦

☐	N25201	B737-824/W	28958/443	0201
☐	N24202	B737-824/W	30429/581	0202
☐	N33203	B737-824/W	30613/591	0203
☐	N35204	B737-824/W	30576/606	0204
☐	N27205	B737-824/W	30577/615	0205
☐	N11206	B737-824/W	30578/618	0206
☐	N36207	B737-824/W	30579/627	0207
☐	N26208	B737-824/W	30580/644	0208
☐	N33209	B737-824/W	30581/647	0209
☐	N26210	B737-824/W	28770/56	0210
☐	N24211	B737-824/W	28771/58	0211
☐	N24212	B737-824/W	28772/63	0212
☐	N27213	B737-824/W	28773/65	0213
☐	N14214	B737-824/W	28774/74	0214
☐	N26215	B737-824/W	28775/76	0215
☐	N12216	B737-824/W	28776/79	0216
☐	N16217	B737-824/W	28777/81	0217
☐	N12218	B737-824/W	28778/84	0218
☐	N14219	B737-824/W	28781/88	0219
☐	N18220	B737-824/W	28929/134	0220
☐	N12221	B737-824/W	28930/153	0221
☐	N34222	B737-824/W	28931/159	0222
☐	N18223	B737-824/W	28932/162	0223
☐	N24224	B737-824/W	28933/165	0224
☐	N12225	B737-824/W	28934/168	0225
☐	N26226	B737-824/W	28935/171	0226

☐	N13227	B737-824/W	28788/262	0227
☐	N14228	B737-824/W	28792/281	0228
☐	N17229	B737-824/W	28793/287	0229
☐	N14230	B737-824/W	28794/296	0230
☐	N14231	B737-824/W	28795/300	0231
☐	N26232	B737-824/W	28942/304	0232
☐	N17233	B737-824/W	28943/328	0233
☐	N16234	B737-824/W	28946/334	0234
☐	N14235	B737-824/W	28947/342	0235
☐	N35236	B737-824/W	28801/367	0236
☐	N14237	B737-824/W	28802/374	0237
☐	N12238	B737-824/W	28804/386	0238
☐	N27239	B737-824/W	28951/391	0239
☐	N14240	B737-824/W	28952/394	0240
☐	N54241	B737-824/W	28953/395	0241
☐	N14242	B737-824/W	28805/402	0242
☐	N18243	B737-824/W	28806/403	0243
☐	N17244	B737-824/W	28954/409	0244
☐	N17245	B737-824/W	28955/411	0245
☐	N27246	B737-824/W	28956/413	0246
☐	N36247	B737-824/W	28807/431	0247
☐	N13248	B737-824/W	28808/435	0248
☐	N14249	B737-824/W	28809/438	0249
☐	N14250	B737-824/W	28957/441	0250
☐	N73251	B737-824/W	30582/650	0251
☐	N37252	B737-824/W	30583/656	0252
☐	N37253	B737-824/W	30584/660	0253
☐	N76254	B737-824/W	30779/667	0254
☐	N37255	B737-824/W	30610/686	0255
☐	N73256	B737-824/W	30611/692	0256
☐	N38257	B737-824/W	30612/706	0257
☐	N77258	B737-824/W	30802/708	0258
☐	N73259	B737-824/W	30803/854	0259
☐	N35260	B737-824/W	30855/862	0260
☐	N77261	B737-824/W	31582/897	0261
☐	N33262	B737-824/W	32402/901	0262
☐	N37263	B737-824/W	31583/906	0263
☐	N33264	B737-824/W	31584/916	0264
☐	N76265	B737-824/W	31585/928	0265
☐	N33266	B737-824/W	32403/930	0266
☐	N37267	B737-824/W	31586/939	0267
☐	N38268	B737-824/W	31587/957	0268
☐	N76269	B737-824/W	31588/966	0269
☐	N73270	B737-824/W	31632/970	0270
☐	N35271	B737-824/W	31589/982	0271
☐	N36272	B737-824/W	31590/987	0272
☐	N37273	B737-824/W	31591/1012	0273
☐	N37274	B737-824/W	31592/1062	0274
☐	N73275	B737-824/W	31593/1077	0275
☐	N73276	B737-824/W	31594/1079	0276
☐	N37277	B737-824/W	31595/1099	0277
☐	N73278	B737-824/W	31596/1390	0278
☐	N79279	B737-824/W	31597/1411	0279
☐	N36280	B737-824/W	31598/1423	0280
☐	N37281	B737-824/W	31599/1425	0281
☐	N34282	B737-824/W	31634/1440	0282
☐	N73283	B737-824/W	31606/1456	0283
☐	N33284	B737-824/W	31635/1475	0284
☐	N78285	B737-824/W	33452/1540	0285
☐	N33286	B737-824/W	31600/1506	0286
☐	N37287	B737-824/W	31636/1509	0287
☐	N76288	B737-824/W	33451/1516	0288
☐	N33289	B737-824/W	31607/1542	0289
☐	N37290	B737-824/W	31601/1567	0290
☐	N73291	B737-824/W	33454/1611	0291
☐	N33292	B737-824/W	33455/1622	0292
☐	N37293	B737-824/W	33453/1743	0293

☐	N33294	B737-824/W	34000/1762	0294
☐	N77295	B737-824/W	34001/1779	0295
☐	N77296	B737-824/W	34002/1787	0296
☐	N39297	B737-824/W	34003/1791	0297
☐	N37298	B737-824/W	34004/1813	0298
☐	N73299	B737-824/W	34005/1821	0299
☐	N78501	B737-824/W	31602/1994	0501
☐	N76502	B737-824/W	31603/2017	0502
☐	N76503	B737-824/W	33461/2023	0503
☐	N76504	B737-824/W	31604/2035	0504
☐	N76505	B737-824/W	32834/2048	0505
☐	N78506	B737-824/W	32832/2065	0506
☐	N87507	B737-824/W	31637/2487	0507
☐	N76508	B737-824/W	31639/2514	0508
☐	N78509	B737-824/W	31638/2523	0509
☐	N77510	B737-824/W	32828/2579	0510
☐	N78511	B737-824/W	33459/2598	0511
☐	N87512	B737-824/W	33458/2602	0512
☐	N87513	B737-824/W	31621/2655	0513
☐	N76514	B737-824/W	31626/2680	0514
☐	N76515	B737-824/W	31623/2713	0515
☐	N76516	B737-824/W	37096/2718	0516
☐	N76517	B737-824/W	31628/2723	0517
☐	N77518	B737-824/W	31605/2768	0518
☐	N76519	B737-824/W	30132/3138	0519
☐	N77520	B737-824/W	31658/3158	0520
☐	N79521	B737-824/W	31662/3169	0521
☐	N76522	B737-824/W	31660/3175	0522
☐	N76523	B737-824/W	37101/3216	0523
☐	N78524	B737-824/W	31642/3224	0524
☐	N77525	B737-824/W	31659/3253	0525
☐	N76526	B737-824/W	38700/3289	0526
☐	N87527	B737-824/W	38701/3305	0527
☐	N76528	B737-824/W	31663/3464	0528
☐	N76529	B737-824/W	31652/3490	0529
☐	N77530	B737-824/W	39998/3521	0530
☐	N87531	B737-824/W	39999/3549	0531
☐	N30401	B737-924/W	30118/820	0401
☐	N79402	B737-924/W	30119/857	0402
☐	N38403	B737-924/W	30120/884	0403
☐	N32404	B737-924/W	30121/893	0404
☐	N72405	B737-924/W	30122/911	0405
☐	N73406	B737-924/W	30123/943	0406
☐	N35407	B737-924/W	30124/951	0407
☐	N37408	B737-924/W	30125/962	0408
☐	N37409	B737-924/W	30126/1004	0409
☐	N75410	B737-924/W	30127/1021	0410
☐	N71411	B737-924/W	30128/1052	0411
☐	N31412	B737-924/W	30129/1112	0412
☐	N37413	B737-924ER/W	31664/2474	0413
☐	N47414	B737-924ER/W	32827/2490	0414
☐	N39415	B737-924ER/W	32826/2516	0415
☐	N39416	B737-924ER/W	37093/2528	0416
☐	N38417	B737-924ER/W	31665/2541	0417
☐	N39418	B737-924ER/W	33456/2547	0418
☐	N37419	B737-924ER/W	31666/2553	0419
☐	N37420	B737-924ER/W	33457/2565	0420
☐	N27421	B737-924ER/W	37094/2577	0421
☐	N37422	B737-924ER/W	31620/2614	0422
☐	N39423	B737-924ER/W	32829/2645	0423
☐	N38424	B737-924ER/W	37095/2651	0424
☐	N75425	B737-924ER/W	33460/2657	0425
☐	N75426	B737-924ER/W	31622/2676	0426
☐	N37427	B737-924ER/W	37097/2707	0427
☐	N75428	B737-924ER/W	31633/2737	0428
☐	N75429	B737-924ER/W	30130/2750	0429

☐	N77430	B737-924ER/W	37098/2774	0430
☐	N77431	B737-924ER/W	32833/2787	0431
☐	N75432	B737-924ER/W	32835/2817	0432
☐	N75433	B737-924ER/W	33527/2842	0433
☐	N37434	B737-924ER/W	33528/2891	0434
☐	N75435	B737-924ER/W	33529/2916	0435
☐	N75436	B737-924ER/W	33531/2947	0436
☐	N37437	B737-924ER/W	33532/2959	0437
☐	N78438	B737-924ER/W	33533/2971	0438
☐	N57439	B737-924ER/W	33534/2990	0439
☐	N45440	B737-924ER/W	33535/2996	0440
☐	N53441	B737-924ER/W	30131/3014	0441
☐	N53442	B737-924ER/W	33536/3027	0442
☐	N38443	B737-924ER/W	31655/3393	0443
☐	N36444	B737-924ER/W	31643/3417	0444
☐	N73445	B737-924ER/W	40000/3615	0445
☐	N38446	B737-924ER/W	31661/3894	0446
☐	N36447	B737-924ER/W	31650/3924	0447
☐	N78448	B737-924ER/W	40003/3942	0448
☐	N81449	B737-924ER/W	31651/3978	0449
☐	N39450	B737-924ER/W	40004/3984	0450
☐	N38451	B737-924ER/W	31646/3990	0451
☐	N68452	B737-924ER/W	40005/4032	0452
☐	N68453	B737-924ER/W	41742/4052	0453
☐	N38454	B737-924ER/W	31640/4068	0454
☐	N34455	B737-924ER/W	41743/4086	0455
☐	N37456	B737-924ER/W	37205/4164	0456
☐	N28457	B737-924ER/W	41744/4182	0457
☐	N38458	B737-924ER/W	37199/4188	0458
☐	N38459	B737-924ER/W	37206/4218	0459
☐	N34460	B737-924ER/W	37200/4224	0460
☐	N39461	B737-924ER/W	37201/4230	0461
☐	N37462	B737-924ER/W	37207/4254	0462
☐	N39463	B737-924ER/W	37208/4260	0463
☐	N37464	B737-924ER/W	41745/4290	0464
☐	N37465	B737-924ER/W	36599/4302	0465
☐	N37466	B737-924ER/W	31644/4326	0466
☐	N38467	B737-924ER/W	33537/4344	0467
☐	N37468	B737-924ER/W	32836/4356	0468
☐	N36469	B737-924ER/W	36600/4374	0469
☐	N37470	B737-924ER/W	37099/4392	0470
☐	N37471	B737-924ER/W	37102/4408	0471
☐	N36472	B737-924ER/W	31653/4436	0472
☐	N38473	B737-924ER/W	38702/4452	0473
☐	N37474	B737-924ER/W	31648/4457	0474
☐	N39475	B737-924ER/W	37100/4473	0475
☐	N36476	B737-924ER/W	38703/4506	0476
☐	N27477	B737-924ER/W	31647/4531	0477
☐	N28478	B737-924ER/W	31649/4546	0478
☐	N68801	B737-924ER/W	42740/4549	0801
☐	N68802	B737-924ER/W	42739/4567	0802
☐	N66803	B737-924ER/W	42817/4589	0803
☐	N69804	B737-924ER/W	42816/4614	0804
☐	N68805	B737-924ER/W	42818/4625	0805
☐	N69806	B737-924ER/W	42742/4661	0806
☐	N68807	B737-924ER/W	42819/4686	0807
☐	N66808	B737-924ER/W	42820/4690	0808
☐	N64809	B737-924ER/W	42821/4718	0809
☐	N69810	B737-924ER/W	42744/4733	0810
☐	N68811	B737-924ER/W	42175/4737	0811
☐	N67812	B737-924ER/W	43530/4758	0812
☐	N69813	B737-924ER/W	43531/4773	0813
☐	N66814	B737-924ER/W	42745/4787	0814
☐	N67815	B737-924ER/W	43532/4795	0815
☐	N69816	B737-924ER/W	42176/4802	0816
☐	N68817	B737-924ER/W	42747/4809	0817
☐	N69818	B737-924ER/W	42177/4825	0818
☐	N69819	B737-924ER/W	43533/4836	0819
☐	N63820	B737-924ER/W	43534/4847	0820
☐	N68821	B737-924ER/W	43535/4868	0821
☐	N68822	B737-924ER/W	42178/4876	0822
☐	N68823	B737-924ER/W	42746/4894	0823
☐	N69824	B737-924ER/W	42179/4907	0824
☐	N66825	B737-924ER/W	42748/4918	0825
☐	N69826	B737-924ER/W	42180/4939	0826
☐	N67827	B737-924ER/W	44581/4950	0827
☐	N66828	B737-924ER/W	44580/4958	0828
☐	N69829	B737-924ER/W	44561/4965	0829
☐	N69830	B737-924ER/W	44560/4976	0830
☐	N66831	B737-924ER/W	44562/5029	0831
☐	N65832	B737-924ER/W	44563/5047	0832
☐	N69833	B737-924ER/W	44565/5074	0833
☐	N68834	B737-924ER/W	44564/5092	0834
☐	N69835	B737-924ER/W	60087/5107	0835
☐	N68836	B737-924ER/W	60088/5118	0836
☐	N66837	B737-924ER/W	60122/5168	0837
☐	N69838	B737-924ER/W	60121/5183	0838
☐	N69839	B737-924ER/W	60316/5214	0839
☐	N69840	B737-924ER/W	42181/5246	0840
☐	N66841	B737-924ER/W	42182/5254	0841
☐	N68842	B737-924ER/W	42183/5258	0842
☐	N68843	B737-924ER/W	60317/5271	0843
☐	N64844	B737-924ER/W	42184/5282	0844
☐	N67845	B737-924ER/W	42185/5286	0845
☐	N67846	B737-924ER/W	42186/5294	0846
☐	N69847	B737-924ER/W	42187/5328	0847
☐	N66848	B737-924ER/W	42188/5339	0848
☐	N62849	B737-924ER/W	42204/5366	0849
☐	N68880	B737-924ER/W	42199/5383	0880♦
☐	N61881	B737-924ER/W	42200/5408	0881
☐	N61882	B737-924ER/W	42201/5416	0882♦
☐	N62883	B737-924ER/W	42202/5463	0883
☐	N62884	B737-924ER/W	42203/5467	0884
☐	N69885	B737-924ER/W	42189/5490	0885
☐	N61886	B737-924ER/W	42190/5505	0886
☐	N61887	B737-924ER/W	42192/5536	0887
☐	N69888	B737-924ER/W	42191/5547	0888
☐	N62889	B737-924ER/W	42193/5559	0889
☐	N63890	B737-924ER/W	42194/5570	0890
☐	N68891	B737-924ER/W	42196/5601	0891
☐	N62892	B737-924ER/W	42195/5620	0892♦
☐	N66893	B737-924ER/W	42197/5734	0893♦
☐	N62894	B737-924ER/W	42198/5783	0894♦
☐	N104UA	B747-422	26902/1141	8104
☐	N105UA	B747-451	26473/985	8105
☐	N107UA	B747-422	26900/1168	8107
☐	N116UA	B747-422	26908/1193	8116
☐	N117UA	B747-422	28810/1197	8117
☐	N118UA	B747-422	28811/1201	8118
☐	N119UA	B747-422	28812/1207	8119
☐	N120UA	B747-422	29166/1209	8120
☐	N121UA	B747-422	29167/1211	8121
☐	N122UA	B747-422	29168/1218	8122
☐	N127UA	B747-422	28813/1221	8127
☐	N128UA	B747-422	30023/1245	8128
☐	N174UA	B747-422	24381/762	8174
☐	N175UA	B747-422	24382/806	8175
☐	N177UA	B747-422	24384/819	8177
☐	N178UA	B747-422	24385/820	8178
☐	N179UA	B747-422	25158/866	8179
☐	N180UA	B747-422	25224/867	8180
☐	N181UA	B747-422	25278/881	8181
☐	N182UA	B747-422	25279/882	8182

	Registration	Type	c/n / l/n	Fleet no.
☐	N197UA	B747-422	26901/1121	8197
☐	N199UA	B747-422	28717/1126	8199
☐	N502UA	B757-222/W	24623/246	5702
☐	N505UA	B757-222/W	24626/254	5705
☐	N510UA	B757-222/W	24780/290	5710
☐	N512UA	B757-222/W	24809/298	5712
☐	N518UA	B757-222/W	24871/311	5718
☐	N543UA	B757-222ER	25698/401	5543
☐	N546UA	B757-222ER/W	25367/413	5546
☐	N548UA	B757-222ER	25396/420	5548
☐	N550UA	B757-222ER	25398/426	5550
☐	N568UA	B757-222/W	26674/498	5468
☐	N587UA	B757-222/W	26713/570	5687
☐	N588UA	B757-222/W	26717/571	5688
☐	N589UA	B757-222ER/W	28707/773	5589
☐	N590UA	B757-222ER/W	28708/785	5590
☐	N595UA	B757-222ER/W	28748/789	5595
☐	N596UA	B757-222ER/W	28749/794	5596
☐	N597UA	B757-222ER/W	28750/841	5597
☐	N598UA	B757-222ER/W	28751/844	5598
☐	N58101	B757-224/W	27291/614	0101
☐	N14102	B757-224/W	27292/619	0102
☐	N33103	B757-224/W	27293/623	0103
☐	N17104	B757-224/W	27294/629	0104
☐	N17105	B757-224/W	27295/632	0105
☐	N14106	B757-224/W	27296/637	0106
☐	N14107	B757-224/W	27297/641	0107
☐	N21108	B757-224/W	27298/645	0108
☐	N12109	B757-224/W	27299/648	0109
☐	N13110	B757-224/W	27300/650	0110
☐	N57111	B757-224/W	27301/652	0111
☐	N18112	B757-224/W	27302/653	0112
☐	N13113	B757-224/W	27555/668	0113
☐	N12114	B757-224/W	27556/682	0114
☐	N14115	B757-224/W	27557/686	0115
☐	N12116	B757-224/W	27558/702	0116
☐	N19117	B757-224/W	27559/706	0117
☐	N14118	B757-224/W	27560/748	0118
☐	N18119	B757-224/W	27561/753	0119
☐	N14120	B757-224/W	27562/761	0120
☐	N14121	B757-224/W	27563/766	0121
☐	N17122	B757-224/W	27564/768	0122
☐	N26123	B757-224/W	28966/781	0123
☐	N29124	B757-224/W	27565/786	0124
☐	N12125	B757-224/W	28967/788	0125
☐	N17126	B757-224/W	27566/790	0126
☐	N48127	B757-224/W	28968/791	0127
☐	N17128	B757-224/W	27567/795	0128
☐	N29129	B757-224/W	28969/796	0129
☐	N19130	B757-224/W	28970/799	0130
☐	N34131	B757-224/W	28971/806	0131
☐	N33132	B757-224/W	29281/809	0132
☐	N17133	B757-224/W	29282/840	0133
☐	N67134	B757-224/W	29283/848	0134
☐	N41135	B757-224/W	29284/851	0135
☐	N19136	B757-224/W	29285/856	0136
☐	N34137	B757-224/W	30229/899	0137
☐	N13138	B757-224/W	30351/903	0138
☐	N17139	B757-224/W	30352/911	0139
☐	N41140	B757-224/W	30353/913	0140
☐	N19141	B757-224/W	30354/933	0141
☐	N75851	B757-324/W	32810/990	0851
☐	N57852	B757-324/W	32811/995	0852
☐	N75853	B757-324/W	32812/997	0853
☐	N75854	B757-324/W	32813/999	0854
☐	N57855	B757-324/W	32814/1038	0855
☐	N74856	B757-324/W	32815/1039	0856
☐	N57857	B757-324/W	32816/1040	0857
☐	N75858	B757-324/W	32817/1042	0858
☐	N56859	B757-324/W	32818/1043	0859
☐	N73860	B757-33N/W	32584/972	0860
☐	N75861	B757-33N/W	32585/976	0861
☐	N57862	B757-33N/W	32586/978	0862
☐	N57863	B757-33N/W	32587/980	0863
☐	N57864	B757-33N/W	32588/985	0864
☐	N77865	B757-33N/W	32589/1003	0865
☐	N78866	B757-33N/W	32591/1007	0866
☐	N77867	B757-33N/W	32592/1008	0867
☐	N57868	B757-33N/W	32590/1017	0868
☐	N57869	B757-33N/W	32593/1018	0869
☐	N57870	B757-33N/W	33525/1031	0870
☐	N77871	B757-33N/W	33526/1032	0871
☐	N641UA	B767-322ER	25091/360	6341
☐	N642UA	B767-322ER	25092/367	6342
☐	N643UA	B767-322ER	25093/368	6343
☐	N644UA	B767-322ER	25094/369	6344
☐	N646UA	B767-322ER	25283/420	6346
☐	N647UA	B767-322ER	25284/424	6347
☐	N648UA	B767-322ER	25285/443	6348
☐	N649UA	B767-322ER	25286/444	6349
☐	N651UA	B767-322ER	25389/452	6351
☐	N652UA	B767-322ER	25390/457	6352
☐	N653UA	B767-322ER	25391/460	6353
☐	N654UA	B767-322ER	25392/462	6354
☐	N655UA	B767-322ER	25393/468	6355
☐	N656UA	B767-322ER	25394/472	6356
☐	N657UA	B767-322ER	27112/479	6357
☐	N658UA	B767-322ER	27113/480	6358
☐	N659UA	B767-322ER	27114/485	6359
☐	N660UA	B767-322ER	27115/494	6360
☐	N661UA	B767-322ER	27158/507	6361
☐	N662UA	B767-322ER	27159/513	6362
☐	N663UA	B767-322ER	27160/514	6363
☐	N664UA	B767-322ER/W	29236/707	6664
☐	N665UA	B767-322ER/W	29237/711	6665
☐	N666UA	B767-322ER/W	29238/715	6666
☐	N667UA	B767-322ER/W	29239/716	6667
☐	N668UA	B767-322ER/W	30024/742	6668
☐	N669UA	B767-322ER/W	30025/757	6669
☐	N670UA	B767-322ER/W	29240/763	6770
☐	N671UA	B767-322ER/W	30026/766	6771
☐	N672UA	B767-322ER/W	30027/773	6772
☐	N673UA	B767-322ER/W	29241/779	6773
☐	N674UA	B767-322ER/W	29242/782	6774
☐	N675UA	B767-322ER/W	29243/800	6775
☐	N676UA	B767-322ER/W	30028/834	6776
☐	N677UA	B767-322ER/W	30029/852	6777
☐	N66051	B767-424ER	29446/799	0051
☐	N67052	B767-424ER	29447/805	0052
☐	N59053	B767-424ER	29448/809	0053
☐	N76054	B767-424ER	29449/816	0054
☐	N76055	B767-424ER	29450/826	0055
☐	N66056	B767-424ER	29451/842	0056
☐	N66057	B767-424ER	29452/859	0057
☐	N67058	B767-424ER	29453/862	0058
☐	N69059	B767-424ER	29454/864	0059
☐	N78060	B767-424ER	29455/866	0060
☐	N68061	B767-424ER	29456/868	0061
☐	N76062	B767-424ER	29457/869	0062
☐	N69063	B767-424ER	29458/872	0063
☐	N76064	B767-424ER	29459/873	0064
☐	N76065	B767-424ER	29460/876	0065

	Reg	Type	c/n	Fleet
☐	N77066	B767-424ER	29461/878	0066
☐	N204UA	B777-222ER	28713/191	2904
☐	N206UA	B777-222ER	30212/216	2906
☐	N209UA	B777-222ER	30215/259	2609
☐	N210UA	B777-222	30216/264	2510
☐	N211UA	B777-222	30217/282	2511
☐	N212UA	B777-222	30218/293	2512
☐	N213UA	B777-222	30219/295	2513
☐	N214UA	B777-222	30220/296	2514
☐	N215UA	B777-222	30221/297	2515
☐	N216UA	B777-222ER	30549/291	2616
☐	N217UA	B777-222ER	30550/294	2617
☐	N218UA	B777-222ER	30222/317	2618
☐	N219UA	B777-222ER	30551/318	2619
☐	N220UA	B777-222ER	30223/340	2620
☐	N221UA	B777-222ER	30552/347	2621
☐	N222UA	B777-222ER	30553/352	2622
☐	N223UA	B777-222ER	30224/357	2623
☐	N224UA	B777-222ER	30225/375	2624
☐	N225UA	B777-222ER	30554/377	2625
☐	N226UA	B777-222ER	30226/380	2626
☐	N227UA	B777-222ER	30555/381	2627
☐	N228UA	B777-222ER	30556/384	2628
☐	N229UA	B777-222ER	30557/388	2629
☐	N768UA	B777-222	26919/11	2368
☐	N769UA	B777-222	26921/12	2369
☐	N771UA	B777-222	26932/3	2371
☐	N772UA	B777-222	26930/5	2372
☐	N773UA	B777-222	26929/4	2473
☐	N774UA	B777-222	26936/2	2374
☐	N775UA	B777-222	26947/22	2375
☐	N776UA	B777-222	26937/27	2376
☐	N777UA	B777-222	26916/7	2377
☐	N778UA	B777-222	26940/34	2478
☐	N779UA	B777-222	26941/35	2379
☐	N780UA	B777-222	26944/36	2380
☐	N781UA	B777-222	26945/40	2481
☐	N782UA	B777-222ER	26948/57	2982
☐	N783UA	B777-222ER	26950/60	2983
☐	N784UA	B777-222ER	26951/69	2984
☐	N785UA	B777-222ER	26954/73	2985
☐	N786UA	B777-222ER	26938/52	2986
☐	N787UA	B777-222ER	26939/43	2987
☐	N788UA	B777-222ER	26942/82	2988
☐	N791UA	B777-222ER	26933/93	2991
☐	N792UA	B777-222ER	26934/96	2992
☐	N793UA	B777-222ER	26946/97	2993
☐	N794UA	B777-222ER	26953/105	2994
☐	N795UA	B777-222ER	26927/108	2995
☐	N796UA	B777-222ER	26931/112	2996
☐	N797UA	B777-222ER	26924/116	2997
☐	N798UA	B777-222ER	26928/123	2998
☐	N799UA	B777-222ER	26926/139	2999
☐	N78001	B777-224ER	27577/161	0001
☐	N78002	B777-224ER	27578/165	0002
☐	N78003	B777-224ER	27579/167	0003
☐	N78004	B777-224ER	27580/169	0004
☐	N78005	B777-224ER	27581/177	0005
☐	N77006	B777-224ER	29476/183	0006
☐	N74007	B777-224ER	29477/197	0007
☐	N78008	B777-224ER	29478/200	0008
☐	N78009	B777-224ER	29479/211	0009
☐	N76010	B777-224ER	29480/220	0010
☐	N79011	B777-224ER	29859/227	0011
☐	N77012	B777-224ER	29860/234	0012
☐	N78013	B777-224ER	29861/243	0013
☐	N77014	B777-224ER	29862/253	0014
☐	N27015	B777-224ER	28678/273	0015
☐	N57016	B777-224ER	28679/279	0016
☐	N78017	B777-224ER	31679/391	0017
☐	N37018	B777-224ER	31680/397	0018
☐	N77019	B777-224ER	35547/617	0019
☐	N69020	B777-224ER	31687/625	0020
☐	N76021	B777-224ER	39776/858	0021
☐	N77022	B777-224ER	39777/868	0022
☐	N27901	B787-8	34821/45	901
☐	N26902	B787-8	34822/50	902
☐	N27903	B787-8	34823/52	903
☐	N20904	B787-8	34824/53	904
☐	N45905	B787-8	34825/55	905
☐	N26906	B787-8	34829/77	906
☐	N29907	B787-8	34830/117	907
☐	N27908	B787-8	36400/124	908
☐	N26909	B787-8	34827/135	909
☐	N26910	B787-8	34826/145	910
☐	N28912	B787-8	34828/186	912
☐	N30913	B787-8	35879/238	913
☐	N38950	B787-9	36401/181	950
☐	N19951	B787-9	36402/223	951
☐	N26952	B787-9	36403/263	952
☐	N35953	B787-9	36404/269	953
☐	N13954	B787-9	36405/275	954
☐	N38955	B787-9	37814/297	955
☐	N45956	B787-9	40918/324	956♦
☐	N27957	B787-9	36409/334	957♦
☐	N27958	B787-9	36406/342	958♦
☐	N27959	B787-9	36407/348	959♦
☐	N26960	B787-9	36408/355	960♦
☐	N29961	B787-9	37811/363	961♦
☐	N36962	B787-9	35880/365	962♦
☐	N17963	B787-9	37812/390	963♦
☐	N27964	B787-9	37813/398	964♦
☐	N27965	B787-9	37815/402	o/o♦
☐	N	B787-9	60143/443	o/o♦
☐	N	B787-9	60144/445	o/o♦

UNITED EXPRESS — *UA / UAL*

	Reg	Type	c/n	Fleet
☐	N465SW	CRJ-200LR	7845	♦
☐	N471CA	CRJ-200ER	7655	
☐	N472CA	CRJ-200ER	7667	
☐	N479CA	CRJ-200ER	7675	
☐	N494CA	CRJ-200ER	7765	♦
☐	N498CA	CRJ-200ER	7792	♦
☐	N507CA	CRJ-200ER	7796	
☐	N593ML	CRJ-200ER	7465	
☐	N679SA	CRJ-200ER	7652	
☐	N701BR	CRJ-200ER	7448	
☐	N702BR	CRJ-200ER	7462	
☐	N709BR	CRJ-200ER	7850	♦
☐	N874AS	CRJ-200ER	7551	♦
☐	N903SW	CRJ-200ER	7425	7425
☐	N905SW	CRJ-200ER	7437	7437
☐	N908SW	CRJ-200ER	7540	7540
☐	N909SW	CRJ-200ER	7558	7558
☐	N910SW	CRJ-200ER	7566	7566
☐	N912SW	CRJ-200ER	7595	7595
☐	N913SW	CRJ-200ER	7597	7597
☐	N915SW	CRJ-200ER	7615	7615
☐	N916SW	CRJ-200ER	7634	7634
☐	N917SW	CRJ-200ER	7641	7641
☐	N918SW	CRJ-200ER	7645	7645

	Reg.	Type	c/n	Fleet
☐	N919SW	CRJ-200ER	7657	7657
☐	N920SW	CRJ-200ER	7660	7660
☐	N923SW	CRJ-200ER	7664	7664
☐	N924SW	CRJ-200ER	7681	7681
☐	N925SW	CRJ-200ER	7682	
☐	N926SW	CRJ-200ER	7687	7687
☐	N927SW	CRJ-200ER	7693	7693
☐	N928EV	CRJ-200ER	8006	
☐	N928SW	CRJ-200ER	7701	7701
☐	N929SW	CRJ-200ER	7703	
☐	N930EV	CRJ-200ER	8014	
☐	N930SW	CRJ-200ER	7713	7713
☐	N932SW	CRJ-200ER	7714	7714
☐	N934SW	CRJ-200ER	7722	7722
☐	N937SW	CRJ-200ER	7735	7735
☐	N938SW	CRJ-200ER	7741	7741
☐	N939SW	CRJ-200ER	7742	7742
☐	N941SW	CRJ-200ER	7750	7750
☐	N943SW	CRJ-200ER	7762	7762
☐	N945SW	CRJ-200ER	7770	7770
☐	N946SW	CRJ-200ER	7776	7776
☐	N947SW	CRJ-200LR	7786	♦
☐	N948SW	CRJ-200ER	7789	7789
☐	N951SW	CRJ-200ER	7795	
☐	N952SW	CRJ-200ER	7805	7805
☐	N954SW	CRJ-200ER	7815	7815
☐	N956SW	CRJ-200ER	7825	7825
☐	N957SW	CRJ-200ER	7829	7829
☐	N958SW	CRJ-200ER	7833	7833
☐	N959SW	CRJ-200ER	7840	7840
☐	N960SW	CRJ-200ER	7853	7853
☐	N961SW	CRJ-200ER	7857	7857
☐	N962SW	CRJ-200ER	7859	7859
☐	N963SW	CRJ-200ER	7865	7865
☐	N964SW	CRJ-200ER	7868	7867
☐	N965SW	CRJ-200ER	7871	7871
☐	N967SW	CRJ-200ER	7872	7872
☐	N969SW	CRJ-200ER	7876	7876
☐	N970SW	CRJ-200ER	7881	7881
☐	N971SW	CRJ-200ER	7947	7947
☐	N973SW	CRJ-200ER	7949	7949
☐	N975SW	CRJ-200ER	7951	7951
☐	N976SW	CRJ-200ER	7952	7952
☐	N978SW	CRJ-200ER	7953	7953
☐	N979SW	CRJ-200ER	7954	7954
☐	N980SW	CRJ-200ER	7955	7955
☐	N982SW	CRJ-200ER	7956	7956
☐	N983CA	CRJ-100ER	7169	
☐	N983SW	CRJ-200ER	7961	7961
☐	N984CA	CRJ-100ER	7171	
☐	N986CA	CRJ-100ER	7174	
☐	N986SW	CRJ-200ER	7967	7967
☐	N988CA	CRJ-100ER	7204	♦
☐	N151GJ	CRJ-702ER	10216	
☐	N152GJ	CRJ-702ER	10218	
☐	N153GJ	CRJ-702ER	10219	
☐	N154GJ	CRJ-702ER	10224	
☐	N155GJ	CRJ-702ER	10225	
☐	N156GJ	CRJ-702ER	10227	
☐	N157GJ	CRJ-702ER	10230	
☐	N158GJ	CRJ-702ER	10237	
☐	N159GJ	CRJ-702ER	10238	
☐	N160GJ	CRJ-702ER	10239	
☐	N161GJ	CRJ-702ER	10253	
☐	N162GJ	CRJ-702ER	10254	
☐	N163GJ	CRJ-702ER	10255	
☐	N164GJ	CRJ-702ER	10256	
☐	N165GJ	CRJ-702ER	10257	
☐	N166GJ	CRJ-702ER	10266	
☐	N167GJ	CRJ-702ER	10269	
☐	N168GJ	CRJ-702ER	10272	
☐	N169GJ	CRJ-702ER	10273	
☐	N170GJ	CRJ-702ER	10280	
☐	N171GJ	CRJ-702ER	10282	
☐	N172GJ	CRJ-702ER	10283	
☐	N173GJ	CRJ-702ER	10287	
☐	N174GJ	CRJ-702ER	10296	
☐	N175GJ	CRJ-702ER	10297	
☐	N501MJ	CRJ-701ER	10047	501
☐	N502MJ	CRJ-701ER	10050	502
☐	N503MJ	CRJ-701ER	10058	503
☐	N504MJ	CRJ-701ER	10066	504
☐	N505MJ	CRJ-701ER	10070	505
☐	N506MJ	CRJ-701ER	10073	506
☐	N507MJ	CRJ-701ER	10077	507
☐	N508MJ	CRJ-701ER	10087	508
☐	N509MJ	CRJ-701ER	10094	509
☐	N510MJ	CRJ-701ER	10101	510
☐	N511MJ	CRJ-701ER	10104	511
☐	N512MJ	CRJ-701ER	10109	512
☐	N513MJ	CRJ-701ER	10111	513
☐	N514MJ	CRJ-701ER	10116	514
☐	N515MJ	CRJ-701ER	10117	515
☐	N516LR	CRJ-701ER	10258	516
☐	N518LR	CRJ-701ER	10259	518
☐	N519LR	CRJ-701ER	10260	519
☐	N521LR	CRJ-701ER	10261	521
☐	N522LR	CRJ-701ER	10262	522
☐	N701SK	CRJ-701ER	10133	10133
☐	N702SK	CRJ-701ER	10136	10136
☐	N703SK	CRJ-701ER	10139	10139
☐	N705SK	CRJ-701ER	10145	10145
☐	N706SK	CRJ-701ER	10149	10149
☐	N707SK	CRJ-701ER	10003	10003
☐	N708SK	CRJ-701ER	10156	10156
☐	N709SK	CRJ-701ER	10159	10159
☐	N710SK	CRJ-701ER	10170	10170
☐	N712SK	CRJ-701ER	10172	10172
☐	N713SK	CRJ-701ER	10174	10174
☐	N715SK	CRJ-701ER	10179	10179
☐	N716SK	CRJ-701ER	10180	10180
☐	N718SK	CRJ-701ER	10184	10184
☐	N719SK	CRJ-701ER	10188	10188
☐	N724SK	CRJ-701ER	10189	10189
☐	N726SK	CRJ-701ER	10190	10190
☐	N727SK	CRJ-701ER	10191	10191
☐	N728SK	CRJ-701ER	10192	10192
☐	N730SK	CRJ-701ER	10193	10193
☐	N732SK	CRJ-701ER	10194	10194
☐	N738SK	CRJ-701ER	10195	10195
☐	N740SK	CRJ-701ER	10196	10196
☐	N742SK	CRJ-701ER	10197	10197
☐	N743SK	CRJ-701ER	10199	10199
☐	N744SK	CRJ-701ER	10200	10200
☐	N745SK	CRJ-701ER	10201	10201
☐	N746SK	CRJ-701ER	10202	10202
☐	N748SK	CRJ-701ER	10203	10203
☐	N750SK	CRJ-701ER	10207	10207
☐	N751SK	CRJ-701ER	10208	10208
☐	N752SK	CRJ-701ER	10209	10209
☐	N753SK	CRJ-701ER	10214	10214
☐	N754SK	CRJ-701ER	10215	10215

☐ N755SK	CRJ-701ER	10220	10220
☐ N756SK	CRJ-701ER	10221	10221
☐ N758SK	CRJ-701ER	10222	10222
☐ N760SK	CRJ-701ER	10223	10223
☐ N762SK	CRJ-702ER	10226	10226
☐ N763SK	CRJ-702ER	10228	10228
☐ N764SK	CRJ-702ER	10229	10229
☐ N765SK	CRJ-702ER	10231	10231
☐ N766SK	CRJ-702ER	10232	10232
☐ N767SK	CRJ-702ER	10233	10233
☐ N768SK	CRJ-702ER	10234	10234
☐ N770SK	CRJ-702ER	10243	10243
☐ N771SK	CRJ-702ER	10244	10244
☐ N772SK	CRJ-702ER	10235	10235
☐ N773SK	CRJ-702ER	10236	10236
☐ N774SK	CRJ-702ER	10240	10240
☐ N776SK	CRJ-702ER	10241	10241
☐ N778SK	CRJ-702ER	10242	10242
☐ N779SK	CRJ-702ER	10276	10276
☐ N780SK	CRJ-702ER	10277	10277
☐ N782SK	CRJ-702ER	10278	10278
☐ N783SK	CRJ-702ER	10281	10281
☐ N784SK	CRJ-702ER	10284	10284
☐ N785SK	CRJ-702ER	10285	10285
☐ N786SK	CRJ-702ER	10286	10286
☐ N787SK	CRJ-702ER	10288	10288
☐ N788SK	CRJ-702ER	10290	10290
☐ N789SK	CRJ-702ER	10291	10291
☐ N790SK	CRJ-702ER	10292	10292
☐ N791SK	CRJ-702ER	10293	10293
☐ N792SK	CRJ-702ER	10294	10294
☐ N793SK	CRJ-702ER	10295	10295
☐ N794SK	CRJ-702ER	10298	10298
☐ N795SK	CRJ-702ER	10299	10299
☐ N796SK	CRJ-702ER	10300	10300
☐ N797SK	CRJ-702ER	10301	10301

☐ N351PH	DHC-8Q-202	490	763
☐ N358PH	DHC-8Q-202	506	775
☐ N359PH	DHC-8Q-202	514	764
☐ N360PH	DHC-8Q-202	515	762
☐ N361PH	DHC-8Q-202	516	767
☐ N362PH	DHC-8Q-202	518	766
☐ N363PH	DHC-8Q-202	520	760
☐ N364PH	DHC-8Q-202	524	765
☐ N365PH	DHC-8Q-202	526	773
☐ N366PH	DHC-8Q-202	510	769
☐ N367PH	DHC-8Q-202	511	774
☐ N368PH	DHC-8Q-202	512	768
☐ N369PH	DHC-8Q-202	513	770
☐ N374PH	DHC-8Q-202	528	771
☐ N375PH	DHC-8Q-202	529	761
☐ N379PH	DHC-8Q-202	530	771

☐ N837CA	DHC-8Q-311	554	355
☐ N838CA	DHC-8Q-311	527	356
☐ N839CA	DHC-8Q-314	553	357
☐ N857CA	DHC-8Q-311	531	359
☐ N876CA	DHC-8Q-311	438	358

☐ N34NG	DHC-8-402Q	4340	828
☐ N188WQ	DHC-8-402Q	4188	778
☐ N190WQ	DHC-8-402Q	4190	779
☐ N191WQ	DHC-8-402Q	4191	780
☐ N195WQ	DHC-8-402Q	4195	781
☐ N196WQ	DHC-8-402Q	4196	[TUS]
☐ N199WQ	DHC-8-402Q	4199	783
☐ N202WQ	DHC-8-402Q	4202	785
☐ N203WQ	DHC-8-402Q	4203	786
☐ N204WQ	DHC-8-402Q	4204	787
☐ N208WQ	DHC-8-402Q	4208	[COE]
☐ N213WQ	DHC-8-402Q	4213	790
☐ N214WQ	DHC-8-402Q	4214	791
☐ N323NG	DHC-8-402Q	4323	821
☐ N328NG	DHC-8-402Q	4328	822
☐ N336NG	DHC-8-402Q	4336	825
☐ N339NG	DHC-8-402Q	4339	827
☐ N341NG	DHC-8-402Q	4341	[GTF]
☐ N342NG	DHC-8-402Q	4342	830
☐ N345NG	DHC-8-402Q	4345	831
☐ N346NG	DHC-8-402Q	4346	832
☐ N356NG	DHC-8-402Q	4356	835

☐ N16501	ERJ-135ER	145145	[IGM]
☐ N16502	ERJ-135ER	145166	[IGM]
☐ N19503	ERJ-135ER	145176	[IGM]
☐ N25504	ERJ-135ER	145186	[IGM]
☐ N14505	ERJ-135ER	145192	[IGM]
☐ N27506	ERJ-135ER	145206	[IGM]
☐ N17507	ERJ-135ER	145215	[IGM]
☐ N14508	ERJ-135ER	145220	[IGM]
☐ N15509	ERJ-135ER	145238	[IGM]
☐ N16510	ERJ-135ER	145251	[IGM]
☐ N16511	ERJ-135ER	145267	[IGM]
☐ N27512	ERJ-135ER	145274	[IGM]
☐ N17513	ERJ-135LR	145292	[IGM]
☐ N14514	ERJ-135LR	145303	[IGM]
☐ N29515	ERJ-135LR	145309	[IGM]
☐ N14516	ERJ-135LR	145323	[IGM]
☐ N24517	ERJ-135LR	145332	[IGM]
☐ N28518	ERJ-135LR	145334	[IGM]
☐ N12519	ERJ-135LR	145366	[IGM]
☐ N16520	ERJ-135LR	145372	[IGM]
☐ N17521	ERJ-135LR	145378	[IGM]
☐ N14522	ERJ-135LR	145383	[IGM]
☐ N27523	ERJ-135LR	145389	[IGM]
☐ N17524	ERJ-135LR	145399	[IGM]
☐ N16525	ERJ-135LR	145403	[IGM]
☐ N11526	ERJ-135LR	145410	
☐ N15527	ERJ-135LR	145413	
☐ N12528	ERJ-135LR	145504	
☐ N28529	ERJ-135LR	145512	
☐ N12530	ERJ-135LR	145533	

The above aircraft are listed by the last three digits, their fleet numbers and the last three of the registation.

☐ N806HK	ERJ-145ER	145112	[GTF]
☐ N807HK	ERJ-145ER	145119	[STL]
☐ N809HK	ERJ-145ER	145187	[LNK]
☐ N810HK	ERJ-145LR	145231	
☐ N812HK	ERJ-145ER	145373	
☐ N829HK	ERJ-145LR	145281	
☐ N832HK	ERJ-145LR	145771	
☐ N834HK	ERJ-145LR	145269	
☐ N835HK	ERJ-145LR	145670	
☐ N836HK	ERJ-145LR	145695	
☐ N839HK	ERJ-145LR	14500829	
☐ N842HK	ERJ-145LR	14500830	
☐ N843HK	ERJ-145LR	14500822	[STL]
☐ N844HK	ERJ-145LR	14500838	
☐ N845HK	ERJ-145LR	14500842	
☐ N846HK	ERJ-145LR	14500855	
☐ N847HK	ERJ-145LR	14500857	
☐ N853HK	ERJ-145MP	145407	[STL]
☐ N854HK	ERJ-145MP	145408	
☐ N855HK	ERJ-145MP	145387	

	Registration	Type	Serial	No.
☐	N856HK	ERJ-145MP	145441	
☐	N857HK	ERJ-145EP	145418	
☐	N18101	ERJ-145XR	145590	101
☐	N18102	ERJ-145XR	145643	102
☐	N24103	ERJ-145XR	145645	103
☐	N41104	ERJ-145XR	145646	104
☐	N14105	ERJ-145XR	145649	105
☐	N11106	ERJ-145XR	145650	106
☐	N11107	ERJ-145XR	145654	107
☐	N17108	ERJ-145XR	145655	108
☐	N11109	ERJ-145XR	145657	109
☐	N34110	ERJ-145XR	145658	110
☐	N34111	ERJ-145XR	145659	111
☐	N16112	ERJ-145XR	145660	112
☐	N11113	ERJ-145XR	145662	113
☐	N18114	ERJ-145XR	145664	114
☐	N17115	ERJ-145XR	145666	115
☐	N14116	ERJ-145XR	145672	116
☐	N14117	ERJ-145XR	145674	117
☐	N13118	ERJ-145XR	145675	118
☐	N11119	ERJ-145XR	145677	119
☐	N18120	ERJ-145XR	145681	120
☐	N11121	ERJ-145XR	145683	121
☐	N12122	ERJ-145XR	145684	122
☐	N13123	ERJ-145XR	145688	123
☐	N13124	ERJ-145XR	145689	124
☐	N14125	ERJ-145XR	145690	125
☐	N12126	ERJ-145XR	145693	126
☐	N11127	ERJ-145XR	145697	127
☐	N24128	ERJ-145XR	145700	128
☐	N21129	ERJ-145XR	145703	129
☐	N21130	ERJ-145XR	145704	130
☐	N31131	ERJ-145XR	145705	131
☐	N13132	ERJ-145XR	145708	132
☐	N13133	ERJ-145XR	145712	133
☐	N25134	ERJ-145XR	145714	134
☐	N12135	ERJ-145XR	145718	135
☐	N12136	ERJ-145XR	145719	136
☐	N11137	ERJ-145XR	145721	137
☐	N17138	ERJ-145XR	145727	138
☐	N23139	ERJ-145XR	145731	139
☐	N11140	ERJ-145XR	145732	140
☐	N26141	ERJ-145XR	145733	141
☐	N12142	ERJ-145XR	145735	142
☐	N14143	ERJ-145XR	145739	143
☐	N21144	ERJ-145XR	145741	144
☐	N12145	ERJ-145XR	145745	145
☐	N17146	ERJ-145XR	145746	146
☐	N16147	ERJ-145XR	145749	147
☐	N14148	ERJ-145XR	145751	148
☐	N16149	ERJ-145XR	145753	149
☐	N11150	ERJ-145XR	145756	150
☐	N16151	ERJ-145XR	145758	151
☐	N27152	ERJ-145XR	145759	152
☐	N14153	ERJ-145XR	145761	153
☐	N21154	ERJ-145XR	145772	154
☐	N11155	ERJ-145XR	145782	155
☐	N10156	ERJ-145XR	145786	156
☐	N12157	ERJ-145XR	145787	157
☐	N14158	ERJ-145XR	145791	158
☐	N17159	ERJ-145XR	145792	159
☐	N12160	ERJ-145XR	145799	160
☐	N13161	ERJ-145XR	14500805	161
☐	N14162	ERJ-145XR	14500808	162
☐	N12163	ERJ-145XR	14500811	163
☐	N11164	ERJ-145XR	14500817	164
☐	N11165	ERJ-145XR	14500819	165
☐	N12166	ERJ-145XR	14500831	166
☐	N12167	ERJ-145XR	14500834	167
☐	N14168	ERJ-145XR	14500840	168
☐	N17169	ERJ-145XR	14500844	169
☐	N16170	ERJ-145XR	14500850	170
☐	N14171	ERJ-145XR	14500859	171
☐	N12172	ERJ-145XR	14500864	172
☐	N14173	ERJ-145XR	14500872	173
☐	N14174	ERJ-145XR	14500876	174
☐	N12175	ERJ-145XR	14500878	175
☐	N11176	ERJ-145XR	14500881	176
☐	N14177	ERJ-145XR	14500888	177
☐	N16178	ERJ-145XR	14500889	178
☐	N14179	ERJ-145XR	14500896	179
☐	N14180	ERJ-145XR	14500900	180
☐	N11181	ERJ-145XR	14500904	181
☐	N33182	ERJ-145XR	14500909	182
☐	N16183	ERJ-145XR	14500914	183
☐	N11184	ERJ-145XR	14500917	184
☐	N17185	ERJ-145XR	14500922	185
☐	N14186	ERJ-145XR	14500924	186
☐	N11187	ERJ-145XR	14500927	187
☐	N14188	ERJ-145XR	14500929	188
☐	N11189	ERJ-145XR	14500931	189
☐	N27190	ERJ-145XR	14500934	190
☐	N11191	ERJ-145XR	14500935	191
☐	N11192	ERJ-145XR	14500936	192
☐	N11193	ERJ-145XR	14500938	193
☐	N11194	ERJ-145XR	14500940	194
☐	N12195	ERJ-145XR	14500943	195
☐	N17196	ERJ-145XR	14500945	196
☐	N21197	ERJ-145XR	14500947	197
☐	N14198	ERJ-145XR	14500951	198
☐	N11199	ERJ-145XR	14500953	199
☐	N27200	ERJ-145XR	14500956	200
☐	N12201	ERJ-145XR	14500959	201
☐	N13202	ERJ-145XR	14500962	202
☐	N14203	ERJ-145XR	14500964	203
☐	N14204	ERJ-145XR	14500968	204
☐	N11535	ERJ-145LR	145518	535
☐	N11536	ERJ-145LR	145520	536
☐	N21537	ERJ-145LR	145523	537
☐	N13538	ERJ-145LR	145527	538
☐	N11539	ERJ-145LR	145536	539
☐	N12540	ERJ-145LR	145537	540
☐	N16541	ERJ-145LR	145542	541
☐	N14542	ERJ-145LR	145547	542
☐	N14543	ERJ-145LR	145553	543
☐	N11544	ERJ-145LR	145557	544
☐	N26545	ERJ-145LR	145558	545
☐	N16546	ERJ-145LR	145562	546
☐	N11547	ERJ-145LR	145563	547
☐	N11548	ERJ-145LR	145565	548
☐	N26549	ERJ-145LR	145571	549
☐	N13550	ERJ-145LR	145575	550
☐	N11551	ERJ-145LR	145411	551
☐	N12552	ERJ-145LR	145583	552
☐	N13553	ERJ-145LR	145585	553
☐	N19554	ERJ-145LR	145587	554
☐	N15555	ERJ-145LR	145594	555
☐	N18556	ERJ-145LR	145595	556
☐	N18557	ERJ-145LR	145596	557
☐	N14558	ERJ-145LR	145598	558
☐	N16559	ERJ-145LR	145603	559
☐	N17560	ERJ-145LR	145605	560

☐	N16561	ERJ-145LR	145610	561
☐	N14562	ERJ-145LR	145611	562
☐	N12563	ERJ-145LR	145612	563
☐	N12564	ERJ-145LR	145618	564
☐	N11565	ERJ-145LR	145621	565
☐	N13566	ERJ-145LR	145622	566
☐	N12567	ERJ-145LR	145623	567
☐	N14568	ERJ-145LR	145628	568
☐	N12569	ERJ-145LR	145630	569
☐	N14570	ERJ-145LR	145632	570
☐	N16571	ERJ-145LR	145633	571
☐	N15572	ERJ-145LR	145636	572
☐	N14573	ERJ-145LR	145638	573
☐	N15574	ERJ-145LR	145639	574
☐	N10575	ERJ-145LR	145640	575
☐	N12900	ERJ-145LR	145511	900
☐	N48901	ERJ-145LR	145501	901
☐	N14902	ERJ-145LR	145496	902
☐	N13903	ERJ-145LR	145479	903
☐	N14904	ERJ-145LR	145477	904
☐	N14905	ERJ-145LR	145476	905
☐	N29906	ERJ-145LR	145472	906
☐	N14907	ERJ-145LR	145468	907
☐	N13908	ERJ-145LR	145465	908
☐	N22909	ERJ-145LR	145459	909
☐	N15910	ERJ-145LR	145455	910
☐	N16911	ERJ-145LR	145446	911
☐	N15912	ERJ-145LR	145439	912
☐	N13913	ERJ-145LR	145438	913
☐	N13914	ERJ-145LR	145430	914
☐	N36915	ERJ-145LR	145421	915
☐	N14916	ERJ-145LR	145415	916
☐	N29917	ERJ-145LR	145414	917
☐	N16918	ERJ-145LR	145397	918
☐	N16919	ERJ-145LR	145393	919
☐	N14920	ERJ-145LR	145380	920
☐	N12921	ERJ-145LR	145354	921
☐	N12922	ERJ-145LR	145338	922
☐	N14923	ERJ-145LR	145318	923
☐	N12924	ERJ-145LR	145311	924
☐	N13975	ERJ-145LR	145163	975
☐	N16976	ERJ-145LR	145171	976
☐	N14977	ERJ-145LR	145175	977
☐	N13978	ERJ-145LR	145180	978
☐	N13979	ERJ-145LR	145181	979
☐	N15980	ERJ-145LR	145202	980
☐	N16981	ERJ-145LR	145208	981
☐	N15983	ERJ-145LR	145239	983
☐	N17984	ERJ-145LR	145246	984
☐	N15985	ERJ-145LR	145248	985
☐	N15986	ERJ-145LR	145254	986
☐	N16987	ERJ-145LR	145261	987
☐	N13988	ERJ-145LR	145265	988
☐	N13989	ERJ-145LR	145271	989
☐	N14991	ERJ-145LR	145278	991
☐	N13992	ERJ-145LR	145284	992
☐	N14993	ERJ-145LR	145289	993
☐	N13994	ERJ-145LR	145291	994
☐	N13995	ERJ-145LR	145295	995
☐	N12996	ERJ-145LR	145296	996
☐	N13997	ERJ-145LR	145298	997
☐	N14998	ERJ-145LR	145302	998
☐	N16999	ERJ-145LR	145307	999

The above aircraft are listed by the last three digits, their fleet numbers and the last three of the registation. Some of the above operate in ExpressJet c/s.

☐	N631RW	ERJ-170SE	17000007	
☐	N632RW	ERJ-170SE	17000050	
☐	N633RW	ERJ-170SE	17000054	
☐	N634RW	ERJ-170SE	17000055	
☐	N635RW	ERJ-170SE	17000056	
☐	N636RW	ERJ-170SE	17000052	
☐	N637RW	ERJ-170SE	17000051	
☐	N638RW	ERJ-170SE	17000053	
☐	N639RW	ERJ-170SE	17000057	
☐	N640RW	ERJ-170SE	17000058	
☐	N641RW	ERJ-170SE	17000062	
☐	N642RW	ERJ-170SE	17000063	
☐	N643RW	ERJ-170SE	17000060	
☐	N644RW	ERJ-170SE	17000061	
☐	N645RW	ERJ-170SE	17000064	
☐	N646RW	ERJ-170SE	17000066	
☐	N647RW	ERJ-170SE	17000067	
☐	N648RW	ERJ-170SE	17000068	
☐	N649RW	ERJ-170SE	17000070	
☐	N650RW	ERJ-170SE	17000071	
☐	N651RW	ERJ-170SE	17000072	
☐	N652RW	ERJ-170SE	17000075	
☐	N653RW	ERJ-170SE	17000076	
☐	N654RW	ERJ-170SE	17000104	
☐	N655RW	ERJ-170SE	17000105	
☐	N656RW	ERJ-170SE	17000113	
☐	N657RW	ERJ-170SE	17000115	
☐	N855RW	ERJ-170SE	17000077	
☐	N856RW	ERJ-170SE	17000078	
☐	N857RW	ERJ-170SE	17000079	
☐	N858RW	ERJ-170SE	17000080	
☐	N859RW	ERJ-170SE	17000082	
☐	N861RW	ERJ-170SE	17000094	
☐	N862RW	ERJ-170SE	17000098	
☐	N863RW	ERJ-170SE	17000100	
☐	N864RW	ERJ-170SE	17000117	
☐	N865RW	ERJ-170SE	17000122	
☐	N103SY	ERJ-175LR	17000390	
☐	N105SY	ERJ-175LR	17000395	
☐	N106SY	ERJ-175LR	17000399	
☐	N107SY	ERJ-175LR	17000400	
☐	N108SY	ERJ-175LR	17000401	
☐	N109SY	ERJ-175LR	17000404	
☐	N110SY	ERJ-175LR	17000405	
☐	N113SY	ERJ-175LR	17000407	
☐	N114SY	ERJ-175LR	17000410	
☐	N116SY	ERJ-175LR	17000411	
☐	N117SY	ERJ-175LR	17000416	
☐	N118SY	ERJ-175LR	17000420	
☐	N119SY	ERJ-175LR	17000421	
☐	N120SY	ERJ-175LR	17000425	
☐	N121SY	ERJ-175LR	17000430	
☐	N122SY	ERJ-175LR	17000431	
☐	N124SY	ERJ-175LR	17000439	
☐	N125SY	ERJ-175LR	17000440	
☐	N127SY	ERJ-175LR	17000441	
☐	N128SY	ERJ-175LR	17000445	
☐	N130SY	ERJ-175LR	17000449	
☐	N131SY	ERJ-175LR	17000450	
☐	N132SY	ERJ-175LR	17000451	
☐	N133SY	ERJ-175LR	17000452	
☐	N134SY	ERJ-175LR	17000458	
☐	N135SY	ERJ-175LR	17000460	
☐	N136SY	ERJ-175LR	17000462	
☐	N138SY	ERJ-175LR	17000466	♦
☐	N139SY	ERJ-175LR	17000468	♦

☐ N140SY	ERJ-175LR	17000470	♦
☐ N141SY	ERJ-175LR	17000472	♦
☐ N142SY	ERJ-175LR	17000475	♦
☐ N143SY	ERJ-175LR	17000476	♦
☐ N144SY	ERJ-175LR	17000482	♦
☐ N145SY	ERJ-175LR	17000484	♦
☐ N146SY	ERJ-175LR	17000491	♦
☐ N148SY	ERJ-175LR	17000492	♦
☐ N149SY	ERJ-175LR	17000495	♦
☐ N150SY	ERJ-175LR	17000499	♦
☐ N151SY	ERJ-175LR	17000503	♦
☐ N721YX	ERJ-175LR	17000493	♦
☐ N722YX	ERJ-175LR	17000496	♦
☐ N723YX	ERJ-175LR	17000498	♦
☐ N724YX	ERJ-175LR	17000502	♦
☐ N725YX	ERJ-175LR	17000506	♦
☐ N726YX	ERJ-175LR	17000507	♦
☐ N727YX	ERJ-175LR	17000509	♦
☐ N728YX	ERJ-175LR	17000510	♦
☐ N729YX	ERJ-175LR	17000512	♦
☐ N730YX	ERJ-175LR	17000518	♦
☐ N731YX	ERJ-175LR	17000520	♦
☐ N732YX	ERJ-175LR	17000521	♦
☐ N88301	ERJ-175LR	17000388	301
☐ N87302	ERJ-175LR	17000394	302
☐ N87303	ERJ-175LR	17000398	303
☐ N89304	ERJ-175LR	17000406	304
☐ N93305	ERJ-175LR	17000412	305
☐ N87306	ERJ-175LR	17000414	306
☐ N84307	ERJ-175LR	17000419	307
☐ N89308	ERJ-175LR	17000422	308
☐ N86309	ERJ-175LR	17000426	309
☐ N88310	ERJ-175LR	17000427	310
☐ N86311	ERJ-175LR	17000429	311
☐ N86312	ERJ-175LR	17000432	312
☐ N89313	ERJ-175LR	17000433	313
☐ N82314	ERJ-175LR	17000436	314
☐ N89315	ERJ-175LR	17000437	315
☐ N86316	ERJ-175LR	17000438	316
☐ N89317	ERJ-175LR	17000442	317
☐ N87318	ERJ-175LR	17000443	318
☐ N87319	ERJ-175LR	17000445	319
☐ N85320	ERJ-175LR	17000454	320
☐ N89321	ERJ-175LR	17000459	321
☐ N86322	ERJ-175LR	17000465	322♦
☐ N85323	ERJ-175LR	17000469	323♦
☐ N86324	ERJ-175LR	17000471	324♦
☐ N88325	ERJ-175LR	17000474	325♦
☐ N88326	ERJ-175LR	17000478	326♦
☐ N88327	ERJ-175LR	17000479	327♦
☐ N88328	ERJ-175LR	17000480	328♦
☐ N83329	ERJ-175LR	17000487	329♦
☐ N88330	ERJ-175LR	17000488	330♦
☐ N88331	ERJ-175LR	17000530	331♦
☐ N88332	ERJ-175LR	17000531	332♦
☐ N82333	ERJ-175LR	17000532	333♦
☐ N86334	ERJ-175LR	17000534	334♦
☐ N88335	ERJ-175LR	17000538	335♦

The above aircraft are listed by the last three digits, their fleet numbers and the last three of the registation.

UPS AIRLINES **5X / UPS**

☐ N120UP	A300F4-622R	805
☐ N121UP	A300F4-622R	806
☐ N122UP	A300F4-622R	807
☐ N124UP	A300F4-622R	808
☐ N125UP	A300F4-622R	809
☐ N126UP	A300F4-622R	810
☐ N127UP	A300F4-622R	811
☐ N128UP	A300F4-622R	812
☐ N129UP	A300F4-622R	813
☐ N130UP	A300F4-622R	814
☐ N131UP	A300F4-622R	815
☐ N133UP	A300F4-622R	816
☐ N134UP	A300F4-622R	817
☐ N135UP	A300F4-622R	818
☐ N136UP	A300F4-622R	819
☐ N137UP	A300F4-622R	820
☐ N138UP	A300F4-622R	821
☐ N139UP	A300F4-622R	822
☐ N140UP	A300F4-622R	823
☐ N141UP	A300F4-622R	824
☐ N142UP	A300F4-622R	825
☐ N143UP	A300F4-622R	826
☐ N144UP	A300F4-622R	827
☐ N145UP	A300F4-622R	828
☐ N146UP	A300F4-622R	829
☐ N147UP	A300F4-622R	830
☐ N148UP	A300F4-622R	831
☐ N149UP	A300F4-622R	832
☐ N150UP	A300F4-622R	833
☐ N151UP	A300F4-622R	834
☐ N152UP	A300F4-622R	835
☐ N153UP	A300F4-622R	839
☐ N154UP	A300F4-622R	840
☐ N156UP	A300F4-622R	845
☐ N157UP	A300F4-622R	846
☐ N158UP	A300F4-622R	847
☐ N159UP	A300F4-622R	848
☐ N160UP	A300F4-622R	849
☐ N161UP	A300F4-622R	850
☐ N162UP	A300F4-622R	851
☐ N163UP	A300F4-622R	852
☐ N164UP	A300F4-622R	853
☐ N165UP	A300F4-622R	854
☐ N166UP	A300F4-622R	861
☐ N167UP	A300F4-622R	862
☐ N168UP	A300F4-622R	863
☐ N169UP	A300F4-622R	864
☐ N170UP	A300F4-622R	865
☐ N171UP	A300F4-622R	866
☐ N172UP	A300F4-622R	867
☐ N173UP	A300F4-622R	868
☐ N174UP	A300F4-622R	869
☐ N570UP	B747-44AF	35667/1388
☐ N572UP	B747-44AF	35669/1396
☐ N573UP	B747-44AF	35662/1401
☐ N574UP	B747-44AF	35663/1403
☐ N575UP	B747-44AF	35664/1406
☐ N576UP	B747-44AF	35665/1410
☐ N577UP	B747-44AF	35666/1412
☐ N578UP	B747-45EM	27154/994
☐ N579UP	B747-45EM	26062/1016
☐ N580UP	B747-428F	25632/968
☐ N581UP	B747-4R7F	25866/1002
☐ N582UP	B747-4R7F	29053/1139
☐ N583UP	B747-4R7F	25867/1008
☐ N401UP	B757-24APF	23723/139
☐ N402UP	B757-24APF	23724/141
☐ N403UP	B757-24APF	23725/143
☐ N404UP	B757-24APF	23726/147

☐ N405UP B757-24APF 23727/149
☐ N406UP B757-24APF 23728/176
☐ N407UP B757-24APF 23729/181
☐ N408UP B757-24APF 23730/184
☐ N409UP B757-24APF 23731/186
☐ N410UP B757-24APF 23732/189
☐ N411UP B757-24APF 23851/191
☐ N412UP B757-24APF 23852/193
☐ N413UP B757-24APF 23853/195
☐ N414UP B757-24APF 23854/197
☐ N415UP B757-24APF 23855/199
☐ N416UP B757-24APF 23903/318
☐ N417UP B757-24APF 23904/322
☐ N418UP B757-24APF 23905/326
☐ N419UP B757-24APF 23906/330
☐ N420UP B757-24APF 23907/334
☐ N421UP B757-24APF 25281/395
☐ N422UP B757-24APF 25324/399
☐ N423UP B757-24APF 25325/403
☐ N424UP B757-24APF 25369/407
☐ N425UP B757-24APF 25370/411
☐ N426UP B757-24APF 25457/477
☐ N427UP B757-24APF 25458/481
☐ N428UP B757-24APF 25459/485
☐ N429UP B757-24APF 25460/489
☐ N430UP B757-24APF 25461/493
☐ N431UP B757-24APF 25462/569
☐ N432UP B757-24APF 25463/573
☐ N433UP B757-24APF 25464/577
☐ N434UP B757-24APF 25465/579
☐ N435UP B757-24APF 25466/581
☐ N436UP B757-24APF 25467/625
☐ N437UP B757-24APF 25468/628
☐ N438UP B757-24APF 25469/631
☐ N439UP B757-24APF 25470/634
☐ N440UP B757-24APF 25471/636
☐ N441UP B757-24APF 27386/638
☐ N442UP B757-24APF 27387/640
☐ N443UP B757-24APF 27388/642
☐ N444UP B757-24APF 27389/644
☐ N445UP B757-24APF 27390/646
☐ N446UP B757-24APF 27735/649
☐ N447UP B757-24APF 27736/651
☐ N448UP B757-24APF 27737/654
☐ N449UP B757-24APF 27738/656
☐ N450UP B757-24APF 25472/659
☐ N451UP B757-24APF 27739/675
☐ N452UP B757-24APF 25473/679
☐ N453UP B757-24APF 25474/683
☐ N454UP B757-24APF 25475/687
☐ N455UP B757-24APF 25476/691
☐ N456UP B757-24APF 25477/728
☐ N457UP B757-24APF 25478/729
☐ N458UP B757-24APF 25479/730
☐ N459UP B757-24APF 25480/733
☐ N460UP B757-24APF 25481/734
☐ N461UP B757-24APF 28265/755
☐ N462UP B757-24APF 28266/759
☐ N463UP B757-24APF 28267/763
☐ N464UP B757-24APF 28268/765
☐ N465UP B757-24APF 28269/767
☐ N466UP B757-24APF 25482/769
☐ N467UP B757-24APF 25483/771
☐ N468UP B757-24APF 25484/774
☐ N469UP B757-24APF 25485/776
☐ N470UP B757-24APF 25486/778
☐ N471UP B757-24APF 28842/813
☐ N472UP B757-24APF 28843/815
☐ N473UP B757-24APF 28846/823
☐ N474UP B757-24APF 28844/879
☐ N475UP B757-24APF 28845/882

☐ N301UP B767-34AF/W 27239/580
☐ N302UP B767-34AF/W 27240/590
☐ N303UP B767-34AF/W 27241/594
☐ N304UP B767-34AF/W 27242/598
☐ N305UP B767-34AF/W 27243/600
☐ N306UP B767-34AF/W 27759/622
☐ N307UP B767-34AF/W 27760/624
☐ N308UP B767-34AF/W 27761/626
☐ N309UP B767-34AF/W 27740/628
☐ N310UP B767-34AF/W 27762/630
☐ N311UP B767-34AF/W 27741/632
☐ N312UP B767-34AF/W 27763/634
☐ N313UP B767-34AF/W 27764/636
☐ N314UP B767-34AF/W 27742/638
☐ N315UP B767-34AF/W 27743/640
☐ N316UP B767-34AF/W 27744/660
☐ N317UP B767-34AF/W 27745/666
☐ N318UP B767-34AF/W 27746/670
☐ N319UP B767-34AF/W 27758/672
☐ N320UP B767-34AF/W 27747/674
☐ N322UP B767-34AF/W 27748/678
☐ N323UP B767-34AF/W 27749/682
☐ N324UP B767-34AF/W 27750/724
☐ N325UP B767-34AF/W 27751/726
☐ N326UP B767-34AF/W 27752/728
☐ N327UP B767-34AF/W 27753/730
☐ N328UP B767-34AF/W 27754/732
☐ N329UP B767-34AF/W 27755/756
☐ N330UP B767-34AF/W 27756/760
☐ N331UP B767-34AF/W 27757/764
☐ N332UP B767-34AF/W 32843/854
☐ N334UP B767-34AF/W 32844/858
☐ N335UP B767-34AF/W 37856/979
☐ N336UP B767-34AF/W 37857/983
☐ N337UP B767-34AF/W 37858/986
☐ N338UP B767-34AF/W 37944/988
☐ N339UP B767-34AF/W 37859/989
☐ N340UP B767-34AF/W 37860/991
☐ N341UP B767-34AF/W 37861/992
☐ N342UP B767-34AF/W 37865/1002
☐ N343UP B767-34AF/W 37945/1003
☐ N344UP B767-34AF/W 37866/1005
☐ N345UP B767-34AF/W 37867/1006
☐ N346UP B767-34AF/W 37868/1008
☐ N347UP B767-34AF/W 37871/1020
☐ N348UP B767-34AF/W 37872/1022
☐ N349UP B767-34AF/W 37947/1024
☐ N350UP B767-34AF/W 37873/1025
☐ N351UP B767-34AF/W 37874/1026
☐ N352UP B767-34AF/W 37875/1028
☐ N353UP B767-34AF/W 37877/1035
☐ N354UP B767-34AF/W 37862/1044
☐ N355UP B767-34AF/W 37863/1046
☐ N356UP B767-34AF/W 37869/1048
☐ N357UP B767-34AF/W 37876/1051
☐ N358UP B767-34AF/W 37864/1053
☐ N359UP B767-34AF/W 37870/1056
☐ N360UP B767-34AF/W 37946/1057
☐ N361UP B767-34AF/W 37878/1059

☐ N250UP MD-11F 48745/596
☐ N251UP MD-11F 48744/592
☐ N252UP MD-11F 48768/601

	Reg	Type	c/n	
☐	N253UP	MD-11F	48439/554	
☐	N254UP	MD-11F	48406/547	
☐	N255UP	MD-11F	48404/523	
☐	N256UP	MD-11F	48405/524	
☐	N257UP	MD-11F	48451/505	
☐	N258UP	MD-11F	48416/466	
☐	N259UP	MD-11F	48417/467	
☐	N260UP	MD-11F	48418/501	
☐	N270UP	MD-11F	48576/574	
☐	N271UP	MD-11F	48572/556	
☐	N272UP	MD-11F	48571/552	
☐	N273UP	MD-11F	48574/566	
☐	N274UP	MD-11F	48575/568	
☐	N275UP	MD-11F	48774/610	
☐	N276UP	MD-11F	48579/599	
☐	N277UP	MD-11F	48578/588	
☐	N278UP	MD-11F	48577/583	
☐	N279UP	MD-11F	48573/559	
☐	N280UP	MD-11F	48634/614	
☐	N281UP	MD-11F	48538/533	
☐	N282UP	MD-11F	48452/472	
☐	N283UP	MD-11F	48484/484	
☐	N284UP	MD-11F	48541/621	
☐	N285UP	MD-11F	48457/498	
☐	N286UP	MD-11F	48453/473	
☐	N287UP	MD-11	48539/571	
☐	N288UP	MD-11F	48540/611	
☐	N289UP	MD-11	48455/487	
☐	N290UP	MD-11F	48456/494	
☐	N291UP	MD-11F	48477/511	
☐	N292UP	MD-11F	48566/543	
☐	N293UP	MD-11F	48473/481	
☐	N294UP	MD-11F	48472/480	
☐	N295UP	MD-11F	48475/489	
☐	N296UP	MD-11F	48474/485	

US AIRWAYS

See American Airlines

US AIRWAYS EXPRESS

See American Eagle

US FOREST SERVICE

	Reg	Type	c/n
☐	N115Z	Basler BT-67	16819/33567
☐	N141Z	DHC-6 Twin Otter 300	803
☐	N143Z	DHC-6 Twin Otter 300	437
☐	N173Z	Short SD.3-30	SH3116
☐	N175Z	Short SD.3-30	SH3115
☐	N178Z	Short SD.3-30	SH3119
☐	N179Z	Short SD.3-30	SH3109

USA JET AIRLINES — U7 / JUS

	Reg	Type	c/n	
☐	N727US	B727-223F	22470/1771	♦
☐	N191US	DC-9-15	45718/17	[YIP]
☐	N192US	DC-9-15RC	47156/228	
☐	N194US	DC-9-15RC	47016/173	
☐	N195US	DC-9-15RC	47017/186	
☐	N196US	DC-9-15RC	47155/216	
☐	N205US	DC-9-32CF	47690/843	
☐	N208US	DC-9-32F	47220/296	
☐	N215US	DC-9-32	47480/607	
☐	N327US	DC-9-33F	47414/536	
☐	N831US	MD-83	49791/1644	
☐	N948AS	MD-82	53021/1801	
☐	N949NS	MD-83	53022/1909	

VIA AIR — VC / SRY

	Reg	Type	c/n	
☐	N802HK	ERJ-145ER	145066	♦
☐	N824HK	ERJ-145LR	145498	♦
☐	N825HK	ERJ-145LR	145510	♦
☐	N833HK	ERJ-145LR	145240	♦
☐	N838HK	ERJ-145LR	145321	♦
☐	N841HK	ERJ-145LR	145382	♦

VIRGIN AMERICA — VX / VRD

	Reg	Type	c/n	
☐	N521VA	A319-112	2773	
☐	N522VA	A319-112	2811	
☐	N523VA	A319-112	3181	
☐	N524VA	A319-112	3204	
☐	N525VA	A319-112	3324	
☐	N526VA	A319-112	3347	
☐	N527VA	A319-112	3417	
☐	N528VA	A319-112	3445	
☐	N529VA	A319-112	3684	
☐	N530VA	A319-112	3686	
☐	N281VA	A320-214/S	6669	♦
☐	N282VA	A320-214/S	6704	♦
☐	N283VA	A320-214/S	6787	♦
☐	N284VA	A320-214/S	6835	♦
☐	N285VA	A320-214/S	6889	♦
☐	N286VA	A320-214/S	6939	♦
☐	N361VA	A320-214/S	5515	
☐	N362VA	A320-214/S	6965	♦
☐	N	A320-214/S	7063	o/o♦
☐	N	A320-214/S	7138	o/o♦
☐	N	A320-214/S	7207	o/o♦
☐	N621VA	A320-214	2616	
☐	N622VA	A320-214	2674	
☐	N623VA	A320-214	2740	
☐	N624VA	A320-214	2778	
☐	N625VA	A320-214	2800	
☐	N626VA	A320-214	2830	
☐	N627VA	A320-214	2851	
☐	N628VA	A320-214	2993	
☐	N629VA	A320-214	3037	
☐	N630VA	A320-214	3101	
☐	N631VA	A320-214	3135	
☐	N632VA	A320-214	3155	
☐	N633VA	A320-214	3230	
☐	N634VA	A320-214	3359	
☐	N635VA	A320-214	3398	
☐	N636VA	A320-214	3460	
☐	N637VA	A320-214	3465	
☐	N638VA	A320-214	3503	
☐	N639VA	A320-214	3016	
☐	N640VA	A320-214	3349	
☐	N641VA	A320-214	3656	
☐	N642VA	A320-214	3670	
☐	N835VA	A320-214	4448	
☐	N836VA	A320-214	4480	
☐	N837VA	A320-214	4558	
☐	N838VA	A320-214	4559	
☐	N839VA	A320-214	4610	
☐	N840VA	A320-214	4616	
☐	N841VA	A320-214	4655	
☐	N842VA	A320-214	4805	
☐	N843VA	A320-214	4814	
☐	N844VA	A320-214	4851	
☐	N845VA	A320-214	4867	

☐	N846VA	A320-214	4894	
☐	N847VA	A320-214	4948	
☐	N848VA	A320-214	4959	
☐	N849VA	A320-214	4991	
☐	N851VA	A320-214	4999	
☐	N852VA	A320-214	5004	
☐	N853VA	A320-214	5034	
☐	N854VA	A320-214	5058	
☐	N855VA	A320-214	5179	

VISION AIR — *V2 / RBY*

☐	N732VA	B737-3T0	23366/1174	
☐	N767VA	B767-222ER	21870/13	[MEX]
☐	N768VA	B767-222ER	21869/11	[ILN]
☐	N769VA	B767-222ER	21866/7	
☐	N402VA	Do228-202K	8085	
☐	N403VA	Do228-202K	8171	
☐	N404VA	Do228-203F	8120	
☐	N405VA	Do228-203F	8144	
☐	N409VA	Do228-201	8097	
☐	N329MX	Do328-100	3049	[BBU]
☐	N431JS	Do328-110	3028	[SDF]

WESTERN AIR EXPRESS — *WAE*

☐	N158WA	SA.226TC Metro II	TC-411	
☐	N160WA	SA.226TC Metro IIA	TC-399	

WESTERN GLOBAL AIRLINES — *WGN*

☐	N344KD	B747-446BCF	26344/929	♦
☐	N356KD	B747-446BCF	26356/1026	♦
☐	N381WA	MD-11F	48523/516	[MZJ]♦
☐	N411SN	MD-11F	48411/453	[MZJ]♦
☐	N412SN	MD-11F	48412/454	>FDX♦
☐	N415JN	MD-11F	48415/576	>FDX
☐	N435KD	MD-11F	48435/478	
☐	N512JN	MD-11F	48512/529	♦
☐	N513SN	MD-11F	48513/564	[OSC]♦
☐	N542KD	MD-11F	48542/570	>FDX♦
☐	N543JN	MD-11F	48543/572	
☐	N544KD	MD-11F	48544/580	o/o
☐	N545JN	MD-11F	48545/587	>AJK
☐	N546JN	MD-11F	48546/589	>FDX♦
☐	N581JN	MD-11F	48581/565	[VCV]♦
☐	N630SN	MD-11F	48630/567	[VCV]♦

WIGGINS AIRWAYS — *WIG*

☐	N24AN	EMB.110P2	110318	
☐	N115WA	EMB.110P1	110451	
☐	N116WA	EMB.110P1	110399	
☐	N117WA	EMB.110P1	110388	
☐	N118WA	EMB.110P2	110250	
☐	N119WA	EMB.110P1	110372	
☐	N120WA	EMB.110P1	110404	
☐	N830AC	EMB.110P1	110205	♦

WORLD ATLANTIC AIRLINES — *KB / WAL*

☐	N802WA	MD-83	53052/1731	
☐	N803WA	MD-82	49507/1425	
☐	N804WA	MD-83	49345/1371	
☐	N805WA	MD-83	53470/2135	
☐	N806WA	MD-83	53251/1909	
☐	N807WA	MD-83	53093/2066	♦

XTRA AIRWAYS — *XP / CXP*

☐	N43XA	B737-4S3	24796/1887	[DHN]
☐	N134AS	B737-484	25314/2124	
☐	N148AS	B737-484	27149/2471	
☐	(N313XA)	B737-484	25313/2109	♦ [N353AS]
☐	N430XA	B737-484	25430/2174	o/o♦
☐	N624XA	B737-86J/W	32624/961	♦
☐	N625XA	B737-86J/W	32625/995	♦
☐	N688XA	B737-4Y0	24688/1876	♦
☐	N917XA	B737-86J/W	32917/1210	♦

OB- PERU

AERCARIBE PERU — *CPR*

☐	OB-2098-P	An-32	1809	♦
☐	OB-2120-P	An-32		♦

AERO TRANSPORTE — *AMP*

☐	OB-1667-P	Beech 1900C	UB-54	
☐	OB-1770-P	Fokker 50	20280	
☐	OB-1778	An-26B-100	14205	
☐	OB-1868-P	An-32	2802	^
☐	OB-1875	Beech 1900D	UE-68	
☐	OB-1907-T	An-32	3107	^
☐	OB-1924-P	An-32	3109	^
☐	OB-1962-T	An-32A	2602	
☐	OB-1985	Beech 1900D	UE-138	
☐	OB-2043-P	Fokker 50	20115	%

^ leased from Transaer; % leased to Rio Amazonas

AMAZON SKY — *AMT*

☐	OB-2015-P	An-26-100	4002	
☐	OB-2085-P	An-32B	3302	

AVIANCA PERU — *T0 / TPU*

☐	N279AV	A330-243	1279	<AVA
☐	N491TA	A320-233	2301	<TAI
☐	N568TA	A321-231	2687	<TAI
☐	N982TA	ERJ-190AR	19000259	<TAI
☐	N984TA	ERJ-190AR	19000273	<TAI
☐	N988TA	ERJ-190AR	19000399	<TAI

LAN PERU — *LP / LPE*

Uses A319-100s and B767-300s with Chilean registrations leased from parent LAN Airlines, Chile.

L. C. PERU — *W4 / LCB*

☐	N240AT	B737-530	24824/2006	♦
☐	N821AC	B737-530	24821/1993	♦
☐	N923LC	B737-55S	26543/2339	♦
☐	N2106A	B737-55S	26542/2337	♦
☐	OB-	B737-530	24944/2051	♦
☐	N436YV	DHC-8Q-202	436	
☐	N444YV	DHC-8Q-202	444	
☐	N447YV	DHC-8Q-202	447	♦
☐	N448YV	DHC-8Q-202	448	
☐	N454YV	DHC-8Q-202	454	
☐	N404AV	DHC-8-402Q	4010	♦
☐	N689AC	DHC-8-402Q	4036	♦

PERUVIAN AIRLINES			P9 / PVN
OB-1839-P	B737-204	22640/867	[LIM]
OB-1841-P	B737-204	22058/629	[LIM]
OB-1851-P	B737-230	22133/772	
OB-1954-P	B737-247	23188/1071	
OB-1955	B737-2T7	22761/850	std
OB-1956	B737-2T7	22762/856	std
OB-1957	B737-236	21806/699	[LIM]
OB-1960-P	B737-33A	23627/1302	[TUS]
OB-1961-P	B737-33A	23629/1311	[TUS]
OB-2036-P	B737-3M8	25071/2039	
OB-2037-P	B737-3Q8	26296/2581	
OB-2041-P	B737-53C	24825/1894	
OB-2079-P	B737-48E	27630/2848	
OB-2089-P	B737-3YO(QC)	23685/1357	
OB-2090-P	B737-3Q8(QC)	24132/1555	[LIM]

SERVICIOS AEREOS DE LOS ANDES			AND
OB-1864	DHC-6 Twin Otter 300	282	
OB-1897-P	DHC-6 Twin Otter 300	521	

STAR PERU			2I / SRU
OB-1769	An-24RV	57310110	[LIM]
OB-1772	An-26B-100	10704	[LIM]
OB-1877-P	BAe146 Srs.100	E1199	
OB-1879-P	BAe146 Srs.100	E1095	
OB-1885-P	BAe146 Srs.200	E2087	
OB-1914-P	BAe146 Srs.300	E3181	
OB-1923-P	BAe146 Srs.300	E3185	
OB-1930-P	BAe146 Srs.200	E2201	
OB-1943-P	BAe146 Srs.200	E2133	
OB-1964-T	BAe146 Srs.200	E2184	[LIM]
OB-1978-T	BAe146 Srs.200QT	E2114	[LIM]
OB-2014-T	BAe146 Srs. 200	E2058	
OB-	CRJ-200ER	7363	♦

OD- LEBANON

MED AIRWAYS			7Y / MED
OD-AMR	CRJ-200ER	7255	

MEA - MIDDLE EAST AIRLINES			ME / MEA
OD-MRL	A320-232	5000	
OD-MRM	A320-232	4632	
OD-MRN	A320-232	4339	
OD-MRO	A320-232	4296	
OD-MRR	A320-232	3837	
OD-MRS	A320-232	3804	
OD-MRT	A320-232	3736	
T7-MRA	A320-214	5162	
T7-MRB	A320-214	5152	
T7-MRC	A320-214	5253	
T7-MRD	A320-214/S	5746	
T7-MRE	A320-232/S	6978	o/o♦
T7-MRF	A320-232/S	7006	o/o♦
OD-RMI	A321-231	1977	
OD-RMJ	A321-231	2055	
OD-MEA	A330-243	984	
OD-MEB	A330-243	998	
OD-MEC	A330-243	995	
OD-MED	A330-243	926	
OD-	A330-243	1725	o/o♦

WINGS OF LEBANON			W7 / WLB
OD-HAJ	B737-3Q8	26313/2704	
4L-IMA	B737-322	24717/1930	<BRZ♦

OE- AUSTRIA

AUSTRIAN AIRLINES			OS / AUA
OE-LDA	A319-112	2131	
OE-LDB	A319-112	2174	
OE-LDC	A319-112	2262	
OE-LDD	A319-112	2416	
OE-LDE	A319-112	2494	
OE-LDF	A319-112	2547	
OE-LDG	A319-112	2652	
OE-LBI	A320-214	1937	
OE-LBJ	A320-214	1553	
OE-LBK	A320-214	1931	
OE-LBL	A320-214	2009	
OE-LBM	A320-214	1504	
OE-LBN	A320-214	0768	
OE-LBO	A320-214	0776	
OE-LBP	A320-214	0797	
OE-LBQ	A320-214	1137	
OE-LBR	A320-214	1150	
OE-LBS	A320-214	1189	
OE-LBT	A320-214	1387	
OE-LBU	A320-214	1478	
OE-LBV	A320-214	1385	
OE-LBW	A320-214	1678	
OE-LBX	A320-214	1735	
OE-LBA	A321-111	0552	
OE-LBB	A321-111	0570	
OE-LBC	A321-111	0581	
OE-LBD	A321-211	0920	
OE-LBE	A321-211	0935	
OE-LBF	A321-211	1458	
OE-LAE	B767-3Z9ER/W	30383/812	
OE-LAT	B767-31AER/W	25273/393	
OE-LAW	B767-3Z9ER/W	26417/448	
OE-LAX	B767-3Z9ER/W	27095/467	
OE-LAY	B767-3Z9ER/W	29867/731	
OE-LAZ	B767-3Z9ER/W	30331/759	
OE-LPA	B777-2Z9ER	28698/87	
OE-LPB	B777-2Z9ER	28699/163	
OE-LPC	B777-2Z9ER	29313/386	
OE-LPD	B777-2Z9ER	35960/607	
OE-LPE	B777-2Q8ER	27607/135	
OE-LGA	DHC-8-402Q	4014	
OE-LGB	DHC-8-402Q	4015	
OE-LGC	DHC-8-402Q	4026	
OE-LGD	DHC-8-402Q	4027	
OE-LGE	DHC-8-402Q	4042	
OE-LGF	DHC-8-402Q	4068	
OE-LGG	DHC-8-402Q	4074	
OE-LGH	DHC-8-402Q	4075	
OE-LGI	DHC-8-402Q	4100	
OE-LGJ	DHC-8-402Q	4104	
OE-LGK	DHC-8-402Q	4280	
OE-LGL	DHC-8-402Q	4310	
OE-LGM	DHC-8-402Q	4319	
OE-LGN	DHC-8-402Q	4326	
OE-LGO	DHC-8-402Q	4281	

	Reg	Type	c/n	Notes
☐	OE-LGP	DHC-8-402Q	4016	
☐	OE-LGQ	DHC-8-402Q	4003	
☐	OE-LGR	DHC-8-402Q	4045	>SWR
☐	OE-LWA	ERJ-195LR	19000314	♦
☐	OE-LWB	ERJ-195LR	19000324	o/o♦
☐	OE-LWC	ERJ-195LR	19000350	o/o♦
☐	OE-LWD	ERJ-195LR	19000411	♦
☐	OE-LWE	ERJ-195LR	19000423	o/o♦
☐	OE-LWF	ERJ-195LR	19000447	o/o♦
☐	OE-LWG	ERJ-195LR	19000464	♦
☐	OE-LWH	ERJ-195LR	19000486	o/o♦
☐	OE-LWI	ERJ-195LR	19000500	o/o♦
☐	OE-LWJ	ERJ-195LR	19000507	o/o♦
☐	OE-LWK	ERJ-195LR	19000523	o/o♦
☐	OE-LWL	ERJ-195LR	19000532	o/o♦
☐	OE-LWM	ERJ-195LR	19000542	o/o♦
☐	OE-LWN	ERJ-195LR	19000553	o/o♦
☐	OE-LWO	ERJ-195LR	19000555	o/o♦
☐	OE-LWP	ERJ-195LR	19000558	o/o♦
☐	OE-LWQ	ERJ-195LR	19000565	o/o♦
☐	OE-LFH	Fokker 70	11554	
☐	OE-LFI	Fokker 70	11529	
☐	OE-LFJ	Fokker 70	11532	
☐	OE-LFP	Fokker 70	11560	
☐	OE-LFQ	Fokker 70	11568	
☐	OE-LFR	Fokker 70	11572	
☐	OE-LVA	Fokker 100	11490	
☐	OE-LVB	Fokker 100	11502	
☐	OE-LVC	Fokker 100	11446	
☐	OE-LVD	Fokker 100	11515	
☐	OE-LVE	Fokker 100	11499	
☐	OE-LVF	Fokker 100	11483	
☐	OE-LVG	Fokker 100	11520	
☐	OE-LVH	Fokker 100	11456	
☐	OE-LVI	Fokker 100	11468	
☐	OE-LVJ	Fokker 100	11359	
☐	OE-LVK	Fokker 100	11397	
☐	OE-LVL	Fokker 100	11404	
☐	OE-LVM	Fokker 100	11361	
☐	OE-LVN	Fokker 100	11367	
☐	OE-LVO	Fokker 100	11460	

All Fokker 70s and 100s sold to Alliance Airways for delivery over next two years.

EUROWINGS AUSTRIA

	Reg	Type	c/n	Notes
☐	OE-	A320-214/S	6636	o/o♦

NIKI — HG / NLY

	Reg	Type	c/n	Notes
☐	OE-LNA	A319-112	3661	
☐	OE-LNB	A319-112	3447	
☐	OE-LNC	A319-112	3728	♦
☐	OE-LND	A319-112	3689	♦
☐	OE-LNE	A319-112	3415	♦
☐	OE-	A319-112	3865	o/o♦
☐	OE-LEA	A320-214	2529	
☐	OE-LEC	A320-214	4316	♦
☐	OE-LED	A320-214	4606	♦
☐	OE-LEE	A320-214	2749	
☐	OE-LEF	A320-214	4368	
☐	OE-LEG	A320-214	4581	
☐	OE-LEH	A320-214	4594	
☐	OE-LEL	A320-214	2668	
☐	OE-LEN	A320-214	3093	♦
☐	OE-LEU	A320-214	2902	
☐	OE-LEX	A320-214	2867	
☐	OE-LEY	A320-214/S	5648	
☐	OE-LNZ	A321-211/S	6979	o/o♦
☐	OE-LES	A321-211	3504	
☐	OE-LET	A321-211	3830	
☐	OE-LEW	A321-211	4611	
☐	OE-LEZ	A321-211	4648	

Aircraft in process of being painted in Air Berlin c/s.

PEOPLE'S VIENNA LINE — PE / PEV

	Reg	Type	c/n	Notes
☐	OE-LMK	ERJ-170STD	17000150	

TYROLEAN JET SERVICE — TJS

	Reg	Type	c/n	Notes
☐	OE-LIP	A319-115CJ	3632	
☐	OE-LOV	A319-115CJ	3513	
☐	OE-LUX	A318-112CJ	4169	

WELCOME AIR — 2W / WLC

	Reg	Type	c/n	Notes
☐	OE-GBB	Do328-110	3078	
☐	OE-LIR	Do328-110	3115	

OH- FINLAND

BLUE1 — K1 / BLF

Ceased operations; plans to restart with CRJ900 leased from CityJet.

FINNAIR — AY / FIN

	Reg	Type	c/n	Notes
☐	OH-LVA	A319-112	1073	
☐	OH-LVB	A319-112	1107	
☐	OH-LVC	A319-112	1309	
☐	OH-LVD	A319-112	1352	
☐	OH-LVG	A319-112	1916	
☐	OH-LVH	A319-112	1184	
☐	OH-LVI	A319-112	1364	
☐	OH-LVK	A319-112	2124	
☐	OH-LVL	A319-112	2266	
☐	OH-LXA	A320-214	1405	
☐	OH-LXB	A320-214	1470	
☐	OH-LXC	A320-214	1544	
☐	OH-LXD	A320-214	1588	
☐	OH-LXF	A320-214	1712	
☐	OH-LXH	A320-214	1913	
☐	OH-LXI	A320-214	1989	
☐	OH-LXK	A320-214	2065	
☐	OH-LXL	A320-214	2146	
☐	OH-LXM	A320-214	2154	
☐	OH-LZA	A321-211	0941	
☐	OH-LZB	A321-211	0961	
☐	OH-LZC	A321-211	1185	
☐	OH-LZD	A321-211	1241	
☐	OH-LZE	A321-211	1978	
☐	OH-LZF	A321-211	2208	
☐	OH-LZG	A321-211/S	5758	
☐	OH-LZH	A321-211/S	5803	
☐	OH-LZI	A321-211/S	5922	
☐	OH-LZK	A321-211/S	5961	
☐	OH-LZL	A321-211/S	6083	
☐	OH-LTM	A330-302E	994	
☐	OH-LTN	A330-302E	1007	
☐	OH-LTO	A330-302E	1013	
☐	OH-LTP	A330-302E	1023	

☐ OH-LTR A330-302E 1067
☐ OH-LTS A330-302E 1078
☐ OH-LTT A330-302E 1088
☐ OH-LTU A330-302E 1173

☐ OH-LQA A340-311 058
☐ OH-LQB A340-313X 835
☐ OH-LQC A340-313X 844
☐ OH-LQD A340-313X 921
☐ OH-LQE A340-313X 938

☐ OH-LWA A350-941 018 ♦
☐ OH-LWB A350-941 019 ♦
☐ OH-LWC A350-941 020 ♦
☐ OH-LWD A350-941 022 o/o♦
☐ OH-LWE A350-941 023 o/o♦
☐ OH-LWF A350-941 028 o/o♦
☐ OH- A350-941 051 o/o♦
☐ OH- A350-941 097 o/o♦

NORDIC REGIONAL AIRLINES BE / FCM

☐ OH-ATE ATR 72-212A 741
☐ OH-ATF ATR 72-212A 744
☐ OH-ATG ATR 72-212A 757
☐ OH-ATH ATR 72-212A 769
☐ OH-ATI ATR 72-212A 783
☐ OH-ATJ ATR 72-212A 792
☐ OH-ATK ATR 72-212A 848
☐ OH-ATL ATR 72-212A 851
☐ OH-ATM ATR 72-212A 916
☐ OH-ATN ATR 72-212A 959
☐ OH-ATO ATR 72-212A 977
☐ OH-ATP ATR 72-212A 1050
☐ OH- ATR 72-600 o/o♦
☐ OH- ATR 72-600 o/o♦
☐ OH- ATR 72-600 o/o♦

☐ OH-LEI ERJ-170LR 17000120
☐ OH-LEK ERJ-170LR 17000127 [EGBP]
☐ OH-LKE ERJ-190LR 19000059
☐ OH-LKF ERJ-190LR 19000066
☐ OH-LKG ERJ-190LR 19000079
☐ OH-LKH ERJ-190LR 19000086
☐ OH-LKI ERJ-190LR 19000117
☐ OH-LKK ERJ-190LR 19000127
☐ OH-LKL ERJ-190LR 19000153
☐ OH-LKM ERJ-190LR 19000160
☐ OH-LKN ERJ-190LR 19000252
☐ OH-LKO ERJ-190LR 19000267
☐ OH-LKP ERJ-190LR 19000416
☐ OH-LKR ERJ-190LR 19000436

ERJ170s & ERJ190s leased from parent company Finnair.

JET TIME FINLAND JTF

☐ OH-JTV B737-7L9/W 28015/785
☐ OH-JTZ B737-73S/W 29083/392

OK- CZECH REPUBLIC

CSA CZECH AIRLINES OK / CSA

☐ OK-MEK A319-112 3043
☐ OK-MEL A319-112 3094
☐ OK-NEM A319-112 3406
☐ OK-NEN A319-112 3436
☐ OK-NEO A319-112 3452
☐ OK-NEP A319-112 3660
☐ OK-OER A319-112 3892 >SVA
☐ OK-PET A319-112 4258 >SVA
☐ OK-REQ A319-112 4713

☐ OK- A320-214 o/o
☐ OK- A320-214 o/o
☐ OK- A320-214 o/o
☐ OK- A320-214 o/o
☐ OK- A320-214 o/o
☐ OK- A320-214 o/o
☐ OK- A320-214 o/o

☐ OK-YBA A330-323E 425

☐ OK-GFQ ATR 72-212A 674 >MAU
☐ OK-GFR ATR 72-212A 681
☐ OK-GFS ATR 72-212A 679
☐ OK-KFN ATR 42-500 637
☐ OK-KFO ATR 42-500 633
☐ OK-KFP ATR 42-500 639

SILVER AIR SLD

☐ OK-SLD LET L-410UVP-E 902503
☐ OK-WDC LET L-410UVP-E 912531

SMARTWINGS QS / TVS

See Travel Service below

TRAVEL SERVICE AIRLINES QS / TVS

☐ OK-HCA A320-214 4699 [BCM]♦
☐ OK-HCB A320-214 2180

☐ OK-SWT B737-7Q8 29346/1264 ^
☐ OK-SWW B737-7Q8 28254/1283 ^
☐ OK-TSA B737-8S3/W 29250/792
☐ OK-TSC B737-8FH/W 35093/2176 >TSC♦
☐ OK-TSD B737-8Q8/W 41795/4895
☐ OK-TSE B737-8ID/W 39437/4775
☐ OK-TSF B737-8GJ/W 37360/2783 >SEJ♦
☐ OK-TSH B737-804/W 28231/538 ^♦
☐ OK-TSI B737-9GJER/W 37363/3843 ♦
☐ OK-TSM B737-9GJER/W 34952/2426 ♦
☐ OK-TVE B737-86Q/W 30294/1469 >SWG
☐ OK-TVF B737-8FH/W 29669/1692 >SWG
☐ OK-TVG B737-8Q8/W 30719/2257 >SWG
☐ OK-TVH B737-8Q8/W 35275/2604 >SWG♦
☐ OK-TVK B737-86N/W 32740/1444 >SEJ
☐ OK-TVL B737-8FN/W 37076/3147 >SEJ
☐ OK-TVM B737-8FN/W 37077/3163 >SWG
☐ OK-TVO B737-8CX/W 32360/1084
☐ OK-TVP B737-8K5/W 32907/1117 >SWG
☐ OK-TVR B737-86N/W 38018/3618 >OMA
☐ OK-TVS B737-86N/W 39404/3633 >SWG
☐ OK-TVT B737-86N/W 39394/3899 >SWG
☐ OK-TVU B737-86N/W 38025/3968 ^>TSC
☐ OK-TVV B737-86N/W 38027/4030 ^>TSC
☐ OK-TVW B737-86Q/W 30295/1600 ^
☐ OK-TVX B737-8Z9/W 33833/1680 >SEJ
☐ OK-TVY B737-8Q8/W 30724/2286 ^>TSC♦

^ operated as Smartwings

VAN AIR EUROPE 6Z / VAA

☐ OK-ASA LET L-410UVP-E 902439 >V9
☐ OK-LAZ LET L-410UVP-E 902504 >V9
☐ OK-RDA LET L-410UVP-E9 861813 >NM
☐ OK-TCA LET L-410UVP-E 902431
☐ OK-UBA LET L-410UVP-E19 892319 >V9

OM- SLOVAKIA

AIR CARGO GLOBAL — UB / CCC

Reg	Type	C/n	
OM-ACA	B747-481F	34016/1360	
OM-ACG	B747-409(BDSF)	24311/869	

AIREXPLORE — ED / AXE

Reg	Type	C/n	
OM-DEX	B737-46J	28867/2879	>MEV
OM-EEX	B737-4Q8	26302/2620	
OM-FEX	B737-8Q8/W	28213/50	<ED
OM-GEX	B737-8AS/W	29919/341	>MEV
OM-HEX	B737-81Q/W	30785/1007	

GO2SKY — RLX

Reg	Type	C/n	
OM-GTA	B737-4Q8	24332/1866	>TCV
OM-GTB	B737-49R	28882/2845	>MSA
OM-GTC	B737-430	27001/2316	std
OM-GTD	B737-46J	27171/2465	♦

TRAVEL SERVICE SLOVAKIA — TVQ

Reg	Type	C/n	
OK-TSG	B737-82R	30666/1460	♦

OO- BELGIUM

BRUSSELS AIRLINES — SN / BEL

Reg	Type	C/n	
OO-SSA(2)	A319-111	2392	
OO-SSB(2)	A319-111	2400	
OO-SSC	A319-112	1086	
OO-SSD	A319-112	1102	
OO-SSE(2)	A319-111	2700	
OO-SSF(2)	A319-111	2763	
OO-SSG	A319-112	1160	
OO-SSH(2)	A319-112	2925	
OO-SSI(2)	A319-111	3895	
OO-SSK	A319-112	1336	
OO-SSM	A319-112	1388	
OO-SSN	A319-112	1963	
OO-SSQ	A319-112	3790	
OO-SSR	A319-112	4275	
OO-SSU	A319-111	2230	
OO-SSV	A319-111	2196	
OO-SSW	A319-111	3255	
OO-	A319-111	1803	o/o♦
OO-SNA	A320-214	1441	
OO-SNB	A320-214	1493	
OO-SNC	A320-214	1797	
OO-SND	A320-214	1838	
OO-SNF(2)	A320-214	2810	
OO-SNG(2)	A320-214	1885	
OO-TCQ	A320-214	2114	♦
OO-SFM	A330-301	030	
OO-SFN	A330-301	037	
OO-SFO	A330-301	045	
OO-SFU	A330-223	324	
OO-SFV	A330-322	095	
OO-SFW	A330-322	082	
OO-SFX(2)	A330-343E	1085	o/o♦
OO-SFY	A330-223	229	
OO-SFZ	A330-223	249	
OO-DWA	Avro 146-RJ100	E3308	
OO-DWB	Avro 146-RJ100	E3315	
OO-DWC	Avro 146-RJ100	E3322	
OO-DWD	Avro 146-RJ100	E3324	
OO-DWE	Avro 146-RJ100	E3327	
OO-DWF	Avro 146-RJ100	E3332	
OO-DWG	Avro 146-RJ100	E3336	
OO-DWH	Avro 146-RJ100	E3340	
OO-DWI	Avro 146-RJ100	E3342	
OO-DWJ	Avro 146-RJ100	E3355	
OO-DWK	Avro 146-RJ100	E3360	
OO-DWL	Avro 146-RJ100	E3361	
G-ECOI	DHC-8-402Q	4224	<BEE
G-ECOK	DHC-8-402Q	4230	<BEE
G-RJXI	ERJ-145EP	145454	<BMR

(2) indicates second use of these marks by type

THOMAS COOK BELGIUM — FQ / TCW

Reg	Type	C/n	
OO-TCH	A320-214	1929	
OO-TCT	A320-212	1402	
OO-TCV	A320-214	1968	♦
OO-TCW	A320-214	1954	♦
OO-TCX	A320-212	1381	♦

TNT AIRWAYS — 3V / TAY

Reg	Type	C/n	
OO-TAQ	BAe146 Srs.200QT	E2078	[EXT]
OO-TAW	BAe146 Srs.200QT	E2089	[YSU]
OE-IAE	B737-4Q8(F)	25105/2505	
OE-IAF	B737-4YO(SF)	25184/2227	
OE-IAG	B737-4Q8(F)	25168/2210	♦
OE-IAJ	B737-476(SF)	24440/2324	♦
OE-IAP	B737-4MO(SF)	29206/3058	
OE-IAQ	B737-4MO(SF)	29207/3078	
OE-IAR	B737-4MO(SF)	29208/3081	
OE-IAS	B737-4MO(SF)	29209/3087	
OE-IAT	B737-4MO(SF)	29210/3091	
OE-IBW	B737-4Q8(F)	25109/2561	
OE-IBZ	B737-34S(SF)	29108/2983	
OO-TNL	B737-34S(SF)	29109/3001	
OO-TNN	B737-45D(SF)	27131/2458	
OO-TNO	B737-49R(SF)	28881/2833	
OO-TNP	B737-4SD(SF)	27256/2589	
OO-TNQ	B737-4MO(SF)	29205/3056	
OO-THA	B747-4HAERF	35232/1381	
OO-THB	B747-4HAERF	35234/1386	
OO-THC	B747-4HAERF	35235/1389	>UAE
OO-THD	B747-4HAERF	35236/1399	>UAE
OE-LFB	B757-23APF	24868/314	♦
OO-TFA	B757-28A(SF)	25622/530	
OO-TSA	B777-FHT	38969/944	
OO-TSB	B777-FHT	39286/963	>SOO
OO-TSC	B777-FHT	37138/977	

TUI AIRLINES BELGIUM — TB / JAF

Reg	Type	C/n	
OO-JAA	B737-8BK/W	29660/2355	
OO-JAD	B737-8K5/W	39093/3601	
OO-JAF	B737-8K5/W	35133/2313	
OO-JAH	B737-8K5/W	37260/3688	
OO-JAO	B737-7K5/W	35141/2603	
OO-JAQ	B737-8K5/W	35148/2790	
OO-JAR	B737-7K5/W	35150/2825	
OO-JAS	B737-7K5/W	35144/2652	
OO-JAU	B737-8K5/W	37250/4345	>SWG
OO-JAV	B737-8K5/W	40943/4407	
OO-JAX	B737-8K5/W	37238/3452	
OO-JAY	B737-8K5/W	40944/4431	
OO-JBG	B737-8K5/W	35142/2660	>SWG

☐	OO-JEF	B737-8K5/W	44271/4805	
☐	OO-JJI	B737-752/W	33793/1597	♦
☐	OO-JLO	B737-8K5/W	34692/2249	
☐	OO-JOS	B737-7K5/W	35282/2585	
☐	OO-JNL	B767-304ER/W	29384/784	♦
☐	OO-JDL	B787-8	34425/137	
☐	OO-JEB	ERJ-190STD	19000607	
☐	OO-JEM	ERJ-190STD	19000603	
☐	OO-JVA	ERJ-190STD	19000689	♦

VLM AIRLINES/CITYJET — *VG / VLM*

☐	OO-VLF	Fokker 50	20208	
☐	OO-VLI	Fokker 50	20226	
☐	OO-VLJ	Fokker 50	20105	
☐	OO-VLL	Fokker 50	20144	
☐	OO-VLM	Fokker 50	20135	>BEE
☐	OO-VLN	Fokker 50	20145	
☐	OO-VLO	Fokker 50	20127	[ANR]
☐	OO-VLP	Fokker 50	20209	^
☐	OO-VLQ	Fokker 50	20159	
☐	OO-VLS	Fokker 50	20109	
☐	OO-VLZ	Fokker 50	20264	
☐	OO-	Sukhoi SSJ 100-95LR		o/o
☐	OO-	Sukhoi SSJ 100-95LR		o/o

See also Cityjet, Ireland WX/BCY;
^ leased to or operated for Vizion Air (W2)

OY- DENMARK

AIR GREENLAND — *GL / GRL*

☐	OY-GRN	A330-223	230	
☐	OY-GRG	DHC-8Q-202	504	
☐	OY-GRH	DHC-8Q-202	488	
☐	OY-GRJ	DHC-8Q-202	496	
☐	OY-GRK	DHC-8Q-202	498	
☐	OY-GRM	DHC-8Q-202	434	
☐	OY-GRO	DHC-8Q-202	482	♦
☐	OY-GRP	DHC-8Q-202	453	♦

ALSIE EXPRESS — *6I / MMD*

☐	OY-CLY	ATR 72-212A	799	
☐	OY-CLZ	ATR 72-212A	818	

ATLANTIC AIRWAYS — *RC / FLI*

☐	OY-RCG	A319-115	5079	
☐	OY-RCH	A319-112	2186	
☐	OY-RCI	A319-112	3905	

BENAIR AIR SERVICE — *BDI*

☐	OY-ASY	EMB.110P1	110308	
☐	OY-BJP	SA.227AC Metro III	AC-499	
☐	OY-MUG	Short SD.3-60	SH3716	
☐	OY-PBH	LET L-410UVP-E20	972736	
☐	OY-PBI	LET L-410UVP-E20	871936	
☐	OY-PBV	Short SD.3-60	SH3747	
☐	OY-PBW	Short SD.3-60	SH3760	

CIMBER — *QI / CIM*

Purchased by SAS to operate its CRJ900s, reported as Red 1.

DANISH AIR TRANSPORT — *DX / DTR*

☐	OY-JRK	A320-231	0444	
☐	OY-JRZ	A320-233	2102	♦
☐	OY-LHD	A320-231	0113	[HEL]
☐	OY-RUP	A320-231	0406	>DNU♦
☐	OY-RUS	A320-231	0447	♦
☐	OY-	A320-212	0409	♦
☐	OY-CJU	ATR 42-300	112	[MEX]♦
☐	OY-JRJ	ATR 42-320	036	
☐	OY-JRY	ATR 42-300	063	
☐	OY-LHA	ATR 72-202	508	
☐	OY-LHB	ATR 72-212	496	
☐	OY-LHC	ATR 72-212	405	
☐	OY-RUB	ATR 72-202	301	
☐	OY-RUD	ATR 72-201	162	
☐	OY-RUF	ATR 42-500	515	
☐	OY-RUG	ATR 72-202	509	
☐	OY-RUO	ATR 42-500	514	>TE
☐	OY-RUR	ATR 72-201	145	♦
☐	OY-JRU	MD-87	49403/1404	
☐	OY-RUE	MD-83	49936/1778	

JET TIME — *JO / JTG*

☐	OY-JZA	ATR 72-600	1110	>SAS
☐	OY-JZB	ATR 72-600	1121	>SAS
☐	OY-JZC	ATR 72-600	1120	>SAS
☐	OY-JZD	ATR 72-600	1131	>SAS
☐	OY-JZE	ATR 72-600	1164	>SAS
☐	OY-JZF	ATR 72-600	1165	>SAS
☐	OY-JZG	ATR 72-600	1171	>SAS
☐	OY-JZH	ATR 72-600	1177	>SAS
☐	OY-JZU	ATR 72-212A	723	>SAS
☐	OY-JZV	ATR 72-212A	789	>SAS♦
☐	OY-JZW	ATR 72-212A	773	>SAS♦
☐	OY-JZY	ATR 72-212A	540	
☐	OY-JZZ	ATR 72-212A	548	>SAS
☐	OY-JTA	B737-33A/W	23631/1337	
☐	OY-JTB	B737-3Y0/W	24464/1753	
☐	OY-JTC	B737-3L9/W	23718/1402	
☐	OY-JTD	B737-3Y0/W	24678/1853	
☐	OY-JTE	B737-3L9/W	27834/2692	
☐	OY-JTF	B737-382(QC)	24364/1657	
☐	OY-JTI	B737-448(F)	25052/2036	
☐	OY-JTJ	B737-301(F)	23741/1498	
☐	OY-JTK	B737-4Y0(SF)	24903/1978	
☐	OY-JTL	B737-42C(F)	24231/1871	
☐	OY-JTM	B737-429(F)	27094/2432	♦
☐	OY-JTS	B737-7K2/W	33465/1316	
☐	OY-JTT	B737-73S/W	29079/194	
☐	OY-JTY	B737-7Q8/W	30727/1005	

NORTH FLYING — *M3 / NFA*

☐	OY-NPD	SA.227DC Metro 23	DC-865B	
☐	OY-NPE	SA.227DC Metro 23	DC-867B	
☐	OY-NPF	SA.227DC Metro 23	DC-880B	
☐	OY-NPG	SA.227DC Metro 23	DC-896B	♦

PRIMERA AIR SCANDINAVIA — *PF / PRI*

☐	OY-PSA	B737-8Q8/W	30688/2280	
☐	OY-PSE	B737-8Q8/W	30664/743	

STAR AIR — *S6 / SRR*

☐	CS-TLZ	B767-375ERF	24086/248	<MMZ♦
☐	OY-SRF	B767-219ER(SF)	23327/134	
☐	OY-SRG	B767-219ER(SF)	23328/149	
☐	OY-SRH	B767-204ER(SF)	24457/256	

	Reg	Type	c/n	
☐	OY-SRI	B767-25E(SF)	27193/527	
☐	OY-SRJ	B767-25E(SF)	27195/535	
☐	OY-SRK	B767-204ER(SF)	23072/107	
☐	OY-SRL	B767-232(SF)	22219/37	
☐	OY-SRM	B767-25E(SF)	27192/524	
☐	OY-SRN	B767-219ER(SF)	23326/124	
☐	OY-SRO	B767-25E(SF)	27194/532	
☐	OY-SRP	B767-232(SF)	22220/38	
☐	OY-SRT	B767-232(F)	22226/78	[GSO]♦

SUN-AIR OF SCANDINAVIA — EZ / SUS

	Reg	Type	c/n	
☐	D-CIRI	Do328-110	3005	<MHS♦
☐	D-CIRP	Do328-120	3006	<MHS
☐	OY-JJB	Do328-310	3199	
☐	OY-JJG	Do328-310	3200	♦
☐	OY-JJH	Do328-310	3171	♦
☐	OY-NCJ	Do328-310	3186	♦
☐	OY-NCL	Do328-310	3192	
☐	OY-NCM	Do328-310	3190	
☐	OY-NCN	Do328-310	3193	
☐	OY-NCO	Do328-310	3210	
☐	OY-NCP	Do328-300	3132	
☐	OY-NCT	Do328-310	3213	
☐	OY-NCU	Do328-300	3122	
☐	OY-NCW	Do328-300	3131	
☐	OY-SVB	BAeJetstream 31	985	
☐	OY-SVF	BAeJetstream 31	686	

Operates as British Airways Express.

THOMAS COOK SCANDINAVIA — DK / VKG

	Reg	Type	c/n	
☐	G-TCDJ	A321-211/S	6526	<TCX♦
☐	OY-TCD	A321-211/S	6314	
☐	OY-TCE	A321-211/S	6342	
☐	OY-TCF	A321-211/S	6351	
☐	OY-TCG	A321-211/S	6389	
☐	OY-TCH	A321-211/S	6438	
☐	OY-TCI	A321-211	6468	
☐	OY-VKC	A321-211	1932	
☐	OY-VKD	A321-211	1960	
☐	G-OMYT	A330-243	301	<TCX♦
☐	OY-VKF	A330-243	309	
☐	OY-VKG	A330-343E	349	
☐	OY-VKH	A330-343E	356	
☐	OY-VKI	A330-343E	357	

P- NORTH KOREA

AIR KORYO — JS / KOR

	Reg	Type	c/n	
☐	P-532	An-24RV	47309707	
☐	P-533	An-24RV	47309708	
☐	P-537	An-24B	67302408	
☐	P-671	An-148-100	03-08	
☐	P-672	An-148-100	04-02	
☐	P-835	Il-18D	188011205	
☐	P-618	Il-62M	2546624	Govt^
☐	P-881	Il-62M	3647853	Govt
☐	P-882	Il-62M	2850236	Govt
☐	P-885	Il-62M	3933913	
☐	P-912	Il-76MD	1003403104	
☐	P-913	Il-76MD	1003404126	
☐	P-914	Il-76MD	1003404146	
☐	P-813	Tu-134B-3	66215	
☐	P-814	Tu-134B-3	66368	
☐	P-551	Tu-154B	75A129	
☐	P-552	Tu-154B	76A143	
☐	P-561	Tu-154B-2	83A573	
☐	P-632	Tu-204-300	1450742364012	
☐	P-633	Tu-204-100	1450741964048	

^ reported re-regd P-883 and operating without regn or titles.

PH- NETHERLANDS

AIS AIRLINES — IS / PNX

	Reg	Type	c/n	
☐	PH-BCI	BAeJetstream 32EP	953	
☐	PH-CCI	BAeJetstream 32	860	♦
☐	PH-DCI	BAeJetstream 32	916	♦
☐	PH-HCI	BAeJetstream 32	864	
☐	PH-LCI	BAeJetstream 31	718	♦
☐	PH-NCI	BAeJetstream 32EP	844	♦
☐	PH-OCI	BAeJetstream 32EP	846	♦
☐	PH-RCI	BAeJetstream 32EP	848	♦

TUI AIRLINES NETHERLANDS — OR / TFL

	Reg	Type	c/n	
☐	G-RAJG	B737-476	24439/2265	<CLJ♦
☐	PH-TFA	B737-8FH/W	35100/2424	
☐	PH-TFB	B737-8K5/W	35149/2820	
☐	PH-TFC	B737-8K5/W	35146/2875	
☐	PH-TFD	B737-86N/W	38014/3588	
☐	PH-TFF	B737-86N/W	35220/2406	
☐	PH-	B737-8K5/W		o/o♦
☐	PH-OYI	B767-304ER/W	29138/783	
☐	PH-TFK	B787-8	36427/182	
☐	PH-TFL	B787-8	37228/245	
☐	PH-TFM	B787-8	36429/281	♦

CORENDON DUTCH AIRLINES — CD / CND

	Reg	Type	c/n	
☐	PH-CDE	B737-8KN/W	35795/2829	
☐	PH-CDF	B737-804/W	28227/452	

DENIM — J7 / DNM

	Reg	Type	c/n	
☐	OY-CHT	ATR 42-300	080	>OVA♦
☐	PH-DND	ERJ-145MP	145406	>EZE
☐	PH-JXN	Fokker 50	20239	
☐	PH-MJP	Fokker 100	11505	

KLM CITYHOPPER — WA / KLC

	Reg	Type	c/n	
☐	PH-EXA	ERJ-190STD	19000655	
☐	PH-EXB	ERJ-190STD	19000658	
☐	PH-EXC	ERJ-190STD	19000659	
☐	PH-EXD	ERJ-190STD	19000661	
☐	PH-EXE	ERJ-190STD	19000687	♦
☐	PH-EXF	ERJ-190STD	19000690	♦
☐	PH-EXG	ERJ-175		o/o♦
☐	PH-EXH	ERJ-175		o/o♦
☐	PH-EXI	ERJ-175		o/o♦
☐	PH-EXJ	ERJ-175		o/o♦
☐	PH-EXK	ERJ-175		o/o♦
☐	PH-EXL	ERJ-175		o/o♦
☐	PH-EXM	ERJ-175		o/o♦
☐	PH-EZA	ERJ-190STD	19000224	
☐	PH-EZB	ERJ-190STD	19000235	
☐	PH-EZC	ERJ-190STD	19000250	
☐	PH-EZD	ERJ-190STD	19000279	
☐	PH-EZE	ERJ-190STD	19000288	
☐	PH-EZF	ERJ-190STD	19000304	
☐	PH-EZG	ERJ-190STD	19000315	
☐	PH-EZH	ERJ-190STD	19000319	
☐	PH-EZI	ERJ-190STD	19000322	

☐	PH-EZK	ERJ-190STD	19000326	
☐	PH-EZL	ERJ-190STD	19000334	
☐	PH-EZM	ERJ-190STD	19000338	
☐	PH-EZN	ERJ-190STD	19000342	
☐	PH-EZO	ERJ-190STD	19000345	
☐	PH-EZP	ERJ-190STD	19000347	
☐	PH-EZR	ERJ-190STD	19000375	
☐	PH-EZS	ERJ-190STD	19000380	
☐	PH-EZT	ERJ-190STD	19000519	
☐	PH-EZU	ERJ-190STD	19000522	
☐	PH-EZV	ERJ-190STD	19000528	
☐	PH-EZW	ERJ-190STD	19000533	
☐	PH-EZX	ERJ-190STD	19000545	
☐	PH-EZY	ERJ-190STD	19000649	
☐	PH-EZZ	ERJ-190STD	19000654	
☐	PH-KZA	Fokker 70	11567	
☐	PH-KZB	Fokker 70	11562	
☐	PH-KZC	Fokker 70	11566	
☐	PH-KZD	Fokker 70	11582	
☐	PH-KZE	Fokker 70	11576	
☐	PH-KZI	Fokker 70	11579	
☐	PH-KZK	Fokker 70	11581	
☐	PH-KZL	Fokker 70	11536	
☐	PH-KZM	Fokker 70	11561	
☐	PH-KZN	Fokker 70	11553	[NWI]
☐	PH-KZP	Fokker 70	11539	
☐	PH-KZR	Fokker 70	11551	
☐	PH-KZS	Fokker 70	11540	
☐	PH-KZT	Fokker 70	11541	
☐	PH-KZU	Fokker 70	11543	
☐	PH-WXC	Fokker 70	11574	
☐	PH-WXD	Fokker 70	11563	

KLM ROYAL DUTCH AIRLINES *KL / KLM*

☐	PH-AKA	A330-303	1287	
☐	PH-AKB	A330-303	1294	
☐	PH-AKD	A330-303	1300	
☐	PH-AKE	A330-303	1381	
☐	PH-AKF	A330-303	1580	
☐	PH-AOA	A330-203	682	
☐	PH-AOB	A330-203	686	
☐	PH-AOC	A330-203	703	
☐	PH-AOD	A330-203	738	
☐	PH-AOE	A330-203	770	
☐	PH-AOF	A330-203	801	
☐	PH-AOI	A330-203	819	
☐	PH-AOK	A330-203	834	
☐	PH-AOM	A330-203	1161	
☐	PH-AON	A330-203	925	
☐	PH-BGD	B737-7K2/W	30366/2675	
☐	PH-BGE	B737-7K2/W	30371/2705	
☐	PH-BGF	B737-7K2/W	30365/2714	
☐	PH-BGG	B737-7K2/W	30367/2835	
☐	PH-BGH	B737-7K2/W	38053/3119	
☐	PH-BGI	B737-7K2/W	30364/3172	
☐	PH-BGK	B737-7K2/W	38054/3292	
☐	PH-BGL	B737-7K2/W	30369/3407	
☐	PH-BGM	B737-7K2/W	39255/3569	
☐	PH-BGN	B737-7K2/W	38125/3584	
☐	PH-BGO	B737-7K2/W	38126/3590	
☐	PH-BGP	B737-7K2/W	38127/3632	
☐	PH-BGQ	B737-7K2/W	39256/3675	
☐	PH-BGR	B737-7K2/W	39446/3728	
☐	PH-BGT	B737-7K2/W	38634/3762	
☐	PH-BGU	B737-7K2/W	39257/3779	
☐	PH-BGW	B737-7K2/W	38128/3797	
☐	PH-BGX	B737-7K2/W	38635/3811	
☐	PH-BCA	B737-8K2/W	37820/3480	
☐	PH-BCB	B737-8K2/W	39443/3648	
☐	PH-BCD	B737-8K2/W	42149/4458	
☐	PH-BCE	B737-8K2/W	42151/4852	
☐	PH-	B737-8K2/W		o/o
☐	PH-	B737-8K2/W		o/o
☐	PH-	B737-8K2/W		o/o
☐	PH-	B737-8K2/W		o/o
☐	PH-BGA	B737-8K2/W	37593/2569	
☐	PH-BGB	B737-8K2/W	37594/2594	
☐	PH-BGC	B737-8K2/W	30361/2619	
☐	PH-BXA	B737-8K2/W	29131/198	
☐	PH-BXB	B737-8K2/W	29132/261	
☐	PH-BXC	B737-8K2/W	29133/305	
☐	PH-BXD	B737-8K2/W	29134/355	
☐	PH-BXE	B737-8K2/W	29595/552	
☐	PH-BXF	B737-8K2/W	29596/583	
☐	PH-BXG	B737-8K2/W	30357/605	
☐	PH-BXH	B737-8K2/W	29597/630	
☐	PH-BXI	B737-8K2/W	30358/633	
☐	PH-BXK	B737-8K2/W	29598/639	
☐	PH-BXL	B737-8K2/W	30359/659	
☐	PH-BXM	B737-8K2/W	30355/714	
☐	PH-BXN	B737-8K2/W	30356/728	
☐	PH-BXU	B737-8BK/W	33028/1936	
☐	PH-BXV	B737-8K2/W	30370/2205	
☐	PH-BXW	B737-8K2/W	30360/2467	
☐	PH-BXY	B737-8K2/W	30372/2503	
☐	PH-BXZ	B737-8K2/W	30368/2533	
☐	PH-BXO	B737-9K2/W	29599/866	
☐	PH-BXP	B737-9K2/W	29600/924	
☐	PH-BXR	B737-9K2/W	29601/959	
☐	PH-BXS	B737-9K2/W	29602/981	
☐	PH-BXT	B737-9K2/W	32944/1498	
☐	PH-BFA	B747-406	23999/725	
☐	PH-BFB	B747-406	24000/732	
☐	PH-BFC	B747-406M	23982/735	
☐	PH-BFD	B747-406M	24001/737	
☐	PH-BFE	B747-406M	24201/763	
☐	PH-BFF	B747-406M	24202/770	
☐	PH-BFG	B747-406	24517/782	
☐	PH-BFH	B747-406M	24518/783	
☐	PH-BFI	B747-406M	25086/850	
☐	PH-BFK	B747-406	25087/854	
☐	PH-BFL	B747-406	25356/888	
☐	PH-BFM	B747-406M	26373/896	[LETL]
☐	PH-BFN	B747-406	26372/969	
☐	PH-BFO	B747-406M	25413/938	[LETL]
☐	PH-BFP	B747-406M	26374/992	
☐	PH-BFR	B747-406M	27202/1014	
☐	PH-BFS	B747-406	28195/1090	
☐	PH-BFT	B747-406	28459/1112	
☐	PH-BFU	B747-406	28196/1127	
☐	PH-BFV	B747-406	28460/1225	
☐	PH-BFW	B747-406	30454/1258	
☐	PH-BFY	B747-406	30455/1302	
☐	PH-CKA	B747-406ERF	33694/1326	^
☐	PH-CKB	B747-406ERF	33695/1328	^
☐	PH-CKC	B747-406ERF	33696/1341	^

^ leased to Martinair

☐	PH-BQA	B777-206ER	33711/454	
☐	PH-BQB	B777-206ER	33712/457	
☐	PH-BQC	B777-206ER	29397/461	

	Reg	Type	c/n	Notes
☐	PH-BQD	B777-206ER	33713/465	
☐	PH-BQE	B777-206ER	28691/468	
☐	PH-BQF	B777-206ER	29398/474	
☐	PH-BQG	B777-206ER	32704/476	
☐	PH-BQH	B777-206ER	32705/493	
☐	PH-BQI	B777-206ER	33714/497	
☐	PH-BQK	B777-206ER	29399/499	
☐	PH-BQL	B777-206ER	34711/552	
☐	PH-BQM	B777-206ER	34712/559	
☐	PH-BQN	B777-206ER	32720/561	
☐	PH-BQO	B777-206ER	35295/609	
☐	PH-BQP	B777-206ER	32721/630	
☐	PH-BVA	B777-306ER	35671/694	
☐	PH-BVB	B777-306ER	36145/706	
☐	PH-BVC	B777-306ER	37582/787	
☐	PH-BVD	B777-306ER	35979/807	
☐	PH-BVF	B777-306ER	39972/915	
☐	PH-BVG	B777-306ER	38867/1020	
☐	PH-BVI	B777-306ER	35947/1029	
☐	PH-BVK	B777-306ER	42172/1106	
☐	PH-BVN	B777-306ER	44549/1280	
☐	PH-BVO	B777-306ER	35946/1292	
☐	PH-BVP	B777-306ER	44555/1376	o/o♦
☐	PH-BVR	B777-306ER	61603	o/o♦
☐	PH-BVS	B777-306ER	61604	o/o♦
☐	PH-BHA	B787-9	36113/356	
☐	PH-BHC	B787-9	38760/368	
☐	PH-BHD	B787-9	38763/381	♦
☐	PH-BHE	B787-9	42485	o/o♦
☐	PH-BHF	B787-9	38765/412	o/o♦
☐	PH-BHG	B787-9	42486/422	o/o♦
☐	PH-BHH	B787-9	38766/449	o/o♦
☐	PH-BHI	B787-9	38767/463	o/o♦
☐	PH-BHK	B787-9		o/o♦
☐	PH-BHL	B787-9	38755/477	o/o♦
☐	PH-BHM	B787-9	38769/500	o/o♦

MARTINAIR — *MP / MPH*

	Reg	Type	c/n	Notes
☐	PH-MPP	B747-412BCF	24061/717	[LETL]
☐	PH-MPQ	B747-412BCF	24975/838	[LETL]
☐	PH-MPS	B747-412BCF	24066/791	
☐	PH-MCP	MD-11CF	48616/577	
☐	PH-MCS	MD-11CF	48618/584	[AMS]
☐	PH-MCU	MD-11F	48757/606	
☐	PH-MCW	MD-11CF	48788/632	

TRANSAVIA AIRLINES — *HV / TRA*

	Reg	Type	c/n	Notes
☐	PH-XRA	B737-7K2/W	30784/873	
☐	PH-XRB	B737-7K2/W	28256/1298	
☐	PH-XRC	B737-7K2/W	29347/1318	
☐	PH-XRD	B737-7K2/W	30659/1329	
☐	PH-XRV	B737-7K2/W	34170/1701	
☐	PH-XRX	B737-7K2/W	33464/1299	
☐	PH-XRY	B737-7K2/W	33463/1292	
☐	PH-XRZ	B737-7K2/W	33462/1278	
☐	PH-HSA	B737-8K2/W	34171/2950	
☐	PH-HSB	B737-8K2/W	34172/3242	
☐	PH-HSC	B737-8K2/W	34173/3266	
☐	PH-HSD	B737-8K2/W	39260/3581	
☐	PH-HSE	B737-8K2/W	39259/3635	
☐	PH-HSF	B737-8K2/W	39261/3998	
☐	PH-HSG	B737-8K2/W	39262/4021	
☐	PH-HSI	B737-8K2/W	42148/4404	
☐	PH-HSJ	B737-8BK/W	42150/4810	
☐	PH-HSK	B737-8K2/W	41330/5354	♦
☐	PH-HSM	B737-8K2/W	42067/5389	♦
☐	PH-HSN	B737-8K2/W	41340	o/o
☐	PH-HSO	B737-8K2/W	41342	o/o
☐	PH-HSW	B737-8K2/W	37160/2880	
☐	PH-HXA	B737-8K2/W	62149/5799	o/o♦
☐	PH-HZD	B737-8K2/W	28376/252	
☐	PH-HZE	B737-8K2/W	28377/277	
☐	PH-HZF	B737-8K2/W	28378/291	
☐	PH-HZG	B737-8K2/W	28379/498	>SCX
☐	PH-HZI	B737-8K2/W	28380/524	
☐	PH-HZJ	B737-8K2/W	30389/549	
☐	PH-HZK	B737-8K2/W	30390/555	
☐	PH-HZL	B737-8K2/W	30391/814	>SCX
☐	PH-HZN	B737-8K2/W	32943/1478	
☐	PH-HZO	B737-8K2/W	34169/2243	>SCX
☐	PH-HZW	B737-8K2/W	29345/1132	
☐	PH-HZX	B737-8K2/W	28248/1126	

PJ- NETHERLANDS ANTILLES

INSEL AIR INTERNATIONAL — *7I / INC*

	Reg	Type	c/n	Notes
☐	PJ-KVL	Fokker 50	20278	
☐	PJ-KVM	Fokker 50	20288	
☐	PJ-KVN	Fokker 50	20299	♦
☐	PJ-	Fokker 70	11541	o/o♦
☐	PJ-MDA	MD-83	49449/1354	[CUR]
☐	PJ-MDB	MD-82	48021/1078	
☐	PJ-MDC	MD-82	49434/1446	
☐	PJ-MDE	MD-82	49971/1755	
☐	PJ-MDF	MD-83	53014/1740	

WIN AIR — *WM / WIA*

	Reg	Type	c/n	Notes
☐	PJ-WCB	DHC-6 Twin Otter 300	793	♦
☐	PJ-WCC	DHC-6 Twin Otter 310	613	♦
☐	PJ-WII	DHC-6 Twin Otter 300	682	
☐	PJ-WIJ	DHC-6 Twin Otter 300	533	
☐	PJ-WIT	DHC-6 Twin Otter 300	588	

PK- INDONESIA

AIRFAST INDONESIA — *AFE*

	Reg	Type	c/n	Notes
☐	PK-OCP	B737-27A	23794/1424	[HLP]
☐	PK-OCF	DHC-6 Twin Otter 400	866	
☐	PK-OCG	DHC-6 Twin Otter 400	868	
☐	PK-OCI	DHC-6 Twin Otter 400	914	♦
☐	PK-OCJ	DHC-6 Twin Otter 300	522	
☐	PK-OCK	DHC-6 Twin Otter 310	616	
☐	PK-OCL	DHC-6 Twin Otter 300	689	
☐	PK-	DHC-6 Twin Otter 400	924	♦
☐	PK-OME	ERJ-135BJ Legacy 600	145516	[HLP]
☐	PK-OCC	IPTN CASA 212-200	210/50N	
☐	PK-OCR	MD-83	53452/2109	♦
☐	PK-OCS	MD-83	53124/1991	
☐	PK-OCT	MD-82	49889/1761	
☐	PK-OCU	MD-82	53017/1797	

ASIALINK CARGO EXPRESS — *KP / AKC*

	Reg	Type	c/n	Notes
☐	PK-KRA	F.27 Friendship 500F	10632	
☐	PK-KRJ	F.27 Friendship 500F	10660	
☐	PK-KRL	F.27 Friendship 500F	10654	
☐	PK-KRP	Fokker 50F	20119	

AVIASTAR MANDIRI — VIT

	Reg	Type	c/n	
☐	PK-BRE	BAe146 Srs.200	E2139	
☐	PK-BRF	BAe146 Srs.200	E2210	
☐	PK-BRI	BAe146 Srs.200	E2227	
☐	PK-BRK	DHC-6 Twin Otter 300	516	♦
☐	PK-BRM	DHC-6 Twin Otter 300	741	♦
☐	PK-BRP	DHC-6 Twin Otter 300	356	
☐	PK-BRQ	DHC-6 Twin Otter 300	702	♦
☐	PK-BRS	DHC-6 Twin Otter 300	299	
☐	PK-BRT	DHC-6 Twin Otter 300	380	

BATIK AIR — ID / BTK

	Reg	Type	c/n	
☐	PK-LAF	A320-214/S	6164	
☐	PK-LAG	A320-214/S	6280	
☐	PK-LAH	A320-214/S	6309	
☐	PK-LAI	A320-214/S	6356	
☐	PK-LAJ	A320-214/S	6361	
☐	PK-LAK	A320-214/S	6372	
☐	PK-LAL	A320-214/S	6505	
☐	PK-LAM	A320-214/S	6628	♦
☐	PK-LAO	A320-214/S	6695	♦
☐	PK-LAP	A320-214/S	6697	♦
☐	PK-LAQ	A320-214/S	6722	♦
☐	PK-LAR	A320-214/S	6782	♦
☐	PK-LAS	A320-214/S	6823	♦
☐	PK-LAT	A320-214/S	6951	o/o♦
☐	PK-LAU	A320-214/S	6962	o/o♦
☐	PK-LAV	A320-214/S	6991	o/o♦
☐	PK-LAW	A320-214/S	7002	o/o♦
☐	PK-	A320-214/S	7050	o/o♦
☐	PK-	A320-214/S	7160	o/o♦
☐	PK-	A320-214/S	7223	o/o♦
☐	PK-	A320-214/S	7231	o/o♦
☐	PK-	A320-214/S	7245	o/o♦
☐	PK-LBK	B737-8GP/W	39822/5048	
☐	PK-LBL	B737-8GP/W	39821/5026	
☐	PK-LBQ	B737-8GP/W	39825/5127	
☐	PK-LBR	B737-8GP/W	40061/5130	
☐	PK-LBS	B737-8GP/W	39827/5157	
☐	PK-LBT	B737-8GP/W	39828/5179	
☐	PK-LBU	B737-8GP/W	38308/5225	
☐	PK-LBV	B737-8GP/W	39831/5255	
☐	PK-LBW	B737-8GP/W	39834/5267	
☐	PK-LBY	B737-8GP/W	39833/5278	
☐	PK-LBZ	B737-8GP/W	39835/5307	
☐	PK-LDE	B737-8GP/W	39836/5315	♦
☐	PK-LDF	B737-8GP/W	38309/5375	♦
☐	PK-LDG	B737-8GP/W	39862/5532	♦
☐	PK-LBG	B737-9GPER/W	38688/4414	
☐	PK-LBH	B737-9GPER/W	38730/4430	
☐	PK-LBI	B737-9GPER/W	38743/4711	
☐	PK-LBJ	B737-9GPER/W	38742/4726	
☐	PK-LBM	B737-9GPER/W	38689/4441	
☐	PK-LBO	B737-9GPER/W	38731/4463	

CARDIG AIR CARGO — 8F / CAD

	Reg	Type	c/n	
☐	PK-BBC	B737-3Y0F	23499/1242	♦
☐	PK-BBS	B737-301SF	23258/1126	
☐	PK-BBY	B737-3Q8(SF)	23535/1301	

CITILINK EXPRESS — QG / CTV

	Reg	Type	c/n	
☐	PK-GLA	A320-233	1635	
☐	PK-GLC	A320-233	0892	
☐	PK-GLD	A320-233	0839	
☐	PK-GLE	A320-232	2598	
☐	PK-GLF	A320-232	2692	
☐	PK-GLG	A320-214	3861	
☐	PK-GLH	A320-214	3147	
☐	PK-GLI	A320-214	3148	
☐	PK-GLJ	A320-232	4961	
☐	PK-GLK	A320-214	5351	
☐	PK-GLL	A320-214	5379	
☐	PK-GLM	A320-214	5394	
☐	PK-GLN	A320-214	5399	
☐	PK-GLO	A320-214	5415	
☐	PK-GLP	A320-214	5511	
☐	PK-GLQ	A320-214	5541	
☐	PK-GLR	A320-214	5551	
☐	PK-GLS	A320-214	5556	
☐	PK-GLT	A320-214	5560	
☐	PK-GLU	A320-214	5571	
☐	PK-GLV	A320-214	5574	
☐	PK-GLW	A320-214	5597	
☐	PK-GLX	A320-214/S	5777	
☐	PK-GLY	A320-214/S	5830	
☐	PK-GLZ	A320-214/S	6118	
☐	PK-GQA	A320-214/S	6207	
☐	PK-GQC	A320-214/S	6224	
☐	PK-GQD	A320-214/S	6243	
☐	PK-GQE	A320-214/S	6270	
☐	PK-GQF	A320-214/S	6322	
☐	PK-GQG	A320-214/S	6333	
☐	PK-GQH	A320-214/S	6408	
☐	PK-GQI	A320-214/S	6434	
☐	PK-GQJ	A320-214/S	6503	
☐	PK-GQK	A320-214/S	6596	♦
☐	PK-GQL	A320-214/S	6753	♦
☐	PK-GQM	A320-214/S	6980	o/o♦
☐	PK-	A320-214/S	7091	o/o♦
☐	PK-	A320-214/S	7221	o/o♦
☐	PK-	A320-214/S	7297	o/o♦
☐	PK-	A320-214/S		o/o♦
☐	PK-GGC	B737-5U3	28727/2937	♦
☐	PK-GGD	B737-5U3	28728/2938	o/o♦
☐	PK-GGE	B737-5U3	28729/2950	♦
☐	PK-GGN	B737-3U3	28735/3029	
☐	PK-GGO	B737-3U3	28736/3032	
☐	PK-GGP	B737-3U3	28737/3037	
☐	PK-GGQ	B737-3U3	28739/3064	
☐	PK-GGR	B737-3U3	28741/3079	

DERAYA AIR TAXI — DRY

	Reg	Type	c/n	
☐	PK-DGA	BAeATP (F)	2026	
☐	PK-DGC	BAeATP (F)	2052	
☐	PK-DSB	Short SD.3-30	SH3056	
☐	PK-DSH	Short SD.3-60	SH3757	
☐	PK-DSR	Short SD.3-30	SH3060	
☐	PK-DSS	Short SD.3-60	SH3743	

DIMONIM AIR

	Reg	Type	c/n	
☐	PK-HVH	ATR 72-202F	373	
☐	PK-HVM	DHC-6 Twin Otter 300	620	♦
☐	PK-HVN	DHC-6 Twin Otter 300	389	♦

EASTINDO

	Reg	Type	c/n	
☐	PK-RGA	Beech 1900D	UE-376	
☐	PK-RGD	Beech 1900D	UE-400	

	EXPRESSAIR		XN / XAR	
☐	PK-TXI	B737-322	24671/1913	
☐	PK-TXJ	B737-3M8	24413/1884	
☐	PK-TXK	B737-2B7	22880/927	
☐	PK-TXY	B737-204	22057/621	
☐	PK-TXZ	B737-36N	28558/2876	
☐	PK-TZA	B737-33V	29340/3121	
☐	PK-TZC	B737-33V	29337/3113	
☐	PK-TXM	Do328-110	3032	
☐	PK-TXN	Do328-110	3030	
☐	PK-TXO	Do328-110	3045	
☐	PK-TXP	Do328-110	3038	
☐	PK-TXQ	Do328-110	3043	
☐	PK-TXW	Do328-110	3044	

	GARUDA INDONESIA		GA / GIA	
☐	PK-GPA	A330-341	138	
☐	PK-GPC	A330-341	140	
☐	PK-GPD	A330-341	144	
☐	PK-GPE	A330-341	148	
☐	PK-GPF	A330-341	153	
☐	PK-GPG	A330-341	165	
☐	PK-GPJ	A330-243	988	
☐	PK-GPK	A330-243	1028	
☐	PK-GPL	A330-243	1184	
☐	PK-GPM	A330-243	1214	
☐	PK-GPN	A330-243	1261	
☐	PK-GPO	A330-243	1288	
☐	PK-GPP	A330-243	1364	
☐	PK-GPQ	A330-243	1410	
☐	PK-GPR	A330-343E	1446	
☐	PK-GPS	A330-243	1474	
☐	PK-GPT	A330-343E	1548	
☐	PK-GPU	A330-343E	1560	
☐	PK-GPV	A330-343E	1577	
☐	PK-GPW	A330-343E	1585	
☐	PK-GPX	A330-343E	1654	♦
☐	PK-GPY	A330-343E	1671	♦
☐	PK-GPZ	A330-343E	1698	♦
☐	PK-GHA	A330-343E	1709	o/o♦
☐	PK-	A330-343E	1723	o/o♦
☐	PK-	A330-343E	1733	o/o♦
☐	PK-	A330-343E		o/o♦
☐	PK-	A330-343E		o/o♦
☐	PK-	A330-243F		o/o♦
☐	PK-	A330-243F		o/o♦
☐	PK-GAA	ATR 72-600	1119	
☐	PK-GAC	ATR 72-600	1132	
☐	PK-GAD	ATR 72-600	1140	
☐	PK-GAE	ATR 72-600	1149	
☐	PK-GAF	ATR 72-600	1152	
☐	PK-GAG	ATR 72-600	1157	
☐	PK-GAH	ATR 72-600	1181	
☐	PK-GAI	ATR 72-600	1191	
☐	PK-GAJ	ATR 72-600	1243	♦
☐	PK-GAK	ATR 72-600	1249	♦
☐	PK-GAL	ATR 72-600	1254	♦
☐	PK-	ATR 72-600		♦
☐	PK-	ATR 72-600		♦
☐	PK-	ATR 72-600		♦
☐	PK-	ATR 72-600		♦
☐	PK-	ATR 72-600		♦
☐	PK-	ATR 72-600		♦
☐	PK-	ATR 72-600		♦
☐	PK-	ATR 72-600		♦
☐	PK-GEG	B737-83N/W	30033/1149	
☐	PK-GEH	B737-83N/W	30643/1106	
☐	PK-GEI	B737-86N/W	29883/1083	
☐	PK-GEJ	B737-86N/W	33003/1121	
☐	PK-GEK	B737-85F/W	30568/793	
☐	PK-GEL	B737-8AS/W	29927/727	
☐	PK-GEM	B737-8AS/W	29928/735	
☐	PK-GEN	B737-8AS/W	29929/753	
☐	PK-GEO	B737-8AS/W	29930/757	
☐	PK-GEP	B737-8AS/W	29931/1020	
☐	PK-GEQ	B737-86N/W	32659/1709	
☐	PK-GFA	B737-86N/W	36549/3331	
☐	PK-GFC	B737-86N/W	39390/3348	
☐	PK-GFD	B737-8U3/W	40807/3337	
☐	PK-GFE	B737-86N/W	36804/3374	
☐	PK-GFF	B737-8U3/W	36436/3370	
☐	PK-GFG	B737-8U3/W	37819/3402	
☐	PK-GFH	B737-8U3/W	36850/3389	
☐	PK-GFI	B737-86N/W	36805/3438	
☐	PK-GFJ	B737-86N/W	37885/3445	
☐	PK-GFK	B737-86N/W	37887/3463	
☐	PK-GFL	B737-86N/W	36808/3505	
☐	PK-GFM	B737-8U3/W	39920/3518	
☐	PK-GFN	B737-86N/W	38033/3607	
☐	PK-GFO	B737-86N/W	39403/3674	
☐	PK-GFP	B737-8U3/W	38821/3684	
☐	PK-GFQ	B737-81D/W	39416/3766	
☐	PK-GFR	B737-81D/W	39417/3802	
☐	PK-GFS	B737-86N/W	36830/3860	
☐	PK-GFT	B737-86N/W	38032/3869	
☐	PK-GFU	B737-86N/W	38040/4482	
☐	PK-GFV	B737-8U3/W	38885/4490	
☐	PK-GFW	B737-8U3/W	39929/4520	
☐	PK-GFX	B737-8U3/W	39928/4453	
☐	PK-GFY	B737-86N/W	38043/4619	
☐	PK-GFZ	B737-86N/W	38044/4635	
☐	PK-GMA	B737-8U3/W	30151/2942	
☐	PK-GMC	B737-8U3/W	30155/3081	
☐	PK-GMD	B737-8U3/W	30156/3100	
☐	PK-GME	B737-8U3/W	30157/3123	
☐	PK-GMF	B737-8U3/W	30140/3129	
☐	PK-GMG	B737-8U3/W	30141/3166	
☐	PK-GMH	B737-8U3/W	30142/3213	
☐	PK-GMI	B737-8U3/W	30143/3243	
☐	PK-GMJ	B737-8U3/W	30144/3249	
☐	PK-GMK	B737-8U3/W	29666/3171	
☐	PK-GML	B737-8U3/W	31763/3177	
☐	PK-GMM	B737-8U3/W	30145/3285	
☐	PK-GMN	B737-8U3/W	30146/3303	
☐	PK-GMO	B737-8U3/W	30147/3327	
☐	PK-GMP	B737-8U3/W	30148/3353	
☐	PK-GMQ	B737-8U3/W	30149/3405	
☐	PK-GMR	B737-8U3/W	30150/3429	
☐	PK-GMS	B737-8U3/W	38071/3855	
☐	PK-GMU	B737-8U3/W	38073/3930	
☐	PK-GMV	B737-8U3/W	38074/3960	
☐	PK-GMW	B737-8U3/W	38069/4026	
☐	PK-GMX	B737-8U3/W	38070/3996	
☐	PK-GMY	B737-8U3/W	38884/4446	
☐	PK-GMZ	B737-8U3/W	38072/4582	
☐	PK-GNA	B737-8U3/W	41310/4692	
☐	PK-GNC	B737-8U3/W	41312/4720	
☐	PK-GND	B737-8U3/W	41794/4761	
☐	PK-GNE	B737-8U3/W	39936/4800	
☐	PK-GNF	B737-8U3/W	39939/4866	

	Reg	Type	c/n	
☐	PK-GNG	B737-8U3/W	39891/4901	
☐	PK-GNH	B737-8U3/W	40547/4961	
☐	PK-GNI	B737-86N/W	41267/4957	
☐	PK-GNJ	B737-8U3/W	41796/4969	
☐	PK-GNK	B737-8U3/W	41798/5049	
☐	PK-GNL	B737-86N/W	41253/5078	
☐	PK-GNM	B737-8U3/W	41322/5057	
☐	PK-GNN	B737-86N/W	41270/5116	
☐	PK-GNO	B737-8U3/W	41800/5109	
☐	PK-GNP	B737-8U3/W	41605/5245	
☐	PK-GNQ	B737-8U3/W	39954/5284	
☐	PK-GNR	B737-8U3/W	39955/5335	
☐	PK-GNS	B737-8U3/W	41607/5385	
☐	PK-GNT	B737-8U3/W	41806/5427	♦
☐	PK-GNU	B737-8U3/W	41812/5613	♦
☐	PK-GNV	B737-8U3/W	41815/5716	♦
☐	PK-GSG	B747-4U3	25704/1011	
☐	PK-GSH	B747-4U3	25705/1029	
☐	PK-GIA	B777-3U3ER	40074/1104	
☐	PK-GIC	B777-3U3ER	40075/1121	
☐	PK-GID	B777-3U3ER	29146/1141	
☐	PK-GIE	B777-3U3ER	29147/1148	
☐	PK-GIF	B777-3U3ER	29148/1203	
☐	PK-GIG	B777-3U3ER	29143/1234	
☐	PK-GIH	B777-3U3ER	29144/1305	♦
☐	PK-GII	B777-3U3ER	29145/1345	♦
☐	PK-GIJ	B777-3U3ER	40072/1332	♦
☐	PK-GIK	B777-3U3ER	40073/1367	♦
☐	PK-GRA	CRJ-1000	19025	
☐	PK-GRC	CRJ-1000	19026	
☐	PK-GRE	CRJ-1000	19027	
☐	PK-GRF	CRJ-1000	19028	
☐	PK-GRG	CRJ-1000	19029	
☐	PK-GRH	CRJ-1000	19030	
☐	PK-GRI	CRJ-1000	19031	
☐	PK-GRJ	CRJ-1000	19032	
☐	PK-GRK	CRJ-1000	19033	
☐	PK-GRL	CRJ-1000	19034	
☐	PK-GRM	CRJ-1000	19035	
☐	PK-GRN	CRJ-1000	19036	
☐	PK-GRO	CRJ-1000	19038	
☐	PK-GRP	CRJ-1000	19039	
☐	PK-GRQ	CRJ-1000	19040	
☐	PK-GRR	CRJ-1000	19042	♦
☐	PK-GRS	CRJ-1000	19043	♦
☐	PK-GRT	CRJ-1000	19044	♦

ATR-72s operated by Garuda Explore and CRJ-1000s by Garuda Explore Jet.

GATARI AIR SERVICE — GHS

	Reg	Type	c/n	
☐	PK-HNS	ATR 42-500	601	
☐	PK-HNT	ATR 42-500	614	

INDONESIA AIR — IDA

	Reg	Type	c/n	
☐	PK-THS	ATR 42-500	559	
☐	PK-THT	ATR 42-500	611	[HLP]
☐	PK-TSY	ATR 42-300	118	[HLP]
☐	PK-TSZ	ATR 42-300	059	[HLP]
☐	PK-TSJ	F.27 Friendship 500	10525	[HLP]
☐	PK-TSO	Fokker 50	20186	
☐	PK-TSP	Fokker 50	20316	

INDONESIA AIRASIA — QZ / AWQ

	Reg	Type	c/n	
☐	PK-AXD	A320-216	3182	
☐	PK-AXE	A320-216	3715	
☐	PK-AXF	A320-216	3765	
☐	PK-AXG	A320-216	3813	
☐	PK-AXH	A320-216	3875	
☐	PK-AXI	A320-216	3963	
☐	PK-AXJ	A320-216	4035	
☐	PK-AXR	A320-216	2881	
☐	PK-AXS	A320-216	2885	
☐	PK-AXT	A320-216	3486	
☐	PK-AXU	A320-216	3549	
☐	PK-AXV	A320-216	4889	
☐	PK-AXW	A320-216	5137	
☐	PK-AXX	A320-216	5215	
☐	PK-AXY	A320-216	5359	
☐	PK-AXZ	A320-216	5420	status?
☐	PK-AZA	A320-214	5165	
☐	PK-AZD	A320-216/S	5627	
☐	PK-AZE	A320-216/S	5098	
☐	PK-AZF	A320-216/S	5706	
☐	PK-AZG	A320-216/S	5657	
☐	PK-AZH	A320-216	5325	
☐	PK-AZI	A320-216	5200	
☐	PK-AZJ	A320-216	5153	

INDONESIA AIRASIA EXTRA — XT / IDX

	Reg	Type	c/n	
☐	PK-XRA	A330-343E	716	
☐	PK-XRC	A330-343E	654	

JAYAWIJAYA DIRGANTARA — JWD

	Reg	Type	c/n	
☐	PK-JRU	F.27 Friendship 500	10629	

JHONLIN AIR TRANSPORT — JLB

	Reg	Type	c/n	
☐	PK-JBA	ATR 72-600	1004	

KALSTAR — KD / KLS

	Reg	Type	c/n	
☐	PK-KSA	ATR 72-600	1080	
☐	PK-KSC	ATR 72-212A	638	
☐	PK-KSD	ATR 72-212A	585	
☐	PK-KSE	ATR 42-320	415	
☐	PK-KSF	ATR 42-500	518	♦
☐	PK-KSG	ATR 72-600	1286	♦
☐	PK-KSI	ATR 42-320	348	
☐	PK-KSO	ATR 42-320	202	
☐	PK-KSU	ATR 72-600	1108	
☐	PK-KSP	B737-59D	26421/2279	
☐	PK-KST	B737-3M8	25040/2017	
☐	PK-KDA	ERJ-195LR	19000029	
☐	PK-KDD	ERJ-190LR	19000110	♦

LION AIRLINES — JT / LNI

	Reg	Type	c/n	
☐	PK-LEF	A330-343E	1675	♦
☐	PK-LEG	A330-343E	1680	♦
☐	PK-LEH	A330-343E	1693	♦
☐	PK-LIF	B737-4Y0	24467/1733	[CGK]
☐	PK-LIH	B737-4Y0	24520/1803	[CGK]
☐	PK-LII	B737-46B	24123/1663	[SUB]
☐	PK-LIR	B737-4Y0	24692/1963	[SUB]
☐	PK-LIS	B737-4Y0	24693/1972	
☐	PK-LIT	B737-4Y0	24512/1777	[CGK]
☐	PK-LIU	B737-3G7	23218/1076	std
☐	PK-LIV	B737-3G7	23219/1090	std
☐	PK-LIW	B737-4Y0	24684/1841	
☐	PK-LJQ	B737-8GP/W	38317/3985	

	Reg	Type	c/n	
☐	PK-LJR	B737-8GP/W	37292/4008	
☐	PK-LJS	B737-8GP/W	37293/4046	
☐	PK-LJU	B737-8GP/W	37294/4071	
☐	PK-LJV	B737-8GP/W	38721/4077	
☐	PK-LJW	B737-8GP/W	37295/4092	
☐	PK-LJY	B737-8GP/W	38722/4125	
☐	PK-LKG	B737-8GP/W	38681/4180	
☐	PK-LKH	B737-8GP/W	37297/4193	
☐	PK-LKI	B737-8GP/W	38724/4206	
☐	PK-LKJ	B737-8GP/W	38682/4226	
☐	PK-LKK	B737-8GP/W	38725/4238	
☐	PK-LKP	B737-8GP/W	38685/4314	
☐	PK-LKQ	B737-8GP/W	38727/4320	
☐	PK-LKR	B737-8GP/W	38686/4332	
☐	PK-LKT	B737-8GP/W	38733/4517	
☐	PK-LKU	B737-8GP/W	38691/4514	
☐	PK-LKV	B737-8GP/W	38735/4583	
☐	PK-LKW	B737-8GP/W	38734/4578	
☐	PK-LKZ	B737-8GP/W	38740/4687	
☐	PK-LOG	B737-8GP/W	38745/4740	
☐	PK-LOH	B737-8GP/W	38744/4762	
☐	PK-LOI	B737-8GP/W	38746/4777	
☐	PK-LOJ	B737-8GP/W	38747/4783	
☐	PK-LOM	B737-8GP/W	38750/4867	
☐	PK-LOO	B737-8GP/W	39814/4879	
☐	PK-LOP	B737-8GP/W	39815/4890	
☐	PK-LOQ	B737-8GP/W	39816/4924	
☐	PK-LOR	B737-8GP/W	39818/4936	
☐	PK-LOV	B737-8GP/W	39817/4954	
☐	PK-LPJ	B737-8GP/W	39869/5530	♦
☐	PK-LPK	B737-8GP/W	39872/5586	♦
☐	PK-LPL	B737-8GP/W	39870/5649	♦
☐	PK-LPM	B737-8GP/W	39874/5709	♦
☐	PK-LPO	B737-8GP/W	39876/5726	♦
☐	PK-LPQ	B737-8GP/W	39877/5747	♦
☐	PK-	B737-8GP/W		o/o♦
☐	PK-	B737-8GP/W		o/o♦
☐	PK-	B737-8GP/W		o/o♦
☐	PK-LFF	B737-9GPER/W	35679/2093	
☐	PK-LFG	B737-9GPER/W	35680/1981	
☐	PK-LFH	B737-9GPER/W	35710/2285	
☐	PK-LFI	B737-9GPER/W	35711/2319	
☐	PK-LFJ	B737-9GPER/W	35712/2349	
☐	PK-LFK	B737-9GPER/W	35713/2437	
☐	PK-LFL	B737-9GPER/W	35714/2461	
☐	PK-LFM	B737-9GPER/W	35715/2485	
☐	PK-LFO	B737-9GPER/W	35716/2504	
☐	PK-LFP	B737-9GPER/W	35717/2455	
☐	PK-LFQ	B737-9GPER/W	35718/2670	
☐	PK-LFR	B737-9GPER/W	35719/2694	
☐	PK-LFS	B737-9GPER/W	35720/2756	
☐	PK-LFT	B737-9GPER/W	35721/2793	
☐	PK-LFU	B737-9GPER/W	35722/2836	
☐	PK-LFV	B737-9GPER/W	35723/2848	
☐	PK-LFW	B737-9GPER/W	35724/2879	
☐	PK-LFY	B737-9GPER/W	35725/2897	
☐	PK-LFZ	B737-9GPER/W	35726/2904	
☐	PK-LGJ	B737-9GPER/W	35727/2934	
☐	PK-LGK	B737-9GPER/W	35728/2984	
☐	PK-LGL	B737-9GPER/W	35729/3008	
☐	PK-LGM	B737-9GPER/W	35730/3075	
☐	PK-LGO	B737-9GPER/W	35731/3093	
☐	PK-LGP	B737-9GPER/W	35732/3111	
☐	PK-LGQ	B737-9GPER/W	35733/3135	
☐	PK-LGR	B737-9GPER/W	35734/3153	
☐	PK-LGS	B737-9GPER/W	35735/3183	
☐	PK-LGT	B737-9GPER/W	35736/3207	
☐	PK-LGU	B737-9GPER/W	35737/3225	
☐	PK-LGV	B737-9GPER/W	37268/3297	
☐	PK-LGW	B737-9GPER/W	37269/3321	
☐	PK-LGY	B737-9GPER/W	37270/3333	
☐	PK-LGZ	B737-9GPER/W	37271/3345	
☐	PK-LHH	B737-9GPER/W	37275/3375	
☐	PK-LHI	B737-9GPER/W	32276/3381	
☐	PK-LHJ	B737-9GPER/W	37272/3411	
☐	PK-LHK	B737-9GPER/W	37273/3423	
☐	PK-LHL	B737-9GPER/W	37274/3441	
☐	PK-LHM	B737-9GPER/W	37277/3513	
☐	PK-LHO	B737-9GPER/W	37278/3555	
☐	PK-LHP	B737-9GPER/W	37279/3573	
☐	PK-LHQ	B737-9GPER/W	37280/3537	
☐	PK-LHR	B737-9GPER/W	37281/3627	
☐	PK-LHS	B737-9GPER/W	37282/3663	
☐	PK-LHT	B737-9GPER/W	37283/3699	
☐	PK-LHU	B737-9GPER/W	38300/3717	
☐	PK-LHV	B737-9GPER/W	37284/3735	
☐	PK-LHW	B737-9GPER/W	38302/3753	
☐	PK-LHY	B737-9GPER/W	37285/3765	
☐	PK-LHZ	B737-9GPER/W	38305/3807	
☐	PK-LJF	B737-9GPER/W	37286/3813	
☐	PK-LJG	B737-9GPER/W	37287/3831	
☐	PK-LJH	B737-9GPER/W	37288/3849	
☐	PK-LJI	B737-9GPER/W	38310/3867	
☐	PK-LJJ	B737-9GPER/W	37289/3888	
☐	PK-LJK	B737-9GPER/W	38311/3900	
☐	PK-LJL	B737-9GPER/W	37290/3918	
☐	PK-LJM	B737-9GPER/W	38313/3936	
☐	PK-LJO	B737-9GPER/W	38315/3954	
☐	PK-LJP	B737-9GPER/W	37291/3966	
☐	PK-LJT	B737-9GPER/W	38720/4056	
☐	PK-LJZ	B737-9GPER/W	37296/4128	
☐	PK-LKF	B737-9GPER/W	38723/4140	
☐	PK-LKL	B737-9GPER/W	38683/4236	
☐	PK-LKM	B737-9GPER/W	38726/4284	
☐	PK-LKO	B737-9GPER/W	38684/4266	
☐	PK-LOF	B737-9GPER/W	38741/4679	
☐	PK-LPF	B737-9GPER/W	39880/5081	
☐	PK-LPH	B737-9GPER/W	39878/5096	
☐	PK-LPI	B737-9GPER/W	38299/5134	
☐	PK-	B737-9GPER/W	39879/5763	o/o♦
☐	PK-	B737-9GPER/W		o/o♦
☐	PK-	B737-9GPER/W		o/o♦
☐	PK-	B737-9GPER/W		o/o♦
☐	PK-	B737-9GPER/W		o/o♦
☐	PK-	B737-9GPER/W		o/o♦
☐	PK-	B737-9GPER/W		o/o♦
☐	PK-	B737-9GPER/W		o/o♦
☐	PK-LHF	B747-412	24063/736	
☐	PK-LHG	B747-412	24065/761	>KNE

MY INDO AIRLINES *MYU*

	Reg	Type	c/n	
☐	PK-MYI	B737-3ZOF	23448/1168	
☐	PK-MYU	B737-3S3F	23811/1445	♦
☐	PK-MYY	B737-347SF	23598/1289	♦

NAM AIR *IN / NIH*

	Reg	Type	c/n	
☐	PK-NAM	B737-524/W	27900/2736	
☐	PK-NAN	B737-524/W	27901/2743	
☐	PK-NAO	B737-524/W	27531/2700	♦
☐	PK-NAP	B737-524/W	27534/2726	♦
☐	PK-NAQ	B737-524/W	27535/2728	♦

NUSANTARA AIR CHARTER — SJK

	Reg	Type	c/n	
☐	PK-JKG	ATR 42-500	667	
☐	PK-JKH	ATR 72-212A	538	♦
☐	PK-JKP	Avro 146-RJ100	E3243	
☐	PK-JKW	BAe146 Srs.200	E2204	

PELITA AIR — 6D / PAS

	Reg	Type	c/n	
☐	PK-PAV	ATR 72-212A	908	♦
☐	PK-PAW	ATR 72-212A	746	
☐	PK-PAX	ATR 42-500	627	
☐	PK-PCN	IPTN CASA 212-200	216/56N	
☐	PK-PCO	IPTN CASA 212-200	215/55N	
☐	PK-PCP	IPTN CASA 212-200	208/48N	
☐	PK-PCQ	IPTN CASA 212-200	207/47N	
☐	PK-PCR	IPTN CASA 212-200	206/46N	
☐	PK-PCS	IPTN CASA 212-200	205/45N	
☐	PK-PCT	IPTN CASA 212-200	204/44N	
☐	PK-PCU	IPTN CASA 212-200	203/43N	
☐	PK-PCV	IPTN CASA 212-200	132/21N	
☐	PK-PCY	IPTN CASA 212-200	39/2N	
☐	PK-PCZ	IPTN CASA 212-200	34/2N	
☐	PK-PSV	DHC-7-103	105	
☐	PK-PSW	DHC-7-103	100	
☐	PK-PSX	DHC-7-103	094	[PCB]
☐	PK-PSY	DHC-7-103	086	[PCB]
☐	PK-PSZ	DHC-7-103	075	[PCB]
☐	PK-PFZ	Fokker 100	11486	
☐	PK-PJJ	Avro 146-RJ85	E2239	
☐	PK-PJN	Fokker 100	11288	

SABANG MERAUKE RAYA — SMC

	Reg	Type	c/n	
☐	PK-ZAB	IPTN CASA 212-200	140/23N	
☐	PK-ZAN	IPTN CASA 212-200	60/4N	
☐	PK-ZAO	IPTN CASA 212-200	64/6N	
☐	PK-ZAQ	IPTN CASA 212-200	277/82N	
☐	PK-ZAV	IPTN CASA 212-200	276/81N	

SRIWIJAYA AIR — SJ / SJY

	Reg	Type	c/n	
☐	PK-CJC	B737-33A	24025/1556	
☐	PK-CJH	B737-2B7	22883/935	
☐	PK-CJI	B737-2B7	23135/1054	
☐	PK-CJK	B737-236	22032/742	[CGK]
☐	PK-CJM	B737-2B7	22884/956	[WJCB]
☐	PK-CJP	B737-2B7	23132/1044	
☐	PK-CJT	B737-33A	24791/1984	
☐	PK-CJW	B737-4Y0	24690/1885	
☐	PK-CJY	B737-3Q8	24698/1846	
☐	PK-CKA	B737-4Q8	25169/2237	
☐	PK-CKD	B737-4Y0	25180/2201	
☐	PK-CKE	B737-3Q8	24987/2268	
☐	PK-CKF	B737-3Y0	25179/2205	
☐	PK-CKH	B737-3Y0	24907/2013	
☐	PK-CKI	B737-3Y0	25187/2248	
☐	PK-CKJ	B737-3L9	27337/2594	
☐	PK-CKK	B737-3L9	27336/2587	
☐	PK-CKL	B737-3Q8	26293/2541	
☐	PK-CKN	B737-4Q8	26281/2380	std
☐	PK-CKP	B737-36N	28559/2882	
☐	PK-CLA	B737-86N/W	28591/233	
☐	PK-CLC	B737-524/W	27323/2616	
☐	PK-CLD	B737-524/W	27333/2660	
☐	PK-CLE	B737-524/W	27326/2633	
☐	PK-CLF	B737-524/W	27330/2648	
☐	PK-CLH	B737-524/W	27327/2634	
☐	PK-CLI	B737-524/W	27332/2659	
☐	PK-CLJ	B737-524/W	27527/2672	
☐	PK-CLK	B737-524/W	27317/2576	
☐	PK-CLL	B737-524/W	27528/2675	
☐	PK-CLN	B737-524/W	27529/2683	
☐	PK-CLO	B737-524/W	27334/2661	
☐	PK-CLQ	B737-81Q/W	29050/444	
☐	PK-CLS	B737-8K5/W	27985/470	
☐	PK-CLT	B737-8K5/W	27991/248	
☐	PK-CLU	B737-524/W	27526/2669	
☐	PK-CME	B737-8Q8/W	30702/1953	
☐	PK-CMF	B737-86Q/W	32885/1147	
☐	PK-CMH	B737-8Q8/W	33699/1309	♦
☐	PK-CMI	B737-8Q8/W	28214/78	♦
☐	PK-CMJ	B737-85P/W	28381/250	♦
☐	PK-CMK	B737-85P/W	28384/420	♦
☐	PK-CML	B737-8Q8/W	30636/768	♦
☐	PK-CMN	B737-86J/W	30876/759	♦
☐	PK-CMO	B737-9LFER/W	41712/5336	♦
☐	PK-CMP	B737-9LFER/W	41843/5190	♦
☐	PK-CMQ	B737-8BK/W	29676/2432	♦

TRANSNUSA AIR SERVICES — TNU

	Reg	Type	c/n	
☐	PK-TNJ	ATR 42-600	1015	
☐	PK-TNV	BAe146 Srs.100	E1124	♦
☐	PK-TNA	Fokker 50	20261	
☐	PK-TNB	Fokker 50	20282	
☐	PK-TNC	Fokker 50	20240	
☐	PK-TND	Fokker 50	20260	
☐	PK-TNS	Fokker 50	20307	
☐	PK-TNR	Fokker 70	11585	

TRANSWISATA PRIMA AVIATION — TWT

	Reg	Type	c/n	
☐	PK-TWW	IPTN CASA 212-200	422/N102	♦
☐	PK-TWN	Fokker 100	11335	

TRAVIRA AIR — TR / TVV

	Reg	Type	c/n	
☐	PK-TVI	ATR 42-600	1017	♦
☐	PK-TVZ	B737-5L9	28996/2998	
☐	PK-TVE	Beech 1900D	UE-338	
☐	PK-TVH	Beech 1900D	UE-364	
☐	PK-TVK	Beech 1900D	UE-375	
☐	PK-TUB	DHC-8Q-315	590	std
☐	PK-TUD	DHC-8Q-315	582	[HLP]

TRIGANA AIR SERVICE — TGN

	Reg	Type	c/n	
☐	PK-YRE	ATR 42-300	027	
☐	PK-YRH	ATR 42-300	097	
☐	PK-YRI	ATR 72-202	326	
☐	PK-YRK	ATR 42-300	106	
☐	PK-YRR	ATR 42-310	214	
☐	PK-YRV	ATR 42-300	190	
☐	PK-YRX	ATR 72-202	342	
☐	PK-YRY	ATR 72-202	201	
☐	PK-YRT	B737-2K5	22599/814	[SUB]
☐	PK-YRZ	B737-3Q8	24700/1924	
☐	PK-YSA	B737-228	23007/948	
☐	PK-YSD	B737-217	22260/784	std
☐	PK-YSG	B737-301(SF)	23930/1539	♦
☐	PK-YSH	B737-3L9	27925/2763	♦
☐	PK-YSY	B737-347SF	23597/1287	
☐	PK-YSZ	B737-320F	23451/1240	
☐	PK-YTZ	B737-4YO	23869/1639	

☐	PK-YRJ	DHC-4 Caribou	27	
☐	PK-YPX	DHC-6 Twin Otter 300	684	
☐	PK-YRF	DHC-6 Twin Otter 300	462	
☐	PK-YRU	DHC-6 Twin Otter 300	685	
☐	PK-YPA	F.27 Friendship 200	10223	[HLP]
☐	PK-YRG	F.27 Friendship 500	10397	std

TRI-MG INTRA ASIA AIRLINES — **GY / TMG**

☐	PK-YGR	B727-223F	20993/1189	[BPN]
☐	PK-YGG	B737-301F	23743/1510	
☐	PK-YGH	B737-36N(F)	28567/2971	
☐	PK-YGP	B737-210C	21822/605	[SZB]
☐	PK-	B737-3G7(F)	24711/1843	♦

WINGS ABADI AIR — **IW / WON**

☐	PK-WFF	ATR 72-212A	869	
☐	PK-WFG	ATR 72-212A	882	
☐	PK-WFH	ATR 72-212A	883	
☐	PK-WFI	ATR 72-212A	871	
☐	PK-WFJ	ATR 72-212A	898	
☐	PK-WFK	ATR 72-212A	905	
☐	PK-WFL	ATR 72-212A	915	
☐	PK-WFM	ATR 72-212A	922	
☐	PK-WFO	ATR 72-212A	936	
☐	PK-WFP	ATR 72-212A	937	
☐	PK-WFQ	ATR 72-212A	943	
☐	PK-WFR	ATR 72-212A	946	
☐	PK-WFS	ATR 72-212A	957	
☐	PK-WFT	ATR 72-212A	961	
☐	PK-WFU	ATR 72-212A	964	
☐	PK-WFV	ATR 72-212A	985	
☐	PK-WFW	ATR 72-212A	1024	
☐	PK-WFY	ATR 72-212A	1048	
☐	PK-WFZ	ATR 72-212A	1055	
☐	PK-WGF	ATR 72-212A	1062	
☐	PK-WGG	ATR 72-600	1063	
☐	PK-WGH	ATR 72-600	1067	
☐	PK-WGI	ATR 72-600	1074	
☐	PK-WGJ	ATR 72-600	1079	
☐	PK-WGK	ATR 72-600	1106	
☐	PK-WGL	ATR 72-600	1118	♦
☐	PK-WGM	ATR 72-600	1168	
☐	PK-WGO	ATR 72-600	1104	
☐	PK-WGP	ATR 72-600	1176	
☐	PK-WGQ	ATR 72-600	1188	
☐	PK-WGR	ATR 72-600	1193	
☐	PK-WGS	ATR 72-600	1134	♦
☐	PK-WGT	ATR 72-600	1220	
☐	PK-WGU	ATR 72-600	1225	
☐	PK-WGV	ATR 72-600	1227	
☐	PK-WGW	ATR 72-600	1234	
☐	PK-WGY	ATR 72-600	1238	
☐	PK-WGZ	ATR 72-600	1244	♦
☐	PK-WHF	ATR 72-600	1247	♦
☐	PK-WHG	ATR 72-600	1250	♦
☐	PK-WHH	ATR 72-600	1256	♦
☐	PK-WHI	ATR 72-600	1263	♦
☐	PK-WHJ	ATR 72-600	1271	♦
☐	PK-WHK	ATR 72-600	1275	♦
☐	PK-WHL	ATR 72-600	1282	♦
☐	PK-WHP	ATR 72-600	1290	♦
☐	PK-WHQ	ATR 72-600	1291	♦
☐	PK-WHR	ATR 72-600	1298	♦
☐	PK-	ATR 72-600	1307	o/o♦
☐	PK-	ATR 72-600		o/o♦
☐	PK-	ATR 72-600		o/o♦
☐	PK-	ATR 72-600		o/o♦

PP- / PR- / PT- BRAZIL

AEROTAXI ABAETE — **ABJ**

☐	PT-GKO	EMB.110E	110119	
☐	PT-MFN	EMB.110C	110040	
☐	PT-MFO	EMB.110C	110058	
☐	PT-MFP	EMB.110C	110105	
☐	PT-MFQ	EMB.110C	110121	
☐	PT-MFS	EMB.110C	110054	

AIR BRASIL CARGO — **BSL**

☐	PR-AIB	B727-227F	21363/1258	
☐	PR-MTJ	B727-2M7F	21952/1693	

AVIANCA BRAZIL — **O6 / ONE**

☐	PR-AVH	A318-122	3001	
☐	PR-AVJ	A318-122	3030	
☐	PR-AVK	A318-122	3062	
☐	PR-AVL	A318-122	3214	
☐	PR-AVO	A318-122	3216	
☐	PR-ONC	A318-121	3371	
☐	PR-OND	A318-121	3390	
☐	PR-ONG	A318-121	3438	
☐	PR-ONH	A318-121	3469	
☐	PR-ONI	A318-121	3509	
☐	PR-ONM	A318-121	3585	
☐	PR-ONO	A318-121	3602	
☐	PR-ONP	A318-121	3606	
☐	PR-ONQ	A318-121	3635	
☐	PR-ONR	A318-121	3642	
☐	PR-AVB	A319-115	4222	
☐	PR-AVC	A319-115	4287	
☐	PR-AVD	A319-115	4336	
☐	PR-ONJ	A319-115	5193	
☐	PR-AVP	A320-214	4891	
☐	PR-AVQ	A320-214	4913	
☐	PR-AVR	A320-214	4941	
☐	PR-AVU	A320-214	4942	
☐	PR-OBB	A320-214/S	6876	[TLS]♦
☐	PR-OBC	A320-214/S	6896	♦
☐	PR-OCA	A320-214/S	6125	
☐	PR-OCB	A320-214/S	6139	
☐	PR-OCD	A320-214/S	6173	
☐	PR-OCH	A320-214/S	6528	
☐	PR-OCI	A320-214/S	6536	
☐	PR-OCM	A320-214/S	6561	♦
☐	PR-OCN	A320-214/S	6598	♦
☐	PR-OCO	A320-214/S	6634	♦
☐	PR-OCP	A320-214/S	6651	♦
☐	PR-OCQ	A320-214/S	6689	♦
☐	PR-OCR	A320-214/S	6712	♦
☐	PR-OCT	A320-214/S	6800	♦
☐	PR-OCV	A320-214/S	6806	♦
☐	PR-OCW	A320-214/S	6813	♦
☐	PR-OCY	A320-214/S	6871	[TLS]♦
☐	PR-ONK	A320-214	5278	
☐	PR-ONL	A320-214	5299	
☐	PR-ONS	A320-214/S	5754	
☐	PR-ONT	A320-214/S	5841	
☐	PR-ONW	A320-214/S	6050	
☐	PR-ONX	A320-214/S	6057	
☐	PR-ONY	A320-214/S	6103	

	Reg	Type	c/n	Notes
☐	PR-ONZ	A320-214/S	6110	
☐	PR-OCG	A330-243	1608	o/o♦
☐	PR-OCX	A330-243	1657	o/o♦
☐	PR-ONV	A330-243F	1506	
☐	PR-	ATR 72-600		o/o♦
☐	PR-	ATR 72-600		o/o♦
☐	PR-	ATR 72-600		o/o♦
☐	PR-	ATR 72-600		o/o♦
☐	PR-OAD	Fokker 100	11370	std
☐	PR-OAF	Fokker 100	11415	
☐	PR-OAG	Fokker 100	11412	[BSB]
☐	PR-OAI	Fokker 100	11417	std
☐	PR-OAJ	Fokker 100	11418	std
☐	PR-OAK	Fokker 100	11425	std
☐	PR-OAL	Fokker 100	11435	std
☐	PR-OAM	Fokker 100	11436	[BSB]
☐	PR-OAS	Fokker 100	11405	[BSB]
☐	PR-OAT	Fokker 100	11411	[CGH]
☐	PR-OAU	Fokker 100	11427	[BSB]

AZUL LINHAS AEREAS AD / AZU

	Reg	Type	c/n	Notes
☐	PR-	A320-251N	7283	o/o♦
☐	PR-	A320-251N		o/o♦
☐	PR-	A320-251N		o/o♦
☐	PR-	A320-251N		o/o♦
☐	PR-	A320-251N		o/o♦
☐	PR-	A320-251N		o/o♦
☐	PR-	A320-251N		o/o♦
☐	PR-	A320-251N		o/o♦
☐	PR-	A320-251N		o/o♦
☐	PR-	A320-251N		o/o♦
☐	PR-AIT	A330-243	529	♦
☐	PR-AIU	A330-243	494	♦
☐	PR-AIV	A330-243	532	
☐	PR-AIW	A330-243	462	
☐	PR-AIX	A330-243	372	
☐	PR-AIY	A330-243	365	
☐	PR-AIZ	A330-243	527	
☐	PR-TKF	ATR 42-500	579	
☐	PP-PTR	ATR 72-212A	785	
☐	PP-PTT	ATR 72-212A	846	
☐	PP-PTU	ATR 72-212A	891	[CNF]
☐	PP-PTX	ATR 72-212A	666	[LFBF]
☐	PP-PTY	ATR 72-212A	911	std
☐	PP-PTZ	ATR 72-212A	918	
☐	PR-AKA	ATR 72-600	1245	♦
☐	PR-AKB	ATR 72-600	1253	♦
☐	PR-AKC	ATR 72-600	1270	♦
☐	PR-AKD	ATR 72-600	1281	♦
☐	PR-AKE	ATR 72-600	1284	♦
☐	PR-AKF	ATR 72-600	1292	♦
☐	PR-AKG	ATR 72-600	1294	[PLU]♦
☐	PR-AQA	ATR 72-600	1052	
☐	PR-AQB	ATR 72-600	1054	
☐	PR-AQC	ATR 72-600	1057	
☐	PR-AQD	ATR 72-600	1060	
☐	PR-AQE	ATR 72-600	1066	
☐	PR-AQF	ATR 72-600	1072	
☐	PR-AQG	ATR 72-600	1076	
☐	PR-AQH	ATR 72-600	1082	
☐	PR-AQI	ATR 72-600	1088	
☐	PR-AQJ	ATR 72-600	1094	
☐	PR-AQK	ATR 72-600	1100	
☐	PR-AQL	ATR 72-600	1102	
☐	PR-AQM	ATR 72-600	1113	
☐	PR-AQN	ATR 72-600	1115	
☐	PR-AQO	ATR 72-600	1138	
☐	PR-AQP	ATR 72-600	1144	
☐	PR-AQQ	ATR 72-600	1166	
☐	PR-AQR	ATR 72-600	1173	
☐	PR-AQS	ATR 72-600	1180	
☐	PR-AQT	ATR 72-600	1190	
☐	PR-AQV	ATR 72-600	1195	
☐	PR-AQW	ATR 72-600	1232	[PLU]
☐	PR-AQX	ATR 72-600	1233	std♦
☐	PR-AQY	ATR 72-600	1236	♦
☐	PR-AQZ	ATR 72-600	1241	♦
☐	PR-ATB	ATR 72-600	969	
☐	PR-ATE	ATR 72-600	972	
☐	PR-ATG	ATR 72-600	988	
☐	PR-ATH	ATR 72-600	991	
☐	PR-ATJ	ATR 72-600	996	
☐	PR-ATK	ATR 72-600	1020	
☐	PR-ATP	ATR 72-600	1026	
☐	PR-ATQ	ATR 72-600	1027	
☐	PR-ATR	ATR 72-600	966	
☐	PR-ATU	ATR 72-600	1033	
☐	PR-ATV	ATR 72-600	1043	
☐	PR-ATW	ATR 72-600	1046	
☐	PR-ATZ	ATR 72-600	1047	
☐	PR-TKI	ATR 72-600	967	
☐	PR-TKJ	ATR 72-600	971	
☐	PR-TKK	ATR 72-600	987	
☐	PR-TKL	ATR 72-600	992	
☐	PR-TKM	ATR 72-600	998	
☐	PP-PJJ	ERJ-190LR	19000163	
☐	PP-PJK	ERJ-190LR	19000178	
☐	PP-PJL	ERJ-190LR	19000189	
☐	PP-PJM	ERJ-190LR	19000432	
☐	PP-PJN	ERJ-190LR	19000441	
☐	PP-PJO	ERJ-190LR	19000450	
☐	PP-PJP	ERJ-190LR	19000460	
☐	PP-PJQ	ERJ-190LR	19000493	
☐	PP-PJR	ERJ-190LR	19000495	
☐	PP-PJT	ERJ-190LR	19000506	
☐	PP-PJU	ERJ-190LR	19000541	
☐	PP-PJV	ERJ-190LR	19000550	
☐	PR-AZA	ERJ-190AR	19000150	
☐	PR-AZB	ERJ-190AR	19000241	
☐	PR-AZC	ERJ-190AR	19000242	
☐	PR-AZD	ERJ-190AR	19000271	
☐	PR-AZE	ERJ-190AR	19000282	
☐	PR-AZF	ERJ-190AR	19000295	
☐	PR-AZG	ERJ-190AR	19000329	
☐	PR-AZH	ERJ-190AR	19000330	
☐	PR-AZI	ERJ-190AR	19000336	
☐	PR-AZL	ERJ-190AR	19000147	
☐	PR-AUA	ERJ-195AR	19000652	
☐	PR-AUB	ERJ-195AR	19000660	
☐	PR-AUC	ERJ-195AR	19000662	
☐	PR-AUD	ERJ-195AR	19000669	
☐	PR-AUE	ERJ-195AR	19000677	
☐	PR-AUF	ERJ-195AR	19000678	
☐	PR-AUH	ERJ-195AR	19000685	
☐	PR-AUI	ERJ-195AR	19000686	
☐	PR-AUJ	ERJ-195AR	19000688	♦
☐	PR-AUK	ERJ-190AR	19000692	♦
☐	PR-AUM	ERJ-195AR	19000693	♦
☐	PR-AUN	ERJ-195AR	19000696	♦

	Reg	Type	C/n	
☐	PR-AUO	ERJ-195AR	19000697	♦
☐	PR-AUP	ERJ-195AR	19000698	♦
☐	PR-AUQ	ERJ-195AR	19000699	♦
☐	PR-AXA	ERJ-195AR	19000491	
☐	PR-AXB	ERJ-195AR	19000498	
☐	PR-AXC	ERJ-195AR	19000510	
☐	PR-AXD	ERJ-195AR	19000514	
☐	PR-AXE	ERJ-195AR	19000521	
☐	PR-AXF	ERJ-195AR	19000530	
☐	PR-AXG	ERJ-195AR	19000540	
☐	PR-AXH	ERJ-195AR	19000569	
☐	PR-AXI	ERJ-195AR	19000575	
☐	PR-AXJ	ERJ-195AR	19000580	
☐	PR-AXK	ERJ-195AR	19000585	
☐	PR-AXL	ERJ-195AR	19000588	
☐	PR-AXN	ERJ-195AR	19000590	
☐	PR-AXO	ERJ-195AR	19000592	
☐	PR-AXP	ERJ-195AR	19000600	
☐	PR-AXQ	ERJ-195AR	19000609	
☐	PR-AXR	ERJ-195AR	19000615	
☐	PR-AXS	ERJ-195AR	19000620	
☐	PR-AXT	ERJ-195AR	19000621	
☐	PR-AXU	ERJ-195AR	19000626	
☐	PR-AXV	ERJ-195AR	19000628	
☐	PR-AXW	ERJ-195AR	19000638	
☐	PR-AXX	ERJ-195AR	19000647	
☐	PR-AXY	ERJ-195AR	19000648	
☐	PR-AXZ	ERJ-195AR	19000650	
☐	PR-AYA	ERJ-195AR	19000237	
☐	PR-AYB	ERJ-195AR	19000239	
☐	PR-AYC	ERJ-195AR	19000240	
☐	PR-AYD	ERJ-195AR	19000247	
☐	PR-AYE	ERJ-195AR	19000260	
☐	PR-AYF	ERJ-195AR	19000353	
☐	PR-AYG	ERJ-195AR	19000356	
☐	PR-AYH	ERJ-195AR	19000361	
☐	PR-AYI	ERJ-195AR	19000366	
☐	PR-AYJ	ERJ-195AR	19000370	
☐	PR-AYK	ERJ-195AR	19000374	
☐	PR-AYL	ERJ-195AR	19000378	
☐	PR-AYM	ERJ-195AR	19000382	
☐	PR-AYN	ERJ-195AR	19000386	
☐	PR-AYO	ERJ-195AR	19000391	
☐	PR-AYP	ERJ-195AR	19000396	
☐	PR-AYQ	ERJ-195AR	19000407	
☐	PR-AYR	ERJ-195AR	19000413	
☐	PR-AYS	ERJ-195AR	19000419	
☐	PR-AYT	ERJ-195AR	19000429	
☐	PR-AYU	ERJ-195AR	19000434	
☐	PR-AYV	ERJ-195AR	19000449	
☐	PR-AYW	ERJ-195AR	19000458	
☐	PR-AYX	ERJ-195AR	19000471	
☐	PR-AYY	ERJ-195AR	19000475	
☐	PR-AYZ	ERJ-195AR	19000484	

COLT TRANSPORTE AEREAS — *XCA*

	Reg	Type	C/n	
☐	PR-IOX	B737-4B6F	26529/2584	
☐	PR-IOY	B737-4B6F	26526/2219	
☐	PR-XCA	B757-28A(ASF)	24235/180	♦

FLYWAYS LINHAS AEREAS — *FYW*

	Reg	Type	C/n	
☐	PP-STY	ATR 72-202	367	♦
☐	PR-TKN	ATR 72-212A	580	

GENSA - GENERAL SERVICES — *GEN*

	Reg	Type	C/n	
☐	PT-SHN	EMB.110P1A	110460	
☐	PT-SOG	EMB.110P1A	110490	

GOL TRANSPORTES AEREOS — *G3 / GLO*

	Reg	Type	C/n	
☐	PR-GEA	B737-7EH/W	37595/3026	
☐	PR-GEC	B737-7EH/W	37608/3678	
☐	PR-GED	B737-7EH/W	37609/3799	
☐	PR-GEE	B737-73V/W	32415/1260	
☐	PR-GEH	B737-76N/W	34757/2241	♦
☐	PR-GEI	B737-76N/W	34758/2266	♦
☐	PR-GEJ	B737-76N/W	34753/2165	♦
☐	PR-GEK	B737-76N/W	34755/2187	♦
☐	PR-GIF	B737-73S	29076/98	
☐	PR-GIG	B737-73S	29077/104	
☐	PR-GIH	B737-76N/W	32743/1503	
☐	PR-GII	B737-7L9	28011/1203	std
☐	PR-GIJ	B737-7L9	28012/1092	std
☐	PR-GIM	B737-73V	30238/913	
☐	PR-GIN	B737-73V	30242/890	
☐	PR-GOG	B737-76Q	30275/900	
☐	PR-GOH	B737-76N	32440/954	
☐	PR-GOI	B737-76N	32574/983	
☐	PR-GOM	B737-76N	28613/463	
☐	PR-GON	B737-76N	30051/436	
☐	PR-GOQ	B737-76N	33417/1215	>VRN
☐	PR-GOR	B737-76N	33380/1231	
☐	PR-GOV	B737-76N	28580/135	
☐	PR-GOW	B737-76N	28584/170	
☐	PR-VBH	B737-73V	30239/944	
☐	PR-VBI	B737-73V	30246/1064	
☐	PR-VBO	B737-73V	30247/1066	
☐	PR-VBV	B737-76N/W	30050/429	
☐	PR-VBW	B737-7BX	30739/758	
☐	PR-VBX	B737-7BX	30738/716	

	Reg	Type	C/n	
☐	PR-GGA	B737-8EH/W	35063/2476	
☐	PR-GGB	B737-8EH/W	35064/2498	
☐	PR-GGD	B737-8EH/W	34275/2588	
☐	PR-GGE	B737-8EH/W	35824/2665	
☐	PR-GGF	B737-8EH/W	35826/2749	
☐	PR-GGG	B737-8EH/W	36566/2809	
☐	PR-GGH	B737-8EH/W	36147/2864	
☐	PR-GGJ	B737-8EH/W	35825/2786	
☐	PR-GGK	B737-8EH/W	35065/2561	
☐	PR-GGL	B737-8EH/W	36148/2890	
☐	PR-GGM	B737-8EH/W	36149/2920	
☐	PR-GGN	B737-8EH/W	35827/2991	
☐	PR-GGO	B737-8EH/W	35828/3025	
☐	PR-GGP	B737-8EH/W	35829/3076	
☐	PR-GGQ	B737-8EH/W	37596/3103	
☐	PR-GGR	B737-8EH/W	36150/3106	
☐	PR-GGT	B737-8EH/W	35830/3115	
☐	PR-GGU	B737-8EH/W	37597/3133	
☐	PR-GGV	B737-8EH/W	37598/3136	
☐	PR-GGW	B737-8EH/W	35831/3165	
☐	PR-GGX	B737-8EH/W	36596/3180	
☐	PR-GGY	B737-8EH/W	37599/3191	
☐	PR-GGZ	B737-8EH/W	37600/3205	
☐	PR-GIT	B737-809	28403/117	
☐	PR-GIU	B737-809	29103/129	
☐	PR-GIV	B737-86N/W	28578/89	
☐	PR-GIW	B737-86N/W	28575/91	std
☐	PR-GOP	B737-8BK	30621/1194	
☐	PR-GTA	B737-8EH/W	34474/1843	
☐	PR-GTB	B737-8EH/W	34475/2020	
☐	PR-GTC	B737-8EH/W	34277/2028	
☐	PR-GTE	B737-8EH/W	34278/2052	
☐	PR-GTF	B737-8EH/W	34279/2061	

	Reg.	Type	C/n	
☐	PR-GTG	B737-8EH/W	34654/2075	
☐	PR-GTH	B737-8EH/W	34655/2091	
☐	PR-GTI	B737-8EH/W	34280/2100	
☐	PR-GTJ	B737-8EH/W	34656/2110	
☐	PR-GTK	B737-8EH/W	34281/2116	
☐	PR-GTL	B737-8EH/W	34962/2215	
☐	PR-GTM	B737-8EH/W	34963/2240	
☐	PR-GTN	B737-8EH/W	34267/2311	
☐	PR-GTO	B737-8EH/W	34964/2332	
☐	PR-GTP	B737-8EH/W	34965/2341	
☐	PR-GTQ	B737-8EH/W	36146/2358	
☐	PR-GTR	B737-8EH/W	34966/2367	
☐	PR-GTT	B737-8EH/W	34268/2407	
☐	PR-GTU	B737-8EH/W	34269/2412	
☐	PR-GTV	B737-8EH/W	34270/2420	
☐	PR-GTY	B737-8EH/W	34273/2464	
☐	PR-GTZ	B737-8EH/W	34274/2468	
☐	PR-GUA	B737-8EH/W	37601/3301	
☐	PR-GUB	B737-8EH/W	35832/3309	
☐	PR-GUC	B737-8EH/W	35835/3430	
☐	PR-GUD	B737-8EH/W	35836/3466	
☐	PR-GUE	B737-8EH/W	35837/3473	
☐	PR-GUF	B737-8EH/W	35838/3508	
☐	PR-GUG	B737-8EH/W	35842/3639	
☐	PR-GUH	B737-8EH/W	35843/3667	
☐	PR-GUI	B737-8EH/W	35844/3722	
☐	PR-GUJ	B737-8EH/W	35851/3745	
☐	PR-GUK	B737-8EH/W	35852/3760	
☐	PR-GUL	B737-8EH/W	35845/3785	
☐	PR-GUM	B737-8EH/W	35846/3823	
☐	PR-GUN	B737-8EH/W	37610/3912	
☐	PR-GUO	B737-8EH/W	35850/4124	
☐	PR-GUP	B737-8HX/W	38876/4114	
☐	PR-GUQ	B737-8EH/W	39604/4160	
☐	PR-GUR	B737-8HX/W	38877/4144	
☐	PR-GUT	B737-8HX/W	38878/4203	
☐	PR-GUU	B737-8EH/W	39607/4248	
☐	PR-GUV	B737-8EH/W	39609/4283	
☐	PR-GUW	B737-8EH/W	39608/4291	
☐	PR-GUX	B737-8EH/W	39611/4319	
☐	PR-GUY	B737-8EH/W	39612/4329	
☐	PR-GUZ	B737-8EH/W	39613/4353	
☐	PR-GXA	B737-8EH/W	39614/4387	
☐	PR-GXB	B737-8EH/W	39615/4382	
☐	PR-GXC	B737-8EH/W	39616/4432	
☐	PR-GXD	B737-8EH/W	39617/4435	
☐	PR-GXE	B737-8EH/W	39618/4501	
☐	PR-GXF	B737-8EH/W	39619/4509	
☐	PR-GXG	B737-8EH/W	39620/4529	
☐	PR-GXH	B737-8EH/W	39621/4544	
☐	PR-GXI	B737-8EH/W	39622/4551	
☐	PR-GXJ	B737-8EH/W	39623/4553	
☐	PR-GXK	B737-8EH/W	39624/4623	
☐	PR-GXL	B737-8EH/W	39625/4591	
☐	PR-GXM	B737-8EH/W	39629/4713	
☐	PR-GXN	B737-8EH/W	39631/4741	
☐	PR-GXO	B737-8EH/W	39632/4757	
☐	PR-GXP	B737-8EH/W	41163/4771	
☐	PR-GXQ	B737-8EH/W	39633/4779	
☐	PR-GXR	B737-8EH/W	39634/4801	
☐	PR-GXT	B737-8EH/W	39636/4844	
☐	PR-GXU	B737-8EH/W	39637/4856	
☐	PR-GXV	B737-8EH/W	39639/4931	
☐	PR-GXW	B737-8EH/W	39640/4933	
☐	PR-GXX	B737-8EH/W	41166/5224	
☐	PR-GXY	B737-8EH/W	40738/5384	
☐	PR-GXZ	B737-8EH/W	40739/5472	♦
☐	PR-GYA	B737-8EH/W	41170/5477	♦
☐	PR-GYB	B737-8EH/W	40741/5645	♦
☐	PR-GYC	B737-8EH/W	40742/5703	♦
☐	PR-GYD	B737-8EH/W	41467/5757	♦
☐	PR-GYE	B737-8EH/W	41179/5760	o/o♦
☐	PR-	B737-8EH/W		o/o
☐	PR-	B737-8EH/W		o/o
☐	PR-	B737-8EH/W		o/o
☐	PR-	B737-8EH/W		o/o

MAP LINHAS AEREAS — PAM

	Reg.	Type	C/n	
☐	PT-MFE	ATR 42-320	295	o/o♦
☐	PR-MPN	ATR 42-320	020	
☐	PR-MPO	ATR 42-320	091	
☐	PR-MPY	ATR 72-202	519	
☐	PR-MPZ	ATR 72-202	523	
☐	PT-LLC	EMB.110P1	110427	
☐	PT-SOF	EMB.110P1A	110486	
☐	PT-WDB	EMB.110C	110551	♦

MODERN LOGISTICS — MWM

	Reg.	Type	C/n	
☐	PP-YBA	B737-4K5F	24125/1687	o/o♦
☐	PR-YBB	B737-4Y0F	24683/1901	o/o♦

PASSAREDO LINHAS AEREAS — Y8 / PTB

	Reg.	Type	C/n	
☐	PP-PTM	ATR 72-212A	798	
☐	PP-PTN	ATR 72-212A	832	♦
☐	PP-PTO	ATR 72-212A	837	
☐	PP-PTP	ATR 72-212A	865	
☐	PP-PTQ	ATR 72-212A	874	
☐	PR-PDA	ATR 72-600	1022	
☐	PR-PDB	ATR 72-600	1028	
☐	PR-PDC	ATR 72-600	1040	
☐	PR-PDD	ATR 72-212A	562	
☐	PR-PDE	ATR 72-212A	565	
☐	PR-PDH	ATR 72-212A	572	
☐	PR-PDI	ATR 72-600	1059	
☐	PR-PDJ	ATR 72-212A	575	
☐	PR-PDK	ATR 72-212A	593	

RICO LINHAS AEREAS — C7 / RLE

	Reg.	Type	C/n	
☐	PT-WJA	EMB.110P1	110265	
☐	PT-WJG	EMB.120RT	120064	
☐	PT-WZM	EMB.120RT	120041	

RIO LINHAS AEREAS — R3 / RIO

	Reg.	Type	C/n	
☐	PR-IOB	B727-264F	22983/1806	
☐	PR-IOC	B727-264F	22984/1813	
☐	PR-IOD	B727-264F	23014/1816	
☐	PR-IOF	B727-214F	21692/1482	
☐	PR-IOG	B727-214F	21691/1480	
☐	PP-WSA	B737-4Q8F	25375/2598	

SIDERAL AIR CARGO — SID

	Reg.	Type	C/n	
☐	PT-MFE	ATR 42-300	295	[MAO]♦
☐	PR-SDF	B737-3H6(SF)	27347/2615	♦
☐	PR-SDG	B737-33A(QC)	25426/2172	♦
☐	PR-SDJ	B737-4YOF	24906/2009	
☐	PR-SDL	B737-3S3F	24060/1519	
☐	PR-SDT	B737-4B6F	26530/2588	♦
☐	PR-SDU	B737-4B6F	24808/1888	
☐	PR-SDV	B737-4Q8F	25377/2717	♦
☐	PR-SDW	B737-3B3(QC)	26851/2267	o/o♦

STERNA LINHAS AEREAS				
☐	PR-STN	A300B4-203F	236	♦

TAM CARGO				M3 / TUS
☐	PR-ABB	B767-316F/W	29881/778	
☐	PR-ABD	B767-316F/W	34245/934	
☐	PR-ACO	B767-346F/W	35817/959	
☐	PR-ACQ	B767-346F/W	35818/960	♦
☐	PR-ADZ	B767-346F/W	35816/956	o/o
☐		B777-F		o/o♦
☐		B777-F		o/o♦

** also known as ABSA Cargo; see also LAN Cargo (CC-)*

TAM LINHAS AEREAS				JJ / TAM
☐	PR-MAL	A319-132	1801	
☐	PR-MAM	A319-132	1826	
☐	PR-MAN	A319-132	1831	
☐	PR-MAO	A319-132	1837	
☐	PR-MAQ	A319-132	1855	
☐	PR-MBN	A319-132	3032	
☐	PR-MBU	A319-132	3588	
☐	PR-MBV	A319-132	3595	
☐	PR-MBW	A319-132	3710	
☐	PR-MYB	A319-112	3727	
☐	PR-MYC	A319-112	3733	
☐	PR-MYL	A319-112	4734	
☐	PR-MYM	A319-112	4756	
☐	PT-MZC	A319-132	1092	
☐	PT-MZE	A319-132	1103	
☐	PT-TMA	A319-132	4000	
☐	PT-TMB	A319-132	4163	
☐	PT-TMC	A319-132	4171	
☐	PT-TMD	A319-132	4192	
☐	PT-TME	A319-132	4389	
☐	PT-TMF	A319-132	2467	
☐	PT-TMG	A319-132	4773	
☐	PT-TMH	A319-132	2784	
☐	PT-TMI	A319-132	5345	
☐	PT-TML	A319-132	2887	♦
☐	(PT-TMM)	A319-132	2886	o/o♦
☐	PR-MAA	A320-232	1595	
☐	PR-MAE	A320-232	1804	
☐	PR-MAG	A320-232	1832	
☐	PR-MAJ	A320-232	1818	
☐	PR-MAK	A320-232	1825	
☐	PR-MAP	A320-232	1857	
☐	PR-MAR	A320-232	1888	
☐	PR-MAS	A320-232	2372	
☐	PR-MAV	A320-232	2393	
☐	PR-MAY	A320-232	2661	
☐	PR-MAZ	A320-232	2513	
☐	PR-MBA	A320-232	2734	
☐	PR-MBB	A320-232	2737	
☐	PR-MBD	A320-232	2838	
☐	PR-MBE	A320-232	2859	
☐	PR-MBF	A320-232	2896	
☐	PR-MBG	A320-232	1459	
☐	PR-MBH	A320-232	2904	
☐	PR-MBL	A320-233	2044	
☐	PR-MBO	A320-232	3156	
☐	PR-MBP	A320-232	1215	
☐	PR-MBQ	A320-232	1652	
☐	PR-MBR	A320-232	1802	
☐	PR-MBS	A320-232	1835	
☐	PR-MBT	A320-233	2014	
☐	PR-MBX	A320-232	1591	
☐	PR-MBY	A320-232	1891	
☐	PR-MBZ	A320-232	1827	
☐	PR-MHA	A320-214	2924	
☐	PR-MHB	A320-214	1692	
☐	PR-MHE	A320-214	3111	
☐	PR-MHF	A320-214	3180	
☐	PR-MHG	A320-214	3002	
☐	PR-MHI	A320-214	3035	
☐	PR-MHJ	A320-214	3047	
☐	PR-MHK	A320-214	3058	
☐	PR-MHM	A320-214	3211	
☐	PR-MHP	A320-214	3266	
☐	PR-MHQ	A320-214	3284	
☐	PR-MHR	A320-214	3313	
☐	PR-MHS	A320-214	3325	[MPL]
☐	PR-MHU	A320-214	3391	
☐	PR-MHV	A320-214	3540	
☐	PR-MHW	A320-214	3630	
☐	PR-MHX	A320-214	3565	
☐	PR-MHY	A320-214	3594	
☐	PR-MHZ	A320-214	3658	
☐	PR-MYA	A320-214	3662	
☐	PR-MYD	A320-214	3750	
☐	PR-MYE	A320-214	3908	
☐	PR-MYF	A320-214	3972	
☐	PR-MYG	A320-214	4320	
☐	PR-MYH	A320-214	4441	
☐	PR-MYI	A320-214	4446	
☐	PR-MYJ	A320-214	4465	
☐	PR-MYK	A320-214	4544	
☐	PR-MYN	A320-214	4953	
☐	PR-MYO	A320-214	4974	
☐	PR-MYP	A320-214	5066	
☐	PR-MYQ	A320-214	5101	
☐	PR-MYR	A320-214	5107	
☐	PR-MYS	A320-214	5109	
☐	PR-MYT	A320-214	5184	
☐	PR-MYU	A320-214	5209	
☐	PR-MYV	A320-214	5222	
☐	PR-MYW	A320-214	5240	
☐	PR-MYX	A320-214	5342	
☐	PR-MYY	A320-214/S	5591	
☐	PR-MYZ	A320-214/S	5621	
☐	PR-TYA	A320-214/S	5643	
☐	PR-TYD	A320-214/S	5749	
☐	PR-TYF	A320-214/S	5752	
☐	PR-TYG	A320-214/S	5845	
☐	PR-TYH	A320-214/S	5883	
☐	PT-MZG	A320-232	1143	
☐	PT-MZH	A320-232	1158	
☐	PT-MZI	A320-232	1246	
☐	PT-MZJ	A320-232	1251	
☐	PT-MZL	A320-232	1376	
☐	PT-MZN	A320-231	0440	
☐	PT-MZT	A320-232	1486	
☐	PT-MZU	A320-232	1518	
☐	PT-MZW	A320-232	1580	
☐	PT-MZY	A320-232	1628	
☐	PT-MZZ	A320-232	1593	
☐	PT-	A320-271N	7126	o/o♦
☐	PT-MXA	A321-231	3222	
☐	PT-MXB	A321-231	3229	
☐	PT-MXC	A321-231	3294	
☐	PT-MXD	A321-231	3761	
☐	PT-MXE	A321-231	3816	

☐	PT-MXF	A321-231	4352	
☐	PT-MXG	A321-231	4358	
☐	PT-MXH	A321-231	4570	
☐	PT-MXI	A321-231	4662	
☐	PT-MXJ	A321-231/S	5528	
☐	PT-MXL	A321-231/S	5947	
☐	PT-MXM	A321-231/S	5987	
☐	PT-MXN	A321-231/S	6097	
☐	PT-MXO	A321-231/S	6121	
☐	PT-MXP	A321-231/S	6163	
☐	PT-MXQ	A321-231/S	6165	
☐	PT-XPA	A321-211/S	6409	
☐	PT-XPB	A321-211/S	6414	
☐	PT-XPC	A321-211/S	6592	♦
☐	PT-XPD	A321-211/S	6632	♦
☐	PT-XPE	A321-211/S	6658	♦
☐	PT-XPF	A321-211/S	6670	♦
☐	PT-XPG	A321-211/S	6685	♦
☐	PT-XPH	A321-211/S	6718	♦
☐	PT-XPI	A321-211/S	6729	♦
☐	PT-XPJ	A321-211/S	6798	♦
☐	PT-XPL	A321-211/S	6895	♦
☐	PT-XPM	A321-211/S	6949	♦
☐	PT-XPN	A321-211/S	7005	o/o♦
☐	PT-	A321-211/S	7081	o/o♦
☐	PT-	A321-211/S	7098	o/o♦
☐	PT-	A321-211/S	7127	o/o♦
☐	PT-	A321-211/S	7128	o/o♦
☐	PT-	A321-211/S	7239	o/o♦
☐	PT-	A321-211/S	7313	o/o♦
☐	PT-	A321-211/S	7323	o/o♦
☐	PT-	A321-211/S	7369	o/o♦
☐	PT-	A321-211/S	7390	o/o♦
☐	PT-MVA	A330-223	232	[LDE]
☐	PT-MVB	A330-223	238	[LDE]
☐	PT-MVC	A330-223	247	
☐	PT-MVD	A330-223	259	
☐	PT-MVE	A330-223	361	[QSC]
☐	PT-MVF	A330-203	466	
☐	PT-MVG	A330-203	472	
☐	PT-MVL	A330-203	700	
☐	PT-MVQ	A330-223	968	
☐	PT-MVS	A330-223	1112	
☐	PR-XTA	A350-941	024	♦
☐	PR-XTB	A350-941	027	o/o♦
☐	PR-XTC	A350-941	035	o/o♦
☐	PR-XTD	A350-941	045	o/o♦
☐	PR-XTE	A350-941	048	o/o♦
☐	PR-XTF	A350-941	064	o/o♦
☐	PR-XTG	A350-941	079	o/o♦
☐	PT-MOA	B767-316ER/W	41995/1049	
☐	PT-MOB	B767-316ER/W	40592/1031	
☐	PT-MOC	B767-316ER/W	41746/1033	
☐	PT-MOE	B767-316ER/W	41996/1052	
☐	PT-MOF	B767-316ER/W	41997/1055	
☐	PT-MOG	B767-316ER/W	29227/698	
☐	PT-MOH	B767-316ER/W	27615/681	♦
☐	PT-MSO	B767-316ER/W	41747/1034	
☐	PT-MSS	B767-316ER/W	41748/1037	
☐	PT-MSV	B767-316ER/W	40593/1038	
☐	PT-MSW	B767-316ER/W	42213/1040	
☐	PT-MSX	B767-316ER/W	41993/1042	
☐	PT-MSY	B767-316ER/W	42214/1043	
☐	PT-MSZ	B767-316ER/W	41994/1045	
☐	PT-MUA	B777-32WER	37664/727	
☐	PT-MUB	B777-32WER	37665/733	
☐	PT-MUC	B777-32WER	37666/740	
☐	PT-MUD	B777-32WER	37667/751	
☐	PT-MUE	B777-32WER	38886/1036	
☐	PT-MUF	B777-32WER	38887/1042	
☐	PT-MUG	B777-32WER	38888/1052	
☐	PT-MUH	B777-32WER	38889/1059	
☐	PT-MUI	B777-32WER	40589/1118	
☐	PT-MUJ	B777-32WER	40588/1128	

TOTAL LINHAS AEREAS — *TTL*

☐	PR-TKB	ATR 42-500	610	
☐	PR-TTH	ATR 42-500	506	♦
☐	PR-TTK	ATR 42-500	504	
☐	PR-TTM	ATR 42-500	551	♦
☐	PR-TTO	B727-2M7F	21200/1206	
☐	PR-TTP	B727-2M7F	21502/1339	
☐	PR-TTW	B727-225F	22438/1685	
☐	PT-MTQ	B727-243F	22053/1620	
☐	PT-MTT	B727-243F	22167/1752	

VARIG — *RG / VRN*

☐	PR-GOQ	B737-76N	33417/1215	<GLO♦
☐	PR-VBF	B737-8EH/W	34276/2716	
☐	PR-VBG	B737-8EH/W	35066/2700	
☐	PR-VBJ	B737-86N/W	36434/2706	
☐	PR-VBK	B737-8EH/W	34271/2445	
☐	PR-VBL	B737-8EH/W	34272/2449	
☐	PR-VBM	B737-7EA	32406/859	[CNF]
☐	PR-VBN	B737-76N	28577/124	[CNF]
☐	PR-VBP	B737-7EA	32407/904	
☐	PR-VBQ	B737-76N	30135/1068	
☐	PR-VBU	B737-76N/W	29905/372	
☐	PR-VBY	B737-73A/W	28499/390	
☐	PR-VBZ	B737-73A/W	28500/414	

Fleet merged & operates on GOL's AOC.

PZ- SURINAME

BLUE WING AIRLINES — *BWI*

☐	PZ-TSA	PZL An-28	1AJ-21	
☐	PZ-TSD	DHC-6 Twin Otter 200	117	
☐	PZ-TSH	DHC-6 Twin Otter 200	145	
☐	PZ-TSN	PZL An-28	1AJ-20	
☐	PZ-TFA	Fokker 70	11556	♦
☐	PZ-TFB	Fokker 70	11570	♦

GUM AIR — *GUM*

☐	PZ-TBN	DHC-6 Twin Otter 310	476	♦
☐	PZ-TBY	DHC-6 Twin Otter 300	646	

SURINAM AIRWAYS — *PY / SLM*

☐	CS-TQP	A330-202	211	<HFY♦
☐	PZ-TCN	B737-36N	28668/2890	
☐	PZ-TCO	B737-36N	28669/2897	
☐	PZ-TCP	A340-311	049	[MZJ]
☐	PZ-TCQ	B737-3Q8	26295/2557	
☐	PZ-TCR	A340-313X	242	♦

P2- PAPUA NEW GUINEA

AIR NIUGINI — *PX / ANG*

☐	P2-PXC	B737-86Q/W	30290/1406	

	Reg	Type	c/n	Notes
☐	P2-PXD	B737-7L9/W	28007/136	
☐	P2-PXE	B737-8BK/W	33024/1688	
☐	P2-PXV	B767-341ER	30341/768	
☐	P2-PXW	B767-383ER	25365/395	
☐	P2-	B787-8		o/o
☐	P2-ANK	DHC-8Q-202	461	^
☐	P2-ANM	DHC-8Q-314	523	^
☐	P2-ANN	DHC-8-315	401	^
☐	P2-ANO	DHC-8-311A	252	^
☐	P2-ANX	DHC-8Q-202	463	^
☐	P2-PXI	DHC-8Q-202	460	^
☐	P2-PXL	DHC-8-314	385	^
☐	P2-PXS	DHC-8-402Q	4262	
☐	P2-PXT	DHC-8-402Q	4329	
☐	P2-PXU	DHC-8-402Q	4316	

^ operates Link PNG

	Reg	Type	c/n	Notes
☐	P2-ANC	Fokker 100	11471	
☐	P2-AND	Fokker 100	11473	
☐	P2-ANE	Fokker 100	11264	
☐	P2-ANF	Fokker 100	11351	
☐	P2-ANH	Fokker 100	11301	
☐	P2-ANJ	Fokker 100	11472	
☐	P2-ANQ	Fokker 100	11451	
☐	P2-ANR	Fokker 70	11578	
☐	P2-ANS	Fokker 70	11580	♦
☐	P2-ANT	Fokker 70	11577	♦
☐	P2-ANU	Fokker 70	11538	♦
☐	P2-ANY	Fokker 70	11551	o/o♦
☐	P2-ANZ	Fokker 70	11563	o/o♦
☐	P2-	Fokker 70	11551	o/o♦
☐	P2-	Fokker 70	11563	o/o♦

PNG AIR — CG / TOK

	Reg	Type	c/n	Notes
☐	P2-ATA	ATR 72-600	1301	♦
☐	P2-ATR	ATR 72-600	1287	♦
☐	P2-	ATR 72-600		o/o♦
☐	P2-	ATR 72-600		o/o♦
☐	P2-EMO	DHC-6 Twin Otter 300	726	
☐	P2-MCC	DHC-6 Twin Otter 200	218	
☐	P2-MCR	DHC-6 Twin Otter 200	219	
☐	P2-MCV	DHC-6 Twin Otter 300	280	
☐	P2-MCX	DHC-6 Twin Otter 310	703	
☐	P2-MCG	DHC-8-102	006	
☐	P2-MCH	DHC-8-102	012	
☐	P2-MCI	DHC-8-102	197	
☐	P2-MCK	DHC-8-102	041	
☐	P2-MCL	DHC-8-102	027	
☐	P2-MCM	DHC-8-103	211	
☐	P2-MCN	DHC-8-102A	380	
☐	P2-MCO	DHC-8-103	366	
☐	P2-MCP	DHC-8-102	033	
☐	P2-MCQ	DHC-8-103A	243	
☐	P2-MCT	DHC-8-102	135	
☐	P2-MCU	DHC-8-102	208	
☐	P2-MCW	DHC-8-102	067	
☐	P2-MCY	DHC-8-102	237	std
☐	P2-LAC	L-382G-35C Hercules	4676	<LYC

ASIA PACIFIC AIRLINES — A6 / MLP

	Reg	Type	c/n	Notes
☐	P2-NAT	DHC-8-103	170	
☐	P2-NAX	DHC-8-103	229	<NJS
☐	P2-NAZ	DHC-8-106	316	<NJS

HEVILIFT - PNG

	Reg	Type	c/n	Notes
☐	P2-AVV	ATR 42-320	304	
☐	P2-KSJ	ATR 42-320	096	
☐	P2-KSL	ATR 42-500	497	
☐	P2-KSR	ATR 42-320	194	
☐	P2-KSV	ATR 42-500	501	
☐	P2-KSB	DHC-6 Twin Otter 300	485	
☐	P2-KSG	DHC-6 Twin Otter 300	509	
☐	P2-KSI	DHC-6 Twin Otter 300	706	
☐	P2-KSO	DHC-6 Twin Otter 300	592	♦
☐	P2-KST	DHC-6 Twin Otter 300	520	
☐	P2-KSU	DHC-6 Twin Otter 300	673	♦
☐	P2-KSW	DHC-6 Twin Otter 310	703	♦
☐	P2-KSY	DHC-6 Twin Otter 400	875	

TRAVEL AIR — 4P

	Reg	Type	c/n	Notes
☐	P2-TAE	Fokker 50	20202	
☐	P2-TAG	Fokker 50	20177	
☐	P2-TAH	Fokker 50	20122	

P4- ARUBA

ARUBA AIRLINES — AG / ARU

	Reg	Type	c/n	Notes
☐	P4-AAA	A320-232	0582	
☐	P4-AAC	A320-232	0573	
☐	P4-AAD	A320-232	0805	♦

CRYSTAL LUXURY AIR

	Reg	Type	c/n	Notes
☐	P4-XTL	B777-29MLR	40955/952	♦
☐	P4-	787-8	35507/17	o/o♦
☐	P4-	787-8	35508/19	o/o♦

INSEL AIR INTERNATIONAL ARUBA — BI / NLU

	Reg	Type	c/n	Notes
☐	PJ-KVG	Fokker 50	20211	
☐	PJ-KVI	Fokker 50	20218	
☐	PJ-KVK	Fokker 50	20219	
☐	P4-FKA	Fokker 70	11528	
☐	P4-FKB	Fokker 70	11537	
☐	P4-FKC	Fokker 70	11583	
☐	P4-MDD	MD-82	49972/1757	
☐	P4-MDG	MD-83	49935/1773	[MZJ]
☐	P4-MDH	MD-83	53624/2277	
☐	P4-MDI	MD-83	49847/1585	♦

TIARA AIR — 3P / TNM

	Reg	Type	c/n	Notes
☐	P4-TIA	Short SD.3-60-100	SH3619	
☐	P4-TIB	Short SD.3-60-100	SH3621	
☐	P4-TIE	B737-322	24249/1638	[MIA]

RA- RUSSIA

AEROBRATSK — BRP

	Reg	Type	c/n	Notes
☐	RA-88205	Yak-40	9630749	
☐	RA-88215	Yak-40K	9630150	

AEROFLOT RUSSIAN AIRLINES — SU / AFL

	Reg	Type	c/n	Notes
☐	VQ-BBA	A319-111	3794	
☐	VQ-BCO	A319-111	3942	
☐	VQ-BCP	A319-111	3998	
☐	VP-BDK	A320-214	2106	

	Reg	Type	C/n	
☐	VP-BEO	A320-214/S	7038	o/o♦
☐	VP-BET	A320-214/S	7071	o/o♦
☐	VP-BID	A320-214	5421	
☐	VP-BJA	A320-214/S	5536	
☐	VP-BJW	A320-214/S	6954	o/o♦
☐	VP-BJY	A320-214/S	6963	o/o♦
☐	VP-BKC	A320-214	3545	
☐	VP-BKX	A320-214	3410	
☐	VP-BKY	A320-214	3511	
☐	VP-BLH	A320-214/S	5565	
☐	VP-BLL	A320-214/S	5572	
☐	VP-BLP	A320-214/S	5578	
☐	VP-BLR	A320-214/S	5585	
☐	VP-BME	A320-214	3699	
☐	VP-BMF	A320-214	3711	
☐	VP-BNL	A320-214/S	5580	
☐	VP-BNT	A320-214/S	5614	
☐	VP-BQP	A320-214	2875	
☐	VP-BQU	A320-214	3373	
☐	VP-BQV	A320-214	2920	
☐	VP-BQW	A320-214	2947	
☐	VP-BRX	A320-214	3063	
☐	VP-BRY	A320-214	3052	
☐	VP-BRZ	A320-214	3157	
☐	VP-BTI	A320-214/S	5873	
☐	VP-BWD	A320-214	2116	
☐	VP-BWE	A320-214	2133	
☐	VP-BWF	A320-214	2144	
☐	VP-BWM	A320-214	2233	
☐	VP-BZO	A320-214	3574	
☐	VP-BZP	A320-214	3631	
☐	VP-BZQ	A320-214	3627	
☐	VP-BZR	A320-214	3640	
☐	VP-BZS	A320-214	3644	
☐	VQ-BAX	A320-214	3778	
☐	VQ-BAY	A320-214	3786	
☐	VQ-BAZ	A320-214	3789	
☐	VQ-BBB	A320-214	3823	
☐	VQ-BBC	A320-214	3835	
☐	VQ-BCM	A320-214	3923	
☐	VQ-BCN	A320-214	3954	
☐	VQ-BEH	A320-214	4133	
☐	VQ-BEJ	A320-214	4160	
☐	VQ-BHL	A320-214	4453	
☐	VQ-BHN	A320-214	4498	
☐	VQ-BIR	A320-214	4625	
☐	VQ-BIT	A320-214	4656	
☐	VQ-BIU	A320-214	4684	
☐	VQ-BIV	A320-214	4649	
☐	VQ-BIW	A320-214	4579	
☐	VQ-BKS	A320-214	4692	
☐	VQ-BKT	A320-214	4712	
☐	VQ-BKU	A320-214	4835	
☐	VQ-BPU	A320-214/S	5921	
☐	VQ-BPV	A320-214/S	5970	
☐	VQ-BPW	A320-214/S	5982	
☐	VQ-BRV	A320-214/S	5967	
☐	VQ-BRW	A320-214/S	5974	
☐	VQ-BSE	A320-214/S	5989	
☐	VQ-BSG	A320-214/S	6017	
☐	VQ-BSH	A320-214/S	6022	
☐	VQ-BSI	A320-214/S	6043	
☐	VQ-BSJ	A320-214/S	6044	
☐	VQ-BSL	A320-214/S	6060	
☐	VQ-BST	A320-214/S	6071	
☐	VQ-BSU	A320-214/S	6090	
☐		A320-214/S	7226	o/o♦

	Reg	Type	C/n	
☐		A320-214/S	7240	o/o♦
☐		A320-214/S	7295	o/o♦
☐	VP-BDC	A321-211	5271	
☐	VP-BEW	A321-211/S	7072	o/o♦
☐	VP-BJX	A321-211/S	6945	o/o♦
☐	VP-BKI	A321-211/S	7137	o/o♦
☐	VP-BOC	A321-211	5720	
☐	VP-BOE	A321-211	5755	
☐	VP-BQR	A321-211	2903	
☐	VP-BQS	A321-211	2912	
☐	VP-BQT	A321-211	2965	
☐	VP-BQX	A321-211	2957	
☐	VP-BRW	A321-211	3191	
☐	VP-BTG	A321-211	5790	
☐	VP-BTL	A321-211	5881	
☐	VP-BTR	A321-211	5913	
☐	VP-BUM	A321-211	3267	
☐	VP-BUP	A321-211	3334	
☐	VP-BWN	A321-211	2330	
☐	VP-BWO	A321-211	2337	
☐	VP-BWP	A321-211	2342	
☐	VQ-BEA	A321-211	4058	
☐	VQ-BED	A321-211	4074	
☐	VQ-BEE	A321-211	4099	
☐	VQ-BEF	A321-211	4103	
☐	VQ-BEG	A321-211	4116	
☐	VQ-BEI	A321-211	4148	
☐	VQ-BHK	A321-211	4461	
☐	VQ-BHM	A321-211	4500	
☐	VQ-BOH	A321-211	5044	
☐	VQ-BOI	A321-211	5059	
☐		A321-211/S	7193	o/o♦
☐		A321-211/S	7202	o/o♦
☐		A321-211/S	7290	o/o♦
☐	VP-BDD	A330-343E	1356	
☐	VP-BDE	A330-343E	1371	
☐	VP-BLX	A330-243	963	
☐	VP-BLY	A330-243	973	
☐	VQ-BBE	A330-243	1014	
☐	VQ-BBF	A330-243	1045	
☐	VQ-BBG	A330-243	1047	
☐	VQ-BCQ	A330-343E	1058	
☐	VQ-BCU	A330-343E	1065	
☐	VQ-BCV	A330-343E	1072	
☐	VQ-BEK	A330-343E	1077	
☐	VQ-BEL	A330-343E	1103	
☐	VQ-BMV	A330-343E	1284	
☐	VQ-BMX	A330-343E	1299	
☐	VQ-BMY	A330-343E	1301	
☐	VQ-BNS	A330-343E	1264	
☐	VQ-BPI	A330-343E	1323	
☐	VQ-BPJ	A330-343E	1328	
☐	VQ-BPK	A330-343E	1345	
☐	VQ-BQX	A330-343E	1232	
☐	VQ-BQY	A330-343E	1247	
☐	VQ-BQZ	A330-343E	1270	
☐	VP-BCD	B737-8LJ/W	41215/5723	♦
☐	VP-BCF	B737-8LJ/W	41216/5767	♦
☐	VP-BON	B737-8LJ/W	41200/5063	
☐	VP-BRF	B737-8LJ/W	41195/4590	
☐	VP-BRH	B737-8LJ/W	41196/4665	
☐	VP-BRR	B737-8LJ/W	41197/4710	
☐	VP-BZA	B737-8LJ/W	41198/4753	
☐	VP-BZB	B737-8LJ/W	41199/4897	
☐	VQ-BVO	B737-8LJ/W	41203/5253	

☐ VQ-BVP B737-8LJ/W 41204/5291
☐ VQ-BWA B737-8LJ/W 41207/5377
☐ VQ-BWB B737-8LJ/W 41209/5468 ♦
☐ VQ-BWC B737-8LJ/W 41210/5480 ♦
☐ VQ-BWD B737-8LJ/W 41211/5516 ♦
☐ VQ-BWE B737-8LJ/W 41213/5652 ♦
☐ VQ-BWF B737-8LJ/W 41214/5690 ♦
☐ B737-8LJ/W 41217 o/o♦
☐ B737-8LJ/W 41218 o/o♦
☐ B737-8LJ/W 41219 o/o♦
☐ B737-8LJ/W 41220 o/o♦
☐ B737-8LJ/W 41221 o/o♦
☐ B737-8LJ/W 41222 o/o♦
☐ B737-8LJ/W 41223 o/o♦
☐ B737-8LJ/W 41224 o/o♦
☐ B737-8LJ/W 41225 o/o♦
☐ B737-8LJ/W 41226 o/o♦
☐ B737-8LJ/W 41227 o/o♦
☐ B737-8LJ/W 41228 o/o♦
☐ B737-8LJ/W 41229 o/o♦
☐ B737-8LJ/W 41239 o/o♦

☐ VP-BGB B777-3M0ER 41679/1068
☐ VP-BGC B777-3M0ER 41680/1079
☐ VP-BGD B777-3M0ER 41681/1084
☐ VP-BGF B777-3M0ER 41686/1097
☐ VQ-BQB B777-3M0ER 41687/1167
☐ VQ-BQC B777-3M0ER 41688/1175
☐ VQ-BQD B777-3M0ER 41682/1185
☐ VQ-BQE B777-3M0ER 41683/1190
☐ VQ-BQF B777-3M0ER 41684/1199
☐ VQ-BQG B777-3M0ER 41689/1205
☐ VQ-BQM B777-3M0ER 41694/1381 o/o♦
☐ VQ-BUA B777-3M0ER 41685/1281
☐ VQ-BUB B777-3M0ER 41690/1294
☐ VQ-BUC B777-3M0ER 41691/1299
☐ B777-3M0ER o/o♦
☐ B777-3M0ER o/o♦

☐ RA-89014 Sukhoi SSJ 100-95B 95025 [SVO]
☐ RA-89015 Sukhoi SSJ 100-95B 95029
☐ RA-89017 Sukhoi SSJ 100-95B 95035
☐ RA-89022 Sukhoi SSJ 100-95B 95039 [SVO]
☐ RA-89023 Sukhoi SSJ 100-95B 95041
☐ RA-89024 Sukhoi SSJ 100-95B 95044
☐ RA-89025 Sukhoi SSJ 100-95B 95047
☐ RA-89026 Sukhoi SSJ 100-95B 95051
☐ RA-89027 Sukhoi SSJ 100-95B 95053
☐ RA-89028 Sukhoi SSJ 100-95B 95059 ♦
☐ RA-89032 Sukhoi SSJ 100-95B 95043
☐ RA-89041 Sukhoi SSJ 100-95B 95063
☐ RA-89042 Sukhoi SSJ 100-95B 95068
☐ RA-89043 Sukhoi SSJ 100-95B 95074
☐ RA-89044 Sukhoi SSJ 100-95B 95076
☐ RA-89045 Sukhoi SSJ 100-95B 95079
☐ RA-89046 Sukhoi SSJ 100-95B 95082
☐ RA-89047 Sukhoi SSJ 100-95B 95084
☐ RA-89051 Sukhoi SSJ 100-95B 95089 ♦
☐ RA-89052 Sukhoi SSJ 100-95B 95088
☐ RA-89056 Sukhoi SSJ 100-95B 95094 ♦
☐ RA-89057 Sukhoi SSJ 100-95B 95097 ♦
☐ RA-89058 Sukhoi SSJ 100-95B 95098 ♦
☐ RA-89059 Sukhoi SSJ 100-95B 95100 o/o♦
☐ RA-89060 Sukhoi SSJ 100-95B 95103 o/o♦
☐ RA-89061 Sukhoi SSJ 100-95B 95090 ♦
☐ RA-89062 Sukhoi SSJ 100-95B 95091 ♦
☐ RA-89063 Sukhoi SSJ 100-95B 95099 ♦
☐ RA-89064 Sukhoi SSJ 100-95B 95101 o/o♦
☐ RA- Sukhoi SSJ 100-95B 95107 o/o♦
☐ RA- Sukhoi SSJ 100-95B 95116 o/o♦
☐ RA- Sukhoi SSJ 100-95B 95124 o/o♦
☐ RA- Sukhoi SSJ 100-95B 95126 o/o♦
☐ RA- Sukhoi SSJ 100-95B 95138 o/o♦

AIRBRIDGE CARGO *RU / ABW*

☐ VQ-BVF B737-46Q(F) 29001/3040 ♦
☐ TF-AMF B747-412BCF 24226/809 <ABD♦
☐ TF-AMP B747-481BDSF 24801/805 <ABD♦
☐ VP-BIG B747-46NERF 35420/1395
☐ VP-BIK B747-46NERF 35421/1400
☐ VP-BIM B747-4HAERF 35237/1402
☐ VQ-BFE B747-83QF 60118/1502 ♦
☐ VQ-BFU B747-8HVF 60117/1501 ♦
☐ VQ-BGZ B747-8HVF 37580/1430
☐ VQ-BHE B747-4KZF 36784/1411
☐ VQ-BIA B747-4KZF 36785/1418
☐ VQ-BLQ B747-8HVF 37581/1448
☐ VQ-BLR B747-8HVF 37668/1452
☐ VQ-BRH B747-8HVF 37669/1463
☐ VQ-BRJ B747-8HVF 37670/1482
☐ VQ-BUU B747-4EVERF 35170/1376
☐ VQ-BVR B747-867F 60687/1505
☐ VQ-BWW B747-406ERF 35233/1382
☐ B747-8HVF o/o♦
☐ B747-8HVF o/o♦
☐ B747-8HVF o/o♦

ALROSA AVIATION *6R / DRU*

☐ RA-46488 An-24RV 27308106
☐ RA-46621 An-24RV 37308708
☐ RA-47272 An-24B 07306402
☐ RA-47694 An-24B 27307601
☐ RA-26552 An-26 3107
☐ RA-26628 An-26 5309
☐ RA-26668 An-26B-100 8201

☐ EI-ECL B737-86N/W 32655/1662
☐ EI-ECM B737-86N/W 32658/1695
☐ EI-FCH B737-83N/W 32576/875
☐ VP-BKD DHC-8-402Q 4162

☐ RA-76360 Il-76TD 1033414492
☐ RA-76420 Il-76TD 1023413446

☐ RA-65146 Tu-134B-3 61000
☐ RA-65653 Tu-134A 0351009
☐ RA-65693 Tu-134B-3 63221 VIP
☐ RA-65715 Tu-134B-3 63536

☐ RA-85654 Tu-154M 89A796
☐ RA-85675 Tu-154M 90A835
☐ RA-85684 Tu-154M 90A851
☐ RA-85728 Tu-154M 92A910
☐ RA-85757 Tu-154M 92A939
☐ RA-85770 Tu-154M 93A952
☐ RA-85782 Tu-154M 93A966 [NOZ]

AMUR AVIAKOMPANIA

☐ RA-13344 An-24RV 37308310
☐ RA-26001 An-26 9705
☐ RA-26048 An-26B 10901
☐ RA-46612 An-24RV 37308609 ♦
☐ RA-87395 Yak-40 9410733
☐ RA-88153 Yak-40 9610746

ANGARA AIRLINES — AGU

	Reg	Type	c/n	
☐	RA-46612	An-24RV	37308609	
☐	RA-46625	An-24RV	37308804	
☐	RA-46662	An-24RV	47309410	
☐	RA-46697	An-24RV	47309908	
☐	RA-46712	An-24RV	57310408	
☐	RA-47366	An-24RV	77310804	
☐	RA-47818	An-24RV	17307107	
☐	RA-47848	An-24B	17307410	
☐	RA-26511	An-26-100	6808	
☐	RA-26543	An-26	2709	
☐	RA-26655	An-26-100	7802	
☐	RA-61709	An-148-100E	27015040009	
☐	RA-61710	An-148-100E	27015040010	
☐	RA-61711	An-148-100E	27515040011	
☐	RA-61713	An-148-100	41-10	
☐	RA-61714	An-148-100	42-01	

ATRAN - AVIATRANS CARGO A/L — V8 / VAS

	Reg	Type	c/n	
☐	VP-BCJ	B737-46Q(SF)	28663/2922	
☐	VP-BCK	B737-46Q(SF)	28758/2939	

AURORA — HZ / SHU

	Reg	Type	c/n	
☐	VP-BDM	A319-111	2069	♦
☐	VP-BDN	A319-111	2072	♦
☐	VP-BDO	A319-111	2091	♦
☐	VP-BUK	A319-111	3281	
☐	VP-BUN	A319-111	3298	
☐	VP-BUO	A319-111	3336	
☐	VP-BWA	A319-111	2052	♦
☐	VP-BWK	A319-111	2222	
☐	VP-BWL	A319-111	2243	
☐	VQ-BBD	A319-131	3838	
☐	VQ-BWV	A319-112	3108	
☐	RA-11364	An-12BK	00347601	
☐	RA-48984	An-12B	402913	
☐	RA-46530	An-24RV	57310009	
☐	RA-73003	B737-2J8	22859/890	[UUS]
☐	RA-73005	B737-232	23100/1038	[UUS]
☐	RA-73006	B737-548	25737/2232	
☐	RA-73013	B737-5L9	28721/2856	
☐	RA-67251	DHC-8Q-311	533	
☐	RA-67252	DHC-8-402Q	4106	o/o♦
☐	RA-67253(2)	DHC-8-311	451	
☐	RA-67254	DHC-8-402Q	4351	♦
☐	RA-67255(2)	DHC-8Q-315	581	
☐	RA-67257	DHC-8-201	457	
☐	RA-67259	DHC-8-201	459	
☐	RA-67261	DHC-8-315	556	
☐	RA-	DHC-8-402Q	4354	o/o♦

AVIACON ZITOTRANS — ZR / AZS

	Reg	Type	c/n	
☐	RA-76370	Il-76TD	1023414458	
☐	RA-76386	Il-76TD	1033418600	
☐	RA-76483	Il-76TD	0063468042	
☐	RA-76502	Il-76TD	1003401004	
☐	RA-76807	Il-76TD	1013405176	
☐	RA-76834	Il-76MD	0093499986	♦
☐	RA-76842	Il-76TD	1033418616	
☐	RA-76846	Il-76TD	0093497936	

AVIASTAR TU — 4B / TUP

	Reg	Type	c/n	
☐	RA-64021	Tu-204-100C	1450742964021	
☐	RA-64024	Tu-204-100C	1450741364024	
☐	RA-64032	Tu-204-100C	1450742264032	

AZUR AIR — ZF / KTK

	Reg	Type	c/n	
☐	RA-46494	An-24RV	27308207	[KJA]
☐	RA-46674	An-24RV	47309606	
☐	RA-46693	An-24RV	47309904	
☐	VP-BAS	B757-28A	28161/723	
☐	VP-BLT	B757-28A	28174/865	
☐	VP-BLV	B757-28A	30043/925	
☐	VP-BPB	B757-231/W	28484/825	[SAW]
☐	VQ-BEY	B757-2Q8/W	29382/1010	
☐	VQ-BEZ	B757-2Q8/W	29377/857	
☐	VQ-BKB	B757-2Q8/W	26271/592	
☐	VQ-BKF	B757-2Q8/W	26268/590	
☐	VQ-BQA	B757-2Q8	30044/954	[DWC]
☐	VP-BXW	B767-3Q8ER/W	27618/727	♦
☐	VQ-BSX	B767-306ER	27612/647	♦
☐	VQ-BSY	B767-306ER	27614/661	♦
☐	VQ-BUO	B767-33AER	27909/591	♦
☐	VQ-BUP	B767-33AER	28043/734	♦

BARKOL AVIAKOMPANIA — VOG

	Reg	Type	c/n	
☐	RA-87227	Yak-40K	9841559	
☐	RA-87280	Yak-40	9322025	
☐	RA-88228	Yak-40	9641750	

BURAL — U4 / BUN

	Reg	Type	c/n	
☐	RA-46408	An-24RV	77304003	♦
☐	RA-46506	An-24RV	37308402	
☐	RA-46614	An-24RV	37308701	
☐	RA-46661	An-24RV	47309305	
☐	RA-47361	An-24RV	67310705	♦
☐	RA-47799	An-24RV	17306808	
☐	RA-93934	An-24B	09902310	♦
☐	RA-89004	Sukhoi SSJ 100-95B	95012	[SVO]♦
☐	RA-89007	Sukhoi SSJ 100-95B	95015	[SVO]♦
☐	RA-	Sukhoi SSJ 100-95B		o/o♦
☐	RA-	Sukhoi SSJ 100-95B		o/o♦

CHUKOTAVIA

	Reg	Type	c/n	
☐	RA-26099	An-26B-100	11905	
☐	RA-26128	An-26B	12702	
☐	RA-26590	An-26B	13910	
☐	RA-46616	An-24RV	37308703	
☐	RA-47159	An-24B	89901701	

DONAVIA — D9 / DNV

	Reg	Type	c/n	
☐	VP-BBT	A319-112	1805	
☐	VP-BBU	A319-112	1630	
☐	VP-BIS	A319-112	1808	
☐	VP-BIV	A319-115LR	3065	
☐	VP-BNB	A319-112	2751	
☐	VP-BNJ	A319-111	2241	
☐	VP-BNN	A319-111	1841	
☐	VP-BQK	A319-111	3179	
☐	VP-BWG	A319-111	2093	
☐	VP-BWJ	A319-111	2179	
☐	RA-89036	Sukhoi SSJ100-95LR	95070	o/o♦
☐	RA-89037	Sukhoi SSJ100-95LR	95077	o/o♦

Reg	Type	C/n	Notes
RA-89038	Sukhoi SSJ100-95LR	95083	o/o♦
RA-	Sukhoi SSJ100-95LR		o/o♦

To be merged into Rossiya during 2016.

FLIGHT INSPECTION & SYSTEMS — LTS

Reg	Type	C/n	Notes
RA-26088	An-26ASLK	11209	
RA-26571	An-26ASLK	3909	
RA-26625	An-26ASLK	5203	
RA-26631	An-26ASLK	5503	
RA-26673	An-26ASLK	8408	
RA-46395	An-24KPA	07306209	

GAZPROMAVIA — 4G / GZP

Reg	Type	C/n	Notes
RA-74008	An-74TK-100	36547095900	
RA-73000	B737-76N	28630/664	
RA-73004	B737-76N	28635/734	
RA-89018	Sukhoi SSJ 100-95LR	95033	
RA-89019	Sukhoi SSJ 100-95LR	95056	
RA-89020	Sukhoi SSJ 100-95LR	95055	
RA-89029	Sukhoi SSJ 100-95LR	95057	
RA-89030	Sukhoi SSJ 100-95LR	95058	
RA-89031	Sukhoi SSJ 100-95LR	95064	
RA-89048	Sukhoi SSJ 100-95LR	95073	
RA-89049	Sukhoi SSJ 100-95LR	95078	
RA-89050	Sukhoi SSJ 100-95LR	95080	♦
RA-89054	Sukhoi SSJ 100-95LR	95092	♦
RA-85625	Tu-154M	87A752	
RA-85751	Tu-154M	92A933	
RA-85774	Tu-154M	93A956	
RA-85778	Tu-154M	93A962	
RA-21505	Yak-40K	9830159	
RA-88186	Yak-40	9620648	
RA-88300	Yak-40K	9641451	
RA-42436	Yak-42D	4520421605018	
RA-42437	Yak-42D	4520436060180	
RA-42438	Yak-42D	4520423609018	
RA-42439	Yak-42D	4520423904019	
RA-42442	Yak-42D	4520422002019	

GLOBUS — GH / GLP

Reg	Type	C/n	Notes
VP-BDF	B737-8Q8/W	30672/1497	♦
VP-BDG	B737-8Q8/W	30669/1479	♦
VP-BDH	B737-8Q8/W	30667/1448	♦
VP-BUG	B737-86J/W	37741/2686	

Subsidiary of S7 Airlines also uses S7 737s on short-term leases.

GROZNY AVIA — ZG / GOZ

Reg	Type	C/n	Notes
RA-42365	Yak-42D	4520424811447	
RA-42379	Yak-42D	4520421014543	
RA-42385	Yak-42D	4520423016309	
RA-42418	Yak-42D	4520423219118	
RA-42451	Yak-42D	4520422708018	♦
RA-42542	Yak-42D	11140804	

IFLY — H5 / RSY

Reg	Type	C/n	Notes
EI-ETI	A330-322	171	
EI-FBU	A330-322	120	
EI-EWT	B757-28A	29381/958	

IKAR — IK / KAR

Reg	Type	C/n	Notes
VP-BPI	B737-83N/W	28244/958	<NWS♦
VP-BPY	B737-83N/W	28247/1091	o/o♦
VQ-BVY	B737-8Q8/W	32841/1705	<NWS♦
VP-BDI	B767-38AER	29618/792	<NWS♦
VP-BMC	B767-3Q8ER	30301/762	<NWS
VP-BOY	B767-3G5ER	29435/720	<NWS
VP-BOZ	B767-3G5ER	28111/612	<NWS
VQ-BTQ	B767-3Q8ER	28207/695	<NWS

IRAERO — IO / IAE

Reg	Type	C/n	Notes
RA-08824	An-24RV	97310810V	
RA-46408	An-24B	77304003	
RA-46640	An-24RV	37308908	
RA-46659	An-24RV	47309306	♦
RA-46846	An-24RV	27307504	
RA-47804	An-24RV	17306903	
RA-47805	An-24RV	17306907	
RA-47821	An-24RV	17307202	♦
RA-48096	An-24RV	57310406	
RA-26051	An-26B	10906	
RA-26131	An-26B	12707	
RA-26138	An-26B	12810	
RA-26515	An-26	6910	
RA-26665	An-26	8108	
RA-26692	An-26B-100	9409	
VP-BAO	CRJ-100ER	7177	
VQ-BEV	CRJ-200ER	7467	♦
VQ-BIX	CRJ-200ER	7546	♦
VQ-BIY	CRJ-200ER	7539	
VQ-BMK	CRJ-200ER	7650	♦
VQ-BML	CRJ-200ER	7650	

IZHAVIA — I8 / IZA

Reg	Type	C/n	Notes
RA-46620	An-24RV	37308707	
RA-46637	An-24RV	37308903	
RA-47315	An-24RV	67310502	
RA-26245	An-26-100	6206	
RA-65577	Tu-134A-3	60475	
RA-42343	Yak-42D	4520421708285	
RA-42368	Yak-42D	4520422914166	
RA-42380	Yak-42D	4520422014549	
RA-42384	Yak-42D	4520423016230	
RA-42421	Yak-42D	4520422303017	
RA-42450	Yak-42D	4520424601019	
RA-42455	Yak-42D	4520424404018	
RA-42549	Yak-42D	11040105	

KHABAROVSK AIRLINES

Reg	Type	C/n	Notes
RA-26101	An-26B	11908	
RA-26105	An-26B-100	12003	
RA-26174	An-26B-100	97308304	
RA-46528	An-24RV	47310007	
RA-46529	An-24RV	57310008	♦
RA-46714	An-24RV	57310105	♦
RA-47321	An-24RV	67310507	
RA-47359	An-24RV	67310608	
RA-47367	An-24RV	77310806	
RA-49264	An-24RT	00911504	♦

KNAAPO — KNM

Reg	Type	C/n	Notes
RA-11371	An-12BP	00347406	
RA-11789^	An-12BP	6343905	
RA-48978^	An-12BK	9346410	[KXK]

^ operates without prefix

KOMIAVIATRANS — KMA

	Reg	Type	C/n	
☐	VQ-BWL	ERJ-145LI	14500804	
☐	VQ-BWM	ERJ-145LI	14500823	
☐	VQ-BWO	ERJ-145LI	14500815	♦
☐	VQ-BWP	ERJ-145LI	145781	
☐	VQ-BWU	ERJ-145LI	145701	♦
☐		ERJ-145LI	145755	o/o
☐		ERJ-145LI	14500839	o/o♦
☐		ERJ-145LI	14500848	o/o♦
☐		ERJ-145LI	14500898	o/o♦
☐		ERJ-145LI	14500882	o/o♦

KOSMOS AIRLINES — KSM

	Reg	Type	C/n	
☐	RA-11025	An-12B	6344103	
☐	RA-12988	An-12B	00347206	
☐	RA-12990	An-12B	00347304	std♦
☐	RA-76416	Il-76TD	0093495854	
☐	RA-65010	Tu-134A	46130	
☐	RA-65576	Tu-134B-3	63285	♦
☐	RA-65719	Tu-134AK	63637	
☐	RA-65726	Tu-134AK	63720	
☐	RA-65771	Tu-134A-3	62445	
☐	RA-65941	Tu-134A-3	60642	
☐	RA-65956	Tu-134A-3	2351709	
☐	RA-85773	Tu-154M	93A955	
☐	RA-85849	Tu-154M	89A815	

KOSTROMA AIR ENTERPRISE — KMW

	Reg	Type	C/n	
☐	RA-26081	An-26B-100	11703	
☐	RA-26595	An-26B	13401	
☐	RA-27210	An-26-100	5410	

KRASAVIA — SSJ

	Reg	Type	C/n	
☐	RA-46466	An-24RV	27307904	
☐	RA-46642	An-24RV	37308910	
☐	RA-46682	An-24RV	47309704	
☐	RA-47306	An-24RV	57310306	
☐	RA-49287	An-24RV	27307607	
☐	RA-26005	An-26	9809	
☐	RA-26008	An-26B-100	9902	
☐	RA-26056	An-26B	11005	
☐	RA-26118	An-26B-100	12207	
☐	RA-26121	An-26B	12305	
☐	RA-26620	An-26B-100	5104	♦
☐	RA-69354	An-32A	1606	std
☐	RA-69355	An-32A	1607	
☐	RA-67017	LET L-410UVP-E10	2812	
☐	RA-67018	LET L-410UVP-E20	2813	
☐	RA-67020	LET L-410UVP-E20	2814	
☐	RA-87900	Yak-40K	9720254	
☐	RA-42340	Yak-42D	4520424606270	♦
☐	RA-42353	Yak-42D	4520424711396	♦
☐	RA-42359	Yak-42D	4520423811417	
☐	RA-42370	Yak-42D	4520422914203	
☐	RA-42388	Yak-42D	4520424016510	♦
☐	RA-42406	Yak-42D	4520424116683	♦
☐	RA-42408	Yak-42D	4520424116698	♦
☐	RA-42458	Yak-42D	4520424207018	♦
☐	RA-42524	Yak-42D	11030603	

LUKIAVIATRANS — PKV

	Reg	Type	C/n	
☐	RA-30039	An-30	0710	
☐	RA-30053	An-30D	1008	
☐	RA-30075	An-30D	1306	
☐	RA-46632	An-30	0201	

MCHS ROSSII — SUM

	Reg	Type	C/n	
☐	RF-31122	An-74P	36547136012	
☐	RF-31350	An-74P	36547097940	
☐	RA-61715	An-148-100EM	27015042015	
☐	RA-61717	An-148-100EM	27015042017	
☐	RF-31121	Be-200ChS	76820003001	
☐	RF-31130	Be-200ChS	76820003102	
☐	RF-31160	Be-200ChS	76820001402	
☐	RF-32765	Be-200ChS	76820001301	
☐	RF-32767	Be-200ChS	76820002501	
☐	RF-32768	Be-200ChS	76820002602	
☐	RA-86570	Il-62M	1356344	
☐	RA-76362	Il-76TD	1033416533	
☐	RA-76363	Il-76TD	1033417540	
☐	RA-76429	Il-76TD	1043419639	
☐	RA-76840	Il-76TD	1033417553	
☐	RA-76841	Il-76TD	1033418601	
☐	RA-76845	Il-76TDP	1043420696	
☐	RA-89066	Sukhoi SSJ 100-95LR	95061	♦
☐	RA-89067	Sukhoi SSJ 100-95LR	95069	♦
☐	RA-42441	Yak-42D	4520421402018	
☐	RA-42446	Yak-42D	4520423308017	

MERIDIAN AIR

	Reg	Type	C/n	
☐	RA-65737	Tu-134B-3	64195	
☐	RA-65798	Tu-134A-3	63179	
☐	RA-65917	Tu-134A-3M	63991	

NK AIR

	Reg	Type	C/n	
☐	RA-42342	Yak-42D	4520421706302	
☐	RA-42373	Yak-42D	4520423914323	
☐	RA-42408	Yak-42D	4520424116698	
☐	RA-42452	Yak-42D	4520424409016	♦

NORDAVIA REGIONAL AIRLINES — 5N / AUL

	Reg	Type	C/n	
☐	RA-47199	An-24RV	27307703	
☐	RA-47305	An-24RV	57310305	
☐	VP-BKU	B737-505	25789/2229	
☐	VP-BKV	B737-505	27155/2449	
☐	VP-BOI	B737-505	24650/1792	
☐	VP-BQI	B737-5Y0	25186/2236	
☐	VP-BQL	B737-5Y0	25185/2220	
☐	VP-BRE	B737-53C	24827/2243	
☐	VP-BRG	B737-53C	24826/2041	
☐	VP-BRI	B737-5Y0	25289/2288	
☐	VP-BRK	B737-5Y0	25288/2286	
☐	VP-BRN	B737-5Y0	25191/2260	
☐	VP-BRP	B737-505	24651/1842	

NORDSTAR — Y7 / TYA

	Reg	Type	C/n	
☐	VQ-BKN	ATR 42-500	827	
☐	VQ-BKO	ATR 42-500	823	
☐	VQ-BKP	ATR 42-500	835	
☐	VQ-BKQ	ATR 42-500	839	
☐	VQ-BPE	ATR 42-500	641	

☐	VP-BKT	B737-33R	28871/2900	
☐	VQ-BDN	B737-8K5/W	32905/1046	
☐	VQ-BDO	B737-8K5/W	32906/1087	
☐	VQ-BDP	B737-8Q8/W	28221/226	
☐	VQ-BDW	B737-8K5/W	27977/9	
☐	VQ-BDZ	B737-8K5/W	27978/40	
☐	VQ-BKR	B737-8AS/W	33559/1443	
☐	VQ-BNG	B737-86J/W	37747/3120	
☐	VQ-BPM	B737-8AS/W	33812/1615	
☐	VQ-BQT	B737-8AS/W	33561/1463	

NORDWIND — *N4 / NWS*

☐	VP-BGH	A321-231	3034	
☐	VP-BRD	A321-231	3120	
☐	VQ-BOD	A321-211	1233	
☐	VQ-BOE	A321-211	1219	
☐	VQ-BRM	A321-231	1276	[LDE]
☐	VQ-BRN	A321-231	1843	
☐	VQ-BRO	A321-232	2927	
☐	VQ-BRU	A321-231	2933	
☐	VP-BOW	B737-8Q8/W	30040/1693	
☐	VP-BPI	B737-83N/W	28244/958	>KAR
☐	VP-BPY	B737-83N/W	28247/1091	
☐	VQ-BPZ	B737-8BK/W	33027/1918	
☐	VQ-BUV	B737-86N/W	32691/2033	
☐	VQ-BVY	B737-8Q8/W	32841/1705	>KAR♦
☐	VP-BDI	B767-38AER	29618/792	>KAR
☐	VP-BMC	B767-3Q8ER	30301/762	>KAR
☐	VP-BOY	B767-3G5ER	29435/720	>KAR
☐	VP-BOZ	B767-3G5ER	28111/612	>KAR
☐	VP-BRL	B767-37D/W	26328/637	[LDE]
☐	VQ-BMQ	B767-306ER	28098/607	[LDE]
☐	VQ-BOG	B767-341ER	30342/774	
☐	VQ-BPT	B767-306ER	27957/587	[LDE]
☐	VQ-BTQ	B767-3Q8ER	28207/695	>KAR
☐	VP-BJB	B777-21BER	27606/121	
☐	VP-BJF	B777-21BER	32703/472	
☐	VQ-BUD	B777-2Q8ER	27608/164	

ORENAIR — *R2 / ORB*

☐	VP-BPG	B737-8AS/W	29924/578	
☐	VQ-BCJ	B737-8AS/W	29932/1030	
☐	VQ-BFY	B737-86N/W	29884/1094	
☐	VQ-BFZ	B737-86N/W	28644/839	
☐	VQ-BIZ	B737-86N/W	28645/840	
☐	VQ-BJC	B737-8K5/W	27992/523	
☐	VQ-BJX	B737-86N/W	32735/1104	
☐	VQ-BNK	B737-8K5/W	30414/703	
☐	VQ-BPX	B737-8Q8/W	35278/2625	
☐	VQ-BSR	B737-8AS/W	33622/2101	
☐	VQ-BSS	B737-8AS/W	33602/2109	
☐	VQ-BUE	B737-8GJ/W	34900/2167	
☐	VQ-BUF	B737-8GJ/W	34897/2069	
☐	VQ-BVU	B737-8LJ/W	41202/5206	
☐	VQ-BVV	B737-8LJ/W	41201/5153	
☐	VQ-BWJ	B737-8LJ/W	41212/5576	♦
☐	VP-BHB	B777-2Q8ER	29402/517	
☐	VP-BLA	B777-2Q8ER	28676/246	
☐	VQ-BNU	B777-2Q8ER	29908/229	

To be merged into Rossiya during 2016.

PETROPAVLOVSK-KAMCHATSKY AIR — *PTK*

☐	RA-26085	An-26B-100	12310
☐	RA-26122	An-26B	12401
☐	RA-26251	An-26-100	9109
☐	RA-28714	An-28	1AJ-006-24
☐	RA-67007	LET L-410UVP-E20	2723
☐	RA-67008	LET L-410UVP-E20	2724
☐	RA-67009	LET L-410UVP-E20	2725
☐	RA-67645	LET L-410UVP-E	902438
☐	RA-67662	LET L-410UVP-E	902520
☐	RA-87385	Yak-40K	9411632
☐	RA-87947	Yak-40K	9621145
☐	RA-87949	Yak-40K	9621345
☐	RA-87988	Yak-40	9541244

POBEDA — *DP / PBD*

☐	VQ-BAW	B737-8MA/W	43666/5386	♦
☐	VQ-BTC	B737-8MA/W	43662/5119	
☐	VQ-BTD	B737-8MA/W	43664/5185	
☐	VQ-BTE	B737-81D/W	39441/5077	
☐	VQ-BTG	B737-8FZ/W	41992/4908	
☐	VQ-BTH	B737-8LJ/W	39947/5051	
☐	VQ-BTI	B737-8LJ/W	39948/5023	
☐	VQ-BTJ	B737-8LJ/W	39950/5133	
☐	VQ-BTS	B737-8FZ/W	41991/4870	
☐	VQ-BWG	B737-8LJ/W	41205/5302	
☐	VQ-BWH	B737-8LJ/W	41206/5318	
☐	VQ-BWI	B737-8LJ/W	41208/5437	♦

POLAR AIRLINES — *PI / RKA*

☐	RA-46333	An-24B	97305510
☐	RA-46510	An-24RV	37308406
☐	RA-46646	An-24RV	37309015
☐	RA-46834	An-24RV	17306801
☐	RA-47260	An-24B	27307802
☐	RA-47352	An-24RV	67310601
☐	RA-47357	An-24RV	67310606
☐	RA-47363	An-24RV	67310707
☐	RA-47786	An-24B	89901601
☐	RA-26030	An-26B-100	10501
☐	RA-26538	An-26-100	47302102
☐	RA-26604	An-26	4506
☐	RA-67623	LET L-410UVP-E	902405
☐	RA-67670	LET L-410UVP-E3	902416
☐	RA-67676	LET L-410UVP-E	872007
☐	RA-67693	LET L-410UVP-E	952624
☐	RA-67694	LET L-410UVP-E	952625

PROGRESS TsSKB AVIAKOMPANIA — *PSS*

☐	RA-26130	An-26B-100	12704
☐	RA-26180	An-26	9737810
☐	RA-26191	An-24B	19902309

PSKOV AVIA — *PSW*

☐	RA-46473	An-24RV	27308101
☐	RA-46651	An-24RV	47309202
☐	RA-46667	An-24RV	47309508
☐	RA-47362	An-24RV	67310706
☐	RA-47697	An-24RV	27307604
☐	RA-26041	An-26B	10707
☐	RA-26086	An-26B	12302
☐	RA-26134	An-26B	12805
☐	RA-26142	An-26B	37312904
☐	RA-26209	An-26B-100	57314302

RED WINGS — *WZ / RWZ*

☐	RA-89001	Sukhoi SSJ 100-95B	95008

	Registration	Type	c/n	Notes
☐	RA-89002	Sukhoi SSJ 100-95B	95010	
☐	RA-89008	Sukhoi SSJ 100-95B	95016	♦
☐	RA-89010	Sukhoi SSJ 100-95B	95018	♦
☐	RA-89021	Sukhoi SSJ 100-95B	95021	
☐	RA-96007	Il-96-300	74393201004	o/o♦
☐	RA-96015	Il-96-300	74393202012	o/o♦
☐	RA-64017	Tu-204-100	1450742564017	
☐	RA-64018	Tu-204-100	1450743164018	std
☐	RA-64019	Tu-204-100	1450743164019	
☐	RA-64020	Tu-204-100	1450743164020	
☐	RA-64022	Tu-204-100	1450743164022	o/o♦
☐	RA-64043	Tu-204-100	1450743764043	
☐	RA-64046	Tu-204-100	1450748664046	
☐	RA-64049	Tu-204-100	1450744864049	
☐	RA-64050	Tu-204-100	1450741964050	

ROSSIYA RUSSIAN AIRLINES — *FV / SDM*

	Registration	Type	c/n	Notes
☐	EI-ETN	A319-111	1654	
☐	EI-ETO	A319-111	1679	
☐	EI-ETP	A319-111	1753	
☐	EI-EYL	A319-111	2465	
☐	EI-EYM	A319-111	2497	
☐	EI-EZC	A319-112	2879	
☐	EI-EZD	A319-112	2913	
☐	VP-BIQ	A319-111	1890	
☐	VP-BIT	A319-112	1761	
☐	VP-BIU	A319-114	0649	
☐	VQ-BAQ	A319-112	1560	
☐	VQ-BAR	A319-112	1488	
☐	VQ-BAS	A319-112	1863	
☐	VQ-BAT	A319-112	1876	
☐	VQ-BAU	A319-112	1851	
☐	VQ-BAV	A319-112	1743	
☐	VP-BWH	A320-214	2151	
☐	VP-BWI	A320-214	2163	
☐	VQ-BCG	A320-214	1200	
☐	VQ-BDQ	A320-214	1767	
☐	VQ-BDR	A320-214	1130	
☐	VQ-BFM	A320-214	1379	
☐	RA-61701	An-148-100B	2701504001	[LED]
☐	RA-61702	An-148-100B	2701504002	[LED]
☐	RA-61703	An-148-100B	2701504003	[LED]
☐	RA-61704	An-148-100B	2701504004	[LED]
☐	RA-61705	An-148-100B	2701504005	[LED]
☐	RA-61706	An-148-100B	2701504006	[LED]
☐	EI-XLC	B747-446	27100/1236	o/o♦
☐	EI-XLE	B747-446	26362/1202	o/o♦
☐	EI-XLF	B747-446	27645/1262	o/o♦
☐	EI-XLG	B747-446	29899/1208	o/o♦
☐	EI-DZH	B767-3Q8ER	29390/870	

Rossiya – Russian State Transport

	Registration	Type	c/n	Notes
☐	RA-61716	An-148-100EA	27015042016	
☐	RA-61718	An-148-100EA	27015042018	
☐	RA-61720	An-148-100EA	42-07	
☐	RA-61722	An-148-100EA	42-09	
☐	RA-73025	A319-115CJ	4024	
☐	RA-73026	A319-115CJ	4679	
☐	RA-86540	Il-62M	3546548	
☐	RA-86710	Il-62M	2647646	
☐	RA-96012	Il-96-300PU	74393201009	
☐	RA-96014	Il-96-300	74393202014	
☐	RA-96016	Il-96-300PU	74393202010	
☐	RA-96017	Il-96-300S	74393202011	
☐	RA-96018	Il-96-300PU	74393202018	
☐	RA-96019	Il-96-300	74393202019	
☐	RA-96020	Il-96-300PU	74393202020	
☐	RA-96021	Il-96-300PU	74393202021	
☐	RA-96022	Il-96-300PU	74393202022	o/o
☐	RA-96023	Il-96-300PU	74393202023	o/o
☐	RA-89039	Sukhoi SSJ 100-95B	95030	♦
☐	RA-89040	Sukhoi SSJ 100-95B	95037	♦
☐	RA-65904	Tu-134A-3	63953	std
☐	RA-65905	Tu-134A-3	63965	
☐	RA-65911	Tu-134A-3	63972	
☐	RA-65921	Tu-134A-3	63997	
☐	RA-85001	Tu-154M	89A820	
☐	RA-64053	Tu-204-300	64053	o/o
☐	RA-64057	Tu-204-300A	1450744164057	
☐	RA-64058	Tu-204-300A	1450744164058	
☐	RA-64059	Tu-204-300A	64059	
☐	RA-64505	Tu-214	42204005	
☐	RA-64506	Tu-214	44204006	
☐	RA-64515	Tu-214SR	44207015	
☐	RA-64516	Tu-214SR	42709016	
☐	RA-64517	Tu-214SR	41709017	
☐	RA-64520	Tu-214PU	44709020	
☐	RA-64521	Tu-214PU	43911021	
☐	RA-64522	Tu-214SUS	43911022	
☐	RA-64524	Tu-214SUS	43003024	
☐	RA-64526	Tu-214SR	526	
☐	RA-64527	Tu-214SR	527	
☐	RA-64528	Tu-214SR	528	
☐	RA-87203	Yak-40	9741456	
☐	RA-87968	Yak-40	9841258	
☐	RA-87969	Yak-40	9831358	
☐	RA-87971	Yak-40D	9831558	
☐	RA-87972	Yak-40	9921658	
☐	RA-88200	Yak-40	9630149	

ROYAL FLIGHT — *ABG*

	Registration	Type	c/n	Notes
☐	VQ-BRF	B737-808/W	34970/2379	♦
☐	VP-BOO	B757-204/W	28834/850	
☐	VQ-BTB	B757-28A/W	28835/858	
☐	VQ-BTF	B757-23A/W	24923/332	
☐	VQ-BTM	B757-256/W	26253/902	
☐	VQ-BTN	B757-256/W	26251/897	
☐	VQ-BTR	B757-28A/W	28171/805	
☐	EI-DZH	B767-3Q8ER	29390/870	o/o♦
☐	EI-EAR	B767-3Q8ER	27616/714	[PVG]♦
☐	EI-ECB	B767-3Q8ER	27617/722	[PVG]♦

RUSLINE — *7R / RLU*

	Registration	Type	c/n	Notes
☐	VP-BMN	CRJ-200ER	7179	
☐	VP-BVB	CRJ-100ER	7245	
☐	VP-BVC	CRJ-200ER	7441	
☐	VP-BVD	CRJ-200ER	7440	
☐	VP-BVK	CRJ-200ER	7408	
☐	VQ-BFB	CRJ-200ER	7637	
☐	VQ-BFF	CRJ-200ER	7470	
☐	VQ-BFI	CRJ-200ER	7671	
☐	VQ-BNA	CRJ-200ER	7473	
☐	VQ-BND	CRJ-200ER	7483	
☐	VQ-BNE	CRJ-100ER	7482	
☐	VQ-BNL	CRJ-100ER	7106	

	Reg	Type	c/n	
☐	VQ-BNY	CRJ-100ER	7108	
☐	VP-CNO	CRJ-100ER	7222	♦
☐	VQ-BBX	EMB.120RT	120205	
☐	VQ-BCB	EMB.120RT	120231	
☐	VQ-BCL	EMB.120ER	120304	
☐	RA-87429	Yak-40	9420535	
☐	RA-88293	Yak-40	9510138	

S7 AIRLINES — *S7 / SBI*

	Reg	Type	c/n	
☐	VP-BHF	A319-114	1819	
☐	VP-BHG	A319-114	1870	
☐	VP-BHI	A319-114	2028	
☐	VP-BHJ	A319-114	2369	
☐	VP-BHK	A319-114	2373	
☐	VP-BHL	A319-114	2464	
☐	VP-BHP	A319-114	2618	
☐	VP-BHQ	A319-114	2641	
☐	VP-BHV	A319-114	2474	
☐	VP-BTN	A319-114	1126	
☐	VP-BTO	A319-114	1129	
☐	VP-BTP	A319-114	1131	
☐	VP-BTQ	A319-114	1149	
☐	VP-BTS	A319-114	1164	
☐	VP-BTT	A319-114	1167	
☐	VP-BTU	A319-114	1071	
☐	VP-BTV	A319-114	1078	
☐	VP-BTW	A319-114	1090	
☐	VP-BTX	A319-114	1091	
☐	VQ-BQW	A319-115LR	2279	
☐	VP-BCP	A320-214	3473	
☐	VP-BCS	A320-214	3490	
☐	VP-BCZ	A320-214	3446	
☐	VP-BDT	A320-214	3494	
☐	VP-BOG	A320-214	5559	
☐	VP-BOJ	A320-214	5607	
☐	VP-BOL	A320-214/S	6066	
☐	VP-BOM	A320-214/S	6171	
☐	VQ-BCI	A320-214	2623	
☐	VQ-BDE	A320-214	3866	
☐	VQ-BDF	A320-214	3880	
☐	VQ-BES	A320-214	4032	
☐	VQ-BET	A320-214	4150	
☐	VQ-BOA	A320-214	5001	
☐	VQ-BPL	A320-214	5026	
☐	VQ-BPN	A320-214	5167	
☐	VQ-BRC	A320-214	5106	
☐	VQ-BRD	A320-214	5031	
☐	VQ-BRG	A320-214	5134	♦
☐	VQ-BQH	A321-211	3070	
☐	VQ-BQI	A321-211	2726	
☐	VQ-BQJ	A321-211	2076	
☐	VQ-BQK	A321-211	2064	
☐	VQ-BMG	B737-8LP/W	41841/5095	o/o♦
☐	VP-BND	B737-83N/W	28245/1054	
☐	VP-BNG	B737-83N/W	30640/1035	
☐	VP-BQD	B737-83N/W	28239/847	
☐	VP-BQF	B737-83N/W	28243/984	
☐	VQ-BKV	B737-8ZS/W	37084/3605	
☐	VQ-BKW	B737-8ZS/W	37085/3654	
☐	VQ-BVK	B737-8GJ/W	41401/5165	
☐	VQ-BVL	B737-8GJ/W	41399/5055	
☐	VQ-BVM	B737-8GJ/W	41400/5094	
☐	VP-BVH	B767-33AER	28495/643	
☐	VQ-BBI	B767-328ER	27428/586	

Leases its 737s to its subsidiary Globus on short term leases.

SARATOV AIRLINES — *6W / SOV*

	Reg	Type	c/n	
☐	VQ-BRX	ERJ-195LR	19000169	
☐	VQ-BRY	ERJ-195LR	19000157	
☐	RA-42316	Yak-42D	4520422202030	[RTW]
☐	RA-42326	Yak-42D	4520424402154	
☐	RA-42328	Yak-42D	4520421505058	
☐	RA-42329	Yak-42D	4520422505093	[RTW]
☐	RA-42356	Yak-42D	4520422811400	
☐	RA-42361	Yak-42D	4520423811427	
☐	RA-42378	Yak-42D	4520421014494	
☐	RA-42389	Yak-42D	4520424016542	
☐	RA-42432	Yak-42D	4520424410016	
☐	RA-42550	Yak-42D	11140205	
☐	RA-42557	Yak-42D	4520423302017	

SEVERSTAL AIRCOMPANY — *D2 / SSF*

	Reg	Type	c/n
☐	RA-67229	CRJ-200LR	7403
☐	RA-67230	CRJ-200LR	7407
☐	RA-67231	CRJ-200LR	7464
☐	RA-67234	CRJ-200ER	7514
☐	RA-67239	CRJ-200ER	7989
☐	RA-67240	CRJ-200ER	8008
☐	RA-87224	Yak-40K	9841259
☐	RA-87954	Yak-40	9811357
☐	RA-88188	Yak-40	9620848
☐	RA-88296	Yak-40	9421634

SHAR INK — *UGP*

	Reg	Type	c/n
☐	RA-74020	An-74TK-100	36547195014
☐	RA-74056	An-74-200	36547098951
☐	RA-76403	Il-76MD	1023412414
☐	RA-76446	Il-76TD	1023412418
☐	RA-76460	Il-76MD	1023410344

SIRIUS AERO — *CIG*

	Reg	Type	c/n	
☐	RA-65574	Tu-134B-3	03564753	♦
☐	RA-65926	Tu-134AK	66101	
☐	RA-65928	Tu-134A-3M	66491	
☐	RA-65978	Tu-134A-3	63357	
☐	RA-87669	Yak-40	9021760	

SKOL AVIAKOMPANIA — *CDV*

	Reg	Type	c/n	
☐	RA-87340	Yak-40	9510939	
☐	RA-87940	Yak-40	9540444	♦
☐	RA-88226	Yak-40	9641350	
☐	RA-88306	Yak-40KD	9640651	

STATE AIRLINE 224 FLIGHT UNIT

	Reg	Type	c/n
☐	RA-82014	An-124-100	9773954732039
☐	RA-82030	An-124-100	9773054732045
☐	RA-82032	An-124-100	9773053832057
☐	RA-82039	An-124-100	9773052055082
☐	RA-82040	An-124-100	9773053355086
☐	RA-82041	An-124-100	9773054055089

Air Force aircraft operated commercially by this unit.

SVERDLOVSK 2ND AIR ENTERPRISE — *UKU*

	Reg	Type	c/n
☐	RA-74006	An-74	36547095896
☐	RA-74048	An-74D	36547098943

☐ RA-87253	Yak-40	9321026	
☐ RA-87503	Yak-40	9520240	
☐ RA-87524	Yak-40	9520641	
☐ RA-87974	Yak-40K	9621346	
☐ RA-88159	Yak-40	9621346	

TURUKHAN AVIA — *UT / TRH*

☐ RA-46468	An-24RV	27307906	♦
☐ RA-46491	An-24RV	27308204	♦
☐ RA-46493	An-24RV	27308206	♦
☐ RA-46494	An-24RV	27308207	♦
☐ RA-46497	An-24RV	27308210	♦
☐ RA-46520	An-24RV	37308506	♦
☐ RA-46532	An-24RV	57310101	♦
☐ RA-46603	An-24RV	37308510	♦
☐ RA-46604	An-24RV	37308601	♦
☐ RA-46609	An-24RV	37308606	♦
☐ RA-46619	An-24RV	37308706	♦
☐ RA-46650	An-24RV	47309201	♦
☐ RA-46689	An-24RV	47309806	♦
☐ RA-46692	An-24RV	47309903	♦
☐ RA-47264	An-24RV	27307806	♦
☐ RA-47295	An-24RV	07306608	♦
☐ RA-47351	An-24RV	67310510	♦
☐ RA-47358	An-24RV	67310607	♦
☐ RA-47820	An-24RV	17307201	♦
☐ RA-49278	An-24RV	47309809	♦
☐ RA-49279	An-24RV	17306905	♦
☐ RA-26102	An-26B	11909	♦
☐ RA-26620	An-26B-100	5104	♦
☐ RA-26662	An-26-100	8101	♦
☐ RA-65052	Tu-134A-3	49825	♦
☐ RA-65083	Tu-134A-3	60090	♦
☐ RA-65560	Tu-134A	60321	♦
☐ RA-65565	Tu-134A-1	63998	♦

URAL AIRLINES — *U6 / SVR*

☐ VP-BBG	A319-111	1579	o/o♦
☐ VP-BJV	A319-112	1603	
☐ VP-BTE	A319-112	1901	
☐ VP-BTF	A319-112	1884	
☐ VQ-BTP	A319-111	3834	
☐ VQ-BTY	A319-112	3385	
☐ VQ-BTZ	A319-112	3388	
☐ VP-BBQ	A320-214	2278	
☐ VP-BDL	A320-232	2343	♦
☐ VP-BFZ	A320-214	0735	
☐ VP-BIE	A320-214	3099	
☐ VP-BMT	A320-214	2349	
☐ VP-BMW	A320-214	2166	
☐ VP-BKB	A320-214	3189	
☐ VP-BTZ	A320-214	3107	
☐ VQ-BAG	A320-214	1063	
☐ VQ-BCY	A320-214	1484	
☐ VQ-BCZ	A320-214	1777	
☐ VQ-BDJ	A320-214	2175	
☐ VQ-BDM	A320-214	2187	
☐ VQ-BFV	A320-214	1152	
☐ VQ-BFW	A320-214	2327	
☐ VQ-BLO	A320-214	1751	
☐ VQ-BNI	A320-214	3472	
☐ VQ-BQN	A320-214	3433	
☐ VQ-BRE	A320-214	2998	
☐ VP-BVP	A321-211	2707	
☐ VQ-BCX	A321-211	1720	
☐ VQ-BDA	A321-211	1012	
☐ VQ-BKG	A321-211	0991	
☐ VQ-BKH	A321-211	0841	
☐ VQ-BKJ	A321-211	0815	
☐ VQ-BOB	A321-211	1905	
☐ VQ-BOC	A321-231	1199	
☐ VQ-BOF	A321-211	0775	
☐ VQ-BOZ	A321-211	2117	

UTAIR AIRLINES — *UT / UTA*

☐ VP-BCB	ATR 42-300	054	std
☐ VP-BLI	ATR 42-300	233	[TOF]
☐ VP-BLO	ATR 42-300	289	std
☐ VP-BPJ	ATR 42-300	165	[TOF]
☐ VP-BPK	ATR 42-300	166	std
☐ VP-BYW	ATR 72-201	174	std
☐ VP-BYX	ATR 72-201	251	std
☐ VQ-BLC	ATR 72-212A	942	♦
☐ VQ-BLD	ATR 72-212A	945	♦
☐ VQ-BLE	ATR 72-212A	950	♦
☐ VQ-BLF	ATR 72-212A	951	♦
☐ VQ-BLG	ATR 72-212A	952	♦
☐ VQ-BLH	ATR 72-212A	953	♦
☐ VQ-BLI	ATR 72-212A	963	♦
☐ VQ-BLJ	ATR 72-212A	965	♦
☐ VQ-BLK	ATR 72-212A	975	♦
☐ VQ-BLL	ATR 72-212A	976	♦
☐ VQ-BLM	ATR 72-212A	980	♦
☐ VQ-BLN	ATR 72-212A	981	♦
☐ VQ-BMA	ATR 72-212A	983	♦
☐ VQ-BMB	ATR 72-212A	984	♦
☐ VQ-BMD	ATR 72-212A	990	♦
☐ VQ-BHZ	B737-46M	28549/2844	
☐ VQ-BIC	B737-45S	28478/3132	>UN
☐ VQ-BID	B737-45S	28477/3131	>UN
☐ VQ-BIE	B737-45S	28476/3103	
☐ VQ-BIF	B737-45S	28474/3028	>UN
☐ VQ-BIG	B737-45S	28473/3014	
☐ VP-BFO	B737-524/W	27319/2590	
☐ VP-BFS	B737-524/W	27532/2712	♦
☐ VP-BFW	B737-524/W	27325/2630	
☐ VP-BVL	B737-524	28926/3069	
☐ VP-BVN	B737-524	27540/2776	
☐ VP-BVZ	B737-524	28925/3066	
☐ VP-BXO	B737-524/W	27314/2566	
☐ VP-BXQ	B737-524/W	27315/2571	
☐ VP-BXR	B737-524/W	27316/2573	
☐ VP-BXU	B737-524/W	27318/2582	
☐ VP-BXY	B737-524/W	27328/2640	
☐ VP-BYK	B737-524	28918/3026	
☐ VP-BYL	B737-524	28920/3048	
☐ VP-BYM	B737-524	28917/3019	
☐ VQ-BAC	B737-524/W	27321/2597	[VKO]
☐ VQ-BAD	B737-524/W	27331/2652	
☐ VQ-BAE	B737-524/W	27320/2596	
☐ VQ-BJL	B737-524/W	28913/2985	
☐ VQ-BJM	B737-524/W	28912/2980	
☐ VQ-BJN	B737-524/W	28911/2973	
☐ VQ-BJO	B737-524/W	28910/2972	
☐ VQ-BJP	B737-524/W	28905/2934	
☐ VQ-BJQ	B737-524/W	28902/2926	
☐ VQ-BJS	B737-524/W	28901/2924	
☐ VQ-BJT	B737-524/W	28900/2913	
☐ VQ-BJU	B737-524/W	28899/2912	

Registration	Type	C/n	Notes
☐ VQ-BJV	B737-524/W	28914/2986	
☐ VQ-BPO	B737-524/W	28903/2927	
☐ VQ-BPP	B737-524/W	28906/2935	
☐ VQ-BPQ	B737-524/W	28907/2956	
☐ VQ-BPR	B737-524/W	28908/2958	
☐ VQ-BPS	B737-524/W	28909/2960	
☐ VP-BUL	B737-8LP/W	41707/4637	[LETL]
☐ VQ-BJF	B737-8AS/W	32778/1140	
☐ VQ-BJG	B737-8AS/W	32779/1167	
☐ VQ-BJH	B737-8AS/W	32780/1178	
☐ VQ-BJI	B737-8AS/W	29936/1236	
☐ VQ-BJJ	B737-8AS/W	29937/1238	
☐ VQ-BMG	B737-8LP/W	41841/5095	[LETL]
☐ VQ-BQP	B737-8GU/W	37553/3646	
☐ VQ-BQQ	B737-8GU/W	37552/3620	
☐ VQ-BQR	B737-8GU/W	36386/3710	
☐ VQ-BQS	B737-8GU/W	36387/3729	
☐ VQ-BRK	B737-8LP/W	41708/4839	[LETL]
☐ VQ-BRP	B737-8LP/W	41709/5002	[LETL]
☐ VQ-BRQ	B737-8LP/W	41710/5019	[LETL]
☐ VQ-BRR	B737-8LP/W	41836/4881	[LETL]
☐ VP-BAB	B767-224ER	30430/811	[LETL]
☐ VP-BAG	B767-224ER	30435/827	
☐ VP-BAI	B767-224ER	30437/839	
☐ VP-BAL	B767-224ER	30439/851	
☐ VP-BAQ	B767-224ER	30431/815	[LETL]
☐ VP-BAU	B767-224ER	30432/819	[LETL]
☐ VP-BAW	B767-224ER	30433/823	[LETL]
☐ VQ-BGH	CRJ-200LR	7114	[LETL]
☐ VQ-BGL	CRJ-200LR	7128	[LETL]
☐ VQ-BGM	CRJ-200LR	7130	[LETL]
☐ VQ-BGO	CRJ-200LR	7135	std
☐ VQ-BGP	CRJ-200LR	7165	[LETL]
☐ VQ-BGQ	CRJ-200LR	7200	[LETL]
☐ VQ-BGT	CRJ-200LR	7266	[LETL]
☐ VQ-BGU	CRJ-200LR	7298	[LETL]
☐ VQ-BGV	CRJ-200LR	7378	[LETL]
☐ VQ-BGW	CRJ-200LR	7391	[LETL]
☐ VQ-BGX	CRJ-200LR	7394	[LETL]

UTAIR CARGO — *TUM*

Registration	Type	C/n	Notes
☐ RA-26010	An-26B	9906	
☐ RA-26104	An-26BRL	12002	[SCW]
☐ RA-88289	An-26B	11804	
☐ RA-74009	An-74	36547095898	
☐ RA-74013	An-74-200	36547098960	
☐ RA-74016	An-74TK-200	365470991034	>UN
☐ RA-74032	An-74TK-200	36547098962	
☐ RA-74035	An-74TK-200	36547098963	>UN
☐ RA-74044	An-74TK-100	36547097936	>UN

UVAUGA — *UHS*

Registration	Type	C/n	Notes
☐ RA-26025	An-26B	10308	
☐ RA-26513	An-26	6810	
☐ RA-26544	An-26	2710	
☐ RA-85609	Tu-154M	84A704	
☐ RA-87315	Yak-40	9331429	
☐ RA-87580	Yak-40	9221222	

VIM AIRLINES — *NN / MOV*

Registration	Type	C/n	Notes
☐ VP-BDY	A319-111	2442	
☐ VP-BDZ	A319-111	2446	
☐ VQ-BTK	A319-111	3403	
☐ VQ-BTL	A319-111	3364	

Registration	Type	C/n	Notes
☐ RA-73009	B757-230	25437/422	>UN
☐ RA-73010	B757-230	25438/428	[HHN]
☐ RA-73011	B757-230	25439/437	
☐ RA-73012	B757-230	25440/443	
☐ RA-73016	B757-230	26433/521	
☐ RA-73017	B757-230	26434/532	
☐ RA-73018	B757-230	26435/537	

VOLGA-DNEPR AIRLINES — *VI / VDA*

Registration	Type	C/n	Notes
☐ RA-82042	An-124-100	9773054055093	
☐ RA-82043	An-124-100	9773054155101	
☐ RA-82044	An-124-100	9773054155109	
☐ RA-82045	An-124-100	9773052255113	
☐ RA-82046	An-124-100	9773052255117	
☐ RA-82047	An-124-100	9773053259121	
☐ RA-82068	An-124-100	9773051359127	♦
☐ RA-82074	An-124-100	9773051459142	
☐ RA-82077	An-124-100	9773054459151	♦
☐ RA-82078	An-124-100	9773054559153	
☐ RA-82079	An-124-100	9773052062157	
☐ RA-82081	An-124-100M	9773051462165	
☐ RA-76503	Il-76-90VD	2113422748	
☐ RA-76511	Il-76-90VD	2123422752	
☐ RA-76950	Il-76-90VD	2053420697	
☐ RA-76951	Il-76-90VD	2073421704	
☐ RA-76952	Il-76-90VD	2093422743	

VOLOGDA AIR ENTERPRISE — *VGV*

Registration	Type	C/n	Notes
☐ RA-87284	Yak-40	9311927	
☐ RA-87400	Yak-40	9421233	♦
☐ RA-87484	Yak-40	9441238	
☐ RA-87494	Yak-40	9541745	♦
☐ RA-87665	Yak-40	9240925	
☐ RA-87842	Yak-40	9321030	
☐ RA-87844	Yak-40	9331330	
☐ RA-87905	Yak-40K	9720754	
☐ RA-87908	Yak-40	9721354	♦
☐ RA-87966	Yak-40	9820958	
☐ RA-88231	Yak-40	9642050	
☐ RA-88251	Yak-40K	9710552	♦

VOSTOK AIRLINES — *VTK*

Registration	Type	C/n	Notes
☐ RA-28920	PZL An-28	1AJ008-06	
☐ RA-28929	PZL An-28	1AJ008-16	
☐ RA-28933	PZL An-28	1AJ008-20	
☐ RA-28941	PZL An-28	1AJ009-07	
☐ RA-28942	PZL An-28	1AJ009-08	
☐ RA-41901	An-38-100	4163847010001	
☐ RA-41902	An-38-100	4163847010002	
☐ RA-41903	An-38-100	4163847010003	

YAKUTIA AIRLINES — *R3 / SYL*

Registration	Type	C/n	Notes
☐ RA-46479	An-24RV	27308007	
☐ RA-46496	An-24RV	27308209	
☐ RA-46665	An-24RV	47309506	♦
☐ RA-47304	An-24RV	57310304	
☐ RA-47352	An-24RV	67310601	♦
☐ RA-47353	An-24RV	67310602	
☐ RA-47360	An-24RV	67310704	♦
☐ RA-47363	An-24RV	67310707	♦
☐ RA-26660	An-26-100	8008	
☐ RA-41250	An-140-100	05A001	[YKS]
☐ RA-41251	An-140-100	07A012	[YKS]
☐ RA-41252	An-140-100	09A014	

☐	RA-41253	An-140-100	36525305032	
☐	VP-BEP	B737-8Q8/W	32797/1287	
☐	VQ-BMP	B737-86N/W	28617/504	
☐	VQ-BOY	B737-85F/W	28825/188	
☐	VQ-BPY	B757-236PCF	25597/441	
☐	VQ-BVI	DHC-8-311	381	
☐	VQ-BVJ	DHC-8-311B	379	
☐	VP-BNU	DHC-8-402Q	4171	std
☐	VP-BOS	DHC-8-402Q	4159	std
☐	RA-89011	Sukhoi SSJ 100-95B	95019	
☐	RA-89012	Sukhoi SSJ 100-95B	95020	
☐	RA-85707	Tu-154M	91A882	[YKS]
☐	RA-85791	Tu-154M	93A975	[YKS]
☐	RA-85794	Tu-154M	93A978	[YKS]
☐	RA-85812	Tu-154M	94A1005	[YKS]

YAMAL AIRLINES — YL / LLM

☐	VP-BBN	A320-232	1918	
☐	VP-BCN	A320-232	1993	
☐	VP-BCU	A320-232	1969	
☐	VP-BHW	A320-232	2413	
☐	VP-BHX	A320-214	2439	
☐	VP-BHZ	A320-214	2419	
☐	VQ-BNR	A320-214	1054	
☐	VQ-BSM	A321-231	1967	
☐	VQ-BSQ	A321-231	1956	
☐	RA-46694	An-24RV	47309904	♦
☐	RA-46695	An-24RV	47309905	♦
☐	VP-BKW	B737-4MO	29204/3051	
☐	VQ-BII	B737-48E	25773/2905	
☐	VQ-BIK	B737-48E	25775/2925	
☐	VQ-BNM	B737-5Q8	28201/2999	
☐	VP-BBA	CRJ-200LR	7607	
☐	VP-BBC	CRJ-200LR	7619	
☐	VP-BBE	CRJ-200LR	7630	
☐	VP-BBM	CRJ-200LR	7738	
☐	VQ-BBV	CRJ-200ER	7454	
☐	VQ-BPA	CRJ-200LR	7583	
☐	VQ-BPB	CRJ-200LR	7573	
☐	VQ-BPC	CRJ-200LR	7570	
☐	VQ-BPD	CRJ-200LR	7567	
☐	VQ-BSA	CRJ-200LR	7910	
☐	VQ-BSB	CRJ-200LR	8010	
☐	RA-89034	Sukohi SSJ100-95LR	95062	♦
☐	RA-89035	Sukohi SSJ100-95LR	95067	♦

RDPL- LAOS

LAO AIRLINES — QV / LAO

☐	RDPL-34188	A320-214	4596	
☐	RDPL-34199	A320-214	4639	
☐	RDPL-34223	A320-214	5356	
☐	RDPL-34224	A320-214	5396	
☐	RDPL-34173	ATR 72-202	870	
☐	RDPL-34174	ATR 72-202	878	
☐	RDPL-34175	ATR 72-202	929	
☐	RDPL-34176	ATR 72-202	938	
☐	RDPL-34222	ATR 72-600	1049	
☐	RDPL-34225	ATR 72-600	1155	
☐	RDPL-34228	ATR 72-600	1189	
☐	RDPL-34168	XIAN MA60	0402	[VTE]
☐	RDPL-34169	XIAN MA60	0403	[VTE]
☐	RDPL-34171	XIAN MA60	0507	[VTE]
☐	RDPL-34172	XIAN MA60	0508	[VTE]

LAO SKYWAY — LLL

☐	HS-SAB	Do228-200	8007	♦
☐	HS-SAE	Do228-200	8124	♦
☐	RDPL-34226	XIAN MA60	0801	♦
☐	RDPL-34262	XIAN MA60	0802	♦
☐	ZS-ATK	LET L-410UVP-E20	062637	♦
☐	ZS-ATN	LET L-410UVP-E20	072639	♦

RP- PHILIPPINES

AIR ASIA ZEST — Z2 / EZD

☐	RP-C8189	A320-216	4797	♦
☐	RP-C8897	A320-232	2141	
☐	RP-C8970	A320-216	3064	
☐	RP-C8971	A320-216	2956	
☐	RP-C8972	A320-216	2826	
☐	RP-C8974	A320-216	3568	
☐	RP-C8975	A320-214	2425	♦
☐	RP-C8986	A320-216	3018	
☐	RP-C8987	A320-214	1286	
☐	RP-C8988	A320-232	2147	
☐	RP-C8993	A320-232	0667	
☐	RP-C8994	A320-233	0743	
☐	RP-C8995	A320-232	0872	
☐	RP-C8996	A320-233	0874	
☐	RP-C8997	A320-232	2576	
☐	RP-C8892	XIAN MA60	0703	[CRK]
☐	RP-C8894	XIAN MA60	0710	[MNL]
☐	RP-C8895	XIAN MA60	0711	[MNL]
☐	RP-C8896	XIAN MA60	0712	[SUB]
☐	RP-C5000	ITPN CASA CN235	2/001N	

AIR SWIFT — T6 / ITI

☐	RP-C4200	ATR 42-500	554	
☐	RP-C4201	ATR 42-500	689	
☐	RP-C4202	ATR 42-600	1205	♦

ASTRO AIR PHILIPPINES — BY / AAV

☐	RP-C8708	MD-83	49946/1898	
☐	RP-C8709	MD-82	53247/1902	♦

CEBU PACIFIC AIR — 5J / CEB

☐	RP-C3191	A319-111	2625
☐	RP-C3192	A319-111	2638
☐	RP-C3193	A319-111	2786
☐	RP-C3194	A319-111	2790
☐	RP-C3195	A319-111	2831
☐	RP-C3196	A319-111	2821
☐	RP-C3197	A319-111	2852
☐	RP-C3198	A319-111	2876
☐	RP-C3237	A320-214	5045
☐	RP-C3238	A320-214	5067
☐	RP-C3242	A320-214	2994
☐	RP-C3243	A320-214	3048
☐	RP-C3244	A320-214	3272
☐	RP-C3249	A320-214	3762
☐	RP-C3250	A320-214	3767
☐	RP-C3260	A320-214	4447
☐	RP-C3261	A320-214	4508

☐	RP-C3262	A320-214	4537	
☐	RP-C3263	A320-214	4574	♦
☐	RP-C3264	A320-214	4852	
☐	RP-C3265	A320-214	4861	
☐	RP-C3266	A320-214	4870	
☐	RP-C3267	A320-214	4927	♦
☐	RP-C3268	A320-214	4993	
☐	RP-C3269	A320-214	5250	♦
☐	RP-C3270	A320-214	5320	♦
☐	RP-C3271	A320-214	5381	
☐	RP-C3272	A320-214/S	5442	
☐	RP-C3273	A320-214/S	5498	
☐	RP-C3274	A320-214/S	5669	
☐	RP-C3275	A320-214/S	5687	
☐	RP-C3276	A320-214/S	5917	
☐	RP-C3277	A320-214/S	5934	
☐	RP-C3278	A320-214/S	6021	
☐	RP-C3279	A320-214/S	6051	
☐	RP-C4100	A320-214/S	6317	
☐	RP-C4101	A320-214/S	6325	
☐	RP-C4102	A320-214/S	6418	
☐	RP-C4103	A320-214/S	6441	
☐	RP-C4104	A320-214/S	6741	♦
☐	RP-C4105	A320-214/S	6777	♦
☐	RP-C4106	A320-214/S	6925	♦
☐	RP-C4107	A320-214/S	6929	♦
☐	RP-C	A320-214/S	7066	o/o♦
☐	RP-C	A320-214/S		o/o♦
☐	RP-C	A320-214/S		o/o♦
☐	RP-C5323	A320-231	0424	^
☐	RP-C3341	A330-343E	1420	
☐	RP-C3342	A330-343E	1445	
☐	RP-C3343	A330-343E	1495	
☐	RP-C3344	A330-343E	1527	
☐	RP-C3345	A330-343E	1552	
☐	RP-C3346	A330-343E	1602	
☐	RP-C3347	A330-343E		o/o
☐	RP-C7250	ATR 72-212A	779	^
☐	RP-C7251	ATR 72-212A	784	^
☐	RP-C7252	ATR 72-212A	820	^
☐	RP-C7253	ATR 72-212A	828	^
☐	RP-C7255	ATR 72-212A	842	^
☐	RP-C7256	ATR 72-212A	847	^
☐	RP-C7257	ATR 72-212A	857	^
☐	RP-C7258	ATR 72-212A	944	^
☐	RP-C	ATR 72-600		o/o♦
☐	RP-C	ATR 72-600		o/o♦
☐	RP-C	ATR 72-600		o/o♦
☐	RP-C	ATR 72-600		o/o♦

^ reported operated as Cebgo.

FIL-ASIAN AIRWAYS — *RI*

☐	RP-C3591	NAMC YS-11A-5	2147	

PACIFIC PEARL AIRWAYS — *PPM*

☐	RP-C8777	B737-232	23088/1018	

PAL EXPRESS — *2P / GAP*

☐	RP-C3227	A320-214	2183	
☐	RP-C3228	A320-214	2162	
☐	RP-C8393	A320-214	4777	
☐	RP-C8395	A320-214	4984	
☐	RP-C8396	A320-214	5007	
☐	RP-C8397	A320-214	5012	
☐	RP-C8398	A320-214	5103	
☐	RP-C8399	A320-214	5310	
☐	RP-C8604	A320-214	3087	
☐	RP-C8606	A320-214	3187	
☐	RP-C8610	A320-214	3310	
☐	RP-C8611	A320-214	3455	
☐	RP-C8615	A320-214	3731	♦
☐	RP-C8616	A320-214	5081	
☐	RP-C8618	A320-214	5140	
☐	RP-C8763	A330-343E	1546	
☐	RP-C3016	DHC-8Q-314	653	
☐	RP-C3017	DHC-8Q-314	657	
☐	RP-C3018	DHC-8Q-314	658	
☐	RP-C3020	DHC-8Q-314	583	
☐	RP-C3030	DHC-8-402Q	4064	
☐	RP-C3031	DHC-8-402Q	4069	
☐	RP-C3032	DHC-8-402Q	4070	
☐	RP-C3033	DHC-8-402Q	4071	
☐	RP-C3036	DHC-8-402Q	4023	

PHILIPPINE AIRLINES — *PR / PAL*

☐	RP-C8609	A320-214	3273	
☐	RP-C8612	A320-214	3553	
☐	RP-C8613	A320-214	3579	
☐	RP-C8614	A320-214	3652	
☐	RP-C8619	A320-214	5315	
☐	RP-C8620	A320-214	5371	
☐	RP-C9901	A321-231/S	5715	
☐	RP-C9902	A321-231/S	5747	
☐	RP-C9903	A321-231/S	5787	
☐	RP-C9905	A321-231/S	5820	
☐	RP-C9906	A321-231/S	5825	
☐	RP-C9907	A321-231/S	5838	
☐	RP-C9909	A321-231/S	6074	
☐	RP-C9910	A321-231/S	6201	
☐	RP-C9911	A321-231/S	6253	
☐	RP-C9912	A321-231/S	6291	
☐	RP-C9914	A321-231/S	6295	
☐	RP-C9915	A321-231/S	6330	
☐	RP-C9916	A321-231/S	6363	
☐	RP-C9917	A321-231/S	6371	
☐	RP-C9918	A321-231/S	6493	
☐	RP-C9919	A321-231/S	6531	
☐	RP-C9921	A321-231/S	6539	
☐	RP-C9923	A321-231/S	6573	
☐	RP-C9924	A321-231/S	6623	
☐	RP-C	A321-231/S	7015	o/o♦
☐	RP-C	A321-231/S	7180	o/o♦
☐	RP-C	A321-231/S	7285	o/o♦
☐	RP-C3330	A330-301	183	[CRK]
☐	RP-C3340	A330-301	203	[CRK]
☐	RP-C8760	A330-343E	1510	
☐	RP-C8762	A330-343E	1531	
☐	RP-C8764	A330-343E	1553	
☐	RP-C8765	A330-343E	1559	
☐	RP-C8766	A330-343E	1566	
☐	RP-C8771	A330-343E	1568	
☐	RP-C8780	A330-343E	1456	
☐	RP-C8781	A330-343E	1460	
☐	RP-C8782	A330-343E	1449	
☐	RP-C8783	A330-343E	1463	
☐	RP-C8784	A330-343E	1467	
☐	RP-C8785	A330-343E	1475	
☐	RP-C8786	A330-343E	1482	
☐	RP-C8789	A330-343E	1504	

□	RP-C3431	A340-313X	176	[GWO]
□	RP-C3435	A340-313X	302	
□	RP-C3436	A340-313X	318	
□	RP-C3437	A340-313X	332	
□	RP-C3438	A340-313X	387	
□	RP-C3439	A340-313X	459	
□	RP-C3441	A340-313X	474	
□	RP-C7772	B777-3F6ER	38719/1153	
□	RP-C7773	B777-3F6ER	38718/1096	
□	RP-C7774	B777-3F6ER	35556/1056	
□	RP-C7775	B777-3F6ER	35555/1022	
□	RP-C7776	B777-36NER	37712/841	
□	RP-C7777	B777-36NER	37709/826	
□	RP-C	B777-3xxER		o/o♦
□	RP-C	B777-3xxER		o/o♦

ROYAL STAR AVIATION

□	RP-C8666	ATR 72-212A	666	o/o♦
□	RP-C9017	ATR 72-202	444	o/o♦
□	RP-C2812	BAeJetstream 32	923	
□	RP-C8298	BAeJetstream 41	41013	
□	RP-C8328	Do328-300	3136	
□	RP-C9555	Do328-310	3160	

SKYJET 5M / MSJ

□	RP-C5255	BAe146 Srs.100	E1104	♦
□	RP-C8538	BAe146 Srs.100	E1015	

SE- SWEDEN

AMAPOLA FLYG APF

□	SE-KTC	Fokker 50F	20124	
□	SE-KTD	Fokker 50F	20125	
□	SE-LEZ	Fokker 50	20128	>RVL
□	SE-LFS	Fokker 50F	20216	♦
□	SE-LIO	Fokker 50	20146	
□	SE-LIP	Fokker 50F	20147	
□	SE-LIR	Fokker 50	20151	>TE
□	SE-LIS	Fokker 50F	20152	
□	SE-LJG	Fokker 50	20168	
□	SE-LJH	Fokker 50	20171	
□	SE-LJI	Fokker 50	20180	
□	SE-LJV	Fokker 50F	20103	
□	SE-LJY	Fokker 50F	20259	
□	SE-MFA	Fokker 50	20118	[BGY]
□	SE-MFB	Fokker 50	20252	
□	SE-MFJ	Fokker 50F	20149	

BRAATHENS REGIONAL DC / GAO

□	SE-MDA	ATR 72-212A	778	
□	SE-MDB	ATR 72-212A	822	
□	SE-MDC	ATR 72-212A	894	>ETS
□	SE-MDH	ATR 72-212A	917	>ETS
□	SE-MDI	ATR 72-212A	930	
□	SE-MKA	ATR 72-600	1276	♦
□	SE-MKB	ATR 72-600	1308	♦
□	SE-MKC	ATR 72-600	1313	♦
□	SE-MKD	ATR 72-600	1331	o/o♦
□	SE-	ATR 72-600		o/o♦
□	SE-ISE	SAAB SF.340A	340A-156	NTJ>
□	SE-ISG	SAAB SF.340B	340B-162	
□	SE-KXK	SAAB 2000	2000-012	>SAS
□	SE-LOM	SAAB 2000	2000-035	
□	SE-LSB	SAAB 2000	2000-043	
□	SE-LSE	SAAB 2000	2000-046	
□	SE-LTU	SAAB 2000	2000-062	
□	SE-LTV	SAAB 2000	2000-063	
□	SE-LTX	SAAB 2000	2000-024	
□	SE-LXH	SAAB 2000	2000-007	
□	SE-LXK	SAAB 2000	2000-056	
□	SE-MFF	SAAB 2000	2000-038	
□	SE-MFK	SAAB 2000	2000-005	>ETS
□	SE-MFM	SAAB 2000	2000-022	

MALMO AVIATION TF / SCW

□	SE-DJN	Avro 146-RJ85	E2231	
□	SE-DJO	Avro 146-RJ85	E2226	
□	SE-DSO	Avro 146-RJ100	E3221	
□	SE-DSP	Avro 146-RJ100	E3242	
□	SE-DSR	Avro 146-RJ100	E3244	
□	SE-DSS	Avro 146-RJ100	E3245	
□	SE-DST	Avro 146-RJ100	E3247	
□	SE-DSU	Avro 146-RJ100	E3248	
□	SE-DSV	Avro 146-RJ100	E3250	
□	SE-DSX	Avro 146-RJ100	E3255	
□	SE-DSY	Avro 146-RJ100	E3263	
□	SE-RJI	Avro 146-RJ100	E3357	

NEXTJET 2N / NTJ

□	SE-LLO	BAeATP	2023	
□	SE-MAK	BAeATP	2040	
□	SE-MAL	BAeATP	2045	
□	SE-MEE	BAeATP	2019	[MMX]
□	SE-MEG	BAeATP	2031	[MMX]
□	SE-MEX	BAeATP	2018	
□	YR-FZA	Fokker 100	11395	<KBP♦
□	SE-ISE	SAAB SF.340A	340A-156	<GAO
□	SE-KXD	SAAB SF.340B	340B-248	
□	SE-KXG	SAAB SF.340B	340A-164	
□	SE-KXI	SAAB SF.340B	340B-176	
□	SE-KXJ	SAAB SF.340B	340B-189	
□	SE-LEP	SAAB SF.340A	340A-127	
□	SE-LJM	SAAB SF.340A	340A-112	
□	SE-LJN	SAAB SF.340A	340A-114	
□	SE-LJS	SAAB SF.340B	340B-215	
□	SE-LJT	SAAB SF.340B	340B-221	
□	SE-LMR	SAAB SF.340A	340A-141	

Operates services for Air Aland (N9 / NVD) in Finland with two of the above SF.340s.

NOVAIR 1I / NVR

□	SE-RDN	A321-231	2211	
□	SE-RDO	A321-231	2216	
□	SE-RDP	A321-231	2410	

SCANDINAVIAN AIRLINES SYSTEM SK / SAS

□	OY-KBO	A319-132	2850	
□	OY-KBP	A319-132	2888	
□	OY-KBR	A319-131	3231	
□	OY-KBT	A319-131	3292	
□	OY-KAL	A320-232	2883	
□	OY-KAM	A320-232	2911	
□	OY-KAN	A320-232	2958	
□	OY-KAO	A320-232	2990	
□	OY-KAP	A320-232	3086	
□	OY-KAR	A320-232	3159	
□	OY-KAS	A320-232	3335	
□	OY-KAT	A320-232	3192	

	Reg	Type	C/n	
☐	OY-KAU	A320-232	3227	
☐	OY-KAW	A320-232	2817	
☐	OY-KAY	A320-232	2856	
☐	SE-RJE	A320-232	1183	
☐	SE-RJF	A320-232	1383	
☐		A320-251N	7236	o/o♦
☐		A320-251N		o/o♦
☐		A320-251N		o/o♦
☐	LN-RKI	A321-232	1817	
☐	LN-RKK	A321-232	1848	
☐	OY-KBB	A321-232	1642	
☐	OY-KBE	A321-232	1798	
☐	OY-KBF	A321-232	1807	
☐	OY-KBH	A321-232	1675	
☐	OY-KBK	A321-232	1587	
☐	OY-KBL	A321-232	1619	
☐	LN-RKH	A330-343E	497	
☐	LN-RKM	A330-343E	496	
☐	LN-RKN	A330-343E	568	
☐	LN-RKO	A330-343E	515	
☐	LN-RKR	A330-343E	1660	♦
☐	LN-RKS	A330-343E	1665	♦
☐	LN-RKT	A330-343E	1697	♦
☐	LN-RKU	A330-343E	1715	o/o♦
☐	LN-RKF	A340-313X	413	
☐	LN-RKG	A340-313X	424	
☐	LN-RKP	A340-313X	167	
☐	OY-KBA	A340-313X	435	
☐	OY-KBC	A340-313X	467	
☐	OY-KBD	A340-313X	470	
☐	OY-KBI	A340-313X	430	
☐	OY-KBM	A340-313X	450	

For ATR 72 fleet see Flybe (G-) & Jet Time (OY-)

	Reg	Type	C/n	
☐	LN-RCT	B737-683	30189/303	
☐	LN-RCU	B737-683	30190/335	
☐	LN-RCW	B737-683	28308/333	
☐	LN-RGK	B737-683	28313/447	
☐	LN-RPA	B737-683	28290/100	
☐	LN-RPB	B737-683	28294/137	
☐	LN-RPE	B737-683	28306/329	
☐	LN-RPF	B737-683	28307/330	
☐	LN-RPG	B737-683	28310/255	
☐	LN-RPS	B737-683	28298/191	
☐	LN-RPT	B737-683	28299/193	
☐	LN-RPW	B737-683	28289/92	
☐	LN-RPX	B737-683	28291/112	
☐	LN-RPY	B737-683	28292/116	
☐	LN-RPZ	B737-683	28293/120	
☐	LN-RRC	B737-683	28300/209	
☐	LN-RRD	B737-683	28301/227	
☐	LN-RRO	B737-683	28288/49	
☐	LN-RRP	B737-683	28311/382	
☐	LN-RRR	B737-683	28309/368	
☐	LN-RRX	B737-683	28296/21	
☐	LN-RRY	B737-683	28297/30	
☐	LN-RRZ	B737-683	28295/149	
☐	SE-DNX	B737-683	28304/270	
☐	SE-DOR	B737-683	28305/290	
☐	LN-RNN	B737-783	28315/464	
☐	LN-RNO	B737-783	28316/476	
☐	LN-RNU	B737-783/W	34548/3116	
☐	LN-RNW	B737-783/W	34549/3210	
☐	LN-RPJ	B737-783	30192/486	
☐	LN-RPK	B737-783	28317/500	

	Reg	Type	C/n	
☐	LN-RRA	B737-783/W	30471/2288	
☐	LN-RRB	B737-783/W	32276/2331	
☐	LN-RRM	B737-783	28314/458	
☐	LN-RRN	B737-783	30191/404	
☐	LN-TUA	B737-705	28211/33	[SNN]
☐	LN-TUD	B737-705	28217/142	
☐	LN-TUF	B737-705	28222/245	
☐	LN-TUJ	B737-705/W	29095/773	
☐	LN-TUK	B737-705/W	29096/794	
☐	LN-TUL	B737-705/W	29097/1072	
☐	LN-TUM	B737-705/W	29098/1116	
☐	SE-RER	B737-7BX	30736/658	
☐	SE-RES	B737-7BX	30737/687	
☐	SE-RET	B737-76N/W	32734/1090	
☐	SE-REU	B737-76N/W	33005/1134	
☐	SE-REX	B737-76N/W	33418/1226	
☐	SE-REY	B737-76N/W	32737/1130	
☐	SE-REZ	B737-76N/W	32738/1392	
☐	SE-RJR	B737-76N/W	33420/1459	
☐	SE-RJS	B737-76N/W	32684/1889	
☐	SE-RJT	B737-76N/W	32741/1487	
☐	SE-RJU	B737-76N/W	29885/1120	
☐	SE-RJX	B737-76N/W	34754/2172	
☐	D-APBC	B737-8BK/W	33016/1588	<PTG♦
☐	LN-RCN	B737-883	28318/529	
☐	LN-RCX	B737-883	30196/733	
☐	LN-RCY	B737-883	28324/767	
☐	LN-RCZ	B737-883	30197/798	
☐	LN-RGA	B737-86N/W	39397/4003	
☐	LN-RGB	B737-86N/W	38034/4280	
☐	LN-RGC	B737-86N/W	41257/4321	
☐	LN-RGD	B737-86N/W	41258/4393	
☐	LN-RGE	B737-86N/W	38037/4376	
☐	LN-RGF	B737-86N/W	38038/4429	
☐	LN-RGG	B737-86N/W	38039/4469	
☐	LN-RGH	B737-86N/W	41266/4770	
☐	LN-RGI	B737-86N/W	35646/4788	
☐	LN-RPL	B737-883	30469/673	
☐	LN-RPM	B737-883	30195/696	
☐	LN-RPN	B737-883	30470/717	
☐	LN-RPO	B737-883	30467/634	
☐	LN-RPR	B737-883	30468/668	
☐	LN-RRE	B737-85P/W	35706/2586	
☐	LN-RRF	B737-85P/W	35707/2610	
☐	LN-RRG	B737-85P/W	35708/2653	
☐	LN-RRH	B737-883/W	34546/2898	
☐	LN-RRJ	B737-883/W	34547/2956	
☐	LN-RRK	B737-883	32278/1169	
☐	LN-RRL	B737-883/W	28328/1424	
☐	LN-RRS	B737-883	28325/1014	
☐	LN-RRT	B737-883	28326/1036	
☐	LN-RRU	B737-883	28327/1070	
☐	LN-RRW	B737-883	32277/1554	
☐	EC-JZV	CRJ-900ER	15117	<ANS♦
☐	OY-KFA	CRJ-900	15206	
☐	OY-KFB	CRJ-900	15211	
☐	OY-KFC	CRJ-900	15218	
☐	OY-KFD	CRJ-900	15221	
☐	OY-KFE	CRJ-900	15224	
☐	OY-KFF	CRJ-900	15231	
☐	OY-KFG	CRJ-900	15237	
☐	OY-KFH	CRJ-900	15240	
☐	OY-KFI	CRJ-900	15242	
☐	OY-KFK	CRJ-900	15244	
☐	OY-KFL	CRJ-900	15246	
☐	OY-KFM	CRJ-900	15250	♦

CRJ-900s to be operated for SAS by Cimber Air.

☐	SE-KXK	SAAB 2000	2000-012	<GAO

SPARROW AVIATION — TE

☐	OY-RUO	ATR 42-500	514	<DTR♦
☐	SE-LIR	Fokker 50	20151	<APF♦

SVERIGEFLYG — 2Q / ETS

☐	SE-MDC	ATR 72-212A	894	<GAO
☐	SE-MDH	ATR 72-212A	917	<GAO
☐	SE-MFK	SAAB 2000	2000-005	<GAO♦

TUIFLY NORDIC — 6B / BLX

☐	SE-DZV	B737-804/W	32904/1302	
☐	SE-RFT	B737-8K5/W	38097/3548	
☐	SE-RFU	B737-8K5/W	37259/3673	
☐	SE-RFV	B737-86N/W	32669/1895	
☐	SE-RFX	B737-8K5/W	37246/3994	
☐	SE-RFY	B737-8K5/W	44272/4827	
☐	SE-RFR	B767-38AER/W	29617/741	

WEST ATLANTIC SWEDEN — PT / SWN

☐	SE-MGJ	ATR 72-202	290	[ATH]
☐	SE-MGN	ATR 72-202	437	♦
☐	SE-KXP	BAeATP (LFD)	2056	
☐	SE-LGU	BAeATP	2022	[MMX]
☐	SE-LGV	BAeATP	2034	[MMX]
☐	SE-LGX	BAeATP	2036	
☐	SE-LGY	BAeATP	2035	
☐	SE-LGZ	BAeATP (LFD)	2021	
☐	SE-LHX	BAeATP (F)	2020	
☐	SE-LHZ	BAeATP (F)	2059	
☐	SE-LNX	BAeATP (F)	2061	
☐	SE-LNY	BAeATP	2062	
☐	SE-LPR	BAeATP (F)	2057	
☐	SE-LPS	BAeATP (LFD)	2043	
☐	SE-LPT	BAeATP (F)	2058	
☐	SE-LPU	BAeATP	2060	
☐	SE-LPV	BAeATP (LFD)	2041	
☐	SE-LPX	BAeATP (F)	2063	
☐	SE-MAF	BAeATP	2002	
☐	SE-MAH	BAeATP	2004	
☐	SE-MAI	BAeATP (LFD)	2010	♦
☐	SE-MAJ	BAeATP (LFD)	2038	
☐	SE-MAM	BAeATP (LFD)	2005	♦
☐	SE-MAN	BAeATP (LFD)	2006	♦
☐	SE-MAO	BAeATP (LFD)	2011	
☐	SE-MAP	BAeATP (LFD)	2037	♦
☐	SE-MAR	BAeATP	2053	
☐	SE-MAY	BAeATP	2044	
☐	SE-MHC	BAeATP (LFD)	2007	♦
☐	SE-MHD	BAeATP (LFD)	2008	o/o♦
☐	SE-MHE	BAeATP (LFD)	2012	♦
☐	SE-MHF	BAeATP (LFD)	2013	o/o♦
☐	SE-MHG	BAeATP (LFD)	2014	♦
☐	SE-MHH	BAeATP (LFD)	2015	o/o♦
☐	SE-MHI	BAeATP (LFD)	2017	♦
☐	SE-MHJ	BAeATP (LFD)	2024	o/o♦
☐	SE-	B737-406F	24959/1949	o/o♦
☐	N791AX	B767-281F	23141/108	<ATN
☐	SE-RLA	B767-232F	22224/76	
☐	SE-RLB	B767-232(SCD)	22222/56	♦
☐	SE-RLC	B767-232(SCD)	22217/27	♦

☐	SE-DUY	CRJ-200F	7023	
☐	SE-RIF	CRJ-200F	7142	

SP- POLAND

ENTER AIR — E4 / ENT

☐	SP-ENA	B737-4Q8	26320/2563	
☐	SP-ENB	B737-4Q8	26299/2602	
☐	SP-ENC	B737-4Q8	25376/2689	
☐	SP-ENE	B737-4Q8	25374/2562	
☐	SP-ENF	B737-4C9	25429/2215	
☐	SP-ENH	B737-405	25795/2867	
☐	SP-ENI	B737-43Q	28489/2827	
☐	SP-ENK	B737-46J	28038/2794	
☐	SP-ENQ	B737-85R/W	29036/164	♦
☐	SP-ENR	B737-8Q8/W	30652/1018	♦
☐	SP-ENT	B737-8AS/W	29926/722	
☐	SP-ENU	B737-83N/W	30675/898	
☐	SP-ENV	B737-8BK/W	33014/1367	
☐	SP-ENW	B737-86J/W	28073/200	
☐	SP-ENX	B737-8Q8	30627/752	
☐	SP-ENY	B737-86N/W	28592/258	
☐	SP-ENZ	B737-85F	28823/174	

EXIN — EXN

☐	SP-EKA	An-26B	12008	
☐	SP-EKB	An-26	1310	[KTW]
☐	SP-EKC	An-26	1407	
☐	SP-EKD	An-26	1402	[KTW]
☐	SP-EKE	An-26	1509	[KTW]
☐	SP-EKF	An-26	1604	[KTW]
☐	SP-FDR	An-26B	11305	
☐	SP-FDT	An-26B	12102	

LOT – POLISH AIRLINES — LO / LOT

☐	SP-LLE	B737-45D	27914/2804	^
☐	SP-LLF	B737-45D	28752/2874	
☐	SP-LLG	B737-45D	28753/2895	^
☐	SP-LRA	B787-8	35938/61	
☐	SP-LRB	B787-8	37894/78	
☐	SP-LRC	B787-8	35940/86	
☐	SP-LRD	B787-8	35941/87	
☐	SP-LRE	B787-8	35939/88	
☐	SP-LRF	B787-8	35942/161	>AEA
☐	SP-LGG	ERJ-145MP	145319	[WAW]
☐	SP-LGH	ERJ-145MP	145329	[WAW]
☐	SP-LGO	ERJ-145MP	145560	[WAW]
☐	SP-LDE	ERJ-170LR	17000029	
☐	SP-LDF	ERJ-170LR	17000035	
☐	SP-LDG	ERJ-170LR	17000065	
☐	SP-LDH	ERJ-170LR	17000069	
☐	SP-LDI	ERJ-170LR	17000073	
☐	SP-LDK	ERJ-170LR	17000074	
☐	SP-LIA	ERJ-175LR	17000125	
☐	SP-LIB	ERJ-175LR	17000132	
☐	SP-LIC	ERJ-175LR	17000134	
☐	SP-LID	ERJ-175LR	17000136	
☐	SP-LIE	ERJ-175LR	17000153	
☐	SP-LIF	ERJ-175LR	17000154	
☐	SP-LIG	ERJ-175LR	17000283	>Govt
☐	SP-LIH	ERJ-175LR	17000288	>Govt
☐	SP-LII	ERJ-175LR	17000290	
☐	SP-LIK	ERJ-175LR	17000303	

☐	SP-LIL	ERJ-175LR	17000306	
☐	SP-LIM	ERJ-175LR	17000311	
☐	SP-LIN	ERJ-175LR	17000313	
☐	SP-LIO	ERJ-175LR	17000321	
☐	SP-LNA	ERJ-195LR	19000415	
☐	SP-LNB	ERJ-195LR	19000444	
☐	SP-LNC	ERJ-195LR	19000462	
☐	SP-LND	ERJ-195LR	19000516	
☐	SP-LNE	ERJ-195LR	19000583	
☐	SP-LNF	ERJ-195LR	19000596	

^ operates as LOT Charters

SKY TAXI — *IGA*

☐	SP-MRB	SAAB SF.340A(QC)	340A-100	
☐	SP-MRC	SAAB SF.340A	340A-143	
☐	SP-MRE	SAAB SF.340A	340A-151	

SMALL PLANET POLSKA — *LLP*

☐	SP-HAB	A320-232	1411	
☐	SP-HAC	A320-233	0739	
☐	SP-HAG	A320-232	1723	
☐	SP-HAH	A320-233	2118	♦
☐	SP-HAI	A320-233	1007	♦
☐	SP-	A321-211	2903	o/o♦
☐	SP-	A321-211	2912	o/o♦
☐	SP-	A321-211	3191	o/o♦
☐	SP-	A321-211	2342	o/o♦

SPRINT AIR — *SRN*

☐	SP-SPA	ATR 72-202F	246	
☐	SP-SPC	ATR 72-202	272	♦
☐	SP-KPC	SAAB SF.340A(QC)	340A-070	
☐	SP-KPE	SAAB SF.340A(QC)	340A-130	
☐	SP-KPH	SAAB SF.340A(QC)	340A-015	
☐	SP-KPK	SAAB SF.340AF	340A-026	
☐	SP-KPL	SAAB SF.340A	340A-038	
☐	SP-KPN	SAAB SF.340A	340A-118	
☐	SP-KPO	SAAB SF.340A(QC)	340A-010	
☐	SP-KPR	SAAB SF.340A(QC)	340A-139	
☐	SP-KPU	SAAB SF.340AF	340A-145	
☐	SP-KPV	SAAB SF.340A	340A-071	
☐	SP-KPZ	SAAB SF.340A	340A-087	

TRAVEL SERVICE POLAND — *3Z / TVP*

☐	SP-TVZ	B737-8BK/W	29643/2303	

ST- SUDAN

AIR TAXI SUDAN — *WAM*

☐	ST-TKO	An-32B	3110	

AIR WEST CARGO — *AWZ*

☐	ST-EWC	Il-76TD	0023438129	
☐	ST-EWX	Il-76TD	1013409282	

ALFA AIRLINES

☐	ST-AQR	Il-76TD	0043453575	
☐	ST-ARP	An-24RV	37308809	
☐	ST-AWT	An-26	3508	
☐	ST-EWD	Il-76TD	0063466989	

ALOK AIR — *LOK*

☐	ST-AWZ	An-24RV	77310808	
☐	S9-TLN	An-24RV		♦

BADR AIRLINES — *J4 / BDR*

☐	C5-BDB	B737-5H6	27354/2637	♦
☐	C5-BDO	B737-36N	28673/2995	♦
☐	C5-BDV	B737-5H6	27356/2654	
☐	EK73772	B737-55S	28472/3004	<TRV♦
☐	EK73775	B737-55S	28475/3096	<TRV♦
☐	ST-BDE	Il-76TD	1013408252	
☐	ST-BDN	Il-76TD	1023413443	
☐	ST-SAL	An-26B	11907	

BENTIU AIR TRANSPORT — *BNT*

☐	ST-NDC	An-26	10908	
☐	ST-SRA	An-26	11807	

BLUE BIRD AVIATION — *BRD*

☐	ET-AKZ	DHC-8-202	469	♦
☐	ET-ALX	DHC-8-202	475	♦
☐	ST-ARH	Fokker 50	20131	♦

DOVE AIR — *DOV*

☐	ST-HIS	An-26B-100	10310	
☐	ST-MRS	Tu-134B-3	63333	

EL MAGAL AVIATION — *MGG*

☐	ST-APJ	An-12BP	2400701	[KRT]
☐	ST-BEN	An-26	6907	

GREEN FLAG AVIATION

☐	ST-BDT	An-74	36547097935	
☐	ST-EWX	Il-76TD	1013409282	
☐	ST-GFD	An-30A-100	0605	
☐	ST-GFF	An-74	36547097932	

KATA TRANSPORTATION COMPANY

☐	ST-AZM	An-12BK	00346907	

NOVA AIRWAYS — *O9 / NOV*

☐	ST-MRA	B737-5C9	26439/2444	♦
☐	ST-NVB	CRJ-200ER	7807	[LJU]
☐	ST-NVC	CRJ-200ER	7686	
☐	ST-NVD	CRJ-200ER	7653	
☐	ST-NVE	CRJ-200ER	7662	
☐	ST-NVG	B737-58E	29122/2991	[ADD]
☐	5Y-BXD	CRJ-100ER	7042	<FFV

SUDAN AIRWAYS — *SD / SUD*

☐	ST-ATA	A300B4-622R	775	[KRT]
☐	ST-ATB	A300B4-622R	666	[KRT]
☐	D6-CAS	A320-214	3040	[KRT]
☐	UR-YAD	A320-211	0726	<ANR
☐	ST-AFA	B707-3J8C	20897/885	[KRT]
☐	C5-MAB	B737-3xx	?	<AAZ♦
☐	5Y-WWA	CRJ-200ER	7350	<♦
☐	5Y-BVZ	ERJ-135LR	145661	<ALW
☐	ST-ASD	Fokker 50	20201	
☐	ST-ASF	Fokker 50	20155	
☐	ST-ASI	Fokker 50	20247	
☐	ST-ASO	Fokker 50	20256	

SUN AIR			**S6 / SNR**
☐ JY-JAY	B737-3S3	29244/3059	<JAV♦
☐ ST-SDA	B737-2T4	23274/1099	
☐ ST-SDB	B737-2T4	23273/1097	>MSL

TARCO AIR			**3T / TRQ**
☐ C5-AAL	B737-332	25996/2488	<AAZ
☐ C5-AAN	B737-522	26687/2402	<AAZ
☐ C5-MAD	B737-3xx	?	<AAZ♦
☐ C5-MAE	B737-3xx	?	<AAZ♦
☐ ST-AWR	Il-76TD	0033447365	
☐ ST-MRL	Yak-42D	4520424116690	
☐ ST-TAB	Yak-42D	4520421401018	
☐ ST-TAC	Yak-42D	4520423304016	
☐ ST-TAR	Yak-42D	4520423307017	[KRT]♦
☐ UR-42426	Yak-42D	4520423304016	♦

SOUTH SUDAN – for fleets see Z8-

SU- EGYPT

AIR ARABIA EGYPT			**E5 / RBG**
☐ SU-AAB	A320-214	3152	

AIR CAIRO			**MC / MSC**
☐ SU-BPU	A320-214	2937	
☐ SU-BPV	A320-214	2966	
☐ SU-BPW	A320-214	3282	
☐ SU-BPX	A320-214	3323	
☐ SU-BSM	A320-214	3626	
☐ SU-BSN	A320-214	3840	♦
☐ SU-GCD	A320-232	2094	

AIR LEISURE			**AL / ALD**
☐ SU-GBM	A340-212	156	
☐ SU-GBN	A340-212	159	
☐ SU-GBO	A340-212	178	
☐ SU-BME	MD-83	49628/1582	

ALEXANDRIA AIRLINES			**XH / KHH**
☐ SU-KHM	B737-5C9	26438/2413	>FDK

ALMASRIA UNIVERSAL AIRLINES			**UJ / LMU**
☐ SU-TCD	A321-231	1366	
☐ SU-TCE	A320-232	0977	
☐ SU-TCF	A320-232	1561	
☐ SU-TCG	A321-211	0852	♦

AMC AIRLINES			**YJ / AMC**
☐ SU-BPZ	B737-86N/W	35213/2300	
☐ SU-BOZ	MD-83	53192/2155	

AVIATOR AIRWAYS			**AVV**
☐ SU-GBJ	B737-566	25352/2169	

CAIRO AVIATION			**CCE**
☐ SU-EAF	Tu-204-120	1450743764027	[CAI]
☐ SU-EAG	Tu-204-120C	1450743764028	[CAI]
☐ SU-EAH	Tu-204-120	1450743164023	[CAI]
☐ SU-EAI	Tu-204-120	1450743164025	[CAI]
☐ SU-EAJ	Tu-204-120C	1450742264029	

EGYPTAIR			**MS / MSR**
☐ SU-GAC	A300B4-203F	255	^
☐ SU-GAS	A300B4-622RF	561	^
☐ SU-GAY	A300B4-622RF	607	^
☐ SU-GBA	A320-231	0165	
☐ SU-GBB	A320-231	0166	
☐ SU-GBC	A320-231	0178	
☐ SU-GBD	A320-231	0194	
☐ SU-GBE	A320-231	0198	
☐ SU-GBF	A320-231	0351	♦
☐ SU-GBG	A320-231	0366	
☐ SU-GBZ	A320-232	2070	
☐ SU-GCA	A320-232	2073	
☐ SU-GCB	A320-232	2079	
☐ SU-GCC	A320-232	2088	
☐ SU-GCL	A320-231	0322	♦
☐ SU-GBT	A321-231	0680	
☐ SU-GBU	A321-231	0687	
☐ SU-GBV	A321-231	0715	
☐ SU-GBW	A321-231	0725	
☐ SU-GCE	A330-243	600	
☐ SU-GCF	A330-243	610	
☐ SU-GCG	A330-243	666	
☐ SU-GCH	A330-243	683	
☐ SU-GCI	A330-243	696	
☐ SU-GCJ	A330-243	709	
☐ SU-GCK	A330-243	726	
☐ SU-GDS	A330-343E	1143	
☐ SU-GDT	A330-343E	1230	
☐ SU-GDU	A330-343E	1238	
☐ SU-GDV	A330-343E	1246	
☐ SU-GBH	B737-566	25084/2019	
☐ SU-GBK	B737-566	26052/2276	
☐ SU-GBL	B737-566	26051/2282	[CAI]
☐ SU-GCM	B737-866/W	35558/2054	
☐ SU-GCN	B737-866/W	35559/2113	
☐ SU-GCO	B737-866/W	35561/2369	
☐ SU-GCP	B737-866/W	35560/2434	
☐ SU-GCR	B737-866/W	35562/2826	
☐ SU-GCS	B737-866/W	35563/2695	
☐ SU-GCZ	B737-866/W	35568/2795	
☐ SU-GDA	B737-866/W	35565/2999	
☐ SU-GDB	B737-866/W	35567/3017	
☐ SU-GDC	B737-866/W	35564/3040	
☐ SU-GDD	B737-866/W	35566/3061	
☐ SU-GDE	B737-866/W	35569/3043	
☐ SU-GDX	B737-866/W	40757/3409	
☐ SU-GDY	B737-866/W	40758/3442	
☐ SU-GDZ	B737-866/W	40759/2472	
☐ SU-GEA	B737-866/W	40760/3492	
☐ SU-GEB	B737-866/W	40800/3677	
☐ SU-GEC	B737-866/W	40801/3819	
☐ SU-GED	B737-866/W	40802/4095	
☐ SU-GEE	B737-866/W	40803/4136	
☐ SU-GBR	B777-266	28424/80	[CAI]
☐ SU-GBS	B777-266	28425/85	
☐ SU-GDL	B777-36NER	38284/850	
☐ SU-GDM	B777-36NER	38285/862	
☐ SU-GDN	B777-36NER	38288/896	
☐ SU-GDO	B777-36NER	38289/907	
☐ SU-GDP	B777-36NER	38290/918	
☐ SU-GDR	B777-36NER	38291/926	

^ operated by Egyptair Cargo MS / MSX

EGYPTAIR EXPRESS — MS / MSE

Reg	Type	C/n	Notes
SU-GCT	ERJ-170LR	17000167	
SU-GCU	ERJ-170LR	17000169	
SU-GCV	ERJ-170LR	17000170	
SU-GCW	ERJ-170LR	17000175	
SU-GCX	ERJ-170LR	17000178	
SU-GCY	ERJ-170LR	17000185	
SU-GDF	ERJ-170LR	17000266	
SU-GDG	ERJ-170LR	17000269	
SU-GDH	ERJ-170LR	17000274	
SU-GDI	ERJ-170LR	17000276	
SU-GDJ	ERJ-170LR	17000282	
SU-GDK	ERJ-170LR	17000284	

FLYEGYPT — FT / FEG

Reg	Type	C/n	Notes
SU-TMG	B737-86J/W	32918/1255	
SU-TMH	B737-8GJ/W	34903/2335	♦

NESMA AIR — NE / NMA

Reg	Type	C/n	Notes
SU-NMA	A320-232	1697	
SU-NMB	A320-232	1732	
SU-NMC	A320-232	2676	

NILE AIR — NP / NIA

Reg	Type	C/n	Notes
SU-BQB	A320-232	3183	
SU-BQC	A320-232	3219	
SU-BQJ	A320-232	2874	♦
SU-BQK	A320-214	3925	♦

PALESTINIAN AIRLINES — PF / PNW

Reg	Type	C/n	Notes
SU-YAH	Fokker 50	20123	>NIN
SU-YAI	Fokker 50	20143	>NIN

PETROLEUM AIR SERVICES — VPS

Reg	Type	C/n	Notes
SU-CBY	CRJ-900	15278	
SU-CCB	CRJ-900	15370	♦
SU-CBA	DHC-7-102	093	
SU-CBB	DHC-7-102	096	[CAI]
SU-CBC	DHC-7-102	097	
SU-CBD	DHC-7-102	098	
SU-CBE	DHC-7-102	099	
SU-CBF	DHC-8Q-315	584	
SU-CBG	DHC-8Q-315	585	
SU-CBH	DHC-8Q-315	594	
SU-CBJ	DHC-8Q-315	607	
SU-CBN	DHC-8Q-315	632	

SX- GREECE

AEGEAN AIRLINES — A3 / AEE

Reg	Type	C/n	Notes
SX-DGF	A319-132	2468	
SX-DGB	A320-232	4165	
SX-DGC	A320-232	4094	
SX-DGD	A320-232	4065	
SX-DGE	A320-232	3990	
SX-DGI	A320-232	3162	
SX-DGJ	A320-232	3316	
SX-DGK	A320-232	3748	
SX-DGL	A320-232	3812	
SX-DGN	A320-232	2828	
SX-DGO	A320-232	3519	
SX-DGR	A320-232	3484	
SX-DGV	A320-232	1856	♦
SX-DGW	A320-232	1909	♦
SX-DGX	A320-232	1996	♦
SX-DGY	A320-232/S	6611	♦
SX-DGZ	A320-232/S	6643	♦
SX-DNA	A320-232/S	6655	♦
SX-DNB	A320-232/S	6832	♦
SX-DNC	A320-232/S	6961	♦
SX-DND	A320-232/S	6989	o/o♦
SX-DNE	A320-232/S	7014	o/o♦
SX-DVG	A320-232	3033	
SX-DVH	A320-232	3066	
SX-DVI	A320-232	3074	
SX-DVJ	A320-232	3365	
SX-DVK	A320-232	3392	
SX-DVL	A320-232	3423	
SX-DVM	A320-232	3439	
SX-DVN	A320-232	3478	
SX-DVQ	A320-232	3526	
SX-DVR	A320-232	3714	
SX-DVS	A320-232	3709	
SX-DVT	A320-232	3745	
SX-DVU	A320-232	3753	
SX-DVV	A320-232	3773	
SX-DVW	A320-232	3785	
SX-DVX	A320-232	3829	
SX-DVY	A320-232	3850	
SX-DGA	A321-231	3878	
SX-DGP	A321-231	3302	
SX-DGQ	A321-231	3322	
SX-DGS	A321-231	1428	♦
SX-DGT	A321-231	1433	♦
SX-DVO	A321-231	3462	
SX-DVP	A321-231	3527	
SX-DVZ	A321-231	3820	

ASTRA AIRLINES — A2 / AZI

Reg	Type	C/n	Notes
SX-DIO	A320-232	0527	
SX-DIP	ATR 72-202	328	>CNF
SX-DIQ	ATR 42-300	130	
SX-DIR	ATR 42-300	278	♦
SX-DIZ	BAe146 Srs.300	E3206	

ELLINAIR — EL / ELB

Reg	Type	C/n	Notes
SX-EMB	A319-132	3705	♦
SX-EMM	A319-132	1703	♦
SX-EMI	Avro 146-RJ85	E2305	
SX-EMS	Avro 146-RJ85	E2296	
LY-GGC	B737-3Q8	24492/1808	<GCA♦

GAINJET — GNJ

Reg	Type	C/n	Notes
SX-ATF	B737-406	25423/2184	
SX-MTF	B737-329	23774/1443	
SX-RFA	B757-23N/W	30232/888	
SX-VIP	B737-3YO	24680/1927	

HERMES AIRLINES — H3 / HRM

Reg	Type	C/n	Notes
SX-BDS	A320-214	0879	>IAW♦
SX-BDT	A320-232	1422	>MLD♦
SX-BHS	A321-111	0642	status?
SX-BHT	A321-211	0666	>MLD
SX-BDU	B737-33R	28873/2975	std♦
SX-BDV	B737-505	25794/2803	[ATH]♦
SX-BDW	B737-37Q	28537/2904	[NWI]♦
SX-BHR	B737-5L9	29234/3068	[LDE]

OLYMPIC AIR — OA / NOA

	Reg	Type	C/n	
☐	SX-BIO	DHC-8-102	330	
☐	SX-BIP	DHC-8-102	347	
☐	SX-BIQ	DHC-8-102	361	
☐	SX-BIR	DHC-8-102	364	
☐	SX-BIT	DHC-8-402Q	4148	
☐	SX-BIU	DHC-8-402Q	4152	
☐	SX-OBA	DHC-8-402Q	4267	
☐	SX-OBB	DHC-8-402Q	4268	
☐	SX-OBC	DHC-8-402Q	4276	
☐	SX-OBD	DHC-8-402Q	4311	
☐	SX-OBE	DHC-8-402Q	4314	
☐	SX-OBF	DHC-8-402Q	4318	
☐	SX-OBG	DHC-8-402Q	4321	
☐	SX-OBH	DHC-8-402Q	4327	

SKY EXPRESS — G3 / SEH

	Reg	Type	C/n	
☐	LY-DAT	ATR 42-500	445	<DNU♦
☐	SX-GRY	ATR 42-300	012A	
☐	SX-LOS	ATR 42-310	107	♦
☐	SX-	ATR 42-320	291	o/o♦
☐	SX-DIA	BAeJetstream 41	41075	
☐	SX-ROD	BAeJetstream 41	41076	
☐	SX-SEH	BAeJetstream 41	41014	

S2- BANGLADESH

BIMAN BANGLADESH AIRLINES — BG / BBC

	Reg	Type	C/n	
☐	S2-ADF	A310-325	700	
☐	S2-ADK	A310-324	594	
☐	S2-AFL	B737-83N/W	28648/888	
☐	S2-AFM	B737-83N/W	28653/948	
☐	S2-AHO	B737-8E9/W	40334/5664	♦
☐	S2-AHV	B737-8E9/W	40335/5715	♦
☐	S2-AFO	B777-3E9ER	40122/964	
☐	S2-AFP	B777-3E9ER	40123/971	
☐	S2-AHK	B777-266ER	32629/362	♦
☐	S2-AHL	B777-266ER	32630/368	♦
☐	S2-AHM	B777-3E9ER	40120/1170	
☐	S2-AHN	B777-3E9ER	40121/1186	
☐	S2-AGQ	DHC-8-402Q	4367	♦
☐	S2-AGR	DHC-8-402Q	4368	♦

BISMILLAH AIRLINES — 5Z / BML

	Reg	Type	C/n	
☐	S2-AAX	HS.748 Srs.2A	1767	
☐	S2-ADW	HS.748 Srs 2A	1766	
☐	S2-AEE	HS.748 Srs 2A	1647	[CXB]

EASY FLY EXPRESS — 8E / EFX

	Reg	Type	C/n	
☐	S2-AIF	SAAB SF.340AC	340A-089	♦

NOVOAIR — VQ / NVQ

	Reg	Type	C/n	
☐	S2-AHG	ATR 72-212A	805	♦
☐	S2-	ATR 72-212A	816	o/o♦
☐	S2-	ATR 72-212A	636	o/o♦
☐	S2-AGJ	ERJ-145EU	145573	
☐	S2-AGK	ERJ-145EU	145546	
☐	S2-AGL	ERJ-145EP	145300	

REGENT AIRLINES — RX / RGE

	Reg	Type	C/n	
☐	S2-AHA	DHC-8Q-314	521	
☐	S2-AHB	DHC-8Q-314	543	
☐	S2-AHC	B737-7V3/W	29360/1644	
☐	S2-AHD	B737-7K5/W	30714/2202	

SKYAIR — C3 / AHW

	Reg	Type	C/n	
☐	9M-PMW	B737-209F	24197/1581	

TRUE AVIATION BD

	Reg	Type	C/n	
☐	S2-AGA	An-26B	13505	>IRV
☐	S2-AGZ	An-26B	13408	>IRV

UNITED AIRWAYS — 4H / UBD

	Reg	Type	C/n	
☐	S2-AFF	A310-325	672	[DAC]
☐	S2-AFW	A310-325	674	[KHI]
☐	S2-AFE	ATR 72-212	385	
☐	S2-AFN	ATR 72-212	379	
☐	S2-AFU	ATR 72-202	402	
☐	S2-AES	DHC-8-103	363	
☐	S2-AEH	MD-83	49937/1784	[DAC]
☐	S2-AEI	MD-83	53183/2071	
☐	S2-AEJ	MD-83	53189/2121	
☐	S2-AEU	MD-83	49790/1643	[DAC]
☐	S2-AFV	MD-83	53377/2057	[DAC]

US BANGLA AIRLINES — BS / UBG

	Reg	Type	C/n	
☐	S2-AGU	DHC-8-402Q	4041	
☐	S2-AGV	DHC-8-402Q	4044	
☐	S2-AGW	DHC-8-402Q	4058	♦

S5- SLOVENIA

ADRIA AIRWAYS — JP / ADR

	Reg	Type	C/n	
☐	S5-AAP	A319-132	4282	
☐	S5-AAR	A319-132	4301	
☐	S5-AAX	A319-111	1000	♦
☐	S5-AAD	CRJ-200LR	7166	[LJU]
☐	S5-AAE	CRJ-200LR	7170	[LJU]
☐	S5-AAG	CRJ-200LR	7384	
☐	ES-ACF	CRJ-701ER	10085	♦
☐	S5-AAY	CRJ-701ER	10080	♦
☐	S5-AAZ	CRJ-701ER	10014	♦
☐	S5-AAK	CRJ-900ER	15128	
☐	S5-AAL	CRJ-900ER	15129	
☐	S5-AAN	CRJ-900ER	15207	
☐	S5-AAO	CRJ-900ER	15215	
☐	S5-AAU	CRJ-900LR	15283	
☐	S5-AAV	CRJ-900LR	15284	
☐	YR-FKA	Fokker 100	11340	<KRP♦
☐	YR-FKB	Fokker 100	11369	<KRP♦

LIPICAN AER

	Reg	Type	C/n	
☐	S5-BBS	SAAB SF.340AF	340A-064	♦
☐	S5-	LET410UVP		♦

SIAVIA — SVB

	Reg	Type	C/n	
☐	F-HAFS	ERJ-145EP	145177	
☐	F-HELA	ERJ-145EU	145167	
☐	F-HFKC	ERJ-145LR	145282	
☐	F-HFKE	ERJ-145LR	145299	♦

SOLINAIR — SOP

	Reg	Type	C/n	
☐	S5-ABW	A300B4-605RF	532	♦

S7- SEYCHELLES

AIR SEYCHELLES — HM / SEY

□	S7-AMI	A320-232	1944	♦
□	S7-SIL	A320-232	1945	♦
□	A6-EYZ	A330-243	807	<ETD
□	S7-ADB	A330-243	751	♦
□	S7-AAF	DHC-6 Twin Otter 300	623	♦
□	S7-AAR	DHC-6 Twin Otter 300	539	♦
□	S7-BRD	DHC-6 Twin Otter 400	899	♦
□	S7-CUR	DHC-6 Twin Otter 400	846	♦
□	S7-DNS	DHC-6 Twin Otter 400	927	♦
□	S7-LDI	DHC-6 Twin Otter 400	898	♦

S9- SAO TOME & PRINCIPE

AFRICA'S CONNECTION — ACH

□	S9-AUN	Do228-201	8076	♦
□	S9-RAS	Do228-201	8068	

TC- TURKEY

ANADOLU JET — TK / AJA

□	TC-SAH	B737-8FH/W	35092/2160	
□	TC-SAI	B737-8AS/W	33818/1685	
□	TC-SAJ	B737-8AS/W	33819/1691	
□	TC-SAK	B737-8AS/W	33820/1696	
□	TC-SAU	B737-8GJ/W	34958/2688	
□	TC-SAV	B737-8GJ/W	34959/2719	
□	TC-SBE	B737-8BK/W	29644/2231	
□	TC-SBF	B737-86Q/W	30296/1647	
□	TC-SBG	B737-86J/W	28071/133	
□	TC-SBI	B737-8AS/W	29920/362	
□	TC-SBJ	B737-8AS/W	29916/210	
□	TC-SBM	B737-8AS/W	29918/307	
□	TC-SBN	B737-86N/W	32690/2250	
□	TC-SBP	B737-86N/W	32672/1932	
□	TC-SBR	B737-86N/W	32693/1951	
□	TC-SBS	B737-8AS/W	29917/298	
□	TC-SBV	B737-86N/W	32736/1113	
□	TC-SBZ	B737-86N/W	28628/573	
□	TC-SCD	B737-8Q8/W	41805/5325	
□	TC-SCE	B737-8Q8/W	41808/5445	♦
□	TC-SCF	B737-8AL/W	40554/5410	♦
□	TC-SCG	B737-8Q8/W	40555/5464	♦
□	TC-SCK	B737-8GJ/W	39428/4348	♦
□	TC-SCL	B737-8GJ/W	39430/4442	♦
□	TC-SUO	B737-86Q/W	30272/824	
□	TC-YAL	ERJ-190LR	19000227	♦
□	TC-YAM	ERJ-190LR	19000403	♦
□	TC-YAN	ERJ-190LR	19000367	♦
□	TC-YAO	ERJ-195LR	19000069	♦
□	TC-YAP	ERJ-195LR	19000084	♦
□	TC-YAR	ERJ-195LR	19000093	♦

B737-800s leased from Sun Express and ERJ-190s & ERJ-195s from Bora Jet.

ATLAS GLOBAL — KK / KKK

□	TC-ATD	A319-112	1124	
□	TC-ABL	A320-214	1390	
□	TC-AGO	A320-232	2029	♦
□	TC-AGU	A320-232	2077	♦
□	TC-ATK	A320-232	2747	
□	TC-ATM	A320-232	2753	
□	TC-ATT	A320-233	1624	
□	UR-AJB	A320-233	0733	<UJX♦
□		A320-232	1663	o/o♦
□	TC-ATB	A321-211	1503	
□	TC-ATE	A321-211	0675	
□	TC-ATF	A321-211	0761	
□	TC-ATH	A321-231	1953	
□	TC-ATR	A321-211	1451	
□	TC-ATY	A321-211	0808	
□	TC-ATZ	A321-211	0823	
□	TC-ETF	A321-231	1438	
□	TC-ETH	A321-231	0968	
□	TC-ETJ	A321-231	0974	
□	TC-ETM	A321-131	0604	
□	TC-ETN	A321-131	0614	
□	TC-ETV	A321-231	1950	

BORAJET — BJ / BRJ

□	TC-YAG	ERJ-190LR	19000263	
□	TC-YAH	ERJ-190LR	19000264	
□	TC-YAI	ERJ-190LR	19000201	
□	TC-YAJ	ERJ-190LR	19000230	
□	TC-YAS	ERJ-195AR	19000050	♦
□	TC-YAT	ERJ-195AR	19000067	o/o♦
□	TC-YAU	ERJ-195AR	19000088	♦

^ leases ERJ-190S & ERJ-195s to Anadolu Jet which fly in their c/s and listed there.

CORENDON AIR — 7H / CAI

□	TC-TJB	B737-3Q8	27633/2878	
□	TC-TJG	B737-86J/W	29120/202	
□	TC-TJH	B737-86J/W	29121/239	
□	TC-TJI	B737-8S3/W	29246/475	
□	TC-TJJ	B737-8S3/W	29247/493	
□	TC-TJL	B737-86J/W	32920/1293	
□	TC-TJM	B737-8Q8/W	28218/160	>CRC
□	TC-TJN	B737-85P/W	28535/480	
□	TC-TJO	B737-86N/W	34253/1866	
□	TC-TJP	B737-8BK/W	33022/1672	
□	TC-TJS	B737-81B/W	34252/1851	♦
□	TC-TJT	B737-8xx		o/o♦
□	TC-TJT	B737-8xx		o/o♦

FREEBIRD AIRLINES — FH / FHY

□	TC-FBH	A320-214	4207	
□	TC-FBO	A320-214	5096	
□	TC-FBR	A320-232	2524	
□	TC-FBV	A320-214	4658	
□	TC-FHB	A320-214	3025	
□	TC-FHC	A320-233	3852	♦
□	TC-FHE	A320-232	2804	
□	TC-FHY	A320-214	3891	♦

IZMIR AIRLINES — 4I / IZM

Owned by Pegasus Airlines with fleet in those colours and included there.

MNG AIRLINES — MB / MNB

□	TC-MCA	A300C4-605R	755	
□	TC-MCC	A300B4-622R	734	
□	TC-MCD	A300B4-605RF	521	
□	TC-MCE	A300B4-605RF	525	

□	TC-MCG	A300B4-622RF	739	
□	TC-MCH	A300B4-622RF	756	o/o♦
□	TC-MND	A300C4-203F	212	[IST]
□	TC-MNV	A300C4-605R	758	
□	TC-MCZ	A330-243F	1332	
□		A330-243F		o/o
□		A330-243F		o/o
□		A330-243F		o/o

MY CARGO AIRLINES — *9T / RUN*

□	TC-ACE	A300B4-203F	154	[SAW]
□	TC-ACU	A300B4-203F	183	[SAW]
□	TC-ACY	A300B4-203F	107	[KHI]
□	TC-ACZ	A300B4-203F	105	[SAW]
□	TC-	A330-2xxF		o/o
□	TC-	A330-2xxF		o/o
□	TC-ACF	B747-481BDSF	25645/979	>SVA
□	TC-ACG	B747-481BDSF	25641/928	>SVA
□	TC-ACH	B747-433BCF	24998/840	>QTR
□	TC-ACJ	B747-433BCF	25075/868	>SVA
□	TC-ACM	B747-428ERF	32867/1318	>SVA♦
□	TC-ACR	B747-428ERF	32866/1315	>SVA♦
□	TC-MCL	B747-412F	32897/1322	♦

ONUR AIR — *8Q / OHY*

□	TC-ONT	A300B4-203	138	[SAW]
□	TC-ONU	A300B4-203	192	[IST]
□	LZ-FBC	A320-214	2540	<HMS♦
□	LZ-FBD	A320-214	2596	<HMS♦
□	TC-OBG	A320-233	0916	
□	TC-OBL	A320-232	0640	
□	TC-OBM	A320-232	0676	
□	TC-OBN	A320-232	2571	
□	TC-OBO	A320-232	2688	
□	TC-OBP	A320-232	0496	[GYR]
□	TC-OBS	A320-232	0543	
□	TC-OBU	A320-232	0661	
□	TC-ODA	A320-233	0912	
□	TC-ODB	A320-232	0580	♦
□	TC-OBF	A321-131	0963	
□	TC-OBJ	A321-231	0835	>GZQ
□	TC-OBK	A321-231	0792	
□	TC-OBR	A321-131	1008	>SVA
□	TC-OBV	A321-231	0806	>SVA
□	TC-OBY	A321-231	0810	
□	TC-OBZ	A321-231	0811	
□	TC-OEA	A321-231	0771	♦
□	TC-ONJ	A321-131	0385	
□	TC-ONS	A321-131	0364	
□	TC-OCA	A330-322	072	
□	TC-OCB	A330-342	098	[IST]
□	TC-OCC	A330-322	143	>SVA
□	TC-OCD	A330-322	087	>SVA
□	TC-OCE	A330-223	353	>SVA♦
□	TC-OCF	A330-223	362	♦
□	TC-OCG	A330-243	345	♦
□	TC-OCH	A330-243	316	♦
□	TC-OCI	A330-243	625	>SVA♦
□	TC-OCJ	A330-243	632	>SVA♦

PEGASUS AIRLINES — *PC / PGT*

□	TC-DCA	A320-214/S	5879	
□	TC-DCB	A320-214/S	5902	
□	TC-DCC	A320-214/S	5950	
□	TC-DCD	A320-214/S	5995	
□	TC-DCE	A320-216/S	6465	
□	TC-DCF	A320-216	3831	♦
□	TC-DCG	A320-216/S	6597	♦
□	TC-DCH	A320-216/S	6619	♦
□	TC-DCI	A320-216/S	6666	♦
□	TC-DCJ	A320-214/S	7145	o/o♦
□	TC-	A320-214	2764	o/o
□	TC-	A320-214/S	7200	o/o♦
□	TC-	A320-251N	7140	o/o♦
□	TC-	A320-251N	7147	o/o♦
□	TC-	A320-251N	7251	o/o♦
□	TC-	A320-251N	7277	o/o♦
□	TC-	A320-251N	7291	o/o♦
□	TC-AAI	B737-82R/W	35699/2712	
□	TC-AAJ	B737-82R/W	35702/2810	
□	TC-AAL	B737-82R/W	35984/2937	
□	TC-AAN	B737-82R/W	38173/3011	
□	TC-AAO	B737-86N/W	28619/534	
□	TC-AAR	B737-86N/W	28624/585	
□	TC-AAS	B737-82R/W	40871/3212	
□	TC-AAT	B737-82R/W	40872/3227	
□	TC-AAU	B737-82R/W	40873/3238	
□	TC-AAV	B737-82R/W	40696/3285	
□	TC-AAY	B737-82R/W	40874/3316	
□	TC-AAZ	B737-82R/W	40875/3325	
□	TC-ABP	B737-82R/W	40876/3326	
□	TC-ACP	B737-82R/W	40697/3354	
□	TC-ADP	B737-82R/W	40720/3526	
□	TC-AEP	B737-82R/W	40724/3563	
□	TC-AGP	B737-82R/W	40728/3579	
□	TC-AHP	B737-82R/W	40721/3600	
□	TC-AIP	B737-82R/W	40877/3602	
□	TC-AIS	B737-82R/W	38174/3857	
□	TC-AJP	B737-82R/W	35983/3617	
□	TC-AMP	B737-82R/W	40723/3622	
□	TC-ANP	B737-82R/W	40722/3637	
□	TC-ARP	B737-82R/W	40727/3652	
□	TC-ASP	B737-82R/W	40011/3662	
□	TC-AVP	B737-82R/W	38175/3877	
□	TC-AZP	B737-82R/W	38176/3896	
□	TC-CCP	B737-86J/W	37746/3109	
□	TC-CPA	B737-82R/W	40725/3909	
□	TC-CPB	B737-82R/W	38177/3947	
□	TC-CPC	B737-82R/W	40878/3972	
□	TC-CPD	B737-82R/W	40726/4013	
□	TC-CPE	B737-82R/W	38178/4023	>MBB
□	TC-CPF	B737-82R/W	40879/4267	
□	TC-CPG	B737-82R/W	40729/4288	
□	TC-CPI	B737-82R/W	40014/4298	
□	TC-CPJ	B737-82R/W	40881/4513	
□	TC-CPK	B737-82R/W	40009/4736	
□	TC-CPL	B737-82R/W	40010/4807	
□	TC-CPM	B737-82R/W	40012/5222	
□	TC-CPN	B737-82R/W	40013/5300	
□	TC-CPO	B737-8AS/W	33641/2222	
□	TC-CPP	B737-804/W	32903/1127	
□	TC-CPR	B737-8GJ/W	34905/2392	
□	TC-CPS	B737-8GJ/W	37366/3628	♦
□	TC-CPU	B737-86N/W	35216/2321	
□	TC-CPV	B737-86J/W	36884/3732	
□	TC-CPY	B737-8H6/W	41767/5615	♦
□	TC-CPZ	B737-8H6/W	41768/5708	♦
□	TC-CRA	B737-8H6/W	41769/5741	♦
□	TC-IZB	B737-86J/W	37743/2834	

☐	TC-IZC	B737-86J/W	37745/3044	
☐	TC-IZD	B737-83N/W	32348/933	
☐	TC-IZE	B737-86J/W	37740/2638	
☐	TC-IZG	B737-8AS/W	33605/2140	
☐	TC-IZI	B737-8GJ/W	34904/2347	
☐	TC-IZJ	B737-82R/W	35700/2435	
☐	TC-	B737-82R/W	40729	o/o♦

SUNEXPRESS XQ / SXS

☐	TC-SED	B737-8CX/W	32361/1098	
☐	TC-SEE	B737-8CX/W	32363/1139	
☐	TC-SEI	B737-8HC/W	61170/5441	♦
☐	TC-SEJ	B737-8HC/W	61171/5517	♦
☐	TC-SEK	B737-8HC/W	61172/5554	♦
☐	TC-SEM	B737-8HC/W	61173/5599	♦
☐	TC-SEN	B737-8HC/W	61174/5486	♦
☐	TC-SEO	B737-8HC/W	61178/5800	o/o♦
☐	TC-SNF	B737-8HC/W	36529/2566	
☐	TC-SNG	B737-8HC/W	36530/2622	
☐	TC-SNH	B737-8FH/W	30826/1732	
☐	TC-SNI	B737-8FH/W	29671/1700	
☐	TC-SNJ	B737-86J/W	30827/1632	
☐	TC-SNN	B737-8HC/W	40775/3250	
☐	TC-SNO	B737-8HC/W	40776/3273	
☐	TC-SNP	B737-8HC/W	40777/3320	
☐	TC-SNR	B737-8HC/W	40754/3352	
☐	TC-SNT	B737-8HC/W	40755/3400	
☐	TC-SNU	B737-8HC/W	40756/3457	
☐	TC-SNV	B737-86J/W	28072/147	
☐	TC-SNY	B737-8K5/W	27981/7	
☐	TC-SNZ	B737-86N/W	28616/483	
☐	TC-SUI	B737-8CX/W	32367/1253	[AYT]
☐	TC-SUL	B737-85F/W	28822/166	
☐	TC-SUM	B737-85F/W	28826/238	
☐	TC-SUU	B737-86Q/W	30274/845	
☐	TC-SUV	B737-86N/W	30807/829	
☐	TC-SUY	B737-86N/W	30806/790	[AYT]
☐	TC-	B737-8HC/W		o/o♦
☐	TC-	B737-8HC/W		o/o♦
☐	TC-	B737-8HC/W		o/o♦
☐	TC-	B737-8HC/W		o/o♦
☐	TC-	B737-8HC/W		o/o♦
☐	TC-	B737-8HC/W		o/o♦
☐	TC-	B737-8HC/W		o/o♦

^ leases B737-800s to Anadolu Jet which fly in their c/s and listed there.

TAILWIND AIRLINES TI / TWI

☐	TC-TLA	B737-4Q8	25107/2526	
☐	TC-TLB	B737-4Q8	25108/2551	
☐	TC-TLC	B737-4Q8	25112/2638	
☐	TC-TLD	B737-4Q8	28199/2826	
☐	TC-TLE	B737-4Q8	27628/2858	
☐	TC-TLG	B737-8K5/W	27983/218	
☐	TC-TLH	B737-8K5/W	27984/220	

TURKISH AIRLINES TK / THY

☐	TC-JCY	A310-304F	478	[IST]
☐	TC-JCZ	A310-304F	480	[IST]
☐	TC-JLM	A319-132	2738	
☐	TC-JLN	A319-132	2739	
☐	TC-JLO	A319-132	2631	
☐	TC-JLP	A319-132	2655	
☐	TC-JLR	A319-132	3142	
☐	TC-JLS	A319-132	4629	
☐	TC-JLT	A319-132	4665	
☐	TC-JLU	A319-132	4695	
☐	TC-JLV	A319-132	4755	
☐	TC-JLY	A319-132	4774	
☐	TC-JLZ	A319-132	4790	
☐	TC-JUA	A319-132	2404	
☐	TC-JUB	A319-132	2414	
☐	TC-JUD	A319-132	2452	
☐	TC-JAI	A320-232	3259	
☐	TC-JBI	A320-232	3308	
☐	TC-JPA	A320-232	2609	
☐	TC-JPB	A320-232	2626	
☐	TC-JPC	A320-232	2928	
☐	TC-JPD	A320-232	2934	
☐	TC-JPE	A320-232	2941	status?
☐	TC-JPF	A320-232	2984	
☐	TC-JPG	A320-232	3010	
☐	TC-JPH	A320-232	3185	
☐	TC-JPI	A320-232	3208	
☐	TC-JPJ	A320-232	3239	
☐	TC-JPK	A320-232	3257	
☐	TC-JPL	A320-232	3303	
☐	TC-JPM	A320-232	3341	
☐	TC-JPN	A320-232	3558	
☐	TC-JPO	A320-232	3567	
☐	TC-JPP	A320-232	3603	
☐	TC-JPR	A320-232	3654	
☐	TC-JPS	A320-232	3718	
☐	TC-JPT	A320-232	3719	
☐	TC-JPU	A320-214	3896	
☐	TC-JPV	A320-214	3931	
☐	TC-JPY	A320-214	3949	
☐	TC-JUE	A320-232	2156	
☐	TC-JUF	A320-232	2164	
☐	TC-JUG	A320-232	2395	
☐	TC-JUI	A320-232	2401	
☐	TC-JUJ	A320-232	2522	
☐	TC-JUK	A320-232	2602	
☐	TC-JMH	A321-231	3637	
☐	TC-JMI	A321-231	3673	
☐	TC-JMJ	A321-231	3688	
☐	TC-JMK	A321-231	3738	
☐	TC-JML	A321-231	3382	
☐	TC-JMM	A321-231	2916	
☐	TC-JMN	A321-231	2919	
☐	TC-JRA	A321-231	2823	
☐	TC-JRB	A321-231	2868	
☐	TC-JRC	A321-231	2999	
☐	TC-JRD	A321-231	3015	
☐	TC-JRE	A321-231	3126	
☐	TC-JRF	A321-231	3207	
☐	TC-JRG	A321-231	3283	
☐	TC-JRH	A321-231	3350	
☐	TC-JRI	A321-231	3405	
☐	TC-JRJ	A321-231	3429	
☐	TC-JRK	A321-231	3525	
☐	TC-JRL	A321-231	3539	
☐	TC-JRM	A321-231	4643	
☐	TC-JRN	A321-231	4654	
☐	TC-JRO	A321-231	4682	
☐	TC-JRP	A321-231	4698	
☐	TC-JRR	A321-231	4706	
☐	TC-JRS	A321-231	4761	
☐	TC-JRT	A321-231	4779	
☐	TC-JRU	A321-231	4788	
☐	TC-JRV	A321-231	5077	

	Reg.	Type	c/n	
□	TC-JRY	A321-231	5083	
□	TC-JRZ	A321-231	5118	
□	TC-JSA	A321-231	5154	
□	TC-JSB	A321-231	5205	
□	TC-JSC	A321-231	5254	
□	TC-JSD	A321-231	5388	
□	TC-JSE	A321-231/S	5450	
□	TC-JSF	A321-231/S	5465	
□	TC-JSG	A321-231/S	5490	
□	TC-JSH	A321-231/S	5546	
□	TC-JSI	A321-231/S	5584	
□	TC-JSJ	A321-231/S	5633	
□	TC-JSK	A321-231/S	5663	
□	TC-JSL	A321-231/S	5667	
□	TC-JSM	A321-231/S	5689	
□	TC-JSN	A321-231/S	6508	
□	TC-JSO	A321-231/S	6563	
□	TC-JSP	A321-231/S	6599	
□	TC-JSR	A321-231/S	6652	
□	TC-JSS	A321-231/S	6657	
□	TC-JST	A321-231/S	6682	
□	TC-JSU	A321-231/S	6709	
□	TC-JSV	A321-231/S	6751	
□	TC-JSY	A321-231/S	6758	
□	TC-JSZ	A321-231/S	6766	
□	TC-JTA	A321-231/S	6781	♦
□	TC-JTD	A321-231/S	6822	♦
□	TC-JTE	A321-231/S	6869	♦
□	TC-JTF	A321-231/S	6987	o/o♦
□	TC-JTG	A321-231/S	6990	o/o♦
□	TC-JTH	A321-231/S	7029	o/o♦
□	TC-JTI	A321-231/S	7089	o/o♦
□	TC-JTJ	A321-231/S	7139	o/o♦
□	TC-JTK	A321-231/S	7146	o/o♦
□	TC-JTL	A321-231/S	7166	o/o♦
□	TC-JTM	A321-231/S	7242	o/o♦
□	TC-JTN	A321-231/S	7268	o/o♦
□	TC-JTO	A321-231/S	7274	o/o♦
□	TC-JCI	A330-243F	1442	
□	TC-JDO	A330-243F	1004	
□	TC-JDP	A330-243F	1092	
□	TC-JDR	A330-243F	1344	
□	TC-JDS	A330-243F	1418	
□	TC-JOU	A330-243F	1550	♦
□	TC-	A330-243F	1722	o/o♦
□	TC-	A330-243F	1750	o/o♦
□	TC-	A330-243F	1768	o/o♦
□	TC-JIL	A330-202	882	
□	TC-JIM	A330-202	901	
□	TC-JIN	A330-202	932	
□	TC-JIO	A330-223	869	
□	TC-JIP	A330-223	876	
□	TC-JIR	A330-223	949	
□	TC-JIS	A330-223	961	
□	TC-JIT	A330-223	977	
□	TC-JIV	A330-223	1213	♦
□	TC-JIY	A330-223	1221	♦
□	TC-JIZ	A330-223	1118	♦
□	TC-JNA	A330-203	697	
□	TC-JNB	A330-203	704	
□	TC-JNC	A330-203	742	
□	TC-JND	A330-203	754	
□	TC-JNE	A330-203	774	
□	TC-JNF	A330-202	463	
□	TC-JNG	A330-202	504	
□	TC-JNH	A330-343E	1150	
□	TC-JNI	A330-343E	1160	
□	TC-JNJ	A330-343E	1170	
□	TC-JNK	A330-343E	1172	
□	TC-JNL	A330-343E	1204	
□	TC-JNM	A330-343E	1212	
□	TC-JNN	A330-343E	1228	
□	TC-JNO	A330-343E	1298	
□	TC-JNP	A330-343E	1307	
□	TC-JNR	A330-343E	1311	
□	TC-JNS	A330-343E	1458	
□	TC-JNT	A330-343E	1476	
□	TC-JNU	A330-243	527	o/o♦
□	TC-JNY	A330-243	532	o/o♦
□	TC-JNZ	A330-303	1487	
□	TC-JOA	A330-303	1501	
□	TC-JOB	A330-303	1514	
□	TC-JOC	A330-303	1522	
□	TC-JOD	A330-303	1529	
□	TC-JOE	A330-303	1571	
□	TC-JOF	A330-303	1616	
□	TC-JOG	A330-303	1620	
□	TC-JOH	A330-303	1622	
□	TC-JOI	A330-303	1629	
□	TC-JOJ	A330-303	1640	
□	TC-JOK	A330-303	1642	
□	TC-JOL	A330-303	1644	
□	TC-JOM	A330-302	1499	♦
□	TC-JON	A330-302	1535	♦
□	TC-LNA	A330-223	874	♦
□	TC-LNB	A330-223	939	♦
□	TC-LNC	A330-303	1696	♦
□	TC-LND	A330-303	1704	o/o♦
□	TC-LNE	A330-303	1706	o/o♦
□	TC-LNF	A330-303	1713	o/o♦
□	TC-LNG	A330-303	1718	o/o♦
□	TC-JDL	A340-311	057	[SAW]
□	TC-JDM	A340-311	115	
□	TC-JDN	A340-313X	180	
□	TC-JIH	A340-313X	270	
□	TC-JII	A340-313X	331	
□	TC-JKK	B737-752/W	34298/1812	
□	TC-JKO	B737-752/W	34300/1848	
□	TC-JFC	B737-8F2/W	29765/80	
□	TC-JFD	B737-8F2/W	29766/87	
□	TC-JFE	B737-8F2/W	29767/95	
□	TC-JFF	B737-8F2/W	29768/99	
□	TC-JFG	B737-8F2/W	29769/102	
□	TC-JFH	B737-8F2/W	29770/114	
□	TC-JFI	B737-8F2/W	29771/228	
□	TC-JFJ	B737-8F2/W	29772/242	
□	TC-JFK	B737-8F2/W	29773/259	
□	TC-JFL	B737-8F2/W	29774/269	
□	TC-JFM	B737-8F2/W	29775/279	
□	TC-JFN	B737-8F2/W	29776/308	
□	TC-JFO	B737-8F2/W	29777/309	
□	TC-JFP	B737-8F2/W	29778/349	
□	TC-JFR	B737-8F2/W	29779/370	
□	TC-JFT	B737-8F2/W	29780/454	
□	TC-JFU	B737-8F2/W	29781/461	
□	TC-JFV	B737-8F2/W	29782/490	
□	TC-JFY	B737-8F2/W	29783/497	
□	TC-JFZ	B737-8F2/W	29784/539	
□	TC-JGA	B737-8F2/W	29785/544	
□	TC-JGB	B737-8F2/W	29786/566	
□	TC-JGC	B737-8F2/W	29787/771	

	Reg	Type	c/n	
☐	TC-JGD	B737-8F2/W	29788/791	
☐	TC-JGF	B737-8F2/W	29790/1088	
☐	TC-JGG	B737-8F2/W	34405/1828	
☐	TC-JGH	B737-8F2/W	34406/1852	
☐	TC-JGI	B737-8F2/W	34407/1873	
☐	TC-JGJ	B737-8F2/W	34408/1880	
☐	TC-JGK	B737-8F2/W	34409/1924	
☐	TC-JGL	B737-8F2/W	34410/1927	
☐	TC-JGM	B737-8F2/W	34411/1944	
☐	TC-JGN	B737-8F2/W	34412/1949	
☐	TC-JGO	B737-8F2/W	34413/1972	
☐	TC-JGP	B737-8F2/W	34414/1978	
☐	TC-JGR	B737-8F2/W	34415/1988	
☐	TC-JGS	B737-8F2/W	34416/1996	
☐	TC-JGT	B737-8F2/W	34417/2009	
☐	TC-JGU	B737-8F2/W	34418/2012	
☐	TC-JGV	B737-8F2/W	34419/2021	
☐	TC-JGY	B737-8F2/W	35738/2592	
☐	TC-JGZ	B737-8F2/W	35739/2654	
☐	TC-JHA	B737-8F2/W	35740/2673	
☐	TC-JHB	B737-8F2/W	35741/2685	
☐	TC-JHC	B737-8F2/W	35742/2708	
☐	TC-JHD	B737-8F2/W	35743/2717	
☐	TC-JHE	B737-8F2/W	35744/2733	
☐	TC-JHF	B737-8F2/W	35745/2748	
☐	TC-JHK	B737-8F2/W	40975/3824	
☐	TC-JHL	B737-8F2/W	40976/3870	
☐	TC-JHM	B737-8F2/W	40980/4041	
☐	TC-JHN	B737-8F2/W	40981/4082	
☐	TC-JHO	B737-8F2/W	40987/4324	
☐	TC-JHP	B737-8F2/W	42000/4336	
☐	TC-JHR	B737-8F2/W	40989/4394	
☐	TC-JHS	B737-8F2/W	40991/4411	
☐	TC-JHT	B737-8F2/W	42001/4423	
☐	TC-JHU	B737-8F2/W	42002/4437	
☐	TC-JHV	B737-8F2/W	40992/4778	
☐	TC-JHY	B737-8F2/W	42003/4798	
☐	TC-JHZ	B737-8F2/W	42004/4814	
☐	TC-JVA	B737-8F2/W	40988/4833	
☐	TC-JVB	B737-8F2/W	40990/4865	
☐	TC-JVC	B737-8F2/W	42005/4886	
☐	TC-JVD	B737-8F2/W	42007/4900	
☐	TC-JVE	B737-8F2/W	42006/4915	
☐	TC-JVF	B737-8F2/W	42008/4934	
☐	TC-JVG	B737-8F2/W	42009/4963	
☐	TC-JVH	B737-8F2/W	60012/5729	♦
☐	TC-JVI	B737-8F2/W	60013/5754	♦
☐	TC-JVJ	B737-8F2/W	60015/5769	♦
☐	TC-JVK	B737-8F2/W	60014/5793	o/o♦
☐	TC-	B737-8F2/W		o/o
☐	TC-	B737-8F2/W		o/o
☐	TC-	B737-8F2/W		o/o
☐	TC-JYA	B737-9F2ER/W	40973/3669	
☐	TC-JYB	B737-9F2ER/W	40974/3693	
☐	TC-JYC	B737-9F2ER/W	40977/3948	
☐	TC-JYD	B737-9F2ER/W	40978/4020	
☐	TC-JYE	B737-9F2ER/W	40979/4044	
☐	TC-JYF	B737-9F2ER/W	40982/4098	
☐	TC-JYG	B737-9F2ER/W	40983/4110	
☐	TC-JYH	B737-9F2ER/W	40984/4134	
☐	TC-JYI	B737-9F2ER/W	40985/4176	
☐	TC-JYJ	B737-9F2ER/W	40986/4308	
☐	TC-JYL	B737-9F2ER/W	42010/5263	
☐	TC-JYM	B737-9F2ER/W	42011/5303	
☐	TC-JYN	B737-9F2ER/W	42012/5387	
☐	TC-JYO	B737-9F2ER/W	42013/5400	
☐	TC-JYP	B737-9F2ER/W	42014/5471	
☐	TC-JJE	B777-3F2ER	40707/895	
☐	TC-JJF	B777-3F2ER	40708/899	
☐	TC-JJG	B777-3F2ER	40791/903	
☐	TC-JJH	B777-3F2ER	40792/906	
☐	TC-JJI	B777-3F2ER	40709/909	
☐	TC-JJJ	B777-3F2ER	40710/913	
☐	TC-JJK	B777-3F2ER	40711/916	
☐	TC-JJL	B777-3F2ER	40793/919	
☐	TC-JJM	B777-3F2ER	40794/923	
☐	TC-JJN	B777-3F2ER	40795/940	
☐	TC-JJO	B777-3F2ER	40796/953	
☐	TC-JJP	B777-3F2ER	40797/959	
☐	TC-JJR	B777-3F2ER	44116/1214	
☐	TC-JJS	B777-3F2ER	44117/1222	
☐	TC-JJT	B777-3F2ER	44118/1233	
☐	TC-JJU	B777-3F2ER	60401/1256	
☐	TC-JJV	B777-3F2ER	44119/1277	
☐	TC-JJY	B777-3F2ER	44120/1287	
☐	TC-JJZ	B777-3F2ER	44122/1291	
☐	TC-LJA	B777-3F2ER	44121/1296	
☐	TC-LJB	B777-3F2ER	44124/1331	
☐	TC-LJC	B777-3F2ER	44123/1337	
☐	TC-LJD	B777-3F2ER	44125/1361	♦
☐	TC-LJE	B777-3F2ER	44126/1368	♦
☐	TC-LJF	B777-3F2ER	44127/1389	o/o♦
☐	TC-LJG	B777-3F2ER	44128/1394	o/o♦
☐	TC-LJH	B777-3F2ER	44129/1403	o/o♦
☐	TC-LJI	B777-3F2ER	44130/1405	o/o♦
☐	TC-	B777-36NER	41818/1140	o/o♦
☐	TC-	B777-36NER	41819/1197	o/o♦
☐	TC-	B777-36NER	42097/1211	o/o♦
☐	TC-	B777-3F2ER		o/o♦
☐	TC-	B777-3F2ER		o/o♦

ULS CARGO — GO / KZU

	Reg	Type	c/n	
☐	TC-KZV	A300B4-103F	041	[SAW]
☐	TC-KZY	A300B4-103F	044	[IST]
☐	TC-LER	A310-308F	646	
☐	TC-SGM	A310-308F	592	
☐	TC-VEL	A310-308F	622	

TF- ICELAND

AIR ATLANTA — CC / ABD

	Reg	Type	c/n	
☐	TF-EAA	A330-223	343	>SVA
☐	TF-EAB	A340-313X	210	>MDG
☐	TF-AAC	B747-481	29262/1199	
☐	TF-AAD	B747-4H6	28426/1130	>SVA
☐	TF-AAE	B747-4H6	27672/1091	>SVA
☐	TF-AAH	B747-4H6	29901/1301	>SVA
☐	TF-AAJ	B747-428	32869/1327	♦
☐	TF-AAK	B747-428	32868/1325	♦
☐	TF-AMF	B747-412BCF	24226/809	>ABW
☐	TF-AMI	B747-412(SF)	27066/940	>SVA
☐	TF-AML	B747-4H6BDSF	27044/1041	>SVA
☐	TF-AMM	B747-4H6BDSF	25700/974	>SVA
☐	TF-AMN	B747-4F6BDSF	27602/1161	>SVA
☐	TF-AMP	B747-481BDSF	24801/805	>ABW
☐	TF-AMQ	B747-412F	26553/1069	>SVA
☐	TF-AMU	B747-48EF	27603/1210	>SVA
☐	TF-AMV	B747-412	28022/1082	>SVA

AIR ICELAND — NY / FXI

☐ TF-JMM Fokker 50 20214 [REK]
☐ TF-JMN Fokker 50 20223
☐ TF-JMR Fokker 50 20243
☐ TF-JMS Fokker 50 20244
☐ TF-JMT Fokker 50 20250

☐ TF-FXA DHC-8-402Q 4022 ♦
☐ TF-FXB DHC-8-402Q 4038 ♦
☐ TF-FXI DHC-8-402Q 4033 ♦
☐ TF-JMG DHC-8-202 445
☐ TF-JMK DHC-8-202 446

BLUEBIRD CARGO — BF / BBD

☐ TF-BBD B737-3Y0(SF) 24463/1701 >ABR
☐ TF-BBE B737-36E(SF) 25256/2123
☐ TF-BBF B737-36E(SF) 25264/2194
☐ TF-BBG B737-36E(SF) 25263/2187
☐ TF-BBH B737-4Y0F 23865/1582
☐ TF-BBJ B737-476F 24436/1998 ♦

ERNIR AIR — FEI

☐ TF-ORA BAeJetstream 32 925
☐ TF-ORC BAeJetstream 32 981
☐ TF-ORD BAeJetstream 31 740 ♦
☐ TF-ORG BAeJetstream 32 986 ♦

ICELANDAIR — FI / ICE

☐ TF-FIA B757-256/W 29310/938
☐ TF-FIC B757-23N/W 30735/931
☐ TF-FIG B757-23APF 24456/237
☐ TF-FIH B757-208(PCF) 24739/273
☐ TF-FII B757-208/W 24760/281
☐ TF-FIJ B757-208/W 25085/368
☐ TF-FIK(4) B757-256/W 26254/905 ♦
☐ TF-FIN B757-208/W 28989/780
☐ TF-FIO B757-208/W 29436/859
☐ TF-FIP B757-208/W 30423/916
☐ TF-FIR B757-256/W 26242/593
☐ TF-FIS B757-256/W 26245/617
☐ TF-FIT(2) B757-256/W 26244/616
☐ TF-FIU B757-256/W 26243/603
☐ TF-FIV B757-208/W 30424/956
☐ TF-FIW B757-27B 24838/302 >
☐ TF-FIX B757-308/W 29434/1004
☐ TF-ISD B757-223/W 24596/344
☐ TF-ISF B757-223/W 24595/337
☐ TF-ISJ B757-256 26249/881 ♦
☐ TF-ISK B757-223/W 24606/379
☐ TF-ISL B757-223/W 25295/423
☐ TF-ISV B757-256 26247/860 ♦
☐ TF-ISY B757-223/W 24594/336 ♦
☐ TF-ISZ B757-223/W 24600/357 ♦
☐ TF-LLX B757-256/W 29311/940

☐ TF-ISN B767-319ER 30586/808 ♦
☐ TF-ISO B767-319ER 29388/785 ♦
☐ TF- B787-8 o/o♦

NORLANDAIR — FNA

☐ TF-NLC DHC-6 Twin Otter 300 413
☐ TF-NLD DHC-6 Twin Otter 300 475

WOW AIR — WW / WOW

☐ TF-BRO A320-232 4305 ♦
☐ TF-DAD A321-211/S 6232
☐ TF-KID A321-211 5681 ♦
☐ TF-MOM A321-211/S 6210
☐ TF-SIS A320-232 4270 ♦
☐ TF-SON A321-211 5733 ♦

TG- GUATEMALA

AERO RUTA MAYA — MMG

☐ TG-JCE DHC-6 Twin Otter 300 422
☐ TG-JOC DHC-6 Twin Otter 200 112 ♦
☐ TG-JCC EMB.110P1 110348
☐ TG-TJD LET L-410UVP 851421

Also operates under the name Jungle Flying.

AVIATECA GUATEMALA — GU / GUG

☐ TG-MYH ATR 42-300 113 [BYH]
☐ TG-TRB ATR 42-300(QC) 317
☐ TG-TRC ATR 72-600 1167
☐ TG-TRD ATR 72-600 1174
☐ TG-TRE ATR 72-600 1196
☐ TG-TRF ATR 72-600 1199

TRANSPORTES AEREOS GUATEMALTECOS — 5U / TGU

☐ TG-CAO BAeJetstream 31 722
☐ TG-TAG EMB.110P1A 110441
☐ TG-TAK EMB.110P1 110405
☐ TG-TAM EMB.110P1 110220
☐ TG-TAN EMB.110P1 110342
☐ TG-TAY EMB.110P1 110218 ♦
☐ TG-BJO SAAB SF.340A 340A-142
☐ TG-TAQ SAAB SF.340A 340A-140 ♦
☐ TG-TAR SAAB SF.340A 340A-116
☐ TG-TAW SAAB SF.340A 340A-117

TI- COSTA RICA

NATURE AIR — 5C / NRR

☐ TI-AZC DHC-6 Twin Otter 300 433
☐ TI-BDZ DHC-6 Twin Otter 300 267
☐ TI-BFO DHC-6 Twin Otter 300 556
☐ TI-BGM LET L-410UVP-E20 902413 ♦
☐ TI-BGO LET L-410UVP-E20 912613 ♦
☐ TI-BGP LET L-410UVP-E20 912530 ♦
☐ TI-BGQ LET L-410UVP-E20 912527 ♦

TJ- CAMEROON

CAMAIR CO — QC / CRC

☐ TC-TJM B737-8Q8/W 28218/160 <CAI♦
☐ TJ-CAC B767-33AER 28138/822
☐ TJ-QCA B737-7BD/W 34480/1900
☐ TJ-QCB B737-7BD/W 33920/1753

☐ TJ-QDA XIAN MA60 ♦
☐ TJ-QDB XIAN MA60 ♦

ELYSIAN AIRLINES — E4 / ELY

☐ TJ-TAA BAe146 Srs.200 E2178

TL- CENTRAL AFRICAN REPUBLIC

KARINOU AIRLINES — U5 / KRN

	Reg	Type	c/n	Notes
☐	TL-AEG	B737-2H4	23109/1016	[BGF]
☐	TL-TSM	B737-36N	28560/2888	

TN- PEOPLE'S REPUBLIC OF CONGO

AIR CONGO INTERNATIONAL

	Reg	Type	c/n	Notes
☐	TN-AHL	XIAN MA60	0405	
☐	TN-AHO	XIAN MA60	0408	
☐	TN-AJF	XIAN MA60	0905	

CANADIAN AIRWAYS CONGO

	Reg	Type	c/n	Notes
☐	TN-AIX	B737-2T5	22632/847	
☐	TN-AJL	MD-82	49278/1183	

EQUAFLIGHT — 5E / EKA

	Reg	Type	c/n	Notes
☐	F-GRGP	ERJ-135ER	145188	
☐	F-HTOP	ERJ-135LR	14500886	
☐	TN-AIJ	EMB.120RT	120209	

TRANS AIR CONGO — Q8 / TSG

	Reg	Type	c/n	Notes
☐	TN-AHI	B737-247	23609/1403	
☐	TN-AIM	B737-232	23083/1008	
☐	TN-AIN	B737-236	23172/1091	
☐	TN-AIZ	B737-33A	25138/2153	
☐	TN-AJJ	B737-3Q8	24986/2192	
☐	TN-MAN	B737-3Q8	26305/2651	♦
☐	TN-	B737-290C	22577/760	♦
☐	TN-	XIAN MA60		o/o♦

TR- GABON

AFRIC AVIATION — L8 / EKG

	Reg	Type	c/n	Notes
☐	TR-LIW	ATR 42-320	148	
☐	ZS-XCC	ATR 42-500	528	<SET♦
☐	ZS-XCG	ATR 42-500	443	<SET♦
☐	ZS-BBM	ERJ-145LR	145597	<SET

GABON AIRLINES — GY / GBK

	Reg	Type	c/n	Notes
☐	TR-LHP	B767-222	21877/46	
☐	TR-LHQ	B767-222	21878/48	
☐	ZS-ATR	ATR 42-320	060	<SET

NOUVELLES AIR AFFAIRES GABON — NVS

	Reg	Type	c/n	Notes
☐	TR-CLB	DHC-8Q-314	545	
☐	TR-LFO	Beech 1900D	UE-313	
☐	TR-LGQ	Fokker 100	11424	

SKY GABON — GV / SKG

	Reg	Type	c/n	Notes
☐	I-MLUT	F.27 Friendship 500	10369	<MNL

TS- TUNISIA

NOUVELAIR — BJ / LBT

	Reg	Type	c/n	Notes
☐	TS-INA	A320-214	1121	>BRQ
☐	TS-INB	A320-214	1175	
☐	TS-INC	A320-214	1744	>DAH
☐	TS-INH	A320-214	4623	
☐	TS-INN	A320-212	0793	>LAAdam
☐	TS-INO	A320-214	3480	>DAH
☐	TS-INP	A320-214	1597	
☐	TS-INQ	A320-214	2158	
☐	TS-INR	A320-214	3487	>DAH

SEVENAIR — UG / TUI

	Reg	Type	c/n	Notes
☐	TS-LBA	ATR 42-300	245	
☐	TS-LBC	ATR 72-202	281	
☐	TS-LBD	ATR 72-202	756	
☐	TS-LBE	ATR 72-202	794	std
☐	TS-ISA	CRJ-900	15091	

Operates as Tunisair Express; reported will be merged with Tunisair.

TUNISAIR — TU / TAR

	Reg	Type	c/n	Notes
☐	TS-IPA	A300B4-605R	558	[TUN]
☐	TS-IPB	A300B4-605R	563	[TUN]
☐	TS-IPC	A300B4-605R	505	
☐	TS-IMJ	A319-114	0869	
☐	TS-IMK	A319-114	0880	
☐	TS-IMO	A319-114	1479	
☐	TS-IMQ	A319-112	3096	
☐	TS-IMC	A320-211	0124	
☐	TS-IMD	A320-211	0205	
☐	TS-IME	A320-211	0123	
☐	TS-IMF	A320-211	0370	
☐	TS-IMG	A320-211	0390	
☐	TS-IMH	A320-211	0402	
☐	TS-IMI	A320-211	0511	
☐	TS-IML	A320-211	0958	
☐	TS-IMM	A320-211	0975	
☐	TS-IMN	A320-211	1187	
☐	TS-IMP	A320-211	1700	
☐	TS-IMR	A320-214	4344	
☐	TS-IMS	A320-214	4689	
☐	TS-IMT	A320-214	5204	
☐	TS-IMU	A320-214	5474	
☐	TS-IMV	A320-214	5610	
☐	TS-IMW	A320-214/S	6338	
☐	TS-IFM	A330-243	1631	♦
☐	TS-IFN	A330-243	1641	♦
☐	TS-IOG	B737-5H3	26639/2253	[TUN]
☐	TS-IOH	B737-5H3	26640/2474	[TUN]
☐	TS-IOI	B737-5H3	27257/2583	[TUN]
☐	TS-IOJ	B737-5H3	27912/2701	
☐	TS-IOK	B737-6H3	29496/268	
☐	TS-IOL	B737-6H3	29497/282	
☐	TS-IOM	B737-6H3	29498/310	
☐	TS-ION	B737-6H3	29499/510	
☐	TS-IOP	B737-6H3	29500/543	
☐	TS-IOQ	B737-6H3	29501/563	
☐	TS-IOR	B737-6H3	29502/816	

TUNISAVIA

	Reg	Type	c/n	Notes
☐	TS-LIB	DHC-6 Twin Otter 300	716	
☐	TS-LSF	DHC-6 Twin Otter 300	575	

TT- CHAD

AIRINTER 1 — HRV

☐	TT-DHT	B737-529	26538/2298	♦
☐	TT-DIZ	B737-5L9	24928/1961	♦
☐	TT-DBC	DC-8-73F	45991/380	>SBO♦

TU- IVORY COAST

AIR COTE D'IVOIRE — HF / VRE

☐	TU-TSA	A319-115LR	2213	
☐	TU-TSB	A319-115LR	2228	
☐	TU-TSN	A319-112	1429	
☐	TU-TSI	DHC-8Q-402	4514	♦
☐	TU-TSK	DHC-8Q-402	4474	
☐	TU-TSL	DHC-8Q-402	4478	

IVOIRIENNE DE TRANSPORTES AERIENS — IVN

☐	TU-PAD	HS.748 Srs. 2B	1799	^

^ reported operates in Afghanistan in East Horizon c/s

TY- BENIN

LYCA CARGO

☐	TY-FSJ	B727-82C/W	19011/387	♦
☐		B727-82C/W	19968/660	o/o♦

T3- KIRIBATI

AIR KIRIBATI — 4A / AKL

☐	T3-AKJ	DHC-6 Twin Otter 300	647	♦
☐	T3-ATC	CASA 212-200	236	
☐	T3-ATI	AVIC II Y-12	0077	
☐	T3-ATJ	CASA 212-200	356	

T8A- PALAU

PALAU PACIFIC AIRWAYS — ED

☐	OM-FEX	B737-8Q8/W	28213/50	<AXE♦

UK- UZBEKISTAN

AVIALEASING — EC / TWN

☐	UK 11418	An-12B	402504	
☐	UK 12001	An-12BP	5343202	
☐	UK 12002	An-12B	402002	

SILK ROAD BUSINESS CARGO — S9 / URS

☐	VP-BSK	A300B4-622RF	788	o/o♦
☐	VQ-BNW	A300B4-622RF	733	

UZBEKISTAN AIRWAYS — HY / UZB

☐	UK 32000	A320-214	4528	Govt
☐	UK 32011	A320-214	4371	
☐	UK 32012	A320-214	4395	
☐	UK 32014	A320-214	4417	
☐	UK 32015	A320-214	4485	
☐	UK 32016	A320-214	4492	
☐	UK 32017	A320-214	4651	
☐	UK 32018	A320-214	4724	
☐	UK 32019	A320-214	4770	
☐	UK 32020	A320-214	4952	
☐	UK 80001	Avro 146-RJ85	E2312	[TAS]
☐	UK 80002	Avro 146-RJ85	E2309	[TAS]
☐	UK 80003	Avro 146-RJ85	E2319	[TAS]
☐	UK 75700	B757-23P	28338/731	Govt
☐	UK 75701	B757-23P	30060/875	
☐	UK 75702	B757-23P	30061/886	
☐	VP-BUH	B757-231	30339/896	
☐	VP-BUI	B757-231	28487/878	
☐	VP-BUJ	B757-231	28488/884	
☐	UK 67000	B767-33PER	35796/958	Govt
☐	UK 67001	B767-33PER/F	28370/635	
☐	UK 67002	B767-33PER/F	28392/650	
☐	UK 67003	B767-33PER	40534/1019	
☐	UK 67004	B767-33PER	40536/1021	
☐	UK 67005	B767-33PER	40533/1047	
☐	UK 67006	B767-33PER	40535/1054	
☐	UK 67007	B767-3CBER	33469/904	♦
☐	VP-BUF	B767-33PER	33078/928	
☐	UK	B787-8	38364/470	♦
☐	UK	B787-8	38364/495	♦
☐	UK 76359	Il-76TD	1033414483	[TAS]
☐	UK 76428	Il-76TD	1043419648	
☐	UK 76449	Il-76TD	1023403058	[TAS]
☐	UK 76794	Il-76TD	0093498954	[TAS]
☐	UK 76805	Il-76TD	1003403109	
☐	UK 91102	Il-114-100	1063800202	[TAS]
☐	UK 91104	Il-114-100	2093800204	
☐	UK 91105	Il-114-100	2063800205	
☐	UK 91106	Il-114-100	2063800206	
☐	UK 91107	Il-114-100	2103800207	
☐	UK 91108	Il-114-100	2073800208	♦
☐	UK 91109	Il-114-100	2073800209	♦

UP- KAZAKHSTAN

AIR ALMATY — K7 / LMY

☐	UP-I7601	Il-76TD	1013409295	
☐	UP-I7618	Il-76TD	0013428831	

AIR ASTANA — KC / KZR

☐	P4-YAS	A319-132	3614	
☐	P4-KBA	A320-232	5401	
☐	P4-KBB	A320-232/S	5613	
☐	P4-KBC	A320-232/S	5734	
☐	P4-KBD	A320-232/S	5870	
☐	P4-KBE	A320-232/S	5968	
☐	P4-KBF	A320-232/S	6037	
☐	P4-KBG	A320-232/S	6029	
☐	P4-VAS	A320-232	3141	
☐	P4-	A320-232/S		o/o
☐	P4-	A320-271N	7124	o/o♦
☐	P4-KDA	A321-231	5357	
☐	P4-KDB	A321-231	5404	
☐	P4-NAS	A321-231	1042	
☐	P4-OAS	A321-231	1204	
☐	P4-EAS	B757-2G5/W	29488/830	
☐	P4-FAS	B757-2G5/W	29489/834	
☐	P4-GAS	B757-2G5/W	28112/708	
☐	P4-KCU	B757-23N/W	27971/690	

☐ P4-MAS B757-28A/W 28833/782

☐ P4-KEA B767-3KYER 42220/1060
☐ P4-KEB B767-3KYER 42221/1062
☐ P4-KEC B767-3KYER 42223/1068
☐ P4- B767-3KYER o/o

☐ P4-KCC ERJ-190LR 19000418
☐ P4-KCD ERJ-190LR 19000431
☐ P4-KCE ERJ-190LR 19000487
☐ P4-KCF ERJ-190LR 19000537
☐ P4-KCG ERJ-190LR 19000543
☐ P4-KCH ERJ-190LR 19000547
☐ P4-KCI ERJ-190LR 19000604
☐ P4-KCJ ERJ-190LR 19000653
☐ P4-KCK ERJ-190LR 19000657
☐ P4- ERJ-190LR o/o
☐ P4- ERJ-190LR o/o

AIR TRUST — *RTR*

☐ UP-I6209 Il-62M 3139956
☐ UP-I7626 Il-76M 1013409303 ♦
☐ UP-I7644 Il-76TD 0033448404

BEK AIR — *Z9 / BEK*

☐ UP-F1004 Fokker 100 11445
☐ UP-F1005 Fokker 100 11500
☐ UP-F1007 Fokker 100 11496
☐ UP-F1009 Fokker 100 11470
☐ UP-F1010 Fokker 100 11527
☐ UP-F1011 Fokker 100 11517
☐ UP-F1012 Fokker 100 11426 ♦
☐ UP-F1014 Fokker 100 11322
☐ UP-Y4021 Yak-40 9302229 [ALA]♦
☐ UP-Y4022 Yak-40 9411533
☐ UP-Y4023 Yak-40 9621148
☐ UP-Y4024 Yak-40 9711552 [ALA]♦

EAST WING — *EWZ*

☐ UP-Y4028 Yak-40F 9710453 ♦
☐ UP-Y4036 Yak-40 9440737 ♦

KAZAIR JET — *KEJ*

☐ UP-AN721 An-72-100D 36572030425
☐ UP-Y4015 Yak-40 9530842

KAZAVIASPAS — *KZS*

☐ UP-AN301 An-30 0604
☐ UP-I7604 Il-76TD 1033414485
☐ UP-T3407 Tu-134A 49912
☐ UP-T5406 Tu-154M 93A965

QAZAQ AIR

☐ P4-AST DHC-8-402Q 4497 <FVS♦
☐ P4-NUR DHC-8-402Q 4494 <FVS♦
☐ P4-QAZ DHC-8-402Q 4502 <FVS♦

SCAT AIRCOMPANY — *DV / VSV*

☐ UP-AN202 An-12BP 3341201
☐ UP-AN404 An-24B 17307303
☐ UP-AN405 An-24B 77303508
☐ UP-AN406 An-24B 77303604
☐ UP-AN407 An-24B 87305305
☐ UP-AN408 An-24B 97305608 [CIT]
☐ UP-AN409 An-24B 07305909
☐ UP-AN410 An-24B 07306104
☐ UP-AN411 An-24B 87304106 [CIT]
☐ UP-AN412 An-24B 87304309
☐ UP-AN413 An-24RV 27309305
☐ UP-AN414 An-24RV 37308305 [CIT]
☐ UP-AN415 An-24RV 47309505
☐ UP-AN416 An-24RV 47309604
☐ UP-AN417 An-24RV 47309910
☐ UP-AN418 An-24B 89901810
☐ UP-AN419 An-24RV 27307609
☐ UP-AN420 An-24B 0706308
☐ UP-AN421 An-24B 07306407
☐ UP-AN424 An-24RV 27307509
☐ UP-AN425 An-24B 79901307
☐ UP-AN426 An-24B 17307406

☐ UP-AN601 An-26 0503

☐ LY-AWD B737-522 26739/2494 <LLC
☐ LY-AWE B737-522 26684/2388 <LLC
☐ LY-AYZ B737-548 25739/2271
☐ LY-AZV B737-7GL/W 37233/2578
☐ UP-B3710 B737-31S 29116/3005
☐ UP-B3712 B737-35B 25069/2053
☐ LY-FLG B757-204 27237/602 <LLC
☐ UP-B5702 B757-21B 25083/359 ^
☐ UP-B5703 B757-21B 25259/392 ^
☐ UP-B5704 B757-21B 25884/461 ^
☐ UP-B6703 B767-332ER 30597/797 ^

☐ UP-CJ004 CRJ-200LR 7901
☐ UP-CJ005 CRJ-200LR 7902
☐ UP-CJ007 CRJ-200LR 7702
☐ UP-CJ008 CRJ-200LR 7365
☐ UP-CJ011 CRJ-200LR 7785
☐ UP-CJ012 CRJ-200ER 7746

☐ UP-Y4203 Yak-42D 4520421116567
☐ UP-Y4210 Yak-42D 4520422306016 [ALA]

^ operated by Sunday Airlines, the charter/leisure arm of SCAT.

SOUTHERN SKY

☐ UP-AN422 An-24B 07306504 ♦
☐ UP-AN423 An-24RV 67310509 ♦

SUNKAR AIR — *AKS*

☐ UP-B3717 B737-322 24664/1877 ♦

ZHETYSU AVIA — *JTU*

☐ UP-Y4018 Yak-40 9812056 ♦
☐ UP-Y4019 Yak-40K 9741855
☐ UP-Y4020 Yak-40 9740256
☐ UP-Y4025 Yak-40 9831958

ZHEZAIR — *ZAV*

☐ UP-L4102 LET L410UVP-E 902512
☐ UP-L4108 LET L410UVP-E20 2801
☐ UP-Y4012 Yak-40K 9741755
☐ UP-Y4013 Yak-40 9731055
☐ UP-Y4014 Yak-40K 9732054

UR- UKRAINE

AEROJET AIRLINES — *BJU*

☐ UR-ALC SAAB SF.340B 340B-163

AEROSTAR **UAR**

☐ UR-DAV Do328-310 3169
☐ UR-WOG Do328-300QC 3118

AEROVIS AIRLINES **VIZ**

☐ UR-CBF An-12BP 2340507
☐ UR-CFB An-12BP 6343802

AIR URGA **3N / URG**

☐ UR-ELM An-24RV 67310506
☐ UR-46311 An-24B 97305307

☐ UR-ELB An-26B 14005 >UN
☐ UR-ELD An-26B 14010 >UN
☐ UR-ELE An-26B 12108 >UN
☐ UR-ELF An-26B-100 12204 >UN
☐ UR-ELG An-26B 12902 >UN
☐ UR-ELH An-26B 12908 >UN
☐ UR-ELI An-26B 14009

☐ UR-APM SAAB SF.340B 340B-230
☐ UR-ARO SAAB SF.340B 340B-276
☐ UR-ELJ SAAB SF.340B 340B-259
☐ UR-ELQ SAAB SF.340B 340B-239
☐ UR-ELS SAAB SF.340B 340B-214
☐ UR-ELU SAAB SF.340B 340B-360
☐ UR-ELV SAAB SF.340B 340B-242
☐ UR-ELZ SAAB SF.340B 340B-359
☐ UR-ESA SAAB SF.340B 340B-449
☐ UR-ESB SAAB SF.340B 340B-426 ♦
☐ UR-IMS SAAB SF.340B 340B-228
☐ UR-IMX SAAB SF.340B 340B-225
☐ UR- SAAB SF.340B 340B-233 ♦

ANTONOV AIRLINES **ADB**

☐ UR-09307 An-22A 043481244
☐ UR-74010 An-74T 36547030450

☐ UR-82007 An-124-100 19530501005
☐ UR-82008 An-124-100M-15019530501006
☐ UR-82009 An-124-100 19530501007
☐ UR-82027 An-124-100 19530502288
☐ UR-82029 An-124-100 19530502630
☐ UR-82072 An-124-100 9773053359136
☐ UR-82073 An-124-100 9773054359139

☐ UR-82060 An-225 19530503763

ATLASJET UKRAINE **UH / UJX**

☐ UR-AJA A320-214 1213
☐ UR-AJB A320-233 0733 >KKK

AVIA EXPRESS

☐ UR-LSA LET L-410UVP-16A 902414 ♦

AZUR AIR UKRAINE **QU / UTN**

☐ UR-UTP B737-8Q8 28226/77
☐ UR-UTQ B737-83N/W 30679/1404
☐ UR-UTR B737-8Q8/W 28215/75

☐ UR-UTX CRJ-200LR 7119 std
☐ UR-UTY CRJ-200LR 7122 [CGN]
☐ UR-UTZ CRJ-200LR 7121 std

BRAVO AIR **BAY**

☐ UR-CNE B737-505 24828/1925 >UKM♦
☐ UR-COB MD-83 53187/2118 >KMF♦
☐ UR-COC MD-83 49808/1836 >KMF♦
☐ UR-COO MD-83 53623/2276 >KMF♦
☐ UR-WRB MD-82 49364/1276 [KBP]

BUKOVYNA AIRLINES **BQ / BKV**

☐ UR-BXI MD-82 53170/2065 >IRA
☐ UR-BXL MD-82 49512/1548 >IRB [MHD]
☐ UR-BXM MD-82 49505/1381 >IRB
☐ UR-BXN MD-82 49569/1405 >IRK
☐ UR-CGS MD-82 49425/1240 >IRB
☐ UR-CGT MD-82 49428/1241
☐ UR-CHW MD-82 49510/1514 >IRA
☐ UR-CHX MD-82 53162/2010 >IRA
☐ UR-CHY MD-82 53171/2067
☐ UR-CHZ MD-82 53169/2063 >IRB
☐ UR-CJA MD-82 49277/1181
☐ UR-CJQ MD-82 49502/1300 >IRB
☐ UR-CJZ MD-82 49506/1400 >IRB

CAVOK AIRLINES **CVK**

☐ UR-CBG An-12BP 6343705 ♦
☐ UR-CCP An-12AP 2340505
☐ UR-CEZ An-12BP 6344304 ♦
☐ UR-CJN An-12B 01348006 ♦
☐ UR-CKC An-74TK-100 36547095905
☐ UR-CKL An-12BK 01348005
☐ UR-CKM An-12BP 02348207
☐ UR-CNN An-12BP 7345004
☐ UR-KDM An-12BK 02348197 ♦

CHALLENGE AERO **5U / CHG**

☐ UR-CLB Yak-40K 9731555 [IEV]♦
☐ UR-CLH Yak-40 9530642 [IEV]♦
☐ UR-ECL Yak-40K 9932059 [SCW]♦
☐ UR-RTS Yak-40 9530541 ♦

CHORNOMORSKI

☐ UR-COD Yak-42D 4520424811442 ♦
☐ UR-COH Yak-42D 4520423606235 ♦

CONSTANTA AIRLINES **UZA**

☐ UR-AKW Yak-40 9731255 ♦
☐ UR-ALM Yak-40K(F) 9741756

DART AIRLINES **DAT**

☐ UR-CEL MD-83 49390/1269 [THR]
☐ UR-CHL MD-83 49395/1286 [IEV]
☐ UR-CJP A320-212 0937 ♦
☐ UR-COF A320-212 0409 [IEV]♦
☐ UR-CON B737-5L9 28997/3008 ♦

DNIPROAVIA **Z6 / UDN**

☐ UR-DNH B737-5Y0 24696/1960 [KBP]
☐ UR-IVK B737-3L9 24571/1815 [KBP]
☐ UR-KIV B737-4Y0 24686/1861 [KBP]

☐ UR-DNA ERJ-145EU 145088 [KBP]
☐ UR-DNB ERJ-145EU 145094
☐ UR-DNE ERJ-145EU 145357 [CFE]
☐ UR-DNF ERJ-145EU 145404
☐ UR-DNG ERJ-145EP 145394 [DNK]
☐ UR-DNI ERJ-145EP 145325 [WAW]
☐ UR-DNK ERJ-145EU 145039 [SVO]

☐ UR-DNL ERJ-145EU 145042 [CFE]
☐ UR-DNN ERJ-145LR 145665 [WAW]
☐ UR-DNO ERJ-145EP 145237 [DNK]
☐ UR-DNP ERJ-145EP 145290
☐ UR-DNQ ERJ-145EP 145315 [WAW]
☐ UR-DNS ERJ-145LR 145652 [KBP]
☐ UR-DNT ERJ-145LR 145709
☐ UR-DNU ERJ-145LR 145738 [KTW]
☐ UR-DNV ERJ-145LR 145445 [KTW]
☐ UR-DNW ERJ-145LR 145316 [WAW]
☐ UR-DNZ ERJ-145LR 145436 [KTW]
☐ UR-DPA ERJ-145LR 145330 [KTW]
☐ UR-DPB ERJ-145LR 145250 [DNK]

ELERON AVIATION COMPANY

☐ UR-CMB Il-76TD 0033446325 ^
☐ UR-CMD Il-76TD 0053460832

^ operated by Alfa Air

EUROPE AIR — *EVP*

☐ UR-BXS Il-76TD 1023411368 ♦
☐ UR-CMC Il-76TD 1013407230 ♦
☐ UR-COE Il-76MD 0093498974 ♦
☐ UR-EAA Il-76TD 0033446350

KHORS AIR — *X9 / KHO*

☐ UR-CMW A319-113 0644 >IZG♦
☐ UR-CNJ A320-211 0311 >IZG♦
☐ UR-CNK A320-211 0426 >IZG♦
☐ UR-COK B737-31S 29055/2923 >CPN♦
☐ UR-CHO MD-82 53231/2107 [THR]
☐ UR-CJE MD-83 49857/1687 [THR]
☐ UR-CLP MD-83 49856/1675 [IEV]

MERIDIAN — *MEM*

☐ UR-BAB An-26B-100 11603
☐ UR-CHT An-26B 5901
☐ UR-MDA An-26-100 7108
☐ UR-MNN An-26B 14403 ♦

MOTOR SICH AIRLINES — *M9 / MSI*

☐ UR-BXC An-24RV 37308902
☐ UR-MSI An-24RV 27307608
☐ UR-11316 An-12BK 9346810
☐ UR-11819 An-12BP 6344009
☐ UR-14005 An-140 36525305021
☐ UR-14007 An-140-100 36525305029
☐ UR-42410 Yak-42D 4520421219029 [OZH]♦
☐ UR-47297 An-24RV 07306610
☐ UR-74026 An-74TK-200 36547096919
☐ UR-88310 Yak-40 9940760

MRK AIRLINES — *6V / MRW*

☐ UR-CGQ SAAB SF.340A 340A-097
☐ UR-CGR SAAB SF.340A 340A-124

STATE AVIATION ENTERPRISE

☐ UR-ABA A319-115CJ 3260
☐ UR-AWB An-74TK-300 36547098984
☐ UR-86527 Il-62M 4037758
☐ UR-86528 Il-62M 4038111
☐ UR-65718 Tu-134A-3 63668

UKRAINE AIR ALLIANCE — *UKL*

☐ UR-CAH An-12BK 8345604
☐ UR-CAJ An-12BK 8346106
☐ UR-CAK An-12BP 6343707
☐ UR-CGV An-12BP 6344610
☐ UR-CGW An-12B 402410
☐ UR-CNT An-12BK 00347505 ♦
☐ UR-CZZ An-12BP 401605

☐ UR-BXQ Il-76TD 1023410360 >MXU

UKRAINE INTERNATIONAL AIRLINES — *PS / AUI*

☐ UR-FAA B737-3Y0(SF) 24462/1691
☐ UR-GAH B737-32Q/W 29130/3105
☐ UR-GAK B737-5Y0/W 26075/2374
☐ UR-GAS B737-528/W 25236/2443
☐ UR-GAT B737-528/W 25237/2464
☐ UR-GAU B737-5Y0/W 25182/2211
☐ UR-GAW B737-5Y0/W 24898/2079
☐ UR-GBA B737-36N/W 28670/2948
☐ UR-GBC B737-5L9 28722/2868
☐ UR-GBD B737-36Q/W 28659/2680

☐ UR-PSA B737-8HX/W 29658/2970
☐ UR-PSB B737-8HX/W 29654/3018
☐ UR-PSC B737-8HX/W 29662/3182
☐ UR-PSD B737-8HX/W 29686/3259
☐ UR-PSE B737-84R/W 38119/3962
☐ UR-PSF B737-84R/W 38120/4018
☐ UR-PSG B737-85R/W 29038/297
☐ UR-PSH B737-85R/W 29040/465
☐ UR-PSM B737-8FZ/W 29674/3140 ♦
☐ UR- B737-84R/W o/o

☐ UR-PSI B737-9KVER/W 41534/4524
☐ UR-PSJ B737-9KVER/W 41535/4654
☐ UR-PSK B737-94XER/W 36086/2910
☐ UR-PSL B737-94XER/W 36087/2928

☐ UR-GEA B767-322ER/W 25280/391
☐ UR-GEB B767-33AER/W 25530/414
☐ UR-GEC B767-33AER/W 25533/454
☐ UR-GED B767-33AER/W 25536/504

☐ UR-EMA ERJ-190STD 19000494
☐ UR-EMB ERJ-190STD 19000501
☐ UR-EMC ERJ-190STD 19000589
☐ UR-EMD ERJ-190STD 19000602
☐ UR-EME ERJ-190STD 19000614

UM AIR — *UF / UKM*

☐ UR-CKX BAe146 Srs.300 E3131 std
☐ UR-CNE B737-505 24828/1925 <BAY
☐ UR-CKN MD-83 53186/2092 >IRB

WIND ROSE — *7W / WRC*

☐ UR-WRH A321-231 2462 >ABQ
☐ UR-WRI A321-231 2682 >ABQ
☐ UR-WRJ A321-231 1869 >ABQ
☐ UR-WRM A320-212 0645
☐ UR-WRO A321-211 0781
☐ UR-WRQ A330-223 296 >ABQ
☐ UR-DNR ERJ-145LR 145641

YAN AIR — *YE / ANR*

☐ UR-CME A320-212 0671
☐ UR-COG B737-301 23937/1587 ♦

	Reg	Type	c/n	Notes
☐	UR-COJ	A321-112	0488	o/o♦
☐	UR-YAD	A320-211	0726	>SUD
☐	UR-CNF	B737-3Z0	27126/2370	
☐	UR-CNP	B737-4Y0	23980/1667	
☐	UR-CJU	MD-83	49631/1596	[THR]
☐	UR-YAB	SAAB SF.340A	340A-134	
☐	UR-YAC	SAAB SF.340A	340A-153	

YUZMASHAVIA — 2N / UMK

	Reg	Type	c/n	Notes
☐	UR-78785	Il-76MD	083489691	
☐	UR-78786	Il-76TD	083490693	
☐	UR-87951	Yak-40K	9810957	[DNK]

ZETAVIA — ZK / ZAV

	Reg	Type	c/n	Notes
☐	UR-CIB	Il-76TD	1003499997	♦
☐	UR-CID	Il-76TD	0063465956	
☐	UR-CIE	Il-76T	093420594	
☐	UR-CIF	Il-76TD	1023412395	
☐	UR-UIG	Il-76TD	1033416515	♦
☐	UR-CIU	Il-76TD	0053458741	
☐	UR-CIV	Il-76TD	0063471147	

VH- AUSTRALIA

AIRNORTH REGIONAL — TL / ANO

	Reg	Type	c/n	Notes
☐	VH-ANK	EMB.120ER	120155	
☐	VH-ANN	EMB.120ER	120203	
☐	VH-ANQ	EMB.120RT	120079	
☐	VH-ANZ	EMB.120RT	120135	
☐	VH-DIL	EMB.120ER	120153	
☐	VH-ANO	ERJ-170LR	17000099	
☐	VH-ANT	ERJ-170LR	17000357	
☐	VH-ANV	ERJ-170LR	17000280	
☐	VH-SWO	ERJ-170LR	17000081	
☐	VH-ANA	SA.227DC Metro 23	DC-871B	
☐	VH-ANW	SA.227DC Metro 23	DC-873B	
☐	VH-ANY	SA.227DC Metro 23	DC-840B	

AIR SOUTH

	Reg	Type	c/n	Notes
☐	VH-YOA	Beech 1900D	UE-143	♦
☐	VH-ZOA	Beech 1900D	UE-85	♦
☐	VH-NHC	EMB.120ER	120152	♦

ALLIANCE AIRLINES — QQ / UTY

	Reg	Type	c/n	Notes
☐	VH-FKO	Fokker 50	20160	
☐	VH-FKV	Fokker 50	20303	
☐	VH-FKW	Fokker 50	20306	
☐	VH-FKX	Fokker 50	20312	
☐	VH-FKZ	Fokker 50	20286	
☐	VH-JFB	Fokker 70	11521	
☐	VH-JFE	Fokker 70	11545	
☐	VH-NKH	Fokker 70	11549	[BNE]
☐	VH-NKU	Fokker 70	11555	
☐	VH-NKZ	Fokker 70	11573	[ADL]
☐	VH-QQR	Fokker 70	11564	
☐	VH-QQV	Fokker 70	11565	
☐	VH-QQW	Fokker 70	11569	
☐	VH-QQX	Fokker 70	11571	
☐	VH-QQY	Fokker 70	11575	
☐	VH-	Fokker 70	11529	o/o♦
☐	VH-	Fokker 70	11532	o/o♦
☐	VH-	Fokker 70	11554	o/o♦
☐	VH-	Fokker 70	11560	o/o♦
☐	VH-	Fokker 70	11568	o/o♦
☐	VH-	Fokker 70	11572	o/o♦
☐	VH-FKA	Fokker 100	11345	
☐	VH-FKC	Fokker 100	11349	
☐	VH-FKD	Fokker 100	11357	
☐	VH-FKF	Fokker 100	11365	
☐	VH-FKG	Fokker 100	11366	
☐	VH-FKJ	Fokker 100	11372	
☐	VH-FKK	Fokker 100	11379	
☐	VH-FKL	Fokker 100	11380	[BNE]
☐	VH-XWM	Fokker 100	11276	
☐	VH-XWN	Fokker 100	11278	
☐	VH-XWO	Fokker 100	11280	
☐	VH-XWP	Fokker 100	11281	
☐	VH-XWQ	Fokker 100	11300	
☐	VH-XWR	Fokker 100	11306	
☐	VH-XWS	Fokker 100	11314	
☐	VH-XWT	Fokker 100	11338	
☐	VH-	Fokker 100	11490	o/o♦
☐	VH-	Fokker 100	11502	o/o♦
☐	VH-	Fokker 100	11446	o/o♦
☐	VH-	Fokker 100	11515	o/o♦
☐	VH-	Fokker 100	11499	o/o♦
☐	VH-	Fokker 100	11483	o/o♦
☐	VH-	Fokker 100	11520	o/o♦
☐	VH-	Fokker 100	11456	o/o♦
☐	VH-	Fokker 100	11468	o/o♦
☐	VH-	Fokker 100	11359	o/o♦
☐	VH-	Fokker 100	11397	o/o♦
☐	VH-	Fokker 100	11404	o/o♦
☐	VH-	Fokker 100	11361	o/o♦
☐	VH-	Fokker 100	11367	o/o♦
☐	VH-	Fokker 100	11460	o/o♦

CASAIR

	Reg	Type	c/n	Notes
☐	VH-KGX	SA.226TC Metro II	TC-326	
☐	VH-NGX	SA.226TC Metro II	TC-287	
☐	VH-OGX	SA.226TC Metro II	TC-395	
☐	VH-WGX	SA.226TC Metro II	TC-312	
☐	VH-ZGX	SA.227TT Merlin III	TT-534	♦

COBHAM AVN SVCS AUSTRALIA — NC / NJS

Operates B717s and other Avro/BAe146s for Qantaslink, which see.

	Reg	Type	c/n	Notes
☐	VH-NJF	BAe146 Srs.300QT	E3198	
☐	VH-NJM	BAe146 Srs.300QT	E3194	^
☐	VH-NJU	Avro 146-RJ85	E2287	♦
☐	VH-NJV	BAe146 Srs.100QT	E1002	^
☐	VH-NJW	Avro 146-RJ85	E2329	^
☐	VH-LCL	DHC-8Q-202	492	
☐	VH-ZZA	DHC-8-202MPA	419	
☐	VH-ZZB	DHC-8-202MPA	424	
☐	VH-ZZC	DHC-8-202MPA	433	
☐	VH-ZZE	DHC-8Q-315MPA	640	
☐	VH-ZZF	DHC-8Q-315MPA	643	
☐	VH-ZZG	DHC-8Q-315MPA	644	
☐	VH-ZZI	DHC-8-202MPA	550	
☐	VH-ZZJ	DHC-8-202MPA	551	
☐	VH-ZZN	DHC-8-315MPA	399	
☐	VH-ZZP	DHC-8-202MPA	411	
☐	VH-NJA	ERJ190LR	19000404	

^ operated as Australian Air Express (XM/XME); also operates as National Jet Express

DE BRUIN AIR

☐	VH-OAE	BAeJetstream 32	851	
☐	VH-OAM	BAeJetstream 32	859	

EXPRESS FREIGHTERS AUSTRALIA — EFA

☐	VH-XMB	B737-376(SF)	23478/1251	^
☐	VH-XML	B737-376(SF)	23486/1286	^
☐	VH-XMO	B737-376(SF)	23488/1352	^
☐	VH-XMR	B737-376(SF)	23490/1390	^
☐	VH-EFR	B767-381F	33510/939	*

^ operated as Australian Air Express (XM/XME);
** flies in Qantas Freght c/s*

JETSTAR AIRWAYS — JQ / JST

☐	VH-JQG	A320-232	2169	
☐	VH-JQL	A320-232	2185	
☐	VH-JQX	A320-232	2197	
☐	VH-VFD	A320-232	4922	
☐	VH-VFF	A320-232	5039	
☐	VH-VFH	A320-232	5211	
☐	VH-VFI	A320-232	5270	
☐	VH-VFJ	A320-232	5311	
☐	VH-VFK	A320-232	5334	
☐	VH-VFL	A320-232	5489	
☐	VH-VFN	A320-232/S	5566	
☐	VH-VFO	A320-232/S	5631	
☐	VH-VFP	A320-232/S	5775	
☐	VH-VFQ	A320-232/S	5780	
☐	VH-VFT	A320-232/S	5532	
☐	VH-VFU	A320-232/S	5814	
☐	VH-VFV	A320-232/S	5858	
☐	VH-VFX	A320-232/S	5871	
☐	VH-VFY	A320-232/S	6362	
☐	VH-VGA	A320-232	4899	
☐	VH-VGD	A320-232	4527	
☐	VH-VGF	A320-232	4497	
☐	VH-VGH	A320-232	4495	
☐	VH-VGI	A320-232	4466	
☐	VH-VGJ	A320-232	4460	
☐	VH-VGN	A320-232	4434	
☐	VH-VGO	A320-232	4356	
☐	VH-VGP	A320-232	4343	
☐	VH-VGQ	A320-232	4303	
☐	VH-VGR	A320-232	4257	
☐	VH-VGT	A320-232	4178	
☐	VH-VGU	A320-232	4245	
☐	VH-VGV	A320-232	4229	
☐	VH-VGY	A320-232	4177	
☐	VH-VGZ	A320-232	3917	
☐	VH-VQA	A320-232	3783	
☐	VH-VQC	A320-232	3668	
☐	VH-VQE	A320-232	3495	
☐	VH-VQF	A320-232	3474	
☐	VH-VQG	A320-232	2787	
☐	VH-VQH	A320-232	2766	
☐	VH-VQJ	A320-232	2703	
☐	VH-VQK	A320-232	2651	
☐	VH-VQL	A320-232	2642	
☐	VH-VQM	A320-232	2608	
☐	VH-VQP	A320-232	2573	
☐	VH-VQQ	A320-232	2537	
☐	VH-VQR	A320-232	2526	
☐	VH-VQS	A320-232	2515	
☐	VH-VQU	A320-232	2455	
☐	VH-VQW	A320-232	2329	
☐	VH-VQZ	A320-232	2292	
☐	VH-XSJ	A320-232	5482	
☐	VH-VWT	A321-231	3717	
☐	VH-VWU	A321-231	3948	
☐	VH-VWW	A321-231	3916	
☐	VH-VWX	A321-231	3899	
☐	VH-VWY	A321-231	1408	
☐	VH-VWZ	A321-231	1195	
☐	VH-VKA	B787-8	36227/123	
☐	VH-VKB	B787-8	36228/134	
☐	VH-VKD	B787-8	36229/142	
☐	VH-VKE	B787-8	36230/162	
☐	VH-VKF	B787-8	36231/175	
☐	VH-VKG	B787-8	36232/189	
☐	VH-VKH	B787-8	36233/200	
☐	VH-VKI	B787-8	36235/257	
☐	VH-VKJ	B787-8	36236/278	
☐	VH-VKK	B787-8	36237/321	
☐	VH-VKL	B787-8	36238/344	
☐	VH-	B787-9		o/o♦
☐	VH-	B787-9		o/o♦
☐	VH-	B787-9		o/o♦

NATIONAL JET EXPRESS

See Cobham Aviation Services

NETWORK AVIATION AUSTRALIA

Operates Fokker 100s for Qantas Link.

PEARL AVIATION

☐	VH-PPF	Do328-110	3057	
☐	VH-PPG	Do328-110	3053	
☐	VH-PPJ	Do328-110	3059	
☐	VH-PPQ	Do328-110	3051	
☐	VH-PPV	Do328-110	3052	
☐	VH-OYB	SA.227DC Metro 23	DC-848B	
☐	VH-OYG	SA.227DC Metro 23	DC-875B	
☐	VH-OYI	SA.227DC Metro 23	DC-839B	
☐	VH-OYN	SA.227DC Metro 23	DC-870B	

PEL-AIR — QWA

☐	VH-EKT	SAAB SF.340AF	340A-085	
☐	VH-KDB	SAAB SF.340AF	340A-008	
☐	VH-KDK	SAAB SF.340AF	340A-016	

QANTAS AIRWAYS — QF / QFA

☐	VH-EBA	A330-202	508	
☐	VH-EBB	A330-202	522	
☐	VH-EBC	A330-202	506	
☐	VH-EBD	A330-202	513	
☐	VH-EBE	A330-202	842	♦
☐	VH-EBF	A330-202	853	♦
☐	VH-EBG	A330-203	887	
☐	VH-EBJ	A330-202	940	♦
☐	VH-EBK	A330-202	945	♦
☐	VH-EBL	A330-203	976	
☐	VH-EBM	A330-203	1061	
☐	VH-EBN	A330-203	1094	
☐	VH-EBO	A330-203	1169	
☐	VH-EBP	A330-203	1174	
☐	VH-EBQ	A330-202	1198	
☐	VH-EBR	A330-202	1251	
☐	VH-EBS	A330-202	1258	

☐	VH-EBV	A330-202	1365	
☐	VH-QPA	A330-303	553	
☐	VH-QPB	A330-303	558	
☐	VH-QPC	A330-303	564	
☐	VH-QPD	A330-303	574	
☐	VH-QPE	A330-303	593	
☐	VH-QPF	A330-303	595	
☐	VH-QPG	A330-303	603	
☐	VH-QPH	A330-303	695	
☐	VH-QPI	A330-303	705	
☐	VH-QPJ	A330-303	712	
☐	VH-OQA	A380-842	014	
☐	VH-OQB	A380-842	015	
☐	VH-OQC	A380-842	022	
☐	VH-OQD	A380-842	026	
☐	VH-OQE	A380-842	027	
☐	VH-OQF	A380-842	029	
☐	VH-OQG	A380-842	047	
☐	VH-OQH	A380-842	050	
☐	VH-OQI	A380-842	055	
☐	VH-OQJ	A380-842	062	
☐	VH-OQK	A380-842	063	
☐	VH-OQL	A380-842	074	
☐	VH-VXA	B737-838/W	29551/1042	
☐	VH-VXB	B737-838/W	30101/1045	
☐	VH-VXC	B737-838/W	30897/1049	
☐	VH-VXD	B737-838/W	29552/1063	
☐	VH-VXE	B737-838/W	30899/1071	
☐	VH-VXF	B737-838/W	29553/1096	
☐	VH-VXG	B737-838/W	30901/1102	
☐	VH-VXH	B737-838/W	33478/1137	
☐	VH-VXI	B737-838/W	33479/1141	
☐	VH-VXJ	B737-838/W	33480/1157	
☐	VH-VXK	B737-838/W	33481/1160	
☐	VH-VXL	B737-838/W	33482/1172	
☐	VH-VXM	B737-838/W	33483/1177	
☐	VH-VXN	B737-838/W	33484/1180	
☐	VH-VXO	B737-838/W	33485/1183	
☐	VH-VXP	B737-838/W	33722/1324	
☐	VH-VXQ	B737-838/W	33723/1335	
☐	VH-VXR	B737-838/W	33724/1340	
☐	VH-VXS	B737-838/W	33725/1352	
☐	VH-VXT	B737-838/W	33760/1412	
☐	VH-VXU	B737-838/W	33761/1420	
☐	VH-VYA	B737-838/W	33762/1532	
☐	VH-VYB	B737-838/W	33763/1534	
☐	VH-VYC	B737-838/W	33991/1612	
☐	VH-VYD	B737-838/W	33992/1706	
☐	VH-VYE	B737-838/W	33993/1712	
☐	VH-VYF	B737-838/W	33994/1727	
☐	VH-VYG	B737-838/W	33995/1736	
☐	VH-VYH	B737-838/W	34180/1815	
☐	VH-VYI	B737-838/W	34181/1840	
☐	VH-VYJ	B737-838/W	34182/1842	
☐	VH-VYK	B737-838/W	34183/1846	
☐	VH-VYL	B737-838/W	34184/1854	
☐	VH-VZA	B737-838/W	34195/2502	
☐	VH-VZB	B737-838/W	34196/2623	
☐	VH-VZC	B737-838/W	34197/2649	
☐	VH-VZD	B737-838/W	34198/2659	
☐	VH-VZE	B737-838/W	34199/2661	
☐	VH-VZL	B737-838/W	34194/3621	
☐	VH-VZM	B737-838/W	34192/3644	
☐	VH-VZO	B737-838/W	34191/3692	
☐	VH-VZP	B737-838/W	39362/3714	
☐	VH-VZR	B737-838/W	34193/3754	
☐	VH-VZS	B737-838/W	39358/3769	
☐	VH-VZT	B737-838/W	34186/3798	
☐	VH-VZU	B737-838/W	34187/3826	
☐	VH-VZV	B737-838/W	34189/3856	
☐	VH-VZW	B737-838/W	39359/3881	
☐	VH-VZX	B737-838/W	34188/3910	
☐	VH-VZY	B737-838/W	39363/3944	
☐	VH-VZZ	B737-838/W	39445/4010	
☐	VH-XZA	B737-838/W	39367/4150	
☐	VH-XZB	B737-838/W	39360/4192	
☐	VH-XZC	B737-838/W	39361/4199	
☐	VH-XZD	B737-838/W	39368/4400	
☐	VH-XZE	B737-838/W	39369/4421	
☐	VH-XZF	B737-838/W	39370/4450	
☐	VH-XZG	B737-838/W	39371/4477	
☐	VH-XZH	B737-838/W	39372/4521	
☐	VH-XZI	B737-838/W	39364/4630	
☐	VH-XZJ	B737-838/W	39365/4669	
☐	VH-XZK	B737-838/W	39366/4705	
☐	VH-XZL	B737-838/W	44573/5009	
☐	VH-XZM	B737-838/W	44574/5018	
☐	VH-XZN	B737-838/W	44575/5060	
☐	VH-XZO	B737-838/W	44576/5108	
☐	VH-XZP	B737-838/W	44577/5164	
☐	VH-	B737-838/W		o/o
☐	VH-	B737-838/W		o/o
☐	VH-	B737-838/W		o/o
☐	N409MC	B747-47UF	30558/1242	<GTI
☐	N493MC	B747-47UF	29254/1179	<GTI
☐	VH-OEB	B747-48E	25778/983	
☐	VH-OEE	B747-438ER	32909/1308	
☐	VH-OEF	B747-438ER	32910/1313	
☐	VH-OEG	B747-438ER	32911/1320	
☐	VH-OEH	B747-438ER	32912/1321	
☐	VH-OEI	B747-438ER	32913/1330	
☐	VH-OEJ	B747-438ER	32914/1331	
☐	VH-OJM	B747-438	25245/875	
☐	VH-OJS	B747-438	25564/1230	
☐	VH-OJT	B747-438	25565/1233	
☐	VH-OJU	B747-438	25566/1239	

QANTASLINK *QF / QFA*

☐	VH-NXD	B717-23S	55062/5031	
☐	VH-NXE	B717-23S	55063/5034	
☐	VH-NXG	B717-2K9	55057/5020	
☐	VH-NXH	B717-2K9	55055/5014	
☐	VH-NXI	B717-2K9	55054/5013	
☐	VH-NXJ	B717-2BL	55166/5116	
☐	VH-NXK	B717-231	55092/5077	
☐	VH-NXL	B717-231	55093/5083	
☐	VH-NXM	B717-231	55094/5084	
☐	VH-NXN	B717-231	55095/5087	
☐	VH-NXO	B717-231	55096/5093	
☐	VH-NXQ	B717-231	55097/5095	
☐	VH-NXR	B717-2BL	55168/5118	
☐	VH-YQS	B717-2BL	55178/5128	
☐	VH-YQT	B717-2BL	55179/5129	
☐	VH-YQU	B717-2BL	55180/5132	
☐	VH-YQV	B717-2BL	55193/5153	
☐	VH-YQW	B717-2BL	55194/5154	♦
☐	VH-YQX	B717-2K9	55053/5016	♦
☐	VH-YQY	B717-2K9	55056/5015	♦
☐	VH-NJC	BAe146 Srs.100	E1013	[ADL]
☐	VH-NJG	BAe146 Srs.200	E2170	
☐	VH-NJH	Avro 146-RJ100	E3301	

	Reg	Type	C/n	
☐	VH-NJI	Avro 146-RJ100	E3265	
☐	VH-NJL	BAe146 Srs.300	E3213	
☐	VH-NJN	BAe146 Srs.300	E3217	
☐	VH-NJP	Avro 146-RJ100	E3354	
☐	VH-NJQ	Avro 146-RJ100	E3328	
☐	VH-NJR	BAe146 Srs.100	E1152	
☐	VH-NJY	Avro 146-RJ100	E3331	
☐	VH-NJZ	BAe146 Srs.300QT	E3126	
☐	VH-SBB	DHC-8Q-315	539	
☐	VH-SBG	DHC-8Q-315	575	
☐	VH-SBI	DHC-8Q-315	605	>SCR
☐	VH-SBJ	DHC-8Q-315	578	[TMW]
☐	VH-SBT	DHC-8Q-315	580	[TMW]
☐	VH-SBV	DHC-8Q-315	595	
☐	VH-SBW	DHC-8Q-315	599	
☐	VH-SCE	DHC-8Q-315	602	
☐	VH-TQD	DHC-8Q-315	598	>SCR
☐	VH-TQE	DHC-8Q-315	596	
☐	VH-TQG	DHC-8-201	430	
☐	VH-TQH	DHC-8Q-315	597	
☐	VH-TQK	DHC-8Q-315	600	>SCR
☐	VH-TQL	DHC-8Q-315	603	>SCR
☐	VH-TQM	DHC-8Q-315	604	>SCR
☐	VH-TQS	DHC-8-202	418	
☐	VH-TQX	DHC-8-202	439	
☐	VH-TQY	DHC-8Q-315	552	
☐	VH-TQZ	DHC-8Q-315	555	[TMW]
☐	VH-LQB	DHC-8-402Q	4343	
☐	VH-LQD	DHC-8-402Q	4371	
☐	VH-LQF	DHC-8-402Q	4375	
☐	VH-LQG	DHC-8-402Q	4376	
☐	VH-LQH	DHC-8-402Q	4431	
☐	VH-LQJ	DHC-8-402Q	4414	
☐	VH-LQK	DHC-8-402Q	4415	
☐	VH-LQL	DHC-8-402Q	4449	
☐	VH-LQM	DHC-8-402Q	4450	
☐	VH-LQQ	DHC-8-402Q	4461	
☐	VH-QOA	DHC-8-402Q	4112	
☐	VH-QOB	DHC-8-402Q	4116	
☐	VH-QOC	DHC-8-402Q	4117	
☐	VH-QOD	DHC-8-402Q	4123	
☐	VH-QOE	DHC-8-402Q	4125	
☐	VH-QOF	DHC-8-402Q	4128	
☐	VH-QOH	DHC-8-402Q	4132	
☐	VH-QOI	DHC-8-402Q	4189	
☐	VH-QOJ	DHC-8-402Q	4192	
☐	VH-QOK	DHC-8-402Q	4215	
☐	VH-QOM	DHC-8-402Q	4217	
☐	VH-QON	DHC-8-402Q	4218	
☐	VH-QOP	DHC-8-402Q	4238	
☐	VH-QOR	DHC-8-402Q	4241	
☐	VH-QOS	DHC-8-402Q	4263	
☐	VH-QOT	DHC-8-402Q	4269	
☐	VH-QOU	DHC-8-402Q	4275	
☐	VH-QOV	DHC-8-402Q	4277	
☐	VH-QOW	DHC-8-402Q	4285	
☐	VH-QOX	DHC-8-402Q	4287	
☐	VH-QOY	DHC-8-402Q	4288	
☐	VH-NHC	Fokker 100	11481	♦
☐	VH-NHF	Fokker 100	11458	
☐	VH-NHG	Fokker 100	11514	
☐	VH-NHI	Fokker 100	11479	
☐	VH-NHJ	Fokker 100	11464	
☐	VH-NHK	Fokker 100	11465	
☐	VH-NHM	Fokker 100	11449	
☐	VH-NHN	Fokker 100	11469	
☐	VH-NHO	Fokker 100	11312	
☐	VH-NHP	Fokker 100	11399	
☐	VH-NHQ	Fokker 100	11506	
☐	VH-NHV	Fokker 100	11482	
☐	VH-NHY	Fokker 100	11467	♦
☐	VH-NQE	Fokker 100	11457	

B717s & Avro.BAe146s opertered by Cobham Aviation Services; Fokker 100s by Network Aviation.
DHC-8-200s & 300s operated by Eastern Australia Airlines; DHC-8-400s by Sunstate Airlines.

REX – REGIONAL EXPRESS ZL / RXA

	Reg	Type	C/n	
☐	VH-EKH	SAAB SF.340B	340B-369	
☐	VH-EKX	SAAB SF.340B	340B-257	
☐	VH-KDQ	SAAB SF.340B	340B-325	
☐	VH-KDV	SAAB SF.340B	340B-322	
☐	VH-KRX	SAAB SF.340B	340B-290	
☐	VH-NRX	SAAB SF.340B	340B-291	
☐	VH-OLL	SAAB SF.340B	340B-175	
☐	VH-OLM	SAAB SF.340B	340B-205	
☐	VH-ORX	SAAB SF.340B	340B-293	
☐	VH-PRX	SAAB SF.340B	340B-303	
☐	VH-REX	SAAB SF.340B	340B-384	
☐	VH-RXE	SAAB SF.340B	340B-275	
☐	VH-RXN	SAAB SF.340B	340B-279	
☐	VH-RXQ	SAAB SF.340B	340B-200	
☐	VH-RXS	SAAB SF.340B	340B-285	
☐	VH-RXX	SAAB SF.340B	340B-209	
☐	VH-SBA	SAAB SF.340B	340B-311	
☐	VH-TRX	SAAB SF.340B	340B-287	
☐	VH-YRX	SAAB SF.340B	340B-178	
☐	VH-ZJS	SAAB SF.340B	340B-186	
☐	VH-ZLA	SAAB SF.340B	340B-371	
☐	VH-ZLC	SAAB SF.340B	340B-373	
☐	VH-ZLF	SAAB SF.340B	340B-374	
☐	VH-ZLG	SAAB SF.340B	340B-375	
☐	VH-ZLH	SAAB SF.340B	340B-376	
☐	VH-ZLJ	SAAB SF.340B	340B-380	
☐	VH-ZLK	SAAB SF.340B	340B-381	
☐	VH-ZLO	SAAB SF.340B	340B-382	
☐	VH-ZLQ	SAAB SF.340B	340B-370	
☐	VH-ZLR	SAAB SF.340B	340B-229	
☐	VH-ZLS	SAAB SF.340B	340B-383	
☐	VH-ZLV	SAAB SF.340B	340B-386	
☐	VH-ZLW	SAAB SF.340B	340B-387	
☐	VH-ZLX	SAAB SF.340B	340B-182	
☐	VH-ZRB	SAAB SF.340B	340B-389	
☐	VH-ZRC	SAAB SF.340B	340B-390	
☐	VH-ZRE	SAAB SF.340B	340B-391	
☐	VH-ZRH	SAAB SF.340B	340B-392	
☐	VH-ZRI	SAAB SF.340B	340B-394	
☐	VH-ZRJ	SAAB SF.340B	340B-396	
☐	VH-ZRK	SAAB SF.340B	340B-397	
☐	VH-ZRL	SAAB SF.340B	340B-398	
☐	VH-ZRM	SAAB SF.340B	340B-400	
☐	VH-ZRN	SAAB SF.340B	340B-393	
☐	VH-ZRY	SAAB SF.340B	340B-401	
☐	VH-ZRZ	SAAB SF.340B	340B-388	
☐	VH-ZXF	SAAB SF.340B	340B-416	♦
☐	VH-ZXS	SAAB SF.340B	340B-179	
☐	VH-	SAAB SF.340B	340B-402	♦
☐	VH-	SAAB SF.340B	340B-420	♦

SHARP AIRLINES SH / SHA

	Reg	Type	C/n	
☐	VH-HWR	SA.227DC Metro 23	DC-851B	

Reg	Type	C/n	Notes
☐ VH-MYI	SA.227DC Metro 23	DC-869B	
☐ VH-SEZ	SA.227AC Metro III	AC-637	
☐ VH-SWK	SA.227DC Metro 23	DC-826B	
☐ VH-UUB	SA.227DC Metro 23	DC-894B	
☐ VH-UUN	SA.227AC Metro III	AC-686	

SHORTSTOP AIR CHARTER

Reg	Type	C/n	Notes
☐ VH-OVM	Douglas DC-3	16354/33102	

SKIPPERS AVIATION — *JW*

Reg	Type	C/n	Notes
☐ VH-XFP	DHC-8-102A	346	
☐ VH-XFQ	DHC-8-106	306	
☐ VH-XFT	DHC-8-102	052	
☐ VH-XFU	DHC-8-102	151	
☐ VH-XFV	DHC-8-314A	350	
☐ VH-XFW	DHC-8-314A	356	
☐ VH-XFX	DHC-8-314A	313	
☐ VH-XFZ	DHC-8-314A	365	
☐ VH-XKI	DHC-8Q-315	587	
☐ VH-XKJ	DHC-8Q-315	588	
☐ VH-XUA	EMB.120ER	120045	
☐ VH-XUB	EMB.120ER	120181	
☐ VH-XUC	EMB.120ER	120208	
☐ VH-XUD	EMB.120ER	120140	
☐ VH-XUE	EMB.120ER	120115	
☐ VH-XUF	EMB.120ER	120207	
☐ VH-XKM	Fokker 100	11410	
☐ VH-XKN	Fokker 100	11420	
☐ VH-WAI	SA.227DC Metro 23	DC-874B	
☐ VH-WAJ	SA.227DC Metro 23	DC-876B	
☐ VH-WAX	SA.227DC Metro 23	DC-877B	
☐ VH-WBA	SA.227DC Metro 23	DC-883B	
☐ VH-WBQ	SA.227DC Metro 23	DC-884B	

SKYTRANS REGIONAL — *N6 / SKP*

Reg	Type	C/n	Notes
☐ VH-QQA	DHC-8-102	005	
☐ VH-QQD	DHC-8-102A	245	^
☐ VH-QQF	DHC-8-102	014	[CNS]
☐ VH-QQG	DHC-8-102	036	
☐ VH-QQI	DHC-8-102	117	
☐ VH-QQK	DHC-8-102A	326	^
☐ VH-QQL	DHC-8-102A	388	
☐ VH-QQM	DHC-8-311	286	[CNS]

^ operated by Maroomba Airlines

SKYTRADERS — *SND*

Reg	Type	C/n	Notes
☐ VH-VCJ	A319-132LR	1880	
☐ VH-VHD	A319-115CJ	1999	♦

TASMAN CARGO AIRLINES — *HJ / AXF*

Reg	Type	C/n	Notes
☐ G-BMRI	B757-236(SF)	24267/211	<DHK♦
☐ VH-TCA	B757-236(SF)	25620/449	

TIGERAIR AUSTRALIA — *TT / TGW*

Reg	Type	C/n	Notes
☐ VH-VNB	A320-232	2906	
☐ VH-VNC	A320-232	3275	
☐ VH-VND	A320-232	3296	
☐ VH-VNF	A320-232	3332	
☐ VH-VNG	A320-232	3674	
☐ VH-VNH	A320-232	3734	
☐ VH-VNJ	A320-232	2982	
☐ VH-VNK	A320-232	3986	
☐ VH-VNO	A320-232	4053	
☐ VH-VNP	A320-232	2952	
☐ VH-VNQ	A320-232	5218	
☐ VH-VNR	A320-232	5900	
☐ VH-XUG	A320-232	6032	
☐ VH-XUH	A320-232/S	6749	♦
☐ VH-VUB	B737-8FE/W	34013/1573	o/o♦

TOLL PRIORITY — *TFR*

Reg	Type	C/n	Notes
☐ VH-TOQ	ATR 42-300F	079	^
☐ VH-TOX	ATR 42-300F	024	^
☐ ZK-FXT	B737-3B7(SF)	23862/1586	<AWK
☐ ZK-JTQ	B737-476(SF)	24442/2371	>AVN
☐ ZK-TLD	B737-3B7(SF)	23706/1499	<AWK
☐ ZK-TLE	B737-3S1(SF)	24834/1896	<AWK♦
☐ ZK-TLJ	B737-476(SF)	24432/1879	<AWK♦
☐ ZK-TLK	B737-476(SF)	24434/1912	<AWK♦
☐ VH-HPE	SA.227DC Metro 23	DC-823B	
☐ VH-UUO	SA.227AC Metro III	AC-530	
☐ VH-UZA	SA.227AT Merlin VI	AT-502	
☐ VH-UZG	SA.227AC Metro III	AC-553	
☐ VH-UZI	SA.227AT Expediter	AT-570	
☐ VH-UZN	SA.227DC Metro 23	DC-881B	
☐ VH-UZP	SA.227AC Metro III	AC-498	
☐ VH-UZS	SA.227AC Metro III	AC-517	
☐ VH-UZW	SA.227AC Metro III	AC-526	

^ operated by Jetcraft Aviation

VIRGIN AUSTRALIA AIRLINES — *DJ / VOZ*

Reg	Type	C/n	Notes
☐ VH-XFC	A330-243	1293	
☐ VH-XFD	A330-243	1306	
☐ VH-XFE	A330-243	1319	
☐ VH-XFG	A330-243	1407	
☐ VH-XFH	A330-243	1452	
☐ VH-XFJ	A330-243	1561	
☐ VH-FVH	ATR 72-212A	954	♦
☐ VH-FVI	ATR 72-212A	955	♦
☐ VH-FVL	ATR 72-212A	974	♦
☐ VH-FVM	ATR 72-212A	979	♦
☐ VH-FVN	ATR 72-600	1039	♦
☐ VH-FVP	ATR 72-600	1025	♦
☐ VH-FVQ	ATR 72-600	1053	♦
☐ VH-FVR	ATR 72-600	1058	♦
☐ VH-FVU	ATR 72-212A	978	♦
☐ VH-FVX	ATR 72-212A	986	♦
☐ VH-FVY	ATR 72-600	1073	♦
☐ VH-FVZ	ATR 72-600	1087	♦
☐ VH-VPI	ATR 72-600	1107	♦
☐ VH-VPJ	ATR 72-600	1169	♦
☐ VH-VBY	B737-7FE/W	34323/1751	
☐ VH-VBZ	B737-7FE/W	34322/1777	
☐ VH-BZG	B737-8FE/W	37822/3355	
☐ VH-VOK	B737-8FE/W	33758/1359	
☐ VH-VOL	B737-8FE/W	33759/1364	
☐ VH-VOM	B737-8FE/W	33794/1373	
☐ VH-VON	B737-8FE/W	33795/1375	
☐ VH-VOO	B737-8FE/W	33796/1377	
☐ VH-VOP	B737-8FE/W	33797/1389	
☐ VH-VOQ	B737-8FE/W	33798/1391	
☐ VH-VOR	B737-8FE/W	33799/1462	
☐ VH-VOS	B737-8FE/W	33800/1483	
☐ VH-VOT	B737-8FE/W	33801/1504	
☐ VH-VOX	B737-8BK/W	33017/1446	
☐ VH-VOY	B737-8FE/W	33996/1551	[MEL]

☐ VH-VUA	B737-8FE/W	33997/1559	
☐ VH-VUB	B737-8FE/W	34013/1573	
☐ VH-VUC	B737-8FE/W	34014/1582	
☐ VH-VUD	B737-8FE/W	34015/1594	
☐ VH-VUE	B737-8FE/W	34167/1676	
☐ VH-VUF	B737-8FE/W	34168/1697	
☐ VH-VUG	B737-8FE/W	34438/1948	
☐ VH-VUH	B737-8FE/W	34440/2003	
☐ VH-VUI	B737-8FE/W	34441/2015	
☐ VH-VUJ	B737-8FE/W	34443/2056	
☐ VH-VUK	B737-8FE/W	36602/2353	
☐ VH-VUL	B737-8FE/W	36603/2356	
☐ VH-VUO	B737-8FE/W	36601/2525	
☐ VH-VUP	B737-8FE/W	36604/2650	
☐ VH-VUQ	B737-8FE/W	36605/2710	♦
☐ VH-VUR	B737-8FE/W	36606/3059	
☐ VH-VUS	B737-8FE/W	36607/3082	
☐ VH-VUT	B737-8FE/W	36608/3132	
☐ VH-VUU	B737-8FE/W	36609/3232	
☐ VH-VUV	B737-8FE/W	37821/3288	
☐ VH-VUW	B737-8KG/W	39449/3398	
☐ VH-VUX	B737-8FE/W	37823/3415	
☐ VH-VUY	B737-8KG/W	39450/3494	
☐ VH-VUZ	B737-8FE/W	39921/3536	
☐ VH-YFC	B737-81D/W	39413/3592	
☐ VH-YFE	B737-81D/W	39414/3623	
☐ VH-YFF	B737-8FE/W	40994/3664	
☐ VH-YFG	B737-8FE/W	40999/3941	
☐ VH-YFH	B737-8FE/W	40996/3801	
☐ VH-YFI	B737-8FE/W	41000/3963	
☐ VH-YFJ	B737-8FE/W	41001/4089	
☐ VH-YFK	B737-8FE/W	41004/3861	
☐ VH-YFL	B737-8FE/W	41002/4047	
☐ VH-YFN	B737-8FE/W	41009/4456	
☐ VH-YFP	B737-8FE/W	41011/4476	
☐ VH-YFQ	B737-8FE/W	41010/4494	
☐ VH-YFR	B737-8FE/W	41012/4543	
☐ VH-YFS	B737-8FE/W	41027/5525	♦
☐ VH-YFT	B737-8FE/W	41028/5557	♦
☐ VH-YFU	B737-8FE/W	41029/5600	♦
☐ VH-YFV	B737-8FE/W	41030/5641	♦
☐ VH-YIA	B737-8FE/W	37824/3718	
☐ VH-YIB	B737-8FE/W	37825/3758	
☐ VH-YID	B737-8FE/W	38709/3851	
☐ VH-YIE	B737-8FE/W	38708/3875	
☐ VH-YIF	B737-8FE/W	38710/3904	
☐ VH-YIG	B737-8FE/W	38711/3921	
☐ VH-YIH	B737-8FE/W	38712/4070	
☐ VH-YIJ	B737-8FE/W	39924/4109	
☐ VH-YIL	B737-8FE/W	38713/4123	
☐ VH-YIM	B737-8FE/W	38716/4119	
☐ VH-YIO	B737-8FE/W	38714/4132	
☐ VH-YIQ	B737-8FE/W	38715/4156	
☐ VH-YIR	B737-8FE/W	39925/4172	
☐ VH-YIS	B737-8FE/W	39926/4201	
☐ VH-YIT	B737-8FE/W	38717/4194	
☐ VH-YIU	B737-8FE/W	40699/4560	
☐ VH-YIV	B737-8FE/W	40698/4571	
☐ VH-YIW	B737-8FE/W	40700/5085	
☐ VH-YIY	B737-8FE/W	40701/5280	
☐ VH-YIZ	B737-8FE/W	40702/5061	
☐ VH-YVA	B737-8FE/W	40995/3680	
☐ VH-YVC	B737-8FE/W	40997/3832	
☐ VH-YVD	B737-8FE/W	40998/3848	
☐ VH-	B737-8FE/W		o/o♦
☐ VH-	B737-8FE/W		o/o♦
☐ VH-	B737-8FE/W		o/o♦
☐ VH-	B737-8FE/W		o/o♦
☐ VH-	B737-8FE/W		o/o♦
☐ VH-VOZ	B777-3ZGER	35302/745	
☐ VH-VPD	B777-3ZGER	37938/756	
☐ VH-VPE	B777-3ZGER	37939/764	
☐ VH-VPF	B777-3ZGER	37940/801	
☐ VH-VPH	B777-3ZGER	37943/898	
☐ VH-ZPA	ERJ-190AR	19000148	
☐ VH-ZPB	ERJ-190AR	19000162	
☐ VH-ZPC	ERJ-190AR	19000170	
☐ VH-ZPD	ERJ-190AR	19000176	
☐ VH-ZPE	ERJ-190AR	19000187	
☐ VH-ZPF	ERJ-190AR	19000193	
☐ VH-ZPG	ERJ-190AR	19000195	
☐ VH-ZPH	ERJ-190AR	19000199	
☐ VH-ZPI	ERJ-190AR	19000202	
☐ VH-ZPJ	ERJ-190AR	19000209	
☐ VH-ZPK	ERJ-190AR	19000218	
☐ VH-ZPL	ERJ-190AR	19000220	
☐ VH-ZPM	ERJ-190AR	19000262	
☐ VH-ZPN	ERJ-190AR	19000312	
☐ VH-ZPO	ERJ-190AR	19000321	
☐ VH-ZPQ	ERJ-190AR	19000412	
☐ VH-ZPR	ERJ-190AR	19000424	
☐ VH-ZPT	ERJ-190AR	19000451	

B777-300s & 24 B737-800s operated by Virgin Australia International (VA / VAU).

VIRGIN AUSTRALIA REGIONAL — *XR / OZW*

☐ VH-FNP	A320-231	0429	
☐ VH-YUD	A320-232	1922	
☐ VH-FNA	Fokker 50	20106	[PER]
☐ VH-FNB	Fokker 50	20107	[PER]
☐ VH-FND	Fokker 50	20129	[PER]
☐ VH-FNE	Fokker 50	20212	
☐ VH-FNF	Fokker 50	20200	
☐ VH-FNH	Fokker 50	20113	
☐ VH-FNI	Fokker 50	20114	
☐ VH-FSL	Fokker 50	20249	[PER]
☐ VH-FNC	Fokker 100	11334	
☐ VH-FNJ	Fokker 100	11489	
☐ VH-FNN	Fokker 100	11326	
☐ VH-FNR	Fokker 100	11488	
☐ VH-FNT	Fokker 100	11461	
☐ VH-FNU	Fokker 100	11373	
☐ VH-FNY	Fokker 100	11484	
☐ VH-FSQ	Fokker 100	11450	
☐ VH-FSW	Fokker 100	11391	
☐ VH-FWH	Fokker 100	11316	♦
☐ VH-FWI	Fokker 100	11318	♦
☐ VH-FZH	Fokker 100	11303	
☐ VH-FZI	Fokker 100	11333	
☐ VH-FZO	Fokker 100	11305	

VN- VIETNAM

JETSTAR PACIFIC AIRLINES — *BL / PIC*

☐ EC-LZF	A320-232/S	5940	<VLG♦
☐ EC-LZM	A320-232/S	5877	<VLG♦
☐ VN-A198	A320-232	4459	
☐ VN-A345	A321-231	2261	
☐ VN-A347	A321-231	2267	
☐ VN-A555	A320-232	2331	
☐ VN-A556	A320-232	2340	

	Reg.	Type	C/n	Notes
☐	VN-A557	A320-232	2670	
☐	VN-A558	A320-232	2922	
☐	VN-A559	A320-232	3012	
☐	VN-A560	A320-232	3621	
☐	VN-A561	A320-232/S	6136	
☐	VN-A562	A320-232	4533	♦
☐	VN-A563	A320-233	2517	♦
☐	TC-	A320-232/S	7213	o/o♦
☐	TC-	A320-232/S		o/o♦
☐	TC-	A320-232/S		o/o♦
☐	TC-	A320-232/S		o/o♦
☐	XY-AGO	A320-214	0973	<MMA♦

VIETJETAIR — VD / VJC

	Reg.	Type	C/n	Notes
☐	LZ-BHG	A320-232	2844	<BGH♦
☐	LZ-BHI	A320-232	3125	<BGH♦
☐	VN-A650	A320-214/S	6457	
☐	VN-A655	A320-214/S	6498	
☐	VN-A656	A320-214/S	6584	♦
☐	VN-A658	A320-214/S	6341	
☐	VN-A659	A320-214/S	6378	
☐	VN-A662	A320-214/S	6738	♦
☐	VN-A663	A320-214/S	6779	♦
☐	VN-A664	A320-214/S	6878	♦
☐	VN-A666	A320-214	3739	
☐	VN-A668	A320-214	3791	
☐	VN-A669	A320-214	4049	
☐	VN-A671	A320-214/S	6958	♦
☐	VN-A672	A320-214/S	6997	o/o♦
☐	VN-A678	A320-214/S	6025	
☐	VN-A680	A320-214	4475	
☐	VN-A681	A320-214	4512	
☐	VN-A682	A320-214/S	5742	
☐	VN-A686	A320-214/S	5822	
☐	VN-A688	A320-214	2712	
☐	VN-A689	A320-214	4190	
☐	VN-A690	A320-214	4415	
☐	VN-A691	A320-214	4504	
☐	VN-A692	A320-214	4907	
☐	VN-A695	A320-214	3646	
☐	VN-A696	A320-214/S	6242	
☐	VN-A699	A320-214	4193	
☐	VN-	A320-214	6498	o/o
☐	VN-	A320-214/S	6773	o/o
☐	VN-	A320-214/S	7167	o/o♦
☐	VN-	A320-214/S	7170	o/o♦
☐	YL-LCP	A320-232	1823	<ART♦
☐	LZ-PMZ	A321-231	1060	<VIM♦
☐	VN-A651	A321-211/S	5295	♦
☐	VN-A660	A321-211/S	6696	♦
☐	VN-A665	A321-211/S	6852	♦
☐	VN-A667	A321-211/S	6936	♦
☐	VN-A	A321-211/S	7143	o/o♦
☐	VN-A	A321-211/S	7241	o/o♦

VIETNAM AIRLINES — VN / HVN

	Reg.	Type	C/n	Notes
☐	VN-A322	A321-231	4311	
☐	VN-A323	A321-231	4669	
☐	VN-A324	A321-231	4703	
☐	VN-A325	A321-231	4737	
☐	VN-A326	A321-231	4783	
☐	VN-A327	A321-231	4826	
☐	VN-A329	A321-231	4863	
☐	VN-A331	A321-231	4945	
☐	VN-A332	A321-231	4971	
☐	VN-A334	A321-231	5164	
☐	VN-A335	A321-231	5241	
☐	VN-A336	A321-231	5247	
☐	VN-A338	A321-231	5251	
☐	VN-A339	A321-231	5275	
☐	VN-A344	A321-231	2255	
☐	VN-A350	A321-231	2974	
☐	VN-A351	A321-231	3005	
☐	VN-A352	A321-231	3013	
☐	VN-A353	A321-231	3022	
☐	VN-A354	A321-231	3198	
☐	VN-A356	A321-231	3315	
☐	VN-A357	A321-231	3355	
☐	VN-A358	A321-231	3600	
☐	VN-A359	A321-231	3737	
☐	VN-A360	A321-231	3862	
☐	VN-A361	A321-231	3964	
☐	VN-A362	A321-231	3966	
☐	VN-A363	A321-231	4136	
☐	VN-A365	A321-231	4213	
☐	VN-A366	A321-231	4277	
☐	VN-A367	A321-231	4315	
☐	VN-A390	A321-231	5297	
☐	VN-A392	A321-231	5306	
☐	VN-A393	A321-231	5340	
☐	VN-A395	A321-231	5385	
☐	VN-A396	A321-231	5392	
☐	VN-A397	A321-231	5418	
☐	VN-A399	A321-231	5438	
☐	VN-A601	A321-231	5456	
☐	VN-A602	A321-231	5469	
☐	VN-A603	A321-231	5495	
☐	VN-A604	A321-231	5555	
☐	VN-A605	A321-231/S	5699	
☐	VN-A606	A321-231/S	5709	
☐	VN-A608	A321-231	5916	
☐	VN-A609	A321-231	5958	
☐	VN-A610	A321-231	5994	
☐	VN-A611	A321-231	6266	
☐	VN-A612	A321-231	6344	
☐	VN-A613	A321-231	6748	♦
☐	VN-A614	A321-231	6810	♦
☐	VN-A615	A321-231	6880	♦
☐	VN-A371	A330-223	275	
☐	VN-A372	A330-223	294	[GWO]
☐	VN-A374	A330-223	299	
☐	VN-A375	A330-223	366	
☐	VN-A376	A330-223	943	[SGN]
☐	VN-A377	A330-223	962	
☐	VN-A378	A330-223	1019	
☐	VN-A379	A330-223	1256	
☐	VN-A381	A330-231	1266	
☐	VN-A383	A330-223	946	
☐	VN-A886	A350-941	014	♦
☐	VN-A887	A350-941	015	♦
☐	VN-A888	A350-941	016	♦
☐	VN-A889	A350-941	017	♦
☐	VN-A	A350-941	056	o/o♦
☐	VN-A	A350-941	067	o/o♦
☐	VN-A	A350-941	086	o/o♦
☐	VN-B210	ATR 72-212A	678	std
☐	VN-B212	ATR 72-212A	685	std
☐	VN-B214	ATR 72-212A	688	std
☐	VN-B218	ATR 72-212A	877	
☐	VN-B219	ATR 72-212A	886	
☐	VN-B220	ATR 72-212A	890	

☐	VN-B221	ATR 72-212A	892	
☐	VN-B223	ATR 72-212A	896	
☐	VN-B225	ATR 72-212A	897	
☐	VN-B233	ATR 72-212A	912	
☐	VN-B236	ATR 72-212A	914	
☐	VN-B237	ATR 72-212A	925	
☐	VN-B239	ATR 72-212A	927	
☐	VN-B240	ATR 72-212A	939	
☐	VN-A141	B777-2Q8ER	28688/436	
☐	VN-A142	B777-2Q8ER	32701/443	
☐	VN-A143	B777-26KER	33502/450	
☐	VN-A144	B777-26KER	33503/453	
☐	VN-A145	B777-26KER	33504/491	
☐	VN-A146	B777-26KER	33505/486	
☐	VN-A861	B787-9	35151/303	♦
☐	VN-A862	B787-9	35152/318	♦
☐	VN-A863	B787-9	35153/333	♦
☐	VN-A864	B787-9	35154/353	♦
☐	VN-A865	B787-9	38761/380	♦
☐	VN-A866	B787-9	38762/388	♦
☐	VN-A867	B787-9	39287/411	o/o♦
☐	VN-A868	B787-9	38288/464	o/o♦
☐	VN-A	B787-9	38768/480	o/o♦
☐	VN-A	B787-9	39289/496	o/o♦

VP-C CAYMAN ISLANDS

CAYMAN AIRWAYS — KX / CAY

☐	VP-CAY	B737-3Q8	26286/2424	
☐	VP-CKW	B737-36E	26322/2769	
☐	VP-CKY	B737-3Q8	26282/2355	
☐	VP-CKZ	B737-36E	27626/2792	
☐	VP-CXA	DHC-6 Twin Otter 300	602	^♦
☐	VP-CXB	DHC-6 Twin Otter 300	563	^♦
☐	VP-CKI	SAAB SF.340B	340B-421	^♦

^ operates as Cayman Airways Express

VQ-T TURKS & CAICOS ISLANDS

AIR TURKS & CAICOS — JY / IWY

☐	VQ-TBC	EMB.120ER	120283	
☐	VQ-TDG	EMB.120ER	120275	
☐	VQ-TEL	EMB.120ER	120273	♦
☐	VQ-TMJ	EMB.120ER	120274	

INTERISLAND

☐	VQ-TGW	DHC-6 Twin Otter 300	330	♦

VT- INDIA

AIRASIA INDIA — I5 / IAD

☐	VT-APJ	A320-216	4346	♦
☐	VT-ATB	A320-216/S	6034	
☐	VT-ATF	A320-216/S	6015	
☐	VT-BLR	A320-216	4070	♦
☐	VT-JRT	A320-216	3448	♦
☐	VT-RED	A320-216/S	5824	

AIR COSTA — LB / LEP

☐	VT-LBR	ERJ-190STD	19000593	
☐	VT-LNR	ERJ-170IGW	17000293	[AMM]
☐	VT-LVR	ERJ-190STD	19000608	
☐	VT-LSR	ERJ-170IGW	17000278	[LIS]
☐	VT-	ERJ-190STD		o/o♦
☐	VT-	ERJ-190STD		o/o♦
☐	VT-	ERJ-190STD		o/o♦

AIR INDIA — AI / AIC

☐	VT-SCA	A319-112	2593	
☐	VT-SCB	A319-112	2624	
☐	VT-SCC	A319-112	2629	
☐	VT-SCF	A319-112	2907	
☐	VT-SCG	A319-112	3271	
☐	VT-SCH	A319-112	3288	
☐	VT-SCI	A319-112	3300	
☐	VT-SCJ	A319-112	3305	
☐	VT-SCK	A319-112	3344	
☐	VT-SCL	A319-112	3551	
☐	VT-SCM	A319-112	3620	
☐	VT-SCN	A319-112	3687	
☐	VT-SCO	A319-112	3822	
☐	VT-SCP	A319-112	3874	
☐	VT-SCQ	A319-112	3918	
☐	VT-SCR	A319-112	3970	
☐	VT-SCS	A319-112	4020	
☐	VT-SCT	A319-112	4029	
☐	VT-SCU	A319-112	4052	
☐	VT-SCV	A319-112	4089	
☐	VT-SCW	A319-112	4121	
☐	VT-SCX	A319-112	4164	
☐	VT-EDC	A320-214	4201	
☐	VT-EDD	A320-214	4212	
☐	VT-EDE	A320-214	4236	
☐	VT-EDF	A320-214	4237	
☐	VT-EPB	A320-231	0045	
☐	VT-EPC	A320-231	0046	
☐	VT-EPF	A320-231	0049	
☐	VT-EPG	A320-231	0050	
☐	VT-EPH	A320-231	0051	
☐	VT-EPI	A320-231	0056	
☐	VT-EPJ	A320-231	0057	
☐	VT-ESB	A320-231	0398	
☐	VT-ESC	A320-231	0416	
☐	VT-ESD	A320-231	0423	
☐	VT-ESE	A320-231	0431	
☐	VT-ESF	A320-231	0432	
☐	VT-ESI	A320-231	0486	
☐	VT-ESJ	A320-231	0490	
☐	VT-ESL	A320-231	0499	
☐	VT-EXA	A320-214/S	6446	
☐	VT-EXB	A320-214/S	6690	♦
☐	VT-EXC	A320-214/S	6715	♦
☐	VT-EXD	A320-214/S	6724	♦
☐	VT-EXE	A320-214/S	6803	♦
☐	VT-PPA	A321-211	3130	
☐	VT-PPB	A321-211	3146	
☐	VT-PPD	A321-211	3212	
☐	VT-PPE	A321-211	3326	
☐	VT-PPF	A321-211	3340	
☐	VT-PPG	A321-211	3367	
☐	VT-PPH	A321-211	3498	
☐	VT-PPI	A321-211	3557	
☐	VT-PPJ	A321-211	3573	
☐	VT-PPK	A321-211	3619	
☐	VT-PPL	A321-211	3752	
☐	VT-PPM	A321-211	3792	
☐	VT-PPN	A321-211	3955	
☐	VT-PPO	A321-211	4002	

Registration	Type	C/n	Notes
☐ VT-PPQ	A321-211	4009	
☐ VT-PPT	A321-211	4078	
☐ VT-PPU	A321-211	4096	
☐ VT-PPV	A321-211	4138	
☐ VT-PPW	A321-211	4155	
☐ VT-PPX	A321-211	4280	
☐ VT-ESN	B747-437	27164/1003	[BOM]
☐ VT-ESO	B747-437	27165/1009	
☐ VT-ESP	B747-437	27214/1034	
☐ VT-EVA	B747-437	28094/1089	
☐ VT-EVB	B747-437	28095/1093	
☐ VT-ALF	B777-237LR	36305/793	
☐ VT-ALG	B777-237LR	36306/800	
☐ VT-ALH	B777-237LR	36307/805	
☐ VT-ALJ	B777-337ER	36308/643	
☐ VT-ALK	B777-337ER	36309/652	
☐ VT-ALL	B777-337ER	36310/656	
☐ VT-ALM	B777-337ER	36311/713	
☐ VT-ALN	B777-337ER	36312/719	
☐ VT-ALO	B777-337ER	36313/798	
☐ VT-ALP	B777-337ER	36314/804	
☐ VT-ALQ	B777-337ER	36315/809	
☐ VT-ALR	B777-337ER	36316/814	
☐ VT-ALS	B777-337ER	36317/864	
☐ VT-ALT	B777-337ER	36318/871	
☐ VT-ALU	B777-337ER	36319/880	
☐ VT-ANA	B787-8	36273/25	
☐ VT-ANB	B787-8	36279/26	
☐ VT-ANC	B787-8	36274/28	
☐ VT-AND	B787-8	36278/29	
☐ VT-ANE	B787-8	36280/30	
☐ VT-ANG	B787-8	36275/32	
☐ VT-ANH	B787-8	36276/35	
☐ VT-ANI	B787-8	36277/46	
☐ VT-ANJ	B787-8	36281/54	
☐ VT-ANK	B787-8	36282/60	
☐ VT-ANL	B787-8	36283/65	
☐ VT-ANM	B787-8	36284/72	
☐ VT-ANN	B787-8	36285/90	
☐ VT-ANO	B787-8	36286/91	
☐ VT-ANP	B787-8	36287/158	
☐ VT-ANQ	B787-8	36288/180	
☐ VT-ANR	B787-8	36289/208	
☐ VT-ANS	B787-8	36290/232	
☐ VT-ANT	B787-8	36291/250	
☐ VT-ANU	B787-8	36292/273	
☐ VT-ANV	B787-8	36293/311	♦
☐ VT-ANW	B787-8	36294/489	o/o♦
☐ VT-ANX	B787-8	36295/511	o/o♦

AIR INDIA EXPRESS — IX / AXB

Registration	Type	C/n	Notes
☐ VT-AXH	B737-8HG/W	36323/2108	
☐ VT-AXI	B737-8HG/W	36324/2132	
☐ VT-AXJ	B737-8HG/W	36325/2142	
☐ VT-AXM	B737-8HG/W	36326/2148	
☐ VT-AXN	B737-8HG/W	36327/2154	
☐ VT-AXP	B737-8HG/W	36328/2177	
☐ VT-AXQ	B737-8HG/W	36329/2258	
☐ VT-AXR	B737-8HG/W	36330/2317	
☐ VT-AXT	B737-8HG/W	36331/2324	
☐ VT-AXU	B737-8HG/W	36332/2381	
☐ VT-AXW	B737-8HG/W	36334/2612	
☐ VT-AXX	B737-8HG/W	36335/2672	
☐ VT-AXZ	B737-8HG/W	36336/2782	
☐ VT-AYA	B737-8HG/W	36337/2861	
☐ VT-AYB	B737-8HG/W	36338/2962	
☐ VT-AYC	B737-8HG/W	36339/3039	
☐ VT-AYD	B737-8HG/W	36340/3122	
☐ VT-	B737-8HG/W		o/o♦
☐ VT-	B737-8HG/W		o/o♦
☐ VT-	B737-8HG/W		o/o♦

AIR INDIA REGIONAL — CD / LLR

Registration	Type	C/n	Notes
☐ VT-ABA	ATR 42-320	390	
☐ VT-ABB	ATR 42-320	392	
☐ VT-ABD	ATR 42-320	356	
☐ VT-ABO	ATR 42-320	406	
☐ VT-AII	ATR 72-600	1197	
☐ VT-AIT	ATR 72-600	1226	
☐ VT-AIU	ATR 72-600	1246	♦
☐ VT-AIV	ATR 72-600	1252	♦
☐ VT-AIW	ATR 72-600	1272	♦
☐ VT-AIY	ATR 72-600	1273	o/o♦
☐ VT-RJB	CRJ-701ER	10217	
☐ VT-RJD	CRJ-701ER	10048	
☐ VT-RJE	CRJ-701ER	10029	

Operating arm of Alliance Air

AIR PEGASUS — OP / PPL

Registration	Type	C/n	Notes
☐ VT-APA	ATR 72-212A	699	
☐ VT-APB	ATR 72-212A	762	♦

BLUE DART AVIATION — BZ / BDA

Registration	Type	C/n	Notes
☐ VT-BDH	B737-25C	24236/1585	[MAA]
☐ VT-BDA	B757-25F(PCF)	28718/752	
☐ VT-BDM	B757-23N(SF)	27598/692	
☐ VT-BDN	B757-25CF	25898/475	
☐ VT-BDO	B757-204(PCF)	26962/440	
☐ VT-BDQ	B757-28A(PCF)	26276/704	

FLYEASY

Registration	Type	C/n	Notes
☐ VT-LPB	ERJ-190LR	19000217	o/o♦
☐ VT-VVA	ERJ-190LR	19000233	o/o♦

GOAIR — G8 / GOW

Registration	Type	C/n	Notes
☐ VT-GOI	A320-214	5016	
☐ VT-GOJ	A320-214	5112	
☐ VT-GOK	A320-214	5232	
☐ VT-GOL	A320-214/S	5463	
☐ VT-GOM	A320-214/S	5552	
☐ VT-GON	A320-214/S	5675	
☐ VT-GOO	A320-214/S	5811	
☐ VT-GOP	A320-214/S	5809	
☐ VT-GOQ	A320-214/S	5990	
☐ VT-GOR	A320-214/S	6072	
☐ VT-WAF	A320-214	3306	
☐ VT-WAG	A320-214	3597	
☐ VT-WAH	A320-214	3616	
☐ VT-WAI	A320-214	3798	
☐ VT-WAJ	A320-214	3827	
☐ VT-WAK	A320-214	3900	
☐ VT-WAL	A320-214	3915	
☐ VT-WAM	A320-214	4399	
☐ VT-WAN	A320-214	4438	
☐ VT-	A320-271N	7047	o/o♦
☐ VT-	A320-271N	7074	o/o♦
☐ VT-	A320-271N	7129	o/o♦
☐ VT-	A320-271N	7181	o/o♦
☐ VT-	A320-271N	7205	o/o♦

☐	VT-	A320-271N	7264	o/o♦

INDIGO AIRLINES 6E / IGO

☐	VT-IAL	A320-232/S	5992	
☐	VT-IAN	A320-232/S	6010	
☐	VT-IAO	A320-232/S	6036	
☐	VT-IAP	A320-232/S	6208	
☐	VT-IAQ	A320-232/S	6247	
☐	VT-IAR	A320-232/S	6275	
☐	VT-IAS	A320-232/S	6289	
☐	VT-IAX	A320-232/S	6287	
☐	VT-IAY	A320-232/S	6336	
☐	VT-IDA	A320-232	4918	
☐	VT-IDB	A320-232	4973	
☐	VT-IDC	A320-232	5073	
☐	VT-IDD	A320-232	5335	
☐	VT-IDE	A320-232	5375	
☐	VT-IDF	A320-232	5426	
☐	VT-IDG	A320-232	5449	♦
☐	VT-IDH	A320-232	5194	♦
☐	VT-IDI	A320-232	5188	♦
☐	VT-IDJ	A320-232	4812	
☐	VT-IDK	A320-232	5228	♦
☐	VT-IDL	A320-232	5120	♦
☐	VT-IDM	A320-232	2204	♦
☐	VT-IDN	A320-232	2334	♦
☐	VT-IDO	A320-232	2275	♦
☐	VT-IDP	A320-232	2359	♦
☐	VT-IDQ	A320-232	2108	o/o♦
☐	VT-IDR	A320-232	2649	♦
☐	VT-IEA	A320-232	4603	
☐	VT-IEB	A320-232	4609	
☐	VT-IEC	A320-232	4614	
☐	VT-IED	A320-232	4630	
☐	VT-IEE	A320-232	4637	
☐	VT-IEF	A320-232	4752	
☐	VT-IEG	A320-232	4762	
☐	VT-IEH	A320-232	4757	
☐	VT-IEI	A320-232	4813	
☐	VT-IEJ	A320-232	4818	
☐	VT-IEK	A320-232	4868	
☐	VT-IEL	A320-232	4888	
☐	VT-IEM	A320-232	4947	
☐	VT-IEN	A320-232	4954	
☐	VT-IEO	A320-232	4965	
☐	VT-IEP	A320-232	5027	
☐	VT-IEQ	A320-232	5036	
☐	VT-IER	A320-232	5076	
☐	VT-IES	A320-232	5090	
☐	VT-IET	A320-232	5094	
☐	VT-IEU	A320-232	5092	
☐	VT-IEV	A320-232	5080	
☐	VT-IEW	A320-232	5155	
☐	VT-IEX	A320-232	5190	
☐	VT-IEY	A320-232	5230	
☐	VT-IEZ	A320-232	5231	
☐	VT-IFA	A320-232	5259	
☐	VT-IFB	A320-232	5262	
☐	VT-IFC	A320-232	5291	
☐	VT-IFD	A320-232	5298	
☐	VT-IFE	A320-232	5313	
☐	VT-IFF	A320-232	5365	
☐	VT-IFG	A320-232	5411	
☐	VT-IFH	A320-232/S	5437	
☐	VT-IFI	A320-232/S	5460	
☐	VT-IFJ	A320-232/S	5473	
☐	VT-IFK	A320-232/S	5476	
☐	VT-IFL	A320-232/S	5507	
☐	VT-IFM	A320-232/S	5537	
☐	VT-IFN	A320-232/S	5577	
☐	VT-IFO	A320-232/S	5641	
☐	VT-IFP	A320-232/S	5676	
☐	VT-IFQ	A320-232/S	5683	
☐	VT-IFR	A320-232/S	5712	
☐	VT-IFS	A320-232/S	5727	
☐	VT-IFT	A320-232/S	5744	
☐	VT-IFU	A320-232/S	5807	
☐	VT-IFV	A320-232/S	5829	
☐	VT-IFW	A320-232/S	5893	
☐	VT-IFX	A320-232/S	5898	
☐	VT-IFY	A320-232/S	5923	
☐	VT-IFZ	A320-232/S	5952	
☐	VT-IGH	A320-232	4008	
☐	VT-IGI	A320-232	4113	
☐	VT-IGJ	A320-232	4156	
☐	VT-IGK	A320-232	4216	
☐	VT-IGL	A320-232	4312	
☐	VT-IGS	A320-232	4328	
☐	VT-IGT	A320-232	4384	
☐	VT-IGU	A320-232	4488	
☐	VT-IGV	A320-232	4481	
☐	VT-IGW	A320-232	4506	
☐	VT-IGX	A320-232	4518	
☐	VT-IGY	A320-232	4535	
☐	VT-IGZ	A320-232	4552	
☐	VT-INP	A320-232	3357	
☐	VT-INQ	A320-232	3414	
☐	VT-INR	A320-232	3453	
☐	VT-INS	A320-232	3457	
☐	VT-INT	A320-232	3497	
☐	VT-INU	A320-232	3541	
☐	VT-INV	A320-232	3618	
☐	VT-INX	A320-232	3782	
☐	VT-INY	A320-232	3863	
☐	VT-INZ	A320-232	3943	
☐	VT-ITA	A320-271N	6744	o/o♦
☐	VT-ITB	A320-271N	6720	o/o♦
☐	VT-ITC	A320-271N	6799	o/o♦
☐	VT-ITD	A320-271N	6819	o/o♦
☐	VT-ITE	A320-271N	6849	o/o♦
☐	VT-ITF	A320-271N	6860	o/o♦
☐	VT-ITG	A320-271N	6868	o/o♦
☐	VT-ITH	A320-271N	6914	o/o♦
☐	VT-ITI	A320-271N	6952	o/o♦
☐	VT-ITJ	A320-271N	6967	o/o♦
☐	VT-ITK	A320-271N	7001	o/o♦
☐	VT-	A320-271N	7185	o/o♦
☐	VT-	A320-271N	7252	o/o♦
☐	VT-	A320-232/S	7033	o/o♦
☐	VT-	A320-232/S	7035	o/o♦
☐	VT-	A320-232/S		o/o♦
☐	VT-	A320-232/S		o/o♦
☐	VT-	A320-232/S		o/o♦
☐	VT-	A320-232/S		o/o♦
☐	VT-	A320-232/S		o/o♦
☐	VT-	A320-232/S		o/o♦

JAGSON AIRLINES JA / JGN

☐	VT-ESQ	Do228-201	8006	
☐	VT-ESS	Do228-201	8017	
☐	VT-EUM	Do228-201	8096	

JET AIRWAYS 9W / JAI

	Reg	Type	c/n	
☐	VT-JWP	A330-202	947	
☐	VT-JWQ	A330-202	956	
☐	VT-JWR	A330-302	1351	
☐	VT-JWS	A330-302	1361	
☐	VT-JWT	A330-302	1370	
☐	VT-JWU	A330-302	1391	
☐	VT-JWV	A330-202	923	
☐	VT-JWW	A330-202	888	♦
☐	VT-JCJ	ATR 72-212A	771	
☐	VT-JCK	ATR 72-212A	775	
☐	VT-JCL	ATR 72-212A	791	
☐	VT-JCM	ATR 72-212A	793	
☐	VT-JCN	ATR 72-212A	825	
☐	VT-JCP	ATR 72-212A	841	
☐	VT-JCQ	ATR 72-212A	843	
☐	VT-JCR	ATR 72-212A	919	
☐	VT-JCS	ATR 72-212A	920	
☐	VT-JCT	ATR 72-212A	924	
☐	VT-JCU	ATR 72-212A	928	
☐	VT-JCV	ATR 72-212A	932	
☐	VT-JCW	ATR 72-212A	933	
☐	VT-JCX	ATR 72-600	1056	
☐	VT-JCY	ATR 72-600	1064	
☐	VT-JCZ	ATR 72-600	1075	
☐	VT-JDC	ATR 72-212A	772	
☐	VT-JDD	ATR 72-212A	758	
☐	VT-JGX	B737-75R/W	34805/2360	
☐	VT-JGY	B737-75R/W	34806/2404	
☐	VT-JBB	B737-8HX/W	36846/2368	
☐	VT-JBC	B737-8HX/W	36847/2388	
☐	VT-JBD	B737-85R/W	35099/2439	
☐	VT-JBE	B737-85R/W	35106/2530	
☐	VT-JBF	B737-85R/W	35082/2550	
☐	VT-JBG	B737-85R/W	35083/2535	
☐	VT-JBH	B737-85R/W	35289/2811	
☐	VT-JBJ	B737-85R/W	36551/2974	
☐	VT-JBK	B737-85R/W	36553/3074	
☐	VT-JBL	B737-85R/W	35651/3000	
☐	VT-JBM	B737-86N/W	36817/3055	
☐	VT-JBN	B737-86N/W	36818/3087	
☐	VT-JBP	B737-86N/W	36819/3101	
☐	VT-JBQ	B737-85R/W	36694/3264	
☐	VT-JBR	B737-85R/W	36695/3281	
☐	VT-JBS	B737-85R/W	36698/3433	
☐	VT-JBU	B737-86N/W	36825/3763	
☐	VT-JBV	B737-86N/W	36827/3836	
☐	VT-JBW	B737-8AL/W	37960/3809	
☐	VT-JBX	B737-8AL/W	37961/3847	
☐	VT-JFA	B737-86N/W	38029/4111	
☐	VT-JFB	B737-86N/W	39401/4127	
☐	VT-JFC	B737-86N/W	38030/4139	
☐	VT-JFD	B737-8AL/W	39051/4205	
☐	VT-JFE	B737-8AL/W	39053/4270	
☐	VT-JFF	B737-8AL/W	39055/4342	
☐	VT-JFG	B737-8AL/W	39057/4428	
☐	VT-JFH	B737-8AL/W	39058/4462	
☐	VT-JFJ	B737-8AL/W	39059/4487	
☐	VT-JFK	B737-8AL/W	39060/4518	
☐	VT-JFL	B737-8AL/W	39061/4579	
☐	VT-JFM	B737-8AL/W	39067/4602	
☐	VT-JFN	B737-8AL/W	39062/4644	
☐	VT-JFP	B737-8AL/W	39068/4696	
☐	VT-JFQ	B737-8AL/W	39063/4727	
☐	VT-JFR	B737-8AL/W	39064/4793	
☐	VT-JFS	B737-8AL/W	39065/4884	
☐	VT-JFT	B737-8AL/W	39066/4932	
☐	VT-JFW	B737-85R/W	42799/4984	
☐	VT-JFX	B737-85R/W	42800/5054	
☐	VT-JFY	B737-85R/W	42804/5068	
☐	VT-JFZ	B737-85R/W	39069/5112	
☐	VT-JGA	B737-85R	30410/1228	
☐	VT-JGE	B737-83N/W	32663/1608	
☐	VT-JGF	B737-8FH/W	29639/1643	
☐	VT-JGG	B737-8FH/W	29668/1686	
☐	VT-JGJ	B737-83N/W	32578/998	
☐	VT-JGK	B737-83N/W	32579/1002	
☐	VT-JGP	B737-85R/W	34798/1920	
☐	VT-JGQ	B737-85R/W	34797/2007	
☐	VT-JGR	B737-85R/W	34799/2044	
☐	VT-JGS	B737-85R/W	34800/2085	
☐	VT-JGT	B737-85R/W	34801/2125	
☐	VT-JGU	B737-85R/W	34802/2170	
☐	VT-JGV	B737-85R/W	34803/2209	
☐	VT-JGW	B737-85R/W	34804/2297	
☐	VT-JNL	B737-85R	29039/326	
☐	VT-JNN	B737-85R	29041/489	
☐	VT-JTA	B737-85R/W	42805/5184	
☐	VT-JTB	B737-85R/W	39070/5196	
☐	VT-JTC	B737-8BK/W	29685/2457	♦
☐	VT-JBY	B737-96NER/W	35227/2621	
☐	VT-JBZ	B737-96NER/W	36539/2596	
☐	VT-JGC	B737-95R	30412/1314	
☐	VT-JGD	B737-95R	33740/1350	
☐	VT-JEH	B777-35RER	35166/678	
☐	VT-JEK	B777-35RER	35165/696	
☐	VT-JEM	B777-35RER	35162/666	
☐	VT-JEQ	B777-35RER	35161/693	

JETKONNECT S2 / JLL

	Reg	Type	c/n	
☐	VT-JLB	B737-7Q8	28250/1142	
☐	VT-JLE	B737-8AS/W	33555/1426	
☐	VT-JLF	B737-8AS/W	33556/1428	
☐	VT-JLH	B737-96NER/W	35223/2559	
☐	VT-JLJ	B737-96NER/W	35225/2590	
☐	VT-SIZ	B737-7BK	33025/1707	
☐	VT-SJA	B737-7BK	33026/1715	
☐	VT-SJI	B737-8K9/W	34399/2030	
☐	VT-SJJ	B737-8K9/W	34400/2053	

QUIKJET CARGO AIRLINES QJA

	Reg	Type	c/n	
☐	VT-SVA	B737-43Q(F)	28490	♦

RELIGARE VOYAGES

	Reg	Type	c/n	
☐	VT-REN	Beech 1900D	UE-410	
☐	VT-REQ	Beech 1900D	UE-407	

SPICEJET SG / SEJ

	Reg	Type	c/n	
☐	LZ-AOA	A319-112	3139	<BGH♦
☐	VT-SLA	B737-7GL/W	34759/2320	♦
☐	VT-SLB	B737-7GL/W	34760/2352	♦
☐	OK-TSF	B737-8GJ/W	37360/2783	<TVS♦
☐	OK-TVK	B737-86N/W	32740/1444	<TVS♦
☐	OK-TVL	B737-8FN/W	37076/3147	<TVS
☐	OK-TVX	B737-8Z9/W	33833/1680	<TVS♦
☐	VT-SGG	B737-8GJ/W	36368/3310	
☐	VT-SGH	B737-8GJ/W	36369/3363	

	Reg	Type	c/n	Notes
□	VT-SGJ	B737-86J/W	29641/1654	
□	VT-SGQ	B737-8GJ/W	37365/3539	
□	VT-SGV	B737-8GJ/W	37362/3830	
□	VT-SGX	B737-8GJ/W	37751/3932	
□	VT-SGY	B737-8GJ/W	37765/3986	
□	VT-SGZ	B737-8GJ/W	39423/4025	
□	VT-SPF	B737-8GJ/W	34896/1861	
□	VT-SPK	B737-8GJ/W	34898/2104	
□	VT-SPP	B737-86N/W	35217/2359	
□	VT-SZA	B737-8GJ/W	39424/4054	
□	VT-SZB	B737-8GJ/W	39427/4225	
□	VT-SZI	B737-8GJ/W	37364/4638	
□	VT-SZJ	B737-8GJ/W	41397/4769	
□	VT-SZK	B737-8GJ/W	41398/4910	
□	VT-SLC	B737-9GJER/W	34956/2608	♦
□	VT-SLD	B737-9GJER/W	34957/2639	♦
□	VT-SPU	B737-9GJER/W	34953/2466	
□	VT-SZL	B737-9GJER/W	34961/2744	♦
□	VT-SUA	DHC-8-402Q	4373	
□	VT-SUB	DHC-8-402Q	4374	
□	VT-SUC	DHC-8-402Q	4377	
□	VT-SUD	DHC-8-402Q	4378	
□	VT-SUE	DHC-8-402Q	4379	
□	VT-SUF	DHC-8-402Q	4382	
□	VT-SUG	DHC-8-402Q	4387	
□	VT-SUH	DHC-8-402Q	4389	
□	VT-SUI	DHC-8-402Q	4395	
□	VT-SUJ	DHC-8-402Q	4396	
□	VT-SUK	DHC-8-402Q	4398	
□	VT-SUL	DHC-8-402Q	4400	
□	VT-SUM	DHC-8-402Q	4402	
□	VT-SUO	DHC-8-402Q	4404	
□	VT-SUP	DHC-8-402Q	4412	

TRUJET — *MG / TRJ*

	Reg	Type	c/n	Notes
□	VT-TMK	ATR 72-212A	858	♦
□	VT-TMP	ATR 72-212A	875	♦
□	VT-TMU	ATR 72-212A	949	♦

VISTARA — *UK / VTI*

	Reg	Type	c/n	Notes
□	VT-TTB	A320-232/S	6223	
□	VT-TTC	A320-232/S	6278	
□	VT-TTD	A320-232/S	6311	
□	VT-TTE	A320-232/S	6343	
□	VT-TTF	A320-232/S	6388	
□	VT-TTG	A320-232/S	6513	
□	VT-TTH	A320-232/S	6735	♦
□	VT-TTI	A320-232/S	6785	♦
□	VT-TTJ	A320-232/S	6865	♦
□	VT-	A320-232/S	7100	o/o♦
□	VT-	A320-232/S	7163	o/o♦

V2- ANTIGUA

LIAT – THE CARIBBEAN AIRLINE — *LI / LIA*

	Reg	Type	c/n	Notes
□	V2-LIA	ATR 72-600	1077	
□	V2-LIB	ATR 72-600	1103	
□	V2-LIC	ATR 72-600	1091	
□	V2-LID	ATR 42-600	1006	♦
□	V2-LIF	ATR 42-600	1008	
□	V2-LIG	ATR 42-600	1009	
□	V2-LIH	ATR 72-600	1112	
□	V2-LIK	ATR 42-600	1012	
□	V2-LIM	ATR 42-600	1018	
□	V2-	ATR 72-600		o/o
□	V2-	ATR 72-600		o/o
□	V2-	ATR 72-600		o/o
□	V2-	ATR 72-600		o/o
□	V2-	ATR 72-600		o/o
□	V2-	ATR 72-600		o/o
□	V2-	ATR 72-600		o/o
□	V2-LDQ	DHC-8-102	113	[JAX]
□	V2-LEU	DHC-8-311B	408	std
□	V2-LFF	DHC-8-311B	410	
□	V2-LFV	DHC-8-311A	283	[ANU]
□	V2-LGB	DHC-8-311A	266	[JAX]
□	V2-LGI	DHC-8-311A	325	
□	V2-LGN	DHC-8-311A	230	std

V5- NAMIBIA

AIR NAMIBIA — *SW / NMB*

	Reg	Type	c/n	Notes
□	V5-ANK	A319-112	3586	
□	V5-ANL	A319-112	3346	
□	V5-ANM	A319-112	5366	
□	V5-ANN	A319-112	5400	
□	V5-ANO	A330-243	1451	
□	V5-ANP	A330-243	1466	
□	V5-NME	A340-311	051	[LDE]
□	V5-NMF	A340-311	047	[LDE]
□	V5-ANF	ERJ-135ER	145243	
□	V5-ANG	ERJ-135ER	145335	
□	V5-ANH	ERJ-135ER	145347	
□	V5-ANI	ERJ-135ER	145252	

WEST AIR AVIATION — *WAA*

	Reg	Type	c/n	Notes
□	V5-WIN	ERJ-145MP	145285	♦

V8- BRUNEI

ROYAL BRUNEI AIRLINES — *BI / RBA*

	Reg	Type	c/n	Notes
□	V8-RBP	A319-132	2023	[BWN]
□	V8-RBR	A319-132	2032	
□	V8-RBS	A320-232	2135	
□	V8-RBT	A320-232	2139	
□	V8-RBU	A320-232	2195	
□	V8-RBV	A320-232	3071	
□	V8-RBW	A320-232/S	6771	♦
□	V8-RBX	A320-232/S	6816	♦
□	V8-DLA	B787-8	34785/128	
□	V8-DLB	B787-8	34786/130	
□	V8-DLC	B787-8	34789/156	
□	V8-DLD	B787-8	34788/166	
□	V8-	B787-8		o/o♦

XA -MEXICO

AEREO CALAFIA — *CFV*

	Reg	Type	c/n	Notes
□	XA-FVT	ERJ-145EP	145157	♦
□	XA-OVB	ERJ-145ER	145083	
□	XA-UVX	ERJ-145EP	145096	♦

AERODAN — *ROD*

	Reg	Type	c/n	Notes
□	XA-YYS	NAMC YS-11A	2077	

AERO JBR — AJB

	Reg	Type	c/n	
☐	XA-UFJ	NAMC YS-11A	2071	

AEROMAR AIRLINES — VW / TAO

	Reg	Type	c/n	
☐	XA-MKH	ATR 72-600	1096	
☐	XA-NLP	ATR 72-600	1086	
☐	XA-SJJ	ATR 42-320	039	
☐	XA-SYH	ATR 42-320	062	
☐	XA-TAH	ATR 42-500	471	
☐	XA-TAI	ATR 42-500	474	
☐	XA-TIC	ATR 42-320	058	
☐	XA-TKJ	ATR 42-500	561	
☐	XA-TLN	ATR 42-500	564	
☐	XA-TPR	ATR 42-500	586	
☐	XA-TPS	ATR 42-500	594	
☐	XA-TRI	ATR 42-500	607	
☐	XA-TRJ	ATR 42-500	608	
☐	XA-UAU	ATR 42-500	462	
☐	XA-UAV	ATR 42-500	476	
☐	XA-UFA	ATR 42-500	412	

Operates AeroMexico Express

AEROMEXICO — AM / AMX

	Reg	Type	c/n	
☐	EI-DRD	B737-752/W	35117/2122	
☐	EI-DRE	B737-752/W	35787/2111	
☐	N423AM	B737-73V/W	32423/1433	
☐	N784XA	B737-752/W	33784/1393	
☐	N788XA	B737-752/W	33788/1439	
☐	N842AM	B737-752/W	32842/1814	
☐	N851AM	B737-752/W	29363/1417	
☐	N904AM	B737-752/W	28262/1565	
☐	N906AM	B737-752/W	29356/1586	
☐	N908AM	B737-752/W	30038/1601	
☐	N997AM	B737-76Q/W	30283/1156	
☐	XA-AAM	B737-752/W	33783/1381	
☐	XA-CTG	B737-752/W	35123/2374	
☐	XA-CYM	B737-752/W	35124/2456	
☐	XA-GOL	B737-752/W	35785/2011	
☐	XA-MAH	B737-752/W	35122/2348	
☐	XA-NAM	B737-752/W	33790/1533	
☐	XA-PAM	B737-752/W	34293/1747	
☐	XA-VAM	B737-752/W	34295/1765	
☐	EI-DRA	B737-852/W	35114/2037	
☐	EI-DRC	B737-852/W	35116/2081	
☐	N342AM	B737-8Z9/W	34262/1720	
☐	N520AM	B737-81Q/W	29052/557	
☐	N825AM	B737-852/W	36699/5091	
☐	N845AM	B737-852/W	36706/5219	
☐	N858AM	B737-8Q8/W	30671/1307	
☐	N859AM	B737-8Q8/W	32796/1272	
☐	N860AM	B737-83N/W	28249/1123	
☐	N861AM	B737-83N/W	30706/929	
☐	N875AM	B737-852/W	36705/5149	
☐	N950AM	B737-852/W	35115/2070	
☐	N957AM	B737-852/W	39957/5379	
☐	N958AM	B737-852/W	39958/5361	
☐	XA-AMA	B737-852/W	36700/4137	
☐	XA-AMB	B737-852/W	36703/4496	
☐	XA-AMC	B737-852/W	36704/4539	
☐	XA-AME	B737-852/W	36708/4559	
☐	XA-AMG	B737-81D/W	39439/4853	
☐	XA-AMJ	B737-852/W	36701/4185	
☐	XA-AMK	B737-852/W	36702/4222	
☐	XA-AML	B737-852/W	36707/5045	
☐	XA-AMM	B737-852/W	39944/4949	
☐	XA-AMN	B737-852/W	39945/4989	
☐	XA-AMO	B737-852/W	43665/5337	♦
☐	XA-AMS	B737-852/W	43661/5295	
☐	XA-AMU	B737-852/W	43657/5512	♦
☐	XA-AMV	B737-852/W	43659/5549	♦
☐	XA-JOY	B737-852/W	35121/2327	
☐	XA-MIA	B737-852/W	35119/2273	
☐	XA-ZAM	B737-852/W	35120/2290	
☐	N745AM	B777-2Q8ER	32718/554	
☐	N746AM	B777-2Q8ER	32719/562	
☐	N774AM	B777-2Q8ER	28689/365	
☐	N776AM	B777-2Q8ER	28692/373	
☐	N782AM	B787-8	37165/330	♦
☐	N783AM	B787-8	37167/359	♦
☐	N961AM	B787-8	35306/115	
☐	N964AM	B787-8	35307/122	
☐	N965AM	B787-8	35308/127	
☐	N966AM	B787-8	35311/155	
☐	N967AM	B787-8	35312/163	
☐	XA-AMR	B787-8	36844/264	
☐	XA-AMX	B787-8	36843/251	
☐		B787-9	43859/483	o/o♦
☐		B787-9	60285/502	o/o♦

AEROMEXICO CONNECT — 5D / SLI

	Reg	Type	c/n	
☐	XA-ACB	ERJ-145LR	145221	[MEX]
☐	XA-ALI	ERJ-145LR	145795	
☐	XA-BLI	ERJ-145LR	145798	
☐	XA-CLI	ERJ-145LR	14500803	
☐	XA-ELI	ERJ-145LR	14500861	
☐	XA-FLI	ERJ-145MP	145444	
☐	XA-ILI	ERJ-145LU	145564	[MEX]
☐	XA-JLI	ERJ-145MP	145426	
☐	XA-KLI	ERJ-145MP	145440	
☐	XA-QLI	ERJ-145LU	145588	[MEX]
☐	XA-RAC	ERJ-145LR	145313	std
☐	XA-RLI	ERJ-145LU	145559	
☐	XA-SLI	ERJ-145LU	145580	
☐	XA-TAC	ERJ-145LR	145475	
☐	XA-TLI	ERJ-145LU	145601	[BNA]
☐	XA-VAC	ERJ-145LR	145232	
☐	XA-VLI	ERJ-145LU	145574	
☐	XA-WAC	ERJ-145LR	145255	
☐	XA-WLI	ERJ-145LU	145434	
☐	XA-XAC	ERJ-145LR	145128	[MEX]
☐	XA-XLI	ERJ-145LU	145456	
☐	XA-YLI	ERJ-145LU	145400	
☐	XA-ZLI	ERJ-145LU	145420	
☐	XA-ACF	ERJ-175LR	17000137	
☐	XA-ACP	ERJ-170SU	17000019	
☐	XA-ACQ	ERJ-170SU	17000042	
☐	XA-ACV	ERJ-170SU	17000046	
☐	XA-ACX	ERJ-175LR	17000126	
☐	XA-ALD	ERJ-170STD	17000025	♦
☐	XA-ALG	ERJ-170STD	17000024	♦
☐	XA-ALH	ERJ-170LR	17000128	♦
☐	XA-GAB	ERJ-175LR	17000147	
☐	XA-GAM	ERJ-170STD	17000141	
☐	XA-GAQ	ERJ-170STD	17000146	
☐	XA-GAY	ERJ-170LR	17000087	♦
☐	XA-GAZ	ERJ-170LR	17000092	♦
☐	XA-SAC	ERJ-170LR	17000139	
☐		ERJ-170STD	17000107	o/o♦
☐		ERJ-170STD	17000112	o/o♦

	Reg	Type	C/n	
☐	XA-AAC	ERJ-190LR	19000121	
☐	XA-ACC	ERJ-190LR	19000499	
☐	XA-ACE	ERJ-190LR	19000518	
☐	XA-ACI	ERJ-190LR	19000525	
☐	XA-ACJ	ERJ-190LR	19000531	
☐	XA-ACK	ERJ-190LR	19000538	
☐	XA-ACM	ERJ-190LR	19000546	
☐	XA-ACN	ERJ-190LR	19000552	
☐	XA-ACS	ERJ-190LR	19000554	
☐	XA-ACT	ERJ-190LR	19000557	
☐	XA-BAC	ERJ-190LR	19000129	
☐	XA-CAC	ERJ-190LR	19000135	
☐	XA-DAC	ERJ-190LR	19000455	
☐	XA-EAC	ERJ-190LR	19000145	
☐	XA-FAC	ERJ-190LR	19000234	
☐	XA-GAD	ERJ-190LR	19000651	
☐	XA-GAE	ERJ-190LR	19000664	
☐	XA-GAF	ERJ-190LR	19000666	
☐	XA-GAG	ERJ-190AR	19000188	
☐	XA-GAH	ERJ-190AR	19000216	
☐	XA-GAI	ERJ-190LR	19000672	
☐	XA-GAK	ERJ-190LR	19000673	
☐	XA-GAL	ERJ-190AR	19000173	
☐	XA-GAR	ERJ-190AR	19000197	
☐	XA-GAW	ERJ-190LR	19000679	
☐	XA-GAX	ERJ-190AR	19000206	
☐	XA-HAC	ERJ-190LR	19000466	
☐	XA-IAC	ERJ-190LR	19000238	
☐	XA-JAC	ERJ-190LR	19000248	
☐	XA-MAC	ERJ-190LR	19000408	
☐	XA-	ERJ-190LR	19000138	o/o♦

AERONAVES TSM — *VTM*

	Reg	Type	C/n	
☐	XA-UJI	Convair 640F	88	
☐	XA-UMI	Convair 640F	48	
☐	XA-UNH	Convair 640F	332	
☐	XA-URL	Convair 640F	104	
☐	XA-UTW	Convair 640F	64	♦
☐	XA-	Convair 640F	463	o/o♦
☐	XA-	DC-9-15RC	47061/207	
☐	XA-	DC-9-15RC	47044/265	
☐	XA-DHL	DC-9-33RC	47193/311	
☐	XA-UOG	DC-9-33RC	47194/324	
☐	XA-UPS	DC-9-33RC	47462/564	
☐	XA-UQT	DC-9-32CF	47147/208	
☐	XA-URM	DC-9-32CF	47148/246	
☐	XA-UUT	DC-9-32F	47355/452	o/o
☐	XA-	DC-9-34	48123/934	o/o
☐	XA-UTX	MD-82SF	49342/1337	♦
☐	XA-UVG	MD-83SF	49663/1437	♦
☐	XA-	MD-82SF	49558/1451	o/o
☐	XA-	MD-82	49562/1475	o/o♦
☐	XA-	MD-82	49804/1669	o/o♦
☐	XA-	MD-82	49990/1770	o/o♦
☐	XA-	MD-82	49162/1110	o/o♦
☐	XA-	MD-82	49267/1239	o/o♦
☐	XA-	MD-82	48013/1000	o/o♦
☐	XA-ADQ	SA.227AC Metro II	TC-409	
☐	XA-ADS	SA.227AC Metro II	TC-404	
☐	XA-AFT	SA.227AC Metro III	AC-581	♦
☐	XA-DCX	SA.227AC Metro III	AC-497	
☐	XA-EEE	SA.227AC Metro III	AC-503	
☐	XA-EGC	SA.227AC Metro III	AC-724	
☐	XA-MIO	SA.227AC Metro III	AC-693B	
☐	XA-PNG	SA.227AC Metro III	AC-687B	
☐	XA-SLW	SA.227AC Metro III	AC-628B	
☐	XA-SUS	SA.227AC Metro III	AC-430B	
☐	XA-TSM	SA.227AC Metro II	AC-412	
☐	XA-TYX	SA.227AC Metro III	AC-627B	
☐	XA-UAL	SA.227AC Metro III	AC-704	
☐	XA-UFO	SA.227AC Metro II	AC-281	
☐	XA-UGJ	SA.226AT Merlin IV	AT-009	
☐	XA-UKJ	SA.227AC Metro III	AC-532	
☐	XA-UMW	SA.227AC Metro III	AC-717	
☐	XA-UNQ	SA.227AC Metro III	AC-565B	
☐	XA-UOC	SA.227AC Metro II	TC-311	♦
☐	XA-UPP	SA.227AC Metro III	AC-736	♦
☐	XA-URZ	SA.227AC Metro III	AC-595	♦
☐	XA-USB	SA.227AC Metro III	AC-761B	♦
☐	XA-USG	SA.226AT Merlin IV	AT-434B	♦
☐	XA-	SA.227AC Metro III	AC-487B	
☐	XA-	SA.227AC Metro III	AC-659B	

AEROUNION — *6R / TNO*

	Reg	Type	C/n	
☐	XA-FPP	A300B4-203F	247	
☐	XA-LRL	A300B4-203F	210	
☐	XA-MRC	A300B4-203F	227	
☐	XA-TWQ	A300B4-203F	045	
☐	XA-EFR	B767-241ER(SF)	23804/178	
☐	XA-LRC	B767-241ER(SF)	23802/172	

AIR TRIBE

	Reg	Type	C/n	
☐	XA-TRB	Convair 580F	52	
☐	XA-UPL	Convair 580F	24	

ALCON SERVICIOS AEREOS — *AOA*

	Reg	Type	C/n	
☐	XA-TND	NAMC YS-11A	2073	

ESTAFETA CARGA AEREA — *E7 / ESF*

	Reg	Type	C/n	
☐	XA-AJA	B737-3Y0(SF)	23747/1363	
☐	XA-ECA	B737-3M8(SF)	24024/1689	
☐	XA-EMX	B737-375F	23707/1388	
☐	XA-ESA	CRJ-100ER	7085	
☐	XA-GGB	B737-3M8(SF)	24023/1675	
☐	XA-SPO	CRJ-100ER	7088	

FLYMEX

	Reg	Type	C/n	
☐	XA-AAS	Do328-300	3127	
☐	XA-ALA	Do328-310	3167	
☐	XA-FAS	Do328-300	3125	

GLOBAL AIR — *DMJ*

	Reg	Type	C/n	
☐	XA-TWR	B737-2H4	21812/611	
☐	XA-UHY	B737-2C3	21016/406	[MEX]
☐	XA-UHZ	B737-201	21816/592	
☐	XA-UMQ	B737-2Q3	24103/1565	

INTERJET — *4O / INJ*

	Reg	Type	C/n	
☐	XA-ABC	A320-214	3690	
☐	XA-ACO	A320-214	1322	
☐	XA-ALM	A320-214	1308	
☐	XA-BAV	A320-214	5372	
☐	XA-BIC	A320-214	3374	
☐	XA-BIO	A320-214	4730	
☐	XA-DOS	A320-214	4235	
☐	XA-EBA	A320-214	2930	♦
☐	XA-ECO	A320-214	4733	
☐	XA-FOG	A320-214	2048	
☐	XA-FUA	A320-214/S	5867	

	Reg	Type	C/n	
☐	XA-GAC	A320-214/S	5933	
☐	XA-IJA	A320-214	1244	
☐	XA-IJT	A320-214	1132	
☐	XA-ILY	A320-214	3123	
☐	XA-ING	A320-214	4304	
☐	XA-INJ	A320-214	1162	
☐	XA-IUA	A320-214/S	5653	
☐	XA-JAV	A320-214	5221	
☐	XA-JCV	A320-214	3514	
☐	XA-JMA	A320-214/S	5665	
☐	XA-KNO	A320-214	2539	
☐	XA-LHG	A320-214/S	5878	
☐	XA-MLR	A320-214	2227	
☐	XA-MTO	A320-214	4924	
☐	XA-MTY	A320-214	1179	
☐	XA-MXM	A320-214	3286	
☐	XA-MYR	A320-214	3021	
☐	XA-NBA	A320-214	2964	♦
☐	XA-RBA	A320-214	3044	♦
☐	XA-SUN	A320-214	4411	
☐	XA-TLC	A320-214	3312	
☐	XA-UHE	A320-214	3149	
☐	XA-VAI	A320-214	3160	
☐	XA-VCT	A320-214	5163	
☐	XA-VFI	A320-214	1780	
☐	XA-VIP	A320-214	3304	
☐	XA-VTA	A320-214	1259	
☐	XA-WAB	A320-214	5358	
☐	XA-XII	A320-214	3508	
☐	XA-YES	A320-214	4933	
☐	XA-ZIH	A320-214	3667	
☐	XA-	A320-214/S	7238	o/o♦
☐	XA-	A321-211/S	7326	o/o♦
☐	XA-ABM	Sukhoi SSJ 100-95B	95036	
☐	XA-ALJ	Sukhoi SSJ 100-95B	95046	
☐	XA-BMO	Sukhoi SSJ 100-95B	95048	
☐	XA-BVM	Sukhoi SSJ 100-95B	95054	♦
☐	XA-GCD	Sukhoi SSJ 100-95B	95052	
☐	XA-IJR	Sukhoi SSJ 100-95B	95024	
☐	XA-JLG	Sukhoi SSJ 100-95B	95023	
☐	XA-JLP	Sukhoi SSJ 100-95B	95042	
☐	XA-JLV	Sukhoi SSJ 100-95B	95028	
☐	XA-LLV	Sukhoi SSJ 100-95B	95049	
☐	XA-LME	Sukhoi SSJ 100-95B	95045	
☐	XA-NGO	Sukhoi SSJ 100-95B	95071	♦
☐	XA-NSG	Sukhoi SSJ 100-95B	95034	
☐	XA-OAA	Sukhoi SSJ 100-95B	95038	
☐	XA-OUI	Sukhoi SSJ 100-95B	95050	♦
☐	XA-PBA	Sukhoi SSJ 100-95B	95040	
☐	XA-PPY	Sukhoi SSJ 100-95B	95066	♦
☐	XA-VAS	Sukhoi SSJ 100-95B	95065	♦
☐	XA-VER	Sukhoi SSJ 100-95B	95081	
☐	XA-	Sukhoi SSJ 100-95B	95072	♦
☐	XA-	Sukhoi SSJ 100-95B	95085	o/o
☐	XA-	Sukhoi SSJ 100-95B	95086	o/o♦
☐	XA-	Sukhoi SSJ 100-95B	95087	o/o♦
☐	XA-	Sukhoi SSJ 100-95B	95102	o/o♦
☐	XA-	Sukhoi SSJ 100-95B	95104	o/o♦
☐	XA-	Sukhoi SSJ 100-95B	95105	o/o♦
☐	XA-	Sukhoi SSJ 100-95B	95106	o/o♦
☐	XA-	Sukhoi SSJ 100-95B	95111	o/o♦
☐	XA-	Sukhoi SSJ 100-95B		o/o♦

MAGNICHARTERS **UJ / GMT**

	Reg	Type	C/n	
☐	XA-MAA	B737-377	23655/1274	
☐	XA-MAD	B737-277	22652/831	
☐	XA-MAE	B737-277	22648/789	
☐	XA-MAI	B737-322	24537/1774	
☐	XA-UNM	B737-322	24248/1636	
☐	XA-UNY	B737-322	24455/1752	
☐	XA-UQA	B737-322	23952/1534	
☐	XA-UQX	B737-33A/W	23827/1444	
☐	XA-UTE	B737-322	24670/1909	
☐	XA-UTS	B737-55D	27130/2448	
☐	XA-UUI	B737-3K2	28085/2722	
☐	XA-UVZ	B737-3B7	22959/1140	♦

MAS AIR CARGO **MY / MAA**

	Reg	Type	C/n	
☐	N420LA	B767-316ERF/W	34627/948	<LCO

See also LAN Cargo (CC-)

MAYAIR **7M / MYI**

	Reg	Type	C/n	
☐	XA-MYI	Short SD.3-60	SH3602	
☐	XA-UUU	Fokker 50	20194	♦

MCS AERO CARGA **MCS**

	Reg	Type	C/n	
☐	XA-MCB	CRJ-200ER(PF)	7058	♦
☐	XA-MCD	CRJ-200ER(PF)	7078	♦
☐	XA-MCS	CRJ-200ER(PF)	7120	♦

TAR AEROLINEAS **LCT**

	Reg	Type	C/n	
☐	XA-BPK	ERJ-145LR	145507	
☐	XA-JFH	ERJ-145LR	145075	♦
☐	XA-MAF	ERJ-145LR	145080	♦
☐	XA-MFH	ERJ-145LR	145568	
☐	XA-NFP	ERJ-145LR	145063	♦
☐	XA-RHF	ERJ-145LR	145481	
☐	XA-SFH	ERJ-145LR	145067	♦
☐	XA-TAR?	ERJ-145LR	145078	♦
☐	XA-	ERJ-145LR	145071	♦

TATSA **TRX**

	Reg	Type	C/n	
☐	XA-UQY	DHC-8-102	160	
☐	XA-URH	DHC-8-102	155	

VIVAAEROBUS **VB / VIV**

	Reg	Type	C/n	
☐	EI-ERH	A320-232	2157	
☐	EI-EUA	A320-232	2210	
☐	XA-TAR	A320-232	2908	
☐	XA-VAA	A320-232/S	6574	♦
☐	XA-VAE	A320-232/S	6602	♦
☐	XA-VAF	A320-232	2443	
☐	XA-VAG	A320-232	2752	
☐	XA-VAH	A320-232	3743	
☐	XA-VAJ	A320-232/S	6750	♦
☐	XA-VAK	A320-232/S	6755	♦
☐	XA-VAN	A320-232/S	6857	♦
☐	XA-VAO	A320-232/S	6875	♦
☐	XA-VAP	A320-232/S	6888	♦
☐	XA-VAQ	A320-232/S	6886	♦
☐	XA-VAR	A320-232/S	6955	♦
☐	XA-VAZ	A320-232	2576	♦
☐	XA-	A320-232/S	7020	o/o♦
☐	XA-	A320-232/S	7043	o/o♦
☐	XA-	A320-232/S		o/o♦
☐	XA-	A320-271N	7060	o/o♦
☐	XA-	A320-271N	7102	o/o♦
☐	XA-	A320-271N	7107	o/o♦
☐	XA-	A320-271N	7153	o/o♦
☐	XA-	A320-271N	7162	o/o♦

☐ EI-EOZ	B737-3Q8	24962/2139	
☐ XA-TAR	B737-301	23259/1132	[MTY]
☐ XA-VAD	B737-3U3	28742/2992	
☐ XA-VIA	B737-3B7	23856/1501	std
☐ XA-VIB	B737-3B7	23378/1339	[CEN]
☐ XA-VIF	B737-301	23552/1382	[MTY]
☐ XA-VIH	B737-301	23554/1408	[MTY]
☐ XA-VIJ	B737-3Y0	24677/1837	[CEN]
☐ XA-VIK	B737-3L9	26442/2277	[MZJ]
☐ XA-VIL	B737-33A	25010/2008	
☐ XA-VIM	B737-33A	25032/2014	
☐ XA-VIQ	B737-33A	27267/2600	std
☐ XA-VIR	B737-33A	27285/2608	
☐ XA-VIS	B737-33A	27457/2756	
☐ XA-VIT	B737-3K2	27635/2721	
☐ XA-VIV	B737-301	23560/1463	[MTY]
☐ XA-VIW	B737-36Q	28660/2883	
☐ XA-VIX	B737-3B7	23312/1162	[MZJ]

VOLARIS — *Y4 / VOI*

☐ N501VL	A319-133	2979	
☐ N502VL	A319-132	3463	
☐ N503VL	A319-132	3491	
☐ N504VL	A319-132	3590	
☐ XA-VOA	A319-132	2771	
☐ XA-VOB	A319-133	2780	
☐ XA-VOC	A319-132	2997	
☐ XA-VOD	A319-133	3045	
☐ XA-VOE	A319-133	3069	
☐ XA-VOF	A319-133	3077	
☐ XA-VOG	A319-133	3175	
☐ XA-VOH	A319-133	3253	
☐ XA-VOI	A319-132	2657	
☐ XA-VOJ	A319-133	3279	
☐ XA-VOK	A319-133	3450	
☐ XA-VOL	A319-132	2666	
☐ XA-VOP	A319-133	4403	
☐ XA-VOQ	A319-133	4422	
☐ N505VL	A320-233	4798	
☐ N506VL	A320-233	4828	
☐ N507VL	A320-233	4832	
☐ N508VL	A320-233	4950	
☐ N509VL	A320-233	5062	
☐ N510VL	A320-233	5207	
☐ N511VL	A320-233	5212	
☐ N512VL	A320-233	5308	
☐ N513VL	A320-233	5322	
☐ N514VL	A320-233	5337	
☐ N515VL	A320-233	5391	
☐ N517VL	A320-232	4741	
☐ N518VL	A320-233	5488	
☐ N519VL	A320-233/S	5510	
☐ N520VL	A320-233/S	5595	
☐ N521VL	A320-233/S	5651	
☐ N522VL	A320-233/S	5776	
☐ N523VL	A320-233/S	6014	
☐ N524VL	A320-233/S	6161	
☐ N525VL	A320-233/S	6332	
☐ N526VL	A320-233/S	6470	
☐ N527VL	A320-233/S	6705	♦
☐ XA-VLB	A320-233/S	5988	
☐ XA-VLC	A320-233/S	5996	
☐ XA-VLD	A320-233/S	6109	
☐ XA-VLE	A320-233/S	6288	
☐ XA-VLF	A320-233/S	6321	
☐ XA-VLK	A320-233/S	6610	♦
☐ XA-VLL	A320-233/S	6778	♦
☐ XA-VLM	A320-233/S	6906	♦
☐ XA-VLN	A320-233/S	6948	♦
☐ XA-VLO	A320-233/S	6969	♦
☐ XA-VOM	A320-233	3624	
☐ XA-VON	A320-232	3672	
☐ XA-VOV	A320-232	3524	
☐ XA-VOW	A320-232	3543	
☐ XA-VOY	A320-233/S	5793	
☐ XA-VOZ	A320-233/S	5819	
☐	A320-233/S	7000	o/o♦
☐	A320-233/S	7088	o/o♦
☐	A320-233/S	7118	o/o♦
☐	A320-233/S	7123	o/o♦
☐	A320-233/S	7325	o/o♦
☐	A320-271N	7051	o/o♦
☐ XA-VLH	A321-231	6558	♦
☐ XA-VLJ	A321-231/S	6601	♦
☐	A321-231/S	7125	o/o
☐	A321-231/S	7196	o/o♦
☐	A321-231/S	7316	o/o♦

XT- BURKINA FASO

AIR BURKINA — *2J / VBW*

☐ XT-ABC	MD-87	49834/1714	
☐ XT-ABD	MD-87	49840/1745	[OLB]
☐ XT-ABS	ERJ-170STD	17000027	
☐ XT-ABT	ERJ-170STD	17000023	

COLOMBE AIRLINES — *CRL*

☐ CS-DVF	ATR 72-202	350	<
☐ XT-	MD-83	49662/1429	

XU- CAMBODIA

BASSAKA AIR — *5B / BSX*

☐ XU-112	A320-214	0648	
☐ XU-113	A320-214	0650	

BAYON AIRLINES — *B9 / BAY*

☐ XU-001	XIAN MA60	1108	
☐ XU-002	XIAN MA60	1109	♦

CAMBODIA ANGKOR AIR — *K6 / VAV*

☐ XU-348	A321-231	5427	
☐ XU-349	A321-231	2480	
☐ XU-350	A321-231	5343	
☐ XU-351	A321-231	2303	
☐ XU-235	ATR 72-212A	899	
☐ XU-236	ATR 72-212A	906	

SKY ANGKOR AIRLINES — *ZA / SWM*

☐ XU-701	A320-212	0421	std
☐ XU-706	A320-214	0986	♦
☐ XU-707	A321-231	1293	♦
☐ XU-708	A320-214	0883	♦
☐ XU-709	A320-214	0914	♦
☐ XU-710	A320-232	2016	

XY- MYANMAR

AIR BAGAN MYANMAR — W9 / JAB

☐ XY-AGF Fokker 100 11282 [RGN]
☐ XY-AIA ATR 72-212 422
☐ XY-AIC ATR 42-320 159 [RGN]
☐ XY-AIK ATR 72-212A 592

AIR KBZ — K7 / KBZ

☐ XY-AIW ATR 72-212A 582
☐ XY-AIY ATR 72-212A 547
☐ XY-AJC ATR 72-212 541
☐ XY-AJD ATR 72-212A 545
☐ XY-AJE ATR 72-600 1068
☐ XY-AJJ ATR 72-600 1085
☐ XY-AJT ATR 72-212A 658
☐ XY-AJW ATR 72-600 1224
☐ XY-AMA ATR 72-600 1162 ♦

AIR MANDALAY — 6T / AMY

☐ XY-AIJ ATR 42-320 268 [RGN]
☐ XY-AIR ATR 72-212 467 [RGN]
☐ XY-ALD ERJ-145EP 145060 ♦
☐ XY-ALE ERJ-145EP 145089 ♦

APEX AIRLINES — SO / XAI

☐ XY-AJV ATR 72-600 1229
☐ XY- ATR 72-600 o/o♦
☐ XY- ATR 72-600 o/o♦

ASIAN WINGS AIRWAYS — AW / AWM

☐ XY-AGN A321-112 0765 [RGN]
☐ XY-AIS ATR 72-212A 626
☐ XY-AIU ATR 72-212A 557
☐ XY-AJQ ATR 72-212A 634

FMI AIR CHARTER — ND

☐ XY-AIB ATR 42-320 178 ♦
☐ XY-AGW CRJ-850LR 7136 ♦
☐ XY-AGY CRJ-200LR 7439 ♦
☐ XY-ALA CRJ-200LR 7486 ♦

GOLDEN MYANMAR AIRLINES — Y5 / GMR

☐ XY-AGS A320-232 1407
☐ XY-AJM ATR 72-600 1148
☐ XY-AJS ATR 72-600 1156

MANN YADANARPON AIRLINES — 7Y / MYP

☐ XY-AJO ATR 72-600 1127
☐ XY-AJP ATR 72-600 1137 ♦

MYANMAR AIRWAYS INTERNATIONAL — 8M / MMA

☐ XY-AGL A320-231 0316 [SAW]
☐ XY-AGO A320-214 0973 >PIC
☐ XY-AGR A319-112 1791
☐ XY-AGU A319-111 1180
☐ XY-AGV A319-111 1247

MYANMAR NATIONAL AIRWAYS — UB / UBA

☐ XY-AEZ ATR 72-212 475
☐ XY-AIF ATR 72-212A 765 VIP
☐ XY-AIG ATR 72-212A 781 VIP
☐ XY-AJN ATR 72-212A 787
☐ XY-AJY ATR 72-600 1267 ♦
☐ XY-AJZ ATR 72-600 1309 ♦

☐ XY-ALB B737-86N/W 43405/5430 ♦
☐ XY-ALC B737-86N/W 43407/5610 ♦
☐ XY-ALF B737-86N/W 43411/5773 ♦
☐ XY-AGP ERJ-190AR 19000154
☐ XY-AGQ ERJ-190AR 19000231
☐ XY-AGB F.28 Fellowship 4000 11184 [RGN]
☐ XY-AGH F.28 Fellowship 4000 11161
☐ XY-AIO XIAN MA60 0806 [RGN]
☐ XY-AIP XIAN MA60 0807

YANGON AIRLINES — YH / AVG

☐ XY-AIM ATR 72-212 479
☐ XY-AIN ATR 72-212 481
☐ XY-AJI ATR 72-212A 797

YA- AFGHANISTAN

AFGHAN JET INTERNATIONAL A/W — HN / AJI

☐ YA-AJH CRJ-200LR 7431
☐ YA-AJK CRJ-200LR 7499

ARIANA AFGHAN AIRLINES — FG / AFG

☐ C5-AAH A320-231 0295 <AAZ♦
☐ YA-CAQ A310-304 496
☐ YA-CAV A310-304ER 497
☐ YA-PIC B737-4YO 26088/2487
☐ YA-PID B737-4YO 26085/2468 ♦
☐ YA-PIE B737-4YO 26086/2475

EAST HORIZON AIR — EA / EHN

☐ EY-201 XIAN MA60 0701 <TJK
☐ TU-PAD HS.748 Srs. 2B 1799 <
☐ YA-EH01 CASA C212-100 AA1-11-9G
☐ YA-EH02 CASA C212-100 A1-12-22
☐ YA-EH03 CASA C212-100 A11-12-31
☐ YA-EH04 CASA C212-100 AA1-4-99
☐ YA-EHC An-24RV 57310203
☐ YA-EHD An-24RV 57310109

KAM AIR — RQ / KMF

☐ YA-KAM B767-222 21879/49
☐ YA-KMC An-24RV 37309008
☐ UR-COB MD-83 53187/2118 <BAY♦
☐ UR-COC MD-83 49808/1836 <BAY♦
☐ UR-COD MD-83 53623/2276 <BAY♦
☐ YA-KMD MD-83 49785/1628
☐ YA-KMF MD-82 49704/1490
☐ YA-KMG MD-83 49567/1367
☐ YA-KMO MD-87 53010/1921
☐ YA-KMZ MD-87 53337/1962

SAFI AIRWAYS — 4Q / SFW

☐ YA-AQS B767-2J6ER 23745/156
☐ YA-HSB B737-3J6 23303/1237 [CAI]
☐ YA-SFL B737-3J6 23302/1224 [CAI]
☐ YA-TTB A340-311 015
☐ YA-TTD A320-214 0994
☐ YA-TTE A319-112 1018
☐ YA-TTF A319-112 0734

YI- IRAQ

AL-NASER AIRLINES — 6N / MHK

YI-APY	B737-201	22274/682	[ADJ]
YI-AQS	B737-48E	25765/2335	

AL-RAFEDAIN FALCON — RFA

YI-BAC	Il-76TD	0083483502	♦

FLY BAGHDAD — IF / FBA

ZS-GAL	A320-231	0064	<♦
ZS-GAS	A320-231	0076	<♦
JY-JAQ	B737-46J	27826/2694	<JAV♦
YI-BAJ	B737-405	24271/1738	[LAN]♦
YI-BAH	CRJ-200LR	7984	♦

IRAQI AIRWAYS — IA / IAW

SX-BDS	A320-214	0879	<HRM♦
YI-ARA	A320-214	5115	
YI-ARB	A320-214	5290	
YI-ARD	A320-214	5464	
YI-AGR	A321-231	4067	
YI-AGS	A321-231	4044	
YI-AQY	A330-202	1339	
YI-APW	B737-2B7	22885/966	
YI-AQK	B737-7BD/W	33935/2315	
YI-AQL	B737-7BD/W	35789/2201	
YI-ASE	B737-81Z/W	40104/4515	
YI-ASF	B737-81Z/W	40105/4719	
YI-ASG	B737-81Z/W	40089/4837	
YI-ASH	B737-81Z/W	40076/4873	
YI-ASI	B737-81Z/W	40077/4943	
YI-ASJ	B737-81Z/W	40090/4921	
YI-ASK	B737-81Z/W	40078/5145	
YI-ASQ	B737-81Z/W	40079/5249	
YI-ASR	B737-81Z/W	40080/5287	
YI-ASS	B737-81Z/W	40081/5322	
YI-AST	B737-81Z/W	40082/5388	
YI-ASU	B737-81Z/W	40087/5598	♦
YI-AQQ	B747-446	27099/1031	
YI-ASA	B747-4H6	28433/1290	
YI-AQM	B767-3P6ER	26235/502	
YI-AQW	B767-3P6ER	26237/544	
YI-AQZ	B777-29MLR	40993/1006	
YI-AQA	CRJ-900LR	15189	
YI-AQB	CRJ-900LR	15202	
YI-AQC	CRJ-900LR	15213	
YI-AQD	CRJ-900LR	15220	
YI-AQE	CRJ-900LR	15265	
YI-AQF	CRJ-900LR	15266	

IRAQ GATE — / IGC

YI-BAG	CRJ-200ER	7958	♦
YI-BAI	CRJ-200ER	7981	♦
YI-	CRJ-200ER	7973	♦

ZAGROSJET — Z4 / GZQ

TC-OBJ	A321-231	0835	<OHY
YI-AQU	A321-231	1878	[IST]

YJ- VANUATU

AIR VANUATU — NF / AVN

YJ-AV1	B737-8Q8/W	30734/2477	[PVG]
YJ-AV8	B737-8SH/W	42052/5750	♦
YJ-AV4	AVIC II Y-12 II	028	
YJ-AV5	AVIC II Y-12 II	029	
YJ-AV6	AVIC II Y-12 II	032	
YJ-AV10	DHC-6 Twin Otter 310	679	
YJ-AV11	DHC-6 Twin Otter 300	564	
YJ-AV71	ATR 72-212A	720	
YJ-AV72	ATR 72-212A	876	

YK- SYRIA

CHAM WINGS AIRLINES — 6Q / SAW

YK-BAA	A320-212	0525	♦
YK-BAB	A320-211	0342	♦
YK-BAC	A320-2xx		♦

FLYDAMAS — 4J / FDK

SU-KHM	B737-5C9	26438/2413	<KHH♦

SYRIAN ARAB AIRLINES — RB / SYR

YK-AKA	A320-232	0886	
YK-AKB	A320-232	0918	
YK-AKC	A320-232	1032	
YK-AKD	A320-232	1076	
YK-AKE	A320-232	1085	
YK-AKF	A320-232	1117	
YK-ANA	An-24B	87304203	
YK-ANC	An-26	3007	
YK-ANE	An-26	3103	
YK-ANF	An-26	3104	
YK-ANG	An-26B	10907	
YK-ANH	An-26B	11406	
YK-AVA	ATR 72-212A	836	
YK-AVB	ATR 72-212A	845	
YK-AGA	B727-294	21203/1188	[DAM]
YK-AGB	B727-294	21204/1194	[DAM]
YK-AGC	B727-294	21205/1198	[DAM]
YK-AGD	B727-269	22360/1670	[DAM]
YK-AGE	B727-269	22361/1716	[DAM]
YK-AGF	B727-269	22763/1788	[DAM]
YK-AHA	B747-SP94	21174/284	[DAM]
YK-AHB	B747-SP94	21175/290	[DAM]
YK-ATA	Il-76M	93421613	
YK-ATB	Il-76M	93421619	
YK-ATD	Il-76M	0013431915	
YK-AYA	Tu-134B-3	63992	
YK-AYB	Tu-134B-3	63994	
YK-AYE	Tu-134B-3	66187	
YK-AYF	Tu-134B-3	63190	
YK-AQA	Yak-40	9341932	
YK-AQB	Yak-40	9530443	
YK-AQD	Yak-40	9830158	
YK-AQE	Yak-40K	9830258	
YK-AQF	Yak-40	9931859	

YL- LATVIA

AIRBALTIC — BT / BTI

Reg	Type	c/n	Notes
☐ YL-BBD	B737-53S	29075/3101	
☐ YL-BBE	B737-53S	29073/3083	
☐ YL-BBI	B737-33A/W	27454/2703	
☐ YL-BBJ	B737-36Q/W	30333/3117	
☐ YL-BBL	B737-33V/W	29334/3089	
☐ YL-BBM	B737-522	26680/2366	
☐ YL-BBN	B737-522	26683/2368	
☐ YL-BBQ	B737-522	26691/2408	
☐ YL-BBR	B737-31S	29266/3092	
☐ YL-BBS	B737-31S	29267/3093	
☐ YL-BBX	B737-36Q/W	30334/3120	
☐ YL-BBY	B737-36Q/W	30335/3129	
☐ YL-	CS300 C Series		♦
☐ YL-	CS300 C Series		♦
☐ YL-BAE	DHC-8-402Q	4289	
☐ YL-BAF	DHC-8-402Q	4293	
☐ YL-BAH	DHC-8-402Q	4296	
☐ YL-BAI	DHC-8-402Q	4302	
☐ YL-BAJ	DHC-8-402Q	4309	
☐ YL-BAQ	DHC-8-402Q	4313	
☐ YL-BAX	DHC-8-402Q	4324	
☐ YL-BAY	DHC-8-402Q	4331	
☐ YL-BBT	DHC-8-402Q	4438	
☐ YL-BBU	DHC-8-402Q	4439	
☐ YL-BBV	DHC-8-402Q	4444	
☐ YL-BBW	DHC-8-402Q	4448	

KS AVIA — KSA

Reg	Type	c/n	Notes
☐ YL-KSA	An-26B	10101	

PRIMERA AIR NORDIC — PF / PRW

Reg	Type	c/n	Notes
☐ YL-PSB	B737-8Q8/W	30722/2261	♦
☐ YL-PSC	B737-86N/W	33419/1251	
☐ YL-PSD	B737-86N/W	28618/514	
☐ YL-PSF	B737-7Q8/W	28210/22	♦
☐ YL-PSG	B737-7BX/W	30743/922	♦
☐ YL-PSH	B737-86N/W	34247/1830	

RAF-AVIA — MTL

Reg	Type	c/n	Notes
☐ YL-RAA	An-26B	11206	
☐ YL-RAB	An-26B	10508	
☐ YL-RAC	An-26	9903	
☐ YL-RAD	An-26B	13909	
☐ YL-RAI	An-26B	9608	♦
☐ YL-RAG	SAAB SF.340AF	340A-052	
☐ YL-RAH	SAAB SF.340AF	340A-081	

SMARTLYNX — 6Y / ART

Reg	Type	c/n	Notes
☐ YL-BBC	A320-211	0142	[MPL]
☐ YL-LCK	A320-214	0936	
☐ YL-LCL	A320-214	0533	
☐ YL-LCM	A320-211	0244	
☐ YL-LCN	A320-211	0662	
☐ YL-LCO	A320-214	1873	
☐ YL-LCP	A320-232	1823	>VJC♦
☐ YL-LCR	A320-214	0984	♦

YN- NICARAGUA

LA COSTENA — W8

Reg	Type	c/n	Notes
☐ YN-CHG	ATR 42-320	323	
☐ YN-CIE	ATR 42-320	400	

YR- ROMANIA

AIR BUCHAREST — BUR

Reg	Type	c/n	Notes
☐ YR-SKI	B737-46J	27213/2585	>♦
☐ YR-TIB	B737-3L9	27924/2760	

AVIRO AIR

Reg	Type	c/n	Notes
☐ YR-AVR	BAe146 Srs.300	E3193	♦

BLUE AIR — 0B / BMS

Reg	Type	c/n	Notes
☐ YR-BAC	B737-377	23653/1260	
☐ YR-BAE	B737-46N	28723/2886	
☐ YR-BAF	B737-322F	24453/1730	
☐ YR-BAG	B737-5L9	24778/1816	
☐ YR-BAJ	B737-430	27002/2323	
☐ YR-BAK	B737-430	27005/2359	
☐ YR-BAO	B737-42C	24813/2062	
☐ YR-BAQ	B737-4D7	28702/2978	
☐ YR-BAR	B737-4Q8	25371/2195	
☐ YR-BAS	B737-430	27007/2367	
☐ YR-BAR	B737-4Z9	25147/2043	♦
☐ YR-BAU	B737-4YO	26066/2301	♦
☐ YR-BAZ	B737-405	24644/1938	
☐ YR-BMA	B737-79P	30651/1267	♦
☐ YR-BMB	B737-85R/W	29037/177	♦
☐ YR-BMC	B737-85F/W	28822/166	o/o♦
☐ YR-BME	B737-86N/W	34251/1817	♦

CARPATAIR — V3 / KRP

Reg	Type	c/n	Notes
☐ YR-FKA	Fokker 100	11340	>ADR
☐ YR-FKB	Fokker 100	11369	>ADR
☐ YR-FZA	Fokker 100	11395	>NTJ

Filed for insolvency 25Jan14 but still operates.

FLY 365 AVIATION

Reg	Type	c/n	Notes
☐ YR-OTL	MD-82	48079/1016	♦

TAROM — RO / ROT

Reg	Type	c/n	Notes
☐ YR-LCA	A310-325	636	
☐ YR-LCB	A310-325	644	
☐ YR-ASA	A318-111	2931	
☐ YR-ASB	A318-111	2955	
☐ YR-ASC	A318-111	3220	
☐ YR-ASD	A318-111	3225	
☐ YR-ATA	ATR 42-500	566	
☐ YR-ATB	ATR 42-500	569	
☐ YR-ATC	ATR 42-500	589	
☐ YR-ATD	ATR 42-500	591	
☐ YR-ATE	ATR 42-500	596	
☐ YR-ATF	ATR 42-500	599	
☐ YR-ATG	ATR 42-500	605	
☐ YR-ATH	ATR 72-212A	861	
☐ YR-ATI	ATR 72-212A	867	
☐ YR-BGA	B737-38J	27179/2524	
☐ YR-BGB	B737-38J	27180/2529	

	Reg	Type	c/n	
☐	YR-BGD	B737-38J	27182/2663	
☐	YR-BGE	B737-38J	27395/2671	
☐	YR-BGF	B737-78J	28440/795	
☐	YR-BGG	B737-78J	28442/827	
☐	YR-BGH	B737-78J	28438/1394	
☐	YR-BGI	B737-78J/W	28439/1419	

YS- EL SALVADOR

AVIANCA CENTRAL AMERICA TA / TAI

	Reg	Type	c/n	
☐	N477TA	A319-132	1952	[MZJ]
☐	N478TA	A319-132	2339	
☐	N479TA	A319-132	2444	
☐	N480TA	A319-132	3057	
☐	N520TA	A319-132	3248	
☐	N521TA	A319-132	3276	
☐	N522TA	A319-132	5219	
☐	N524TA	A319-132	5280	
☐	N694AV	A319-132/S	6068	
☐	N695AV	A319-132/S	6099	
☐	N703AV	A319-132/S	5406	
☐	N723AV	A319-115/S	6167	
☐	N490TA	A320-232	2282	
☐	N491TA	A320-233	2301	>TPU
☐	N492TA	A320-233	2434	
☐	N493TA	A320-233	2917	
☐	N494TA	A320-233	3042	
☐	N495TA	A320-233	3103	
☐	N496TA	A320-233	3113	
☐	N497TA	A320-233	3378	
☐	N498TA	A320-233	3418	
☐	N499TA	A320-233	3510	
☐	N603AV	A320-214/S	5840	
☐	N680TA	A320-233	3538	
☐	N683TA	A320-233	4906	
☐	N684TA	A320-233	4944	
☐	N685TA	A320-233	5068	
☐	N686TA	A320-214	5238	
☐	N687TA	A320-233	1334	
☐	N689TA	A320-214	5333	
☐	N564TA	A321-231	2862	
☐	N568TA	A321-231	2687	>TPU
☐	N570TA	A321-231	3869	
☐	N692AV	A321-231/S	5936	
☐	N693AV	A321-231/S	6002	
☐	N697AV	A321-231/S	6190	
☐	N725AV	A321-231/S	6219	
☐	N742AV	A321-231/S	6861	♦
☐	N935TA	ERJ-190AR	19000205	
☐	N936TA	ERJ-190AR	19000215	
☐	N937TA	ERJ-190AR	19000221	
☐	N938TA	ERJ-190AR	19000228	
☐	N982TA	ERJ-190AR	19000259	>TPU
☐	N983TA	ERJ-190AR	19000265	
☐	N984TA	ERJ-190AR	19000273	>TPU
☐	N985TA	ERJ-190AR	19000287	
☐	N986TA	ERJ-190AR	19000360	
☐	N987TA	ERJ-190AR	19000393	
☐	N988TA	ERJ-190AR	19000399	>TPU
☐	N989TA	ERJ-190AR	19000482	
☐		ERJ-190AR		o/o

VECA AIRLINES VU / VAR

	Reg	Type	c/n	
☐	N1235V	A319-132	2718	♦
☐	N1821V	A319-132	2383	

YU- SERBIA

AIR SERBIA JU / ASL

	Reg	Type	c/n	
☐	YU-APA	A319-132	2277	
☐	YU-APB	A319-132	2296	
☐	YU-APC	A319-131	2621	
☐	YU-APD	A319-132	2335	
☐	YU-APE	A319-132	3252	
☐	YU-APF	A319-132	3317	
☐	YU-API	A319-132	1140	
☐	YU-APJ	A319-132	1159	
☐	YU-APG	A320-232	2587	
☐	YU-APH	A320-232	2645	
☐	YU-ALN	ATR 72-202	180	
☐	YU-ALO	ATR 72-202	186	
☐	YU-ALP	ATR 72-202	189	
☐	YU-ALT	ATR 72-212A	555	
☐	YU-ALU	ATR 72-212A	536	
☐	YU-ALV	ATR 72-212A	727	♦
☐	YU-ANF	B737-3H9	23330/1136	[BEG]
☐	YU-ANH	B737-3H9	23415/1171	[BEG]
☐	YU-ANL	B737-3H9	23716/1321	[BEG]
☐	YU-ANV	B737-3H9	24140/1524	[BEG]
☐	YU-ANW	B737-3H9	24141/1526	[BEG]

AVIOLET JU

	Reg	Type	c/n	
☐	YU-AND	B737-3H9	23329/1134	
☐	YU-ANI	B737-3H9	23416/1175	
☐	YU-ANJ	B737-3H9	23714/1305	♦
☐	YU-ANK	B737-3H9	23715/1310	♦

YV VENEZUELA

NOTE: *aircraft with marks ending in T are probably not active and some may be awaiting overhaul*

AERO EJECUTIVOS VEJ

	Reg	Type	c/n	
☐	YV1854	Douglas DC-3	6135	
☐	YV201T	Douglas DC-3	11775	
☐	YV211T	Douglas DC-3	10201	^
☐	YV212T	Douglas DC-6B	44419/491	
☐	YV214T	Douglas DC-6	43708/347	^
☐	YV-426C	Douglas DC-3	4093	
☐	YV-440C	Douglas DC-3	2201	

^ wears AECA titles

AEROMED

	Reg	Type	c/n
☐	YV1752	LET L-410UVP-E	861719
☐	YV2027	LET L-410UVP-E	861713

AEROPOSTAL VH / ALV

	Reg	Type	c/n	
☐	YV139T	DC-9-51	47695/806	[CCS]
☐	YV505T	MD-82	49794/1600	
☐	YV529T	MD-83	53024/1825	
☐	YV563T	MD-82	53225/2086	
☐	YV2793	MD-82	49796/1713	
☐	YV2957	MD-82	53233/2110	
☐	YV2992	MD-82	53206/2034	
☐	YV3097	MD-82	49969/1719	♦

ALBATROS AIRLINES — G2 / GAL

YV3001	B737-5L9	28995/2947	
YV2814	EMB.120RT	120130	
YV2776	EMB.120RT	120150	
YV2777	EMB.120RT	120074	

ASERCA AIRLINES — R7 / OCA

YV119T	DC-9-31	47271/389	std
YV368T	DC-9-32	47518/614	std
YV372T	DC-9-32	47575/680	std
YV1492	DC-9-31	45864/130	[CCS]
YV1663	DC-9-31	48144/1039	[CCS]
YV2220	DC-9-31	48155/1050	std
YV2259	DC-9-31	48120/949	std
YV2431	DC-9-31	48119/943	std
YV2434	DC-9-32	47473/598	[CCS]
YV2444	DC-9-32	47282/446	[CCS]
YV153T	MD-82	49486/1317	
YV493T	MD-82	49517/1633	
YV494T	MD-82	49521/1690	
YV593T	MD-83	49848/1592	
YV2749	MD-82	49258/1161	
YV2754	MD-82	49259/1162	
YV2971	MD-83	53472/2178	
YV2990	MD-83	53473/2183	
YV3024	MD-83	53453/2112	

AVIOR AIRLINES — 9V / ROI

YV343T	B737-232	23101/1041	[BLA]
YV344T	B737-232	23081/1005	[BLA]♦
YV2732	B737-2Y5	23848/1418	
YV2794	B737-232	23089/1019	
YV2823	B737-232	23090/1020	
YV2928	B737-401	23885/1512	
YV2937	B737-2Y5	23847/1414	
YV2946	B737-401	23886/1487	
YV2998	B737-2Y5	23848/1418	♦
YV3011	B737-401	23989/1716	
YV3012	B737-401	23990/1732	
YV3151	B737-2T5	22979/950	♦
YV3157	B737-4B7	24862/1910	♦
YV3158	B737-401	23984/1674	♦
YV	B737-4B7	24781/1874	o/o♦
YV	B737-4B7	24812/1892	o/o♦

AVIOR REGIONAL — RGR

YV2917	Fokker 50	20193	
YV2936	Fokker 50	20195	
YV2948	Fokker 50	20198	
YV2976	Fokker 50	20188	[PZO]
YV2977	Fokker 50	20187	[PZO]
YV3010	Fokker 50	20237	[PZO]♦

COMERAVIA — CVV

YV396T	Short SD.3-60	SH3713	
YV1232	LET L-410UVP	810640	
YV1233	LET L-410UVP	851427	
YV1332	LET L-410UVP	831028	
YV1333	LET L-410UVP-E	861709	♦

CONVIASA — VO / VCV

YV1004	A340-211	031	[CCS]
YV1005	ATR 42-320	491	[CCS]
YV1008	ATR 42-320	346	[CCS]
YV1009	ATR 42-320	487	
YV1850	ATR 72-201	276	[CCS]
YV2421	ATR 72-212	482	[MYR]
YV2422	ATR 72-212	486	[CCS]
YV101T	B737-291	21747/555	std
YV378T	B737-25A	23789/1392	[LIM]
YV475T	B737-230	22124/727	[LIM]
YV476T	B737-230	22121/720	[LIM]
YV1007	B737-322	23949/1493	
YV2558	B737-232	23096/1028	[CCS]
YV2559	B737-232	23097/1029	
EC-LNA	B747-446	26346/897	<PLM♦
YV1111	CRJ-701ER	10270	[FLL]
YV1115	CRJ-701ER	10271	
YV2088	CRJ-701ER	10274	
YV2115	CRJ-701ER	10275	
YV2849	ERJ-190AR	19000509	
YV2850	ERJ-190AR	19000505	
YV2851	ERJ-190AR	19000515	
YV2911	ERJ-190STD	19000610	
YV2912	ERJ-190STD	19000612	
YV2913	ERJ-190AR	19000622	
YV2943	ERJ-190AR	19000634	
YV2944	ERJ-190AR	19000635	
YV2953	ERJ-190AR	19000643	
YV2954	ERJ-190AR	19000644	
YV2964	ERJ-190AR	19000645	
YV2965	ERJ-190AR	19000646	
YV2966	ERJ-190AR	19000485	
YV3016	ERJ-190ECJ Lineage 1000	19000177	
YV3052	ERJ-190IGW	19000675	
YV3071	ERJ-190IGW	19000676	

COSTA AIRLINES — COT

YV550T	CRJ-200LR	7172	
YV	CRJ-200ER	7851	o/o♦

ESTELAR LATINOAMERICA — E4 / ETR

YV497T	B737-247	23603/1361	
YV498T	B737-2E3	22703/811	
YV2722	B737-2Y5	24031/1523	
YV2792	B737-2B7	22887/976	
YV2918	B737-329	23773/1441	

LASER — QL / LER

YV167T	DC-9-32	47281/427	[CCS]
YV331T	DC-9-31	48157/1054	
YV332T	DC-9-31	48158/1056	[CCS]
YV469T	MD-81	53299/2075	
YV480T	MD-81	53043/1982	
YV492T	MD-81	53301/2082	
YV1240	MD-81	49907/1734	
YV1243	MD-81	49908/1749	
YV2923	MD-82	49563/1485	
YV2927	MD-82	49924/1759	
YV2945	MD-82	49564/1486	
YV3053	MD-82	49566/1497	
YV3145	MD-82	49565/1496	♦
YV	MD-82	49919/1744	o/o♦

LINEA TURISTICA AEREOTUY — LD / TUY

☐	YV382T	ATR 42-320	110	
☐	YV2757	ATR 42-320	206	
☐	YV1184	DHC-7-102	030	
☐	YV1185	DHC-7-102	005	[CCS]
☐	YV-640C	DHC-7-102	017	[CCS]

PERLA AIRLINES — DP / PLV

☐	YV335T	MD-82	49232/1178	
☐	YV529T	MD-83	53024/1825	

RUTACA — 5R / RUC

☐	YV169T	B737-2S3	21776/577	
☐	YV170T	B737-2M8	21231/462	std
☐	YV369T	B737-230	22113/649	std
☐	YV379T	B737-230	22115/694	std
☐	YV380T	B737-230	22127/745	
☐	YV390T	B737-230	22128/752	
☐	YV397T	B737-236	23225/1102	std♦
☐	YV472T	B737-242	22074/619	std
☐	YV1007	B737-322	23949/1493	o/o
☐	YV1381	B737-2S3	21774/563	
☐	YV2556	B737-3G7	24712/1869	o/o♦
☐	YV3063	B737-3Q8	26311/2681	
☐	YV	B737-244	22581/796	o/o

SBA AIRLINES — S3 / BBR

☐	CS-TFZ	A330-243	1008	<HFY♦
☐	YV1421	ATR 42-320	300	std
☐	YV1422	ATR 42-320	340	std
☐	YV1423	ATR 42-320	360	[CCS]
☐	YV1424	ATR 42-320	368	std
☐	YV2314	ATR 42-300	038	[CCS]
☐	YV288T	B757-21B	24402/233	[MEX]
☐	YV304T	B757-21B	24714/262	
☐	YV450T	B757-236	24370/218	
☐	YV528T	B767-3P6ER	24349/244	
☐	YV545T	B767-3P6ER	23764/158	
☐	YV612T	B767-351ER/W	26608/559	♦
☐	YV348T	MD-82	49120/1071	std
☐	YV481T	MD-82	49846/1581	
☐	YV485T	MD-83	49668/1467	

SOLAR CARGO — 4S / OLC

☐	YV1402	An-26	7207	[VLN]
☐	YV1403	An-26	9810	[VLN]
☐	YV524T	DC-10-30F	47840/337	

SUNDANCE AIR — SUV

☐	YV1544	LET L-410UVP	831032	
☐	YV2063	LET L-410UVP	831010	

TRANSAVEN — VEN

☐	YV1417	LET L-410UVP	830939	
☐	YV2082	LET L-410UVP-E	902430	
☐	YV2083	LET L-410UVP-E	892314	

TRANSCARGA INT'L AIRWAYS — T9 / TIW

☐	YV560T	A300B4-203F	261	
☐	YV562T	A300B4-203F	274	
☐	YV	A300B4-203F	152	o/o
☐	YV	A300B4-203F	220	o/o
☐	YV	A300B4-203F	234	o/o
☐	YV	A300B4-203F	259	o/o♦
☐	YV2546	EMB.120RTF	120017	
☐	YV2694	EMB.120RTF	120021	

TRANSMANDU

☐	YV1019	BAeJetstream 32	911	
☐	YV2456	BAeJetstream 32	884	
☐	YV2532	BAeJetstream 32	965	♦
☐	YV2536	BAeJetstream 32	966	

TURPIAL AIRLINES

☐	YV	B737-4S3	24795/1870	o/o♦

VENESCAR INTERNACIONAL — V4 / VEC

☐	YV2308	ATR 42-300F	061	
☐	YV2309	B727-31F	20114/712	std
☐	YV478T	B727-2Q4F	22424/1683	[SFB]
☐	YV567T	B737-4Q3F	29487/3122	
☐	YV573T	B737-4Q3F	26606/2898	♦

VENEZOLANA — VNE

☐	YV179T	BAeJetstream 31	759	
☐	YV180T	BAeJetstream 31	770	
☐	YV-1084C	BAeJetstream 31	734	
☐	YV-1085C	BAeJetstream 31	729	
☐	YV290T	BAeJetstream 41	41020	♦
☐	YV268T	B737-232	23099/1035	std
☐	YV287T	B737-217	22728/911	std
☐	YV296T	B737-2T5	22024/641	
☐	YV302T	B737-2T5	23087/1013	std
☐	YV502T	B737-291	21598/512	
☐	YV513T	B737-230	23158/1089	
☐	YV535T	B737-230	23153/1075	std
☐	YV191T	MD-83	49392/1272	
☐	YV514T	MD-82	49511/1537	
☐	YV	MD-82	49513/1568	o/o

Z- ZIMBABWE

AIR ZIMBABWE — UM / AZW

☐	Z-WPA	B737-2N0	23677/1313	
☐	Z-WPB	B737-2N0	23678/1405	
☐	Z-WPC	B737-2N0	23679/1415	[HRE]
☐	Z-WPD	BAe146 Srs.200	E2065	[HRE]
☐	Z-WPE	B767-2N0ER	24713/287	
☐	Z-WPF	B767-2N0ER	24867/333	
☐	Z-WPK	XIAN MA60	0302	[HRE]
☐	Z-WPM	A320-214	0630	[JNB]
☐	Z-WPN	A320-211	1973	

FASTJET ZIMBABWE — FN / FJW

☐	Z-FJE	A319-131	2281	♦

FLYAFRICA.COM — Z7 / FZW

☐	Z-FAA	B737-55S	26539/2300	
☐	Z-FAB	B737-55S	26540/2317	
☐	Z-	B737-5xx	26541/2319	o/o♦

GLOBAL AFRICA AVIATION — Z3 / SMJ

☐	Z-GAA	MD-11F	48410/495	♦

☐	Z-GAB	MD-11F	48746/597	
☐	Z-GAC	MD-11F	48756/623	

ZK- NEW ZEALAND

AIR CHATHAMS CV / CVA

☐	ZK-CIB	Convair 580F	327A	
☐	ZK-CIE	Convair 580	399	
☐	ZK-CIF	Convair 580	381	
☐	ZK-AWP	Douglas DC-3C	16387/33135	

AIR FREIGHT NZ AFN

☐	ZK-FTA	Convair 580F	168	
☐	ZK-KFH	Convair 580F	42	
☐	ZK-KFJ	Convair 580F	114	
☐	ZK-KFL	Convair 580F	372	
☐	ZK-KFS	Convair 5800	277	

AIR NEW ZEALAND NZ / ANZ

☐	ZK-OAB	A320-232	4553	
☐	ZK-OJA	A320-232	2085	
☐	ZK-OJB	A320-232	2090	
☐	ZK-OJC	A320-232	2112	
☐	ZK-OJD	A320-232	2130	
☐	ZK-OJE	A320-232	2148	
☐	ZK-OJF	A320-232	2153	
☐	ZK-OJG	A320-232	2173	
☐	ZK-OJH	A320-232	2257	
☐	ZK-OJI	A320-232	2297	
☐	ZK-OJK	A320-232	2445	
☐	ZK-OJM	A320-232	2533	
☐	ZK-OJN	A320-232	2594	
☐	ZK-OJO	A320-232	2663	
☐	ZK-OJQ	A320-232	4584	
☐	ZK-OJR	A320-232	4884	
☐	ZK-OJS	A320-232	4926	
☐	ZK-OXA	A320-232/S	5629	
☐	ZK-OXB	A320-232/S	5682	
☐	ZK-OXC	A320-232/S	5847	
☐	ZK-OXD	A320-232/S	5962	
☐	ZK-OXE	A320-232/S	5993	
☐	ZK-OXF	A320-232/S	6182	
☐	ZK-OXG	A320-232/S	6460	
☐	ZK-OXH	A320-232/S	6471	
☐	ZK-OXI	A320-232/S	6533	
☐	ZK-OXJ	A320-232/S	6694	
☐	ZK-OXK	A320-232/S	6706	♦
☐	ZK-OXL	A320-232/S	7086	o/o♦
☐	ZK-NCG	B767-319ER/W	26912/509	
☐	ZK-NCI	B767-319ER/W	26913/558	
☐	ZK-NCJ	B767-319ER/W	26915/574	
☐	ZK-NCK	B767-319ER/W	26971/663	
☐	ZK-NCL	B767-319ER/W	28745/677	
☐	ZK-OKA	B777-219ER	29404/534	
☐	ZK-OKB	B777-219ER	34376/537	
☐	ZK-OKC	B777-219ER	34377/546	
☐	ZK-OKD	B777-219ER	29401/550	
☐	ZK-OKE	B777-219ER	32712/564	
☐	ZK-OKF	B777-219ER	34378/575	
☐	ZK-OKG	B777-219ER	29403/591	
☐	ZK-OKH	B777-219ER	34379/605	
☐	ZK-OKM	B777-319ER	38405/902	
☐	ZK-OKN	B777-319ER	38406/911	
☐	ZK-OKO	B777-319ER	38407/921	
☐	ZK-OKP	B777-319ER	39041/972	
☐	ZK-OKQ	B777-319ER	40689/984	
☐	ZK-OKR	B777-319ER	44546/1206	
☐	ZK-OKS	B777-319ER	44547/1237	
☐	ZK-NZC	B787-9	41988/126	
☐	ZK-NZD	B787-9	41989/133	
☐	ZK-NZE	B787-9	34334/169	
☐	ZK-NZF	B787-9	34335/213	
☐	ZK-NZG	B787-9	37963/236	
☐	ZK-NZH	B787-9	37964/351	
☐	ZK-NZI	B787-9	37965/456	o/o♦
☐	ZK-NZJ	B787-9	37966/468	o/o♦
☐	ZK-NZK	B787-9	43217/490	o/o♦

AIR NEW ZEALAND LINK NZ / NZA

☐	ZK-MCA	ATR 72-212A	597	
☐	ZK-MCB	ATR 72-212A	598	
☐	ZK-MCC	ATR 72-212A	714	
☐	ZK-MCF	ATR 72-212A	600	
☐	ZK-MCJ	ATR 72-212A	624	
☐	ZK-MCO	ATR 72-212A	628	
☐	ZK-MCP	ATR 72-212A	630	
☐	ZK-MCU	ATR 72-212A	632	
☐	ZK-MCW	ATR 72-212A	646	
☐	ZK-MCX	ATR 72-212A	687	
☐	ZK-MCY	ATR 72-212A	703	
☐	ZK-MVA	ATR 72-600	1051	
☐	ZK-MVB	ATR 72-600	1065	
☐	ZK-MVC	ATR 72-600	1084	
☐	ZK-MVD	ATR 72-600	1117	
☐	ZK-MVE	ATR 72-600	1182	
☐	ZK-MVF	ATR 72-600	1228	
☐	ZK-MVG	ATR 72-600	1264	♦
☐	ZK-MVH	ATR 72-600	1304	♦
☐	ZK-MVI	ATR 72-600	1306	♦
☐	ZK-MVJ	ATR 72-600	1319	o/o♦
☐	ZK-MVK	ATR 72-600	1328	o/o♦
☐	ZK-MVL	ATR 72-600		o/o♦
☐	ZK-MVM	ATR 72-600		o/o♦
☐	ZK-MVO	ATR 72-600	1299	♦
☐	ZK-EAB	Beech 1900D	UE-425	
☐	ZK-EAC	Beech 1900D	UE-426	
☐	ZK-EAD	Beech 1900D	UE-427	
☐	ZK-EAE	Beech 1900D	UE-428	
☐	ZK-EAF	Beech 1900D	UE-429	
☐	ZK-EAG	Beech 1900D	UE-430	
☐	ZK-EAH	Beech 1900D	UE-431	
☐	ZK-EAJ	Beech 1900D	UE-433	std
☐	ZK-EAN	Beech 1900D	UE-437	
☐	ZK-EAO	Beech 1900D	UE-438	
☐	ZK-EAP	Beech 1900D	UE-439	
☐	ZK-NEA	DHC-8Q-311	611	
☐	ZK-NEB	DHC-8Q-311	615	
☐	ZK-NEC	DHC-8Q-311	616	
☐	ZK-NED	DHC-8Q-311	617	
☐	ZK-NEE	DHC-8Q-311	618	
☐	ZK-NEF	DHC-8Q-311	620	
☐	ZK-NEG	DHC-8Q-311	621	
☐	ZK-NEH	DHC-8Q-311	623	
☐	ZK-NEJ	DHC-8Q-311	625	
☐	ZK-NEK	DHC-8Q-311	629	
☐	ZK-NEM	DHC-8Q-311	630	
☐	ZK-NEO	DHC-8Q-311	633	
☐	ZK-NEP	DHC-8Q-311	634	
☐	ZK-NEQ	DHC-8Q-311	636	

	Reg	Type	c/n	Notes
☐	ZK-NER	DHC-8Q-311	639	
☐	ZK-NES	DHC-8Q-311	641	
☐	ZK-NET	DHC-8Q-311	642	
☐	ZK-NEU	DHC-8Q-311	647	
☐	ZK-NEW	DHC-8Q-311	648	
☐	ZK-NEZ	DHC-8Q-311	654	
☐	ZK-NFA	DHC-8Q-311	659	
☐	ZK-NFB	DHC-8Q-311	670	
☐	ZK-NFI	DHC-8Q-311	671	

AIRWORK NEW ZEALAND — *AWK*

	Reg	Type	c/n	Notes
☐	ZK-FXT	B737-3B7(SF)	23862/1586	>TFR
☐	ZK-JTQ	B737-476	24442/2371	>TFR
☐	ZK-PAK	B737-476F	24444/2454	♦
☐	ZK-TLA	B737-3B7(SF)	23383/1425	
☐	ZK-TLD	B737-3B7(SF)	23706/1499	>TFR
☐	ZK-TLE	B737-3S1(SF)	24834/1896	>TFR
☐	ZK-TLJ	B737-476(SF)	24432/1879	>TFR♦
☐	ZK-TLK	B737-476(SF)	24434/1912	>TFR♦
☐	ZK-ECI	BAeJetstream 32EP	946	
☐	ZK-ECJ	BAeJetstream 32EP	969	
☐	ZK-PAX	F.27 Friendship 500	10596	
☐	ZK-POH	F.27 Friendship 500	10680	
☐	ZK-NSS	SA.227AC Metro III	AC-692B	
☐	ZK-POB	SA.227AC Metro III	AC-606B	
☐	ZK-POE	SA.227DC Metro 23	CC-843B	
☐	ZK-POF	SA.227DC Metro 23	CC-844B	

JETCONNECT — *QF / QNZ*

	Reg	Type	c/n	Notes
☐	ZK-ZQA	B737-838/W	34200/2989	
☐	ZK-ZQB	B737-838/W	34201/3006	
☐	ZK-ZQC	B737-838/W	34202/3048	
☐	ZK-ZQD	B737-838/W	34203/3515	
☐	ZK-ZQE	B737-838/W	34185/3542	
☐	ZK-ZQF	B737-838/W	34204/3552	
☐	ZK-ZQG	B737-838/W	34190/3683	
☐	ZK-ZQH	B737-838/W	39357/3743	

JETSTAR NEW ZEALAND — *JQ / SCR*

	Reg	Type	c/n	Notes
☐	VH-SBI	DHC-8Q-315	605	<QFA♦
☐	VH-TQD	DHC-8Q-315	598	<QFA♦
☐	VH-TQK	DHC-8Q-315	600	<QFA♦
☐	VH-TQL	DHC-8Q-315	603	<QFA♦
☐	VH-TQM	DHC-8Q-315	604	<QFA♦

KIWI REGIONAL AIRLINES — *KRL*

	Reg	Type	c/n	Notes
☐	ZK-KRA	SAAB SF.340A(QC)	340A-065	♦

ZP- PARAGUAY

AMASZONAS DEL PARAGUAY — *AZP*

	Reg	Type	c/n	Notes
☐	ZP-CRN	CRJ-200ER	7866	♦

ZS- SOUTH AFRICA

AFRICA CHARTER AIRLINE — *FSK*

	Reg	Type	c/n	Notes
☐	ZS-SID	B737-244F	22583/809	♦
☐	ZS-TFT	B737-3Q8	26301/2623	♦

AIRLINK — *4Z / LNK*

	Reg	Type	c/n	Notes
☐	ZS-ASW	Avro 146-RJ85	E2313	
☐	ZS-ASX	Avro 146-RJ85	E2314	
☐	ZS-ASY	Avro 146-RJ85	E2316	
☐	ZS-ASZ	Avro 146-RJ85	E2318	
☐	ZS-PUL	BAe146 Srs.200	E2064	[JNB]
☐	ZS-SSH	Avro 146-RJ85	E2285	
☐	ZS-SSI	Avro 146-RJ85	E2383	
☐	ZS-SSJ	Avro 146-RJ85	E2385	
☐	ZS-SSK	Avro 146-RJ85	E2251	
☐	ZS-SYO	Avro 146-RJ85	E2394	
☐	ZS-SYP	Avro 146-RJ85	E2393	
☐	ZS-TCO	Avro 146-RJ85	E2388	
☐	ZS-TCP	Avro 146-RJ85	E2389	
☐	ZS-NRE	BAeJetstream 41	41048	
☐	ZS-NRF	BAeJetstream 41	41050	
☐	ZS-NRG	BAeJetstream 41	41051	
☐	ZS-NRH	BAeJetstream 41	41054	
☐	ZS-NRI	BAeJetstream 41	41061	
☐	ZS-NRJ	BAeJetstream 41	41062	
☐	ZS-OEX	BAeJetstream 41	41103	
☐	ZS-OMZ	BAeJetstream 41	41037	
☐	ZS-DFA	ERJ-145MP	145165	
☐	ZS-OTM	ERJ-135LR	145485	>SZL
☐	ZS-OTN	ERJ-135LR	145491	
☐	ZS-OUV	ERJ-135LR	145493	
☐	ZS-SJX	ERJ-135LR	145428	
☐	ZS-SNV	ERJ-135LR	145551	
☐	ZS-SNW	ERJ-135LR	145720	
☐	ZS-SNX	ERJ-135LR	145620	
☐	ZS-SNZ	ERJ-135LR	145725	
☐	ZS-SUV	ERJ-135LR	145663	
☐	ZS-SWN	ERJ-135LR	145453	
☐	ZS-SWV	ERJ-135LR	145737	
☐	ZS-SYB	ERJ-145MP	145308	
☐	ZS-SYT	ERJ-135LR	145358	>SZL
☐	ZS-TCB	ERJ-135ER	145210	
☐	ZS-TCE	ERJ-135LR	145356	
☐	ZS-TFK	ERJ-135LR	145249	
☐	ZS-TFL	ERJ-135LR	145368	

AWESOME AVIATION — *ASM*

	Reg	Type	c/n	Notes
☐	ZS-FAB	Beech 1900D	UE-227	♦
☐	ZS-FAN	Beech 1900D	UE-198	
☐	ZS-JAG	Beech 1900D	UE-115	
☐	ZS-PRG	Beech 1900D	UE-90	
☐	ZS-SEM	Beech 1900D	UE-91	
☐	ZS-SNO	Beech 1900D	UE-96	

CEM AIR — *5Z / CEM*

	Reg	Type	c/n	Notes
☐	ZS-CEM	Beech 1900D	UE-182	♦
☐	ZS-CMA	Beech 1900D	UE-259	
☐	ZS-CMI	Beech 1900D	UE-218	♦
☐	ZS-OMB	Beech 1900D	UE-81	
☐	ZS-OUG	Beech 1900D	UE-14	♦
☐	ZS-PKB	Beech 1900D	UE-3	
☐	ZS-PYU	Beech 1900D	UE-107	
☐	ZS-CMB	CRJ-100ER	7215	>PFZ
☐	ZS-CMD	CRJ-100ER	7141	>PFZ
☐	ZS-CMR	CRJ-100ER	7326	>ATC
☐	ZS-CRJ	CRJ-100ER	7338	>ATC
☐	ZS-KEM	CRJ-200ER	7297	>ATC
☐	ZS-	CRJ-100ER	7292	std♦
☐	ZS-	CRJ-100ER	7293	o/o
☐	ZS	CRJ-200ER	8028	std♦
☐	ZS	CRJ-200ER	8037	std♦
☐	ZS-	CRJ-100ER	7109	o/o♦

☐	ZS-DHC	DHC-8-102	030	

COMAIR — MN / CAW

☐	ZS-OAA	B737-4L7	26960/2483	^
☐	ZS-OAF	B737-4S3	25116/2061	*
☐	ZS-OAG	B737-4H6	27168/2435	^
☐	ZS-OAM	B737-4S3	24164/1702	^
☐	ZS-OAO	B737-4S3	24163/1700	^
☐	ZS-OAP	B737-4S3	24167/1736	^
☐	ZS-OAR	B737-476	28152/2829	
☐	ZS-OAT	B737-476	28150/2773	
☐	ZS-OAV	B737-4H6	27086/2426	^
☐	ZS-OKG	B737-376	23483/1264	^
☐	ZS-OKK	B737-376	23485/1277	^
☐	ZS-OTF	B737-436	25305/2147	^
☐	ZS-OTG	B737-436	25840/2197	^
☐	ZS-OTH	B737-436	25841/2222	^
☐	ZS-ZWA	B737-8LD/W	40851/4094	*
☐	ZS-ZWB	B737-8LD/W	40852/4229	*
☐	ZS-ZWC	B737-8LD/W	40853/4252	*
☐	ZS-ZWD	B737-8LD/W	40855/4279	*
☐	ZS-ZWE	B737-8LD/W	40854/5518	*♦
☐	ZS-ZWF	B737-8LD/W	40856/5606	*♦
☐	ZS-ZWG	B737-8LD/W	40972/5770	^♦
☐	ZS-ZWI	B737-85R/W	30403/749	^
☐	ZS-ZWO	B737-8K2/W	28373/51	*
☐	ZS-ZWP	B737-86N/W	28612/455	*
☐	ZS-ZWQ	B737-8K2/W	28374/57	*
☐	ZS-ZWR	B737-85P/W	28382/256	^
☐	ZS-ZWS	B737-86N/W	32732/1056	*
☐	ZS-ZWT	B737-8K5/W	27990/246	*

^ British Airways colours and titles;
** operates as Kulula.com division*

DHL AVIATION AFRICA — DHV

☐	HB-AFH	ATR 72-202F	313	<FAT
☐	HB-AFP	ATR 72-201F	381	<FAT♦
☐	HB-AFR	ATR 72-201F	195	<FAT
☐	ZS-OVP	ATR 42-300F	088	<SET

FAIR AVIATION — FAV

☐	ZS-BIL	B737-277	22650/806	♦
☐	ZS-SIK	B737-244	22590/854	[JNB]♦
☐	ZS-SIL	B737-244	22591/859	♦
☐	ZS-SMO	BAe146 Srs.300	E3169	♦
☐	ZS-SOP	BAe146 Srs.300	E3187	♦

FEDERAL AIR — TV / PDF

☐	ZS-DRC	Beech 1900C-1	UC-166	♦
☐	ZS-OXN	Beech 1900D	UE-83	
☐	ZS-PJY	Beech 1900D	UE-204	
☐	ZS-PUC	Beech 1900D	UE-84	
☐	ZS-PWY	Beech 1900D	UE-87	

FLYSAFAIR — FA / SFR

☐	ZS-IAB	B737-210C	20917/344	^
☐	ZS-JRC	B737-42JF	27143/2457	UN
☐	ZS-JRD	B737-4Y0	24917/2071	
☐	ZS-JRE	B737-4Y0	26065/2284	
☐	ZS-JRF	B737-4L7F	26961/2517	
☐	ZS-JRI	B737-4Q8	25095/2265	
☐	ZS-JRK	B737-4Q8	25096/2278	
☐	ZS-JRL	B737-46M	28550/2847	♦
☐	ZS-SIF	B737-244F	22585/828	^
☐	ZS-SIS	B737-236	21801/669	[JNB]
☐	ZS-SJR	B737-844/W	32631/1176	♦
☐	ZS-SMJ	B737-3Y0F	23500/1243	[JNB]

☐	ZS-JIV	L-382G-30 Hercules	4673	
☐	ZS-JIZ	L-382G-35C Hercules	4695	
☐	ZS-OPS	L-382G-42C Hercules	4799	♦
☐	ZS-ORB	L-382G-14C Hercules	4248	
☐	ZS-RSC	L-382G-28C Hercules	4475	
☐	ZS-RSF	L-382G-31C Hercules	4562	
☐	ZS-RSG	L-382G-31C Hercules	4565	

☐	ZS-OBF	MD-82	48019/1001	[JNB]
☐	ZS-OPX	MD-83	53012/1736	[JNB]
☐	ZS-OPZ	MD-83	49617/1464	[JNB]
☐	ZS-SKB	MD-83	49966/2047	>RNX
☐	ZS-TRI	MD-83	49707/1487	

^ operated as Bid Air Cargo

GLOBAL AIRWAYS

☐	YL-RGA	A320-231	0053	o/o♦

GRYPHON AIR — GP / GRF

☐	ZS-EVE	B737-230	22123/726	
☐	ZS-GAB	MD-82	49165/1117	
☐	ZS-GAG	DC-9-32	47190/240	[JNB]
☐	ZS-GAU	DC-9-32	47798/914	
☐	ZS-JDS	MD-82	49254/1156	o/o♦
☐	ZS-TRJ	MD-87	49829/1678	

INTER AIR — D6 / ILN

☐	ZS-IJA	B737-201	22751/857	[JNB]
☐	ZS-IJB	B767-266ERM	23180/99	
☐	ZS-IJI	B707-323C	19517/614	[PTG]
☐	ZS-IJJ	B737-2H7C	20591/309	
☐	ZS-IJK	B727-61	19176/290	[PTG]
☐	ZS-SIH	B737-244	22587/835	

MANGO — JEJ

☐	ZS-SJG	B737-8BG/W	32353/711	
☐	ZS-SJH	B737-8BG/W	32354/725	
☐	ZS-SJK	B737-8BG/W	32355/807	
☐	ZS-SJL	B737-8BG/W	32356/819	
☐	ZS-SJO	B737-8BG/W	32357/918	♦
☐	ZS-SJP	B737-8BG/W	32358/955	
☐	ZS-SJT	B737-844/W	32633/1225	
☐	ZS-TGB	B737-36Q	29327/3023	♦

PHOEBUS APOLLO AVIATION — PE / PHB

☐	ZS-DIW	Douglas DC-3	11991	
☐	ZS-PAI	Douglas DC-4	27319	
☐	ZS-PAK	DC-9-32	47368/505	
☐	ZS-PAL	DC-9-33RC	47704/819	[JNB]
☐	9J-PAA	ATL-98 Carvair	27314/21	

ROVOS AIR — 6P / VOS

☐	ZS-ARV	Convair 340-67	228	
☐	ZS-BRV	Convair 340-67	215	
☐	ZS-CRV	Douglas DC-3	13331	

SOLENTA AVIATION — SL / SET

☐	ZS-AFR	ATR 42-500	643	
☐	ZS-ATR	ATR 42-300F	060	>GBX
☐	ZS-LUC	ATR 42-320	032	
☐	ZS-OVP	ATR 42-300F	088	>DHV
☐	ZS-OVR	ATR 42-300F	116	[MGL]

☐	ZS-OVS	ATR 42-320F	075	
☐	ZS-XCA	ATR 72-212	463	[MGL]
☐	ZS-XCB	ATR 72-212	460	std♦
☐	ZS-XCC	ATR 42-500	528	>EKG
☐	ZS-XCD	ATR 42-300F	228	
☐	ZS-XCE	ATR 72-202	396	
☐	ZS-XCG	ATR 42-500	443	>EKG
☐	ZS-AEA	Beech 1900D	UE-385	
☐	ZS-MKE	Beech 1900D	UE-44	>DHV
☐	ZS-NAC	Beech 1900D	UE-28	
☐	ZS-NPT	Beech 1900C-1	UC-113	>DHV
☐	ZS-OCX	Beech 1900D	UE-321	
☐	ZS-OHE	Beech 1900C-1	UC-48	
☐	ZS-OLY	Beech 1900D	UE-39	
☐	ZS-OYC	Beech 1900D	UE-117	
☐	ZS-OYE	Beech 1900D	UE-200	
☐	ZS-OYJ	Beech 1900D	UE-273	
☐	ZS-OYK	Beech 1900D	UE-318	
☐	ZS-PJX	Beech 1900D	UE-102	
☐	ZS-TIL	Beech 1900D	UE-21	♦
☐	ZS-ZED	Beech 1900D	UE-260	
☐	ZS-BBC	ERJ-145LU	145395	♦
☐	ZS-BBD	ERJ-145LU	145242	♦
☐	ZS-BBH	ERJ-145LR	145604	
☐	ZS-BBI	ERJ-145LR	145223	^
☐	ZS-BBJ	ERJ-145LR	145277	^
☐	ZS-BBK	ERJ-135LR	145396	
☐	ZS-BBM	ERJ-145LR	145597	>EKG
☐	ZS-ZAA	LET 410UVP-E20	2919	
☐	ZS-ZAB	LET 410UVP-E20	2920	
☐	ZS-ZAC	LET 410UVP-E20	3001	
☐	ZS-ZAD	LET 410UVP-E20	3003	
☐	ZS-ZAE	LET 410UVP-E20	3007	♦
☐	ZS-ZAF	LET 410UVP-E20	3008	♦

^ operates Fky Blue Crane (7B)

SOUTH AFRICAN AIRWAYS SA / SAA

☐	ZS-SFG	A319-131	2326	
☐	ZS-SFH	A319-131	2355	
☐	ZS-SFI	A319-131	2375	
☐	ZS-SFJ	A319-131	2379	
☐	ZS-SFK	A319-131	2418	
☐	ZS-SFL	A319-131	2438	
☐	ZS-SFM	A319-131	2469	
☐	ZS-SFN	A319-131	2501	
☐	ZS-SZA	A320-232	5637	
☐	ZS-SZB	A320-232	5680	
☐	ZS-SZC	A320-232	5956	
☐	ZS-SZD	A320-232	6007	
☐	ZS-SZE	A320-232	6147	
☐	ZS-SZF	A320-232	6189	
☐	ZS-SZG	A320-232	6200	
☐	ZS-SZH	A320-232	6306	
☐	ZS-SZI	A320-232	6439	
☐	ZS-SZJ	A320-232	6478	
☐	ZS-SZY	A320-232	5011	
☐	ZS-SZZ	A320-232	4990	
☐	ZS-SXU	A330-243	1271	
☐	ZS-SXV	A330-243	1249	
☐	ZS-SXW	A330-243	1236	
☐	ZS-SXX	A330-243	1223	
☐	ZS-SXY	A330-243	1210	
☐	ZS-SXZ	A330-243	1191	
☐	ZS-	A330-343E	1745	o/o♦
☐	ZS-SNA	A340-642	410	
☐	ZS-SNB	A340-642	417	
☐	ZS-SNC	A340-642	426	
☐	ZS-SND	A340-642	531	
☐	ZS-SNE	A340-642	534	
☐	ZS-SNF	A340-642	547	
☐	ZS-SNG	A340-642	557	
☐	ZS-SNH	A340-642	626	
☐	ZS-SNI	A340-642	630	
☐	ZS-SXA	A340-313E	544	
☐	ZS-SXB	A340-313E	582	
☐	ZS-SXC	A340-313E	590	
☐	ZS-SXD	A340-313E	643	
☐	ZS-SXE	A340-313E	646	
☐	ZS-SXF	A340-313E	651	
☐	ZS-SXG	A340-313X	378	
☐	ZS-SXH	A340-313X	197	
☐	ZS-SBA	B737-3Y0F	26070/2349	
☐	ZS-SBB	B737-3Y0F	26072/2369	
☐	ZS-SJA	B737-8S3/W	29248/561	
☐	ZS-SJB	B737-8S3/W	29249/653	
☐	ZS-SJC	B737-85F/W	28828/565	
☐	ZS-SJD	B737-85F/W	28829/582	
☐	ZS-SJE	B737-85F/W	28830/669	
☐	ZS-SJF	B737-85F/W	30006/688	
☐	ZS-SJM	B737-85F/W	30476/789	
☐	ZS-SJN	B737-85F/W	30569/850	
☐	ZS-SJS	B737-844/W	32632/1205	
☐	ZS-SJU	B737-844/W	32634/1383	
☐	ZS-SJV	B737-844/W	32635/1407	

SOUTH AFRICAN EXPRESS XZ / EXY

☐	ZS-NMC	CRJ-200ER	7225	
☐	ZS-NMD	CRJ-200ER	7233	
☐	ZS-NME	CRJ-200ER	7240	
☐	ZS-NMF	CRJ-200ER	7287	
☐	ZS-NMG	CRJ-200ER	7772	
☐	ZS-NMH	CRJ-200ER	7787	
☐	ZS-NMI	CRJ-200ER	7153	
☐	ZS-NMJ	CRJ-200ER	7161	^
☐	ZS-NMK	CRJ-200ER	7198	
☐	ZS-NML	CRJ-200ER	7201	
☐	ZS-NMM	CRJ-200ER	7234	
☐	ZS-NMN	CRJ-200ER	7237	
☐	ZS-NBF	CRJ-701	10028	
☐	ZS-NBG	CRJ-701	10039	
☐	ZS-NMO	DHC-8-402Q	4122	
☐	ZS-NMS	DHC-8-402Q	4127	
☐	ZS-YBP	DHC-8-402Q	4142	
☐	ZS-YBR	DHC-8-402Q	4144	
☐	ZS-YBT	DHC-8-402Q	4146	
☐	ZS-YBU	DHC-8-402Q	4344	
☐	ZS-YBW	DHC-8-402Q	4350	
☐	ZS-YBX	DHC-8-402Q	4366	
☐	ZS-YBY	DHC-8-402Q	4370	
☐	ZS-YBZ	DHC-8-402Q	4175	

^ operates as Maluti Sky in Lesotho

STAR AIR CARGO BRH

☐	ZS-PUI	B737-2B7	22890/986	
☐	ZS-SFX	B737-2B7	22889/983	std
☐	ZS-SGE	B737-2T4	22371/717	[MEX]
☐	ZS-SPU	B737-3S3	24059/1517	♦
☐	ZS-SVT	B737-2K9	23405/1178	

ZS-SVV	B737-236	22030/693	[JNB]
ZS-VDB	B737-31L	27345/2625	
ZS-VDP	B737-31L	27346/2636	

Z8- SOUTH SUDAN

GOLDEN WINGS AVIATION

ZS-BGW	DHC-8-311	250	♦
ZS-	DHC-8-311	414	♦
ZS-SKA	Fokker 70	11559	♦

KUSH AVIATION — KUH

EK4104	LET L410UVP-3	861606	
EY-324	An-32A	1709?	
ET-AKU	Fokker 50	20333	<ETH
ST-ALM	An-32B	3409	
ST-APS	Il-76TD	1023409316	
ST-ASX	Il-76TD	73479392	
ST-KNF	An-26	13006	
5Y-SIA	Fokker 100	11307	<
5Y-BSM	LET L-410UVP-E3	871939	<RRV
5Y-NIK	LET L-410UVP-E19	912619	<RRV

3B- MAURITIUS

AIR MAURITIUS — MK / MAU

3B-NBF	A319-112	1592	
3B-NBH	A319-112	1936	
3B-NBL	A330-202	1057	
3B-NBM	A330-202	883	
3B-NAU	A340-312	076	
3B-NAY	A340-313X	152	
3B-NBD	A340-313X	194	
3B-NBE	A340-313X	268	
3B-NBI	A340-313E	793	
3B-NBJ	A340-313E	800	
OK-GFQ	ATR 72-212A	674	<CSA♦
3B-NBG	ATR 72-212A	690	
3B-NBN	ATR 72-212A	921	

3C- EQUATORIAL GUINEA

AIR ANNOBON

ZS-SOR	BAe146 Srs.300	E3155	
3C-MAA	Avro 146-RJ85	E2365	

CEIBA INTERCONTINENTAL — C2 / CEL

3C-LLG	ATR 42-300	335	[LPA]
3C-LLH	ATR 42-500	671	
3C-	ATR 42-500		o/o♦
3C-LLI	ATR 72-212A	790	
3C-LLM	ATR 72-212A	810	
CS-FAF	B737-8FB/W	41159/4973	
3C-LLW	B737-8FB/W	41158/5180	
3C-LLY	B737-8FB/W	41157/4782	
3C-LLU	B767-306	30393/781	
CS-TQX	B777-2FBLR	40668/937	<WHT
3C-MAB	B777-2FBLR	60116/1258	o/o
RA-76384	Il-76TD-90	1033401015	<♦

CRONOS AIRLINES — C8 / CRA

ZS-SOP	BAe146 Srs.300	E3187	
3C-AKK	BAe146 Srs.200	E2069	
ZS-AKK	ERJ-135LR	145301	
ZS-	ERJ-135LR	145283	♦

EQUATORIAL CONGO AIRLINES — LC

HB-JJB	B737-306	27421/2438	<PTI♦
HB-JJD	B757-236/W	25807/610	<PTI
HB-JJE	B757-204/W	27219/596	<PTI
HB-JJF	B767-316ER/W	27613/652	<PTI
HB-JJH	B737-752/W	33791/1557	<PTI

PUNTO AZUL — ZR

ZS-DFC	ERJ-145MP	145339	
3C-MAC	ERJ-145MP	145244	♦

TANGO AIRWAYS

3C-TAN	MD-82	49987/1760	

3D- SWAZILAND

SWAZILAND AIRLINK — SA / SZL

ZS-SYT	ERJ-135LR	145358	<LNK
ZS-OTM	ERJ-135LR	145485	<LNK♦

4K- AZERBAIJAN

AZERBAIJAN AIRLINES — J2 / AHY

4K-AZ03	A319-111	2516	
4K-AZ04	A319-111	2588	
4K-AZ05	A319-111	2788	
4K-AZ54	A320-211	0331	
4K-AZ77	A320-214	2846	
4K-AZ78	A320-214	2853	
4K-AZ79	A320-214	2865	
4K-AZ80	A320-214	2991	
4K-AZ83	A320-214	2685	
4K-AZ84	A320-214	3006	
4K-AZ85	A340-542	886	
4K-AZ86	A340-542	894	
4K-AI08	A340-642	779	♦
4K-AZ11	B757-22L	29305/894	
4K-AZ12	B757-22L	30834/947	
4K-AZ38	B757-256	26246/620	
4K-AZ43	B757-2M6	23453/100	
4K-AZ81	B767-32LER	40343/1004	
4K-AZ82	B767-32LER/W	41063/1030	
VP-BBR	B787-8	37920/211	
VP-BBS	B787-8	37921/247	
4K-AZ52	ERJ-170	17000002	
4K-AZ64	ERJ-190AR	19000627	
4K-AZ65	ERJ-190AR	19000630	
4K-AZ66	ERJ-190AR	19000631	
4K-AZ67	ERJ-190AR	19000636	
4K-	ERJ-190AR		o/o
4K-	ERJ-190AR		o/o

SILK WAY AIRLINES — ZP / AZQ

4K-AZ23	An-12BK	8345605	
4K-AZ25	An-12BP	3341209	♦
4K-AZ63	An-12BP	9346308	
4K-AZ93	An-12BK	7345203	

	Reg	Type	c/n	Note
☐	4K-AZ19	Il-76TD	53460820	
☐	4K-AZ31	Il-76TD	1013405184	
☐	4K-AZ40	Il-76TD	1043419632	
☐	4K-AZ41	Il-76TD	1093420673	
☐	4K-AZ60	Il-76MD	0093499982	♦
☐	4K-AZ61	Il-76TD	1023412411	
☐	4K-AZ100	Il-76TD-90	2073421708	
☐	4K-AZ101	Il-76TD-90	2083421716	

SILK WAY WEST AIRLINES — 7L / AZG

	Reg	Type	c/n	Note
☐	VQ-BVB	B747-83QF	44444/1501	
☐	VQ-BVC	B747-83QF	44937/1496	
☐	VQ-BWY	B747-83QF	60120/1521	♦
☐	VQ-	B747-83QF		o/o♦
☐	VQ-	B747-83QF		o/o♦
☐	VQ-	B747-83QF		o/o♦
☐	4K-SW008	B747-4R7F	29732/1231	
☐	4K-SW888	B747-4R7F	29730/1203	

SKYWIND — AZH

	Reg	Type	c/n	Note
☐	4K-78129	Il-76MD	83489683	

4L- GEORGIA

BRAVO AIR — BRZ

	Reg	Type	c/n	Note
☐	4L-BKI	An-26	3709	♦
☐	4L-GSS	An-26	5106	
☐	4L-IKE	An-26	5407	
☐	4L-IMA	B737-322	24717/1930	>WLB♦

GEORGIAN AIRWAYS — A9 / TGZ

	Reg	Type	c/n	Note
☐	4L-TGI	B737-505	26336/2805	
☐	4L-TGM	B737-76N/W	29904/347	
☐	4L-TGN	B737-7BK/W	33015/1384	
☐	4L-GAL	CRJ-200ER	7076	
☐	4L-TGB	CRJ-200LR	7442	
☐	4L-TGL	ERJ-170LR	17000093	♦

LUFTLINE GEORGIA — GX / LLS

	Reg	Type	c/n	Note
☐	4L-GSN	B737-405	24643/1860	♦

TCA - THE CARGO AIRLINES — TZS

	Reg	Type	c/n	Note
☐	4L-ABA	A300B4-203F	157	
☐	4L-ABI	A300C4-203F	277	
☐	4L-AMS	A300B4-203F	126	♦
☐	4L-BIC	A300C4-203F	292	
☐	4L-ACE	B747-329(SF)	24837/810	♦
☐	4L-KAB	B747-246F	22477/494	♦

4O- MONTENEGRO

MONTENEGRO AIRLINES — YM / MGX

	Reg	Type	c/n	Note
☐	4O-AOA	ERJ-195LR	19000180	
☐	4O-AOB	ERJ-195LR	19000283	
☐	4O-AOC	ERJ-195LR	19000358	
☐	4O-AOD	ERJ-195LR	19000665	
☐	4O-AOK	Fokker 100	11272	[TGD]
☐	4O-AOL	Fokker 100	11268	[TGD]
☐	4O-AOM	Fokker 100	11321	
☐	4O-AOP	Fokker 100	11332	
☐	4O-AOT	Fokker 100	11350	std

4R- SRI LANKA

FITS AIR — 8D / EXV

	Reg	Type	c/n	Note
☐	4R-EXD	Il-18GrM	187009802	[RKV]
☐	4R-EXH	F.27 Friendship 500RF	10642	[BTH]
☐	4R-EXJ	DC-8-63CF	46049/479	[NBO]
☐	4R-EXK	F.27 Friendship 500RF	10631	[SUB]
☐	4R-EXM	MD-82SF	53217/2053	

HELITOURS

	Reg	Type	c/n	Note
☐	4R-HTN	XIAN MA-60	0708	
☐	4R-HTO	XIAN MA-60	0709	

MIHIN LANKA — MJ / MLR

	Reg	Type	c/n	Note
☐	4R-MRC	A321-231	3106	
☐	4R-MRD	A321-231	1946	
☐	4R-MRE	A320-232	2731	
☐	4R-MRF	A319-112	1893	

SRILANKAN AIRLINES — UL / ALK

	Reg	Type	c/n	Note
☐	4R-ABK	A320-214	2584	
☐	4R-ABL	A320-232	2345	
☐	4R-ABM	A320-214	4694	
☐	4R-ABN	A320-214	4869	
☐	4R-ABO	A320-214	4915	
☐	4R-ABP	A320-214	5086	
☐	4R-ABQ	A321-231	3397	
☐	4R-ABR	A321-231	3636	
☐	4R-ALA	A330-243	303	
☐	4R-ALB	A330-243	306	
☐	4R-ALC	A330-243	311	
☐	4R-ALD	A330-243	313	
☐	4R-ALG	A330-243	404	
☐	4R-ALH	A330-243	627	
☐	4R-ALJ	A330-243	456	
☐	4R-ALL	A330-343E	1564	
☐	4R-ALM	A330-343E	1583	
☐	4R-ALN	A330-343E	1604	
☐	4R-ALO	A330-343E	1650	
☐	4R-ALP	A330-343E	1669	♦
☐	4R-ALQ	A330-343E	1687	♦
☐	4R-ALR	A330-343E	1689	♦
☐	4R-ADF	A340-313X	374	[CMB]
☐	4R-	A350-941	052	o/o♦
☐	4R-	A350-941	055	o/o♦
☐	4R-	A350-941	060	o/o♦

4X- ISRAEL

ARKIA ISRAEL AIRLINES — IZ / AIZ

	Reg	Type	c/n	Note
☐	4X-AVT	ATR 72-212A	884	
☐	4X-AVU	ATR 72-212A	587	
☐	4X-AVX	ATR 72-212A	656	
☐	4X-BAU	B757-3E7	30178/906	
☐	4X-BAW	B757-3E7	30179/912	
☐	4X-EMA	ERJ-195LR	19000172	
☐	4X-EMB	ERJ-190LR	19000616	

AYIT AVIATION & TOURISM — AYT

	Reg	Type	c/n	Note
☐	4X-AHP	DHC-6 Twin Otter 100	75	
☐	4X-AGP	Short SC.7 Skyvan 3-100	SH1893	♦
☐	4X-AVP	Short SD.3-60	SH3758	

CAL CARGO AIR LINES — 5C / ICL

	Reg	Type	C/n	
☐	4X-ICA	B747-4EVERF	35172/1383	
☐	4X-ICB	B747-412F	26561/1042	
☐	4X-ICM	B747-271C	21965/438	
☐	4X-ICO	B747-230F	23348/625	[MHV]
☐	4X-	B747-412(BCF)	24227/831	o/o♦

EL AL ISRAEL AIRLINES — LY / ELY

	Reg	Type	C/n	
☐	4X-EHA	B737-958ER/W	41552/4632	831
☐	4X-EHB	B737-958ER/W	41553/4697	832
☐	4X-EHC	B737-958ER/W	41554/4990	833
☐	4X-EHD	B737-958ER/W	41555/5311	834
☐	4X-EHE	B737-958ER/W	41556/4840	835
☐	4X-EHF	B737-958ER/W	41557/5772	♦
☐	4X-EHH	B737-958ER/W	41558/5791	o/o♦
☐	4X-EKA	B737-858/W	29957/204	801
☐	4X-EKB	B737-858/W	29958/249	802
☐	4X-EKC	B737-858/W	29959/314	803
☐	4X-EKE	B737-758	29961/442	702
☐	4X-EKF	B737-8HX/W	29638/2766	806
☐	4X-EKH	B737-85P/W	35485/2871	807
☐	4X-EKI	B737-86N/W	28587/192	812
☐	4X-EKJ	B737-85P/W	35486/2908	808
☐	4X-EKL	B737-85P/W	35487/2941	809
☐	4X-EKM	B737-804/W	30465/502	816*
☐	4X-EKO	B737-86Q/W	30287/1308	813*
☐	4X-EKP	B737-8Q8/W	30639/935	814
☐	4X-EKR	B737-804/W	30466/505	817
☐	4X-EKS	B737-8Q8/W	36433/2702	815
☐	4X-EKT	B737-8BK/W	33030/1968	810*
☐	4X-EKU	B737-8Z9/W	33834/1938	818*

** operates for "UP" a low cost subsidiary with same AOC*

	Reg	Type	C/n	
☐	4X-ELA	B747-458	26055/1027	201
☐	4X-ELB	B747-458	26056/1032	202
☐	4X-ELC	B747-458	27915/1062	203
☐	4X-ELD	B747-458	29328/1215	204
☐	4X-ELE	B747-412	26551/1045	205
☐	4X-ELF	B747-412F	26563/1036	207
☐	4X-ELH	B747-412	26555/1075	208
☐	EC-LZO	B767-35DER	27902/577	<PVG♦
☐	4X-EAF	B767-27EER	24854/326	[TLV]
☐	4X-EAJ	B767-330ER	25208/381	635
☐	4X-EAK	B767-3Q8ER	27600/655	612
☐	4X-EAL	B767-33AER	27477/780	613
☐	4X-EAM	B767-3Q8ER	28132/692	614
☐	4X-EAN	B767-3Q8ER	27993/619	♦
☐	4X-EAP	B767-3Y0ER	24953/405	634
☐	4X-EAR	B767-352ER	26262/583	633
☐	EC-MIA	B777-28EER	28685/400	<PVG♦
☐	4X-ECA	B777-258ER	30831/319	101
☐	4X-ECB	B777-258ER	30832/325	102
☐	4X-ECC	B777-258ER	30833/335	103
☐	4X-ECD	B777-258ER	33169/405	104
☐	4X-ECE	B777-258ER	36083/648	105
☐	4X-ECF	B777-258ER	36084/655	106

ISRAIR — 6H / ISR

	Reg	Type	C/n	
☐	4X-ABF	A320-232	4354	
☐	4X-ABG	A320-232	4413	
☐	4X-	A320-232	7110	o/o♦
☐	4X-ATH	ATR 72-212A	931	
☐	4X-ATI	ATR 72-212A	962	
☐	4X-ATM	ATR 42-320	069	[BYH]
☐	4X-ATN	ATR 42-320	053	[BYH]

5A- LIBYA

NOTE: *many aircraft damaged or written off in recent military action; status unclear*

AFRIQIYAH AIRWAYS — 8U / AAW

	Reg	Type	C/n	
☐	5A-ONC	A319-111	3615	
☐	5A-OND	A319-111	3657	
☐	5A-ONI	A319-111	4004	dam
☐	5A-ONA	A320-214	3224	
☐	5A-ONB	A320-214	3236	
☐	5A-ONM	A320-214	4521	dam
☐	5A-ONN	A320-214	5414	dam
☐	5A-ONO	A320-214	5448	
☐	5A-ONH	A330-202	1043	dam
☐	5A-ONP	A330-202	1472	dam

AIR LIBYA — 7Q / TLR

	Reg	Type	C/n	
☐	5A-DKV	B727-2D6	22374/1711	[BEN]
☐	5A-DKX	B727-2D6	22765/1801	[BEN]
☐	5A-FLA	Avro 146 RJ100	E3232	
☐	5A-FLB	Avro 146 RJ100	E3234	dam
☐	5A-FLC	BAe146 Srs.200	E2077	

BURAQ AIR — UZ / BRQ

	Reg	Type	C/n	
☐	TS-INA	A320-214	1121	<LBT♦
☐	5A-DGR	BAeJetstream 32	945	
☐	5A-DMG	B737-8GK/W	34948/2074	
☐	5A-DMH	B737-8GK/W	34949/2106	dam
☐	5A-MAB	B737-406	24857/1902	
☐	5A-WAC	B737-4B6	26531/2453	
☐	5A-WAD	B737-55D	27419/2401	dam

GHADAMES AIR TRANSPORT — OG / GHT

	Reg	Type	C/n	
☐	5A-WAT	A320-212	0438	
☐	C5-AEB	DC-9-32	48146/1044	[JNB]

GLOBALAIR — 5S / GAK

	Reg	Type	C/n	
☐	5A-DNO	Il-76T	0043451509	
☐	5A-DQB	Il-86	51483208069	[FJR]

LIBYAN AIR CARGO — LCR

	Reg	Type	C/n	
☐	5A-DOA	An-26B	12306	
☐	5A-DOB	An-26B	12307	
☐	5A-DOC	An-26B	12308	
☐	5A-DOD	An-26B	12406	
☐	5A-DOE	An-26B	13003	
☐	5A-DOF	An-26B	13007	std
☐	5A-DOG	An-26-100	13008	
☐	5A-DOJ	An-26	13104	
☐	5A-DON	An-26B	13009	
☐	5A-DOQ	An-26B	13202	
☐	5A-DOU	An-26B-100	13201	
☐	5A-DOV	An-26B-100	13109	std
☐	5A-DKL	An-124-100	19530502761	std
☐	5A-DKN	An-124-100	19530502792	[TIP]
☐	5A-DNY	Il-62M	3052657	
☐	5A-DNB	Il-76TD	0023437086	[TIP]
☐	5A-DNC	Il-76TD	0023437084	[TIP]
☐	5A-DND	Il-76TD	0033445299	[TIP]
☐	5A-DNH	Il-76TD	0033446356	[TIP]

☐ 5A-DRS	Il-76M	1033414474	
☐ 5A-DJQ	L-382G-40C Hercules	4798	
☐ 5A-DJR	L-382E-15C Hercules	4302	
☐ 5A-DOM	L-382G-62C Hercules	4992	
☐ 5A-DOO	L-382G-64C Hercules	5000	

LIBYAN AIRLINES — LN / LAA

☐ ER-AXO	A320-231	0357	<KPM♦
☐ 5A-LAH	A320-214	4405	dam
☐ 5A-LAJ	A320-214	4490	dam♦
☐ 5A-LAK	A320-214	4526	
☐ 5A-LAO	A320-214	5373	dam
☐ 5A-LAP	A320-214	5405	
☐ 5A-LAQ	A320-214	5494	
☐ TS-INN	A320-212	0793<LBTdam	
☐ 5A-LAR	A330-202	1412	
☐ 5A-LAS	A330-202	1424	[TIP]
☐ 5A-LAT	A330-202	1505	
☐ 5A-LAU	A330-202	1543	♦
☐ 5A-LAF	ATR 42-500	691	
☐ 5A-LAG	ATR 42-500	802	[TIP]
☐ 5A-LAA	CRJ-900LR	15120	dam
☐ 5A-LAD	CRJ-900LR	15214	
☐ 5A-LAE	CRJ-900LR	15216	[TIP]
☐ 5A-LAL	CRJ-900LR	15256	dam
☐ 5A-LAM	CRJ-900LR	15257	
☐ 5A-LAN	CRJ-900LR	15258	dam
☐ 5A-DCT	DHC-6 Twin Otter 300	627	
☐ 5A-DCV	DHC-6 Twin Otter 300	637	
☐ 5A-DCX	DHC-6 Twin Otter 300	641	
☐ 5A-DCZ	DHC-6 Twin Otter 300	645	
☐ 5A-DDE	DHC-6 Twin Otter 300	677	
☐ 5A-DHY	DHC-6 Twin Otter 300	661	
☐ 5A-DJG	DHC-6 Twin Otter 300	744	
☐ 5A-DJH	DHC-6 Twin Otter 300	747	
☐ 5A-DJI	DHC-6 Twin Otter 300	757	
☐ 5A-DJJ	DHC-6 Twin Otter 300	769	

LIBYAN WINGS — YL / LWA

☐ 5A-WLA	A319-112	2878	
☐ 5A-WLB	A319-112	2954	

PETRO AIR — PEO

☐ 5A-AGR	DHC-8-315	601	
☐ 5A-DLX	DHC-8-311	254	
☐ 5A-PAA	ERJ-170LR	17000275	[MUC]
☐ 5A-PAB	ERJ-170LR	17000279	
☐ 5A-PAC	DHC-6 Twin Otter 400	854	
☐ 5A-SOC	ERJ-170LR	17000162	

5B- CYPRUS

COBALTAIR

☐ 5B-	A320-2xx		o/o♦
☐ 5B-	A320-2xx		o/o♦

TUS AIRWAYS — U8

☐ 5B-DER	SAAB SF.340B	340B-167	♦

5H- TANZANIA

AIR TANZANIA — TC / ATC

☐ ZS-CMR	CRJ-100ER	7326	<CEM♦
☐ ZS-CRJ	CRJ-100ER	7338	<CEM♦
☐ ZS-KEM	CRJ-200ER	7297	<CEM♦
☐ 5H-MWG	DHC-8-311	462	

FASTJET — FN / FTZ

☐ 5H-FJA	A319-111	2176	
☐ 5H-FJC	A319-112	1145	
☐ 5H-FJD	A319-131	2268	
☐ 5H-FIF	A319-131	2308	♦
☐ 5H-FJG	A319-112	2891	♦
☐ M-AMRM	ATR 72-212A	826	o/o♦

PRECISIONAIR — PW / PRF

☐ 5H-PAG	ATR 42-320	384	[DAR]
☐ 5H-PWA	ATR 72-212A	780	
☐ 5H-PWB	ATR 72-212A	834	
☐ 5H-PWC	ATR 72-212A	866	
☐ 5H-PWD	ATR 72-212A	880	
☐ 5H-PWE	ATR 42-500	815	
☐ 5H-PWF	ATR 42-500	819	[DAR]
☐ 5H-PWG	ATR 72-212A	923	
☐ 5H-PWH	ATR 72-600	1001	
☐ 5H-PWI	ATR 72-600	1003	

REGIONAL AIR SERVICES — 8N / REG

☐ 5H-KEG	DHC-6 Twin Otter 310	799	

SAFARI EXPRESS AIRWAYS

☐ 5H-SPB	Beech 1900D	UE-300	
☐ 5H-SPC	Beech 1900D	UE-319	

TROPICAL AIR — TOA

☐ 5H-AMI	ATR 42-312	151	
☐ 5H-ATR	ATR 42-320	308	
☐ 5H-CRY	LET L-410UVP-E20	982631	

ZANAIR — B4 / TAN

☐ 5H-LET	LET L-410UVP-E9	892226	
☐ 5H-ZAP	LET L-410UVP-E9	871824	

5N- NIGERIA

AERO CONTRACTORS — AJ / NIG

☐ 5N-BIZ	B737-4B7	24558/1845	
☐ 5N-BJA	B737-4B7	24873/1931	
☐ 5N-BKQ	B737-522	26695/2423	
☐ 5N-BKR	B737-522	26699/2485	
☐ 5N-BLC	B737-522	26692/2421	
☐ 5N-BLD	B737-522	26675/2345	
☐ 5N-BLE	B737-522	26672/2343	
☐ 5N-BLG	B737-522	25387/2179	
☐ 5N-BOB	B737-42C	24232/2060	
☐ 5N-BOC	B737-42C	24814/2270	
☐ 5N-BOT	B737-4U3	25713/2531	^[IST]
☐ 5N-BOU	B737-4U3	25715/2537	^
☐ 5N-BOV	B737-4U3	25716/2540	^[IST]
☐ 5N-BOW	B737-4U3	25718/2548	^[IST]
☐ 5N-BPQ	B737-4MO	29201/3018	

	Reg	Type	c/n	Notes
☐	5N-BPR	B737-4MO	29202/3025	
☐	5N-BQI	B737-48E	25766/2543	^
☐	5N-BQL	B737-4M0	29203/3049	

^ *Hak Air c/s*

	Reg	Type	c/n	Notes
☐	5N-BJO	DHC-8Q-311	534	
☐	5N-BPT	DHC-8-402Q	4078	
☐	5N-BPU	DHC-8-402Q	4079	

AIR PEACE — APK

	Reg	Type	c/n	Notes
☐	5N-BQO	B737-36N/W	28571/3022	♦
☐	5N-BQP	B737-33R	28870/2899	♦
☐	5N-BQQ	B737-524/W	27533/2725	
☐	5N-BQR	B737-528/W	25235/2428	
☐	5N-BQS	B737-524/W	27530/2686	
☐	5N-BRN	B737-528	25234/2411	
☐	5N-BQU	B737-36N	28564/2936	♦
☐	5N-BQT	Do328-300	3221	

ALLIED AIR CARGO — 4W / AJK

	Reg	Type	c/n	Notes
☐	N545JN	MD-11F	48545/587	<WGN♦
☐	5N-JRT	B737-4YOF	26081/2442	
☐	5N-OTT	B737-406SF	24529/1770	
☐	5N-RKT	B737-4Q8F	26300/2604	

ARIK AIR — W3 / ARA

	Reg	Type	c/n	Notes
☐	5N-JIC	A330-223	891	
☐	5N-JID	A330-223	927	
☐	CS-TFW	A340-542	910	[LOS]
☐	CS-TFX	A340-542	912	[LOS]
☐	5N-MJC	B737-7BD/W	33932/2234	
☐	5N-MJD	B737-7BD/W	36073/2248	
☐	5N-MJE	B737-7GL/W	34761/2401	
☐	5N-MJF	B737-7GL/W	34762/2427	
☐	5N-MJG	B737-7BD/W	33944/2576	
☐	5N-MJH	B737-7BD/W	36719/2589	
☐	5N-MJI	B737-76N/W	28640/799	[MLA]
☐	5N-MJJ	B737-76N/W	28641/809	
☐	5N-MJK	B737-76N/W	30830/855	
☐	5N-MJN	B737-86N/W	35638/2789	
☐	5N-MJO	B737-86N/W	35640/2819	
☐	5N-MJP	B737-8JE/W	38970/3030	
☐	5N-MJQ	B737-8JE/W	38971/3065	
☐	5N-	B787-9		o/o♦
☐	5N-	B787-9		o/o♦
☐	5N-JEA	CRJ-900ER	15058	
☐	5N-JEB	CRJ-900ER	15059	
☐	5N-JEC	CRJ-900ER	15054	
☐	5N-JED	CRJ-900ER	15114	
☐	5N-JEE	CRJ-1000	19037	
☐	5N-BKU	DHC-8-402Q	4207	
☐	5N-BKV	DHC-8-402Q	4219	
☐	5N-BKW	DHC-8-402Q	4465	
☐	5N-BKX	DHC-8-402Q	4470	

ASSOCIATED AIR CARGO — SCD

	Reg	Type	c/n	Notes
☐	5N-BHV	B727-227F	21364/1261	[LOS]
☐	5N-BJX	B727-225F	20627/947	[LOS]
☐	5N-BNQ	B727-2B7F	22162/1717	
☐	5N-BIT	EMB.120RT	120050	
☐	5N-BJM	ERJ-145LR	14500984	

AZMAN AIR — AZM

	Reg	Type	c/n	Notes
☐	5N-HAI	B737-36N	28570/3010	
☐	5N-SYS	B737-56N	28565/2944	♦
☐	5N-YSM	B737-36N	28557/2862	
☐	5N-	B737-5L9	29235/3076	o/o♦

CAVERTON HELICOPTERS — YC / CJR

	Reg	Type	c/n	Notes
☐	5N-BJV	DHC-6 Twin Otter 300	816	
☐	5N-SHE	DHC-6 Twin Otter 400	864	♦

CHANCHANGI AIRLINES — 3U / NCN

	Reg	Type	c/n	Notes
☐	5N-BMB	B737-3J6	25079/2016	
☐	5N-BMC	B737-3Z0	25089/2027	[BEG]
☐	5N-IZB	B737-2X6C	23292/1113	

DANA — DO / DAV

	Reg	Type	c/n	Notes
☐	5N-AUN	Do228-201	8076	
☐	5N-DOB	Do228-202	8026	
☐	5N-DOW	Do328-110	3070	
☐	5N-DOX	Do328-110	3073	
☐	5N-DOY	Do328-110	3089	

DANA AIR — 9J / DAN

	Reg	Type	c/n	Notes
☐	5N-BRG	Beech 1900D	UE-7	♦
☐	5N-BRH	Beech 1900D	UE-26	
☐	5N-BKI	MD-83	49482/1309	[NAP]
☐	5N-DEV	MD-83	49947/1900	
☐	5N-JAI	MD-83	53016/1850	
☐	5N-JOY	MD-83	49944/1888	
☐	5N-SAI	MD-83	53018/1779	
☐	5N-SRI	MD-83	53020/1789	

FIRST NATION AIRWAYS — FRN

	Reg	Type	c/n	Notes
☐	5N-FND	A319-113	0647	
☐	5N-FNE	A319-113	0660	
☐	5N-FNF	A319-112	1612	o/o♦

JED AIR

	Reg	Type	c/n	Notes
☐	5N-BMS	B737-2RBC	21710/546	

KABO AIR — N2 / QNK

	Reg	Type	c/n	Notes
☐	5N-JRM	B747-251B	23549/651	[KAN]
☐	5N-MAD	B747-251B	23547/642	
☐	5N-MDK	B747-422	26878/966	
☐	5N-RDK	B747-4F6	28959/1158	♦

MAX AIR — NR / NGL

	Reg	Type	c/n	Notes
☐	5N-BLY	B747-2F9	22773/893	[KAN]♦
☐	5N-BMG	B747-346	23638/658	
☐	5N-DBM	B747-346	23968/693	
☐	5N-DDK	B747-346	23967/692	
☐	5N-HMB	B747-438	25067/857	
☐	5N-MBB	B747-346	24018/694	

MED-VIEW AIRLINES — VL / MEV

	Reg	Type	c/n	Notes
☐	OM-DEX	B737-46J	28867/2879	<AXE♦
☐	OM-GEX	B737-8AS/W	29919/341	<AXE♦
☐	5N-BQM	B737-5Q8	28055/3024	
☐	5N-MAA	B737-4D7	28703/2962	
☐	5N-MAB	B737-4D7	28704/2968	♦
☐	5N-BQN	B767-352ER/W	26261/575	♦

OVERLAND AIRWAYS — OJ / OLA

☐	5N-BCO	Beech 1900D	UE-225	
☐	5N-BCP	Beech 1900D	UE-116	
☐	5N-BCR	ATR 42-300	031	
☐	5N-BCS	ATR 42-300	025	
☐	5N-BND	ATR 42-300	363	
☐	5N-BPE	ATR 72-202	316	
☐	5N-BPF	ATR 72-202	352	
☐	5N-BPG	ATR 72-202	365	
☐	5N-BRQ	ATR 42-320	351	♦

TOPBRASS AVIATION — BRL

☐	5N-TBA	DHC-8-315	608	
☐	5N-TBC	DHC-8-315	614	

5R- MADAGASCAR

AIR MADAGASCAR — MD / MDG

☐	TF-EAB	A340-313X	210	<ABD
☐	5R-EAA	A340-313X	319	
☐	5R-EJA	ATR 72-600	1239	♦
☐	5R-EJB	ATR 72-600	1248	♦
☐	5R-MJE	ATR 72-212A	694	
☐	5R-MJF	ATR 72-212A	698	
☐	5R-MJG	ATR 42-500	649	
☐	5R-EBA	B737-86N/W	35212/2277	♦
☐	5R-MFL	B737-3Z9	24081/1515	
☐	5R-MGC	DHC-6 Twin Otter 300	328	
☐	5R-MGD	DHC-6 Twin Otter 300	329	
☐	5R-MGF	DHC-6 Twin Otter 300	482	

5T- MAURITANIA

MAURITANIAN AIRLINES INT'L — L6 / MAI

☐	5T-CLA	B737-55S	28469/2849	
☐	5T-CLB	B737-55S	28470/2861	
☐	5T-CLC	B737-7EE/W	34263/1739	
☐	5T-CLD	ERJ145LR	14500852	

5U- NIGER

NIGER AIRLINES — 6N / NIN

☐	N966SM	B737-201	22354/736	♦
☐	SU-YAH	Fokker 50	20123	<PNW
☐	SU-YAI	Fokker 50	20143	<PNW

5V- TOGO

ASKY AIRLINES — KP / SKK

☐	ET-ANG	B737-7K9/W	34401/2216	<ETH
☐	ET-ANH	B737-7K9/W	34402/2270	<ETH
☐	ET-AOK	B737-790/W	33012/1306	<ETH
☐	ET-ANW	DHC-8-402Q	4320	<ETH
☐	ET-ANX	DHC-8-402Q	4330	<ETH
☐	ET-AQC	DHC-8-402Q	4421	<ETH
☐	ET-AQD	DHC-8-402Q	4427	<ETH
☐	ET-AQE	DHC-8-402Q	4428	<ETH
☐	ET-AQF	DHC-8-402Q	4429	<ETH

5W- SAMOA

POLYNESIAN AIRLINES — PH / PAO

☐	5W-FAW	DHC-6 Twin Otter 300	827	
☐	5W-FAY	DHC-6 Twin Otter 300	690	
☐	5W-STF	DHC-6 Twin Otter 300	402	

5X- UGANDA

EAGLE AIR UGANDA — H7 / EGU

☐	5X-EBZ	Beech 1900C	UC-174	
☐	5X-EIV	LET L-410UVP-E9	962632	
☐	5X-GNF	LET L-410UVP-E8	892320	

UGANDA AIR CARGO — UCC

☐	5X-UCF	L-382G-11C Hercules	4610	
☐	5X-UOF	L-382G-23C Hercules	4388	
☐	5X-UXZ	AVIC Y-12 IV	027	
☐	5X-UYX	AVIC Y-12 IV	026	
☐	5X-UYZ	AVIC Y-12 IV	021	

5Y- KENYA

AFRICAN EXPRESS AIRWAYS — XU / AXK

☐	5Y-AXD	DC-9-32	47088/180	
☐	5Y-AXF	DC-9-32	47093/237	
☐	5Y-AXG	CRJ-100/200	?	
☐	5Y-AXJ	EMB.120RT	120078	
☐	5Y-AXO	EMB.120RT	120259	♦
☐	5Y-AXL	MD-82	49204/1179	
☐	5Y-AXN	MD-82	49207/1189	

AIRKENYA EXPRESS — P2 / XAK

☐	5Y-BGH	DHC-6 Twin Otter 300	574	
☐	5Y-BIO	DHC-6 Twin Otter 300	579	
☐	5Y-PJP	DHC-6 Twin Otter 310	424	
☐	5Y-BMP	DHC-7-1O2	080	[WIL]♦
☐	5Y-CDK	DHC-7-110	054	
☐	5Y-BTZ	DHC-8-102	203	
☐	5Y-BRU	LET L-410UVP-E9	912539	

ALS — K4 / ALW

☐	5Y-BVO	DHC-8-102	007	UN
☐	5Y-BXH	DHC-8-102	205	UN
☐	5Y-BXI	DHC-8-102	376	UN
☐	5Y-BXU	DHC-8-102	344	
☐	5Y-BZI	DHC-8-102	105	UN
☐	5Y-CAU	DHC-8-103	010	
☐	5Y-PRV	DHC-8-102	185	UN
☐	5Y-STN	DHC-8-102	179	UN
☐	5Y-BVY	ERJ-135LR	145599	
☐	5Y-BVZ	ERJ-135LR	145661	>SUD
☐	5Y-CAV	ERJ-145MP	145385	UN

ASTRAL AVIATION — 8V / ACP

☐	5Y-GMA	B727-2Q9F	21930/1508	
☐	5Y-MWM	B727-227F	21247/1217	♦
☐	5Y-SAN	DC-9-34CF	47706/821	[NBO]
☐	5Y-UAE	DC-9-34CF	47707/823	

AVRO EXPRESS

☐ 5Y-BXT HS.748 Srs.2B 1701
☐ 5Y-CBI HS.748 Srs.2B 1784
☐ 5Y-PFA HS.748 Srs.2B 1736 UN♦

BLUEBIRD AVIATION — *BBZ*

☐ 5Y-VVI DHC-8-402Q 4056 UN
☐ 5Y-VVN DHC-8-102 062
☐ 5Y-VVO DHC-8-402Q 4066
☐ 5Y-VVP DHC-8-106 339
☐ 5Y-VVR DHC-8-102 204
☐ 5Y-VVS DHC-8-102A 349
☐ 5Y-VVT DHC-8-102A 362
☐ 5Y-VVU DHC-8-402Q 4008
☐ 5Y-VVW DHC-8-402Q(F) 4011
☐ 5Y-VVX DHC-8-402Q 4018
☐ 5Y-VVY DHC-8-402Q(F) 4009
☐ 5Y-VVZ DHC-8-402Q(PF) 4024

☐ 5Y-VVF Fokker 50 20136
☐ 5Y-VVG Fokker 50 20137
☐ 5Y-VVH Fokker 50 20203
☐ 5Y-VVJ Fokker 50 20133
☐ 5Y-VVK Fokker 50 20213

☐ 5Y-HHC LET L-410A 720204
☐ 5Y-VVE LET L-410UVP-E20 922726
☐ 5Y-VVL LET L-410UVP-E7 872018
☐ 5Y-VVM Beech 1900D UE-175

BLUE SKY AVIATION

☐ 5Y-BOD LET L-410UVP-E20 982727
☐ 5Y-BPH LET L-410UVP
☐ 5Y-BSA LET L-410UVP-E9 892323

DAC EAST AFRICA

☐ 5Y-BWR CRJ-200LR 7004 [WIL]
☐ 5Y-WWA CRJ-200ER 7350 >SUD

☐ 5Y-BTP DHC-8-102 104 [WIL]
☐ 5Y-BWG DHC-8-311 406
☐ 5Y-DAC DHC-8-102 251 [WIL]
☐ 5Y-ENA DHC-8-102 297
☐ 5Y-GRS DHC-8-106 355 o/o
☐ 5Y-MOC DHC-8-311 374 [WIL]
☐ 5Y-PTA DHC-8-315 397 UN
☐ 5Y-QHW DHC-8-402Q 4052
☐ 5Y-WJF DHC-8Q-202 456

FLY SAX — *B5 / EXZ*

☐ 5Y-BSS Beech 1900C UC-88 ♦
☐ 5Y-BUZ DHC-8-106 253 ♦
☐ 5Y-CCT CRJ-100ER 7040 ♦
☐ 5Y-EEE F.28 Fellowship 4000 11229
☐ 5Y-SAX DC-9-15 45740/62
☐ 5Y-SSR CRJ-200ER 7386 ♦
☐ 5Y-XXA DC-9-14 45725/19

FLY540 — *5H / FFV*

☐ 5X-FFN F.27 Friendship 500CRF 10531 [WIL]
☐ 5Y-BTT Beech 1900C UC-125
☐ 5Y-BVG Beech 1900D UE-62
☐ 5Y-BXB DHC-8-102 213
☐ 5Y-BXC CRJ-100ER 7184
☐ 5Y-BXD CRJ-100ER 7042 >NOV

☐ 5Y-CCL CRJ-100ER 7011 [WIL]♦
☐ 5Y-CGF CRJ-200LR 7373 ♦

FREEDOM AIRLINE EXPRESS

☐ 5Y-FAN CRJ-100LR 7113 ♦
☐ 5Y- EMB.120ER 120314 ♦

JAMBO JET — *JX*

☐ 5Y-KQA B737-3U8 28746/2863
☐ 5Y-KQB B737-3U8 28747/2884
☐ 5Y-KYM B737-306 28719/2930
☐ 5Y-QOE DHC-8-402Q 4065 ♦

JUBBA AIRWAYS KENYA — *3J / JBW*

☐ 5Y-BXG B737-247 23519/1299 [JIB]
☐ 5Y-BXZ B737-247 23516/1257
☐ 5Y-BZL B737-4B7 24550/1793 [NBO]
☐ 5Y-CCR B737-3Z0 27521/2738 [WIL]
☐ 5Y-JAA A320-212 0445 ♦

KENYA AIRWAYS — *KQ / KQA*

☐ 5Y-KQC B737-3U8(SF) 29088/3034
☐ 5Y-KQD B737-3U8 29750/3095
☐ 5Y-KYN B737-306 28720/2957

☐ 5Y-KQF B737-76N/W 30136/1145
☐ 5Y-KQG B737-7U8/W 32371/1242
☐ 5Y-KQH B737-7U8/W 32372/1327

☐ 5Y-CYA B737-8HX/W 40549/5115
☐ 5Y-CYB B737-8HX/W 40550/5170
☐ 5Y-CYC B737-86N/W 43400/5237
☐ 5Y-CYD B737-8HX/W 40553/5372
☐ 5Y-CYE B737-86N.W 43408/5669 ♦
☐ 5Y-KYD B737-86N/W 35632/2690
☐ 5Y-KYE B737-86N/W 35286/2757
☐ 5Y-KYF B737-86N/W 35637/2803
☐ 5Y- B737-8HX/W o/o♦

☐ 5Y-KQS B777-2U8ER 33683/522 [NBO]
☐ 5Y-KQT B777-2U8ER 33682/514 [NBO]
☐ 5Y-KQU B777-2U8ER 33681/479 [NBO]
☐ 5Y-KZX B777-36NER 42097/1211 [AMS]
☐ 5Y-KZY B777-36NER 41819/1197 [AMS]
☐ 5Y-KZZ B777-36NER 41818/1140 [AMS]

☐ 5Y-KZA B787-8 35510/157
☐ 5Y-KZB B787-8 35511/184
☐ 5Y-KZC B787-8 36040/192
☐ 5Y-KZD B787-8 36041/204
☐ 5Y-KZE B787-8 36042/212
☐ 5Y-KZF B787-8 36043/224
☐ 5Y-KZG B787-8 36044/289
☐ 5Y-KZH B787-8 36045/307 ♦
☐ 5Y-KZJ B787-8 36046/317 ♦

☐ 5Y-FFA ERJ-190AR 19000562
☐ 5Y-FFB ERJ-190AR 19000572
☐ 5Y-FFC ERJ-190AR 19000577
☐ 5Y-FFD ERJ-190AR 19000579
☐ 5Y-FFE ERJ-195AR 19000586
☐ 5Y-FFF ERJ-190AR 19000594
☐ 5Y-FFG ERJ-190AR 19000599
☐ 5Y-FFH ERJ-190AR 19000619
☐ 5Y-FFJ ERJ-190AR 19000633
☐ 5Y-FFK ERJ-190AR 19000642
☐ 5Y-KYH ERJ-170LR 17000230
☐ 5Y-KYK ERJ-170LR 17000111

☐ 5Y-KYP	ERJ-190AR	19000398	
☐ 5Y-KYQ	ERJ-190AR	19000440	
☐ 5Y-KYR	ERJ-190AR	19000468	
☐ 5Y-KYS	ERJ-190AR	19000478	
☐ 5Y-KYT	ERJ-190AR	19000544	

MOMBASA AIR SAFARI — RRV

☐ 5Y-WOW	Douglas DC-3TP	14165/25610	
☐ 5Y-BSM	LET L-410UVP-E3	871939	>KUH
☐ 5Y-NIK	LET L-410UVP-E19	912619	>KUH

RUDUFU

☐ 5Y-SKN	Fokker 50	20110	♦
☐ 5Y-SVN	Fokker 50	20116	♦
☐ 5Y-WFA	Fokker 50	20121	♦

SAFARI LINK AVIATION — F2 / XLK

☐ 5Y-SLD	DHC-8-102	331	
☐ 5Y-SLF	DHC-6 Twin Otter 300	513	

SAFE AIR COMPANY — K3 /SAQ

☐ 5Y-TCO	HS.748-2B	1772	♦

SILVERSTONE AIR SERVICES

☐ 5Y-	F.27 Friendship 500F	10471	o/o♦
☐ 5Y-	F.27 Friendship 500F	10658	o/o♦

SKYWARD EXPRESS

☐ 5Y-SMI	DHC-8-311	404	♦
☐ 5Y-SMK	DHC-8-311	407	♦

SKYWARD INT'L AVIATION — SEW

☐ 5Y-JXJ	Fokker 50	20232	
☐ 5Y-JXK	Fokker 50	20233	
☐ 5Y-MIS	Fokker 50	20111	
☐ 5Y-SED	Fokker 50	20108	
☐ 5Y-SIA	Fokker 100	11307	>KUH
☐ 5Y-SMZ	Fokker 50	20192	♦

748 AIR SERVICES — SVT

☐ 5Y-IHO	DHC-8-106	268	
☐ 5Y-JGM	DHC-8-102A	287	>UN
☐ 5Y-MAJ	DHC-8-103	153	♦
☐ 5Y-RHM	DHC-8-102A	177	>UN♦
☐ 5Y-SMJ	DHC-8-402Q	4013	>UN

6O- SOMALIA

JUBBA AIRWAYS — 6J / JUB

☐ EY-329	Fokker 50	20130	<ASW♦

SOM-AIR

☐ 5Y-CDP	DC-9-32	48145/1042	

6V- SENEGAL

ASECNA — XKX

☐ 6V-AFW	ATR 42-300	117	

SENEGAL AIRLINES — DN / SGG

☐ F-GSEU	A330-243	635	<XPF♦
☐ 6V-	ERJ-145EP	145045	♦

6Y- JAMAICA

AIR JAMAICA — JM / AJM

See Caribbean Airlines (9Y-).

FLY JAMAICA AIRWAYS — OJ / FJM

☐ N524AT	B757-23N	30233/895	
☐ N767WA	B767-319ER	24876/413	

7O- YEMEN

BLUE BIRD AVIATION — BBY

☐ 7O-ADH	DHC-6 Twin Otter 310	764	
☐ 7O-ADI	DHC-6 Twin Otter 300	664	
☐ 7O-ADU	DHC-8-102A	327	
☐ 7O-ADY	DHC-8-103	333	
☐ 7O-BBC	DHC-8-202	432	♦

FELIX AIRWAYS — FO / FXX

☐ 7O-FAB	CRJ-702NG	10268	[SAH]
☐ 7O-FAI	CRJ-200ER	7307	
☐ 7O-FAJ	CRJ-200ER	7308	std

YEMENIA — IY / IYE

☐ 7O-ADA	B727-2NB	21842/1512	govt♦
☐ 7O-ADD	L-382C-86D Hercules	4827	
☐ 7O-ADE	L-382C-86D Hercules	4825	
☐ 7O-ADF	Il-76TD	1033418578	
☐ 7O-ADR	A310-324ET	568	[CAI]
☐ 7O-ADV	A310-325	702	[JIB]
☐ 7O-ADW	A310-325	704	
☐ 7O-AFA	A320-232	4653	
☐ 7O-AFB	A320-232	4690	

7P- LESOTHO

MALUTI SKY — 7D / MSU

☐ ZS-NMJ	CRJ-200ER	7161	♦

7Q- MALAWI

MALAWIAN AIRLINES — 3W / MWI

☐ ET-AQB	DHC-8-402Q	4419	<ETH
☐ ET-ARB	B737-7Q8/W	30687/2252	<ETH♦

NYASSA AIR TAXI

☐ 7Q-STA	DHC-5D Buffalo	107	♦
☐ 7Q-STB	DHC-5D Buffalo	95A	UN♦

7T- ALGERIA

AIR ALGERIE — AH / DAH

☐ TS-INC	A320-214	1744	<LBT♦
☐ TS-INO	A320-214	3480	<LBT♦
☐ TS-INR	A320-214	3487	<LBT♦
☐ 7T-VJA	A330-202	1613	
☐ 7T-VJB	A330-202	1630	
☐ 7T-VJC	A330-202	1649	
☐ 7T-VJV	A330-202	644	
☐ 7T-VJW	A330-202	647	

Reg	Type	c/n	Notes
7T-VJX	A330-202	650	
7T-VJY	A330-202	653	
7T-VJZ	A330-202	667	
7T-VUI	ATR 72-212A	644	
7T-VUJ	ATR 72-212A	648	
7T-VUK	ATR 72-212A	652	
7T-VUL	ATR 72-212A	672	
7T-VUM	ATR 72-212A	677	
7T-VUN	ATR 72-212A	684	
7T-VUO	ATR 72-212A	901	
7T-VUP	ATR 72-212A	903	
7T-VUQ	ATR 72-212A	909	
7T-VUS	ATR 72-212A	913	
7T-VUT	ATR 72-600	1223	
7T-VUV	ATR 72-600	1258	♦
7T-VUW	ATR 72-600	1266	♦
7T-	ATR 72-600	1280	o/o♦
7T-VVQ	ATR 72-212A	676	
7T-VVR	ATR 72-212A	683	
7T-VJQ	B737-6D6	30209/1115	
7T-VJR	B737-6D6	30545/1131	
7T-VJS	B737-6D6	30210/1150	
7T-VJT	B737-6D6	30546/1152	
7T-VJU	B737-6D6	30211/1164	
7T-VJJ	B737-8D6	30202/610	
7T-VJK	B737-8D6	30203/640	
7T-VJL	B737-8D6	30204/652	
7T-VJM	B737-8D6	30205/691	
7T-VJN	B737-8D6	30206/751	
7T-VJO	B737-8D6	30207/868	
7T-VJP	B737-8D6	30208/896	
7T-VKA	B737-8D6/W	34164/1748	
7T-VKB	B737-8D6/W	34165/1768	
7T-VKC	B737-8D6/W	34166/1773	
7T-VKD	B737-8D6/W	40858/3406	
7T-VKE	B737-8D6/W	40859/3446	
7T-VKF	B737-8D6/W	40860/3471	
7T-VKG	B737-8D6/W	40861/3596	
7T-VKH	B737-8D6/W	40862/3625	
7T-VKI	B737-8D6/W	40863/3658	
7T-VKJ	B737-8D6/W	40864/3691	
7T-VKK	B737-8D6/W	60747/5479	♦
7T-VKL	B737-8D6/W	60748/5700	♦
7T-	B737-8D6/W		o/o
7T-	B737-8D6/W		o/o
7T-	B737-8D6/W		o/o
7T-	B737-8D6/W		o/o♦
7T-	B737-8D6/W		o/o♦
7T-	B737-8D6/W		o/o♦
7T-VJG	B767-3D6ER	24766/310	
7T-VJH	B767-3D6ER	24767/323	
7T-VJI	B767-3D6ER	24768/332	
7T-VHL	L-382-51D Hercules	4886	

AIR EXPRESS ALGERIA

Reg	Type	c/n	Notes
ZS-ORV	Beech 1900D	UE-42	<♦
ZS-OYD	Beech 1900D	UE-191	<♦
TT-AVH	LET L-410UVP-E20	3006	♦
ZS-OOF	LET L-410UVP-E20	871920	<
ZS-OUE	LET L-420	012735A	<
ZS-OXR	LET L-410UVP-E20	972730	<
7T-VAE	LET L-410UVP-E20	872011	
7T-VAF	LET L-410UVP-E20	082629	
7T-VAG	LET L-410UVP-E20	2915	

STAR AVIATION ALGERIA

Reg	Type	c/n	Notes
7T-VNB	Beech 1900D	UE-305	
7T-VND	DHC-6 Twin Otter 300	502	
7T-VNE	DHC-6 Twin Otter 300	717	
7T-VNG	Beech 1900D	UE-296	

TASSILI AIRLINES — SF / DTH

Reg	Type	c/n	Notes
7T-VCA	B737-8ZQ/W	40884/3575	
7T-VCB	B737-8ZQ/W	40885/3606	
7T-VCC	B737-8ZQ/W	40886/3747	
7T-VCD	B737-8ZQ/W	40887/3786	
7T-VIO	Beech 1900D	UE-366	
7T-VIP	Beech 1900D	UE-369	
7T-VIQ	Beech 1900D	UE-381	
7T-VCL	DHC-8-402Q	4167	
7T-VCM	DHC-8-402Q	4169	
7T-VCN	DHC-8-402Q	4173	
7T-VCO	DHC-8-402Q	4178	
7T-VCP	DHC-8-202	661	
7T-VCQ	DHC-8-202	664	
7T-VCR	DHC-8-202	665	
7T-VCS	DHC-8-202	666	

8Q- MALDIVES

FLYME MALDIVES — VP / VQI

Reg	Type	c/n	Notes
8Q-VAV	ATR 72-212A	701	
8Q-VAW	ATR 72-212A	702	
8Q-	ATR 72-600	1069	o/o♦

MALDIVIAN — Q2 / DQA

Reg	Type	c/n	Notes
8Q-IAN	A320-214	2347	
8Q-IAI	A321-211	2599	
8Q-IAE	DHC-6 Twin Otter 310	629	♦
8Q-IAF	DHC-6 Twin Otter 300	447	♦
8Q-IAG	DHC-6 Twin Otter 200	226	♦
8Q-IAJ	DHC-6 Twin Otter 300	276	
8Q-IAL	DHC-6 Twin Otter 300	358	
8Q-AMD	DHC-8-202	429	
8Q-IAK	DHC-8Q-315	557	
8Q-IAM	DHC-8Q-311	499	
8Q-IAO	DHC-8Q-314	544	
8Q-IAP	DHC-8Q-315	491	
8Q-IAQ	DHC-8Q-202	542	
8Q-IAR	DHC-8Q-314	591	♦
8Q-IAS	DHC-8Q-315	546	

MALDIVIAN AIR TAXI

Reg	Type	c/n	Notes
8Q-MAD	DHC-6 Twin Otter 300	273	
8Q-MAF	DHC-6 Twin Otter 300	449	
8Q-MAH	DHC-6 Twin Otter 300	374	
8Q-MAI	DHC-6 Twin Otter 300	279	
8Q-MAJ	DHC-6 Twin Otter 300	837	
8Q-MAO	DHC-6 Twin Otter 300	259	
8Q-MAP	DHC-6 Twin Otter 310	571	
8Q-MAT	DHC-6 Twin Otter 200	146	
8Q-MAW	DHC-6 Twin Otter 300	722	
8Q-MAX	DHC-6 Twin Otter 300	755	
8Q-MAZ	DHC-6 Twin Otter 300	774	
8Q-MBA	DHC-6 Twin Otter 300	691	
8Q-MBB	DHC-6 Twin Otter 300	659	
8Q-MBC	DHC-6 Twin Otter 300	256	
8Q-MBD	DHC-6 Twin Otter 300	283	

	Reg	Type	C/n	
☐	8Q-MBE	DHC-6 Twin Otter 300	561	
☐	8Q-MBF	DHC-6 Twin Otter 300	375	
☐	8Q-MBG	DHC-6 Twin Otter 300	288	
☐	8Q-MBH	DHC-6 Twin Otter 300	585	
☐	8Q-OEQ	DHC-6 Twin Otter 100	44	

MEGA GLOBAL AIR SERVICES — 5M / MEG

	Reg	Type	C/n	
☐	8Q-MEE	B767-306ER	27959/609	♦
☐	8Q-MEF	B767-306ER	27960/625	♦
☐	8Q-MEG	B767-3P6ER	24496/270	
☐	8Q-MEH	B767-3Y0ER	26206/487	
☐	8Q-MEI	B757-28AER/W	25623/528	

TRANS MALDIVIAN AIRWAYS — TMW

	Reg	Type	C/n	
☐	8Q-TAB	DHC-6 Twin Otter 300	582	
☐	8Q-TAC	DHC-6 Twin Otter 300	580	
☐	8Q-TAE	DHC-6 Twin Otter 300	372	
☐	8Q-TMB	DHC-6 Twin Otter 300	587	
☐	8Q-TME	DHC-6 Twin Otter 300	798	
☐	8Q-TMF	DHC-6 Twin Otter 300	657	
☐	8Q-TMG	DHC-6 Twin Otter 300	597	
☐	8Q-TMH	DHC-6 Twin Otter 300	668	
☐	8Q-TMI	DHC-6 Twin Otter 300	754	
☐	8Q-TMJ	DHC-6 Twin Otter 300	781	
☐	8Q-TMK	DHC-6 Twin Otter 300	751	
☐	8Q-TML	DHC-6 Twin Otter 300	640	
☐	8Q-TMN	DHC-6 Twin Otter 300	700	
☐	8Q-TMO	DHC-6 Twin Otter 300	234	
☐	8Q-TMP	DHC-6 Twin Otter 300	652	
☐	8Q-TMQ	DHC-6 Twin Otter 300	753	
☐	8Q-TMR	DHC-6 Twin Otter 300	270	
☐	8Q-TMS	DHC-6 Twin Otter 300	663	
☐	8Q-TMT	DHC-6 Twin Otter 300	454	
☐	8Q-TMU	DHC-6 Twin Otter 300	467	
☐	8Q-TMV	DHC-6 Twin Otter 300	625	
☐	8Q-TMW	DHC-6 Twin Otter 300	768	
☐	8Q-TMX	DHC-6 Twin Otter 400	848	
☐	8Q-TMY	DHC-6 Twin Otter 400	849	
☐	8Q-TMZ	DHC-6 Twin Otter 400	850	

9A- CROATIA

CROATIA AIRLINES — OU / CTN

	Reg	Type	C/n	
☐	9A-CTG	A319-112	0767	
☐	9A-CTH	A319-112	0833	
☐	9A-CTI	A319-112	1029	
☐	9A-CTL	A319-112	1252	
☐	9A-CTJ	A320-214	1009	
☐	9A-CTK	A320-214	1237	
☐	9A-CQA	DHC-8-402Q	4205	
☐	9A-CQB	DHC-8-402Q	4211	
☐	9A-CQC	DHC-8-402Q	4258	
☐	9A-CQD	DHC-8-402Q	4260	
☐	9A-CQE	DHC-8-402Q	4300	
☐	9A-CQF	DHC-8-402Q	4301	

EUROPEAN COASTAL

	Reg	Type	C/n	
☐	9A-TOB	DHC-6 Twin Otter 300	244	♦
☐	9A-TOC	DHC-6 Twin Otter 200	45	♦
☐	(9A-TOF)	DHC-6 Twin Otter 310	696	o/o♦
☐		DHC-6 Twin Otter 310	666	o/o♦

LIMITLESS AIRWAYS — LIM

	Reg	Type	C/n	
☐	9A-SLA	A320-214	0828	

TRADE AIR — 8P / TDR

	Reg	Type	C/n	
☐	9A-BTD	Fokker 100	11407	
☐	9A-BTE	Fokker 100	11416	

9G- GHANA

AFRICA WORLD AIRLINES — AW / AFW

	Reg	Type	C/n	
☐	9G-AET	ERJ-145LI	14500992	
☐	9G-AEU	ERJ-145LI	14500996	
☐	9G-AFB	ERJ-145LI	14501059	

AIR GHANA — GHN

	Reg	Type	C/n	
☐	9G-AGL	B737-4Q8(F)	25163/2264	

STARBOW AIRLINES — S9 / IKM

	Reg	Type	C/n	
☐	EC-MIY	ATR 72-212A	498	<SWT♦
☐	9G-SBA	BAe146 Srs.300	E3125	[ACC]
☐	9G-SBB	BAe146 Srs.300	E3123	
☐	9G-SBC	BAe146 Srs.300A	E3183	
☐	9G-SBD	BAe146 Srs.200	E2059	
☐	A6-FLR	DHC-8-402Q	4486	<FVS

9H- MALTA

AIR MALTA — KM / AMC

	Reg	Type	C/n	
☐	9H-AEL	A319-112	2332	
☐	9H-AEM	A319-112	2382	
☐	9H-AEI	A320-214	2189	
☐	9H-AEK	A320-214	2291	
☐	9H-AEN	A320-214	2665	
☐	9H-AEO	A320-214	2768	
☐	9H-AEP	A320-214	3056	
☐	9H-AEQ	A320-214	3068	

HIFLY MALTA — 5M / HFM

	Reg	Type	C/n	
☐	9H-SUN	A340-313X	367	♦
☐	9H-TQM	A340-313X	117	♦

MEDAVIA — N5 / MDM

	Reg	Type	C/n	
☐	9H-AET	Do328-110	3117	
☐	9H-AEW	DHC-8-102	222	
☐	9H-AFD	DHC-8Q-315	458	
☐	9H-AFH	Beech 1900D	UE-372	
☐	9H-AFI	Beech 1900D	UE-31	

VALORFLY — V7 / VLF

	Reg	Type	C/n	
☐	9H-VLA	B737-430	27003/2328	std♦

VVB AVIATION — SGO

	Reg	Type	C/n	
☐	9H-VVB	B737-4K5	24901/1854	♦
☐	9H-	B737-4QB	24706/1996	o/o♦

9J- ZAMBIA

PROFLIGHT ZAMBIA — PO / PFZ

	Reg	Type	C/n	
☐	9J-PCS	BAeJetstream 32	824	
☐	9J-PCT	BAeJetstream 32	903	
☐	9J-PCU	BAeJetstream 32	800	
☐	9J-	BAeJetstream 31	691	♦
☐	9J-PCW	BAeJetstream 41	41034	
☐	9J-PCX	BAeJetstream 41	41035	

☐	ZS-CMB	CRJ-100ER	7215	<CEM
☐	ZS-CMD	CRJ-100ER	7141	<CEM♦

STABO AIR — 4P / SBO

☐	TT-DBC	DC-8-73AF	45991/380	<HRV

9K- KUWAIT

JAZEERA AIRWAYS — J9 / JZR

☐	9K-CAI	A320-214	3919	
☐	9K-CAJ	A320-214	3939	
☐	9K-CAK	A320-214	4162	
☐	9K-CAL	A320-214	5033	
☐	9K-CAM	A320-214	5625	
☐	9K-CAN	A320-214	5833	
☐	9K-CAO	A320-214	6124	

KUWAIT AIRWAYS — KU / KAC

☐	9K-AMA	A300B4-605R	673	[KWI]
☐	9K-AMB	A300B4-605R	694	[KWI]
☐	9K-AMC	A300B4-605R	699	[KWI]
☐	9K-AMD	A300B4-605R	719	[KWI]
☐	9K-AME	A300B4-605R	721	[KWI]
☐	9K-ALA	A310-308	647	[KWI]
☐	9K-ALB	A310-308	649	[KWI]
☐	9K-ALC	A310-308	663	[KWI]
☐	9K-ALD	A310-308	648	[KWI]
☐	9K-AKA	A320-212	0181	
☐	9K-AKB	A320-212	0182	
☐	9K-AKC	A320-212	0195	
☐	9K-AKD	A320-212	2046	Govt
☐	9K-AKE	A320-214/S	6350	
☐	9K-AKF	A320-214/S	6375	
☐	9K-AKG	A320-214/S	6458	
☐	9K-AKH	A320-214/S	6476	
☐	9K-AKI	A320-214/S	6500	
☐	9K-AKJ	A320-214/S	6516	♦
☐	9K-AKK	A320-214/S	6538	♦
☐	9K-APA	A330-243	1626	
☐	9K-APB	A330-243	1643	
☐	9K-APC	A330-243	1653	♦
☐	9K-APD	A330-243	1678	♦
☐	9K-APE	A330-243	1681	♦
☐	9K-ANA	A340-313	089	
☐	9K-ANB	A340-313	090	
☐	9K-ANC	A340-313	101	
☐	9K-AND	A340-313	104	
☐	9K-ADE	B747-469M	27338/1046	Govt
☐	9K-AOA	B777-269ER	28743/125	
☐	9K-AOB	B777-269ER	28744/145	

9M- MALAYSIA

AIRASIA — AK / AXM

☐	9M-AFA	A320-214	2612	
☐	9M-AFB	A320-214	2633	
☐	9M-AFC	A320-214	2656	
☐	9M-AFD	A320-214	2683	
☐	9M-AFE	A320-214	2699	
☐	9M-AFF	A320-214	2760	
☐	9M-AFG	A320-216	2816	
☐	9M-AFI	A320-216	2842	
☐	9M-AFO	A320-216	2989	
☐	9M-AFP	A320-216	3000	
☐	9M-AFS	A320-216	3117	
☐	9M-AFT	A320-216	3140	
☐	9M-AFU	A320-216	3154	
☐	9M-AFV	A320-216	3173	
☐	9M-AFW	A320-216	3404	
☐	9M-AFY	A320-216	3194	
☐	9M-AFZ	A320-216	3201	
☐	9M-AHA	A320-216	3223	
☐	9M-AHB	A320-216	3232	
☐	9M-AHD	A320-216	3291	
☐	9M-AHE	A320-216	3327	
☐	9M-AHF	A320-216	3353	
☐	9M-AHG	A320-216	3370	
☐	9M-AHH	A320-216	3427	
☐	9M-AHJ	A320-216	3477	
☐	9M-AHL	A320-216	3521	
☐	9M-AHM	A320-216	3536	
☐	9M-AHP	A320-216	3582	
☐	9M-AHQ	A320-216	3628	
☐	9M-AHR	A320-216	3701	
☐	9M-AHS	A320-216	3776	
☐	9M-AHT	A320-216	3997	
☐	9M-AHV	A320-216	4079	
☐	9M-AHX	A320-216	4263	
☐	9M-AHY	A320-216	4293	
☐	9M-AHZ	A320-216	4361	
☐	9M-AJA	A320-216/S	5897	
☐	9M-AJB	A320-216/S	5905	
☐	9M-AJC	A320-216/S	5914	
☐	9M-AJD	A320-216/S	5863	
☐	9M-AJE	A320-216/S	5908	
☐	9M-AJG	A320-216/S	6048	
☐	9M-AJH	A320-216/S	6064	
☐	9M-AJI	A320-216/S	6075	
☐	9M-AJJ	A320-216/S	6084	
☐	9M-AJK	A320-216/S	6088	
☐	9M-AJL	A320-216/S	6105	
☐	9M-AJM	A320-216/S	6096	
☐	9M-AJN	A320-216/S	6145	
☐	9M-AJO	A320-216/S	6149	
☐	9M-AJP	A320-216/S	6158	
☐	9M-AJQ	A320-216/S	6204	
☐	9M-AJR	A320-216/S	6215	
☐	9M-AJS	A320-216	4989	
☐	9M-AJT	A320-216/S	6262	♦
☐	9M-AJU	A320-216/S	6492	
☐	9M-AJV	A320-216	4147	♦
☐	9M-AJW	A320-216	3610	♦
☐	9M-AJX	A320-216	4462	♦
☐	9M-AQA	A320-216	4404	
☐	9M-AQB	A320-216	4458	
☐	9M-AQC	A320-216	4793	
☐	9M-AQD	A320-216	4882	
☐	9M-AQE	A320-216	4571	
☐	9M-AQF	A320-216	4582	
☐	9M-AQG	A320-216	4477	
☐	9M-AQH	A320-216	4969	
☐	9M-AQI	A320-216	4486	
☐	9M-AQM	A320-216	5149	
☐	9M-AQN	A320-216	5272	
☐	9M-AQO	A320-216	5347	
☐	9M-AQP	A320-216	5397	
☐	9M-AQQ	A320-216/S	5428	
☐	9M-AQR	A320-216/S	5430	
☐	9M-AQS	A320-216	5431	

	Reg	Type	c/n	Notes
☐	9M-AQU	A320-216/S	5505	
☐	9M-AQV	A320-216/S	5619	
☐	9M-AQX	A320-216/S	5547	
☐	9M-AQY	A320-216/S	5846	
☐	9M-AQZ	A320-216/S	5888	
☐	9M-	A320-216/S	7030	o/o♦
☐	9M-	A320-216/S	7057	o/o♦
☐	9M-	A320-216/S	7136	o/o♦
☐	9M-	A320-216/S	7164	o/o♦

AIRASIA X — *D7 / XAX*

	Reg	Type	c/n	Notes
☐	9M-XAA	A330-301	054	
☐	9M-XAD	A330-202	330	[KUL]
☐	9M-XBB	A330-343E	1646	[LDE]♦
☐	9M-XBC	A330-343E	1659	♦
☐	9M-XXA	A330-343E	952	
☐	9M-XXB	A330-343E	974	
☐	9M-XXC	A330-343E	1048	
☐	9M-XXD	A330-343E	1066	>PIA
☐	9M-XXE	A330-343E	1075	
☐	9M-XXF	A330-343E	1126	
☐	9M-XXG	A330-343E	1131	
☐	9M-XXH	A330-343E	1165	
☐	9M-XXI	A330-343E	1411	
☐	9M-XXJ	A330-343E	1423	
☐	9M-XXK	A330-343E	1433	>KNE
☐	9M-XXP	A330-343E	1481	
☐	9M-XXS	A330-343E	1533	
☐	9M-XXT	A330-343E	1549	
☐	9M-XXU	A330-343E	1581	
☐	9M-XXV	A330-343E	1589	
☐	9M-XXW	A330-343E	1596	
☐	9M-XXY	A330-343E	1600	
☐	9M-XXZ	A330-343E	1612	♦
☐	9M-	A330-343E	1670	o/o
☐	9M-	A330-343E	1674	o/o
☐	9M-	A330-343E	1712	o/o♦
☐	9M-	A330-343E	1729	o/o♦
☐	9M-	A330-343E	1734	o/o♦
☐	9M-	A330-343E	1743	o/o♦
☐	9M-XAB	A340-313X	273	[LDE]
☐	9M-XAC	A340-313X	278	[SZW]

ASIA CARGO AIRLINES — *3G / GSB*

	Reg	Type	c/n	Notes
☐	9M-GSA	B737-4B7(F)	24559/1847	
☐	9M-GSB	B737-46Q(SF)	28661/2910	

EAGLEXPRESS AIR CHARTER — *9A / EZX*

	Reg	Type	c/n	Notes
☐	9M-AZL	A330-243	261	>KNE♦
☐	9M-ACM	B747-428M	25628/934	>KNE♦
☐	9M-MPD	B747-4H6	25701/997	>SVA
☐	9M-MPK	B747-4H6	28427/1147	>SVA
☐	9M-MPM	B747-4H6	28435/1152	>SVA

FIREFLY — *FY / FFM*

	Reg	Type	c/n	Notes
☐	9M-FIA	ATR 72-600	1093	
☐	9M-FIB	ATR 72-600	1128	
☐	9M-FIC	ATR 72-600	1158	
☐	9M-FID	ATR 72-600	1178	
☐	9M-FIE	ATR 72-600	1235	
☐	9M-FIF	ATR 72-600	1259	♦
☐	9M-FIG	ATR 72-600	1262	♦
☐	9M-FIH	ATR 72-600	1285	o/o♦
☐	9M-	ATR 72-600		o/o
☐	9M-	ATR 72-600		o/o
☐	9M-	ATR 72-600		o/o♦
☐	9M-	ATR 72-600		o/o♦
☐	9M-FYA	ATR 72-212A	812	
☐	9M-FYB	ATR 72-212A	814	
☐	9M-FYC	ATR 72-212A	821	
☐	9M-FYD	ATR 72-212A	830	
☐	9M-FYE	ATR 72-212A	840	
☐	9M-FYF	ATR 72-212A	860	
☐	9M-FYG	ATR 72-212A	868	
☐	9M-FYH	ATR 72-212A	934	
☐	9M-FYI	ATR 72-212A	935	
☐	9M-FYJ	ATR 72-212A	941	
☐	9M-FYK	ATR 72-212A	947	
☐	9M-FYL	ATR 72-212A	948	

MALAYSIA AIRLINES — *MH / MAS*

	Reg	Type	c/n	Notes
☐	9M-MKA	A330-322	067	[SZB]
☐	9M-MTA	A330-322E	1209	
☐	9M-MTB	A330-322E	1219	
☐	9M-MTC	A330-322E	1229	
☐	9M-MTD	A330-322E	1234	
☐	9M-MTE	A330-322E	1243	
☐	9M-MTF	A330-322E	1281	
☐	9M-MTG	A330-322E	1318	
☐	9M-MTH	A330-322E	1336	
☐	9M-MTI	A330-322E	1337	
☐	9M-MTJ	A330-323E	1347	
☐	9M-MTK	A330-323E	1388	
☐	9M-MTL	A330-323E	1395	
☐	9M-MTM	A330-323E	1431	
☐	9M-MTN	A330-323E	1470	
☐	9M-MTO	A330-343E	1489	
☐	9M-MUA	A330-223F	1136	
☐	9M-MUB	A330-223F	1148	
☐	9M-MUC	A330-223F	1164	
☐	9M-MUD	A330-223F	1180	
☐	9M-MNA	A380-841	078	
☐	9M-MNB	A380-841	081	
☐	9M-MNC	A380-841	084	
☐	9M-MND	A380-841	089	
☐	9M-MNE	A380-841	094	
☐	9M-MNF	A380-841	114	
☐	9M-FFD	B737-85F/W	30007/746	
☐	9M-FFE	B737-85F/W	30567/761	
☐	9M-FFF	B737-8FZ/W	39320/3690	
☐	9M-MLE	B737-8FH/W	35105/2501	
☐	9M-MLF	B737-8FZ/W	29657/3335	
☐	9M-MLG	B737-8FZ/W	31779/3395	
☐	9M-MLH	B737-8FZ/W	31723/3435	
☐	9M-MLI	B737-8FZ/W	31793/3503	
☐	9M-MLJ	B737-8FZ/W	39319/3564	
☐	9M-MLK	B737-8FZ/W	39321/3778	
☐	9M-MLL	B737-8FZ/W	39322/3834	
☐	9M-MLM	B737-8H6/W	39323/3885	
☐	9M-MLN	B737-8H6/W	39324/4042	
☐	9M-MLO	B737-8H6/W	39325/4085	
☐	9M-MLP	B737-8H6/W	39326/4208	
☐	9M-MLQ	B737-8H6/W	39327/4237	
☐	9M-MLR	B737-8H6/W	39328/4257	
☐	9M-MLS	B737-8H6/W	39333/4618	
☐	9M-MLT	B737-8H6/W	39334/4656	
☐	9M-MLU	B737-8H6/W	39940/4872	
☐	9M-MLV	B737-8H6/W	39941/4917	
☐	9M-MSA	B737-8H6/W	40143/4346	
☐	9M-MSB	B737-8H6/W	40144/4385	

☐	9M-MSC	B737-8H6/W	40145/4405	
☐	9M-MSD	B737-8H6/W	40146/4447	
☐	9M-MSE	B737-8H6/W	40147/4502	
☐	9M-MSF	B737-8H6/W	40148/4512	
☐	9M-MSG	B737-8H6/W	40149/4574	
☐	9M-MSH	B737-8H6/W	40150/4616	
☐	9M-MSI	B737-8H6/W	40151/4640	
☐	9M-MSJ	B737-8H6/W	40152/4685	
☐	9M-MXA	B737-8H6/W	40128/3421	
☐	9M-MXB	B737-8H6/W	40129/3458	
☐	9M-MXC	B737-8H6/W	40130/3495	
☐	9M-MXD	B737-8H6/W	40131/3577	
☐	9M-MXE	B737-8H6/W	40132/3723	
☐	9M-MXF	B737-8H6/W	40133/3806	
☐	9M-MXG	B737-8H6/W	40134/3873	
☐	9M-MXH	B737-8H6/W	40135/3911	
☐	9M-MXI	B737-8H6/W	40136/4105	
☐	9M-MXJ	B737-8H6/W	40137/4131	
☐	9M-MXK	B737-8H6/W	40138/4217	
☐	9M-MXL	B737-8H6/W	40139/4246	
☐	9M-MXM	B737-8H6/W	40140/4276	
☐	9M-MXN	B737-8H6/W	40141/4287	
☐	9M-MXO	B737-8H6/W	40142/4317	
☐	9M-MXP	B737-8H6/W	40153/4723	
☐	9M-MXQ	B737-8H6/W	40154/4749	
☐	9M-MXR	B737-8H6/W	40155/4772	
☐	9M-MXS	B737-8H6/W	40156/4815	
☐	9M-MXT	B737-8H6/W	40157/4848	
☐	9M-MXU	B737-8H6/W	40158/4930	
☐	9M-MXV	B737-8H6/W	40159/4964	
☐	9M-MXW	B737-8H6/W	40160/5040	
☐	9M-MXX	B737-8H6/W	40161/5052	
☐	9M-MXY	B737-8H6/W	40162/5208	
☐	9M-	B737-8H6/W		o/o
☐	9M-	B737-8H6/W		o/o
☐	9M-MPN	B747-4H6	28432/1247	[SZB]
☐	9M-MPP	B747-4H6	29900/1296	[KUL]
☐	9M-MPR	B747-4H6F	28434/1371	
☐	9M-MPS	B747-4H6F	29902/1374	
☐	9M-MRA	B777-2H6ER	28408/64	std
☐	9M-MRE	B777-2H6ER	28412/115	std
☐	9M-MRL	B777-2H6ER	29065/329	std
☐	9M-MRM	B777-2H6ER	29066/336	std
☐	9M-MRN	B777-2H6ER	28419/394	[KUL]
☐	9M-MRP	B777-2H6ER	28421/496	[KUL]
☐	9M-MRQ	B777-2H6ER	28422/498	[KUL]

MALINDO AIRWAYS — *OD / MXD*

☐	9M-LMF	ATR 72-600	1081	
☐	9M-LMG	ATR 72-600	1089	
☐	9M-LMH	ATR 72-600	1095	
☐	9M-LMJ	ATR 72-600	1123	
☐	9M-LMK	ATR 72-600	1130	
☐	9M-LML	ATR 72-600	1135	
☐	9M-LMM	ATR 72-600	1147	
☐	9M-LMO	ATR 72-600	1154	
☐	9M-LMP	ATR 72-600	1161	
☐	9M-LMQ	ATR 72-600	1179	
☐	9M-LMR	ATR 72-600	1186	
☐	9M-LNF	B737-9GPER/W	38687/4368	
☐	9M-LNG	B737-9GPER/W	38729/4380	
☐	9M-LNH	B737-9GPER/W	38732/4484	
☐	9M-LNJ	B737-9GPER/W	38690/4495	
☐	9M-LNK	B737-9GPER/W	38737/4600	
☐	9M-LNL	B737-9GPER/W	38736/4592	
☐	9M-LNM	B737-8GP/W	39826/5122	
☐	9M-LNP	B737-8GP/W	39830/5195	
☐	PK-LNQ	B737-8GP/W	39857/5435	♦
☐	9M-LNR	B737-8GP/W	39863/5438	♦
☐	9M-LNS	B737-8GP/W	39858/5503	♦
☐	9M-LNT	B737-8GP/W	39866/5513	♦
☐	9M-LNU	B737-8GP/W	39865/5574	♦
☐	9M-LNV	B737-8GP/W	39867/5635	♦
☐	9M-LNW	B737-8GP/W	39875/5616	♦
☐	9M-LNY	B737-8GP/W	39871/5654	♦

MASWINGS — *MY / MWG*

☐	9M-MWA	ATR 72-212A	817	
☐	9M-MWB	ATR 72-212A	856	
☐	9M-MWC	ATR 72-212A	863	
☐	9M-MWD	ATR 72-212A	873	
☐	9M-MWE	ATR 72-212A	885	
☐	9M-MWF	ATR 72-212A	889	
☐	9M-MWG	ATR 72-212A	895	
☐	9M-MWH	ATR 72-212A	900	
☐	9M-MWI	ATR 72-212A	904	
☐	9M-MWJ	ATR 72-212A	910	
☐	9M-MYA	ATR 72-600	1099	
☐	9M-MYB	ATR 72-600	1153	
☐	9M-MYC	ATR 72-600	1170	
☐	9M-MYD	ATR 72-600	1187	
☐	9M-	ATR 72-600		o/o
☐	9M-	ATR 72-600		o/o
☐	9M-	ATR 72-600		o/o
☐	9M-	ATR 72-600		o/o
☐	9M-	ATR 72-600		o/o
☐	9M-	ATR 72-600		o/o♦
☐	9M-	ATR 72-600		o/o♦
☐	9M-	ATR 72-600		o/o♦
☐	9M-	ATR 72-600		o/o♦
☐	9M-SSA	DHC-6 Twin Otter 400	880	
☐	9M-SSB	DHC-6 Twin Otter 400	883	
☐	9M-SSC	DHC-6 Twin Otter 400	886	
☐	9M-SSD	DHC-6 Twin Otter 400	893	
☐	9M-SSE	DHC-6 Twin Otter 400	894	
☐	9M-SSF	DHC-6 Twin Otter 400	909	
☐	9M-MGB	Fokker 50	20156	[SZB]
☐	9M-MGE	Fokker 50	20166	[SZB]

MHS AVIATION

☐	9M-STL	Beech 1900D	UE-373	
☐	9M-STM	Beech 1900D	UE-374	

RAYA AIRWAYS — *TH / RMY*

☐	9M-TGB	B727-2F2F	22998/1810	[SZB]
☐	9M-TGE	B727-247F	21697/1471	
☐	9M-TGF	B727-247F	21698/1474	
☐	9M-TGG	B727-247F	21699/1485	
☐	9M-TGH	B727-247F	21701/1493	
☐	9M-TGJ	B727-247F	21700/1489	[SZB]
☐	9M-TGK	B727-247F	21392/1305	[SZB]
☐	9M-TGM	B727-225F	22549/1737	[SZB]
☐	9M-TGN	B727-225F	21856/1537	[SZB]
☐	9M-RYA	B757-26D(PCF)	24472/235	♦
☐	N761CX	B767-223(SCD)	22318/111	<ATN♦

RAYANI AIR — *RN / RKT*

☐	9M-RKA	B737-4H6	27083/2403	♦
☐	9M-RKB	B737-4H6		♦

9N- NEPAL

BUDDHA AIR			U4 / BHA
☐ 9N-AIM	ATR 42-320	388	
☐ 9N-AIN	ATR 42-320	403	
☐ 9N-AIT	ATR 42-320	409	
☐ 9N-AJO	ATR 72-212A	535	
☐ 9N-AJS	ATR 72-212A	531	
☐ 9N-AJX	ATR 72-212A	578	
☐ 9N-AEE	Beech 1900D	UE-286	
☐ 9N-AEW	Beech 1900D	UE-328	
☐ 9N-AGH	Beech 1900D	UE-409	

GOMA AIR			
☐ 9N-AKY	LET L410UVP-E20	2917	♦
☐ 9N-AKZ	LET L410UVP-E20	3005	♦

NEPAL AIRLINES			RA / RNA
☐ 9N-AKW	A320-233/S	6445	
☐ 9N-AKX	A320-233/S	6555	
☐ 9N-ACA	B757-2F8	23850/142	
☐ 9N-ACB	B757-2F8C	23863/182	
☐ 9N-ABM	DHC-6 Twin Otter 300	455	♦
☐ 9N-ABT	DHC-6 Twin Otter 300	812	std♦
☐ 9N-ABU	DHC-6 Twin Otter 300	814	
☐ 9N-ABX	DHC-6 Twin Otter 300	830	
☐ 9N-AKS	Harbin Y-12E	?	♦

SAURYA AIRLINES			S1
☐ 9N-ALE	CRJ-200ER	7493	

SIMRIK AIRLINES			RMK
☐ 9N-AGI	Beech 1900C	UC-97	
☐ 9N-AGL	Beech 1900C	UC-108	
☐ 9N-	Beech 1900		♦
☐ 9N-AIE	Do228-202K	8165	
☐ 9N-AJH	Do228-202	8198	

TARA AIR			
☐ 9N-ABM	DHC-6 Twin Otter 300	455	
☐ 9N-AET	DHC-6 Twin Otter 300	619	
☐ 9N-AEV	DHC-6 Twin Otter 300	729	
☐ 9N-AHH	DHC-6 Twin Otter 400	926	♦
☐ 9N-AKL	DHC-6 Twin Otter 400	921	♦
☐ 9N-AHS	Do228-212	8218	
☐ 9N-AKE	Do228-202	8244	♦
☐ 9N-AKK	Do228-212	8239	♦

YETI AIRLINES			YT / NYT
☐ 9N-AHU	BAeJetstream 41	41072	
☐ 9N-AHV	BAeJetstream 41	41077	
☐ 9N-AHW	BAeJetstream 41	41078	
☐ 9N-AHY	BAeJetstream 41	41066	
☐ 9N-AIB	BAeJetstream 41	41017	
☐ 9N-AIH	BAeJetstream 41	41085	
☐ 9N-AJC	BAeJetstream 41	41096	

9Q- DEMOCRATIC REPUBLIC OF CONGO

AIR KASAI			
☐ 9Q-CFL	An-26B	14008	
☐ 9Q-CFM	An-26B-100	10405	
☐ 9Q-CFP	An-26	10605	
☐ 9Q-CFA	LET L-410UVP-E	871921	
☐ 9Q-CFG	LET L-410UVP-E3	571911	

AIR KATANGA			
☐ 9Q-CYD	Beech 1900C	UB-40	
☐ N704PG	ERJ-135LR	145174	♦

AIR TROPIQUES			
☐ 9Q-CEJ	Beech 1900C	UB-74	
☐ 9Q-CEO	LET L-410UVP	820837	

BLUE AIRLINES			
☐ 9Q-CZO	An-26	13402	

BLUESKY AIRLINES			
☐ 9Q-CSZ	MD-83	53063/1851	♦

BUSY BEE CONGO			
☐ 9Q-CSW	LET L-410A	730209	
☐ 9Q-CTD	LET L-410A	00-02	

COMPAGNIE AFRICAINE D'AVIATION			FPV
☐ 9Q-CPB	A320-211	0279	
☐ 9Q-CAT	A320-212	0189	[CHR]
☐ 9Q-CHB	A320-212	0427	♦
☐ 9Q-DSB	A321-211	0677	♦
☐ 9Q-CAB	Fokker 50	20276	
☐ 9Q-CBL	Fokker 50	20206	♦

CONGO AIRWAYS			
☐ 9Q-CLU	A320-216	3362	♦
☐ 9Q-CKD	A320-216	3412	♦

GOMAIR			
☐ 9Q-CBX	B737-291	22089/632	♦
☐ 9Q-CGD	B737-3S3(QC)	23788/1393	♦
☐ 9Q-	B737-3M8(QC)	24021/1630	o/o♦

KATANGA WINGS			
☐ 9Q-CKW	MD-83	49458/1406	

KIN AVIA			
☐ 9Q-CEG	LET L-410UVP-E	912607	
☐ 9Q-CEN	LET L-410UVP-E3	892325	
☐ 9Q-CKA	LET L-410UVP-E	861722	
☐ 9Q-CMA	LET L-410UVP-E	902515	
☐ 9Q-CRJ	LET L-410UVP-E	872006	

SERVICES AIR			
☐ 9Q-CNJ	B727-2S2F	22934/1828	
☐ 9Q-CSS	B727-2S2F	22924/1818	
☐ 9Q-CVN	B727-2S2F	22933/1827	
☐ 9Q-CVS	B727-2S2F	22931/1825	

	Reg.	Type	c/n	
☐	9Q-CVV	B727-2S2F	22935/1829	
☐	9Q-	B727-2S2F	22925/1819	♦

TRANS AIR CARGO SERVICE — TSG

	Reg.	Type	c/n	
☐	9Q-CMP	B727-22C	19892/640	♦
☐	9Q-CJG	DC-8-62F	46110/487	
☐	9Q-CJO	DC-8-73CF	46133/534	♦

XL TRADING

	Reg.	Type	c/n	
☐	9Q-CNH	F.27 Friendship 500	10550	[QRA]
☐	9Q-CNL	F.27 Friendship 500	10634	

9V- SINGAPORE

JETSTAR ASIA AIRWAYS — 3K / JSA

	Reg.	Type	c/n	
☐	9V-JSA	A320-232	2316	
☐	9V-JSB	A320-232	2356	
☐	9V-JSE	A320-232	2423	
☐	9V-JSF	A320-232	2453	
☐	9V-JSH	A320-232	2604	
☐	9V-JSI	A320-232	4443	
☐	9V-JSJ	A320-232	4515	
☐	9V-JSK	A320-232	4772	
☐	9V-JSL	A320-232	4786	
☐	9V-JSM	A320-232	4872	
☐	9V-JSN	A320-232	4914	
☐	9V-JSO	A320-232	5305	
☐	9V-JSP	A320-232	5323	
☐	9V-JSQ	A320-232/S	5390	
☐	9V-JSR	A320-232	5433	
☐	9V-JSS	A320-232/S	5472	
☐	9V-JSU	A320-232/S	5708	
☐	9V-JSV	A320-232/S	5813	

SCOOT — TZ / SC0

	Reg.	Type	c/n	
☐	9V-OTC	B777-212ER	25809/86	[SIN]
☐	9V-OTD	B777-212ER	28510/90	[SIN]
☐	9V-OFA	B787-8	37117/314	♦
☐	9V-OFB	B787-8	37118/335	♦
☐	9V-OFC	B787-8	37120/349	♦
☐	9V-OFD	B787-8	37121/375	♦
☐	9V-OFE	B787-8	37122/415	o/o♦
☐	9V-OFF	B787-8	37123/474	o/o♦
☐	9V-OJA	B787-9	37112/240	
☐	9V-OJB	B787-9	37113/272	
☐	9V-OJC	B787-9	37114/284	♦
☐	9V-OJD	B787-9	37115/308	♦
☐	9V-OJE	B787-9	37116/316	♦
☐	9V-OJF	B787-9	37119/337	♦
☐	9V-	B787-9		o/o♦
☐	9V-	B787-9		o/o♦
☐	9V-	B787-9		o/o♦

SILKAIR — MI / SLK

	Reg.	Type	c/n	
☐	9V-SBC	A319-132	1228	[XSP]
☐	9V-SBE	A319-132	2568	
☐	9V-SBF	A319-132	3104	
☐	9V-SBG	A319-132	4215	
☐	9V-SBH	A319-132	4259	
☐	9V-SLG	A320-233	2252	
☐	9V-SLI	A320-233	2775	
☐	9V-SLJ	A320-233	3570	
☐	9V-SLK	A320-233	3821	
☐	9V-SLL	A320-233	4118	
☐	9V-SLM	A320-233	4457	
☐	9V-SLO	A320-233	5050	
☐	9V-SLP	A320-233	5089	
☐	9V-SLQ	A320-233	5296	
☐	9V-SLR	A320-233	5531	
☐	9V-SLS	A320-233	5794	
☐	9V-MGA	B737-8SA/W	44217/4765	
☐	9V-MGB	B737-8SA/W	44218/4808	
☐	9V-MGC	B737-8SA/W	44219/4882	
☐	9V-MGD	B737-8SA/W	44220/4926	
☐	9V-MGE	B737-8SA/W	44221/5017	
☐	9V-MGF	B737-8SA/W	44222/5089	
☐	9V-MGG	B737-8SA/W	44223/5140	
☐	9V-MGH	B737-8SA/W	44224/5148	
☐	9V-MGI	B737-8SA/W	44225/5260	
☐	9V-MGJ	B737-8SA/W	44226/5355	
☐	9V-MGK	B737-8SA/W	44227/5422	♦
☐	9V-MGL	B737-8SA/W	44228/5531	♦
☐	9V-MGM	B737-8SA/W	44229/5572	♦
☐	9V-MGN	B737-8SA/W	44230/5596	♦
☐	9V-	B737-8SA/W		o/o♦
☐	9V-	B737-8SA/W		o/o♦
☐	9V-	B737-8SA/W		o/o♦

SINGAPORE AIRLINES — SQ / SIA

	Reg.	Type	c/n	
☐	9V-SSA	A330-343E	1485	
☐	9V-SSB	A330-343E	1517	
☐	9V-SSC	A330-343E	1544	
☐	9V-SSD	A330-343E	1562	
☐	9V-SSE	A330-343E	1597	
☐	9V-SSF	A330-343E	1609	
☐	9V-SSG	A330-343E	1633	
☐	9V-SSH	A330-343E	1648	
☐	9V-SSI	A330-343E	1666	♦
☐	9V-STA	A330-343E	978	
☐	9V-STB	A330-343E	983	
☐	9V-STC	A330-343E	986	
☐	9V-STD	A330-343E	997	
☐	9V-STE	A330-343E	1006	
☐	9V-STF	A330-343E	1010	
☐	9V-STG	A330-343E	1012	
☐	9V-STH	A330-343E	1015	
☐	9V-STI	A330-343E	1085	[BOD]
☐	9V-STK	A330-343E	1099	[SIN]
☐	9V-STL	A330-343E	1105	
☐	9V-STM	A330-343E	1107	
☐	9V-STN	A330-343E	1124	
☐	9V-STO	A330-343E	1132	
☐	9V-STQ	A330-343E	1149	
☐	9V-STR	A330-343E	1156	
☐	9V-STT	A330-343E	1382	
☐	9V-STU	A330-343E	1401	
☐	9V-STV	A330-343E	1427	
☐	9V-STW	A330-343E	1447	
☐	9V-STY	A330-343E	1453	
☐	9V-STZ	A330-343E	1477	
☐	9V-SMA	A350-941	026	o/o♦
☐	9V-SMB	A350-941	030	o/o♦
☐	9V-SMC	A350-941	031	o/o♦
☐	9V-SMD	A350-941	037	o/o♦
☐	9V-SME	A350-941	041	o/o♦
☐	9V-SM	A350-941	054	o/o♦
☐	9V-SM	A350-941	062	o/o♦
☐	9V-SM	A350-941	068	o/o♦

☐	9V-SM	A350-941	077	o/o♦
☐	9V-SM	A350-941	081	o/o♦
☐	9V-SKA	A380-841	003	
☐	9V-SKB	A380-841	005	
☐	9V-SKC	A380-841	006	
☐	9V-SKD	A380-841	008	
☐	9V-SKE	A380-841	010	
☐	9V-SKF	A380-841	012	
☐	9V-SKG	A380-841	019	
☐	9V-SKH	A380-841	021	
☐	9V-SKI	A380-841	034	
☐	9V-SKJ	A380-841	045	
☐	9V-SKK	A380-841	051	
☐	9V-SKL	A380-841	058	
☐	9V-SKM	A380-841	065	
☐	9V-SKN	A380-841	071	
☐	9V-SKP	A380-841	076	
☐	9V-SKQ	A380-841	079	
☐	9V-SKR	A380-841	082	
☐	9V-SKS	A380-841	085	
☐	9V-SKT	A380-841	092	
☐	9V-SQJ	B777-212ER	30875/406	
☐	9V-SQK	B777-212ER	33368/428	
☐	9V-SQL	B777-212ER	33370/451	
☐	9V-SQM	B777-212ER	33372/485	
☐	9V-SQN	B777-212ER	33373/487	
☐	9V-SRJ	B777-212ER	28527/372	
☐	9V-SRL	B777-212ER	32334/409	
☐	9V-SRM	B777-212ER	32320/438	
☐	9V-SRO	B777-212ER	32321/447	
☐	9V-SRP	B777-212ER	33369/448	
☐	9V-SRQ	B777-212ER	33371/449	
☐	9V-SVA	B777-212ER	28524/350	[ASP]
☐	9V-SVB	B777-212ER	28525/353	
☐	9V-SVC	B777-212ER	28526/355	
☐	9V-SVD	B777-212ER	30869/366	[ASP]
☐	9V-SVE	B777-212ER	30870/374	
☐	9V-SVF	B777-212ER	30871/378	
☐	9V-SVG	B777-212ER	30872/398	
☐	9V-SVH	B777-212ER	28532/407	
☐	9V-SVI	B777-212ER	32316/412	
☐	9V-SVJ	B777-212ER	32335/415	
☐	9V-SVL	B777-212ER	32336/422	
☐	9V-SVM	B777-212ER	30874/430	
☐	9V-SVN	B777-212ER	30873/431	
☐	9V-SVO	B777-212ER	28533/471	
☐	9V-SNA	B777-312ER	42240/1279	
☐	9V-SNB	B777-312ER	42241/1340	
☐	9V-SNC	B777-312ER	42242/1355	♦
☐	9V-SWA	B777-312ER	34568/586	
☐	9V-SWB	B777-312ER	33377/592	
☐	9V-SWD	B777-312ER	34569/600	
☐	9V-SWE	B777-312ER	34570/602	
☐	9V-SWF	B777-312ER	34571/603	
☐	9V-SWG	B777-312ER	34572/604	
☐	9V-SWH	B777-312ER	34573/615	
☐	9V-SWI	B777-312ER	34574/618	
☐	9V-SWJ	B777-312ER	34575/623	
☐	9V-SWK	B777-312ER	34576/644	
☐	9V-SWL	B777-312ER	34577/673	
☐	9V-SWM	B777-312ER	34578/701	
☐	9V-SWN	B777-312ER	34579/703	
☐	9V-SWO	B777-312ER	34580/708	
☐	9V-SWP	B777-312ER	34581/710	
☐	9V-SWQ	B777-312ER	34582/716	
☐	9V-SWR	B777-312ER	34583/722	
☐	9V-SWS	B777-312ER	34584/729	
☐	9V-SWT	B777-312ER	34585/759	
☐	9V-SWU	B777-312ER	42235/1124	
☐	9V-SWV	B777-312ER	42236/1136	
☐	9V-SWW	B777-312ER	42237/1184	
☐	9V-SWY	B777-312ER	42238/1250	
☐	9V-SWZ	B777-312ER	42239/1266	
☐	9V-SYF	B777-312	30868/360	
☐	9V-SYG	B777-312	28528/364	
☐	9V-SYH	B777-312	32317/420	
☐	9V-SYI	B777-312	32327/484	
☐	9V-SYJ	B777-312	33374/503	
☐	9V-SYK	B777-312	33375/505	[SIN]
☐	9V-SYL	B777-312	33376/515	

SINGAPORE AIRLINES CARGO — *SQ / SQC*

☐	9V-SFF	B747-412F	28026/1105	
☐	9V-SFG	B747-412F	26558/1173	
☐	9V-SFI	B747-412F	28027/1256	♦
☐	9V-SFJ	B747-412F	26559/1285	[SIN]
☐	9V-SFK	B747-412F	28030/1298	
☐	9V-SFM	B747-412F	32898/1333	
☐	9V-SFN	B747-412F	32899/1342	
☐	9V-SFO	B747-412F	32900/1349	
☐	9V-SFP	B747-412F	32902/1364	
☐	9V-SFQ	B747-412F	32901/1369	

TIGER AIRWAYS — *TR / TGW*

☐	9V-TRA	A319-132	3757	
☐	9V-TRB	A319-132	3801	
☐	9V-TAE	A320-232	2724	
☐	9V-TAF	A320-232	2728	
☐	9V-TAM	A320-232	4181	[KUL]
☐	9V-TAN	A320-232	4210	
☐	9V-TAO	A320-232	4421	
☐	9V-TAP	A320-232	4445	[KUL]
☐	9V-TAQ	A320-232	4469	
☐	9V-TAR	A320-232	4491	
☐	9V-TAS	A320-232	4493	
☐	9V-TAT	A320-232	4532	
☐	9V-TAU	A320-232	4561	
☐	9V-TAV	A320-232	4608	
☐	9V-TAZ	A320-232	4879	
☐	9V-TJR	A320-232	4645	
☐	9V-TRD	A320-232	4931	
☐	9V-TRH	A320-232/S	5496	
☐	9V-TRI	A320-232/S	5596	
☐	9V-TRK	A320-232/S	5697	
☐	9V-TRL	A320-232/S	5721	
☐	9V-TRM	A320-232/S	5805	
☐	9V-TRN	A320-232/S	5915	
☐	9V-TRW	A320-232/S	5605	
☐	9V-TRX	A320-232/S	5662	
☐	9V-	A320-232/S	7203	o/o♦

9XR- RWANDA

RWANDAIR — *WB / RWD*

☐	9XR-	A330-243	1741	o/o♦
☐	9XR-	A330-343E	1754	o/o♦
☐	9XR-WF	B737-84Y/W	40892/3737	
☐	9XR-WG	B737-84Y/W	40893/3817	

☐	9XR-WJ	B737-7K5/W	30717/2228	
☐	9XR-WK	B737-7K5/W	30726/2298	
☐	9XR-	B737-84Y/W		o/o♦
☐	9XR-	B737-84Y/W		o/o♦
☐	9XR-WH	CRJ-900	15286	
☐	9XR-WI	CRJ-900	15287	
☐	9XR-WL	DHC-8-402Q	4464	
☐	9XR-WM	DHC-8-402Q	4498	♦

9Y- TRINIDAD & TOBAGO

CARIBBEAN AIRLINES — **BW / BWA**

☐	9Y-TTA	ATR 72-600	968	
☐	9Y-TTB	ATR 72-600	973	
☐	9Y-TTC	ATR 72-600	989	
☐	9Y-TTD	ATR 72-600	993	
☐	9Y-TTE	ATR 72-600	997	
☐	9Y-ANU	B737-8Q8/W	28235/697	
☐	9Y-BGI	B737-8Q8/W	28232/547	
☐	9Y-GEO	B737-8Q8/W	28225/433	
☐	9Y-JMC	B737-8Q8/W	28252/1195	
☐	9Y-JMD	B737-8Q8/W	30720/2235	
☐	9Y-JME	B737-86J/W	32919/1279	
☐	9Y-JMF	B737-8Q8/W	30730/2399	
☐	9Y-KIN	B737-8Q8/W	28234/680	
☐	9Y-MBJ	B737-85P/W	33980/2245	
☐	9Y-POS	B737-8Q8/W	28230/506	
☐	9Y-SXM	B737-8HO/W	37935/3716	
☐	9Y-TAB	B737-8Q8/W	28233/598	

See also Air Jamaica (6Y-)

CORPORATE & VIP AIRCRAFT

☐	AP-SSH	ERJ-135BJ Legacy 600	14501029	♦
☐	A4O-AA	A320-232	2566	
☐	A4O-AJ	A319-133CJ	4992	
☐	A4O-HMS	B747-8HO BBJ	39749/1466	o/o
☐	A4O-OMN	B747-430	32445/1292	
☐	A4O-SO	B747-SP27	21785/405	
☐	A6-AAB	Avro 146-RJ100	E3387	std
☐	A6-AAM	A318-112CJ Elite	1599	
☐	A6-ADL	ERJ-135BJ Legacy 650	14501141	
☐	A6-AIN	B737-7Z5/W BBJ1	29268/280	
☐	A6-AJC	A318-112CJ Elite	3985	
☐	A6-AJI	ERJ-190ECJ Lineage 1000	19000261	
☐	A6-ALN	B777-2ANER	29953/252	
☐	A6-AUH	B737-8EX/W BBJ2	33473/1196	
☐	A6-CAS	A318-112CJ Elite	4211	♦
☐	A6-CJE	A319-115CJ	4822	
☐	A6-COM	B747-433M	25074/862	
☐	A6-CPC	ERJ-135BJ Legacy 600	14500960	
☐	A6-DAS	B737-7Z5/W BBJ1	29858/530	
☐	A6-DFR	B737-7BC/W BBJ1	30884/747	
☐	A6-DLM	A320-232	2403	
☐	A6-DPW	ERJ-135BJ Legacy 600	14500955	
☐	A6-ESH	A319-133CJ	0910	
☐	A6-FLL	ERJ-135BJ Legacy 600	14501051	
☐	A6-FLO	ERJ-135BJ Legacy 600	14501096	
☐	A6-FZZ	B737-8KN/W	40277/5492	♦
☐	A6-GGC	ERJ-135BJ Legacy 600	14500972	♦
☐	A6-GGP	B747-412F	28032/1224	
☐	A6-HEH	B737-8AJ/W BBJ2	32825/1602	
☐	A6-HHS	ERJ-190ECJ Lineage 1000	19000296	
☐	A6-HMS	A320-232	3379	
☐	A6-HRM	B747-422	26903/1171	
☐	A6-HRS	B737-7E0/W BBJ1	29251/150	
☐	A6-IGT	ERJ-190ECJ Lineage 1000	19000362	
☐	A6-KAH	ERJ-190ECJ Lineage 1000	19000236	
☐	A6-MMM	B747-422	26906/1185	
☐	A6-MRM	B737-8EC/W BBJ2	32450/787	
☐	A6-MRS	B737-8EO/W BBJ2	35238/1966	
☐	A6-NKL	ERJ-135BJ Legacy 600	14500944	
☐	A6-NLA	ERJ-135BJ Legacy 600	14501075	
☐	A6-PFA	B747-8KB BBJ	37500/1440	
☐	A6-PFC	B787-8	35303/141	
☐	A6-PJE	ERJ-135BJ Legacy 600	14500972	
☐	A6-RJ1	Avro 146-RJ85	E2323	
☐	A6-RJ2	Avro 146-RJ85	E2325	
☐	A6-RJU	B737-77W/W BBJ1	62468/5718	♦
☐	A6-RJV	B737-77W/W BBJ1	62467/5564	♦
☐	A6-RJX	B737-7AKW BBJ1	29865/241	
☐	A6-RJY	B737-7Z5W BBJ1	29857/445	
☐	A6-RJZ	B737-7Z5/W BBJ1	29269/432	
☐	A6-SHJ	A320-232X (ACJ320)	6659	♦
☐	A6-SIL	B777-35RER	36563/802	
☐	A6-VAS	ERJ-135BJ Legacy 650	14501156	
☐	A6-YMA	ERJ-135BJ Legacy 650	14501190	
☐	A7-AAG	A320-232	0927	
☐	A7-AAH	A340-313X	528	
☐	A7-AFE	A310-308	667	
☐	A7-HBJ	B747-8KB BBJ	37075/1449	♦
☐	A7-HHE	B747-8KB BBJ	37544/1439	
☐	A7-HHH	A340-541	495	
☐	A7-HHJ	A319-133CJ	1335	
☐	A7-HHK	A340-211	026	
☐	A7-HHM	A330-202	605	
☐	A7-HJJ	A330-202	487	
☐	A7-HSJ	A320-232CJ Prestige	5255	
☐	A7-MBK	A320-232CJ Prestige	4170	
☐	A7-MED	A319-133CJ	4114	
☐	A7-MHH	A319-115CJ	3994	
☐	A9C-AWL	Avro 146-RJ100	E3386	
☐	A9C-BA	B727-2M7/W RE	21824/1595	
☐	A9C-BDF	Avro 146-RJ85	E2390	
☐	A9C-DAA	B737-268	22050/622	std
☐	A9C-HAK(1)	B747-SPZ5	23610/676	std
☐	A9C-HAK(2)	B747-4F6	28961/1174	♦
☐	A9C-HMH	B767-4FSER	34205/965	
☐	A9C-HMK	B747-4P8	33684/1324	
☐	A9C-HWR	Avro 146-RJ85	E2306	
☐	A9C-ISA	B737-86J/W	37750/5314	♦
☐	A9C-MTC	ERJ-135BJ Legacy 600	14500975	
☐	B-3073	Challenger 850	8109	♦
☐	B-3078	Challenger 850	8110	♦
☐	B-3096	ERJ-135BJ Legacy 650	14501145	std
☐	B-3097	ERJ-135BJ Legacy 650	14501151	
☐	B-3098	ERJ-135BJ Legacy 650	14501155	
☐	B-3099	ERJ-135BJ Legacy 650	14501173	
☐	B-3203	ERJ-190ECJ Lineage 1000	19000453	
☐	B-3219	ERJ-190ECJ Lineage 1000	19000534	
☐	B-3220	ERJ-190ECJ Lineage 1000	19000641	
☐	B-3280	ERJ-135BJ Legacy 650	14501210	♦
☐	B-3281	ERJ-135BJ Legacy 650	14501222	♦
☐	B-3290	ERJ-135BJ Legacy 650	14501206	
☐	B-3291	ERJ-135BJ Legacy 650	14501207	

	Reg	Type	c/n	
☐	B-3293	ERJ-135BJ Legacy 650	14501180	
☐	B-3295	ERJ-135BJ Legacy 650	14501203	
☐	B-3296	ERJ-135BJ Legacy 650	14501174	
☐	B-3370	Challenger 850	7950	
☐	B-3373	Challenger 850	8112	♦
☐	B-3563	Challenger 850	8100	
☐	B-3570	Challenger 850	8102	
☐	B-3676	Challenger 850	8107	♦
☐	B-3799	ERJ-135BJ Legacy 650	14501161	
☐	B-3999	B737-79L/W BBJ	41090/3636	
☐	B-4004	Tu-154M	85A714[NAY]	♦
☐	B-4005	CRJ-200LR	7138	♦
☐	B-4006	CRJ-200LR	7149	♦
☐	B-4007	CRJ-200LR	7180	♦
☐	B-4010	CRJ-200LR	7189	♦
☐	B-4011	CRJ-200LR	7193	♦
☐	B-4014	Tu-154M	90A847	♦
☐	B-4028	Tu-154M	93A967[NAY]	♦
☐	B-4050	Tu-154M	86A730[NAY]	♦
☐	B-4060	CRJ-701ER	10164	♦
☐	B-4061	CRJ-701ER	10183	♦
☐	B-4062	CRJ-701ER	10187	♦
☐	B-4063	CRJ-701ER	10204	♦
☐	B-4064	CRJ-701ER	10206	♦
☐	B-4065	CRJ-702ER	10336	♦
☐	B-4066	CRJ-702	10337	♦
☐	B-4067	CRJ-702	10339	♦
☐	B-4068	CRJ-702	10341	♦
☐	B-4069	CRJ-702	10342	♦
☐	B-4661	CRJ-702	10335	♦
☐	B-4662	CRJ-702	10338	♦
☐	B-4701	CRJ-200LR	7639	♦
☐	B-4702	CRJ-200LR	7455	♦
☐	B-5266	B737-7AK/W BBJ1	29866/408	
☐	B-5273	B737-73W/W BBJ1	38633/3329	
☐	B-5286	B737-7GJ/W BBJ1	41658/3866	
☐	B-5818	B737-7ZW/W BBJ1	43826/4593	♦
☐	B-6186	A318-112CJ Elite	3333	
☐	B-6188	A318-112CJ Elite	3617	
☐	B-6418	A319-133CJ	4042	
☐	B-6435	A319-133CJ	4428	
☐	B-6933	A319-133CJ	4583	
☐	B-6936	A318-112CJ Elite	4732	
☐	B-7695	CRJ-200ER	7268	
☐	B-7697	Challenger 850	8089	
☐	B-7767	Challenger 850	8106	
☐	B-7795	Challenger 850	8098	
☐	B-7797	Challenger 850	8096	
☐	B-?	Challenger 850	8111	o/o♦
☐	B-8415	A320-232CJ Prestige	4388	♦
☐	B-54111	A319-115CJ	5792	♦
☐	B-55411	A318-112CJ Elite	3886	
☐	B-77777	A318-112CJ Elite	3363	
☐	B-99999	ERJ-135BJ Legacy 600	145644	
☐	B-HRS	BAeJetstream 41	41102	
☐	B-HRT	BAeJetstream 41	41104	
☐	B-LEX	B737-7EI/W BBJ1	34683/1859	
☐	C-FFAL	B737-2RRC	21711/573	
☐	C-FLKY	CRJ-200 Execliner	7779	♦
☐	C-FPAW	B747-SPJ6	21934/467	
☐	C-FPHS	B737-53A	24970/1977	
☐	C-GCPW	Do328-300	3129	
☐	C-GDTD	Challenger 850	8067	
☐	C-GFIO	CRJ-200ER	7526	
☐	C-GFSJ	DHC-8-103	017	std
☐	C-GNVC	CRJ-200ER	7519	

	Reg	Type	c/n	
☐	C-GOIA	SF.340B	340B-347	
☐	C-GSLL	Challenger 850	8103	
☐	C-GSUA	Challenger 890	15182	
☐	C-GSUF	Challenger 890	15271	
☐	C-GSUM	Challenger 890	15158	
☐	C-GSUW	Challenger 850	8047	
☐	C-GTFF	B747-SPB5	22484/507	
☐	C-GXNR	B737-2S2C	21929/608	
☐	CN-MBH	B747-48EM	28551/1131	♦
☐	CN-MBP	ERJ-135BJ Legacy 600	14501117	
☐	CN-MVI	B737-8KB/W BBJ2	37545/2696	
☐	CN-SHS	ERJ-190ECJ Lineage 1000	19000307	
☐	CN-SSH	ERJ-135BJ Legacy 600	14501114	
☐	CP-2634	BAe146 Srs.200	E2096	
☐	CS-TFY	A320-232	1868	
☐	C5-AMH	B737-4H6	26444/2308	♦
☐	C5-CGA	Do328-300	3121	♦
☐	C5-GAF	B727-95	19252/327	
☐	C5-GOG	B727-1H2/W	20533/869	
☐	C5-MAF	ERJ-135BJ Legacy 600	14501098	♦
☐	C5-RTG	Il-62MK	1356234	
☐	C9-SPM	ERJ-145EP	145114	
☐	D-AACM	B737-8JM/W BBJ2	37663/3024	
☐	D-AAIJ	Challenger 850	8065	
☐	D-ACBN	A319-115CJ	3243	
☐	D-ACRN	CRJ-200LR	7486	
☐	D-ADCP	ERJ-135BJ Legacy 600	14501067	
☐	D-ADCR	ERJ-135BJ Legacy 650	14501135	
☐	D-ADDD	CRJ-200ER	7529	♦
☐	D-ADNA	A319-133CJ	1053	
☐	D-AERO	ERJ-135BJ Legacy 650	14501216	♦
☐	D-AFUN	ERJ-135BJ Legacy 650	14501168	
☐	D-AHOX	ERJ-135BJ Legacy 650	14501213	♦
☐	D-AJET	ERJ-135BJ Legacy 650	14501166	
☐	D-AJOY	Challenger 850	8069	
☐	D-AKAT	ERJ-135BJ Legacy 600	14501038	
☐	D-ALEX	A319-115CJ/S	5963	
☐	D-ALXX	A319-115CJ	4470	
☐	D-APGS	A319-115CJ	3046	♦
☐	D-ATRA	A320-232	0659	
☐	D-AVAN	ERJ-135BJ Legacy 600	14501092	
☐	D-AVIB	ERJ-135BJ Legacy 600	14501109	
☐	D-BADA	Do328-310	3224	
☐	D-BADC	Do328-310	3216	
☐	D-BDTB	Do328-310	3147	
☐	D-BDTC	Do328-310	3149	
☐	D-BDTD	Do328-310	3181	
☐	D-BGAS	Do328-300	3139	
☐	D-BJET	Do328-300	3207	
☐	D-CATZ	Do328-100	3090	
☐	D-CIRD	Do328-110	3011status?	
☐	D-CIRI	Do328-110	3005>SUS	
☐	D-CIRO	Do328-110	3025	
☐	D-CIRP	Do328-110	3006>SUS	
☐	D-CMHA	Do328-100	3023	
☐	D-CMHB	Do328-130	3110	
☐	D-CMHC	Do328-110	3022	♦
☐	D-CPWF	Do328-100	3112	
☐	D2-EBC	ERJ-145LR	145003	
☐	D2-FFW	ERJ-145MP	145360	
☐	D2-FHK	Do-328-310	3161	
☐	D2-MAN	B707-321B	20025/780	
☐	D2-TPR	B707-3J6B	20715/870	
☐	EI-EEZ	Challenger 850	8085	
☐	EK RA01	A319-132	0913	

☐	EP-AGA	B737-286	21317/483	
☐	ER-BCA	B727-230F	20905/1091	♦
☐	ER-KKL	ERJ-135BJ Legacy 650	14501191	
☐	EW-001PA	B737-8EV/W BBJ2	33079/1075	
☐	EW-001PB	B767-32KER	33968/926	
☐	EW-301PJ	Challenger 850	8057	
☐	EW-85815	Tu-154M	95A1010	
☐	EX-00001	Tu-154M	92A945	♦
☐	EY-65788	Tu-134A-3	62835	
☐	EZ-B024	Challenger 870	10332	
☐	F-GVTH	DC-9-21	47308/474	
☐	F-HFKD	ERJ-135BJ Legacy 600	14500933	♦
☐	F-HGNT	A320-212	0234	
☐	F-WTBR	B737-79V/W BBJ1	61040/5279	♦
☐	G-BVRJ	Avro 146-RJ70	E1254	
☐	G-CJMD	ERJ-135BJ Legacy 600	14500994	
☐	G-CMAS	ERJ-135BJ Legacy 650	14501142	
☐	G-GLEG	ERJ-135BJ Legacy 650	14500998	♦
☐	G-HUBY	ERJ-135BJ Legacy 600	14500854	
☐	G-JOTR	Avro 146-RJ85	E2294	♦
☐	G-LALE	ERJ-135BJ Legacy 600	14501017	
☐	G-LEGC	ERJ-135BJ Legacy 600	14501025	
☐	G-LUXE	BAe146 Srs.300	E3001	
☐	G-NMAK	A319-115CJ	2550	
☐	G-NOAH	A319-115CJ	3826	
☐	G-OFOA	BAe146 Srs.100	E1006	
☐	G-OFOM	BAe146 Srs.100	E1144	
☐	G-OSRA	B727-2S2F	22938/1832	
☐	G-OSRB	B727-2S2F	22929/1823	
☐	G-OTGL	ERJ-135BJ Legacy 650	14501162	
☐	G-OWTN	ERJ-145EP	145010	
☐	G-PEPI	ERJ-135BJ Legacy 600	14500873	
☐	G-RADY	Challenger 850	8081	
☐	G-RHMS	ERJ-135BJ Legacy 600	14501072	
☐	G-SHAL	Challenger 850	8066	
☐	G-SMLA	BAe146-200A	E2047	
☐	G-SUGR	ERJ-135BJ Legacy 650	14501199	
☐	G-SYLJ	ERJ-135BJ Legacy 600	14500937	
☐	G-SYNA	ERJ-135BJ Legacy 650	14501127	
☐	G-TBAE	BAe146 Srs.200	E2018	
☐	G-TCSX	B757-2K2	26330/717	
☐	G-THFC	ERJ-135BJ Legacy 600	14500954	
☐	G-TYPH	BAe146 Srs.200	E2200	
☐	G-WIRG	ERJ-135BJ Legacy 650	14501184	
☐	HB-JFL	ERJ-135BJ Legacy 600	14501057	
☐	HC-CGO	ERJ-145LR	14500987	
☐	HL7227	B737-7HF/W BBJ1	35977/2047	
☐	HL7759	B737-7EG/W BBJ1	35990/2107	
☐	HL7787	B737-75G/W BBJ1	36852/2475	
☐	HL8080	A319-115X/S	5768	
☐	HL8290	B737-7GE/W BBJ1	41375/4325	
☐	HP-1A	ERJ-135BJ Legacy 600	14501066	
☐	HS-CMV	B737-4Z6	27906/2698	11-111
☐	HS-NVA	ERJ-135LR	14501077	2112
☐	HS-NVB	ERJ-135LR	14501125	2113
☐	HS-TYQ	A310-324	591	60201
☐	HS-TYR	A319-115CJ	1908	60202
☐	HS-TYS	B737-8Z6/W	35478/1955	55-555
☐	HS-TYT	A320-214X (ACJ320)	6112	60203
☐	HZ-A2	A320-214	3164	
☐	HZ-A3	A320-214	0764	
☐	HZ-A4	A319-112	1494	
☐	HZ-A5	A318-112CJ Elite	2910	
☐	HZ-A10	ATR 42-500	859	
☐	HZ-A11	ATR 72-600	1184	
☐	HZ-A15	A320-216	3261	
☐	HZ-AB	A330-243CJ	1676	♦

☐	HZ-AB1	L-1011-500 TriStar	1247	
☐	HZ-AB3	B727-2U5 RE	22362/1657	
☐	HZ-AC	A319-115X/S	6727	♦
☐	HZ-AFAS	MD-11	48533/544	[JED]
☐	HZ-AIF	B747-SP68	22503/529	[JED]
☐	HZ-ATR	B737-9FG BBJ3	39317/3219	
☐	HZ-FM1	B737-528	27425/2730	
☐	HZ-HAA	B737-529/W	25419/2165	
☐	HZ-HMED	B757-23A	25495/599	
☐	HZ-HM1	B747-468	28343/1265	
☐	HZ-HM1A	B747-3G1	23070/592	
☐	HZ-HM1B	B747-SP68	21652/329	
☐	HZ-HM1C	B747-SP	22750/560	
☐	HZ-HMS1	B747-8JA BBJ	40065/1446	
☐	HZ-HMS2	A340-213	204	
☐	HZ-HM7	MD-11	48532/532	[JED]
☐	HZ-HR5	B737-8AN/W BBJ2	32438/779	
☐	HZ-HY2	A320-232	3402	
☐	HZ-IAM	ERJ-135BJ Legacy 600	14501055	
☐	HZ-MF1	B737-7FG/W BBJ1	33405/1204	
☐	HZ-MF2	B737-7AJ/W BBJ1	33499/1217	
☐	HZ-MF6	B737-9FGER/W BBJ3	39318/3399	
☐	HZ-MF7	B787-8 BBJ	40053/149	o/o
☐	HZ-MF8	B787-8 BBJ	40059/193	o/o
☐	HZ-MF9	B777-3FGER	61518/1271	
☐	HZ-MIS	B737-2K5	22600/816	
☐	HZ-NSA	A310-304	431	
☐	HZ-RCA	A318-112CJ Elite	3932	
☐	HZ-RKR	B727-121	19006/262	
☐	HZ-SKY	A340-642X	924	♦
☐	HZ-SKY1	A340-211	009	♦
☐	HZ-SKI	B727-212 RE	21460/1340	
☐	HZ-WBT7	B747-4J6	25880/926	
☐	HZ-XY7	A320-214	2165	
☐	I-TALY	A340-541	748	♦
☐	JY-AAG	ERJ-190-100ECJ Lineage	19000278	
☐	JY-ASX	A340-642X	924	
☐	JY-CMC	ERJ-135BJ Legacy 650	14501126	
☐	J2-KBA	B727-191	19394/418	
☐	LX-DIO	B737-97YER/W BBJ3	62515/5659	♦
☐	LX-GJC	A318-112CJ Elite	3100	
☐	LX-GVV	A319-115CJ	3542	
☐	LX-MCE	A319-115CJ	2592	
☐	LX-MOI	ERJ-135BJ Legacy 600	14500841	
☐	LX-NVB	ERJ-135BJ Legacy 600	14501002	
☐	LX-OLA	ERJ-135BJ Legacy 600	14500995	
☐	LX-RLG	ERJ-135BJ Legacy 600	14500967	
☐	LY-LTY	Challenger 850	8055	
☐	LY-TVG	B737-7ZF/W BBJ1	60406/5028	
☐	LY-VTA	CRJ-200ER	7617	
☐	LY-ZAB	Challenger 850	7248	
☐	LZ-AOB	A319-112	3188	
☐	M-AAKV	ERJ-135BJ Legacy 650	14501183	
☐	M-ABEC	ERJ-135BJ Legacy 600	14501031	
☐	M-ANGA	ERJ-135BJ Legacy 600	14501086	
☐	M-ANTA	Challenger 850	8094	
☐	M-ARSL	ERJ-135BJ Legacy 600	14500802	
☐	M-AZIZ	B737-505	24649/2225	[FJR]
☐	M-BETY	Do328-310	3176	
☐	M-BIRD	ERJ-135BJ Legacy 600	14500993	♦
☐	M-CPRS	ERJ-135BJ Legacy 650	14501160	♦
☐	M-DSCL	ERJ-135BJ Legacy 600	14500851	std
☐	M-DWWW	Challenger 850	8080	std
☐	M-ESGR	ERJ-135BJ Legacy 600	14501016	
☐	M-FAHD	B727-176 RE	19254/298	
☐	M-FTOH	B727-269	22359/1652	

	Registration	Type	c/n	
☐	M-FZMH	Challenger 850	8068	
☐	M-HHHH	A318-112CJ Elite	4650	
☐	M-HLAN	Challenger 850	8104	
☐	M-IABU	A340-313X	955	
☐	M-ILAN	ERJ-135BJ Legacy 650	14501192	♦
☐	M-IMAK	ERJ-135BJ Legacy 650	14501140	
☐	M-JCCA	ERJ-135BJ Legacy 650	14501182	
☐	M-KATE	A319-133CJ	4151	
☐	M-KPCO	ERJ-135BJ Legacy 600	14500973	
☐	M-LILJ	Challenger 850	8060	
☐	M-LILY	Challenger 850	8108	
☐	M-NJSS	ERJ-135BJ Legacy 600	145686	
☐	M-OLEG	ERJ-135BJ Legacy 600	14500991	
☐	M-RBUS	A319-115CJ	3856	
☐	M-RCCG	ERJ-135BJ Legacy 600	14501113	
☐	M-RISE	B757-23N/W	27972/694	
☐	M-RRBK	ERJ-135BJ Legacy 650	14501136	std
☐	M-SBAH	ERJ-190ECJ Lineage 1000	19000225	
☐	M-SEXY	ERJ-135BJ Legacy 650	14501221	♦
☐	M-SFAM	MD-87	53042/1969	
☐	M-STAR	B727-2X8/W	22687/1984	
☐	M-STRY	Avro 146-RJ70	E1267	♦
☐	M-TAKE	Challenger 850	8079	
☐	M-URUS	B737-7GC/W BBJ1	34622/1785	
☐	M-YBBJ	B737-7HE/W BBJ1	36027/2068	
☐	M-YBUS	A320-214CJ	6069	
☐	M-YKBO	ERJ-135BJ Legacy 650	14501211	♦
☐	N1TS	B737-7JY/W BBJ1	39109/3461	
☐	N3DE	ERJ-145LR	145626	
☐	N6GD	ERJ-135BJ Legacy 600	14500983	
☐	N25AZ	B727-130	18370/134	
☐	N28CG	Do328-100	3024	
☐	N28MS	B787-8 BBJ	35309/143	o/o
☐	N30MP	B727-121	18998/239	std
☐	N35LX	B737-330	23528/1290	
☐	N38CG	Do328-100	3034	
☐	N42WA	CRJ-200LR	7024	
☐	N43PR	B737-75V/W BBJ1	28581/126	
☐	N44KS	SAAB SF.340A	340A-050	
☐	N45NA	DC-9-33RC	47410/480	
☐	N46VA	ERJ-145LR	145103	♦
☐	N50TC	B737-72T/W BBJ1	29024/131	
☐	N53NA	ERJ-135BJ Legacy 600	145770	
☐	N57TT	Do328-300	3205	
☐	N60GH	CRJ-200ER	7274	
☐	N63AG	ERJ-135BJ Legacy 600	14501061	
☐	N73HK	B737-2S9	21957/618	
☐	N84AW	ERJ-135BJ Legacy 600	14500982	♦
☐	N88ZL	B707-330B	18928/457	
☐	N89FE	ERJ-135 Legacy 600	14501058	
☐	N89LD	ERJ-135SE	145648	
☐	N90R	B737-7EL/W BBJ1	32775/889	
☐	N92SR	B737-7JR/W BBJ1	37111/2595	
☐	N96AP	CRJ200XR Hemisphere	7730	
☐	N106EC	ERJ-135BJ Legacy 600	14501106	
☐	N108MS	B737-7BC/W BBJ1	33102/1111	
☐	N111VM	B737-7GV/W BBJ1	36090/2196	
☐	N114M	BAe146 Srs.100	E1068	
☐	N119NA	B757-223/W	24487/236	
☐	N124LS	ERJ-135BJ Legacy 600	14500948	
☐	N127BG	ERJ-135BJ Legacy 600	14501064	
☐	N127NK	DC-9-21	47361/488	
☐	N131BC	Do328-310	3168	
☐	N135SK	ERJ-135BJ Legacy 600	14500989	
☐	N135SL	ERJ-135BJ Legacy 600	145711	
☐	N138DE	ERJ-145LR	145129	
☐	N141SH	CRJ-200LR	7206	
☐	N144DC	B757-225	22191/2	
☐	N146FF	BAe146 Srs.200	E2049	
☐	N162W	BAC111-401AK	087	
☐	N162WC	B737-7BC/W BBJ1	30329/384	
☐	N164W	BAC111-401AK	090	
☐	N165W	B737-247	19605/57	
☐	N168CF	MD-87	49670/1453	
☐	N170EH	ERJ-170-100LR	17000059[BNA]	♦
☐	N188JT	ERJ-135BJ Legacy 600	145699	
☐	N189DR	ERJ-135BJ Legacy 600	14500925	
☐	N220AU	DC-10-10	46501/2	
☐	N226G	B757-23A	25491/511	
☐	N226HY	ERJ-135BJ Legacy 600	14501014	
☐	N227GV	ERJ-190-100ECJ Lineage	19000159	
☐	N227WE	ERJ-135BJ Legacy 600	14501018	
☐	N234BZ	ERJ-135LR	145388	
☐	N241EC	ERJ-145EP	145021	
☐	N260DV	B737-75T/W BBJ1	29142/167	
☐	N267SK	ERJ-145LR	145268	
☐	N279AD	B737-4Q8	26279/2221	♦
☐	N286CH	ERJ-145XR	14501185	
☐	N286FM	ERJ-145XR	14501186	
☐	N286DP	ERJ-145XR	14501178	
☐	N286HF	ERJ-145XR	14501177	
☐	N286SJ	ERJ-145XR	14501153	
☐	N287KB	MD-87	49768/1595	
☐	N296TX	Challenger 850	8053	
☐	N301SR	B737-7JU/W BBJ1	38854/3727	
☐	N304CE	Do328-300	3184	
☐	N309DP	Do328-100	3095	
☐	N311AG	B727-117 RE	20512/858	
☐	N313CG	ATR 42-320F	358	
☐	N315TS	B737-7CU/W BBJ1	30772/554	
☐	N317LL	ERJ-135BJ Legacy 600	14501007	
☐	N321GG	B737-5H6	26445/2377	
☐	N325JF	ERJ-135SE	145499	std
☐	N328CK	Do328-300	3137	
☐	N328GT	Do328-310	3183	
☐	N328LN	Do328-310	3150	
☐	N328WW	Do328-300	3116	
☐	N330AU	MD-10-30F	46800/96	
☐	N330MX	Do328-120	3067	
☐	N333BH	ERJ-135BJ Legacy 650	14501167	
☐	N356BZ	ERJ-135LR	145288	♦
☐	N359SK	Do328-300	3202	
☐	N366FM	ATR 42-500	549	
☐	N370BC	B737-205	23468/1262	
☐	N371BC	B737-8EF/W BBJ2	32971/996	
☐	N373RB	ERJ-135BJ Legacy 600	14500957	
☐	N380BJ	B737-7JZ/W BBJ1	37700/3128	
☐	N386AZ	ERJ-145XR	14501159	
☐	N386CH	ERJ-135SE	145467	
☐	N389LS	L-1011-500 TriStar	1250[RKT]	
☐	N391EF	Do328-110	3091	
☐	N403RW	ERJ-135LR	145262	
☐	N406BN	B727-291F	19991/521	
☐	N406FJ	Do328-300	3156	
☐	N407FJ	Do328-310	3157	
☐	N411FJ	Do328-310	3166	
☐	N419FJ	Do328-310	3173	
☐	N419LP	ERJ-135BJ Legacy 600	145555	
☐	N429FJ	Do328-310	3194	
☐	N430FJ	Do328-310	3209	
☐	N444HE	B737-39A/W	23800/1409	
☐	N455BJ	B747-8LQ/W BBJ2	41060/1459	

	Reg.	Type	c/n	
☐	N459AD	ERJ-145MP	145185	
☐	N470DC	ERJ-135BJ Legacy 600	14500946	
☐	N472NA	BAe146 SRs.200	E2138	
☐	N473PS	Do328-110	3010	
☐	N474NA	BAe146 Srs.200	E2084	
☐	N480SJ	CRJ200XR Hemisphere	7755	
☐	N494TG	ERJ-135BJ Legacy 600	145678	
☐	N500DE	ERJ-145EP	145084	
☐	N500LS	B737-73T/W BBJ1	29054/143	
☐	N500PR	Challenger 800	7846	
☐	N500VP	B737-2H4	22062/640	
☐	N501LS	Challenger 800	7584	
☐	N502BJ	B737-8ZE/W BBJ2	42215/4952	
☐	N502MG	B727-191	19391/309	
☐	N503JT	ERJ-135BJ Legacy 600	14501032	
☐	N504BJ	B737-82Z/W BBJ2	60686/5129	
☐	N505LL	DHC-8-315	415	
☐	N508RH	ERJ-145LR	145769	♦
☐	N509RH	ERJ-145LR	145517	♦
☐	N515JT	ERJ-135BJ Legacy 600	14500950	
☐	N520JG	CRJ-701ER	10052	♦
☐	N522AX	DC-10-30ER	48315/436	
☐	N529DB	Challenger 800	7152	
☐	N545EF	Do328-110	3093	
☐	N546JB	Challenger 850	8078	♦
☐	N540M	ERJ-135LR	14500977	♦
☐	N548M	ERJ-135ER	145364	
☐	N549M	ERJ-135LR	145450	
☐	N556MA	BAe146 Srs.200	E2106	std
☐	N560WK	DHC-8Q-315	560	
☐	N563AW	DHC-8Q-315	563	
☐	N567WK	DHC-8Q-315	567	
☐	N568AW	DHC-8Q-315	568	
☐	N569AW	DHC-8Q-315	569	
☐	N570AW	DHC-8Q-315	570	
☐	N577EF	Do328-110	3077	
☐	N580ML	ERJ-135BJ Legacy 600	14500990	
☐	N588AH	ERJ-190ECJ Lineage 1000	19000140	♦
☐	N589AW	DHC-8Q-315	589	
☐	N593AN	MD-83	53093/2066	
☐	N597CJ	ERJ-135BJ Legacy 600	14501015	
☐	N598DB	ERJ-135BJ Legacy 650	14501195	♦
☐	N600LP	ERJ-135BJ Legacy 600	14500863	
☐	N600TN	ERJ-135BJ Legacy 600	145505	
☐	N600YC	ERJ-135BJ Legacy 600	14501069	
☐	N601LS	Challenger 800	7008	
☐	N602JF	BAeJetstream 41	41038	
☐	N605WG	ERJ-135BJ Legacy 600	14500980	
☐	N606DH	B727-130	18365/52	
☐	N608EC	ERJ-135BJ Legacy 650	14501128	
☐	N610G	B757-22L	29304/870	
☐	N611BV	ERJ-135BJ Legacy 600	145637	♦
☐	N615PA	B727-243	21266/1227	
☐	N615PG	ERJ-135BJ Legacy 600	14501004	
☐	N624RH	B707-338C	19624/689	
☐	N632RF	SAAB SF.340A	340A-042	
☐	N634AR	DHC-8-103	003	
☐	N637AR	DHC-8-102	265	
☐	N639CS	B737-4YO	26073/2375	
☐	N640CS	B737-4YO	26078/2431	
☐	N645HM	Do328-110	3013	
☐	N650JV	ERJ-135BJ Legacy 650	14501181	
☐	N660CP	B737-7BD/W	36721/2646	
☐	N660JM	ERJ-135BJ Legacy 600	145642	
☐	N661EC	ERJ-135BJ Legacy 600	14501001	
☐	N661JM	ERJ-135BJ Legacy 600	145730	♦
☐	N665PF	ERJ-135BJ Legacy 650	14501165	♦
☐	N666RD	CRJ-900LR	15277	
☐	N666GL	ERJ-190ECJ Lineage 1000	19000317	
☐	N668CP	B737-76N/W	38028/4072	
☐	N673BF	B767-238ER	23402/133	
☐	N678RS	Challenger 850	7176	
☐	N682RW	MD-81	48006/966	
☐	N688FD	B737-7EG/W BBJ1	40586/4130	♦
☐	N688JC	ERJ-135BJ Legacy 650	14501139	
☐	N697BJ	DC-9-32	47799/918	
☐	N698SS	B727-223	21369/1275	
☐	N702RS	SAAB SF.340B	340B-233	
☐	N702SJ	Challenger 800	7489	
☐	N703RS	SAAB SF.340B	340B-252	
☐	N707JT	B707-138B	18740/388	[MIA]
☐	N711WM	Challenger 800	7140	
☐	N712JM	B737-73W/W BBJ1	40116/4465	
☐	N713JM	B737-8LZ/W BBJ2	42510/4499	
☐	N715AV	CRJ-100ER	7158	♦
☐	N719AV	CRJ-200-100ER	7159	♦
☐	N720MM	B737-7BC/W BBJ1	33010/1037	
☐	N721UF	B737-7BC/W BBJ1	30327/356	
☐	N724CL	B727-151	19121/264	
☐	N724YS	B727-281 RE	21474/1378	
☐	N725BD	ERJ-135BJ Legacy 600	14501034	
☐	N727AH	B727-121	19261/422	
☐	N727DL	SAAB SF.340A	340A-036	
☐	N727EL	B727-227F	21463/1353	
☐	N727NK	B727-212	21945/1502	
☐	N728PH	ERJ-135BJ Legacy 600	14500985	
☐	N730MM	ERJ-190ECJ Lineage 1000	19000632	♦
☐	N732KA	B737-59D	25065/2028	
☐	N734A	ERJ-170LR	17000318	
☐	N735A	ERJ-170LR	17000319	
☐	N735TS	ERJ-135LR	145386	std
☐	N736A	ERJ-170LR	17000320	
☐	N737A	B737-7AX	30181/648	
☐	N737AG	B737-7BF/W BBJ1	30496/301	
☐	N737AJ	B737-2H4	23054/969	
☐	N737AT	B737-7HJ/W BBJ1	36756/2405	
☐	N737CC	B737-74Q/W BBJ1	29135/206	
☐	N737ER	B737-7CJ/W BBJ1	30754/516	
☐	N737GG	B737-8KT/W BBJ2	40118/3369	
☐	N737KA	B737-7BX	30740/776	
☐	N737L	B737-7CG/W BBJ1	30751/401	
☐	N737LE	B737-75V/W BBJ1	28579/312	
☐	N737M	B737-8EQ/W BBJ2	33361/1124	
☐	N738A	B737-7AX	30182/690	
☐	N742PB	B737-73U/W BBJ1	29200/234	
☐	N742SP	ERJ-135BJ Legacy 600	14500884	
☐	N743A	B737-7AX	30184/925	
☐	N744VG	B747-41R	32745/1287	♦
☐	N745A	B737-7AX	30185/978	
☐	N747A	B747-SP27	21992/447	
☐	N747GE	B747-121	19651/25	
☐	N747GF	B747-446	26355/1024	
☐	N747NA	B747-SP21	21441/306	
☐	N752SP	ERJ-135BJ Legacy 600	14500903	
☐	N757AF	B757-2J4/W	25155/371	
☐	N757AG	B757-256	29306/920	
☐	N757HW	B757-225	22194/5	
☐	N757MA	B757-24Q	28463/739	
☐	N757SS	B757-236	22176/14	
☐	N760CC	ERJ-190ECJ Lineage 1000	19000656	♦

☐	N767A	B767-2AXER	33685/903	
☐	N767KS	B767-24QER	28270/629	
☐	N770BB	B757-2J4/W	25220/387	
☐	N777AS	B777-24QER	29271/174	
☐	N777UE	A318-112CJ	5478	
☐	N721CX	DC-8-72CF	46013/427	♦
☐	N787RR	B747-267B	21966/446	
☐	N788DP	B737-79U/W BBJ1	29441/111	
☐	N788LS	B737-3L9	24220/1602	
☐	N789LS	B737-35B	24269/1628	
☐	N800AK	B727-123QX/W RE	20045/596	
☐	N800AW	DHC-8Q-315	573	
☐	N800KS	B737-7BC/W BBJ1	30782/586	
☐	N801MR	DHC-8Q-202	606	
☐	N802MR	DHC-8Q-202	612	
☐	N803MR	DHC-8Q-202	626	
☐	N804CE	ERJ-135LR	145326	
☐	N804MS	B767-3P6ER	27255/525	♦
☐	N804X	Challenger 700	10002	
☐	N805MR	DHC-8Q-202	655	
☐	N805X	CRJ-701ER	10091	♦
☐	N806MR	DHC-8Q-315	662	
☐	N807MR	DHC-8Q-315	663	
☐	N808MR	DHC-8Q-315	667	
☐	N809TD	ERJ-135BJ Legacy 600	14500809	
☐	N810TD	ERJ-135BJ Legacy 650	14501194	
☐	N813BB	SAAB 2000	2000-044	
☐	N817NA	DC-8-72	46082/458	
☐	N818HR	ERJ-135BJ Legacy 600	14501105	
☐	N827TV	ERJ-135BJ Legacy 600	14500971	
☐	N829RN	ERJ-135SE	145361	
☐	N834BA	B737-73Q/W BBJ1	29102/101	
☐	N835BA	B737-7BC/W BBJ1	30572/491	
☐	N836BA	B737-7BC/W BBJ1	30756/569	
☐	N839BA	B737-77Z/W BBJ1	62699/5749	o/o♦
☐	N843BB	B737-436	25843/2244	
☐	N850JL	Challenger 850	8088	
☐	N865LS	ERJ-135BJ Legacy 600	14501080	
☐	N870DC	Challenger 870	10314	
☐	N872DC	Challenger 870	10322	
☐	N874TW	B757-223/W	24524/248	
☐	N880DF	DC-9-32	47635/754	
☐	N880DP	MD-83	49504/1363	
☐	N887LS	B737-74U/W BBJ1	29233/197	
☐	N888AU	CRJ-200 Phoenix	7211	
☐	N888GY	CRJ-200 ExecLiner	7471	
☐	N888ML	ERJ-135BJ Legacy 600	14500818	
☐	N888TY	B737-7AH/W BBJ1	29749/456	
☐	N888WU	CRJ-200 ExecLiner	7481	
☐	N888YF	B737-7BC/W BBJ1	33036/1060	
☐	N889ML	ERJ-190-100ECJ Lineage	19000438	
☐	N890RL	CRJ-200ER	7717	
☐	N894JW	ERJ-135 Legacy 600	145789	
☐	N895CL	Challenger 850	8095	
☐	N898JS	ERJ-135BJ Legacy 600	14501071	
☐	N900EM	ERJ-135BJ Legacy 600	14500976	
☐	N900LH	Do328-110	3014	
☐	N902WG	B737-2H6	22620/822	
☐	N903TB	B757-2Q8/W	28172/772	
☐	N904FL	ERJ-135BJ Legacy 600	145780	
☐	N905FL	ERJ-135BJ Legacy 600	145775	
☐	N905NA	B747-123	20107/86	
☐	N907EF	Do328-110	3104	
☐	N908FL	ERJ-135BJ Legacy 600	14500942	
☐	N908JE	B727-131	20115/735	
☐	N909MT	ERJ-135BJ Legacy 600	14501011	
☐	N909TT	ERJ-135BJ Legacy 600	14501044	
☐	N910FL	ERJ-135BJ Legacy 600	14500952	
☐	N910TE	L-1011-1 TriStar	193L-1064	♦
☐	N912JC(3)	ERJ-135BJ Legacy 600	14501215	♦
☐	N912NB	B737-2H4	22675/839	
☐	N925FL	ERJ-135BJ Legacy 600	14500825	
☐	N926FM	ERJ-135SE	145466	
☐	N929EF	Do328-110	3026	
☐	N930HB	B737-7ZH/W	38751/3796	
☐	N932NA	DC-9-32CF	47476/569	
☐	N939AJ	ERJ-135BJ Legacy 600	14500939	
☐	N941EF	Do328-110	3016	
☐	N953EF	Do328-110	3075	
☐	N959BP	B737-7BD/W	36720/2628	
☐	N966JS	ERJ-135BJ Legacy 600	14500966	
☐	N966MS	ERJ-190ECJ Lineage 1000	19000683	
☐	N972EX	B737-505	24645/2072	♦
☐	N974EC	ERJ-135BJ Legacy 600	14500974	
☐	N974VV	DC-10-40	46974/274	
☐	N975EF	Do328-110	3031	
☐	N977JG	B737-73Q/W BBJ1	30789/602	♦
☐	N979PF	ERJ-135BJ Legacy 600	14500979	♦
☐	N980ST	B737-4B3	24750/1916	
☐	N981EE	ERJ-190ECJ Lineage 1000	19000559	
☐	N986AK	MD-87	49412/1424	♦
☐	N987AK	MD-87	49404/1430	♦
☐	N987GC	MD-87	53040/1897	
☐	N990ST	B737-4YO	24493/1751	
☐	N999YG	Challenger 800	7075	
☐	N1023C	ERJ-135SE	145550	
☐	N1800C	Challenger 800	7351	
☐	N1977H	ERJ-135BJ Legacy 650	14501198	♦
☐	N2708E	B737-7LT/W BBJ1	39095/4148	o/o
☐	N2767	B767-238ER	23896/183	
☐	N3618F	A319-115CJ	2748	
☐	N7600K	B737-7BC/W BBJ1	32628/953	
☐	N8587H	ERJ-135BJ Legacy 650	14501175	
☐	N8767	B737-7EG/W BBJ1	32807/926	
☐	N8860	DC-9-15	45797/51	
☐	N17773	B727-227	21045/1133	
☐	N31019	L-1011-1 TriStar	193B-1066	♦
☐	N77286	CRJ-200ER	7286	♦
☐	N79711	B737-7BQ/W BBJ1	30547/423	
☐	N92225	SAAB 2000	028	
☐	OD-TAL	CRJ-200SE	7086	
☐	OE-IBK	ERJ-135BJ Legacy 600	14501110	
☐	OE-ICE	A318-112CJ	4503	
☐	OE-IDB	ERJ-135BJ Legacy 600	14500999	
☐	OE-IDH	ERJ-135BJ Legacy 600	14501026	
☐	OE-IIB	Fokker 100	11403	
☐	OE-IIC	Fokker 100	11406	
☐	OE-IID	Fokker 100	11368	
☐	OE-IIM	ERJ-135BJ Legacy 600	14501048	♦
☐	OE-ILX	B737-8DR/W BBJ2	32777/882	
☐	OE-IML	ERJ-135BJ Legacy 650	14501143	
☐	OE-IRF	B737-7JU/W BBJ1	38855/3825	
☐	OE-IRK	ERJ-135BJ Legacy 600	14500916	
☐	OE-ISA	Challenger 850	8043	
☐	OE-ISF	Challenger 850	8056	
☐	OE-ITA	ERJ-135BJ Legacy 650	14501133	
☐	OE-IZA	ERJ-135BJ Legacy 650	14501201	♦
☐	OE-IZZ	Challenger 850	8052	
☐	OE-LJG	A319-115CJ	4353	
☐	OE-LUV	ERJ-190ECJ Lineage 1000	19000571	♦

	Reg	Type	c/n	
☐	OE-LUX	A318-112 Elite	4169	
☐	OK-GGG	ERJ-135BJ Legacy 600	14500986	
☐	OK-JNT	ERJ-135BJ Legacy 600	14501087	
☐	OK-OWN	ERJ-135BJ Legacy 600	14501200	
☐	OK-ROM	ERJ-135BJ Legacy 600	14501039	
☐	OK-SLN	ERJ-135BJ Legacy 600	145796	
☐	OK-SUN	ERJ-135BJ Legacy 600	14500963	
☐	OK-SYN	ERJ-135BJ Legacy 600	14501189	
☐	OM-BYE	Yak-40	9440338	
☐	OM-BYL	Yak-40	9940560	
☐	OM-BYO	Tu-154M	89A803	
☐	OM-BYR	Tu-154M	98A1012	
☐	OO-ARO	ERJ-135BJ Legacy 650	14501214	♦
☐	OO-NGI	ERJ-190ECJ Lineage 1000	19000611	
☐	OY-NNA	Challenger 850	8073	
☐	OY-VEG	Challenger 850	8075	
☐	OY-VGA	Challenger 850	8077	
☐	PH-AQF	B737-8Z6/W	62445/5609	♦
☐	PH-KBX	Fokker 70	11547	
☐	PH-LCI	Bae Jetstream 31	718	
☐	PH-MKH	Fokker 100	11242[WOE]	
☐	PK-DHK	ERJ-135BJ Legacy 600	14501046	
☐	PK-RJA	ERJ-135BJ Legacy 650	14501134	
☐	PK-RJI	Fokker 100	11328	
☐	PK-RJP	ERJ-135BJ Legacy 600	14501172	
☐	PK-RNI	ERJ-135BJ Legacy 600	14501045	
☐	PK-RSS	ERJ-135BJ Legacy 600	14501020	
☐	PK-OKE	ERJ-135LR	145726	
☐	PP-ADV	ERJ-190-100ECJ Lineage	19000568	
☐	PP-FJA	ERJ-135BJ Legacy 650	14501138	
☐	PP-INC	ERJ-135BJ Legacy 650	14501179	
☐	PP-JLO	ERJ-135BJ Legacy 600	14501090	
☐	PP-NLR	ERJ-135BJ Legacy 650	14501149	
☐	PP-VVA	ERJ-135LR	145702	
☐	PP-VVV	ERJ-135BJ Legacy 600	14501099	
☐	PR-AZT	ATR 72-202	450	
☐	PR-AVX	ERJ-135BJ Legacy 600	14501037	
☐	PR-BBS	B737-7BC/W BBJ1	32575/861	
☐	PR-CBY	ERJ-135BJ Legacy 650	14501187	
☐	PR-CID	B737-33A	25033/2025	
☐	PR-CRG	ERJ-135BJ Legacy 650	14501169	
☐	PR-DPF	ERJ-145EP	145127	
☐	PR-ITU	ERJ-135BJ Legacy 650	14501137	
☐	PR-IUH	ERJ-135BJ Legacy 600	145717	
☐	PR-JDJ	ERJ-135BJ Legacy 650	14501131	
☐	PR-NIO	ERJ-135BJ Legacy 600	14501012	
☐	PR-ODF	ERJ-135BJ Legacy 600	14501054	
☐	PR-ORE	ERJ-135BJ Legacy 600	145625	
☐	PR-PFN	ERJ-145LR	145002	
☐	PT-FKK	ERJ-135BJ Legacy 650	14501188	
☐	PT-LEG	ERJ-135BJ Legacy 650	14501197	
☐	PT-SKW	ERJ-135BJ Legacy 600	14501006	
☐	PZ-TZE	Do328-300	3114	
☐	P4-AEG	ERJ-135BJ Legacy 600	14501111	♦
☐	P4-AFK	B737-7FY/W BBJ1	36493/2211	
☐	P4-ASL	B737-7BH/W BBJ1	29791/336	
☐	P4-BBJ	B737-7AV/W BBJ1	30070/244	
☐	P4-CLA	B767-2DXER	32954/861	
☐	P4-FLY	B727-122	19148/473	
☐	P4-FSH	B747-SP31	21963/441	
☐	P4-KAZ	B737-7EJ/W BBJ1	32774/853	
☐	P4-KUL	ERJ-135BY Legacy 600	14500978	
☐	P4-LIG	B737-7JF/W BBJ1	37592/2752	
☐	P4-MAK	B737-7HZ/W BBJ1	40761/3425	
☐	P4-MES	B767-33AER	33425/909	
☐	P4-MGU	A319-115CJ	5445	
☐	P4-MIS	A319-115CJ	3133	
☐	P4-MSG	ERJ-135BJ Legacy 600	14500913	
☐	P4-NGK	B737-7HZ/W BBJ1	37583/2869	
☐	P4-RLA	A319-133CJ	4319	
☐	P4-RYY	ERJ-135BJ Legacy 600	14500941	
☐	P4-SLK	ERJ-135BJ Legacy 650	14501147	
☐	P4-SMS	ERJ-135BJ Legacy 650	14501123	
☐	P4-SUN	ERJ-135BJ Legacy 600	14501074	
☐	P4-SVM	ERJ-135BJ Legacy 600	14501060	
☐	P4-MCO	DHC-8Q-315	549	
☐	P4-NOF	B737-4YO	23976/1651	♦
☐	P4-VNL	A319-115CJ	2921	
☐	RA-02857	ERJ-135BJ Legacy 600	145549	
☐	RA-02858	ERJ-135BJ Legacy 600	145586	
☐	RA-42402	Yak-42D	4520422116583	
☐	RA-42412	Yak-42D	4520422219055	
☐	RA-42424	Yak-42D	4520421502016	
☐	RA-42427	Yak-42D	4520422305016	
☐	RA-42440	Yak-42D	4520424210018	
☐	RA-64010	Tu-204-300	1450743164010	
☐	RF-64519	Tu-214ON	42709019	
☐	RA-64523	Tu-214VPU	42305023	
☐	RA-65692	Tu-134B-3	63215	
☐	RA-65721	Tu-134A-3M	66130	
☐	RA-65723	Tu-134A-3M	66440	
☐	RA-65830	Tu-134A-3	12093	
☐	RA-65908	Tu-134AK	63870	
☐	RA-65930	Tu-134A-3M	66500	
☐	RA-65932	Tu-134A-3	66405	Std
☐	RA-65979	Tu-134A-3	63158	
☐	RA-65984	Tu-134A-3	63400	
☐	RA-67218	Challenger 850	8074	
☐	RA-67219	Challenger 850	8090	
☐	RA-67220	Challenger 850	8091	
☐	RA-67233	Challenger 850	8105	
☐	RA-74015	An-74-200	36547098969	
☐	RA-74047	An-74-200	36547097941	♦
☐	RA-85019	Tu-154M	05A1019	
☐	RA-85084	Tu-154M	08A1004	
☐	RA-85155	Tu-154M	10A1000	
☐	RA-85360	Tu-154B-2	79A360	
☐	RA-85446	Tu-154B-2	80A446	♦
☐	RA-85510	Tu-154B-2	82A510	
☐	RA-85565	Tu-154B-2	82A565	
☐	RA-85572	Tu-154B-2	83A572	♦
☐	RA-85586	Tu-154B-2	83A586	
☐	RA-85594	Tu-154B-2	83A594	
☐	RA-85605	Tu-154B-2	84A605	
☐	RA-85686	Tu-154M	90A854	
☐	RA-86539	Il-62M	2344615	
☐	RA-86555	Il-62M	4547315	
☐	RA-87216	Yak-40	9510440	
☐	RA-87286	Yak-40	9310128	
☐	RA-87273	Yak-40	9310927	
☐	RA-87382	Yak-40	9411332	
☐	RA-87429	Yak-40	9420535	
☐	RA-87496	Yak-40	9541945	
☐	RA-87569	Yak-40D	9220222	
☐	RA-87953	Yak-40K	9811157	
☐	RA-87983	Yak-40	9540644	
☐	RA-88216	Yak-40	9630250	
☐	RA-88269	Yak-40	9720753	♦
☐	RA-88293	Yak-40	9510138	
☐	RA-88294	Yak-40	9331029	
☐	RA-88297	Yak-40	9530142	
☐	RA-88298	Yak-40K	9930160	

☐	RA-88306	Yak-40KD	9640651	
☐	RA-89053	Sukhoi SSJ 100-95LR	95009	♦
☐	RA-96104	Il-96-400VPU	97693201004	♦
☐	RF-65153	Tu-134AK	66198	
☐	RF-85855	Tu-154M	86A723	
☐	RF-88301	Yak-40K	9641251	
☐	RP-C8638	CRJ-200ER	7756	
☐	RP-C9258	Do328-110	3036	♦
☐	RDPL-34177	An-74TK-100	365470991005	
☐	SE-DJG	ERJ-135BJ Legacy 600	14501042	
☐	SP-DLB	ERJ-135BJ Legacy 600	14501100	
☐	SP-FMG	ERJ-135BJ Legacy 600	14501102	
☐	SP-LIG	ERJ-175LR	17000283	<LOT
☐	SP-LIH	ERJ-175LR	17000288	<LOT
☐	ST-PRA	Il-62M	2357711	
☐	SU-GGG	A340-212	061	
☐	SX-BKO	ERJ-145SA	145374	374
☐	SX-BKP	ERJ-145SA	145671	671
☐	SX-BKQ	ERJ-145SA	145729	729
☐	SX-BKR	ERJ-145SA	145757	757
☐	SX-DGM	ERJ-135BJ Legacy 600	14501023	
☐	SX-IFA	MD-83	49809/1843	
☐	S5-ABL	ERJ-135BJ Legacy 600	14501008	
☐	S5-ACK	ATR 72-212	369	
☐	S9-SVE	B727-30	18366/98	
☐	TC-ANA	A319-115CJ	1002	
☐	TC-DIA	ERJ-135BJ Legacy 650	14501148	
☐	TC-EJA	CRJ-200ER	7763	
☐	TC-GVS	ERJ-135BJ Legacy 600	14501003	
☐	TC-TUR	A330-243	1240	
☐	TJ-ALG	F.28 Fellowship 4000	11227	
☐	TL-YJT	B727-251	21155/1169	
☐	TR-KJD	ATR 42-312	131	
☐	TR-KPR	B777-236	27108/17	♦
☐	TS-IOO	B737-7H3/W BBJ1	29149/348	
☐	TS-KRT	A340-541	902	o/o
☐	TT-ABC	MD-87	49888/1692	
☐	TT-ABD	B737-74Q/W BBJ1	29136/225	
☐	TT-ABE	ATR 42-300	230	
☐	TU-VAA	Fokker 100	11245	
☐	TU-VAO	B727-2Y4RE/W	22968/1815	[JNB]
☐	TU-VAS	A319-133CJ	2192	
☐	TY-24A	B727-256	20819/1018	
☐	TZ-001	B727-2K5/W	21853/1640	
☐	TZ-PRM	B737-7BC/W BBJ1	30328/377	♦
☐	T7-KAS	ERJ-135BJ Legacy 600	14501079	
☐	T7-LRK	ERJ-135BJ Legacy 600	14501021	
☐	T7-OAM	Challenger 850	8084	♦
☐	T7-SAU	A340-541	563	
☐	T7-UBS	ERJ-135BJ Legacy 650	14501122	
☐	UN-65683	Tu-134A	62199	
☐	UN-85463	Tu-154B-2	80A463	
☐	UN-87488	Yak-40	9441638	
☐	UN-87816	Yak-40	9230724	
☐	UP-A2001	A320-214CJ Prestige	3199	
☐	UP-A2101	A321-211CJ	5538	
☐	UP-A3001	A330-243	863	
☐	UP-B5701	B757-2M6ER	23454/102	
☐	UP-C8502	Challenger 850	8049	
☐	UP-C8503	Challenger 850	8093	
☐	UP-C8505	Challenger 850	8054	
☐	UP-CJ001	CRJ100ER	7359	
☐	UP-CJ009	CRJ100ER	7354	♦
☐	UP-CL001	Challenger 870	10289	
☐	UP-EM007	ERJ-135BJ Legacy 650	14501146	
☐	UP-EM010	ERJ-135BJ Legacy 650	14501154	
☐	UP-EM017	ERJ-135BJ Legacy 650	14501176	♦

☐	UP-T3405	Tu-134A-3	31218	
☐	UP-T3406	Tu-134A-3	40150	
☐	UP-T3409	Tu-134B-3	62820	
☐	UP-T5401	Tu-154M	91A889	
☐	UP-T5406	Tu-154M	93A965	
☐	UP-Y4006	Yak-40K	9740556	
☐	UP-Y4008	Yak-40	9541741	
☐	UP-Y4015	Yak-40	9530842	
☐	UP-Y4033	Yak-40K	9641050	
☐	UP-Y4202	Yak-42D	4520423402116	
☐	UP-Y4204	Yak-42D	4520423408016	
☐	UP-Y4206	Yak-42D	4520423403018	
☐	UP-42721	Yak-42D	4520423310017	
☐	UP-87850	Yak-40	9441738	
☐	UR-ALM	Yak-40K	9741756	
☐	UR-AWB	An-74TK-300	36547098984	
☐	UR-CLH	Yak-40	9530642	
☐	UR-DAP	Yak-40	9521241	
☐	UR-ICD	Challenger 850	8072	
☐	UR-RTS	Yak-40	9530541	
☐	UR-RUS	CRJ-200LR	7990	
☐	UR-UKR	An-148-100B	0101	
☐	VH-JGB	ERJ-135LR	145728	
☐	VH-JTG	ERJ-135LR	145687	
☐	VH-JZG	ERJ.135LR	145713	
☐	VH-VEM	SAAB SF.340B	340B-364	
☐	VH-VEO	SAAB SF.340B	340B-366	
☐	VH-VEP	SAAB SF.340B	340B-377	
☐	VH-VLT	ERJ-135BJ Legacy 600	14501107	
☐	VP-BAP	B727-121	19260/412	
☐	VP-BAT	B747-SP21	21648/367	
☐	VP-BBJ	B737-72U/W BBJ1	29273/146	
☐	VP-BBW	B737-7BJ/W BBJ1	30076/179	
☐	VP-BBZ	B737-8LX/W BBJ2	39899/4035	
☐	VP-BCL	Challenger 870	10247	
☐	VP-BDA	B787-9	37109/293	♦
☐	VP-BDB	B737-9LB/W BBJ3	38890/3033	
☐	VP-BDJ	B727-123	20046/605	
☐	VP-BED	A319-115CJ	3073	
☐	VP-BEL	B737-74T/W BBJ1	29139/189	
☐	VP-BER	CRJ-200ER	7508	std
☐	VP-BEX	A319-115CJ	2706	
☐	VP-BFT	B737-7JB/W BBJ1	36714/2340	
☐	VP-BGL	ERJ-135BJ Legacy 600	14500961	std
☐	VP-BHM	DC-8-62	46111/491	
☐	VP-BHS	DC-8-72	46067/455	std
☐	VP-BIZ	B737-7AU/W BBJ1	34477/1825	
☐	VP-BJJ	B737-7BC/W BBJ1	30330/415	
☐	VP-BKG	A318-112CJ	4878	
☐	VP-BKS	B767-3P6ER	27254/522	
☐	VP-BLK	B747-SP31	21961/415	
☐	VP-BMS	A340-541	560	
☐	VP-BNY	Challenger 850	8097	
☐	VP-BNZ	B737-7HD/W BBJ1	35959/2029	
☐	VP-BOP	B737-73W/W BBJ1	40117/3701	
☐	VP-BPZ	B727-117 RE	20327/797	
☐	VP-BRT	B737-7BC/W BBJ1	32970/988	
☐	VP-BWR	B737-79T/W BBJ1	29317/265	
☐	VP-BYA	B737-7AN/W BBJ1	29972/642	
☐	VP-BZL	B737-8DV/W BBJ2	32915/969	
☐	VP-CAA	ERJ-135BJ Legacy 600	14501091	
☐	VP-CAC	A330-243 ACJ330	1053	
☐	VP-CAD	A319-115CJ	5040	
☐	VP-CAE	B737-7KK BBJ1	38608/3208	
☐	VP-CAL	B777-2KQER	40753/891	
☐	VP-CAN	ERJ-135BJ Legacy 650	14501120	
☐	VP-CAQ	B737-2V6	22431/803	

☐	VP-CBA	B737-2W8	22628/820	std
☐	VP-CBB	B737-8AW/W BBJ2	32806/912	
☐	VP-CBE	A330-202	1321	
☐	VP-CBH	MD-82	53577/2189	wfu
☐	VP-CBI	MD-82	53581/2204	
☐	VP-CCJ	A319-133CJ	2421	
☐	VP-CDD	A340-642X	924	♦
☐	VP-CEC	B737-9HW/W BBJ3	37546/2725	
☐	VP-CGX	A319-115CJ Elite	4956	
☐	VP-CHA	A320-232CJ/S Prestige	5182	
☐	VP-CLL	ERJ-135BJ Legacy 650	14501217	♦
☐	VP-CIA	A319-115X	4228	♦
☐	VP-CIE	A319-133CJ	1589	
☐	VP-CKH	A318-112CJ Elite	3530	
☐	VP-CKK	B737-9JAER/W BBJ3	37560/2664	
☐	VP-CKS	A318-112CJ Elite	3238	
☐	VP-CLL	ERJ-135BJ Legacy 600	14501052	std
☐	VP-CLR	B737-7EM/W BBJ1	34865/1865	
☐	VP-CME	B767-231EM	22567/30	
☐	VP-CMJ	A319-111CJ	4768	♦
☐	VP-CMK	ERJ-135BJ Legacy 600	14501083	
☐	VP-CNI	MD-87	49767/1587	
☐	VP-CON	Challenger 850	8083	
☐	VP-CPA	B737-7AW/W BBJ1	30031/251	
☐	VP-CPP	CRJ-200LR	7625	
☐	VP-CRA	ERJ-135BJ Legacy 650	14501196	♦
☐	VP-CSK	B737-8GG/W BBJ2	34620/1803	
☐	VP-CSN	A319-115CJ	3356	
☐	VP-CTF	MD-87	49777/1634	
☐	VP-CVX	A319-133CJ	1212	
☐	VP-CWJ	ERJ-135BJ Legacy 650	14501152	
☐	VP-CYB	A318-112 Elite	5545	♦
☐	VP-CZW	B737-7JW/W BBJ	38408/4730	♦
☐	VP-CZY	B727-2P1 RE	21595/1406	
☐	VQ-BCS	ERJ-135BJ Legacy 600	14501089	♦
☐	VQ-BDD	A318-112CJ Elite	3751	
☐	VQ-BFP	ERJ-135BJ Legacy 600	14501049	
☐	VQ-BFQ	ERJ-135BJ Legacy 600	14501062	
☐	VQ-BFR	ERJ-135BJ Legacy 650	14501121	♦
☐	VQ-BFS	ERJ-135BJ Legacy 650	14501132	♦
☐	VQ-BKK	A319-115CJ	1485	
☐	VQ-BMS	B747-SP21	21649/373	
☐	VQ-BNQ	Challenger 800	7136	
☐	VQ-BOS	B737-8GQ/W	35792/2351	
☐	VQ-BOV	Challenger 850	8092	
☐	VQ-BSK	B747-8ZV BBJ	42096/1468	
☐	VQ-BTA	B737-7P3/W BBJ1	29188/217	
☐	VQ-BVQ	A319-133CJ	4842	
☐	VT-AOK	ERJ-135BJ Legacy 650	14501157	
☐	VT-AOL	ERJ-135BJ Legacy 650	14501158	
☐	VT-AOP	ERJ-190-100ECJ Lineage	19000203	
☐	VT-ARE	CRJ-100ER	7163	
☐	VT-BSF	ERJ-135BJ Legacy 600	14500901	
☐	VT-CKP	ERJ-135BJ Legacy 600	14501094	
☐	VT-IAH	A319-115CJ	2837	
☐	VT-IBP	Challenger 850	8070	
☐	VT-JMN	ERJ-135ER	145233	
☐	VT-JSI	ERJ-135LR	14500893	
☐	VT-KJG	ERJ-135BJ Legacy 650	14501202	
☐	VT-VJM	A319-133CJ	2650	
☐	VT-	ERJ-135BJ Legacy 650	14501218	♦
☐	V8-ALI	B747-430	26426/910	
☐	V8-BKH	A340-212	046	
☐	V8-MHB	B767-27GER	25537/517	
☐	V8-	B787-8 BBJ	44572/325	o/o♦
☐	XA-AYJ	ERJ-190ECJ Lineage 1000	19000243	
☐	XA-FJA	ERJ-145LR	145098	♦
☐	XA-KAD	ERJ-135BJ Legacy 600	14501035	♦
☐	XA-LBO	ERJ-135BJ Legacy 600	14500970	
☐	XA-MAX	ERJ-135BJ Legacy 600	145540	
☐	XA-MHA	ERJ-135BJ Legacy 600	14500965	std
☐	XA-RWS	ERJ-135BJ Legacy 600	14500969	
☐	XB-NSU	B737-217	22257/756	
☐	XC-	Do328-310	3220	
☐	XC-MEX	B787-8	40695/6TP-01	
☐	XT-BFA	B727-282 RE	22430/1715	
☐	YI-APX	A300B4-203	239	
☐	YK-SQG	Yak-40K	9941959	
☐	ZK-ECI	BAeJetstream 32EP	946	
☐	ZS-AAK	Do328-300	3162	
☐	ZS-AAT	Do328-300	3146	
☐	ZS-AJS	Do328-120	3029	♦
☐	ZS-ECB	ERJ-135BJ Legacy 600	14500832	
☐	ZS-IOC	Do328-300	3219	
☐	ZS-JSM	BAeJetstream 41	41052	
☐	ZS-NEX	B767-35DER	24865/322	♦
☐	ZS-NOM	BAeJetstream 41	41047	
☐	ZS-PVX	B727-2N6RE	22825/1805	
☐	ZS-PYB	DC-9-14	45706/61	
☐	ZS-RSA	B737-7ED/W BBJ1	32627/826	
☐	3C-EGE	B737-7FB/W BBJ1	33367/1189	
☐	3C-QQH	ERJ-145EP	145076	
☐	3DC-SWZ	MD-87	53041/1945	
☐	4K-8888(1)	B727-251	22543/1700[GYD]	
☐	4K-8888(2)	A319-115CJ	2487	♦
☐	4K-AI01	B767-32LER	40342/990	
☐	4K-AI07	A320-214X CJ	6285 [BSL]	
☐	4K-AI08	A340-642	779 [BSL]	
☐	4K-AZ10	Tu-154M	98A1013	
☐	4K-AZ808	ATR 42-500	673	
☐	4L-GAA	Challenger 850	8046	
☐	4X-AOT	B737-297	21740/562	
☐	5A-CAA	An-74TK-300	3654701211080	♦
☐	5A-ONE	A340-213	151	
☐	5A-UAD	Challenger 850	8087	
☐	5H-ABG	DHC-8Q-315	574	
☐	5H-CCM	F.28 Fellowship 3000	11137	
☐	5H-TGF	Fokker 50	20231	
☐	5N-BMH	Do328-300	3120	
☐	5N-BOZ	ERJ-145EU	145617	
☐	5N-BSM	ERJ-135ER	145189	♦
☐	5N-BSN	ERJ-135ER	145198	♦
☐	5N-FGT	B737-7N6/W BBJ1	34260/1746	
☐	5N-RSG	ERJ-135BJ Legacy 600	14500891	
☐	5N-SPE	Do328-300	3151	
☐	5N-SPM	Do328-300	3141	
☐	5N-	ERJ-145LR	145488	
☐	5R-MRM	B737-3Z9	24081/1515	
☐	5U-GRN	B737-75U/W BBJ1	28976/158	
☐	5V-TAI	F.28 Fellowship 1000	11079	std
☐	5V-TGF	DC-8-62H	46071/469	
☐	5Y-BWR	CRJ-100LR	7004	
☐	5Y-CAR	CRJ-200ER	7186	
☐	6V-AEF	B727-2M1/W RE	21091/1134	
☐	6V-ONE	A319-115CJ	1556	
☐	7Q-WPB	ERJ-135LR	145676	
☐	7T-VPE	ATR 72-600	1200	
☐	7T-VPF	ATR 72-600	1280	♦
☐	7T-VPP	A340-540	917	
☐	9H-AGF	A319-133CJ	5261	
☐	9H-AHA	B737-505	24647/2143	
☐	9H-OME	B737-505	24274/2035	
☐	9H-YES	B737-5Q8	25167/2173	♦

	Reg	Type	C/n	
☐	9H-AJW	B737-3U3	28733/2969	♦
☐	9H-AVK	A319-115CJ	4622	
☐	9H-AVM	B757-23A/W	24527/249	
☐	9H-BBJ	B737-7BC/W BBJ1	30791/623	
☐	9H-BOO	Challenger 850	8051	♦
☐	9H-BVJ	Challenger 850	8071	
☐	9H-CLG	Challenger 850	8063	
☐	9H-CLX	A330-243	451	♦
☐	9H-GGG	B737-7ZX/W BBJ1	40119/4620	
☐	9H-ILA	Challenger 850	8101	♦
☐	9H-ILI	Challenger 850	8048	♦
☐	9H-ILV	Challenger 850	8082	
☐	9H-ILY	Challenger 850	8076	♦
☐	9H-ILZ	Challenger 850	8086	
☐	9H-JOY	CRJ200ER	7644	♦
☐	9H-JPC	ERJ-135BJ Legacy 600	14501010	
☐	9H-MTF	B737-329	23774/1443	
☐	9H-SBJ	Sukohi SSJ100-95LR	95060	♦
☐	9H-WFC	ERJ-135BJ Legacy 600	14500988	
☐	9K-GAA	B747-8JK BBJ	38636/1434	
☐	9K-GBA	A340-542	1091	
☐	9K-GBB	A340-542	1102	
☐	9K-GCC	B737-9BQ/W BBJ3	37632/2965	
☐	9K-GEA	A319-115CJ	3957	
☐	9M-NAA	A319-115CJ	2949	
☐	9M-NAB	A320-214CJ Prestige	4199	
☐	9Q-CDC	B727-30	18934/222	
☐	9Q-CLK	B707-138B	17702/64	

MILITARY

	Serial	Type	C/n	
☐	OB2	Do328-110	3083	(A2)
☐	554	A320-214CJ Prestige	3723	(A4O)
☐	555	A320-214CJ Prestige	4117	(A4O)
☐	556	A320-214CJ Prestige	4795	(A4O)
☐	769	Tu-204-120CE	1450743664030	(B)
☐	3701	B737-8AR/W	30139/428	(B)
☐	15001	A310-304	446	(C)
☐	15002	A310-304	482	(C)
☐	15003	A310-304	425	(C)
☐	921	B737-58N	28866/2929	(CC)
☐	922	B737-330QC	23524/1272	(CC)
☐	985	B767-3YOER	26205/474	(CC)
☐	FAB-61	C-130B Hercules	3549	(CP)♦
☐	FAB-65	C-130B Hercules	3588	(CP)
☐	FAB-90	F.27M Friendship 400M	10578	(CP)
☐	FAB-96	XIAN MA60	0503	(CP)
☐	FAB-97	XIAN MA60	0504	(CP)
☐	FAB-100	BAe146 Srs.200	E2080	(CP)std
☐	FAB-101	BAe146 Srs.200	E2041	(CP)std
☐	FAB-102	BAe146 Srs.200	E2023	(CP)std
☐	FAB-103	BAe146 Srs.200	E2040	(CP)std
☐	FAB-104	BAe146 Srs.200	E2024	(CP)std
☐	FAB-105	BAe146 Srs.200	E2022	(CP)♦
☐	FAB-106	BAe146 Srs.200	E2048	(CP)♦
☐	FAB-111	B727-224	23449/1756	(CP)♦
☐	FAB-112	B737-2Q3	23117/1033	(CP)♦
☐	FAB-113	B737-2Q3	23481/1241	(CP)
☐	FAB-114	B737-230	22135/781	(CP)♦
☐	FAB-115	B737-322	24653/1810	(CP)
☐	FAB-116	B737-230	22122/721	(CP)
☐	FAB-117	B737-230	22636/808	(CP)
☐	FAB-118	B737-230	22139/791	(CP)
☐	10+21	A310-304	498	(D)
☐	10+23	A310-304	503	(D)
☐	15+01	A319-133CJ	3897	(D)
☐	15+02	A319-133CJ	4060	(D)
☐	16+01	A340-313X	274	(D)
☐	16+02	A340-313X	355	(D)
☐	T-501	ERJ-135BJ Legacy 600	14500981	(D2)
☐	T.22-1	A310-304	550	(EC)
☐	T.22-2	A310-304	551	(EC)
☐	1002	B707-3J9C	20832/886	(EP)std
☐	1002	B707-3J9C	21124/910	(EP)
☐	1581	B757-260ER	26058/496	(ET)
☐	F-RADA	A310-304	421	(F)
☐	F-RADB	A310-304	422	(F)
☐	F-RADC	A310-304	418	(F)
☐	F-RAJA	A340-211	075	(F)
☐	F-RAJB	A340-212	081	(F)
☐	F-RARF	A330-223	240	(F)
☐	QQ101	Avro 146-RJ100	E3368	(G)
☐	ZE700	BAe146 Srs.100	E1021	(G)
☐	ZE701	BAe146 Srs.100	E1029	(G)
☐	ZE707	BAe146 Srs.200QC	E2211	(G)
☐	ZE708	BAe146 Srs.200QC	E2188	(G)
☐	FAE-051	ERJ-135BJ Legacy 600	14501082	(HC)
☐	FAE-620	B727-230	21620/1419	(HC)
☐	FAE-630	B737-236	21798/658	(HC)
☐	FAE-691	B727-134	19691/487	(HC)
☐	FAC0001	B737-74V/W BBJ1	29272/323	(HK)
☐	FAC0002	F.28 Fellowship 1000	11992	(HK)
☐	FAC1041	F.28 Fellowship 3000C	11162	(HK)
☐	FAC1202	B767-276ER	24157/253	(HK)
☐	FAC1209	B737-46BSF	25262/2088	(HK)
☐	FAC1215	ERJ-135BJ Legacy 600	14501095	(HK)
☐	PNC-0242	ATR 42-320	380	(HK)
☐	10001	B747-4B5	26412/1284	(HL)
☐	85101	B737-3Z8	23152/1073	(HL)
☐		B787-8	41987/11	(HL)
☐	FAH-001	ERJ-135BJ Legacy 600	14501041	(HR)
☐	1084	ERJ-135LR	14501084	HS-AMP
☐	1124	ERJ-135LR	14501124	(HS)
☐	2112	ERJ-135LR	14501077	HS-NVA
☐	2113	ERJ-135LR	14501125	HS-NVB
☐	11-111	B737-4Z6	27906/2698	HS-CMV
☐	55-555	B737-8Z6/W	35478/1955	HS-TYS
☐	99-999	B737-448	24866/1867	HS-HRH
☐	60201	A310-324	591	HS-TYQ
☐	60202	A319-115	1908	HS-TYR
☐		B737-8Z6/W	62445/5609	(HS)o/o♦
☐	HZ-101	B737-7DP/W BBJ1	32805/940	(HZ)
☐	HZ-102	B737-8DP/W BBJ2	32451/836	(HZ)
☐	HZ-124	A340-213	004	(HZ)
☐	MM62174	A319-115CJ	1157	(I)
☐	MM62209	A319-115CJ	1795	(I)
☐	MM62243	A319-115CJ	2507	(I)
☐	MM	A340-541	748	I-TALY♦
☐	20-1101	B747-47C	24730/816	(JA)
☐	20-1102	B747-47C	24731/839	(JA)
☐	T-01	B757-23A	25487/470	(LV)std
☐	T-02	F.28 Fellowship 4000	11203	(LV)std
☐	T-03	F.28 Fellowship 1000	11028	(LV)std
☐	T-04	B737-5H6	26456/2527	(LV)std
☐	01-0015	B737-7DM/W BBJ1	32916/979	(N)
☐	01-0040	B737-7DM/W BBJ1	29971/684	(N)
☐	01-0041	B737-7DM/W BBJ1	33080/1089	(N)
☐	02-0042	B737-7FD/W BBJ1	33500/1223	(N)
☐	02-0201	B737-7CP/W BBJ1	30755/545	(N)
☐	02-0202	B737-7CP/W BBJ1	30753/481	(N)

	Registration	Type	c/n	
☐	02-0203	B737-7BC/W BBJ1	33434/1211	(N)
☐	05-0730	B737-7DM/W BBJ1	34807/1908	(N)
☐	05-0932	B737-7DM/W BBJ1	34808/2008	(N)
☐	05-4613	B737-7DM/W BBJ1	34809/2141	(N)
☐	09-0015	B757-2Q8/W	25044/369	(N)
☐	09-0016	B757-2Q8/W	28160/721	(N)
☐	09-0540	B737-7DM/W BBJ1	40706/3512	(N)
☐	44105	B757-2xx	?	(N)
☐	82-8000	B747-2G4B	23824/679	(N)
☐	92-9000	B747-2G4B	23825/685	(N)
☐	98-0001	B757-2GW/W	29025/783	(N)
☐	98-0002	B757-2GW/W	29026/787	(N)
☐	99-0003	B757-2GW/W	29027/824	(N)
☐	99-0004	B757-2GW/W	29028/829	(N)
☐	FAP-350	B737-244	19707/82	(OB)
☐	FAP-352	B737-282	23042/967	(OB)
☐	FAP-356	B737-528	27426/2739	(OB)
☐	2801	A319-115CJ	2801	(OK)
☐	3085	A319-115CJ	3085	(OK)
☐	CE-01	ERJ-135ER	145449	(OO)
☐	CE-02	ERJ-135LR	145480	(OO)
☐	CE-03	ERJ-145LR	145526	(OO)
☐	CE-04	ERJ-145LR	145548	(OO)
☐	A-001	B737-8U3/W BBJ2	41706/3902	(PK)
☐	A-2801	F.28 Fellowship 1000	11042	(PK)
☐	A-2802	F.28 Fellowship 3000R	11113	(PK)
☐	A-2803	F.28 Fellowship 3000R	11117	(PK)
☐	A-3804	F.28 Fellowship 4000	11234	(PK)
☐	A-7304	B737-2Q8	21518/522	(PK)
☐	A-7305	B737-4U3	25714/2535	(PK)
☐	A-7306	B737-4U3	25719/2549	(PK)
☐	A-7307	B737-5U3	28730/2952	(PK)♦
☐	AI-7301	B737-2X9	22777/868	(PK)
☐	AI-7302	B737-2X9	22778/947	(PK)
☐	AI-7303	B737-2X9	22779/985	(PK)
☐	2101	A319-133CJ	2263	(PP)
☐	2115	B737-2N3	21165/441	(PP)
☐	2116	B737-2N3	21166/445	(PP)
☐	2520	ERJ-145ER	145023	(PP)
☐	2521	ERJ-145ER	145020	(PP)
☐	2522	ERJ-145ER	145027	(PP)
☐	2523	ERJ-145ER	145028	(PP)
☐	2524	ERJ-145EP	145034	(PP)
☐	2525	ERJ-145ER	145038	(PP)
☐	2526	ERJ-145ER	145137	(PP)
☐	2550	ERJ-145LR	145350	(PP)
☐	2560	ERJ-135LR	145600	(PP)
☐	2561	ERJ-135LR	145608	(PP)
☐	2580	ERJ-135BJ Legacy 600	145412	(PP)
☐	2581	ERJ-135BJ Legacy 600	145462	(PP)
☐	2582	ERJ-135BJ Legacy 600	145495	(PP)
☐	2583	ERJ-135BJ Legacy 600	145528	(PP)
☐	2584	ERJ-135BJ Legacy 600	14500997	(PP)
☐	2585	ERJ-135BJ Legacy 600	14501078	(PP)
☐	2590	ERJ-190LR	19000214	(PP)
☐	2591	ERJ-190LR	19000277	(PP)
☐	88179	Yak-40	9631947	(RA)♦
☐	RP-1250	F.28 Fellowship 3000	11153	(RP)
☐	145-209	ERJ-135ER	145209	(SX)
☐	374	ERJ-145SA	145374	SX-BKO
☐	135L-484	ERJ-135BJ Legacy 600	145484	(SX)
☐	671	ERJ-145SA	145671	SX-BKP
☐	729	ERJ-145SA	145729	SX-BKQ
☐	757	ERJ-145SA	145757	SX-BKR
☐	A36-001	B737-7DT/W BBJ1	30829/738	(VH)
☐	A36-002	B737-7DF/W BBJ1	30790/613	(VH)
☐	K2412	B737-2A8	23036/977	(VT)
☐	K2413	B737-2A8	23037/982	(VT)
☐	K3186	B737-2A8	20484/275	(VT)
☐	K3187	B737-2A8	20483/273	(VT)
☐	K3601	ERJ-135BJ Legacy 600	14500867	(VT)
☐	K3602	ERJ-135BJ Legacy 600	14500880	(VT)
☐	K3603	ERJ-135BJ Legacy 600	14500910	(VT)
☐	K3604	ERJ-135BJ Legacy 600	14500919	(VT)
☐	K5012	B737-7HI/W BBJ1	36106/2118	(VT)
☐	K5013	B737-7HI/W BBJ1	36107/2325	(VT)
☐	K5014	B737-7HI/W BBJ1	36108/2425	(VT)
☐	PF-801	Do328-300		(XA)
☐	TP-01	B757-225/W	22690/151	(XA)
☐	TP-02	B737-33A	24095/322	(XA)
☐	TP-03	B737-322	24361/1694	(XA)
☐	3501	B727-114	18912/169	(XA)
☐	3520	B737-2B7	23133/1049	(XA)
☐	3526	B737-8MC/W	44437/5595	(XA)♦
☐	4101	ERJ-145SA	145190	(XA)
☐	4111	ERJ-145MPA	145694	(XA)
☐	4112	ERJ-145MPA	145723	(XA)
☐	"KOC001"	A320-232	4507	(XU)
☐	0001	A319-133CJ	1468	(YV)std
☐	0207	B737-2N1	21167/442	(YV)
☐	NZ7571	B757-2K2	26633/519	(ZK)
☐	NZ7572	B757-2K2	26634/545	(ZK)
☐	295	B707-366C	20919/888	(4X)
☐	NAF916	B737-505	25791/2351	(5N)
☐	KAF308	Fokker 70	11557	(5Y)
☐	G-530	F.28 Fellowship 3000	11125	(9G)
☐	M28-01	F.28 Fellowship 1000	11088	(9M)
☐	M53-01	B737-7H6/W BBJ1	29274/397	(9M)

NOTES

NOTES

NOTES

NOTES

NOTES

Would you like to know more about airline fleets?

Air-Britain's **Airline Fleets 2016** lists the full fleets of around 2,500 operators in 200 countries including most small twins and commercially-used singles and helicopters. The airline two-and three-letter codes are given together with bases and airport codes. C/ns, most recent previous identity, fleet numbers, aircraft names, non-standard colour schemes and lease details are also included. Aircraft in non-airline use, full indices of all airline codes, operators and major airports also contribute to this valuable reference.

Indispensible for the serious airline enthusiast, this A5 hardback book will run to around 720 pages and will be available in early May.

Did you know that there are other Quick Reference titles available?

Business Jets and Turboprops 2016 (BizQR) lists all such aircraft currently in service by registration or military serial, with c/ns. Known reservations are also included. In A5 softback format with 184 pages at £10.95 to non-members, or £8.95 to members. Available now.

UK, IoM and Ireland Civil Registers 2016 (UKQR) includes registrations and types of all currently registered G-, M-, ZJ-, 2- and EI- aircraft together with a list of foreign-registered aircraft based in the UK. Also featured are current military serials, a military/civil registration decode, base index and museums listing. A5 softback format, expected to be 192 pages and available in April at £10.95 to non-members, or £8.95 to members.

European Registers Handbook 2016 is a mixed-media publication with current civil registers of 45 countries (not UK) in QR registration/type format in an A4 softback book of over 500 pages together with a fully searchable CD giving full c/ns, identities and additional information, plus photographs from 2015 events. CD available May, book available May/June.

Other annual hardback publications are:

The Civil Aircraft Registers of the British Isles 2016. This larger-format volume of 650 pages gives full type, c/n, previous identities, date registered, owners, bases and airworthiness details of all current aircraft and many additional reference features. Available May.

Business Jets International 2016 contains full production lists of every type, past and present, in c/n order together with a 77,000-entry registration–c/n index. Available mid-2016.

Keep an eye on our web based shop **www.air-britain.co.uk** and advertisements in leading magazines for prices and availability.**Air-Britain membership** offers many advantages, not least reduced prices on all our publications as shown above. All members receive the quarterly A4 magazine *Aviation World* which contains 52 pages of news, features and photographs, many in colour. There is one 160-page monthly A5 magazine *Air-Britain News* throughout the year, and a choice of two other A4 quarterlies – *Archive* and *Aeromilitaria* – for the civil and military enthusiast respectively, together with access to exclusive websites, an information service and travel.

Membership in 2016, including *Aviation World* and *Air-Britain News*, costs £48 (UK), £67 (Europe) and £72 (Rest of the World). There are several possible combinations of magazines and also overseas rates. *Air-Britain News* is also available in electronic format for Windows 8 and iPad users, offering full colour throughout and extra photo pages. In addition it is available up to a week before the printed version pops through UK letterboxes and there is a great saving in time and postal charges for overseas members – see our website for full details.

Full details may be found on www.air-britain.co.uk or write to Air-Britain, 1 Rose Cottages, 179 Penn Road, Hazlemere, High Wycombe, Bucks HP15 7NE for a free information pack.